ADVANCES IN THE CHEMISTRY

OF THE COORDINATION COMPOUNDS

Edited by Stanley Kirschner
Professor of Inorganic Chemistry
At Wayne State University

Proceedings of the Sixth International Conference on Coordination Chemistry, held at Wayne State University, Detroit, Michigan, August 27 to September 1, 1961

THE MACMILLAN COMPANY   NEW YORK, 1961

FOREWORD

Although the first coordination compounds to be studied were purely inorganic in nature, the field has grown so greatly that the study of coordination compounds now includes large portions of organic chemistry and some areas of biochemistry. Coordination phenomena, long applied in analytical chemistry and electrochemistry, have in recent years found application in the study of catalysis, reaction inhibitors, and biological processes.

The rapid growth of interest in coordination chemistry during the last decade has been accompanied by, and doubtless catalyzed by, the numerous conferences and symposia at which chemists have discussed the chemistry of these remarkable substances. The first conference of the series of which the one held at Wayne State University is a part was a very informal meeting arranged in 1951 by Dr. Joseph Chatt at Welwyn, England and sponsored by Imperial Chemical Industries. Nearly all of those in attendance at this first meeting were from the British Isles. There were, however, three or four men from the Continent, so the meeting can properly be called an international one. This symposium was so successful and the participants felt they gained so much from it that, even before they adjourned, it was decided that other meetings of the same sort should be held. Accordingly, the Danish Chemical Society invited coordination chemists to meet in Copenhagen in the Summer of 1953. This meeting, too, was extremely successful and stimulated interest in a continuing series of international conferences. The Koninklijke Nederlandse Chemische Vereniging sponsored the third conference, which was convened in Amsterdam in the Spring of 1955. This was followed by similar meetings in Rome in 1957 and in London in 1959. Each of these meetings has been arranged by the chemical society in the host country without any over-all international supervision and each, therefore, has operated under a different type of organization and has had its own distinctive atmosphere. Attendance at most of the conferences has been small, so chemists from all parts of the world have been able to become well acquainted on a basis of personal friendship. This has stimulated interest in the meetings and has greatly facilitated discussion of chemical problems. Indeed, the meetings have been so pleasant and so productive of research ideas that those who have taken part in them have come to feel that attendance is almost a "must." Continuance of the series is thus assured.

At each of the recent meetings, an informal group of those present has gathered to receive invitations for future meetings. The enthusiasm of the group is so great and the interest in coordination chemistry is so high that there have been more invitations than could possibly be accepted, and there is now a waiting list of countries that seek to entertain future conferences. The next meeting is to be held in Stockholm in June of 1962. While no definite plans have been laid for meetings to follow that one, Moscow, Zurich and Haifa have all been mentioned as sites for future meetings.

The proceedings of each of the International Conferences on Coordination Compounds (except the first) have been published in book form and have been widely used by students and research chemists. In many cases, the demand has far outrun the supply and reprinting has been necessary.

The Division of Inorganic Chemistry of the American Chemical Society invited the coordination chemists to attend a conference in the United States in the Summer of 1961. It has been generously aided in co-sponsorship by the United States Air Force, The International Union of Pure and Applied Chemistry, and Wayne State University, to all of whom we express out great thanks.

In addition to the series of meetings, of which this one is a part, there have been other meetings on coordination compounds during this past decade. These, too, have been significant and highly successful. We should mention particularly the International Symposium on the Chemistry of Coordination Compounds which was held in Allahabad under the auspices of the National Academy of Sciences of India in February, 1959. While it is highly desirable that coordination chemists from all parts of the world should meet to become acquainted and to discuss their researches, it is clear that the world is still too large to allow all chemists to meet with their colleagues frequently. The next best plan, perhaps, is to have two or three series of meetings with liberal exchange of published information and with such mutual attendance as can be arranged.

Urbana, Illinois   JOHN C. BAILAR, JR.
April 1961

PREFACE

The organization of an international conference such as the Sixth International Conference on Coordination Chemistry has proved to be a most interesting undertaking. The two attitudes observed by the Executive Secretary to have permeated this Conference throughout its entire development are understanding and cooperation. This understanding and cooperation have been forthcoming not only from the members of the Executive Committee and the Committee on Invitations and Papers listed below but also from many others. The authors whose works are presented here have had to meet extremely early deadlines so that this book could be available at the Conference, and they have exhibited wonderful cooperation in this regard. Many outstanding research investigators in coordination chemistry have shown complete understanding when they were asked not to present papers at this meeting but to participate in other ways. As a result, several younger chemists in the field and chemists who had not been able to participate to a great extent in past international conferences in coordination chemistry were able to present papers on the limited program.

The Executive Secretary wishes to express his sincere appreciation not only to the members of the Executive Committee and the Committee on Invitations and Papers for their necessary and invaluable contributions, but also to the Sponsors and Contributors (see pages vii–viii), without whose help the activities of this Conference would have been severely restricted. Further, special thanks must also go to many persons at Wayne State University, including Vice President Randall Whaley, Dean J. Russell Bright, Dean Victor A. Rapport, Professor Wilfried Heller, Dr. John Oliver, Miss Virginia Blackwell, and Mrs. Lila Isaacs—an excellent secretary who is able to maintain a truly magnificent serenity, even under the most trying conditions—for their significant contributions to the success of the Conference.

Finally, my own deep appreciation and gratitude go to my wife and children for their understanding and the willing sacrifices they have made as a result of having a husband and father who is the Executive Secretary of an international conference.

Detroit, Michigan
April, 1961

STANLEY KIRSCHNER

SIXTH INTERNATIONAL CONFERENCE ON COORDINATION CHEMISTRY
WAYNE STATE UNIVERSITY
DETROIT, MICHIGAN

EXECUTIVE COMMITTEE

John C. Bailar, Jr., Chairman
University of Illinois, Urbana, Illinois

Arthur Adamson
University of Southern California, Los Angeles, California

Fred Basolo
Northwestern University, Evanston, Illinois

Stanley Kirschner, Executive Secretary
Wayne State University, Detroit, Michigan

SPONSORS

Division of Inorganic Chemistry, American Chemical Society

International Union of Pure and Applied Chemistry

United States Air Force, Office of Scientific Research

Wayne State University

COMMITTEE ON INVITATIONS AND PAPERS

Fred Basolo, Chairman
Northwestern University, Evanston, Illinois

Arthur Adamson
University of Southern California, Los Angeles, California

John C. Bailar, Jr.
University of Illinois, Urbana, Illinois

D. H. Busch
The Ohio State University, Columbus, Ohio

F. A. Cotton
Massachusetts Institute of Technology, Cambridge, Massachusetts

E. L. King
University of Wisconsin, Madison, Wisconsin

H. Sternberg
U.S. Bureau of Mines, Pittsburgh, Pennsylvania

H. Taube
University of Chicago, Chicago, Illinois

CONTRIBUTORS

Climax Molybdenum Co. of Michigan
Detroit, Michigan

Detroit Section, American Chemical Society
Detroit, Michigan

Ethyl Corporation
Detroit, Michigan

Ford Motor Company
Dearborn, Michigan

General Motors Corporation
Warren, Michigan

Metal & Thermit Corporation
Rahway, New Jersey, and
Ferndale, Michigan

Parke, Davis and Company
Detroit, Michigan

U. S. Rubber Company
Detroit, Michigan

Wyandotte Chemicals Corporation
Wyandotte, Michigan

TABLE OF CONTENTS

CONFERENCE LECTURES

THEORIES OF BONDING IN COORDINATION COMPOUNDS

C. J. BALLHAUSEN

Institute of Physical Chemistry
University of Copenhagen
Copenhagen, Denmark

Any valid theory dealing with the bonding in chemical compounds
must of necessity be semi-empirical. If it were possible to calculate
the electronic structures "exactly" we would not need any "theories
of bonding"; everything would follow from the solution of the Schröd-
inger equation. However, as repeated ad infinitum, a solution of this
equation is not possible for any but the simplest molecules, and
the bonding theories therefore aim at extracting the *principal* features of the various phenomena. However, it is clear that the greater
the simplifications and approximations, the more we must satisfy ourselves with a final result which, of necessity, can only be qualitative.

If we now turn our attention toward the complexes, what are the
questions we want answered? These fall into two classes: (1) "Collective behaviour" exemplified by complexity constants and kinetic
behaviour and (2) "Single species behaviour" dealing with, for instance, the magnetism, spectra, and resonance of a single molecule.
Since the treatment of the first group also requires the theory of statistical mechanics, we will omit it here, and concentrate upon the
second group.

The all important question for the coordination compounds of the
transition metals is thus: How do we describe and characterize the
bonding between the central ion and the ligands in terms of some
electronic theory? In modern times three methods have been used to
solve the problems of the nature of these bonds and to account for the
other properties of the complexes:

(1) The molecular orbital method
(2) The valence bond theory
(3) The crystal- or ligand-field theory

Until recently most chemists working with the complexes of the
transition metal ions have been primarily interested in the application
of the valence bond theory, as exemplified by Pauling[1] in his famous
book *The Nature of the Chemical Bond*. Special emphasis was laid
upon the magnetic properties of the complexes, and a seemingly successful theory was built upon these features.

3

However, more than twenty-five years have passed since Van Vleck[2,3] demonstrated the superiority of the crystal-field approach in the discussion of the magnetic properties of inorganic complexes. Now it should be stated that for the complexes under discussion both the valence-bond picture and the crystal-field picture can be considered a specialization of the molecular orbital method. Indeed, the most useful approach to these compounds is now called the ligand-field theory which is really nothing more than a "hybridization" of the ideas of Bethe[4] and Van Vleck[2,3] with those of Mulliken.[5] Thus the best features of both the valence-bond theory and the crystal-field theory are incorporated in the ligand-field theory, and it is this theory with which we shall be primarily concerned. First, however, a few words concerning the pure crystal-field theory.[6]

The crystal-field theory treats an inorganic complex as if such a compound could be regarded as an "ionic" molecule. It is then evident that the central metal atom in the complex is subjected to an electrical field originating from the surrounding atoms or molecules, analogous to what would take place if the atom were located in a little cavity inside a crystalline lattice. Such a "crystalline field" would of course destroy the spherical symmetry of the free atom; it is the consequences of this situation which are dealt with by the crystal-field theory. The model considers an isolated molecule, and it handles the electrons of the central metal ion as if they were subjected to an electric field originating from the surrounding ligands.

The electrons on the ligands are not allowed to overlap and mix with the electrons of the metal ion; as a result the role played by the ligands is rather limited. Of course they can be polarized by the metal ion of the complex, but the motions of the ligand electrons are assumed to remain unaffected by such factors as whether the electrons of the metal ion are in an excited state or not. Thus the ligands are only supposed to provide a constant electric potential, possessing the symmetry of the ligands, in which the electrons of the metal ion can move.

It was realized later that this point of view does not impair the usefulness of the theory. Indeed Van Vleck showed that the theory of molecular orbitals provides an explanation for the validity of the above point of view. It must only be remembered that the word "ionic" as used in the crystal field theory is not to be taken in any way to represent the truth.

The quantal treatment of the crystal-field model is therefore easy. The Hamiltonian for the electrons of the metal ion consists of two terms

$$\mathcal{H} = \mathcal{H}_F + U$$

where $\mathcal{H}_F$ is the Hamiltonian for the free ion and $\mathcal{U}$ is the potential provided by its ligands. It is supposed that the eigenfunctions and eigenvalues of $\mathcal{H}_F$ are known. Accordingly the potential $\mathcal{U}$ is regarded as a perturbation which determines the electronic motions and term values of the metal ion in the complex. We notice that the whole problem can be regarded as a sort of intramolecular Stark-effect.

Written out in greater detail we have for the Hamiltonian of a metal ion possessing i electrons:

$$\mathcal{H} = - \frac{\hbar^2}{2m} \sum_i \nabla_i^2 - \sum_i \frac{Ze^2}{r_i} + \frac{1}{2} \sum_{i \neq j} \frac{e^2}{r_{ij}} + \sum_i \xi_i(r)\,\vec{1}_i \cdot \vec{s}_i + \mathcal{U}$$

With the exception of the term in $\mathcal{U}$, the Hamiltonian is exactly the Hamiltonian for the free ion. However, when we perturb the eigenvalues for the free ions with $\mathcal{U}$ it is of course very important to know how $\mathcal{U}$ compares in order of magnitude with the two other perturbing quantities: The electronic repulsion term $\Sigma\, e^2/r_{12}$ and the spin orbit term $\xi_i(r)\,\vec{1} \cdot \vec{s}$. It is seen that three cases can be realised:

1) $\mathcal{U} < \xi(r)\,\vec{1} \cdot \vec{s} \lesssim e^2/r_{12}$ (Complexes of the rare earths)
2) $\xi(r)\,\vec{1} \cdot \vec{s} < \mathcal{U} < e^2/r_{12}$ (Complexes of the first transition group)
3) $\mathcal{U} > e^2/r_{12} \gtrsim \xi(r)\,\vec{1} \cdot \vec{s}$ ("Covalent" complexes)

It is customary to call the second case "the weak crystalline field case" and the third case "the strong crystalline field case." Of course there is no real distinction between the three cases; analytically they go over into each other. The reason we distinguish between them is simply in order to specify our starting point. In actual cases the complexes of the rare earths are found in case one, while the complexes of the first transition group are found somewhere in between cases two and three, and can be described starting from either point of view. On the other hand, the complexes of the second and third transition series are best treated using a "strong field" approximation.

If we look at the effect of a crystalline field coming from an octahedron on the d-electrons of a metal ion, we get the now well-known picture of a splitting; the five-fold degenerate d-levels split into a lower orbital three-fold degenerate level called t_{2g} and a higher lying two-fold degenerate level called e_g. The energy separation between these two subshells is usually called $10\,Dq$. It is by now even more well known, that the spectral and bulk magnetic properties of the complex ions can be completely accounted for using this picture.

So far the only role of the ligands has been to produce a "crystalline" field, causing the splitting of the various orbitals of the metal atom. Now such a point of view is equivalent to regarding a complex molecule as held together by pure ionic forces, replacing any inherent bonding by point charges attracting and repulsing each other. However, we know from Earnshaw's theorem of electrostatics that no system of charges can be in stable equilibrium while at rest. Obviously a modification in our view of the bonding is needed in order to save the situation. It is true that in the pure crystal-field theory we very seldom utilize any specific features of the orbitals; for the most part it is only their symmetry properties that are used. However, the crux of the matter is the following: Will the inclusion of a more realistic bonding scheme produce a splitting of the orbitals in the way the crystal-field theory demands? To this question the answer is fortunately yes.

As mentioned earlier we will call this second approximation the ligand-field theory because it acknowledges the presence of the ligands to a much greater extent than the pure crystalline-field theory. Hence the ligand-field method differs from the crystalline-field procedure in that the structural unit for the wave function is the whole complex ion, rather than the single central atom.

A question which naturally arises is, what proof do we have for the claimed superiority of the molecular orbital description over the pure crystalline-field model? Quite apart from the more indirect evidence such as the impossibility of fitting certain magnetic experiments[7] and absorption band intensities[8] without using the molecular orbital scheme, a very direct proof for the "covalency" of certain complexes has been given by Owen and Stevens.[9] They found that the paramagnetic resonance spectrum of $IrCl_6^{2-}$ showed a hyperfine structure which could only be interpreted as originating from the Cl^- ions. Similar experiments yielding identical results have since been performed by Tinkham[10] on the complexes MnF_2, FeF_2 and CoF_2. These experiments give us clear proof that the magnetic electrons move in a molecular orbital extending over the entire complex, and hence that an M.O. scheme is closer to the truth than a crystalline-field description.

The LCAO method may be used to construct orbitals for the complex. These orbitals are of the form

$$\Psi = \alpha \, \Psi \, (\Gamma) + \beta \sum_j a_j \Psi_j$$

where $\Psi \, (\Gamma)$ is a wavefunction of the central atom and $\sum_j a_j \Psi_j$ is a linear combination of ligand wave functions.

Let us first consider the so-called σ-bonds in an octahedral complex. These orbitals are symmetric about the line joining the ligand and the central atom. The coefficients α and β determine the extent of mixing of the metal orbital with the ligand orbitals. The values of α and β are in principle obtained by a variational calculation. If we neglect the overlap between the central-atom and ligand orbitals, the following relation holds for α and β:

$$\alpha^2 + \beta^2 = 1$$

or

$$\beta = \sqrt{1 - \alpha^2}$$

In order for the electron to be shared equally between the metal and the ligands, α must be equal to β. The solution of the equation then yields $\alpha = \beta = \pm \sqrt{\frac{1}{2}}$. This case corresponds to Pauling's covalent orbitals.

It can be seen that the transition from the crystal-field theory to the ligand-field theory depends upon the value of α. If α is equal to one, this corresponds to the crystal-field case. Furthermore the smaller the value of α the more the complex deviates from strict crystalline-field theory. The Pauling theory *assumes* $\alpha = \sqrt{\frac{1}{2}}$, corresponding to complete mixing of metal and ligand orbitals, but this assumption is usually further from the truth than the assumption $\alpha = 1$, the "ionic case."

It is very important to realize that the solution to the quadratic secular equation associated with the determination of the mixing coefficients for a molecular orbital yields two solutions. The lower root represents a lower energy than is found in the separated system, hence we call it a bonding orbital. The upper root, on the other hand, yields a higher energy than found for the free atoms, hence we call it an anti-bonding orbital. The anti-bonding orbital is usually distinguished from the bonding orbital by means of a star. We may picture the bonding as shown in Fig. 1.

Let us now consider the bonding scheme in a complex possessing O_h symmetry, assuming that only σ-bonding is operative (Fig. 2). On the left are placed the energy levels of the gaseous metal ion, on the right the energy levels of the free ligand. In the middle of the figure are then placed the levels for the combined orbitals of the complex.

Each of the ligand's σ-orbitals contains two electrons. Consequently the bonding scheme must accomodate 12 electrons plus the electrons coming from the central ion. For instance, for $Ti(H_2O)_6^{+3}$, the lone pair of electrons on each water molecule are taken to be the σ-electrons; the metal atom, on the other hand, has one $3d$ electron. The electronic molecular configuration of this complex is thus

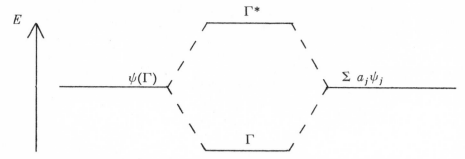

Fig. 1. Bonding and antibonding levels in LCAO theory. To the left and right are presented the energy levels for the separated complex while the levels for the resulting compound are in the center.

$(a_{1g}{}^b)^2(t_{1u})^6(e_g{}^b)^4(t_{2g})$. Notice that the twelve σ-electrons occupy all the bonding orbitals, placing a single electron in the non-bonding t_{2g} orbital.

The level above the t_{2g} orbital is the anti-bonding $e_g{}^*$ orbital. In the crystal-field theory the energy difference between the e_g and the t_{2g} orbital is taken as $10\,Dq$; here in the molecular orbital theory we

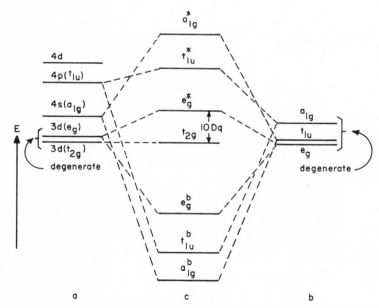

Fig. 2. Bonding scheme for an octahedral complex: energy levels for the gaseous metal ion (a); energy levels for the ligands (b); and energy levels for the combined metal and ligand orbitals (c).

notice that $10\,Dq$ must be interpreted as the energy difference between the *antibonding* e_g^* and the t_{2g} level. Formally, therefore, this case is not distinguishable from the "ionic" bonding pattern. However, the magnitude of $10\,Dq$ in the ligand-field theory depends entirely upon how strong the bonding is. If π-bonding is present, the value of $10\,Dq$ will be modified because the t_{2g} orbital can now participate in the bonding. Quantitatively therefore, $10\,Dq$ is immoderately sensitive to changes in the bonding situation.

The important question must then be whether it is possible to calculate the quantity $10\,Dq$ from basic principles. This is not an easy task; indeed, in the only two attempts so far made, Kleiner[11] obtained a value for chrome alum of $Dq = -550$ cm^{-1}, the experimental value being $Dq = 1750$ cm^{-1}. Tanabe and Sugano[12] obtained $Dq = 4750$ cm^{-1} for the same compound. Both of these results are thus in serious disagreement with experiments. The reason for Kleiner's bad result is the neglect in his calculation of the exchange forces between the $3\,d$ orbitals of the central ion and the ligand orbitals. The inclusion of this effect will, as shown by Tanabe and Sugano, correct the sign of Dq.

There are one or two additional points where the inclusion of exchange effects may be of great importance. It is found experimentally that the Condon-Slater integrals F_n and the spin-orbit coupling parameter ξ are somewhat reduced in the complexes from their free ion values.[13] Even if the reduction of the term distances can be rationalized using a purely crystal-field approximation,[14] the reduction of ξ cannot be explained in this way, since it requires a withdrawing of charge from the central ion. This effect is thus a clear indication that "covalent" bonds are operative. Unfortunately, however, the calculation of Tanabe and Sugano did not lead to diminished values of ξ and F_n. All in all, it may be stated that a complete theoretical explanation of these phenomena is badly needed.

A much less rigorous scheme for the calculation of Dq than the one utilized by the Japanese authors has been put forward by Wolfsberg and Helmholz.[15] These authors were interested in the energy levels of the tetrahedral molecules MnO_4^- and $CrO_4^=$, but their procedure may just as well be applied to octahedral complexes.

It may be appropriate to mention here that Pauling's valence bond approximation has fallen into disrepute during recent years because of the neglect of the antibonding levels. Looking once more at Fig. 2 it can be seen that placing e_g^* at a very high energy (or perhaps even forgetting it) will lead to the well-known serious difficulties if the number of d-electrons exceeds 6, which is the number of electrons we can place in the three-fold degenerate t_{2g} orbital. For example, it is not only difficult to account for the magnetism of the complexes in any rational way, but it is completely impossible to give any account at all of the excited states of the complex. No explanation of the absorption spectra of the complex ions can then be given in terms of Pauling's theory. This is of course just the field where the ligand-field theory has obtained its greatest triumphs.

I want to emphazise as strongly as possible, that the usual picture given in textbooks, of "boxes" in which the electrons are placed, at best is misleading, and, in the case where the number of metal d-electrons exceeds six, is completely wrong as well. Consider for instance octahedrally coordinated Ni^{++}. This is usually pictured as

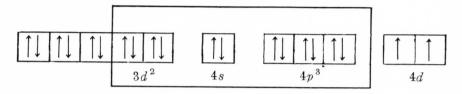

First of all this implies that the electrons in the boxes labelled $d^2 sp^3$ have the same energy as the other d-electrons. This is of course wrong, in fact they themselves don't even have the same energy. But worst of all, the last two d-electrons are *not* in $4d$. We know for sure that they are in the antibonding $(3d)^*$ level. Using the above picture of the "bonding," it is completely impossible to understand the electronic features of Ni^{++}; why, then, use it, let alone teach it? Matters become even worse if the bonding of more complicated molecules—for instance, the sandwich compounds—are treated using a "box" model. This is bound to end in disaster.

It is a curious (and saddening!) thought that when all of the above was said by Van Vleck in the thirties, alas all the chemists apparently had deaf ears.

Returning to the molecular orbital description of the complexes, it is very unfortunate (but not unexpected!) that the calculation of the "mixing coefficients" α and β in the molecular orbitals of the complex is nearly impossible. However, it has been found that it is possible to estimate the mixing of metal- and ligand-orbitals using certain experimental results, or in other words to achieve our goal using a semi-empirical theory. Since the full description of some of these methods would lead us far afield into the theory of magnetic resonance, and, furthermore, since some of the problems involved are not fully understood at the present time, we shall mention only some of the most important features.

The first method for the evaluation of the mixing coefficients is due to Stevens[16] and Owen.[13] Their method depends upon the fact that the orbital magnetic moment of an unpaired d-electron is reduced, if the magnetic electron is spread out in a molecular orbital over the entire molecule.

The second way of estimating the wave-functions for the magnetic electrons, is by observing the "hyperfine structure" in the electron paramagnetic resonance spectrum.

Griffiths, Owen and Ward[17] found, as already mentioned, an anomalous hyperfine structure in the paramagnetic resonance spectrum of $IrCl_6^{-2}$ which could only be explained as arising from the interaction of the magnetic spin of the electron with the nuclear spin of the chlorine ion. This effect can also be used for the elucidation of the mixing coefficients.[18]

The third way of estimating the "covalent" character of the bonding is very closely related to the above method. Instead of looking at the paramagnetic resonance of the electron, we look at the nuclear magnetic resonance of the ligands. This technique is due to Shulman *et al.*,[19] and is certainly the most direct way possible of measuring the electronic density of the magnetic electrons at a point removed from the center of the cation.

The initial experiment of Shulman *et al.* was performed using a crystal of MnF_2. It was found that the nuclear F^{19} resonance frequency was shifted from the free-ion F^- value by a surprisingly large internal field. This large shift was explained as due to the mixing of the fluoride orbitals with the manganese orbitals.[19,20] What takes place is a so-called spin-polarization. That is due to the presence of the unpaired electrons; the F^- nuclei, which usually have an equal amount of α and β spin electrons surrounding them, are left with an electronic cloud in which the α and β electrons are no longer exactly paired off. This results in a net internal magnetic field at the F^{19} nuclei, and hence a shift in the resonance condition takes place.

The isotropic shift is given by the fractional probability density of α and β spin evaluated at the fluorine nucleus; where (S.D.) stands for spin density:

$$f_s = \left[\frac{(S.D.)_\alpha - (SD)_\beta}{(S.D.)_\beta} \right]_{nucleus}$$

Experimentally this quantity can be calculated[20,21] from the measured resonance shift, parallel to the situation in the electronic resonance experiment dealt with earlier.

The above quantity f_s can be related to the bonding parameters as follows. Let us, for simplicity, look at a diatomic molecule AB, with the atomic wavefunctions ψ and Φ centered at A and B respectively (Fig. 3).

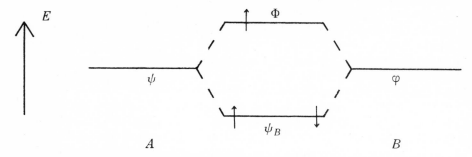

Fig. 3. Bonding and antibonding orbitals in the case of spin polarization.

The bonding orbital is constructed as

$$\Psi_b = N\left(\lambda\psi + \varphi\right)$$

and the antibonding orbital is given by

$$\Phi = N^*\left(\psi + a\varphi\right)$$

Here, due to normalization and orthogonality properties we have

$$N^{-2} = \lambda^2 + 1 + 2\lambda S$$
$$N^{*-2} = a^2 + 1 + 2aS$$
$$\lambda + a\lambda S + a + S = 0$$

with the overlap integral, S, defined as

$$S = \int \psi\,\varphi\,d\tau$$

If the bonding orbital is mostly made up of the φ wavefunction we have $\lambda \ll 1$. It follows then that in the antibonding orbital the greatest contribution comes from ψ, and that consequently, $a \ll 1$. With these conditions and if S is much less than one the above equations reduce to

$$N^{-2} \approx 1$$
$$N^{*-2} \approx 1$$
$$a = -\left(\lambda + S\right)$$

The total wavefunction for the three electron system is, to the zero order given by the antisymmetrized product function

$$\left|\,\Psi_b\left(\alpha\right)\Psi_b\left(\beta\right)\Phi\left(\alpha\right)\,\right|$$

The α and β spin densities in the *bonding* orbital pair off, and what is left is an unpaired α spin-density located in the antibonding orbital:

$$(\text{S.D.})_\alpha = \int \left|\,\Phi\,\right|^2 d\tau$$

The spin density of ψ evaluated at B is negligible, or in other words, both of the wavefunctions ψ and φ are very localized. Then the unbalanced spin density as evaluated at B is

$$N^{*-2} a^2 \mid \varphi(B) \mid^2$$

and the fractional probability charge f_s is

$$f_s = \frac{N^{*-2} a^2 \mid \varphi(B) \mid^2}{N^{-2} \mid \varphi(B) \mid^2} = (\lambda + S)^2$$

This whole picture is directly applicable to MnF_2, if we interpret ψ as the wavefunction for the Mn^{2+} ion, and φ as the fluoride $2s$ wavefunction.[20] Experiments yield a value of $f_s = 0.50 \times 10^{-2} . S$, calculated from Hartree-Fock wavefunctions, is equal to 0.05, and we obtain $\lambda \simeq 0.02$. Hence we notice that the antibonding magnetic electrons mostly move in the metal e_g orbitals, and that consequently the pure crystalline-field model, at least for this complex, ought to be a good approximation.

It is even possible to sort out the σ and π contributions to the bonding. Reference is made here to the work by Shulman and Knox.[21,22] These authors estimated the fraction of unpaired $2s$ together with $f_\sigma - f_\pi$, and the difference between the fraction of unpaired $2p\sigma$ and $2p\pi$, for a series of compounds. This and similar work is very important, because it will in the end enable us to "map" the electronic density of the magnetic electrons, and since the method has also been shown to work[23] for very complicated systems as the big chelate compounds of Ni^{2+}.

The method of molecular orbitals is also capable of describing more complicated systems—for instance, ferrocene, $Fe(C_5H_5)_2$. The more intuitive feeling we have for the bonding of the simple "classical" complexes breaks completely down in this and similar cases. The most complete calculations of ferrocene so far performed[24,25] show, for example that of the eighteen valence electrons present (10 π-electrons from the two rings and 8 electrons from the iron), twelve will be placed in six strongly bonding molecular orbitals. The remaining six electrons (which in a certain sense can be thought of as the π-electrons in benzene) will then determine the "chemical" features of ferrocene. It may be mentioned that the spectrum[25] as well as the behaviour towards protons in ferrocene can be accounted for in this way.[26]

All in all I think we must conclude that the basic features of the bonding found in complexes can only be described using a molecular orbital picture.

It is recorded in the literature that the parrot of Captain Silver in *Treasure Island* used to call out "Pieces of eight, pieces of eight."

In the same way, many chemists in the past and present have called out "Rules of eighteen, Rules of eighteen." Even if this may be true in some cases, I hope to have demonstrated that the question of the bonding in the complexes sometimes is a bit more "complex."

REFERENCES

1. L. Pauling, *The Nature of the Chemical Bond*, Cornell University Press, 1939.
2. J. H. Van Vleck, *J. Chem. Phys.* **3**, 803, 807 (1935).
3. J. H. Van Vleck and A. Sherman, *Rev. Mod. Phys.* **7**, 167 (1935).
4. H. Bethe, *Ann. Phys.*, [5], **3**, 135 (1929).
5. R. S. Mulliken, *Phys. Rev.*, **40**, 55 (1932).
6. L. Orgel, *Transition-Metal Chemistry*, Methuen and Co., Ltd., London, 1960.
7. J. Owen, *Diss. Far. Soc.*, **19**, 127 (1955).
8. C. J. Ballhausen and A. D. Liehr, *Mol. Spectroscopy*, **2**, 342 (1958); *ibid.*, **4**, 190 (1960).
9. J. Owen and K. W. H. Stevens, *Nature*, **171**, 836 (1953).
10. M. Tinkham, *Proc. Roy. Soc. (London)*, **A236**, 535 (1956).
11. W. H. Kleiner, *J. Chem. Phys.*, **20**, 1784 (1952).
12. Y. Tanabe and S. Sugano, *J. Phys. Soc. (Japan)*, **11**, 864 (1956).
13. J. Owen, *Proc. Roy. Soc. (London)*, **A227**, 183 (1955).
14. H. B. Gray and C. J. Ballhausen, *Acta Chem. Scand.*, **15** (1961).
15. M. Wolfsberg and L. Helmholz, *J. Chem. Phys.*, **20**, 837 (1952).
16. K. W. H. Stevens, *Proc. Roy. Soc., (London)*, **A219**, 542 (1953).
17. J. H. E. Griffiths, J. Owen, and I. M. Ward, *Proc. Roy. Soc. (London)*, **A219**, 526 (1953); *ibid.*, **A226**, 96 (1954).
18. M. Tinkham, *Proc. Roy. Soc. (London)*, **A236**, 549 (1956).
19. R. G. Shulman and V. Jaccarino, *Phys. Rev.*, **108**, 1219 (1957).
20. F. Keffer, T. Oguchi, W. O'Sullivan and J. Yamashita, *Phys. Rev.*, **115**, 1553 (1959).
21. R. G. Shulman and K. Knox, *Phys. Rev. Letters*, **4**, 603 (1960).
22. R. G. Shulman and K. Knox, *Phys. Rev.*, **119**, 94 (1960).
23. W. D. Phillips and R. E. Benson, *J. Chem. Phys.*, **33**, 607 (1960).
24. E. M. Shustorovich and M. E. Dyatkina, *Doklady Akademii Nauk USSR*, **128**, 1234 (1959).
25. J. P. Dahl and C. J. Ballhausen, *Mat. Fys. Medd. Dan. Vid. Selsk.*
26. C. J. Ballhausen and J. P. Dahl, *Acta Chem. Scand.*, **15**, (1961).

KINETICS AND MECHANISMS OF
REACTIONS OF COORDINATION COMPOUNDS

ROBERT E. CONNICK

Department of Chemistry
University of California
Berkeley, California

This paper deals with two rather distinct aspects of rates of coordination reactions. The first part is concerned with the exchange of water molecules in and out of the first coordination sphere of metal ions, while the second part deals with the rates and mechanisms of interconversion of the nine monomeric chloride complexes of Ru(III).

Water Exchange

One of the most difficult types of coordination rates to measure is the exchange of bulk solvent water molecules with water molecules in the first coordination sphere of hydrated metal ions. When the reaction is slow, e.g., with Cr^{+3}, the rate may be followed by an isotopic sampling technique.[1] For the great majority of aquated metal ions, however, the rate is so great that some other method must be applied. Nuclear magnetic resonance offers such a method.

Numerous measurements have been made of the effect on the proton resonance of water of the addition of metal ions to solutions. In attempting to interpret such data in terms of the rate at which water molecules go in and out of the first coordination sphere it is never certain whether the protons move independently of the oxygens or whether the whole water molecule is exchanged. By making measurements on the oxygen isotope O^{17}, the results yield information directly on the motion of the oxygen of the water molecule. The results reported here will be concerned only with this type of measurement.

Data on the rates of water exchange for the paramagnetic ions Mn^{2+}, Cu^{2+}, Fe^{3+}, Cr^{3+}, and Ni^{2+} have been reported.[2] This work has been repeated more recently[3] using water enriched in O^{17} with the results shown in Table 1. The quantity k_1 is defined as the first order rate constant for the reaction:

$$M(H_2\overset{*}{O})^{+n} + H_2O \xrightarrow{k_1} M(H_2O)^{+n} + H_2\overset{*}{O}$$

The inverse of k_1 is the lifetime of a particular water molecule on the metal ion.

Limits on the rates of water exchange for a number of diamagnetic metal ions have been obtained by Jackson, Lemon, and Taube[4] using a different technique. They found at room temperature that the lifetime of a water molecule on the metal ion was greater than $ca.$ 10^{-4} sec for Be^{2+}, Al^{3+}, and Ga^{3+}, while it was less than $ca.$ 10^{-4} sec for Mg^{2+}, Sn^{2+}, Ba^{2+}, Hg^{2+}, and Bi^{3+}.

By studying the effect of temperature on the nuclear magnetic resonance it should be possible to tell whether the observed rate actually equals the water exchange rate, or whether it is indeed only a lower limit. In the case of paramagnetic cations the quantity observed is the increase in width of the resonance of the O^{17} caused by the paramagnetic ion. When expressed in radians per second this quantity equals the rate of transverse relaxation, which is the rate at which the nuclei lose their precessional coherence in the plane at right

TABLE 1: LOWER LIMITS FOR THE FIRST-ORDER RATE CONSTANTS
FOR WATER EXCHANGE AT $ca.$ $26\,^{\circ}C$

Ion	Lower Limit to k_1, sec^{-1}
Mn^{++}	2×10^7
Cu^{++}	3×10^6
Co^{++}	3×10^5
Ni^{++}	3×10^4
Fe^{3+}	2×10^4

angles to the large magnetic field. The rate of transverse relaxation is controlled by the slower of the two processes: (a) the rate at which water molecules enter and leave the first coordination sphere, and (b) the rate at which the transverse relaxation occurs within the first coordination sphere of the paramagnetic ions. These two processes will have different temperature coefficients in general. Process (a) should exhibit a positive temperature coefficient of the magnitude expected for a normal chemical reaction. Process (b) will have a smaller positive temperature coefficient or in certain cases a negative temperature coefficient.

The temperature dependence of the transverse relaxation of manganous ion has been investigated by Mr. T. Swift of this laboratory with the following results. The rate of transverse relaxation arising from the presence of the manganous ion shows a positive temperature coefficient at low temperatures and a negative temperature coefficient at high temperatures. The data can be interpreted in a manner similar to that of Bernheim *et al.*,[5] for the corresponding case of the nuclear magnetic resonance of protons in aqueous solutions of manganous ion. The one additional feature is that at low temperatures it is necessary to introduce a term corresponding to a rate of exchange of water molecules which is comparable to the rate of transverse relaxation in the first coordination sphere of the manganous ion.[6] Thus one has the situation that near room temperature the relaxation is governed partly by both processes. The resulting value of k_1 at 25° of 5×10^7 sec^{-1} agrees well with the rate constant for the exchange of protons found by Bernheim *et al.*,[5] and substantiates the suggestion of Pearson *et al.*[7] that the protons exchange through exchange of the entire water molecule.

Similar temperature studies are underway on other paramagnetic ions.

Interconversion of Chloride Complexes of Ru(III)

With the identification[8] of the nine monomeric ruthenium(III) chloride complexes, one has a rather extensive group of similar complexes for studying the effect on rates of reaction of replacing water molecules by chloride ions in the coordination sphere of the metal ion and of measuring the relative effects of *cis* and *trans* arrangements. The results reported here were obtained by Dr. D. A. Fine and Dr. E. E. Mercer in this laboratory.

Approximate values of the equilibrium quotients expressed in moles per liter are given in Tables 2 and 3. It is presumed that the ruthenium is octahedrally coordinated and that any of the six positions not occupied by chloride ion are filled with water molecules. The identification of the *cis* and *trans* species is not certain; it is based on the observation in a number of similar cases that the *trans* isomer is held less tightly by an ion-exchange resin than the *cis* species.[9]

The most striking observation concerning the rates of interconversion is the tremendous increase in the rate of replacement of a

TABLE 2: FORMATION QUOTIENTS FOR SUCCESSIVE CHLORIDE COMPLEXES AT 25 °C

Reaction	Equilibrium Quotient	Ionic Strength
$RuCl^{2+} + Cl^- = RuCl_2^+$	~ 30 M^{-1}	$0.1\ M$
$RuCl_2^+ + Cl^- = RuCl_3$	2.7 M^{-1}	$0.1\ M$
$RuCl_3 + Cl^- = RuCl_4^-$	0.8 M^{-1}	$3\ \ M$
$RuCl_4^- + Cl^- = RuCl_5^{2-}$	$\sim 0.14\ M^{-1}$	$5\ \ M$
$RuCl_5^{2-} + Cl^- = RuCl_6^{3-}$	~ 0.1 M^{-1}	$5\ \ M$

TABLE 3: *TRANS-CIS* EQUILIBRIUM QUOTIENTS AT 25 °C

Reaction	Equilibrium Quotient	Ionic Strength
$RuCl_2^+$ (*trans*) = $RuCl_2^+$ (*cis*)	~ 1	0.1 M
$RuCl_3$ (*trans*) = $RuCl_3$ (*cis*)	0.3	0.1 M
$RuCl_4^-$ (*trans*) = $RuCl_4^-$ (*cis*)	4.	3 M

chloride ion by a water molecule as one increases the number of chlorides bound to the ruthenium. Thus the half-time for loss of a chloride ion from $RuCl^{2+}$ is probably greater than one year at room temperature whereas the conversion of $RuCl_6^{3-}$ to $RuCl_5^{2-}$ occurs in less than a few seconds; i.e., more than 10^7-fold faster. Qualitatively this result is in agreement with the crystal-field theory which predicts that the activation energy would decrease as chlorides replace water molecules because the crystal-field splitting, according to spectral observations, is less for chloride ion than for water.[10] Acceptance of this conclusion must be tempered by the fact that relative rates of reaction of ligands do not follow the spectral series closely[10] and that ferric ion, which should have no crystal-field stabilization, shows a similar increase in lability with an increasing number of chlorides.[11]

Another possible rationalization of the above effect is that the chloride ions remaining on the ruthenium may more readily adjust their electron clouds to the strained electronic configuration existing in the activated complex. The much greater polarizability of chloride ion is evidence for the possibility of such an effect.

Reference to the equilibrium quotients of Table 1 shows that the great change in rates does not arise from effects in the equilibrium configurations. Thus simple electrostatic and steric effects seem unlikely sources of an explanation. Nor is there evidence from the equilibrium data for any drastic change in the bond character in the successive complexes.

Rate laws have been established and rate constants measured for several of the interconversions. The reactions connecting $RuCl^{2+}$ and $RuCl_3$ are shown in Table 4. All are first order reactions except the addition of Cl^- to $RuCl_2^+$ which is second order. There is no effect of a hydrogen ion on the rates in the neighborhood of 0.1 M H^+.

Assuming no inversion in configuration on the loss or gain of a chloride ion, as is found for other similar reactions in acidic solution,[10] the data of Table 4 are seen to be consistent with a *trans* labilizing effect. Thus a position opposite a chloride appears to have enhanced reactivity relative to a position opposite a water molecule.

TABLE 4: RATE CONSTANTS FOR INTERCONVERSIONS AT 25°C

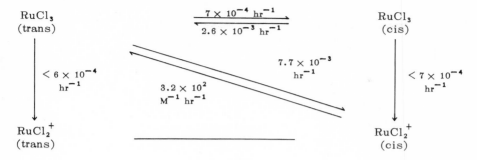

The *trans* $RuCl_3$ goes to *cis* $RuCl_2^+$ and vice versa; the *trans* $RuCl_3$ loses a chloride at least ten times more rapidly than a *cis* $RuCl_3$.

The ease with which isomerization of $RuCl_3$ occurs is rather striking; it may be accounted for in the following way. Presumably a chloride is held more tightly than a water molecule, and it is likely that water exchange is occurring rather rapidly. A small fraction of the times when a water molecule is lost the chlorides may change their configuration as the new water molecule enters. As a partial check on the above hypothesis, it would be interesting to measure the water exchange rate.

Qualitative observations have been made on the other rates of interconversion of the complexes. As far as is known the results are similar to those of Table 4 in that a *trans* effect appears to control the course of the reactions. These results will be reported in more detail.

REFERENCES

1. J. P. Hunt and H. Taube, *J. Chem. Phys.*, **19**, 602 (1951).
2. R. E. Connick and R. E. Poulson, *J. Chem. Phys.*, **30**, 759 (1959).
3. R. E. Connick and E. D. Stover, to be published.
4. J. A. Jackson, J. F. Lemon, and H. Taube, *J. Chem. Phys.*, **32**, 553 (1960).
5. R. A. Bernheim, T. H. Brown, H. S. Gutowsky, and D. E. Woessner, *J. Chem. Phys.*, **30**, 950 (1959).
6. H. M. McConnell, *J. Chem. Phys.*, **28**, 430 (1958).
7. R. G. Pearson, J. Palmer, M. M. Anderson, and A. L. Allred, *Z. für Electrochem.*, **64**, 110 (1960).
8. (a) H. H. Cady and R. E. Connick, *J. Am. Chem. Soc.*, **80**, 2646 (1958); (b) R. E. Connick and D. A. Fine, *J. Am. Chem. Soc.*, **82**, 4187 (1960); D. A. Fine, Thesis, University of California Lawrence Radiation Laboratory Report UCRL-9059, Feb. 2, 1960.
9. (a) E. L. King and R. P. Walters, *J. Am. Chem. Soc.*, **74**, 447 (1952); (b) J. T. Hougen, K. Schlug, and E. L. King, *ibid.*, **79**, 519 (1957);

    (c) E. L. King, M. J. M. Woods, and H. S. Gates, *ibid.*, **80**, 5015 (1958); (d) M. Mori, M. Shibata and J. Azami, *Nippon Kagaku Zasshi*, **76**, 1003 (1955); (e) M. Mori, M. Shibata, and M. Nanasawa, *Bull. Chem. Soc. Japan*, **29**, 247 (1956).

10. F. Basolo and R. G. Pearson, *Mechanisms of Inorganic Reactions*, John Wiley and Sons, Inc., New York, 1958.

11. R. E. Connick and C. P. Coppel, *J. Am. Chem. Soc.*, **81**, 6389 (1959).

THE SYNTHESIS OF COORDINATION COMPOUNDS

FRANCIS P. DWYER

Biological Inorganic Chemistry Section
John Curtin School of Medical Research
Australian National University
Canberra, A. C. T., Australia

Since the time of Werner, there have been no dramatic advances in the synthetic methods of coordination chemistry, but rather an increasing awareness of the fundamental principles involved. Much has been learned, from comprehensive studies of dissociation constants and of complex equilibria in aqueous solution, about the affinities of ligands and the best experimental conditions for their coordination to metals. The resultant sophistication in metal complexes has been notably enhanced in the last decade by kinetic studies of substitution reactions and the mechanisms of electron transfer. Synthetic work is now considered hardly respectable except as a means to a physical measurement or to demonstrate or elucidate a theoretical concept. Though the emphasis has passed from synthesis to properties and theoretical development, it is, nevertheless, opportune that the classical, half-intuitive syntheses should be examined in the light of present knowledge, and that attention should be directed to simpler and quantitatively more satisfactory methods.

Cobalt(III) Complexes

The unique position of cobalt in coordination chemistry, both as regards the number and variety of known complexes, and their relative ease of synthesis, arises from three factors: the lability of the aquo Co^{2+} ion and Co(II) complexes in general, the inertness of the Co(III) complexes towards substitution, and the slow rates of electron transfer between Co(II) and Co(III) complexes. Though an analogous situation exists with chromium, the strong reducing action of the Cr(II) ion introduces difficulties. With the heavier analogs of cobalt, (rhodium and iridium) the bivalent states for the most part are inaccessible, and the tervalent states (usually complex) comparatively inert.

Though synthesis involving ligand substitution in Co(III) complexes can often be effected, the usual procedure is to assemble the complex in the Co(II) state and then oxidise. Some consideration of the factors cited above is valuable. The aerial oxidation at room temperature of an aqueous mixture of cobalt(II) salt, ammonium chloride, and a high concentration of ammonia yields a mixture of Co(III) ammines containing 4, 5 and 6 coordinated ammonias with the other positions filled with aquo and/or chloro groups. From the known rates of ligand exchange with these Co(III) complexes under the above-cited experimental conditions it can be concluded that there is a qualitative but not necessarily a quantitative identity between the oxidised product and the mixture of species likely to be present in the unoxidised solution. This can only be the case if the Co(II) species are all being oxidised at various rates. Because of the rapid attainment of equilibrium between the Co(II) complexes and the observed comparative slowness of the oxidation reaction, one might anticipate almost exclusively one Co(III) complex, i.e., corresponding to the most easily oxidised Co(II) complex. The redox potential of the oxidising agent, which is usually at least 0.5 volt more negative than the irreversible Co(II) – Co(III) complex couples, is not important, but rather its accessibility to one Co(II) complex rather than to another. Movement of the equilibrium undoubtedly favors the most rapidly oxidised species in the final product, even though it may occur in minimal amounts in the equilibrium mixture. In aqueous solution in the presence of ammonia the $[Co(NH_3)_6]^{3+}$ ion is thermodynamically stable.[1] Thermodynamically unstable species are preserved not only by their inertness to direct substitution, but probably, in most instances, by the slowness of electron transfer (oxidation) towards Co(II) species. The relatively fast rate[2] of the reaction $[Coen_3]^{2+} + [Co(NH_3)_6]^{3+} \longrightarrow [Coen_3]^{3+} + [Co(NH_3)_6]^{2+}$ in the presence of ethylenediamine, which involves a free-energy decrease, would not seem a general phenomenon. There is apparently only an infinitesimal exchange in the reverse reaction. It will be evident, however, that a condition for the synthesis of thermodynamically unstable Co(III) complexes is that the rate of electron transfer between Co(II) complexes and the oxidising agent must be fast compared with the transfer between Co(II) and Co(III) complexes.

Since, almost inevitably, the Co(II) solution to be oxidised will contain a mixture of complexes, efforts are generally made to ensure the maximum concentration of the reduced species appropriate to the synthesis. This difficulty is, of course, most obvious where "mixed" complexes, e.g., $[Coen_2Cl_2]Cl$, are being prepared. Simple variation in the ratios of ligands often suffices. The composition of the mixture of ammonia, ammonium salts, Co^{2+} ion, and nitrite ion determines whether $[Co(NH_3)_3(NO_2)_3]$, $NH_4[Co(NH_3)_4(NO_2)_2]$, or $[Co(NH_3)_4(NO_2)_2]NO_3$ is the predominant product.[3,4,5] Composition can be controlled semi-quantitatively rather than intuitively by knowledge of the relative complexing tendencies of the ligands towards the Co(II) state. Precise knowledge, however, is lacking about dissociation constants in the more complex equilibria, e.g., $[Co(NH_3)_4(NO_2)_2] \rightleftharpoons Co^{2+} + 4NH_3 + 2NO_2^-$.

The reduction of the oxidising agent usually leads to pH changes. The common agents, O_2 and H_2O_2 generate hydroxyl ion, persulfates are converted to bisulfates, lead dioxide and red lead yield different amounts of the weakly basic litharge, permanganate and dichromate consume hydrogen ions. These pH changes must be taken into account in order to avoid continuous change in the effective ligand-metal ratio, and to avoid hydroxo complexes; but they may be used advantageously. These principles are illustrated in the recent syntheses of the ethylenediaminebis(oxalato) cobaltate(III), and oxalato bis(ethylenediamine) cobalt(III) ions.[6] The stability of the bis(oxalato) cobaltate(II) ion is low, and precipitation of cobalt(II) oxalate in aqueous solution can only be prevented by a very high concentration of oxalate ions (potassium oxalate). The concentration of free ethylenediamine must be controlled to prevent the existence of appreciable amounts of the favored $[Coen_2C_2O_4]^0$, or $[Coen_3]^{2+}$ ion in the equilibrium, whilst maintaining the overall stoichiometry. This was done by using ethylenediamine dihydrochloride. Lead dioxide was found to be the best oxidising agent at 100°, the litharge formed liberating a slow, fairly constant, amount of free ethylenediamine. The deep green tris(oxalato)cobaltate(III) ion was apparently not formed at any stage of the reaction. The preparation of the $[Coen_2C_2O_4]^+$ ion in good yield necessitated that the concentration of the free ethylenediamine be kept sufficiently high to obviate the formation of any $[Coen(C_2O_4)_2]^-$ ion in the oxidation—otherwise the highly insoluble $[Coen_2C_2O_4][Coen(C_2O_4)_2]$ would be precipitated—but not so high that very much $[Coen_3]^{2+}$ would be present. Oxidation with lead dioxide of a mixture of cobalt(II) sulfate, and ethylenediamine oxalate (2 mol), gave the desired complex. The lead(II) ion was precipitated continuously as sulfate. It is not known whether oxidation occurs on the surface of lead dioxide or free radicals (OH) are involved.

The completion of any synthesis requires isolation of the product in a pure form. An obvious help is the use of oxidising agents that yield water: oxygen and hydrogen peroxide, or those that can be precipitated such as lead dioxide, red lead, or selenium dioxide which is reduced to insoluble selenium. Chlorine or bromine often attack the ligand rapidly or become implicated in the complex, e.g., in the preparation of $[CoEDTA \cdot Br]^{2-}$ ion.[7,8] Potassium dichromate is contraindicated because of the possibility of contamination with Cr(III) complexes, and, like potassium permanganate, because of the necessity of eliminating soluble Mn(II) and Cr(III) salts. An excellent starting material for many Co(III) complex syntheses is sodium tris(carbonato-cobaltate(III), which reacts directly with weakly acidic, but does not destroy, easily oxidisable substances.[9,10] With ethylenediamine di-hydrochloride, (3 mols), $[Coen_3]^{3+}$ ion was obtained smoothly with the liberation of carbon dioxide. Dithiols displaced the carbonate group without appreciable oxidation, to yield the tris(dithio)cobaltate(III) complexes. The low solubility of $Na_3[Co(CO_3)_3]$ is a practical disadvantage; the potassium salt, if it could be isolated easily,[10] would be better.

Very soluble complex cations can often be isolated conveniently as the tri-iodide anion, either by adding potassium tri-iodide or a mixture of acetic acid and potassium iodide followed by hydrogen peroxide. The tri-iodide is then converted to the iodide by passing sulfur dioxide through a cold alcoholic suspension. Complex anions or cations are often useful precipitating agents. It is generally desirable that the ionic charges be the same to effect the least solubility. The tris(carbonato) cobaltate(III) ion was first isolated as the hex-ammine cobalt(III) salt.[11] The very soluble aquo(propylenediamine-tetra-acetic) chromate(III) ion has been isolated as the insoluble *trans*-dinitrobis(ethylenediamine) cobalt(III) salt,[12] and this cation then eliminated with sodium perchlorate.

Substitution Reactions in the Synthesis of Co(III) Complexes

Substitution of one ligand for another is a common synthetic procedure. Though at one time many of these reactions were envisaged as being quite analogous to double decomposition, kinetic and mechanism studies have shown that often a series of intermediate complexes precedes the final product. In the reaction $[Coen_2Cl_2]^+ + C_2O_4^{2-} \longrightarrow [Coen_2C_2O_4]^+ + 2Cl^-$, aquation and isomerisation precede the addition of the oxalate group, probably attached then as a unidentate ligand. Much more effective syntheses are possible as the result of such information.

The substitution of nitro and carbonato groups for aquo groups in *cis*-diaquobis(ethylenediamine) cobalt(III) ion proceeds with full retention of the configuration—the two Co-O bonds remaining intact. This has been shown by oxygen isotope studies with the former substitution[13] and by the reaction of bicarbonate ion with the optically pure isomers in the latter.[14] The reverse action $[Coen_2Co_3]^+ + 2H^+ \xrightarrow{20°} cis\text{-}[Coen_2(H_2O)_2]^{3+} + H_2O + CO_2$ also proceeds with the retention of configuration. A mixture of the *cis* and *trans* isomers was obtained in almost quantitative yield by the reaction $2CoCl_2 + 2en \cdot 2HCl + PbO_2 + 2H_2O \xrightarrow{100°} 2[Coen_2(H_2O)_2]Cl_3 + PbCl_2$. After cooling, and removal of the lead chloride (and excess dioxide), the aqueous mixture was stirred at 80 ° with lithium carbonate until strongly alkaline, when both di-aquo isomers were transformed to the carbonato complex.[14] Isomerisation of the *trans* diaquo complex proceeds slowly in acid and alkaline solution but rapidly in neutral solution.[15] After removal of the excess lithium carbonate, and addition of a little calcium chloride to eliminate carbonate ion, the $[Coen_2CO_3]Cl$ could be precipitated in high yield, (85%) by adding alcohol, in which both LiCl and $CaCl_2$ are soluble. Treatment with cold dilute hydrochloric acid yielded a solution of *cis*-$[Coen_2-(H_2O)_2]Cl_3$ which could be transformed quantitatively to *cis*-$[Coen_2(NO_2)_2]Cl$ by allowing to stand with sodium nitrite. Evaporation of the solution of $[Coen_2(H_2O)_2]Cl_3$ to dryness yielded *cis*-$[Coen_2Cl_2]Cl$ quantitatively. In this instance, isomerisation is known to occur in the hot solution, the equilibrium being displaced as the less soluble *cis* isomer separates.[16]

A potentially valuable substance for the preparation of bis(oxalato) complexes is Durrant's salt $K_4[(Co(C_2O_4)_2OH)_2]$. This can be expected to behave as two bis(oxalato) hydroxo-aquo cobalt(III) anions in substitution reactions with, for example, glycine to yield the glycinatobis(oxalato) cobaltate(III) ion.

Dismutation in Substitution Reactions

"Mixed" amine complexes have been usually prepared by replacement of chloro, nitro and/or ammonia groups. Werner,[17] for instance, used the series of reactions $[Co(NO_2)_3(NH_3)_3] \xrightarrow{en} [Coen\ NH_3(NO_2)_3] \xrightarrow{pn} [Coenpn(NO_2)_2]^+$ to prepare dinitro(ethylenediamine)(propylenediamine) cobalt(III) ion. All ten of the theoretical isomers (geometrical and optical) were claimed to have been isolated. A similar reaction sequence[18] has been used to prepare chloro(ethylenediamine)-(diethylenetriamine) cobalt(III) chloride, the final nitro group being eliminated with hydrochloric acid.

A number of "mixed" tris(diamines) have been synthesised by the reaction between *cis*- and *trans*-dichlorobis(diamine) cobalt(III) salt and another diamine with or without solvent, at room temperature, or up to 100 °. In this way were prepared propylenediamine bis(ethylenediamine) cobalt(III),[19] 1,10-phenanthroline bis(ethylenediamine) cobalt(III),[20] *trans*-1-2-cyclopentanediamine bis(ethylenediamine) cobalt(III) ions.[20] The attempted synthesis of ethylenediamine bis(cyclopentanediamine) cobalt(III) chloride, yielded only a mixture of $[Coen_3]Cl_3$ and $[Co(cptdin)_3]Cl_3$. Attention was drawn to the simultaneous production of $[Coen_3]Cl_3$ in some of the above syntheses.

A systematic survey of substitution of chloro and nitro groups by diamines, made during studies of the stereospecific effects of optically active ligands in octahedral complexes, has shown that substantial dismutation takes place. The reaction of l-propylenediamine and cis- or $trans$-dichlorobis(ethylenediamine)cobalt(III) chloride in water, methanol or dimethyl formamide was found to yield a practically inseparable mixture of tris-diamines.[21] After fractional crystallization, the molar ratio l-pn/en was found to vary from 0.00 to 2.0 in various fractions. As will be shown later, all of the possible tris(diamine) complexes were formed in the synthesis. It might be emphasised that elemental analysis of the reaction product does not necessarily have any significance where strict stoichiometry has been observed with the reactants. Because of partial racemate formation, recrystallisation may not separate mixtures of tris(diamine) complexes derived from chemically similar bases.

Partition chromatography on cellulose has now been used[14] to study the composition of the reaction product obtained from l-propylenediamine (1 mol), and cis-dichloro- and cis-dinitrobis(ethylenediamine) chlorides in dimethylformamide, (25 °), and water, (90 °) respectively. Preliminary tests on paper strips using 3% concentrated hydrochloric acid in water-saturated n-butanol as eluent showed four bands. The fastest moving material was identified by a marker of L-[Co-pn$_3$]Cl$_3$, but markers showed that the most intense, slowest moving band coincided with either d,l-[Coen$_3$]Cl$_3$, or D[Co l-pn$_3$]Cl$_3$. In some tests small amounts of cobalt(II) salts and/or unchanged [Coen$_2$(NO$_2$)$_2$]Cl were detected. After separation of the faster moving substances, the slow moving band was separated into four components by using as eluent perchloric acid in water-saturated butanol. These separations were also carried out on a large scale on cellulose pulp (0.6 Kg) in a column (2' long × 3" diameter). The various fractions were extracted with water and the solid obtained by evaporation. Identification was made by analysis, and the en/pn ratio. The substances obtained in order of elution were: hydrochloric acid, L-[Co l-pn$_3$]Cl$_3$, L-[Co l-pn$_2$en]Cl$_3$, L-[Coen$_2$ l-pn]Cl$_3$; perchloric acid, D-[Co l-pn$_3$]Cl$_3$, D-[Co l-pn$_2$en]Cl$_3$, D-[Co en$_2$ l-pn]Cl$_3$, D,L-[Coen$_3$]Cl$_3$. The relative amounts of the substances isolated are shown in Table 1. The latter data were obtained from paper strips, from which the respective bands were cut, eluted with water and estimated spectrophotometrically.

The same substances were obtained by the serial oxidation of mixtures of ethylenediamine, l-propylenediamine, (2:1, and 1:2), cobalt chloride (1 mol), and hydrochloric acid, (1 mol) in the presence of charcoal. The relative amounts of the tris(diamines) formed (Table 1) are determined by the ratios of the two bases, their relative affinities

TABLE 1: ETHYLENEDIAMINE-*l*-PROPYLENEDIAMINECo(III) COMPLEXES

	From [Coen$_2$Cl$_2$]Cl %	From [Coen$_2$(NO$_2$)$_2$]Cl %	Direct Synthesis *l*-pn/en = 1:2 %	*l*-pn/en = 2:1 %
L-[Coen$_2$ *l*-pn]$^{3+}$	27	28	27	15
L-[Coen *l*-pn$_2$]$^{3+}$	10	17	18	37
L-[Co- *l*-pn$_3$]$^{3+}$	13	4	6	30
D-[Co en$_2$*l*-pn]$^{3+}$	17.5	15.5	13	7
D-[Co en *l*-pn$_2$]$^{3+}$	1	3.5	3	5
D-[Co *l*-pn$_3$]$^{3+}$	<1	1	<1	2
D,L-[Co en$_3$]$^{3+}$	31	31	32	4

for the metal, and, as well, the stereospecific limiting function of the *l*-propylenediamine.

Similarly, the reaction product from 1,10-phenanthroline, (1 mol) and *cis*-[Coen$_2$Cl$_2$]Cl (1 mol) in water at 95°, using aqueous-butanol-hydrochloric acid eluent on paper was found to consist of four substances.[14] The two minor components have been identified as the simple tris compounds [Coen$_3$]Cl$_3$ and [Co phen$_3$]Cl$_3$. Presumably, the main products, present in roughly equal amounts, were [Coen$_2$phen]Cl$_3$ and [Coen phen$_2$]Cl$_2$.

The synthesis of chloro(ethylenediamine)(diethylenetriamine) cobalt(III) chloride quoted above[18] can be carried out by either of two reaction sequences to the mono(nitro) complex which is then treated with concentrated hydrochloric acid:

(1) $[Co(NH_3)_3(NO_2)_3] \xrightarrow{\text{dien}} [Co\ NH_3(dien)(NO_2)_2]^+ \xrightarrow{\text{en}}$

$$[Co\ en(dien)NO_2]^{2+}$$

(2) $[Co(dien)(NO_2)_3] \xrightarrow{\text{en}} [Co(dien)en\ NO_2]^{2+}$

Fractional crystallisation from methanol and ethanol with the object of separation of the three possible geometrical isomers, also showed that both reaction sequences yielded appreciable amounts of [Coen$_3$]Cl$_3$ and [Co dien$_2$]Cl$_3$ as well as cobalt(II) chloride.

The racemization of [Co en$_3$]$^{3+}$ ion in the presence of hot aqueous ethylenediamine has been shown to involve both [Coen$_3$]$^{3+}$ ion and free ethylenediamine in the activated state, presumably as a 7- or 8-covalent spin-free intermediate.[22] This observation has been confirmed by Dwyer and Sargeson,[23] who showed, in addition, that if sufficient ethylenediamine was present, some [Co en$_3$]Cl$_2$ resulted. Complete conversion of the Co(III) to the Co(II) complex, which could be isolated in crystalline form, was found to occur when [Co en$_3$]Cl$_3$ was heated at 110° in a sealed tube.

It will be evident from Table 1 that the replacement of chloro and nitro groups from [Co en$_2$Cl$_2$]Cl and [Co en$_2$(NO$_2$)$_2$]Cl is not a typical substitution reaction, since the composition of the product is very similar to that derived from the oxidation of the stoichiometric mixture of the bases and cobalt(II) chloride. In methanol or dimethylform-amide solution, dissociation of a chlorine atom from the [Co en$_2$Cl$_2$]$^+$ ion to yield a 5-covalent intermediate may well precede the addition of propylenediamine, as a unidentate ligand, which then completes its coordination by the dissociation or displacement of the second chlorine atom. Dismutation would appear to necessitate a 7- or 8-covalent spin-free intermediate from which either ethylenediamine or propylene-diamine may dissociate. With the [Co en$_2$(NO$_2$)$_2$]$^+$ ion, the higher temperatures used, and the slower rates of reaction suggest a similar mechanism, but a [Co en$_2$ pn(NO$_2$)$_2$]$^+$ intermediate cannot be excluded. When l-[Coen$_2$Cl$_2$]I was allowed to react in methanol with ethylenediamine, the recovered [Co en$_3$Cl$_3$] was slightly levorotatory, ($[\alpha]_D = -5°$). From the specific rotation of the pure tris complex ($[\alpha]_D = -154°$), it will be seen that there is some 3% retention of configuration in the reaction. It has been shown that dissociation of a chlorine atom from [Co en$_2$Cl$_2$]Cl is contemporaneous with racemization and isomerisation in methanol solution.[24] The small retention of configuration gives no clear indication of the extent of the dismutation reaction, nor can calculations be readily made from the data in Table 1 because of unknown stereospecific influences.

Dismutation does not appear to occur, nor is any Co(II) complex detectable in the reaction between *cis*-[Co en$_2$Cl$_2$]Cl with liquid or alcoholic ammonia. It might be thought that hydroxyl ion, a strong nucleophile, is an important factor, but 1,10-phenanthroline is a weak base, and yields, as we have seen a mixture of products. Further, the usual mixture of tris(diamines) results[14] from the reaction of *cis*-[Co en$_2$(NO$_2$)$_2$]Cl and aqueous propylenediamine in the presence of acetic acid, (pH, 6.5).

Catalysts and Co(III) Complexes

Charcoal was first used by Bjerrum[25] as a catalyst in a series of experiments designed to bring about rapid equilibrium between cobalt complexes in solution. The equilibrium in the reactions [Co(NH$_3$)$_6$]$^{3+}$ + H$_2$O $\rightleftharpoons$ NH$_4^+$ + [Co(NH$_3$)$_5$OH]$^{2+}$ $\rightleftharpoons$ [Co(NH$_3$)$_5$H$_2$O]$^{3+}$ + NH$_3$ lies far to the right and is attained very slowly. Catalysis was observed with colloidal mercury or platinum in a nitrogen atmosphere and in the presence of Co^{2+} ion, but charcoal proved to be most effective even in the absence of the latter ion. Earlier, Schwarz and Kronig[26] had shown that when [Co(NH$_3$)$_6$]Cl$_3$ was shaken with charcoal in aqueous solution, the color changed to purplish red, due, they presumed, to the formation of the chloropentammine complex, and, as well, ammonia was liberated. Bjerrum[27] found that oxidation of a mixture of Co(II) salt, ammonium salt and ammonia in the presence of charcoal yielded the $[Co(NH_3)_6]^{3+}$ ion almost exclusively. Charcoal may also be added to the standard synthetic mixture used for the preparation of tris(ethylenediamine) cobalt(III) chloride when aerial oxidation proceeds very much more rapidly.[14] Dwyer and Garvan[12] have found that the Co(II) complexes of polyaminocarboxylic acids are oxidised incompletely by hydrogen peroxide, but subsequent addition of charcoal and the passage of air through the solution effects almost quantitative oxidation.

The use of charcoal in synthetic procedures necessitates strict cognisance of its true function in bringing about equilibrium between the various possible *Co(III)* species. In many reactions the desired product is not the complex with the lowest free-energy amongst those that may be formed—e.g., $[Co\,en_2(H_2O)_2]^{3+}$ from Co(II) salts and ethylenediamine (2 mols)—and labilisation of the Co(III) state thus defeats the synthetic objective. This aspect of the catalysis is illustrated by the work of Bailar and Work,[28] who aerated solutions containing hexammine cobalt(III) and nitrite ions in the presence of charcoal. Although the relative bonding tendencies of ammonia and nitrite towards Co(III) appear to be similar, free-energies favor the neutral complex $[Co(NH_3)_3(NO_2)_3]$, which was formed almost exclusively.

The charcoal catalysed racemization of *dextro*-tris(ethylenediamine)cobalt(III) ion in aqueous solution at 90 ° was discovered by Douglas.[29] With catalytically active charcoal, (vide infra), racemization can be effected at room temperature in 15 minutes, though in the absence of catalyst, the optical activity appears to persist indefinitely in boiling aqueous solution. Charcoal brings about racemization of the ethylenediaminetetraacetatocobaltate(III) ion, at room temperature in 15 minutes.

Although Schwarz and Kronig[26] did not observe the formation of any Co(II) salts or complexes in their experiments and Bjerrum[25] found that addition of Co^{2+} ion was unnecessary in the presence of charcoal, some reduction of the Co(III) complex does, in fact, always occur. At 100 °, after boiling $[Co\,en_3]Cl_3$ solution in the presence of charcoal for 3 minutes, approximately 4% cobalt(II) ion was detected after acidification; but at room temperature only a few parts per million were found, although racemization was complete in both instances.[30]

Charcoal and other surface extended catalysts—e.g., silica gel, colloidal metals—probably act by rendering the paramagnetic spin-free state of Co(III) more accessible. The transition from spin-paired to spin-free involves some expansion of the complex, and bond labilisation. Rearrangements as well as ligand dissociation are facilitated. Because of the non-equivalence of the electronic states, the potential of most complex cobalt(II) – complex cobalt(III) couples is irreversible, and the rates of electron transfer are slow. The potential[31] of the couple [Co en$_3$]$^{2+}$ spin-free – [Co en$_3$]$^{3+}$ spin-paired is usually taken as + 0.232 V., but the potential of the couple [Co en$_3$]$^{2+}$ spin-free – [Co en$_3$]$^{3+}$ spin-free is probably very much more negative. As a result, the mild reducing action of charcoal can be expected to yield some reduced Co(III) complex.

As pointed out previously, the slow rate of electron transfer between Co(II) and Co(III) complexes is a valuable property in the synthesis of many mixed Co(III) complexes. The rate of electron transfer, however, is enormously catalysed[30] by charcoal. For example the complete electron-transfer racemization of d-[Co en$_3$]Cl$_3$ in the presence of d-l[Co en$_3$]Cl$_2$ required 8 days at 25°, but, in the presence of charcoal, less than 2 minutes. The catalytic equilibration and racemisation reactions thus appear to occur by two routes: (1) labilisation through a spin-free activated state on the catalyst surface, and (2) rapid electron transfer between the equivalent (labile) Co(II) complexes—generated as a by-product of (1)—and the spin-paired Co(III) complex. Dwyer and Sargeson[30] have found that acid inhibits the racemization, and the small rotational loss observed (6%), coincides almost completely with the amount of Co(II) salt found (4%), in the solution. This suggests that racemization in the absence of acid was due chiefly to the catalyst-mediated electron transfer. However under other circumstances route (1) may well be predominant.

Most varieties of activated charcoal appear to catalyse the racemization of [Co en$_3$]$^{3+}$ ion in hot solution, but not at room temperature. Freshly activated samples operate at the lower temperatures, but slowly deteriorate. Aging appears to be associated with the loss of reducing centers. This can often be rectified by the addition of small amounts of a reducing agent such as iodide or sulfite ion. Finely divided metals—Pt, Pd, Rh, Hg—also promote the spin-free state, but traces of reducing agent are necessary to make them efficient equilibrium catalysts.[30] More active catalysts—Raney nickel, copper, silver—in the presence of halide ion, are themselves reducing agents, and complete decomposition of Co(III) complexes may occur.

Chromium(III) Complexes

Like cobalt the Cr(II) state is labile and may be used to assemble the complex, which is then oxidised, usually by oxygen, to the inert

Cr(III) complex. Data on the electron exchange rates between Cr(II) and Cr(III) complexes are scanty, but for most complexes slow rates are to be expected. The positive potential of the Cr^{2+} aq.–Cr^{3+} aq. couple introduces manipulative difficulties in the preparation and storage of the Cr(II) salts, and in the assemblage of the Cr(II) complex. Some ligands, e.g., 1,10-phenanthroline are reduced. As a result, direct addition of ligand to the Cr(III) state, by displacement of aquo or chloro groups, is to be preferred. The slow rates of displacement of aquo groups, especially by nitrogen donors, have led to the use of anhydrous salts. Tris(ethylenediamine) chromium(III) salts are usually prepared by the action of anhydrous ethylenediamine on the anhydrous chloride or sulfate.[32] In aqueous solution chromium(III) hydroxide and various red or purple "olated" complexes result. It has been shown that charcoal catalyses the direct formation of $[Cr\ en_3]^{3+}$ ion but not $[Cr(NH_3)_6]^{3+}$ in aqueous solution. The catalysis is of low efficiency, and the mechanism is obscure. It is inconceivable that even traces of Cr(II) ion or complex ion may be formed by such a weak reducing agent. One can speculate that in some way the Cr–O bond is weakened, though general labilisation, as with Co(III) complexes, is contra-indicated by the observation of Bjerrum and Lamm[33] that charcoal has very little effect on the rate of aquation of $[Cr(NH_3)_6]^{3+}$ ion. Rollinson and Bailar[32] have surveyed the preparative methods for hexammine chromium(III) salts, all of which necessitate the use of anhydrous chromium(III) chloride, and, usually, liquid ammonia. The reaction generally becomes very slow when the chloropentammine stage is reached, but may be catalysed by sodium amide. The amide ion is a strongly nucleophilic reagent, and the replacement of the chlorine atom is quite analogous to substitution reactions involving hydroxyl ion. The intermediate amide complex by reaction with ammonia regenerates the amide ion.

Traces of zinc dust are sometimes added to synthetic mixtures involving anhydrous chromium(III) chloride in alcohol, e.g., the preparation[34] of $[Cr\ bipy_2Cl_2]Cl$. The small amounts of Cr(II) salt produced probably accelerate the dissolution of the anhydrous salt in the alcohol—a phenomenon well-known when water is the solvent and ascribed to electron transfer—but it is not certain that any effect is exerted on the rate of formation of the Cr(III) complex. Coordination of bases through the hexa-aquochromium(III) ion can often be effected in suitable anhydrous solvents. Green $CrCl_3 \cdot 6H_2O$ when dissolved in hot dimethylformamide coordinates with ethylenediamine[14] and 1,10-phenanthroline[35] to yield $[Cr\ en_3]Cl_3$ and $Cr\ phen\ Cl_3$. Hexa-(urea)chromium(III) chloride 3-hydrate is often a good starting material, and has been used in aqueous solution to prepare potassium tris(thio-oxalato)chromate(III). Rapid hydrolysis of the thio-oxalate ion, and the slow displacement of water from the aquo-Cr(III) ion operate together to give poor yields.[36] The hexa-urea complex also reacts with warm anhydrous ethylenediamine to give [Cr en$_3$]Cl$_3$ in good yield.[14]

The problem of the slow replacement of coordinated water has been overcome in some syntheses by the use of dichromate salts. The classic example is the production of ammonium tetra(thiocyanato) di-amminechromate(III) by the pyrolysis of a mixture of ammoniumdi-chromate and thiocyanate. Bis- and tris(oxalato)complexes usually are prepared from potassium dichromate and oxalic acid. In the synthesis of *cis*-diaquobis(oxalato)chromate(III) ion,[37] a homogeneous mixture is moistened and then heated to start the reaction, which proceeds spontaneously with the liberation of carbon dioxide, reduction to the Cr(III) state, and complex formation in the almost complete absence of liquid water. The coordination chemistry of chromium is not nearly so comprehensive as that of cobalt. Considerable scope remains for the development of new synthetic methods.

REFERENCES

1. H. Taube, *Chem. Reviews,* **50,** 73 (1952).
2. W. B. Lewis, C. D. Coryell and J. W. Irvine, *J. Chem. Soc.,* **1940,** S.386.
3. S. M. Jorgensen, *Z. anorg. Chem.,* **5,** 192 (1894); **17,** 468 (1898).
4. W. G. Palmer, *Experimental Inorganic Chemistry,* Cambridge, 1954, pp. 537-539.
5. W. E. Cooley, C. F. Liu and J. C. Bailar, *J. Am. Chem. Soc.,* **81,** 4189 (1959).
6. F. P. Dwyer, I. K. Reid and F. L. Garvan, *ibid,* **83,** (1961).
7. L. M. Morris and D. H. Busch, *ibid.,* **78,** 5178 (1956).
8. G. Schwarzenbach, *Helv. chim. Acta,* **32,** 839 (1949).
9. H. F. Bauer and W. C. Drinkard, *J. Am. Chem. Soc.,* **82,** 5031 (1960).
10. M. Mori, *Bull. Soc. Chem. Japan,* **29,** 883 (1956).
11. T. P. McCutcheon and W. J. Schuele, *J. Am. Chem. Soc.,* **75,** 1845 (1953).
12. F. P. Dwyer and F. L. Garvan, *ibid.,* **83,** (1961).
13. R. K. Murmann and H. Taube, *ibid.,* **78,** 4886 (1956).
14. F. P. Dwyer and A. M. Sargeson, Unpublished work.
15. J. Bjerrum and S. E. Rasmussen, *Acta Chem. Scand.,* **6,** 1265 (1952).
16. F. Basolo and R. G. Pearson, *Mechanism of Inorganic Reactions,* Wiley, New York, 1958, p. 242.
17. A. Werner and A. P. Smirnoff, *Helv. chim. Acta,* **1,** 5 (1918).
18. R. G. Pearson, C. R. Boston and F. Basolo, *J. Phys. Chem.,* **59,** 304 (1955).
19. P. Pfeiffer, I. Grassman and H. Pietsch, *Z. anorg. Chem.,* **58,** 301 (1908).
20. F. M. Jaeger and H. B. Blumendal, *Z. anorg. Chem.,* **175,** 161 (1928).
21. F. P. Dwyer and A. M. Sargeson, *J. Am. Chem. Soc.,* **81,** 5269 (1959).
22. W. H. Gehman and W. C. Fernelius, *J. Inorg. Nuclear Chem.,* **9,** 71 (1959).

23. F. P. Dwyer and A. M. Sargeson, *J. Phys. Chem.* In press.
24. D. D. Brown and R. S. Nyholm, *J. Chem. Soc.,* **1953,** 2696.
25. J. Bjerrum, *Metal Ammine Formation in Aqueous Solution,* P. Haase, Copenhagen, 1941, pp. 235–251.
26. R. Schwarz and W. Kronig, *Ber.,* **56,** 208 (1923).
27. J. Bjerrum and J. P. McReynolds, *Inorganic Syntheses,* **2,** 216 (1946).
28. J. C. Bailar and J. B. Work, *J. Am. Chem. Soc.,* **67,** 176 (1945).
29. B. E. Douglas, *ibid.,* **76,** 1020 (1954).
30. F. P. Dwyer and A. M. Sargeson, *Nature,* **187,** 1022 (1960).
31. Ref. 25, pp. 223–233.
32. C. L. Rollinson and J. C. Bailar, *J. Am. Chem. Soc.,* **65,** 250 (1943).
33. J. Bjerrum and C. G. Lamm, *Acta Chem. Scand.* **9,** 216 (1955).
34. F. H. Burstall and R. S. Nyholm, *J. Chem. Soc.,* **1952,** 3570.
35. J. A. Broomhead, Thesis, Australian National University, 1961.
36. F. P. Dwyer and A. M. Sargeson, *J. Am. Chem. Soc.,* **81,** 2335 (1959).
37. Ref. 4, pp. 387–388.

STRUCTURE AND STEREOCHEMISTRY
OF COORDINATION COMPOUNDS

R. J. GILLESPIE

Department of Chemistry,
McMaster University
Hamilton, Ontario, Canada

The stereochemistry of inorganic molecules and complex ions is generally discussed in terms of the simple valence-bond theory that has been developed by Pauling and others according to which the directional character of covalent bonds is attributed to their being formed from directed atomic orbitals such as p or d orbitals, or from sp^n or $sp^m d^n$ hybrid orbitals. [1,2] Although this theory has had a long and justified popularity, it has a number of limitations and it is the purpose of this paper to discuss an alternative theory which appears to be able to account for some of the features of molecular structure for which the valence-bond theory does not seem to provide adequate explanations. As an example of one of the limitations of the valence-bond theory we may consider five and six-coordination. The bonds are regarded as being formed from directed hybrid orbitals formed from a set of one s, three p, and either one or two d orbitals. However the set of five d-orbitals are not spatially equivalent, and if the $d_{x^2-y^2}$ orbital is chosen, valence-bond theory predicts a square pyramidal bond arrangement but if the d_{x^2} orbital is chosen, a trigonal bipyramidal bond arrangement is predicted. Similarly for six coordination the set of six $sp^3 d_{x^2-y^2} d_{z^2}$ hybrid orbitals is associated with an octahedral molecular shape, whereas the set of six $sp^3 d_{xz} d_{yz}$ hybrid orbitals is associated with a trigonalprism bond arrangement. The difficulty is that there is no very satisfactory way of choosing between these alternatives. Arguments based on the possibility of slightly better overlap with one type of orbital than the other are not very helpful because the real shapes of the orbitals are only known approximately and the extent of overlap can only be calculated approximately. If it is known that the shape of a molecule is, for example, octahedral, then the bonding orbitals may be conveniently described as being formed from $sp^3_{x^2-y^2} d_{z^2}$ hybrid orbitals on the

34

central atom, but this does not explain why the molecule has an octahedral shape in the first place.

Sidgwick and Powell's Postulates

Sidgwick and Powell[3] pointed out in 1940 that the arrangement of the electron pairs in the valency shell of an atom appears to depend only on the total number of electron pairs including both bonding pairs and lone-pairs. For 2, 3, 4, 5 and 6 electron pairs in a valency shell they gave the spatial arrangements shown in Table 1. More recently Gillespie and Nyholm[4] have shown that these empirical postulates can be used to account for the shapes of virtually all the molecules and complex ions of the non-transition elements having a total of not more than six electron pairs in the valency shell of the central atom. These rules also apply to molecules in which the central atom is a transition element if it has a d^0 or a d^{10} configuration. Some examples are given in Table 1. For transition elements with 1 to 9 non-bonding electrons in their valency shells, however these simple rules need some modification as is discussed later.

The Spin Correlation Theory

Since these empirical postulates are so successful in accounting for molecular shape, it is important to consider their quantum mechanical basis. The arrangement or spatial correlation of the electrons in a valency shell arises from their mutual interactions which are of two kinds: electrostatic repulsion, which gives rise to charge correlation between the electrons; and the interaction that arises from the operation of the Pauli exclusion principle, which gives rise to spin correlation between the electrons.[5] It is a physical consequence of the Pauli exclusion principle, which states that the total wave function for any polyelectronic system must be antisymmetric to electron interchange, that electrons with parallel spins tend to keep apart, while electrons with opposite spins tend to be drawn together.[5] Spin correlation causes the electrons in a valency shell to arrange themselves in close pairs of opposite spin which keep as far apart from each other as possible.[5,6] Thus, as a consequence of the operation of the Pauli exclusion principle, the electrons in a valency shell are arranged in the same manner as if there were a repulsive force acting between pairs of opposite spin. This apparent repulsive force is of exactly the same nature as that which comes into play when two inert gas atoms or closed-shell ions are brought together. As the electron orbitals overlap, the Pauli exclusion principle operates so

TABLE 1: ARRANGEMENTS OF ELECTRON PAIRS IN VALENCY SHELLS AND THE SHAPES OF MOLECULES*

Number of Electron Pairs in Valency Shell	Arrangement	Number of Bonding Pairs	Number of Lone Pairs	Shape of Molecule	Examples
2	Linear	2	0	Linear	$HgCl_2$, $Ag(CN)_2^-$
3	Equilateral triangle	3	0	Equilateral triangle	BF_3
		2	1	V-Shape	$SnCl_2$ (vapour)
4	Tetrahedron	4	0	Tetrahedral	BF_4^-, $TiCl_4$, $Zn(NH_3)_2Cl_2$, $Cu(CN)_4^{3-}$
		3	1	Trigonal pyramid	NH_3, PCl_3
		2	2	V-shape	H_2O, F_2O
5	Trigonal bipyramid	5	0	Trigonal bipyramid	PCl_5, $NbCl_5$, $TaCl_5$
		4	1	SeF_4†	SeF_4, $TeCl_4$, $(CH_3)_2TeCl_2$, PbO
		3	2	T-shape	ClF_3, BrF_3, $C_6H_5 ICl_2$
		2	3	Linear	ICl_2^-, I_3^-
6	Octahedron	6	0	Octahedron	MOF_6, PCl_6^-, $SnCl_6^{2-}$, TiF_6^{2-}, VF_6^-
		5	1	Square pyramid	IF_5, $SbCl_5^{2-}$
		4	2	Square	ICl_4^-

*Non-transition elements and transition elements with d^0 and d^{10} configurations.

†The lone-pair is in an equatorial position.

as to keep electrons of parallel spin out of the same region of space: thus the electron distribution of each atom or ion is distorted and the energy of the system is raised so that there is in effect a repulsive force between the two atoms or ions. Pairs of electrons in any two orbitals of the same atom will "repel" each other in an exactly similar manner. Thus as a consequence of spin correlation it is evident that two electron pairs in a valency shell will have a linear arrangement, three pairs a planar triangular arrangement, and four pairs a tetrahedral arrangement, as these arrangements maximise the distance between any pair of electrons and thus minimise their interactions.[7]

The most probable arrangements for more than four electron pairs are not so obvious. We now consider a possible method by which they may be obtained. If we make the assumption that all the electron pairs in a valency shell are at the same average distance from the nucleus, then we need only consider their angular distribution and each electron pair may be represented as a point moving on the surface of a sphere whose radius equals the average distance of the electrons from the nucleus. The problem then reduces to that of finding the most stable arrangement of a given number of such points under the action of an appropriate law of force. The repulsive forces that exist between the closed shells of two inert gas atoms or ions with inert gas configurations are negligibly small when there is very little overlap between the electron shells but increase rapidly with increasing overlap. These forces are generally represented as being approximately proportional to some large inverse power of the interelectron distance, i.e., the repulsive force is proportional to $1/r^n$ where r is the average distance between the electron pairs and n is in the range 8–12. The repulsive force between the electron pairs in a valency shell may be described in the same manner. If the repulsive force were due to electrostatic interaction alone, then the interaction would be described by the inverse square law. It has been shown that the most probable arrangements of 2, 3, 4, 5, 6, 8 and 9 electron pairs are the same for both the $1/r^n$ and $1/r^2$ force laws and are the linear, planar triangular, tetrahedral, trigonalbipyramidal, octahedral, square antiprism and the "3.3.3" arrangement respectively (Table 2 and Fig. 1). For seven electron pairs the most stable arrangement for a $1/r^n$ force law is the "1.3.3" arrangement while for the $1/r^2$ force law it is the pentagonal bipyramid.[6] For two to six electron pairs these are exactly the arrangements postulated by Sidgwick and Powell which have been shown to account for the shapes of virtually all the molecules of the non-transition elements. It seems reasonable to suppose, therefore, that this method also cor-

TABLE 2: EQUILIBRIUM ARRANGEMENTS OF SIMILAR PARTICLES ON THE SURFACE OF A SPHERE

Number of Particles	Arrangement
2	Linear
3	Equilateral triangle
4	Tetrahedron
5	Trigonal bipyramid
6	Octahedron
7	Pentagonal bipyramid, $(1/r^2)$; "1.3.3",* $(1/r^n)$
8	Square antiprism
9	"3.3.3"†

*This arrangement is obtained by adding one extra point over the centre of one rectangular face of a trigonal prism.

†This arrangement is obtained by adding an extra point over each rectangular face of a trigonal prism.

rectly predicts the arrangements of eight and nine electron pairs. These predicted arrangements are now compared with the experimentally observed shapes of molecules with a central atom having these numbers of electron pairs. Seven-coordination for which the predictions of this method are not quite so certain is also considered.

Eight-Coordination

For eight electron pairs the predicted arrangement is the square antiprism; therefore, we expect the shape of a molecule or complex ion whose central atom has eight bonding and no non-bonding electron pairs in its valency shell to be that of a square antiprism (Fig. 2). The cubic arrangement which has often been suggested for eight-coordination is obviously unstable with respect to the square antiprism, as turning one face of a cube through 45° to obtain a square antiprism, increases the distance between any pair of corners on these opposite faces and thereby decreases the interaction between electron pairs in these positions. It is interesting to find that the *only* shape that has been found for eight-coordinated molecules with no non-bonding electrons in their valency shells is the square antiprism. One other shape is known for eight-coordination, namely that found for $Mo(CN)_8^{4-}$, but in this case the central atom is a transition-metal with two non-bonding d-electrons; this is discussed later.

Only two simple mononuclear complexes involving eight-coordination have had their structures determined, namely the tantalum octafluoride ion, TaF_8^{3-}, and thorium acetylacetonate, $Th(C_5H_7O_2)_4$ and both have the predicted square antiprism structure.[8,9] However, eight-coordination is also found in a number of polynuclear com-

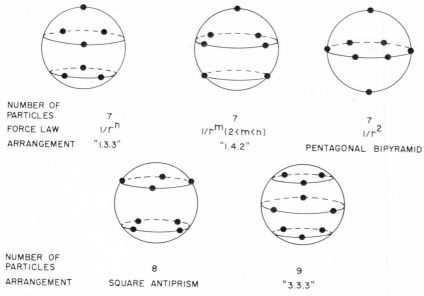

NUMBER OF
PARTICLES   7   7   7
FORCE LAW $1/r^n$ $1/r^m (2 < m < n)$ $1/r^2$
ARRANGEMENT   "1.3.3"   "1.4.2"   PENTAGONAL BIPYRAMID

NUMBER OF
PARTICLES   8   9
ARRANGEMENT   SQUARE ANTIPRISM   "3.3.3"

Fig. 1. Equilibrium arrangements of particles on the surface of a sphere:

Number of particles	7	7	7
Force law	$1/r^n$	$1/r^m$ $(2 < m < n)$	$1/r^2$
Arrangement	"1.3.3"	"1.4.2"	Pentagonal bipyramid
Number of particles		8	9
		Square antiprism	"3.3.3"

plexes whose structures have been determined. Lundgren has investigated a number of basic salts of Ce(IV) and Th(IV),[10,11,12] In
$Th(OH)_2CrO_4 \cdot H_2O$, and $Th(OH)_2SO_4$ there are polynuclear complex
ions with the formula $[Th(OH)_2^{2+}]_n$ in which each thorium atom is

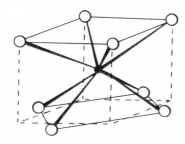

Fig. 2. Square-antiprism eight-coordination.

bonded to four OH groups arranged in the form of a square. Eight-coordination around each thorium is completed by four oxygen atoms from each of four separate chromate or sulphate groups; these four oxygen atoms also being arranged at the corners of a square that is parallel to, but rotated through 45°, the square formed by the OH groups. There is, therefore, a square antiprism of oxygen atoms around each thorium atom. The compound $CeOSO_4 \cdot H_2O$ contains polynuclear ions of the formula $(CeO^{2+})_n$ in which each Ce is coordinated to three oxygen atoms at three of the corners of a square. The square is completed by a water molecule and again square antiprism eight-coordination around the cerium atoms is completed by four oxygen atoms from sulphate groups. The basic sulphate with the formula $Ce_6O_4(OH)_6(SO_4)_6$, however, has a different structure containing the finite complex ion $[Ce_6O_4(OH)_4]^{12+}$ (Fig. 3). In this ion the metal atoms are situated at the corners of an octahedron and are surrounded by eight oxygen atoms at the corners of a cube. Thus each cerium is coordinated to four oxygen atom arranged at the corners of a square. Square-antiprism eight-coordination around the cerium is completed by four more oxygen atoms, one from each of four sulphate groups. Crystalline hydrated zirconyl chloride, $ZrOCl_2 \cdot 8H_2O$, has been found to contain the cy-

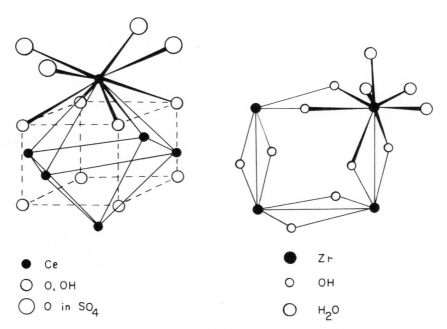

● Ce   ● Zr

○ O, OH   ○ OH

◯ O in SO_4 ◯ H_2O

Fig. 3a and b. Structures of $[Ce_6O_4(OH)_6](SO_4)_6$ and $[Zr_4(OH)_8(H_2O)_{16}]^{8+}$.

clic tetranuclear cation $[Zr_4(OH)_8(H_2O_{16})]^{8+}$ which has the structure shown in Fig. 3.[13] The four zirconium atoms are arranged in the form of a square, with two OH groups bridging each pair of zirconium atoms along the sides of the square, one OH being above and the other below the plane of the square. Four water molecules are also bonded to each zirconium and they are arranged in such a way as to complete a square antiprism arrangement of ligands around the zirconium atom.

The $Mo_6Cl_8^{4+}$ Cation

Brosset[14] has determined the structure of the $Mo_6Cl_8^{4+}$ cation and shown that it consists of a regular octahedron of molybdenum atoms circumscribed by a cube of chlorine atoms, each molybdenum atom lying approximately in the plane of four chlorine atoms constituting a face of the cube, (Fig. 4). Each molybdenum atom is therefore bonded to eight other atoms: four molybdenum atoms at the adjacent corners of the octahedron and four chlorine atoms at the corners of a square, which is parallel to, but rotated through 45° with respect to, the square formed by the four molybdenum atoms. There is therefore a very distorted square antiprism arrangement of ligands around each molybdenum atom. However, the arrangement of the bonding electrons must approximate more closely a square antiprism than the arrangement of the ligands. Each chlorine forms three bonds to molybdenum atoms and the Mo-Cl-Mo angles are only 60°. However,

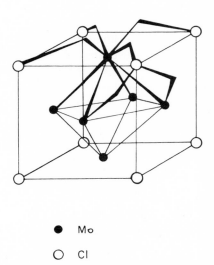

●   Mo

○   Cl

Fig. 4. Structure of the $Mo_6Cl_8^{4+}$ ion.

it is most unlikely that three of the four electron pairs in the valency shell of a chlorine atom would be so close together. The most probable arrangement for four electron pairs is tetrahedral and the angle between bonding pairs is unlikely to be less than 90° since at this angle repulsions between the electron pairs of second row elements become relatively large.[15] It is very probable that the angles between the three bonding pairs at each chlorine are slightly greater than 90° and this can only be reconciled with the structure of the complex if the Mo—Cl bonds are bend—i.e., if the most probable location of the bonding pair is not on the line joining the two nuclei. If this is the case, then the arrangement of electron pairs around each molybdenum approximates closely the expected square antiprism.

Nine-Coordination

For nine electron pairs the predicted arrangement is the "3.3.3" arrangement, i.e., the trigonal prism with an electron pair opposite the centre of each of its three rectangular faces. Therefore molecules whose central atom has a valency shell containing nine-bonding electron pairs and no non-bonding electron pairs would be expected to have this structure (Fig. 5). Unfortunately no mononuclear complexes of this type have had their structures determined. The only nine-coordinated mononuclear complex ion whose structure is known is the $Nd(H_2O)_9^{3+}$ ion in crystalline $Nd(BrO_3)_3 \cdot 9H_2O$ [16] which does have the structure shown in Fig. 5, although the neodymium atom has two non-bonding 4f electrons which appear to have no effect on the arrangement of the nine-bonding pairs. The effect of non-bonding electrons on the arrangements of bonding electrons in transition and lanthanide element complexes is discussed later. Nine-coordination has been found in a number of crystalline solids that do not contain discrete complex ions. For example, crystalline $SrCl_2 \cdot 6H_2O$ con-

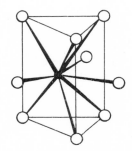

Fig. 5. Nine-coordination.

tains infinite one-dimensional complex ions $[Sr(H_2O)_6^{2+}]_n$ in which the strontium atom is nine-coordinated by water molecules having the predicted "3.3.3" arrangement.[16] Barium chloride has a structure involving the same nine-coordinated arrangement of chlorine atoms around each barium atom.[16] Lead and some lanthanide dihalides and some actinide and lanthanide trihalides and trihydroxides also have structures involving the same type of nine-coordination of the metal atom. Although in these cases the metal atom also has non-bonding electrons, these do appear to affect the arrangement of the bonding electrons. It is interesting to note that the structure shown in Fig. 5 is the only one that has been found for nine-coordination.

Seven-Coordination

For seven electron pairs the most probable arrangement for a $1/r^n$ force law is an octahedron somewhat distorted by a seventh pair opposite one of its faces, i.e., a "1.3.3" arrangement, while for an inverse square force law the equilibrium arrangement of seven particles is the pentagonal bipyramid, i.e., a "1.5.1" arrangement. It seems reasonable to suppose that as the exponent n is decreased, the equilibrium arrangement will pass from the "1.3.3" arrangement to the "1.5.1" arrangement through an intermediate "1.4.2" arrangement, i.e., a trigonal prism that is distorted by the seventh pair opposite one of its rectangular faces (Fig. 1). It is interesting to find that iodine heptafluoride and the ions $UO_2F_5^{3-}$ and ZrF_7^{3-} have the pentagonal bipyramid structure based on the "1.5.1" arrangement of seven electron pairs, while the ions TaF_7^{2-}, NbF_7^{2-} and $NbOF_6^{2-}$ have a distorted trigonal prism structure based on the "1.4.2" arrangement of seven electron pairs. In the A-modification of the M_2O_3 oxides of La, Ce, Pr, and Nd the metal atoms are seven-coordinated by oxygen atoms which have the distorted octahedral arrangement based on the "1.3.3" arrangement of seven electron pairs. The factors which determine which of these three possible shapes are adopted in any particular molecule or complex ion are not clear at the present time.

The Effect of Non-bonding Electrons on Molecular Shape

For molecules and ions containing up to six electron pairs in the valency shell of the central atom any non-bonding electrons are found to occur in localised pairs which play an equal part with the bonding pairs in determining the stereochemistry. Thus, the angular shape of the water molecule is essentially determined by the presence of two non-bonding electron pairs and the fact that the IF_5

molecule has a square pyramidal rather than a trigonal bipyramidal shape is essentially determined by the presence of a non-
bonding electron pair. However, when there are more than six
electron pairs in the valency shell, non-bonding electrons do
not in general appear to have such an important influence on molecular shape. For example, in the six-coordinated complexes of
the transition metals there are six bonding pairs and one or
more non-bonding d-electrons. The arrangement of six ligands in a
transition metal complex is invariably octahedral, i.e., it is the same
as would be obtained in the absence of the non-bonding d-electrons.
In terms of the Sidgwick and Powell postulates one would have to
say that the non-bonding d electrons were not part of the valency
shell but were occupying an inner non-bonding shell that interacted
only slightly with the ligand electrons. This would correspond to a
weak-field complex in ligand-field theory. In such weak-field complexes the d electrons as far as possible occupy separate orbitals
keeping their spins parallel and such complexes are therefore paramagnetic. However many ligands do interact quite strongly with the
non-bonding d-electrons as is shown for example by the spin-pairing
and consequent reduction in the magnetic moment that occurs in
strong-field complexes. According to the ligand-field theory the
electric field of six octahedrally arranged ligands causes a splitting
of the five d-orbitals, which are degenerate in the absence of an external field, into a group of three, d_{xy}, d_{xz}, and d_{yz}, of low energy
(d_ϵ orbitals) and a group of two, $d_{x^2-y^2}$ and d_{z^2}, of higher energy
(d_γ orbitals). Calculation of the energy difference between the d_ϵ
and the d_γ orbitals on the basis of the simple electrostatic theory,
however, gives values that are considerably smaller than those that
are obtained experimentally.[17] This is because this theory ignores
the other important interaction between the electrons, namely, spin-
correlation arising from the operation of the Pauli exclusion principle. Thus, as the orbital containing the lone pair electrons on the
ligand atom approaches and overlaps the d orbitals of the metal atom
the d electrons are forced away from the ligands into orbitals which
have a minimum of interaction with the ligand orbitals; for an octahedral complex these are the d_ϵ orbitals. Transition elements of the
first transition series never have coordination numbers greater than
six; although their valency shells can contain up to nine electron
pairs, three of these must be non-bonding electron pairs occupying d_ϵ
orbitals. The question then arises as to why these nine electron
pairs do not have the "3.3.3" arrangement with the six ligands at
the corners of a trigonal prism and three electron pairs in the
equatorial positions (Fig. 5).

It appears that for a valency shell containing six bonding electron pairs the system has a lower energy if any non-bonding electrons, up to a maximum of six, occupy "delocalised" atomic d_ϵ orbitals rather than localised hybrid orbitals similar to the bonding pairs. The analagous situation for four bonding and one non-bonding electron pair confined to move in a plane is shown in Fig. 6; in this case (a) is of lower energy than (b). It appears likely, however, that the energy difference between these two different electron arrangements may not be very large and, in suitable cases, the "localised" arrangement of the non-bonding electrons may be preferred. This may be the case in ferrocene and related molecules.

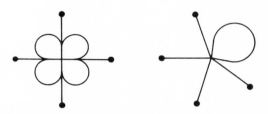

Fig. 6. Possible arrangements of four bonding electron pairs and a single non-bonding pair in a plane.

There are nine electron pairs in the valency shell of the iron atom of ferrocene. Three pairs may be regarded as bonding each of the two cyclopentadiene groups; the six bonding pairs having a trigonal prism arrangement, while the six non-bonding electrons form three localised pairs, one opposite each rectangular face of the trigonal prism (Fig. 7). The electron pairs presumably have this "3.3.3" arrangement because if the ferrocene molecule had a structure based on the octahedral arrangement of six bonding electron pairs the d_ϵ orbitals would have their maxima directed towards the C-C bonds of the cyclopentadiene groups. In the structure shown in Fig. 7, however, the non-bonding electrons are located as far away as possible from the ligands. Some evidence for the existence of localised lone-pairs on the iron atom in ferrocene is provided by the observation that this molecule is weakly basic and that protonation appears to take place on the iron atom and presumably, therefore, on one of the localised lone pairs. [18]

For weak-field or spin-free complexes the interaction between the ligand electron pairs and the non-bonding d electrons is too weak to cause any deviation from the expected octahedral structure for any

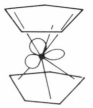

Fig. 7. Bonding in the ferrocene molecule.

number of d electrons. The non-bonding d electron orbitals are closer
to the nucleus than the bonding electron pairs and they overlap or
interact with each other to a negligible extent. For spin-paired or
strong-field complexes, the interaction between the bonding electron-
pairs and the d electrons is sufficiently large to cause them to move
into the d_ϵ orbitals. If there are more than six non-bonding d electrons, they cannot all move out of the way of the ligand electrons in
this way and there must be some distortion of the octahedron. It is
noteworthy, however, that the distortion that is observed is not an angular distortion, such as is produced by non-bonding electrons in valency shells containing less than six electron-pairs but the octahedron is distorted so that two *trans*-bonds become longer than the other
four as in $Pd(diarsine)_2I_2$ [19] or in various Cu(II) complexes.[20] According to ligand-field theory in complexes with 7, 8 or 9 d electrons 1, 2 or 3 of these respectively must occupy the d_ϵ orbitals. If
one or two of these electrons are in the d_{z^2} orbital or one in the
$d_{x^2-y^2}$ and two in the d_{z^2} then they will repel the two ligands on the
z-axis so that these two bonds are longer than the other four. An
alternative way of looking at this is to recall that if there were 10 d
electrons they would constitute a spherical closed shell but when
one, two or three d electrons are missing, the shell is no longer symmetrical but may be regarded as approximately elliptical in shape, and
this causes a corresponding distortion of the octahedral arrangement
of the bonding electron pairs.

The $Mo(CN)_8^{4-}$ and $U_6O_4(OH)_4^{12+}$ Ions

In the complex ions $Mo(CN)_8^{4-}$ and $U_6O_4(OH)_4^{12+}$ the metal atoms
have a valency shell containing eight bonding pairs and two non-
bonding electrons.

The $U_6O_4(OH)_4^{12+}$ ion has the same structure as the corresponding
cerium complex ion in which there is a square antiprism arrangement
of ligands around the metal atom. Uranium(IV) compounds are gener-

ally paramagnetic and therefore the non-bonding electrons probably occupy two separate $5f$ orbitals. This uranium complex may therefore be regarded as being of the weak-field type in which there is only a small interaction between the non-bonding $5f$ electrons and the eight bonding pairs which is not sufficient to distort the favoured square-antiprism arrangement of the eight bonding pairs.

The $Mo(CN)_8^{4-}$ ion, which is dimagnetic, does, however, have a different structure than is shown in Fig. 8. Evidently this must be regarded as a strong-field complex in which there is strong in-

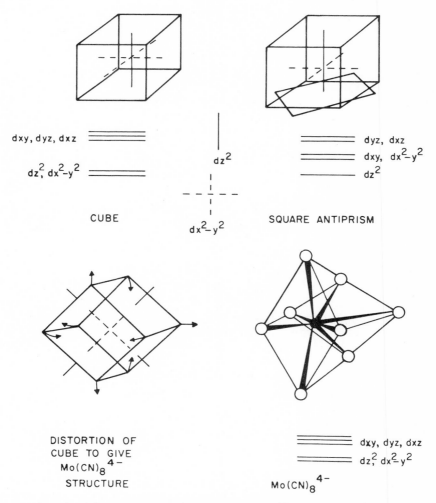

Fig. 8. Cubic, square-antiprism, and $Mo(CN)_8^{4-}$ eight-coordination.

teraction between the bonding electron-pairs and the non-bonding electrons. Figure 8 shows the splitting of the d-levels produced by cubic, square antiprism and the $Mo(CN)_8^{4-}$ arrangements of ligands. For the square antiprism arrangement of ligands the d_{z^2} orbital has a lower energy than the other d-orbitals and could accommodate the non-bonding pair without any appreciable distortion of the square antiprism arrangement. It is very likely that the stability of the $Mo(CN)_8^{4-}$ ion is at least partly due to the formally non-bonding pair being involved in double bonding with the cyanide groups as occurs in other transition metal complex cyanides such as $Fe(CN)_6^{3-}$. The orientation of the d_{z^2} orbital however, is such that it cannot overlap to any appreciable extent with the $2p$ orbitals of the carbon atoms. Very much better overlap with the $2p$ orbitals of all eight carbon atoms would be achieved if the eight cyanide groups had a cubic arrangement and the non-bonding pair occupied the $d_{x^2-y^2}$ orbital. However, the cubic arrangement of the ligands does not minimise the bonding electron interactions, and the cubic arrangement will if possible distort to a more stable arrangement. If there are no non-bonding pairs, or if a single non-bonding pair is free to occupy the d_{z^2} orbital then the cube distorts to give the square antiprism, but if the non-bonding pair is in the $d_{x^2-y^2}$ orbital then the square antiprism cannot be the most stable arrangement since this orbital has lobes directed towards four of the ligands. However the cube can be distorted as indicated in Fig. 8 so as to maintain a minimum interaction between the bonding pairs and the non-bonding electrons in the $d_{x^2-y^2}$ orbital and at the same time reduce the interaction between the bonding pairs. This distortion produces the $Mo(CN)_8^{4-}$ structure. We conclude, therefore, that the $Mo(CN)_8^{4-}$ structure is a consequence of the interactions between the eight bonding and one non-bonding electron pairs and of the tendency of the non-bonding pair to occupy the $d_{x^2-y^2}$ orbital so that it can take part in double bonding with the cyanide groups.

REFERENCES

1. L. Pauling, *Nature of the Chemical Bond*, 3rd Edition, Cornell University Press, 1960.
2. G. E. Kimball, *J. Chem. Phys.*, **8**, 188 (1940).
3. N. V. Sidgwick and H. M. Powell, *Proc. Roy. Soc.*, **176**, 153 (1940).
4. R. J. Gillespie and R. S. Nyholm, *Quart. Revs.*, **9**, 339 (1957).
5. J. W. Linnett, *Wave Mechanics and Valency*, Methuen, London, 1961.
6. R. J. Gillespie, *Can. J. Chem.*, **38**, 818 (1960).
7. P. G. Dickens and J. W. Linnett, *Quart. Revs.* **9**, 291 (1957).
8. J. L. Hoard, W. J. Martin, M. E. Smith and J. F. Whitney, *J. Am. Chem. Soc.*, **76**, 3820 (1954).

9. D. Grednic and B. Matokovic, *Nature*, **182**, 465 (1958).
10. G. Lundgren, *Arkiv Kemi*, **6**, 59 (1953).
11. G. Lundgren, *ibid.*, **2**, 535 (1950).
12. G. Lundgren, *Rev. Trav. Chim.*, **75**, 585 (1956).
13. A. Clearfield and P. A. Vaughan, *Acta Cryst.*, **9**, 555 (1956).
14. C. Brosset, *Arkiv. Kemi Mineral. Geol.*, **A22**, 1 (1946).
15. R. J. Gillespie, *J. Am. Chem. Soc.*, **82**, 5978 (1960).
16. A. F. Wells, *Structural Inorganic Chemistry*, Oxford University Press, 2nd Edition, 1950.
17. L. E. Orgel, *An Introduction to Transition Metal Chemistry*, Methuen, London, 1960.
18. T. J. Curphy, J. O. Santer, M. Rosenblum and J. H. Richards, *J. Am. Chem. Soc.*, **82**, 5250 (1960).
19. C. M. Harris, R. S. Nyholm and N. C. Stephenson, *Nature*, **177**, 1127 (1956).
20. J. D. Dunitz and L. E. Orgel, *Advances in Inorganic Chemistry and Radiochemistry*, **2**, 1, (1960).

HYDROGEN AND ORGANIC DERIVATIVES OF TRANSITION METALS

G. WILKINSON

Imperial College of Science and Technology
London, England

The subject of this paper covers such a diverse and rapidly expanding range of transition metal chemistry that to survey all of the developments since the last International Conference on Coordination Chemistry is an impossible task, but unfortunately it is not necessary to do so since a number of reviews [1-5] have recently been published in addition to the excellent comprehensive summaries of recent work.[6] In both of these areas, however, we are dealing mainly with diamagnetic molecular or ionic species, soluble in organic or other solvents, and containing hydrogen atoms bound either to the metal atom or to carbon ligands. These species are hence especially amenable to study by high-resolution nuclear magnetic resonance techniques; indeed some recent advances could not have been made so quickly, if at all, without this physical tool. Accordingly I have chosen to discuss those topics where n.m.r. measurements have been essential to or extensively used in the elucidation of the problems at hand.

TRANSITION METAL TO HYDROGEN BONDS AND BONDING INTERACTIONS

Metal to Hydrogen Bonding

It is now some years since it was observed that hydrogen atoms which are directly bound to transition metal atoms in the complexes $(\pi-C_5H_5)_2ReH$[7] and $HCo(CO)_4$,[8] have exceptionally large chemical shifts to high fields. Since it was thought that this high-field shift might indicate high electron density at the proton and a very close association of the hydrogen and metal atoms, an attempt was made[9] to ascertain the metal to hydrogen distance by a broad-line n.m.r. study at low temperatures of the only readily accessible suitable compound, $H_2Fe(CO)_4$. From the measured inter-proton distance it was possible, by making certain reasonable assumptions about the symmetry of the molecule, to estimate the Fe-H distance. This estimate, *ca.* 1.1 Å, showed that the Fe-H distance was comparable with, if not actually smaller than, the radius of the metal atom itself. No other estimates of transition metal to hydrogen bond distances are yet available, although they are very desirable; they are not easy to measure. Although this sole estimate could be said to substantiate the view that the bond can be pictured as a proton buried in the electron density of the metal atom, it is hazardous to assume similar short distances in other compounds with M——H bonds; nor is it justifiable to conclude, since all species with M——H bonds thus far measured show, like $H_2Fe(CO)_4$, one or more high-field resonance lines, that the M——H bond distance is similarly short. In the first place, it appears from both spectroscopic and dimensional evidence that in the hydrocarbonyls the metal-carbon monoxide skeleton is not extensively distorted by the hydrogen atoms——i.e., the latter do not appear to occupy a bond position——so that, for example, $HMn(CO)_5$ in its physical properties[10] resembles $Fe(CO)_5$ and its infrared spectrum[11] shows that it is certainly not octahedral. By contrast X-ray diffraction measurements[12]——which do not show up the hydrogen atoms however——have shown that in $[(C_2H_5)_3P]_2PtBrH$ the ligand atoms are approximately square planar with the hydrogen atom apparently occupying a normal bond position. In the di-π-cyclopentadienyl metal hydrides discussed below, it also seems necessary to require that a bond position be occupied by hydrogen. It is clear that further structural studies on hydride complexes are desirable.

Concerning the characteristic high-field line, it must be noted that so far all of the shifts have been measured in solutions or for pure liquids; however, it seems unlikely that solvent effects can be responsible for the large shifts. It is known that electron density effects are by no means the sole or even most important factors influencing chemical shifts. If the atom to which hydrogen is bound has non-bonding electrons, then these can have induced in them, by the applied magnetic field, paramagnetic electron circulation which generates a counter field at the proton site resulting in the shift of the proton resonance to higher fields.[13] Thus in the hydrogen halides, the paramagnetic effect increases with increasing size of the halogen atom so that in hydrogen iodide[14] the shift approaches the region observed for protons bound to transition metal atoms. For the latter, however, the shifts are much greater than those where hydrogen is bound to other heavy metal atoms such as tin or lead. Hence the high-field shift may be due to the fact that any non-bonding

electrons will be in d or hybrid d orbitals. An additional complication is that when π-bonding ligands are also present on the metal
atom, the metal to ligand bonds will have some π-character; thus
these bonds will show marked magnetic anisotropy and could give
rise to long-range magnetic effects at the proton site (cf., the discussion of olefin complexes below). When π-C_5H_5 rings are present,
circulating currents in the rings may have an effect, in addition to
any effects due to secondary π-bonding, in the metal-to-ligand bond.
No estimates of the likely magnitudes of these effects in transition
metal complexes have yet been made. However, it certainly seems
that the absolute magnitude of the proton shifts can have little if any
significance or correlation with the electron density at the proton
site. The above effects should depend on the orientation and symmetries of non-bonding electrons and on the dispositions of metal to
ligand π-bonds and could be expected to vary widely in complexes of
different stereochemistries. So far there certainly appears to be little
connection or correlation of the position of the high-field line with
the mass of the metal atom, nature of the ligands, M—H stretching
frequencies or chemical activity of the M—H bond; it can be expected that the shifts of hydrogen atoms bound to complex groupings
of different electronegativity will reflect this factor but it may be
small compared to the other effects.

In spite of the lack of understanding of the reasons for it, the high-
field line, in the obvious absence of HI or a few other compounds
such as porphyrins and certain paramagnetic complexes, can be
taken as unequivocal proof of the presence of an M—H bond in a
diamagnetic complex. The measurements are sensitive and are especially important for studying solutions of labile, air-sensitive or
otherwise non-isolable species where other methods such as infrared
spectra or chemical reactions—e.g., with carbon tetrachloride—cannot be used. In aqueous or strong acid media the n.m.r. method is the
only easy way of demonstrating the presence of M—H bonds.

Complexes in Lower Oxidation States as Hydride Complexes

The first utilization of n.m.r. in this respect was for the yellow
solutions obtained by treatment of cobaltous cyanide with sodium
amalgam, which had previously been considered to contain a lower
complex cyanide.[15] A high-field line was observed, while in the
corresponding rhodium analog the line was a doublet due to indirect
coupling of the proton and Rh^{103} nuclear spins through the bonding
electrons, a fact which also confirms the presence of the Rh-H bond;
it is a pity that more transition metal nuclei do not have spin $\frac{1}{2}$ since
the coupling constants could perhaps give some useful information.

Many other cases of what were previously thought to be complexes of lower oxidation states but which are in fact hydride complexes are now coming to light. Thus the rhodium compound made twenty years ago by Nyholm, through treatment of rhodium chloride and diphenyl-methylarsine with hypophosphorous acid and formulated as a dimeric Rh(II) complex, has been shown by infrared and chemical studies to be $HRhCl_2(AsMePh_2)_2$.[16] Similarly the complexes prepared by Vaska[17] and formulated as being of the type $Ru(Os)Cl(PPh_3)_3$ with the metal in the I oxidation state have recently been shown[18] to be carbonyl hydrides such as $HRu(Os)Cl(CO)(PPh_3)_3$. The formation of hydrides, carbonyl, or carbonyl hydride metal complexes by the inter-action of metal halides in the presence of substituted phosphine and similar ligands with alcohols, usually in presence of base,[18,19] is believed[18] to be due to hydride transfer from the α-carbon atom of the alcohol or alkoxide ion. It is to be noted that the compounds with one carbon monoxide and one hydrogen are reported without comment[18] as having three bands around $2000 \, cm^{-1}$; since only two frequencies are to be expected, the products may be *cis-trans* isomeric mixtures. It has also been shown[20] that iridium hydride species with triphenylphos-phine, arsine or stibine, e.g., $HIrCl(SbPh_3)_3$, can be obtained by heating the halide salt with the ligand in alcoholic solutions. Some of the so-called platinum zerovalent compounds with triphenylphos-phine[21] are unquestionably also hydrides, as perhaps are products derived from them.

Perhaps the most interesting case of a "lower" oxidation state is that of the celebrated "rhenide" ion. Examination[22] of aqueous perrhenate solutions reduced by sodium amalgam first showed that Re-H bonds were present since a high-field line was found. In view of this finding, Floss and Grosse reviewed[23] their earlier preparative and analytical studies on crystalline "rhenides" which they had formulated as salts of the ion $[Re(H_2O)_4]^-$. The authors now con-clude that their analytical data and oxidation equivalents are con-sistent with stoicheiometries such as $Ba[ReH_4]_2 \cdot 4H_2O$. The infra-red spectra of the potassium and barium salts show bands at ca. $2000 \, cm^{-1}$ in accord with the expected region for Re-H stretches, and a resemblance to the spectra of aluminohydrides is claimed. Tracer studies have shown that the behaviour of technetium is simi-lar,[23] which is to be expected since both ReO_4^- and TcO_4^- show a polarographic wave[24] corresponding to an eight-electron reduction (atom transfer is of course actually involved). It is not certain, how-ever, that the reduction in aqueous solutions gives the same ion as that obtained by the method used to isolate the crystalline salts, namely reduction of perrhenate by potassium in ethylenediamine. Further, a very similar preparative procedure has been alleged to give a crystalline salt, which from oxidation equivalents, stoicheiometry and by estimation of the H/Re ratio by measurement of the intensity of the high-field line in a solution of known rhenium concentration against a chloroform standard, has a hydrogen to rhenium ratio of about $7:1$.[25] It is by no means impossible that complex species other than ReH_4^- exist, but rigorous proof is so far lacking.

Although so far no other hydrido species of the rhenium type have been prepared for other metals, it is possible that they can be obtained for other elements by different methods. Indeed, it has been found[26] that the interaction of lithium hydride and rhodium metal at $ca.$ 600° gives a liquid phase without evolution of gas. The black crystalline solid is suggested to be Li_4RhH_4 and Li_4RhH_5, mainly on the basis of stoicheiometry and X-ray powder patterns.

With the exception of the hydridorhenium(III) ion, most of the complexes with transition metal to hydrogen bonds have had π-bonding ligands also present. Such ligands are not essential for the formation of M—H bonds, although the case of electron transfer to the metal atom or the ease of homolytic fission of the M—H bond will obviously depend on several factors such as the stability of the oxidation state of the metal and on the electron affinity of the metal-ligand system. There has been accumulated a good deal of evidence to show that labile complex species with transition metal to hydrogen bonds are formed in reactions of molecular hydrogen with various metal species and also in the oxidation of metal ions by hydrogen atoms.[27] One well-defined example exists of a reasonably stable complex ion with a non π-bonding ligand, which also illustrates the substitution in an octahedral complex ion (probably occurring initially through ion-pair formation) by hydride ion using borohydride ion as the source in aqueous solution.[28] The solution obtained from dichlorobisethylenediaminerhodium (III) ion showed a high-field line split by the Rh^{103} nucleus into a doublet. Similar hydride ion displacements have been made for various other complex ions although in some cases, such as that of the pentammine rhodium salts, concentrations high enough for n.m.r. study cannot be obtained. From the absorption spectra of these hydride ammine ions, it should be possible to determine the position of hydride ion in the spectrochemical series. It may be noted that hydride ion substitution in the pentacyanohalogenocobaltic complexes, $[Co(CN)_5X]^{3-}$, gives the same species ($[Co(CN)_5H]^{3-}$) obtained in other ways (see above), and the latter ion is hence best regarded as a Co(III) species. Hence, the action of sodium amalgam on the cobaltous cyanide must cause oxidation presumably by hydrogen atoms (cf. ref. 27).

Protonation of Metal Atoms in Complexes

The compound $(\pi\text{-}C_5H_5)_2ReH$ provided the first demonstration not only of the high-field n.m.r. line and of the region for M—H stretching frequencies, but also of the protonation of a transition metal atom in a complex to form an M^+—H bond. In aqueous dioxan solution, the compound was a base somewhat weaker than ammonia. It now has been shown that even the neutral di-π-cyclopentadienyl iron, ruthenium and osmium compounds, $(\pi\text{-}C_5H_5)_2M$, can behave as bases, though very weak ones, being protonated only by boron trifluoride aquate.[29(a)] This discovery followed the previous isolation by Rosenblum of a stable salt, $C_{10}H_{10}FeHAlCl_4$, during studies of the mechanism of the Friedel-Crafts reactions of ferrocene; it seems clear that the hydrogen exchange of ferrocene and its derivatives in sulfuric acid[29(a,b)] proceeds through initial formation of $(\pi\text{-}C_5H_5)_2FeH^+$. This ferrocenonium ion shows the characteristic high-field resonance line and, as with $(\pi\text{-}C_5H_5)_2ReH$, the $\pi\text{-}C_5H_5$ resonance line is split into a doublet by electron-coupled spin-spin interaction. Important information on these di-π-cyclopentadienyl metal hydride species comes from the n.m.r. spectra[30] of the neutral molecule $(\pi\text{-}C_5H_5)_2TaH_3$ and the ions $(\pi\text{-}C_5H_5)_2WH_3^+$. In these species, the high-field line has a complex pattern characteristic of A_2X and A_2B systems respectively; thus, in the tantalum compound there is a triplet, relative intensity one, and a doublet, relative intensity two. This clearly indicates that two of the hydrogen atoms are in equivalent environments while the third is different. Hence we can consider all of the $(\pi\text{-}C_5H_5)_2MH_x$ species to have three orbitals, two of which are equivalent, which can hold either hydrogen atoms or lone pairs which are stereochemically and chemically active. Although, for example, $(\pi\text{-}C_5H_5)_2ReH$ will have two such lone pairs, only one proton is taken up—but this is not surprising since on electrostatic grounds the second base constant will be exceedingly small. Theoretical studies[31] have shown that if the $\pi\text{-}C_5H_5$ to metal axes in $(\pi\text{-}C_5H_5)_2MH_x$ compounds are non-linear, there are indeed three orbitals of the type required and it is significant that there is very little loss in the metal-to-ring bounding energy by such a distortion even to a $\pi\text{-}C_5H_5\text{-}M\text{-}\pi\text{-}C_5H_5$ angle of $150°$.

At the last Conference, Sternberg and Wender[32] suggested that on the evidence of protonation of $(\pi\text{-}C_5H_5)_2ReH$, some of the reactions of carbonyls such as $Fe(CO)_5$ and $[\pi\text{-}C_5H_5Fe(CO)_2]_2$ in acid media could involve protonated species. Although the particular species they invoked are not always formed, their suggestion has been realised by protonation of a variety of carbonyl species[33] such as $Fe(CO)_5$, $(Ph_3P)Fe(CO)_4$, $C_4H_6Fe(CO)_3$ in strong acids such as sulfuric, trifluoroacetic, fluorosulfonic and fluoroboric. In certain cases, such as that of $[\pi\text{-}C_5H_5Fe(CO)_2]_2$, it can be shown by comparing the intensities of the high-field and $\pi\text{-}C_5H_5$ resonance lines that only one proton is taken up on the metal atom.

The suggestion[34] that the unusual proton affinities of the 1:10-phenanthroline- and 22'bipyridine-iron(II) dicyanide is due to protonation of the metal atom does not appear to be sound. It is highly unlikely that in such a case two protons would be readily taken up by the metal atom as is observed, and in fact we have been unable to detect a high-field proton resonance line in sulfuric acid solutions of the complexes. The available data are quite consistent with protonation of the nitrogen atom in the cyanide groups. We have been unable to obtain clear infrared evidence for N——H bonding in the di-hydrochloride salt, but poorly defined spectra are similarly obtained for pure acids such as $H_4[Fe(CN)_6]$ which must also of necessity have N——H bonds.

Other Metal-Hydrogen Interactions

Although in the above sections we have been concerned with well-defined metal-to-hydrogen bonds, cases are now appearing of interaction between transition metal atoms and hydrogen atoms attached to other groups which are more akin to hydrogen bonds.

Thus in ferrocenyl and ruthenocenyl alcohols, there is clear evidence[35] for intramolecular bonding which can be regarded as unsymmetrical hydrogen bonding. Although the metal atom is not very electronegative, it fulfills one of the functions necessary for hydrogen bonding in having, as the protonation studies show, lone pairs which can serve as donors, just as can the π-electrons in aromatic systems or the $\pi\text{-}C_5H_5$ ring itself. For the ferrocenyl alcohols, both types of hydrogen bonding occur and in 2-ferrocenylethanol, for example, hydroxyl stretching frequencies at 3632, 3605 and 3533 cm^{-1} have been assigned to the free, π-bonded and Fe-bonded hydroxyl absorptions respectively. From the previous discussion of the non-linearity of the $\pi\text{-}C_5H_5$-to-metal axes, it seems reasonable to assume that some angularity will be introduced also on metal-hydrogen bonding. There does not appear to be any intermolecular metal-hydrogen bonding although intermolecular π-bonding does occur[35] and this has been attributed to the greater accessibility of the $\pi\text{-}C_5H_5$ ring electron density compared with the more sterically hindered iron atom. It seems more likely that this is a reflection of the much weaker donor power of the non-bonding electrons on the metal.

A different type of metal-hydrogen interaction is that observed for the compounds which have a methylene group on a hydrocarbon ligand bound to a metal atom such that one of the hydrogen atoms must point towards (*endo*) the metal atom. Examples have been found in the cyclopentadiene[36,37] and π-cyclohexadienyl[38] complexes where it was shown that *endo* C-H$_\alpha$ stretching frequency is not only abnormally strong for a C-H stretching frequency but is also displaced to unusually low wavenumbers, e.g., in π-$C_5H_5CoC_5H_6$ to 2742 cm^{-1}; the proton resonance lines fall in the normal aliphatic region, however, though the *endo* proton occurs at higher fields than the *exo* proton line. The hydrogen atoms responsible for the C-H$_\alpha$ stretches are chemically reactive, being quite readily and rapidly transferred to various substrates. The observations are consistent with a weakening of the C-H$_\alpha$ bond by interaction with the metal atom.

In the case of the compounds π-$C_5H_5MC_5H_6$, the C-H$_\alpha$ stretch is much broader than in the compounds where benzene or other ligands occupy the π-C_5H_5 site and this fact, together with the unusual splittings observed on the corresponding C-D stretching vibration, suggests that the hydrogen atom may be tunnelling from one ring to the other through an excited state involving a metal-to-hydrogen bond, with angular rings as in the di-π-cyclopentadienyl hydrides. Such a transition state would also be consistent with the chemical behaviour; from the splittings in the n.m.r. spectrum we can be sure, however, that there is no such effect in the ground state of the molecule. The reversible reactions of the type

$$\pi\text{-}C_5H_5Fe(CO)_2PPh_3^+ \underset{-H^-}{\overset{+H^-}{\rightleftharpoons}} C_5H_6Fe(CO)_2PPh_3$$

may well be occurring through intermediate states with M—H bonds, and it is significant that all of these compounds with a C-H$_\alpha$ grouping react rapidly with carbon tetrachloride, as do many compounds which have a normal transition metal-to-hydrogen bond; whereas other complexes such as $C_7H_8Mo(CO)_3$ or $C_7H_{10}Fe(CO)_3$, where both hydrogen atoms of the methylene group are further from the metal atom, do not react with CCl_4, even though triphenylmethyltetrafluoroborate will abstract a hydride ion from them.

π-BONDED HYDROCARBON DERIVATIVES OF TRANSITION METALS

N.m.r. Spectra of Hydrocarbon Metal Complexes

There continues to be a very rapid development in this area of chemistry.[3-6] With the recognition of the π-allyl, π-cyclohexadienyl and carbonium ion complexes discussed below it now seems that there are very few unsaturated hydrocarbon systems capable of being π-bonded to a transition metal atom left uninvestigated. One obvious exception is that of the cyclopropenyl grouping, which should give complexes such as π-$C_3H_3Co(CO)_3$ or π-C_3H_3Ni-π-C_5H_5, it being isoelectronic with the π-allyl complexes.

An important aspect of recent work has been the study of n.m.r. spectra of hydrocarbon metal complexes. So far, relatively little information has been gleaned from the absolute positions of the single proton resonance lines observed in the symmetrically delocalised cyclic π-bonded systems, although there have been attempts[39] to account for the magnitudes of the shifts for the parent hydrocarbon entities $C_5H_5^-$, C_6H_6 and $C_7H_7^+$ in terms of ring currents. The position of a resonance line of a hydrogen atom bound to carbon depends on several factors, one of the more important being the local charge on the carbon atom. Induced circulation of electrons around atoms in bonds and around π-electron systems like aromatic rings can affect the hydrogen shifts and when a hydrocarbon is bound to a transition metal atom, even more complications are introduced since the π-electron density is distorted by bonding to the metal in a manner which is far from clear at present. Hence, most of the n.m.r. studies have been made for olefin and similar partially delocalised π-bonded metal complexes which give complex n.m.r. spectra. Interest has been primarily with the pattern of the resonance lines due to chemical shifts and electron coupled spin-spin interactions and their detailed assignments, rather than with the less understandable line positions as such. From the patterns—number of peaks and relative areas—it is often possible to say a great deal about the structures of complexes and it is now relatively easy to assign with quite a high degree of certainty most, if not all, of the lines in very complex spectra which only two years ago would have been regarded as too difficult to assign. Nevertheless, at the present time the reasons for some of the observed splittings and line positions are not too clear.

As examples of complex spectra we can note those of the azuleneiron carbonyls,[40] since here the great differences between the spectra of the complexes and of the parent hydrocarbons—where the patterns have received a satisfactory interpretation on the basis of charge densities on the ring carbon atoms—is clearly apparent. By consideration of deutero and other substituted azuleneiron complex spectra and from previous observations[36] that in metal-bonded conjugated diene systems the terminal proton resonances move upfield while the central proton resonances stay more or less in the uncoordinated olefin region, it was possible to assign essentially all of the lines. The 4:6:8-trimethylazulene complex showed three methyl resonance lines showing the non-equivalence of the 4- and 8-methyl groups in the complex; the splitting of the methyl lines by adjacent protons in the seven-membered ring differed also, leading to the view that the non-equivalence was due to a real difference in electron distribution on the two sides of the seven-membered ring. In the case of the guaiazuleneiron complex, the spectra could be interpreted only on the basis of an equimolar isomeric mixture, and this was subsequently confirmed by chemical separation. The spectra thus implied the fixing of the double bonds into one Kekulé form and a satisfactory complete assignment of the lines was possible. The splittings also indicated that one of the double bonds in the seven-membered ring was not involved in metal-bonding, a situation also found for the cycloheptatriene iron tricarbonyl[42] discussed below. It is of interest to note that the X-ray structure of dibenzene-chromium is alleged to indicate alternate long (1.45 Å) and short (1.36 Å) bonds suggesting some localisation of electron density.[41]

Merely by considering the n.m.r. patterns it is often possible to show that certain structures for molecules or ions are not feasible. Thus the n.m.r. spectra readily show, for example, that "cyclo-octatrieneiron tricarbonyl" is bicyclo[4,2,0]octa-2,5-dieneiron tricarbonyl[42] while "dicyclopentadienenickel" is π-cyclopentadienyl π-cyclopentenylnickel.[43] It is in such cases that n.m.r. is especially useful since it can give unequivocal answers not obtainable, or which are ambiguous, from infrared and other short-term methods of study. However, n.m.r. cannot prove that a particular structure is the correct one in the sense of providing sure stereochemical dispositions of atoms or groups in molecules—for example, to argue from the fact that the terminal protons of the diene system in cyclopentadiene compounds occur at high fields in the normal aliphatic region could imply that the carbon atom to which they are bound has sp^3 tetrahedral bonds but this is denied by infrared evidence.[36] This particular observation, whilst useful in assigning spectra, illustrates the point made earlier that chemical shifts can be due to factors as yet imperfectly understood. At the present time, X-ray crystal studies have been made only on two olefin compounds, $C_7H_8Mo(CO)_3$[44] and $C_4H_6Fe(CO)_3$,[45] for which the detailed n.m.r. assignments have been made.[46,46] For $C_7H_8Mo(CO)_3$ it appears that σ-bonded structures are excluded and that there are alternate long and short bonds in the coordinated triene system. Assuming a somewhat idealized structure, an attempt has been made[46] to interpret the observed n.m.r. shifts by assuming that the major factor affecting the chemical shift of the protons is the "long-range shielding magnetic effects" due to the magnetic moment induced by the applied field in the π-electrons in the coordinated double bonds. Such long-range effects have been invoked to qualitatively explain shifts in organic molecules with fair success.[47] In the metal complexes, however, a special complication arises in trying to decide how the π-electron density in a double bond is distorted by coordination to the metal atom. By analogy with organic systems it is assumed that the long-range effects can be represented crudely by placing a point magnetic dipole at some position along the metal to C-C axis. If there were an appreciable amount of metal-to-ligand double bonding, the dipole would be expected to point perpendicular or at some angle to this axis, but it is found that the main features of the spectrum can be reproduced fairly well if the dipole points along the metal to C-C axis and is located at a distance about one-third of the way from the C-C bond axis to the metal. This approach, though obviously very crude, does lead also to separation of the central and terminal proton resonances for coordinated conjugated dienes such as those of cyclopentadiene. In the case of butadiene iron tricarbonyl, the X-ray studies[45] indicate that the planar carbon skeleton of the olefin has equal C-C distances although the central and terminal proton resonances are widely separated.[36,42] All that can be said at the present time is that the two observations are not incompatible, since the actual electron density distribution within the molecule is not obtained from X-ray data, but it is this important unknown factor which influences the chemical shifts.

π-Allyl and Related Metal Complexes

The main recent developments in the preparative chemistry of π-bonded hydrocarbon metal complexes have been concerned with what we could call asymmetric π-bonded entities in contrast to the symmetric π-bonded entities such as $C_5H_5^-$, C_6H_6 or $C_7H_7^+$. Of the new systems, π-allyl, π-cyclohex- and pent-enyl, π-cyclohexadienyl or π-cycloheptadienyl, the allyl systems are so far the most extensive. Although allyl alcohol platinum complexes have long been known and allylic intermediates in interactions of allyl compounds with metals have been postulated,[48] the first hydrocarbon complex to be isolated appears to be the product $C_6H_7Co(CO)_3$ from the interaction of cobalt hydrocarbonyl with butadiene,[49(a)] which was later[49(b)] formulated as having a metal-to-carbon σ-bond in addition to a metal-to-C$=$C donor bond. The first clear suggestion that the allyl group as such could be bound to a metal was made[50,51] in connection with the products from the interaction of palladous chloride with allyl alcohol. The preparation of complexes of other metals by direct methods, such as interaction of carbonylate salts with allyl chloride, by a number of workers[52] (one study being particularly extensive[53]) together with n.m.r. studies have now amply confirmed that the allyl group can be π-bonded to metal atoms acting as a formal three-electron donor like nitric oxide. Of particular interest is that for substituted allyls, *anti* and *syn* isomers (related to the central hydrogen atom) can be characterised.[52 c, d, 53] Also of interest is the relationship between the σ-allyl and π-allyl complexes which is particularly clear-cut in the case of the manganese carbonyls where both types can be isolated.[52 b, 53]

As could be expected, cyclic systems containing an allylic grouping can also be π-bonded to metals and π-cyclopentenyl and π-cyclohexenyl complexes have been unequivocally demonstrated by n.m.r. studies.[43] There are also a few π-bonded complexes of a somewhat similar type where instead of a π-electron system delocalised over three carbon atoms as in the allylic derivatives, there is a π-electron system delocalised over five carbon atoms bound to the metal.[38,42] These derivatives can be considered as being formally analogous to π-C_5H_5 derivatives. The π-cyclohexadienyl manganese carbonyl and π-cyclopentodienyl iron derivatives are best prepared by hydride ion attack on the corresponding arene-metal salts and can be converted back to the latter by removal of hydride ion so that, as with the π-C_5H_5-C_5H_6 and π-C_7H_7-C_7H_8 complexes, there is a reversible hydride ion transfer reaction involved.

Protonation of Olefin-metal Complexes

While protonation of many metal complexes in strong acids leads to the formation of transition metal-hydrogen bonds, certain olefin metal carbonyls show quite a different behaviour. These complexes are ones in which not all of the π-electrons of the unsaturated hydrocarbon ligand are involved in bonding to the metal atom, so that protonation can occur on the ligand to give a new C—H bond, leaving what is best regarded as a carbonium ion π-bonded to the metal atom.

It was shown by n.m.r., infrared and chemical studies[42,55] that cycloheptatrieneiron tricarbonyl has a lone non-coordinated double bond, a situation which also best explains some features of the n.m.r. spectra of the azuleneiron carbonyls.[40] With hydrogen bromide, $C_7H_8Fe(CO)_3$ gave a salt of the ion $C_7H_9Fe(CO)_3^+$ which was formulated as a π-cycloheptadienyl derivative.[42] On dissolution in concentrated sulfuric acid, the same cationic species was formed by protonation.[54] This ion with a -CO_3 group bound to it was also obtained[55] by the action of trityltetrafluoroborate on $C_7H_8Fe(CO)_3$, while with this reagent the π-cycloheptadieneiron tricarbonyl[42,55] $C_7H_{10}Fe(CO)_3$ gave the $C_7H_9Fe(CO)_3^+$ ion by hydride abstraction.

These ions, like the π-cyclohexadienyl complexes, have a π-electron system delocalised over five carbon atoms bound to the metal.

A more interesting case is that of the well-known cyclooctatetraene iron tricarbonyl which, both on the basis of stoichiometry and a simple molecular-orbital picture,[56] have only four low-lying π-electrons involved in metal bonding, so that four essentially non-bonding π-electrons reside on the ligand. On dissolution in concentrated sulfuric acid,[54] $C_8H_8Fe(CO)_3$ gives a stable solution from which crystalline salts can be isolated. The n.m.r. spectrum is quite complex, but nevertheless can be elucidated by deuteration using deuterosulfuric acid in conjunction with proton-spin decoupling studies of certain of the bands. The data are quite consistent with the formation of the ion $C_8H_9Fe(CO)_3^+$ where a bicyclic carbonium ion is bound to the metal.

Other metal complexes with lone double bonds on the ligands, e.g., bicyclooctatetraenemolybdenum tetracarbonyl or cyclononatrienemolybdenum tetracarbonyl should similarly give cationic species on protonation. It could also be expected that abstraction of a hydride ion from the methylene group of a norbornadiene metal complex would leave the non-classical carbonium ion bound to the metal.

REFERENCES*

1. M. L. H. Green, *Angew. Chem.*, **72**, 719 (1960).
2. J. Lewis, *Science Progress*, XLIX, No. 193, 67 (1961); J. Chatt and B. L. Shaw, *XVIIth Int. Cong. Pure and Appl. Chem.*, p. 147, Butterworths, London, 1960.
3. G. Coates, *Organometallic Compounds*, 2nd Ed., Methuen, London, 1960.
4. H. Zeiss, Editor, *Organometallic Chemistry*, A. C. S. Monograph No. 147, Reinhold Publishing Corp., New York, 1960.
5. P. L. Pauson, Tilden Lecture, *Proc. Chem. Soc.*, **297** (1960).
6. D. W. A. Sharp, *Annual Reports*, **1960, 1961**, Chemical Society London.
7. (a) J. Birmingham and G. Wilkinson, *J. Am. Chem. Soc.*, **77**, 3421 (1955).
   (b) M. L. H. Green, L. Pratt and G. Wilkinson, *J. Chem. Soc.*, 3916 (1958).
8. R. A. Friedel, I. Wender, S. L. Shufler and H. W. Sternberg, *J. Am. Chem. Soc.*, **77**, 3951 (1955).
9. E. O. Bishop, J. L. Down, P. R. Emtage, R. E. Richards and G. Wilkinson, *J. Chem. Soc.*, 2484 (1959).
10. W. Hieber and G. Wagner, *Z. Naturforsch.*, **13b**, 339 (1958).
11. F. A. Cotton, J. L. Down and G. Wilkinson, *J. Chem. Soc.*, **833** (1959).
12. P. G. Owston, J. M. Partridge, and J. M. Rowe, *Acta Cryst.*, **13**, 246 (1960).

*Literature survey covers journals received in London up to March 24, 1961.

13. J. A. Pople, *Proc. Roy. Soc.* **A239**, 541, 550 (1957).
14. W. G. Schneider in *Hydrogen Bonding*, D. Hadzi, Editor, Pergamon Press, 1959.
15. W. P. Griffith and G. Wilkinson, *J. Chem. Soc.*, 2757 (1959).
16. J. Lewis, R. S. Nyholm, and G. K. N. Reddy, *Chem. and Ind.*, 1386 (1960).
17. L. Vaska, *Z. Naturforsch.*, **15**, 56 (1960); L. Vaska and E. M. Sloane, *J. Am. Chem. Soc.*, **82**, 1263 (1960).
18. J. Chatt and B. L. Shaw, *Chem. and Ind.*, 290 (1961).
19. *Idem, ibid.*, 931 (1960).
20. L. Vaska, *J. Am. Chem. Soc.*, **83**, 756 (1961).
21. L. Malatesta and C. Cariello, *J. Inorg. Nucl. Chem.*, **8**, 561 (1958); *J. Chem. Soc.*, 2323 (1958).
22. R. Colton, J. A. W. Dalziel, W. P. Griffith and G. Wilkinson, *Nature*, **183**, 1755 (1959).
23. J. G. Floss and A. V. Grosse, *J. Inorg. Nuclear Chem.*, **16**, 36, 44 (1960).
24. R. Colton, J. A. W. Dalziel, W. P. Griffith and G. Wilkinson, *J. Chem. Soc.*, 71 (1960) and references cited therein.
25. A. Ginsberg, Ph.D. Dissertation, Chemistry Department, Columbia University, New York, 1960; A. Ginsberg, J. M. Miller, J. R. Cavanaugh, and B. P. Dailey, *Nature*, **185**, 528 (1960).
26. J. D. Farr, *J. Inorg. Nucl. Chem.*, **14**, 202 (1960).
27. See J. Halpern, G. Czapski, J. Jortner and G. Stein, *Nature*, **186**, 629 (1960) and references quoted therein.
28. G. Wilkinson, *Proc. Chem. Soc.*, 72 (1961).
29. (a) T. J. Curphey, J. O. Santer, M. Rosenblum and J. H. Richards, *J. Am. Chem. Soc.*, **82**, 5249 (1960).
    (b) A. N. Nesmeyanov, D. N. Kursanov, V. N. Setkina, N. V. Kislyakova, and N. S. Kochetkova, *Tetrahedron Letters*, 41 (1961).
30. J. McCleverty and G. Wilkinson, *Chem. and Ind.*, 288 (1961); M. L. H. Green, J. McCleverty, L. Pratt and G. Wilkinson, unpublished results.
31. C. J. Ballhausen and J. P. Dahl, *Acta Chem. Scand.*, 1961 (in press).
32. H. W. Sternberg and I. Wender, International Conference on Coordination Chemistry, Chemical Society Special Publication No. 13, p. 35, London, 1959.
33. A. Davison and G. Wilkinson, *Proc. Chem. Soc.*, 356 (1960).
34. A. A. Schiltz, *J. Am. Chem. Soc.*, **82**, 3000, 5779 (1960).
35. D. S. Trifan and R. Bacskai, *J. Am. Chem. Soc.*, **82**, 5011 (1960).
36. M. L. H. Green, L. Pratt and G. Wilkinson, *J. Chem. Soc.*, 3753 (1959); 989 (1960).
37. A. Davison, M. L. H. Green and G. Wilkinson, *J. Chem. Soc.* (1961; in press).
38. G. Winkhaus and G. Wilkinson, *Proc. Chem. Soc.*, 311 (1960) and *J. Chem. Soc.*, in press, (1961).
39. G. Fraenkel, R. E. Carter, A. McLachlan and J. H. Richards, *J. Am. Chem. Soc.*, **82**, 5846 (1960) and earlier references cited therein.
40. R. Burton, L. Pratt and G. Wilkinson, *J. Chem. Soc.*, 4290 (1960).
41. F. Jellinek, *Nature*, **187**, 871 (1960).
42. R. Burton, L. Pratt and G. Wilkinson, *J. Chem. Soc.*, 594 (1961).
43. E. O. Fischer and H. Werner, *Tetrahedron Letters*, 17 (1961); D. Jones, G. W. Parshall, L. Pratt and G. Wilkinson, *ibid.*, 48 (1961).

44. J. D. Dunitz and P. L. Pauling, *Helv. Chim. Acta*, **43**, 2188 (1960).

45. O. S. Mills and G. Robinson, *Proc. Chem. Soc.*, 421 (1960).

46. M. A. Bennett, L. Pratt and G. Wilkinson, *J. Chem. Soc.* 2037 (1961).

47. For discussion and references see L. M. Jackman, *Applications of Nuclear Magnetic Resonance Spectroscopy in Organic Chemistry*, p. 124 et seq., Pergamon Press, London, 1959; H. Conroy in *Advances in Organic Chemistry*, Vol. 2, p. 281, Interscience Publishers, New York, 1960.

48. See for example P. Pfeiffer and H. Hoyer, *Z. anorg. Chem.*, **211**, 241 (1933); L. F. Hatch and R. R. Estes, *J. Am. Chem. Soc.*, **67**, 1731 (1945).

49. (a) H. B. Jonassen, R. I. Stearns, J. Kenttamaa, D. W. Moore and A. G. Whitaker, *J. Am. Chem. Soc.*, **80**, 2586 (1958);
    (b) C. L. Aldridge, H. B. Jonassen, and E. Pulkkinen, *Chem. and Ind.*, 374 (1960).

50. I. I. Moiseev, E. A. Federovskaya, and Y. K. Syrkin, *Zhur. neorg. Khim.*, **4**, 2461 [1218] (1959).

51. J. Schmidt and W. Hafner, *Angew. Chem.*, **71**, 284 (1959); cf. also R. Huttel and J. Kratzer, *ibid.*, **71**, 456 (1959).

52. (a) R. F. Heck and D. S. Breslow, *J. Am. Chem. Soc.*, **82**, 750 (1960).
    (b) H. D. Kaez, R. B. King, and F. G. A. Stone, *Z. Naturforsch.*, **15b**, 682 (1960).
    (c) H. C. Dehm and J. C. W. Chien, *J. Am. Chem. Soc.*, **82**, 4429 (1960).
    (d) D. W. Moore, H. B. Jonassen, T. B. Joyner, and A. J. Bertrand, *Chem. and Ind.*, 1304 (1960).
    (e) B. L. Shaw, *Proc. Chem. Soc.*, 247 (1960).

53. W. R. McClellan, H. H. Hoehn, H. N. Cripps, E. L. Muetterties, and B. W. Howk, *J. Am. Chem. Soc.* (1961; in press).

54. A. Davison, W. McFarlane, L. Pratt and G. Wilkinson, *Chem. and Ind.* (1961; in press).

55. H. J. Dauben and D. J. Bertelli, *J. Am. Chem. Soc.*, **83**, 498 (1961).

56. F. A. Cotton, *J. Chem. Soc.*, 400 (1960) and references given therein.

THE BIOCHEMICAL SIGNIFICANCE OF COORDINATION COMPOUNDS

R. J. P. WILLIAMS

Wadham College and Inorganic Chemistry Laboratory
Oxford, England

Let us consider two elements, molybdenum and cobalt, and show how a knowledge of their coordination chemistry helps in the understanding of the biochemical significance of these elements. These elements are chosen because molybdenum is involved in catalysis of several oxidation-reduction reactions in biochemical systems, whereas cobalt is involved in several different enzymes, both of known and unknown functional significance, but which are not obviously connected with oxidation of substrates.

Molybdenum

An understanding of the function of molybdenum in biological systems depends upon an understanding of its chemistry. We (here I refer to Mr. P. C. H. Mitchell and myself) have therefore conducted an experimental survey of the properties of this element. In aqueous solution and in the absence of oxygen all valence states between three and six and including these two can be stabilised by combination with chosen ligands. The valence states three and four, but not in general the valence states five and six, form complexes much like those of other transition elements (Table 1). Thus the complexes $[MoCl_6]^{3-}$, $[Mo(CNS)_6]^{3-}$, and $[Mo(CN)_8]^{4-}$ are formed from a simple cation M^{n+} and ligands. On the other hand the complexes of five- and six-valent molybdenum are complexes of the "Yl" ions, of which MoO^{3+} and MoO_2^{2+} respectively are the most important, e.g. [MoO (phenolate)$_3$], $[MoOCl_5]^{2-}$, MoO_2(8-hydroxyquinoline)$_2$ and $[MoO_2F_4]^{2-}$. Although much is known of the complex formation by simple ions M^{n+} little has been done on the "Yl" complexes MO^{n+}. We treat this problem first.

TABLE 1: INORGANIC COMPLEXES OF MOLYBDENUM

Ligand	Mo(III) d^3	Mo(IV) d^2	Mo(V) d^1
Cl^-	K_3MoCl_6 $\mu_{eff} = 3.66$ (3 spins) $\lambda_{max} = $ 395 495 $\nu_{max} = $ 25,320 20,200 $\varepsilon_{max} = $ 83 49	K_2MoCl_6 ?	$(NH_4)_2MoOCl_5$ 1.7 (1 spin)
NCS^-	$(NH_4)_3Mo(NCS)_6$ $\mu_{eff} = 3.75$ (3 spins) $\lambda_{max} = $ uv $\nu_{max} = $ uv $\varepsilon_{max} = $?	$(pyH)_2Mo(NCS)_6$ 3.0 to 3.5 410 420 465 24,390 23,810 17,700 3 to 6×10^4	$(NH_4)_2MoO(NCS)_5$ 1.7 (1 spin) $\cdots$ $(pyH)_2MoO_2(NCS)_3$ Diamagnetic Dimeric in nitrobenzene Peak at 463 (21,600) with $\varepsilon_{max} = 10^4$
CN^-	$K_4Mo(CN)_7 \cdot 2H_2O$ $\mu_{eff} = 1.77$ (1 spin) $\lambda_{max} = $ 505* $\nu_{max} = $ 19,800 $\varepsilon_{max} = $ 66	$K_4Mo(CN)_8$ diamagnetic 370* 27,030 158	$K_3Mo(CN)_8$ 1.66 (1 spin) 377 386 400 26,530 25,910 25,000 1000–1200

*main peaks.

Complex Formation by Molybdyl(V) and (VI) Ions*

Unlike the uranyl ions the molybdyl ions cannot be studied as free aqueous ions. Presumably the much smaller size of the central atom leads to ready hydrolysis even in acid solution. A similar effect of size is observed in a comparison between beryllium and the other divalent cations of group IIA of the periodic table. Thus complexes of molybdenum must be studied in very acid solutions or in non-aqueous media. In many cases it has proved possible to prepare the complexes only in the solid state. We refer to these solids first.

In Table 2 we list some of the solid compounds we have prepared and analysed. We also note that MoO_2^{2+} is capable of forming compounds with simple ligands such as fluoride and hydroxide, but that the complexes with chloride are very much less easily obtained, presumably because they are much less stable, and those with heavier halides are doubtful or non-existent. In the molybdenum thiocyanate complexes it is the nitrogen atom which is combined with the molybdenum, Mo-NCS, and the infrared frequency of the C-N bond classifies this as one of the most ionic of thiocyanate complexes.[6] Both the manner of combination with thiocyanate and the relative stabilities of the halide complexes places MoO_2^{2+} amongst Chatt's[7] a-type ions. The formation of complexes with organic compounds agrees with this classification. MoO_2^{2+} forms complexes with anionic ligands, e.g. edta, 8-hydroxyquinoline, and dibasic aliphatic acid anions. MoO^{3+} is similar to MoO_2^{2+} in preferring the nitrogen to the sulphur end of the thiocyanate anion and in its preference for fluoride over the other halides, but it has a considerable affinity for some of the latter halides. This is shown by the formation of complexes such as $[MoOCl_5]^{2-}$ which are stable in aqueous acid solutions. However in more alkaline solution the halide complexes dimerise and hydrolyse like most other complexes of five-valent molybdenum. We return to this point later. Dimerisation does not occur in uranyl(V) chemistry and hydrolysis is only observed at high pH values.[1] The relative stability of the thiocyanate and chloride complexes of Mo(V) as compared with Mo(VI) shows that the change to a lower valency has introduced more b-type character into the chemistry of the element. This is also borne out by the combination with organic ligands. The

---

*Here a digression to some inorganic chemistry is not entirely out of place. The chemistries of the "Yl" ions of the transition elements in the periodic table illustrate all the trends which are featured by their simpler cations. The higher the valency, the lower the atomic number of the central ion, the more the ion shows a = type character[7], Table 2. The exception as with simple ions, is provided by the central ions with f-electron rather than d-electron cores. In this case the exceptions are the actinide "Yl" ions, which behave the most like a-type elements.[7]

TABLE 2: COMPLEXES OF MOLYBDENUM(V)

Ligand	Compound Empirical Formula	Mag. Susc.* $\chi_A \times 10^6$	Temp. °K	Visible Spectrum λ_{max} (mμ)	ε_{max}
EDTA	$Na_2Mo_2O_4EDTA \cdot 4H_2O$	33	292	298	9600 w
				385	380
NCS⁻	$(pyH)_2MoO_2(NCS)_3$ [e]	diamag.		463	13500 a
Phenol	$MoCl_2(OPh)_3$ [e]	60	289	465	11000 bz
		50	132		
Acac	$Mo(OH)_3 acac_2 \cdot 3H_2O$	1366	291	490	5000 bz
		1466	135		
Oxine	$MoO(OH)_2 oxine_2$	175 a	291	540	a
		1400 b	291		
		190 a	137		
		1560 b	138		
Phenolates:					
p-HO·C$_6$H$_4$·COOH	$MoCl_2L_3$	...		441	ca 10⁴ c
C$_6$H$_5$OH[e]		60	289	465	11,000 bz
		50	132		
p-MeC$_6$H$_4$OH		18	291	490	4100 bz
1:1 complexes:					
Oxine	*in solution*			388	a
				405	a
5-Meoxine				435	1600 n
o-phen	$MoO(OH)Cl_2phen$	270	293	528	1860

Inorganic:					
MoCl$_5$	solid	ca. 1000[c]	305		
		ca. 5500	78		
Chloro	(NH$_4$)$_2$MoOCl$_5$	1200	300	ca 450	16
				700	
Fluoro	NaMoF$_6$	1150[d]	300 at 300		
NCS$^-$	(NH$_4$)$_2$MoO(NCS)$_5$	1175	at 298		
CN	K$_3$Mo(CN)$_8$	1175		377	1200
				386	1280
				400 sh	940

*Magnetic susceptibilities in cgs per one Mo. The value expected for one spin at ca. 300°K. is ca. 1200×10^{-6}. Low values imply strong electron-electron interaction.

Solvents for spectra (in last column): w, water; a, alcohol; bz, benzene; c, chloroform; n, nitrobenzene.

Oxine complexes: a was precipitated from alkaline solution and b from acid solution. A chloro complex, MoOCl oxine$_2$ was pptd. from alcohol and had $\chi = 770 \times 10^{-6}$ at 293°K. and the solution in pyridine had peaks at $\lambda_{max} = 383$ and 593 with extinction coefficients 3640 and 1870 respectively.

c - Values from Knox and Coffey, JACS, 81, 5 (1959). MoCl$_5$ obeys a Curie-Weiss law with $\mu = 1.52$ at room temperature and $\Delta = -23°C$.

Solid MoCl$_5$ has chlorine bridges with Mo-Mo 3.84 Å. (Sands and Zalkin, Act. Cryst., 12, 723 (1959).

d - Hargreaves and Peacock, JCS, 1958, 3776.

e - Known to be dimeric.

MoO^{3+} ion forms complexes with dithiol, ortho-phenanthroline, as well as with oxine and anionic ligands such as edta, phenolates and simple carboxylic acids. All these complexes (see Table 2) show a great tendency to polymerise, presumably forming metal-metal bonds, as the dimers have magnetic moments of less than one electron per molybdenum. The formation of the Mo(V) dimers illustrates a point of great significance to inorganic chemistry and to the understanding of the function of Mo(V) in biological systems. *The one d electron of Mo(V) is very exposed to the neighbouring atoms.**

The general chemistry of molybdenum(V) is reminiscent of that of iron (III) in the following respects: (1) The cations form complexes with a very similar series of ligands. (2) Ferric ions, like Mo(V) ions, have a considerable tendency to polymerise, e.g., in acetate, phenanthroline and hydroxide complexes. (3) The complexes of ferric ion also have spectrophotometric properties in common with molybdenum (V) complexes. In particular both sets of complexes have intense absorption bands in the visible. Table 3 lists the parallels between their spectra. Now we know that the ferric spectra originate in charge

TABLE 3: SPECTRA OF MOLYBDENUM(V) AND IRON(III) COMPLEXES*

Ligand	λ_{max}Fe(III) mμ	λ_{max}Mo(V) mμ
EDTA	300	380
p-carboxy-phenol	u.v.	440
Acetylacetonate	470	490
Thiocyanate	490	463
Phenolate	558	465
p-Cresolate	576	490
Oxinate	580	540

*All extinction coefficients are $> 10^3$.

transfer excitation from the ligands to the ferric ion,[3,9] for the more reducing the ligand, i.e., the better its electron donor power and the more the intense charge transfer absorption band moves into the visible. This is also true of the intense absorption band of Mo(V) complexes and it appears as if Mo(V) is not only easily oxidised to Mo(VI) but that it can act as a relatively readily reducible cation going down to Mo(IV). This need not imply that Mo(IV) complexes are easily obtained

---

*$2/d$-electrons and d-orbitals of elements early in a transition series and in later transitions series appear to be strongly exposed to ligands. We will shortly publish a discussion of this effect and its influences upon the stability and absorption spectra of such valence states as Cr(II), V(II), etc.[8] As in Mo^V, chemistry complexes with unsaturated ligands are surprisingly stable.

but they are fairly readily accessible excited states of molybdenum(V). The parallel in complex ion chemistry between iron and molybdenum, both in the ligands with which they form complexes and in the spectra of these complexes, is also found in biochemistry for both cations are associated with flavoproteins. Their charge transfer spectra indicate that the d states of the metal interact strongly with the ligands. A further piece of evidence also shows that this interaction between the $4d$ states of the molybdenum(V) ion and the ligands bound to it is strong. We have found [11] that the dimerised compound Mo_2Cl_4 (phenolate)$_6$ shows a characteristic new absorption band in the solid state (which is a molecular crystal structure) as compared with solutions and that the solid, which has metallic lustre, is *a moderate semi-conductor* with a thermal activation energy for conduction of some 30 Kcals.[11] The relevance of this observation to biochemists lies in the nature of some of the substrates and co-enzymes of Mo(V) and Fe(III) enzymes.[†] Amongst substrates of xanthine oxidase [10] are salicylaldehydes, purines and xanthines, which are all phenols. The flavine co-enzymes are both phenols and aromatic imines. Aromatic imines, e.g., dipyridyl and ortho-phenanthroline, interact with Mo(V) in much the same way as do phenols. Thus if the Mo(V) or Fe(III) of the enzymes is bound to either substrate or co-enzyme, we anticipate that the complex will show a charge transfer spectrum and that electron transfer from metal to ligand will be facile. The spectra of Mo(V)-flavin enzymes cannot be understood from a study of the components alone and it may well be that the charge-transfer Mo(V) band underlies and is confused with the band due to flavin alone (see Table 2).

The molybdenum valence state (IV) is formed with great difficulty. Only in the octa-cyanide is it peculiarly stabilised by favourable ligand-field symmetry which forces it into a diamagnetic, strong field condition. In other complexes it is not necessarily to be expected that this valence state will be diamagnetic. The only other compounds we have examined are $Mo(CNS)_6^{2-}$ and MoO_2 which are paramagnetic. Mo(IV) disproportionates readily. Molybdenum(III) complexes are well known and easily prepared. When octahedral they are often unstable in solution but are hydrolysed only slowly in water

---

[†]Some flavo-proteins contain both iron and molybdenum. The facts that both iron and molybdenum complexes show charge-transfer spectra and that their complexes are semi-conductors in the solid state make it possible that the oxidation-reduction reactions utilise the electron transport path Fe · substrate $\overset{e}{\longleftrightarrow}$ coenzyme · Mo where a direct exchange of an electron takes place between a co-enzyme and a substrate. The exchange is made possible by the presence of the two metal ions which activate the two organic molecules. This type of mechanism could account for certain features of xanthine oxidase reactions. [10]

as expected from their d^3 configuration. This observation is of importance as it is not to be expected that substrate exchange can be rapid in molybdenum(III) complexes.

Relative Stability of Different Valence States

From the properties of molybdenum(V) complexes in the solid and solution states it seems probable that electron transfer to and from the metal ion is facile. Thus oxidation or reduction should be very rapid. This is observed. It is also important, especially in a biological system, that the redox potential between the valence states is poised in a correct relationship to the potentials of the molecules which are to be oxidised or reduced. We have therefore made some studies of the redox potentials of molybdenum couples. The results are listed in Fig. 1. Although this study has only just begun, it shows that, just as in the cases of iron and copper, the control of the potentials of the molybdenum redox couples, the relative stability of the valence states, is readily achieved by suitable complex formation. Fig. 1 shows the relative stabilities with three complexing agents. Whereas cyanide stabilises Mo(IV) in a highly specific manner, this valence state is of very low stability with chloride and hydroxide (not observed) or thiocyanate. On the other hand, three-valent and five-valent molybdenum are often of somewhat similar stability with respect to the six-valent state. We suspect that this is also true of many other complexes with organic ligands. The molybdenum potentials in the table refer to acid solution. Both Mo(V) and to a greater degree Mo(VI) will be increas-

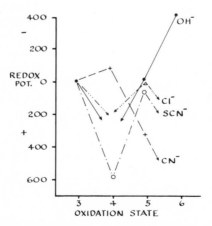

Fig. 1. The redox potentials (millivolts) of some molybdenum complexes, using the 3-valent states as an arbitrary zero.

ingly stabilised relative to other valence states on going into neutral and alkaline solution. Their cations are derived from the acids $Mo^{VI}(OH_2)_6$ which gives the nominal complex-forming cation $MoO_2 \cdot (OH_2)_4^{2+}$, and $Mo^V(OH_2)_6$ which gives the nominal complex-forming cation $MoO(H_2O)_5^{3+}$. The $Mo^{III}(H_2O)_6$ ion is a very weak acid and is probably little stabilised by change of pH. At neutral pH we estimate then that the reduction potential of the Mo^{VI}/Mo^V couple is about -0.2 to -0.4 volts while that of the Mo^V/Mo^{III} is about -0.6 to -1.0 volts. This would appear to put the molybdenum(III) valence state outside the potentials of a biological system but leaves the Mo(V)/ Mo(VI) potential very close to that of the flavins, -0.25 volts. We find it very difficult to make any certain predictions about Mo(IV), but the very pronounced difficulties which are associated with the study of this valence state even in acid solution, suggest that the valence state will be unstable in neutral solution except perhaps in particular field symmetries.

Reactions of Molybdenum with Riboflavin

We will now consider some experiments more nearly related to a biological system. We have studied the reduction of riboflavin in water by Mo(V). The experiments must be performed in circumstances which are far from ideal. Molybdenum(V) can only be kept as a mo- nomer in acid solution and in the absence of oxygen. On addition of such an acid solution to a buffer solution at pH 9.0 (borate buffer) there is undoubtedly considerable (virtually complete) and rapid hy- drolysis and dimerisation. If riboflavin is present in the buffer, there is also a slow reduction of riboflavin to its radical and then to the radical dimer, $Mo^V + FAD \longrightarrow Mo^{VI} + FADH \longrightarrow$ dimer. This reaction does not go to completion but gives an equilibrium mixture. The dimerisation of both Mo(V) and the radical probably prevent the further reaction from occurring Mo(V) + FADH $\longrightarrow$ Mo(VI) + $FADH_2$. We have also shown that molybdate is partially reduced by the fully reduced riboflavin $FADH_2$ and once again equilibrium is set up—this time favouring the reduced riboflavin. At pH 9.0 the two potentials in the riboflavin system, FAD $\rightleftharpoons$ FADH and FADH $\rightleftharpoons$ $FADH_2$ are both close to -0.30 volts. Thus the reduction potential of the Mo(V)/ Mo(VI) couple at this pH must also be near -0.25 volts in agreement with the calculated value (see above). In the study of these systems we have had no reason to suppose that either Mo(IV) or Mo(III) were present in any quantity.

We have been unable to show unequivocally that Mo(V) forms a com- plex with riboflavin in any of its three states although some work makes this a possibility which must be examined very carefully. The problem involves the Mo(V) dimers, the inevitable reduction of the ligand, and the fact that all the species absorb in similar spectral regions.

Molybdenum-Containing Enzymes

Many biochemists will consider the approach to molybdenum enzymes which I have outlined laborious, unnecessary and perhaps even unrewarding. No consideration has been given to the protein of the enzyme. I would now like to show that this is not so, and that in conjunction with certain biochemical studies our work throws some light on molybdenum enzymes. Our first problem concerns the way in which molybdenum is bound to the enzyme. The resting enzyme in the oxidised state holds Mo(VI) firmly from pH 2-10. A strong possibility for this combination is the binding of the molybdyl ion, $[MoO_2^{2+}]X$. Here X is likely to be one or more anionic groups, e.g. carboxylate, of the protein. It is more improbable that molybdenum (VI) is bound to either sulphur or aliphatic nitrogen of the protein, but it could be bound to aromatic nitrogen and/or phenolic oxygen of the co-enzyme or substrates. Some substrates of the molybdenum enzymes are given in Table 4. The best studied of these enzymes is xanthine oxidase. In the work on this enzyme, it has been shown by electron spin resonance measurements that on reduction with substrate there is a signal due to molybdenum which is produced and disappears in a time sequence similar to that of the signal due to the radical of riboflavin. In the early work,[12] which was probably carried out on *inactive* enzyme, it was not possible to say whether the molybdenum was reduced to the (III) or the (V) valent state. As I have pointed out above, there are good chemical reasons for supposing that the reduction could only be to Mo(V). Dr. Bray has told me of further independent experiments on the enzyme which lead more directly to the view that Mo(V) and not Mo(III) is involved. These results will be published shortly. On addition of a slight excess of reducing agent to the *active* enzyme both the spin resonance signal of the flavin and that

TABLE 4: SOME MOLYBDENUM-CONTAINING ENZYMES[13]

Enzyme	Substrates
xanthine oxidase	xanthines, pterins, purines
aldehyde oxidase	aldehydes, quinoline and pyridine derivatives
nitrate reductase	nitrate
nitrite reductase (?)	nitrite

of the molybdenum disappear but the Mo(V) signal re-appears with still larger quantities of reducing agent. A very considerable excess of the strongest reducing agent that can be added, dithionite, to an *inactive* enzyme, produces the strongest molybdenum(V) signal (almost 100% in some experiments). At least in the *inactive* preparation then it seems impossible to reduce Mo(V). It would *appear* however that molybdenum(V) is further reduced in the *active* enzyme for the E.S.R. signal disappears with a slight excess of reducing agent.[12] An alternative explanation of this reduction is that molybdenum(V) returns to molybdenum(VI) with complete reduction of the flavin. A plausible scheme is given in Fig. 2.

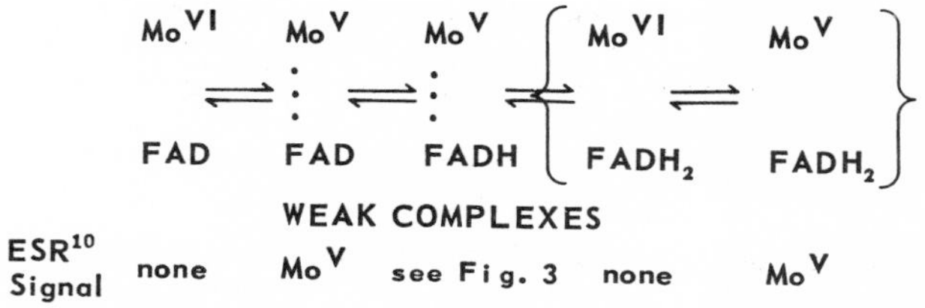

The steps in parenthesis are *in vitro* steps only. It is supposed that inactive Xanthine Oxidase gives no intermediate complexes.

Fig. 2. Active xanthine oxidase reduction (hypothetical).

The scheme introduces no valences of molybdenum other than those that have been produced in model experiments, and contains steps in accord with known model reactions. The scheme suggests that there is a complex between Mo(V) and FAD. Also, in the second complex Mo(V)——FADH two radicals are postulated close to one another in space. We should expect a splitting of the two E.S.R. signals due to the field of one radical affecting the energy states of the other. The situation is well-recognised for two identical radicals. The signals would then be as in Fig. 3(b). The observed signal[12] is rather similar, shown schematicly in Fig. 3(c). Whatever the explanation of the observed signal[24] the case of adjacent radicals is one of great importance in biological systems. Electron-spin resonance is almost the only method which will detect such a situation.[14] Molybdenum enzymes are also involved in the series of reduction steps from nitrate to ammonia. Although a good deal is known of these enzymes the work is not yet in a state to be tackled from the point of view of model systems. However, in all these systems it would appear that the function of Mo(V) is to introduce an odd electron into an organic or inorganic molecule. Elsewhere we have discussed this function of

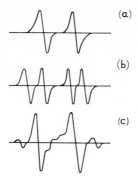

Fig. 3. The electron spin resonance signals for (a) two independent radicals, (b) two strongly interacting radicals, (c) two strongly interacting radicals which may or may not be formed in the presence of one another and which can be present in very different proportions. (c) is to be compared with signals observed by Bray et al.[10]

a metal complex in some copper (cupric) and iron (ferric) enzymes.[1,2,4] We will now consider the function of cobalt in certain enzymes.

Cobalt Complexes

The chemistry of the complexes of the two stable valence states of cobalt has been well studied. In the divalent state cobalt forms complexes which, as far as their thermodynamic stability is concerned, fall with almost monotonous regularity between iron(II) and nickel-(II). Deviations from this regularity are found when ferrous goes over into the low-spin state, e.g., with o-phenanthroline, when the stability of its complexes exceeds that of cobaltous complexes, and when the properties of the ligand, usually large size and high polarisability, do not permit an octahedral coordination about the three cations.[2] In the latter case the stability of the cobaltous complexes sometimes exceeds that of nickel, e.g., in their chlorides. It is a feature of the chemistry of the cobaltous ion that the cation is reluctant to assume the low-spin configuration, doing so only in cyanide and partially in phthalocyanine and porphyrin complexes. *In these low-spin complexes the odd electron is very exposed to substrates or ligands.* It is also a feature of this ion that in the high-spin state and in octahedral coordination the extinction coefficient of the complexes (pink) is low, < 10, but in the same electron configuration and in a tetrahedral environment or other environments with no center of symmetry the extinction coefficient (blue) approaches 1,000. In the latter case the extinction coefficient is the higher the better the electron donor properties of the ligands. In the formation of complexes the cobaltous ion shows no striking preference for nitrogen rather than oxygen type ligands.[1]

This information has proved of immediate applicability to the problems of biochemistry. Carboxy-peptidase is an enzyme responsible for peptide bond hydrolysis. It contains zinc, which is essential for reactivity.[15] The zinc is apparently bound at a site of low symmetry by relatively few coordinating centres—two or three, as judged by the following properties: (a) The zinc is capable of further coordination to o-phenanthroline. (b) The zinc is readily exchangeable with radioactive zinc or with a large number of other cations. This is in marked contrast to the behaviour of zinc in enzymes such as carbonic anhydrase and the DPN dependent enzymes, although the zinc is slowly exchangeable in the latter cases. (c) When zinc is exchanged with cobaltous, the apo-enzyme complex formed is blue, indicating that the coordinating groups available to the cobaltous ion do not permit it to form a regular octahedral complex. The cobaltous enzyme has the same properties as the zinc enzyme even exceeding it in activity.[15] (d) The relative stabilities of the manganous, nickelous and cobaltous complexes show that zinc is the most stable and that cobaltous is nearly as stable as zinc. This suggests again an irregular coordination site, for the stability of zinc complexes only exceeds that of nickel when the cations are forced to assume irregular coordination. As cobaltous much prefers octahedral coordination with the most common types of coordinating group available from a protein, i.e. in model nitrogen or oxygen complexes, we must presume that the irregular geometry is forced upon the cation by the protein despite the fact that the number of binding groups is small. Now the most common ligand which brings about all these effects in model systems is sulphur and we therefore suggested that the cations in carboxypeptidase be bound to a sulphur group and it was this group which caused the cations to form non-octahedral complexes.[17] Dr. Vallee and his associates proved simultaneously by chemical analytical methods (a superior approach) that the zinc was bound to sulphur. In collaboration with him, we have recently suggested that as the second atom binding the cation is a nitrogen group either of imidazole or of a terminal amine group.[16] This follows from a study of the relative stability of the carboxy-peptidase complexes and those of model ligands. This is illustrated in Fig. 4. Whereas there is a linear 1 : 1 correlation between the stability constants of the carboxy-peptidase complexes and those of bidentate nitrogen-sulphur model ligands, there is no such correlation with other models. The whole of this study illustrates how thinking about coordination compounds can help

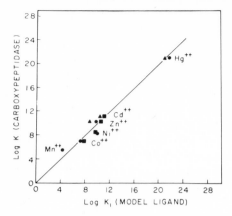

Fig. 4. Correlation of log K for carboxypeptidase with log K_1 for sulphur-nitrogen ligands; ●, cysteine; ■, mercapto-ethylamine; ▲, glutathione.

in the study of biological systems. Even the two facts, (1) that zinc is commonly found in enzymes and cobaltous and nickel are not and (2) that zinc complexes exceed in stability complexes of cobaltous and nickel only when the ligands are of large size and polarisability, led us to suggest from the stabilities of model complexes that the zinc in enzymes might be expected to be bound to sulphur. This argument[17] was based upon the assumption that the cations and ligands of a biological system are in thermodynamic equilibrium.* (We have expanded on this point at a recent conference.)[5] It follows from this assumption that the cation found in the biological system in conjunction with a given enzyme may have no imperative connection with the metal requirement for activity of the enzyme *in vitro*. *In vitro* we can alter the relative amounts of cations available to a biological substance from the values obtaining through cosmological processes and through the relative chemistry of the earth, soil, and living substances. When a metal-enzyme which contains a given metal is

---

*Here [17] we assumed implicitly that the protein binds the metal by a few groups, i.e., *two or three*. A possibility which we neglected is that the irregular geometry of a protein could lead to a coordination site for the cation composed of a *larger* number of groups in an *irregular* configuration, e.g., 4 or 5 coordination. In such a case the sequence of stabilities could be Zn^{II} and $Co^{II} > Ni^{II}$ independent of the nature of the binding groups as found when steric hindrance prevents octahedral coordination in model complexes, e.g., (1) chloride and (2) 2-methyl-8-hydroxyquinoline complexes. [18] Such high coordination of irregular stereo-chemistry is expected to be rare in metal-protein complexes but it is possible in the case of carbonic anhydrase. [19]

treated with another metal in excess, then often exchange occurs. [15] The properties of the new metallo-enzyme may or may not now depend upon the cation inserted. In the case of carboxypeptidase it is known that the insertion of cations which have similar coordination chemistry to zinc, e.g., cobaltous and manganous, give rise to metallo-enzymes which are new carboxypeptidases and very similar to zinc carboxypeptidase. Strictly they are not new for the biochemical system is probably not homogeneous and "should" contain amounts of the cobaltous and manganous enzymes as well as of the zinc enzyme. These amounts (*in vivo*) are regulated by the complicated set of stability constants which pertain *specifically* to a given metal. This applies equally to all metallo-enzymes catalysing acid-base reactions. (I have deliberately restricted attention to the cations zinc, cobaltous and nickel, avoiding cupric and ferrous because the latter can undergo oxidation or reduction which would invalidate comparisons.) If more unusual cations are added to the enzyme, e.g., mercuric and cadmium, then, although the enzyme does not have carboxy-peptidase activity, it has esterase activity (Table 5). Dr. Vallee and myself[16] have attempted to show how this change in the activity of the enzyme on change of the metal is related to the properties of the cations and is independent of the character of the protein (Fig. 5). This is the hypothesis of the active site carried to an extreme as there is no need to invoke changes in protein character to explain changes in enzyme activity.

The cobaltous cation is found (*in vivo*) in argininase. The enzyme is not said to be noticeably coloured blue or purple. If closer inspection confirms this observation, then the coordination site in this case is a nearly regular octahedron. It will be a case of a cobaltous

TABLE 5: RELATIVE CARBOXYPEPTIDASE AND ESTERASE ACTIVITIES OF DIFFERENT METALLO-"CARBOXYPEPTIDASES"[15]

Metal	Peptidase Activity* (arbitrary units)	Esterase Activity[†] (arbitrary units)
Zinc (natural)	7.0	1.5
Cobalt	12.0	1.8
Nickel	8.0	1.0
Manganous	2.8	0.4
Cadmium	0.0	2.3
Mercuric	0.0	1.6

*Peptidase activity was measured with

$$C_6H_5 \cdot CH_2 \cdot OCO \cdot NH \cdot CH_2 \cdot CO \cdot NH \cdot CH \cdot (CO_2H) \cdot CH_2 \cdot C_6H_5 \cdot$$

[†]Esterase activity was measured with

$$C_6H_5 \cdot CO \cdot NH \cdot CH_2 \cdot CO \cdot O \cdot CH \cdot (CO_2H) \cdot CH_2 \cdot C_6H_5 \cdot$$

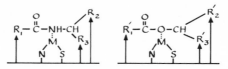

Fig. 5. Suggested complexes for peptidase and esterase activity in same enzyme.

pink complex in a biological system. As the cation can be replaced by nickel and zinc while activity is retained, but not by manganous or magnesium, we suggest that the required binding groups of the enzyme or the substrates to the cobalt are most likely to be about three nitrogen atoms together with about three oxygen groups which may be water or carboxylate.

This discussion of cobaltous chemistry and its biological significance shows how important it is to utilise the known coordination chemistry of cations in the examination of enzymes. Especially important is the change of cation in an enzyme to one not found in a biological system but one which has analytically interesting properties. Such properties can often be correlated with the geometry and binding groups of the active site. A series of cobalt complexes which have been intensively studied recently are the cobalamins, of which vitamin B_{12}, a cyanide complex, is the best known. We have studied some properties of this series of complexes. (Mr. J. Pratt is largely responsible for the work I shall summarise.) The first point concerns the oxidation-reduction reaction of the B_{12} compounds. It is known that the vitamin is in the Co(III) state but that it is reduced by hydrogen in the presence of a palladium or platinum surface. A similar reaction takes place with borohydride. The reduced forms are readily re-oxidised by molecular oxygen and many oxidising agents. These reactions place the redox potential of the vitamin somewhere near that of hydrogen. This would roughly be where one would predict the potential of the cobalt from its coordinating groups. The vitamin is stable only in the absence of sunlight. u.v. light leads to a replacement of cyanide by water giving vitamin $B_{12(a)}$. Presumably the initial step of the reaction is similar to the model photo-redox reactions of cobaltic complexes so thoroughly studied by Adamson.[20] This suggests that an internal photo-chemical reduction of B_{12} is easy. Vitamin B_{12a} is also easily reduced by chromous, borohydride, and hydrogen and is re-oxidised by molecular oxygen. From our knowledge of the cobalt(III)/cobalt(II) and cobalt(II)/cobalt(I) potentials, we would expect that the (III)/(II) potentials of the complexes of B_{12}-like compounds would become more negative in the order of ligands in the sixth coordination position—water > ammines > cyanide

—but that the unsaturated groups which stabilise Co(III) relative to cobalt(II), e.g., cyanide, isocyanide, and dipyridyl, also stabilise cobalt(I). The Corrin ring system is similar to this group of ligands and vitamin B_{12} complexes can undoubtedly be reduced to the cobalt (I) state by reagents such as borohydride. The products have an absorption maximum at 305–315 mμ (Table 6). Now in the cobalamin co-enzymes the cobalt is bound by the Corrin ring (or by a ring system of similar ligand properties, see below) and either by two adenines, A_2 or one adenine and one benzimidazole, AB. Such groups are expected to make the redox potential of the co-enzymes not very different from that of $B_{12(a)}$. Reduction to both divalent and monovalent cobalt must be easy in these compounds. *In vivo* all the complexes are likely to be in low-valent states as the redox potential maintained in a biological cell is much lower than that of the hydrogen electrode. Possibly cobalt(I) is present to a large degree.

TABLE 6: VITAMIN B_{12} COMPLEXES, ABSORPTION SPECTRA MAXIMA (mμ)*

Ligand bound	u.v. maxima	Visible maxima
H_2O	350	525
NH_3	354	530
imidazole	357	540
thiocyanate	358	540
pyridine	361	545
cyanide	365	560
(dicyanide)	368	575

*The ligand sequence is that of increasing electron acceptor power. The dicyanide spectrum has peculiarities which we will analyze elsewhere.

We now turn to the spectrophotometric properties of the complexes (Tables 6 and 7). Vitamin B_{12} has band maxima at around 360 mμ and between 500 and 600 mμ. These bands are affected by changes in coordination in much the same way as the bands of low-spin iron porphyrins [3] (Table 6). Cyanide shifts the bands to longer wavelengths. Saturated amines, and water to a greater extent, shift the bands to shorter wavelengths. These observations are consistent with the nature of π to π' transitions where the electrons in the excited state are more concentrated away from the nitrogen atoms than in the ground state.

The spectra of the yellow cobalamin co-enzymes A_2 and the borohydride reduction products of B_{12a} are totally different (Fig. 6). The former have band maxima at 305 mμ (rather flat and ill-defined), at 375 mμ (this absorption is weak; the stronger absorption is at 360 mμ), and rather ill-defined absorption in the region of 400–450 mμ.

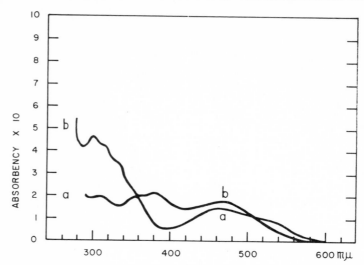

Fig. 6. Comparison of spectra of (a) γ-picoline cobalamin ($1.9 \cdot 10^{-5}$M) after three days in the dark and (b) adenylcobamide coenzyme ($2.06 \cdot 10^{-5}$M).

We conclude that the conjugated system of the Corrin ring is broken, as illustrated in Fig. 7, but fully reduced at $C_8 - C_9$. We now turn to some other evidence of this change. Of the two types of co-enzymes the di-adenine compound (A_2) has only a yellow form independent of pH while the mono-adenine mono-benzimidazole (AB) form is red in alkali and yellow in acid. In acid the two forms have very similar spectra. This suggests that the reaction with alkali is blocked in the di-adenine form. Now we can prepare compounds from vitamin B_{12a} which have spectra very like the red form and which change to the yellow form with change of pH in much the same way as the AB co-enzyme (Table 7). The reagents which bring about this change are sodium sulphite, (stannous chloride), sodium thiosulphate and sodium sulphide. Common features of these new compounds and the AB co-enzymes, apart from the spectra, are their sensitivity to u.v. light, which gives B_{12a} again or a compound very similar to it, the action of cyanide which produces the purple di-cyanide compound, and *their resistance to oxidation by molecular oxygen.* All the above reagents can be thought of as reducing agents introducing hydrogen or as coordinating agents. We consider that in alkali these compounds have the intact Corrin ring. Compounds like the yellow co-enzymes, A_2, can be prepared by the action of γ-picoline. The compound behaves like a methyl derivative of B_{12} in which the Corrin ring conjugation is broken. We suggest that in the yellow form (acid AB and A_2)

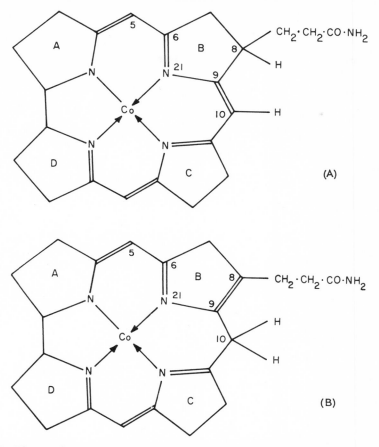

Fig. 7. The corphyrin skeleton of crystalline vitamin B_{12}(A) and of a possible tautomeric form (B). We believe now that the di-adenine co-enzymes are reduced forms of B with C_8–C_9 a single bond and no negative charge on the ring.

the Corrin ring is bent as we suggested in an earlier paper. The double bond in the C_8–C_9 position should be ignored in reduced forms.) It is bent by the attack of hydrogen or methyl groups on the "incipient" carbonium ion, C_{10}, induced by the cobalt atom. The problem of the valence of the cobalt in these compounds can only be solved by measurements of magnetic moment. Unfortunately the values so far obtained by different workers are very discordant and their conclusions are not always acceptable from their evidence. However from the information in Table 7 and the magnetic data we consider that, rather than dealing with one substance in solution which has

TABLE 7: POSITIONS OF ABSORPTION PEAKS OF B_{12} DERIVATIVES (mμ)

Derivative	Action of		
	Light	Cyanide	Borohydride
B_{12} (the monocyanide) 360, 535, 575	B_{12a} 350, 520	B_{12} (dicyanide)	initially 307
B_{12a} (the mono-hydrate) 350, 520 acid; 358, 525 alkali	none	dicyanide	312, 375, 520
Me_2SO_4† compound { acid 318, 353, 415 ; alkali (307), 362, 530 }	B_{12a}*	a cyanide*	plus cyanide or pyridine 307, 380, 450
bisulphite compound { acid 352, 415 ; alkali 307, 362, 530 }	B_{12a}*	a cyanide* and slowly B_{12} dicyanide	
γ-picoline 315, 460 compound	some B_{12} pyridine (stable)	a cyanide* (slowly)	
Co-enzyme A_2 307, (375), 455		slowly to dicyanide	no effect
Co-enzyme AB acid 302, 455; alkali 307, (375), 520		slowly to dicyanide	no effect

*A compound which closely resembles a known compound, either B_{12a} or the dicyanide, but which is not identical with it.
†The reaction with dimethyl sulphate may well be due to sulphite.

simple redox properties, we are dealing with a very flexible compound. It can exist in two ring forms, and in at least two, (I) and (III), oxidation states in each ring form. Moreover it is far from certain that the oxidation states will be simple spin states rather than equilibrium mixtures of different spin states especially in the Co(II) forms. If we are correct, the remarkable flexibility of reaction of B$_{12}$ derivatives in biological systems, stems from the presence in one molecule of an "incipient" carbonium ion, C$_{10}$, and a two-electron redox system. The combination has all the characteristics of a flavin or DPN co-enzyme in that the change of oxidation state by two units can induce change of molecular configuration. Thus the system could be likened to the molybdenum system we have described above; a transition metal ion combined with an organic aromatic system must be treated as a unit. The cation introduces charge into the organic group and the organic group gives spatial significance to the redox reactions which the complex undergoes. This type of effect could well be general to many metal ion/co-enzyme cofactors and it is not essential that the metal should be capable of undergoing oxidation-reduction changes. The presence of positive charge may in itself be sufficient as we have discussed in the case of zinc/DPN reactions (Fig. 8). Finally this mechanism of attack on B$_{12}$ co-enzymes is very like that

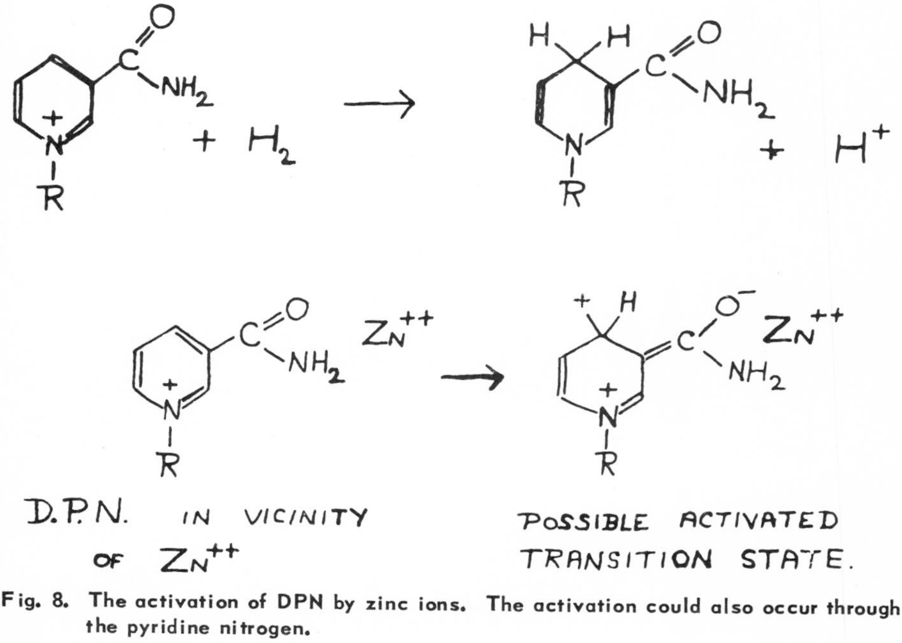

Fig. 8. The activation of DPN by zinc ions. The activation could also occur through the pyridine nitrogen.

we have described to explain the intermediate states of peroxidase and catalase[3] and it is capable of extension to the explanation of the migration of charge in the electron transport chain and in chloroplasts.

In conclusion I wish to emphasise that the work and ideas I have discussed originate only in part from myself and I would like to draw attention to my co-workers, Mr. J. M. Pratt and Mr. P. C. H. Mitchell. Our thanks are due Dr. E. Lester Smith and the Wellcome Trust for guidance and financial help.

REFERENCES*

1. R. J. P. Williams, *Biol. Rev. Cambridge Phil. Soc. 28,* 381 (1953), and *Special Lectures in Biochemistry,* 1954–55, University College, London, H. K. Lewis and Co., London, 1956.
2. R. J. P. Williams, *The Enzymes,* (Ed. P. D. Boyer, H. Lardy and K. Myrbäck) Academic Press, New York, p. 391.
3. R. J. P. Williams, A. S. Brill and R. J. P. Williams, Symposium on Haemitin Enzymes, Australia, 1959, *Biochem. J. 78,* 246 and 253 (1961).
4. R. J. P. Williams, National Academy of Sciences (U. S. A.), *Symposium on Metal Ions in Biology* (1960).
5. R. J. P. Williams, *Vth International Congress of Biochemistry,* Moscow, 1961.
6. P. C. H. Mitchell and R. J. P. Williams, *J. Chem. Soc. (London),* 1960, 1912.
7. S. Ahrland, J. Chatt, and N. R. Davies, *Quart. Rev., Chem. Soc. (London),* 12, 265 (1958).
8. J. Crabtree, W. C. Fernelius, D. Marsh, J. C. Tomkinson, R. J. P. Williams, to be published.
9. J. C. Tomkinson, and R. J. P. Williams, *J. Chem. Soc. (London),* 1958, 2070.
10. R. C. Bray, and R. C. Bray, T. Värngård, and A. Ehrenberg, to be published.
11. P. S. Braterman and R. J. P. Williams, to be published.
12. R. C. Bray, B. G. Malmström, and T. Värngård, *Biochem. J.,* 73, 193 (1959).
13. M. Dixon and E. C. Webb, *Enzymes,* Longmans, London, 1958, p. 185–227.
14. D. C. Borg, National Academy of Sciences (U. S. A.), *Symposium on Metal Ions in Biology* (1960).
15. There are a long series of papers on this metallo-enzyme by Vallee and co-workers, see *IVth Int. Congress of Biochem.* Vol. VIII, 138, Pergamon Press (London)
16. B. L. Vallee and R. J. P. Williams, to be published.

---

*The parochial character of the references arises from an emphasis on our own recent work. No attempt has been made to survey the vast literature on molybdenum or cobalt containing enzymes, for which the reader is referred to standard monographs. References (1) and (2) are given as a general introduction to the whole subject.

17. R. J. P. Williams, *Nature*, **188**, 322 (1960).
18. R. J. P. Williams, *J. Phys. Chem.*, **58**, 121 (1954).
19. These remarks are made as a result of a discussion by Dr. B. G. Malmström, who has prepared several metallo-carbonic anhydrases recently. (See contributions by B. G. Malmström and R. J. P. Williams at *Vth International Congress of Biochemistry*, Moscow).
20. A. W. Adamson, *Discussions Faraday Soc.*, **29**, 1960, 163.
21. J. M. Pratt and R. J. P. Williams, *Biochem. and Biophys. Acta*, **46**, 191, (1961).
22. The B_{12} literature is covered in the many publications of Prof. D. C. Hodgkin, Dr. E. Lester Smith, and Prof. H. A. Barker and their co-authors.
23. *Note added in proof.* Our own measurements indicate that the cobalt ion is in the (I) or (II) state.
24. An alternative explanation invokes the resonance signal due to Fe(II) or Fe(III). Again two radicals are postulated close together in space.

SIGNIFICANCE OF COMPLEXES IN CATALYTIC PROCESSES

H. ZEISS

Monsanto Research S. A.
Zürich, Switzerland

In one of the reliable dictionaries of the English language may be found the following definitions:

> **Catalysis** (fr. Gr. *katalysis,* dissolution), acceleration of a reaction produced by a substance, called the "catalyst," which may be recovered practically unchanged at the end of the reaction.
> **Complex,** a whole made up of complicated or interrelated parts.

These definitions illustrate the difficulties which a discussion of the role of complexes in catalysis entails, since both of these word formations contain loose terminology and are vague, incomplete and ambiguous. As a consequence catalysis and complexes mean many things to many persons, depending upon the particular field of interest of the individual. I should imagine that the petroleum engineer would think of 'catalytic cracking,' the polymer chemist of Ziegler catalyst, the biochemist of haemoglobin or cytochrome, and so on, when this subject is brought to mind. It is apparent, therefore, that there is no clear and unequivocal definition of catalysis, meaning the same to all, because these processes are still incompletely understood. Perhaps by concentrating our attention on the chemical function of the complex in catalytic reactions we may derive a more common comprehension of catalysis and at the same time make some progress toward better defining it. The immensity of this phenomenon in our world requires that we do so.

The most dramatic example of the role of metal complexes in catalysis, in my opinion, is that provided by iron in the decomposition of hydrogen peroxide into water and oxygen.[1] Whereas the ferric ion, hydrated by water, $Fe(OH_2)_6^{+3}$, has a very small catalytic efficiency in this reaction at $0°$, the porphyrin environment of iron in haem increases iron's activity by a factor of 10^3, and when haem is inserted into a protein structure to form catalase, this catalytic power of iron rises to 10^5 m.l.$^{-1}$ s.$^{-1}$, an incredible jump of ten powers of 10 over that of the "bare" ferric ion. Surely one must learn more of catalytic processes in which complexes exhibit such phenomenal increases in efficiency. And the role of iron in catalase is not confined only to hydrogen peroxide decomposition. Catalase acts also as a peroxidase and as a catalyst in oxidative phosphorylation. However, it is not my purpose to examine biological mechanisms in this paper. This example is intended as a goal of our understanding. We must go back to simpler systems.

Our own entry into the subject under discussion dates back to the discovery of triphenylchromium(III) by Dr. Walter Herwig in my laboratory in Dayton.[2] Several years prior to this (1954)[3] we had proposed that the polyphenylchromium compounds (Hein) arising from the reaction of phenyl Grignard in ether with chromium(III) halide were in fact chromium(I) "sandwich" complexes in which the aromatic components, e.g., benzene, biphenyl, were bonded through their π-electrons to the empty dsp orbitals of chromium.[4a] In a further study of this Grignard-metal halide synthesis of π-complexes[2] we succeeded not only in isolating the triphenylchromium(III) compound, according to

$$3(C_6H_5)_2Mg \cdot MgBr_2 + 2CrCl_3 \longrightarrow 2(C_6H_5)_3Cr \cdot 3THF +$$
$$\text{(in tetrahydrofuran)}$$

$$3MgBr_2 + 3MgCl_2$$

but also in rearranging it, e.g., by washing it with diethyl ether, to the π-complexed "sandwich" structures. These complexes are thermally stable at moderate temperatures and are relatively inert to air in their cationic form and to water in either the cationic or zerovalent state; but triphenylchromium(III) and other aryl and alkyl derivatives of chromium(III) are quite sensitive to water and oxygen. However, when bis-benzenechromium(O), for example, is heated to its melting point, 284°, *in vacuo*, it decomposes into benzene and atomic chromium.[5] At the instant of release of the chromium atom from the zerovalent complex we would expect it to be a nascent form of chromium and consequently highly reactive. At this temperature and in its experimental environment the chromium atom finds nothing better to do than to form a metal mirror.

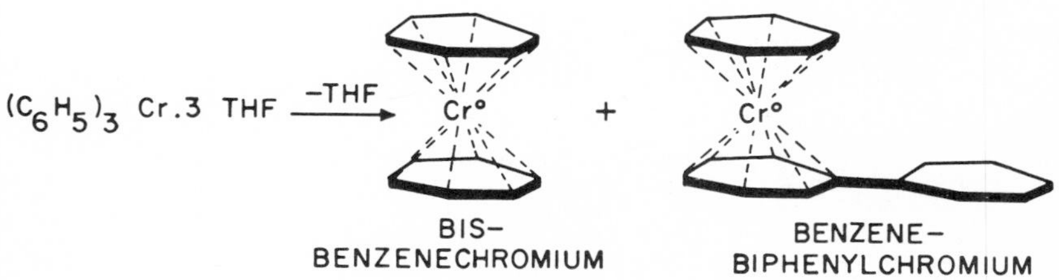

$(C_6H_5)_3$ Cr.3 THF $\xrightarrow{-THF}$ Cr° + Cr°

BIS-
BENZENECHROMIUM

BENZENE-
BIPHENYLCHROMIUM

Fig. 1.

I have dwelt on this conversion of chromium(III) in its chloride salt to the highly reactive chromium(0) atom by way of the Grignard process, reductive rearrangement into π-complex and finally thermal release, since these steps will be applied presently to other systems.

An attempt to isolate diphenylchromium(II) from the reaction of phenyl Grignard and chromium(II) halide was not successful owing to the facile rearrangement of this organochromium(II) derivative into the π-complexes shown in Fig. 1.[6] The ease with which diphenylchromium(II) reverts to complex form bears an important relationship to the chemistry of the phenylcobalt(II) compounds which we shall consider shortly. However, diarylchromium(II) compounds, e.g., dimesitylchromium, can be isolated if the aryl substituents possess structural features, e.g., o-methyl groups, which interfere with the internal oxidative-reductive rearrangement to π-complexes.[7]

The stability of the chromium(0) complexes which include also hexacarbonylchromium, benzene-tricarbonylchromium, etc., is dependent upon the ability of the chromium atom, atomic no. 24, to achieve a krypton-like configuration, 36, by d^2sp^3 coordination, having octahedral geometry. Consider once again the physical state of

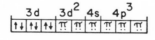

Fig. 2.

the zerovalent chromium atom when the complex is thermally decomposed. The benzene or biphenyl rings plating chromium are abruptly removed, the chromium atom is laid bare, and in this state cannot be regarded as "colloidal" or "finely divided" but rather as "hot" chromium. This procedure, incidentally, represents a new method of preparing a transition metal in a reactive form.

In our stoichiometric experiments with the phenyl Grignard-chromium halide systems in the preparation of phenylchromium derivatives and π-complexes, no evidence for the existence of partially phenylated chromium, e.g., $C_6H_5CrCl_2$ or $(C_6H_5)_2CrCl$, was found. This is mentioned with reference to the experiments of Dessy,[8] which provide no basis for the formulation of phenyl Grignard as a mixed aryl-metal halide, i.e., R-MgX. His evidence in fact supports the formulation, $R_2Mg \cdot MgX_2$, for the Grignard reagent. I would suggest here that our predilection for the historical and incorrect formula of the Grignard reagent may be penalizing our thinking about Grignard reactions in particular and about organometallic chemistry in general.

The study of the effect of metal halides on Grignard systems, particularly phenyl Grignard, in ether was undertaken some years ago by Kharasch[9] and continued until his death. One of the chief results of this large body of work was the demonstration of the catalytic effect of several transition metal halides, notably those of cobalt and nickel, in decomposing phenyl Grignard to biphenyl. The decrease in catalytic activity of the metal halides in ascending in atomic number to copper or descending to chromium (Table 1) is striking in that the

TABLE 1: CATALYTIC EFFICIENCY OF METAL HALIDES IN THE DECOMPOSITION OF PHENYL GRIGNARD IN THE PRESENCE OF BROMOBENZENE

Metal Halide	Metal Atomic No.	Yield of % $(C_6H_5)_2$
$CuCl_2$	29	6
$NiCl_2$	28	72
$CoCl_2$	27	86
$FeCl_3$	26	47
$MnCl_2$	25	21
$CrCl_3$	24	7

metals which show no activity are precisely those which are now known to form stable derivatives under Grignard conditions. Phenylcopper, for example, is stable up to 80 ° at which point it decomposes into biphenyl and copper. In ether, triphenylchromium(III) rearranges to the stable π-complexes. Those remaining metals having little or no activity, Fe and Mn, are known to form either stable π-complexes with aromatic systems or isolable σ-bonded derivatives. Cobalt(II) and nickel(II), the two active metals, do not form bis-benzene complexes. This experimental result is readily explicable in terms of the stabilization acquired by Cr(O), Mn(I) and Fe(II), having an effective atomic number of 24, in achieving a krypton configuration by sharing 12 π-electrons. Cobalt (25-27) and nickel (26-28) cannot do this.

Arylcobalt(II) compounds have been claimed. In one paper[10] both arylcobalt halides and diarylcobalt were reported to have been isolated from reactions of naphthyl and phenyl Grignard reagents with cobalt(II) halides. The phenylcobalt products were described as being quite unstable. We have formed dimesitylcobalt(II) in tetrahydrofuran[11] and have found that it has limited stability at room temperature. It will be recalled that diphenylchromium(II) too was quite labile, reverting immediately to π-complex, and that dimesitylchromium(II) was isolable. We suggest, therefore, that diphenylcobalt behaves similarly in undergoing oxidative-reductive rearrangement but in doing so forms biphenyl and cobalt(O) in an atomic, not colloidal, state. The essential difference here is that chromium(O) is accomodated in its zerovalent form by internal rearrangement to π-complex, a path which cobalt(II) is unable to follow. Under the Grignard conditions employed by Kharasch, i.e., boiling ether and long periods of time, cobalt(O) is produced in nascent form and of course in a considerably more reactive atmosphere than that in which chromium(O) is produced from bis-benzenechromium(O) at 284° *in vacuo*.

The reactive atmosphere which the Kharasch school at Chicago provided was that of added organic halides for the most part. It became clear early in these studies that the biphenyl which was produced when catalytic amounts of cobalt(II) halide were added to phenyl Grignard-organic halide solutions in ether was derived from the phenyl Grignard, since alkyl as well as aryl halides were effective in promoting the production of biphenyl. Thus it became clear that the added organic halide was functioning as part of the catalytic system in conjunction with cobalt. A mechanism was proposed to account for these results, as they were understood at that time, which was distinguished by its emphasis on a free radical process.

$$C_6H_5MgX + CoCl_2 \longrightarrow C_6H_5CoCl + MgXCl$$
$$C_6H_5CoCl \longrightarrow C_6H_5 \cdot + \cdot CoCl$$
$$\cdot CoCl + R\text{-}X \longrightarrow R \cdot + CoClX$$
$$2C_6H_5 \cdot \longrightarrow (C_6H_5)_2$$
$$2R \cdot \longrightarrow R\text{-}R$$

This mechanism has not been seriously challenged in the past. Wilds and McCormack[12] suggested an alternate path which was based more upon analogy with other organometallic systems rather than upon an unknown cobalt(I) halide intermediate.

$$2C_6H_5MgX + CoCl_2 \longrightarrow (C_6H_5)_2Co + 2MgXCl$$
$$(C_6H_5)_2Co \longrightarrow (C_6H_5)_2 + Co(O)$$
$$Co + R\text{-}X \longrightarrow R_2 + CoX_2$$

Until recently there has been no experimental basis for reaching a decision regarding the validity of either process or the rejection of both.

Our previous discussion[4b] of the behavior of diarylchromium(II) and-cobalt(II) supports the first two steps of the Wilds-McCormack proposal, i.e.,

$$(C_6H_5)_2Mg + CoCl_2 \rightarrow (C_6H_5)_2Co + MgCl_2$$
$$(C_6H_5)_2Co \rightarrow (C_6H_5)_2 + Co(0)$$

We regard an earlier counter-argument citing the ineffectiveness of colloidal cobalt in these reactions as irrelevant, since, as has been emphasized before, the atomic cobalt produced here is a different chemical entity both in structure and reactivity. The isolation of diarylcobalt compounds and the reported existence of arylcobalt halides support the first steps of both mechanisms. However, in rewriting the first step of the Kharasch mechanism using correct Grignard structure, the process no longer seems quite so simple. That is, stepwise reaction leads to the short-lived phenylmagnesium halide which must

$$(C_6H_5)_2Mg + CoCl_2 \dashrightarrow C_6H_5MgCl + C_6H_5CoCl$$

revert back to diphenylmagnesium or undergo further reaction with added organic halide. The alternative is complete reaction which is the first step of the Wilds-McCormack scheme.

The concept of an intermediate cobalt(I) halide in these systems is not supported by new chemical evidence. The cobalt(II) halide-phenyl Grignard system to which the organic halide, 3-phenoxypropyl bromide, had been added was found to result in the evolution of cyclopropane and the formation of phenol.[13] The Kharasch mechanism invoked the production of an organic radical which eliminated the

$$C_6H_5O-CH_2CH_2CH_2-Br + \cdot CoCl \qquad C_6H_5O-CH_2CH_2CH_2 \cdot +$$

$$CoClBr$$

phenoxy fragment in forming cyclopropane. However, Slaugh[14] has now shown this path to be improbable since his generation of the 3-phenoxypropyl radical in dilute solution by the decarbonylation of 4-phenoxybutraldehyde produces no trace of cyclopropane.

$$C_6H_5O-CH_2CH_2CH_2-CHO \xrightarrow{(t\text{-}BuO)_2} C_6H_5O-CH_2CH_2CH_3 + CO$$

Since 3-phenoxypropyl bromide is somewhat representative of the list of organic halides which have been added to the phenyl Grignard-cobalt(II) halide system, it is perhaps not too daring to suggest that the cobalt(I) halide radical is not involved with these either.

In the particular example just described we suppose that the phenoxypropyl bromide is attacked by atomic cobalt forming from the decomposition of diphenylcobalt(II) into biphenyl. The product, 3-phenoxypropyl cobalt(II) bromide, eliminates phenoxide ion, producing

$$C_6H_5O—CH_2CH_2CH_2^- \overset{+}{C}oBr \rightarrow C_6H_5O^- + (CH_2)_3 + \overset{+}{C}oBr$$

cyclopropane and liberating cobalt(II) ion for further participation. This ionic scheme is generally applicable to other organic halides. However, in the case of polyfunctional halides, such as the acyl halides, and of special structures, such as those having tertiary hydrogen, where free radical attack by zerovalent cobalt may be favored, the process can involve the production of organic radicals.

Finally, there is now also direct evidence that metals are produced in an atomic state in the metal halide-Grignard systems. Wang and Yang[15] find that the hydrogenation of 1-octene proceeds far faster in the presence of a catalyst prepared from equivalent amounts of propyl Grignard and nickel(II) chloride than in the presence of W-2 Raney nickel under the same conditions. The production of atomic nickel by the decomposition of dialkylnickel(II) is consistent with this result.

Interceptive reactions of the organo-transition metal compounds before or during their rearrangement to π-complex or decomposition to bare metal represent a new approach to chemical synthesis. Organochromium derivatives are reacted with acetylenes to yield, *inter al.,* benzenes, naphthalenes, phenanthrenes, anthracenes, styrenes, stilbenes, and cyclopentadienes; and with carbon monoxide to give carbonyl compounds and hexacarbonylchromium(O).[4a] Organocobalt(II) is particularly distinguished for its ability to trimerize 2-butyne with a catalytic efficiency which increases rapidly with acetylene concentration.[11] Organonickel(II) responds in a most sensitive way to changes in the stoichiometric concentrations of tolane in producing hexaphenylbenzene and organonickel polymer.[7]

These syntheses proceed through highly reactive intermediate complexes, including perhaps those of the cyclobutadienes, and therefore present a wide area for the preparation of known and unknown structures by using pure or mixed ligand reagents. The limitations of this general method of constructing molecules by taking advantage of the coordinating power of the transition metals and their attraction for organic ligands are not known presently. There are a sufficient number of examples now at hand to permit an optimistic view.

Thus, we have observed how a metal compound becomes a complex by rearrangement (π-complex formation) or by interaction with solvent or other reactants (coordination). We then have seen how the metal complex becomes intimately involved in synthesis either by internal reaction within its own confines or externally with its environment; or, by decomposition into another reactive species (atomic metal).

This is to say, the organometallic reagent becomes the complex which becomes the center or origin (catalyst) of the chemical process. This merging of the parts into the whole, catalysis, does not require (except economically) the stipulation that the catalyst be recovered, either practically or completely unchanged. It does require that a uniquely active center be created which permits, accelerates or inhibits a specific chemical reaction.

REFERENCES

1. M. Calvin, *Science,* **130,** 1170 (1959).
2. W. Herwig and H. Zeiss, *J. Am. Chem. Soc.,* **81,** 4798 (1959).
3. H. Zeiss, M. Tsutsui and L. Onsager, Abstr., 126th Meeting, Am. Chem. Soc., New York, 1954, p. 29–0.
4a. H. Zeiss, *Organometallic Chemistry,* Reinhold Publ. Corp., New York, 1960, pp. 380–388.
4b. *Cf.* reference 4a, pp. 396–397. Also, M. Tsutsui has chosen to review this discussion, Abstr., 139th Meeting, Am. Chem. Soc., St. Louis, 1961, p. 28–0.
5. H. Zeiss and W. Herwig, *Ann.,* **606,** 209 (1957).
6. H. Zeiss and M. Tsutsui, *J. Am. Chem. Soc.,* **81,** 1367 (1959).
7. H. Zeiss and M. Tsutsui, *J. Am. Chem. Soc.,* **82,** 6255 (1960).
8. R. E. Dessy, *J. Org. Chem.,* **25.** 2260 (1960).
9. M. S. Kharasch and O. Reinmuth, *Grignard Reactions of Nonmetallic Halides,* Prentice-Hall, New York, 1954. Chapter 5.
10. O. L. Ingles and J. B. Polya, *J. Chem. Soc.,* 2280 (1949).
11. H. Zeiss and M. Tsutsui, *J. Am. Chem. Soc.,* **83,** 825 (1961).
12. A. L. Wilds and W. B. McCormack, *J. Org. Chem.,* **14,** 45 (1949).
13. M. S. Kharasch, G. Stampa and W. Nudenberg, *J. Org. Chem.,* **18,** 575 (1953).
14. L. H. Slaugh, Abstr., Am. Chem. Soc., 138th Meeting, New York, 1960, p. 50-P.
15. T.-I. Wang and N. C. Yang, *ibid.,* New York, 1960, p. 51-P.

THE STABILITY OF COORDINATION COMPOUNDS

K. B. YATSIMIRSKII

Department of Chemistry
Ivanovo Chemical and Technological Institute
Ivanovo, U.S.S.R.

The stability of coordination compounds is usually characterized by the equilibrium constant of the reaction of their formation from its constituent particles (i.e., by the stability constant) or by the equilibrium constant of their dissociation reaction into their constituents (metal and ligand ion). These constants (stability constants) are related by a simple dependence on change of free enthalpy (ΔZ) and, therefore, the idea of stability of coordination compounds is essentially a thermodynamic one. Besides changing free enthalpy (or free energy), it is of importance to know the change of enthalpy (ΔH) of the above reactions, as it is by changes in enthalpy that the strength of chemical bonds is characterized.

For the purpose of theoretical analysis, it is most important to know the stability of gaseous complex particles, that is, the change of ΔZ and ΔH in reactions of the type:

$$M_{(gas)} + nL_{(gas)} = [ML_n]_{(gas)} \tag{1}$$

where M is a metal ion and L = ligand, the signs of charges are omitted to simplify the equation.

In the case of reaction (1) complex formation phenomenon is considered in its purest aspect. Here this phenomenon is not complicated by solvation, or formation and destruction of the lattice, etc.

The direct experimental determination of ΔH and ΔZ for the reactions of type (1) has not hitherto been realized. However, in many cases it is possible to make a rather exact theoretical calculation of the above quantities with the help of corresponding thermodynamic cycles.

Any cycle of this type will include either the lattice energy of a complex compound, that is, the change in energy of a process of the type:

$$[ML_n]X_{m(c)} = [ML_n]_{(gas)} + mX_{(gas)} \tag{2}$$

or the solvation energy of the complex ion, representing the change in energy of the process:

$$[ML_n]_{solv.} = [ML_n]_{gas} \qquad (3)$$

For the calculation of the lattice energy of coordination compounds we propose to use equation (1) of A. F. Kapustinskii. This equation, including the latest precise definitions, has the form:

$$U = 287.2 \frac{Z_K Z_A \Sigma n}{r_K + r_A} \left(1 - \frac{0.345}{r_K + r_A}\right) + 2.5 Z_K Z_A \Sigma n \qquad (4)$$

where U is the lattice energy, Z_K and Z_A = the charges of the cation and anion, r_K and r_A = their radii, and Σn = the total number of particles in a "molecule" of the salt. One or both ions are complex. With the help of equation (4), it is possible to calculate the lattice energy of many salts to within 1–2%.[2,3]

By using such a simple cycle, we calculated the heats of formation of some ammine ions of the $[M(NH_3)_6]^{2+}$ type, aquo ions of the $[M(H_2O)_6]^{2+}$ type, and some other complex ions, all in the gaseous phase:

$$MX_{2(c)} + 6L_{(gas)} \xrightarrow{\Delta H_c} [ML_6]X_{2(c)}$$

$$\downarrow u \qquad\qquad\qquad \uparrow -U_K$$

$$M^{2+}_{(gas)} + 2X^-_{(gas)} + 6L_{(gas)} \xrightarrow{\Delta H_K} [ML_6]^{2+}_{(gas)} + 2X^-_{(gas)}$$

whence it follows:

$$\Delta H_K = \Delta H_c + U_K - U. \qquad (5)$$

It is also possible to use a cycle such as:

$$M^{2+}_{aq} + 6L_{aq} \xrightarrow{\Delta H_{aq}} [ML_6]^{2+}_{aq}$$

$$\downarrow \Lambda_M + 6\lambda \qquad\qquad \uparrow -\Lambda_K$$

$$M^{2+}_{(gas)} + 6L_{(gas)} \xrightarrow{\Delta H_K} [ML_6]^{2+}_{(gas)}$$

and hence:

$$\Delta H_K = \Delta H_{aq} + \Lambda_K - \Lambda_M - 6\lambda. \qquad (6)$$

The data obtained by us are given in Table 1. ΔH_K values are calculated from equation (5). The reliability of these values is confirmed by the data obtained which are independent of the nature of the anion X. In most cases the data have been obtained as the mean of 3–4 values.

TABLE 1: THERMODYNAMIC CHARACTERISTICS OF THE REACTIONS OF THE TYPE:

$$M^{2+}_{(gas)} + 6L_{(gas)} = ML^{2+}_{6(gas)}$$

Cations :	$[M(NH_3)_6]^{2+}$				:	$[M(H_2O)_6]^{2+}$			
	$-\Delta H_K$	$:-\Delta S_K$	$:-\Delta Z_K$	$: \lg K$	:	$-\Delta H_K$	$-\Delta S_K$	$:-\Delta Z_K$	$: \lg K$
Ca^{2+}	273	138	232	170	:	291	138	250	184
Cr^{2+}	344	138	303	222		...	138	...	...
Mn^{2+}	339	138	298	219		308	138	267	196
Fe^{2+}	361	138	320	235		...	138	...	...
Co^{2+}	396	138	355	261		365	138	324	238
Ni^{2+}	410	138	369	271		373	138	332	244
Cu^{2+}	410	138	369	271		374	138	333	244
Zn^{2+}	394	138	353	259		359	138	318	233

For instance, the heat of formation of ammine ions was calculated from the chloride, bromide and iodide of the given metal. The values of ΔS are estimated approximately on the basis of N. Kobozev's rule.[4] The values of ΔZ and log K have been calculated with the help of well-known equations.

For explaining the observed course of changing ΔH and ΔZ, the following ideas may be used. The interaction between ligands and the central cation may be divided into three hypothetical stages: (1) The electrostatic interaction of an ion-ion or ion-dipole type. The energy of electrostatic interaction W can be easily calculated by the charges of reacting particles, their radii or their dipole moments. (2) The orientation and deformation of d-orbitals in the field of ligands and the rearrangement of electrons in such a way that they occupy the lowest energy levels. This gives the gain in energy which is known as the energy of extrastabilisation by the ligand field, E. (3) The formation of partly covalent σ-bonds.

The change of energy in this stage (the quantity C) depends on the difference between the electron affinity of a cation (the energy of the process $M^{n+}_{(gas)} + 2e^- = M^{n-2}_{(gas)}$) and the ionisation energy of a ligand (the energy of the process $L^{-m}_{(gas)} = L^{2-m}_{(gas)} + 2e$).

The formation of π-bonds also makes a contribution to the value of C. The total energetic effect of reaction (1) may be expressed by an equation such as:

$$-\Delta H_K = W + E + C \qquad (7)$$

The correctness of this idea can be confirmed by consideration of the following points. The value C, apparently, is insignificant for co-ordination compounds formed by eight-electron cations, even if in the corresponding compounds there is a considerable degree of covalent bond formation.

The values of ΔH_K for many coordination compounds formed by these ions may be calculated by the use of the very simple formulae for ion-ion or ion-dipole interaction.[5]

The value C sharply increases with an increase in the electron affinity of a cation (ionisation potential of an atom). In this connection, the stability of coordination compounds increases with an increase in ionisation potential. This fact has attracted the attention of many investigators.[6,7]

The effect of ligand-field, as it is seen from Table 1, has its maximum value for nickel coordination compounds. Such an effect really must take place in the case of octahedral configuration. The correctness of equation (7) may be confirmed by use of an analogous equation for the calculation of lattice energy.[8] The process of crystal formation from gaseous ions is very similar to the process of particle formation of coordination compounds from the initial particles. The correctness of equation (7) is confirmed by analysis of the following data about the stability of coordination compounds in aqueous solutions.

There are very few data about the stability of complex particles in the gaseous state. The lack of these data is connected with the great difficulty in calculating the lattice energy or heats of solvation of complex ions (mainly because of the absence of data about the effective radii of complex ions). Perhaps in the future there will be the possibility of direct investigation of some gaseous complex particles with the help of mass spectrometric methods.

The investigation of equilibria of the dissociation and formation reactions of coordination compounds in solutions has recently made remarkable progress. The number of coordination compounds studied in this regard now exceeds 2000. The reactions taking place in a solution can be represented by a general scheme such as:

$$MS_m + nL = ML_n + mS \tag{8}$$

or one of the steps

$$MS_m + L = MS_{m-1} L + S \tag{8a}$$

where S is a molecule of a solvent.

The destruction of the solvated ion MS_m (aquo-ion in water, ammino-ion in ammonia, etc.) and formation of a coordination compound with ligands L always take place in similar equilibrium processes. The equilibrium constant of such a process is essentially a ratio of the stability constant of the complex ion ML_n to the stability constant of the solvated ion MS_m .

The change of energy in the processes in question is determined by the difference of energies of formation of gaseous particles, ML_n and MS_m, by the difference of their solvation energies, by the energy of solvation, L, and by the energy of vaporization of solvent, $-S$.

As in the investigation of equilibria in a given solvent, one always deals with solvated particles, the reaction equations (8) and (8a) may be simplified:

$$M + nL = ML_n \tag{9}$$

$$M + L = ML \tag{9a}$$

All particles taking part in these equilibria are solvated. There are many methods for the experimental determination of stability constants. The first investigations in this field were completed at the very beginning of the twentieth century.[9,10]

During further progress of these investigations, the work of N. Bjerrum and J. Bjerrum (especially including the classical work "Metal-Ammine Formation in Aqueous Solution") played an outstanding role. The idea of stepwise complex formation was especially fruitful. This idea was evolved in many countries and particularly in the USSR, as a result of the work of A. K. Babko and his co-workers. The pH-metric method of determining the equilibrium concentrations of ligands and calculating from them the "formation function"—$\bar{n}$ developed by J. Bjerrum was also very important. Almost half of the stability constants available in literature have been obtained by this method.

Further investigation of the stability of coordination compounds has been extensively carried out in many countries (including the works of Leden, Schwarzenbach, Sillen and others).

At present there are rather complete compilations of stability constants,[11,12,13] reviews of experimental methods for determining stability constants, and mathematical treatments of the obtained results. Therefore, one can limit oneself to the enumeration of the principal groups of methods and dwell in detail on the essence of the newer methods.

The direct determination of equilibrium concentrations of M and L by analytical methods can be accomplished only by investigations of slowly dissociating and forming coordination compounds of the type ML_n. A large majority of the methods of determining the stability constants (or instability constants) is based on the investigation of dependence of some property of the solution, P, on the concentration of ligand, L.

This dependence can usually be represented as follows:

$$P = P_0[M] + P_1[ML] + \ldots + P_i[ML_i] + \ldots + P_n[ML_n] \tag{10}$$

where $P_0, P_1, \ldots P_i \ldots P_n$ are the values of property P at unimolar concentration of M, $ML \ldots ML_i \ldots ML_n$, respectively, and in the absence of other complexes.

The quantity P is then divided by the total concentration of metal salt, C_M°, and the dependence of $\overline{P}$ is expressed in terms of the concentration of the ligand, L:

$$\overline{P} = \frac{P_0 + P_1 \beta_1 [L] + P_2 \beta_2 [L]^2 + \ldots + P_i \beta_i [L]^i + \ldots + P_n \beta_n [L]^n}{1 + \beta_1 [L] + \beta_2 [L]^2 + \ldots + \beta_i [L]^i + \ldots + \beta_n [L]^n} \quad (11)$$

The most reliable and simple methods are those by which a property of the solution is determined only by the concentration of free metal ions or by the concentration of only one form of a complex compound (for example, ML_i). The properties which depend only on the concentration of free metal ions are as follows: electrode potential, the solubility of salts of the type $M_p X_q$, and biological activity. Frequently, the extraction is determined only by the concentration of electro-neutral particles of the type, MA_p°.

Under certain conditions, some other properties of the solution can be determined only from concentrations of the type ML_i ($P_i \neq 0$, $P_0 = P_1 = P_2 = \ldots = P_n = 0$). These properties are: the ability for ion exchange to occur (in the absence of other particles of the type ML_i with the same sign of charge), absorption of light at definite wavelengths, and the rates of reactions catalysed only by the definite compound ML_i. In some cases it is possible to distinguish the value P connected with the existence of a given complex with the help of special methods. It is possible, for example, to measure the absorbtion curves of a number of solutions of varying concentration, L, but constant total concentration, M. Each absorbtion curve can be resolved into separate bands. The height of each band is determined only by the concentration of the definite form of a coordination compound (for instance, ML_i).

Finally, some properties, apparently, are always determined by a summation of all (or several) particles of the type ML_i. These properties are: conductivity, the heat of mixing solutions M with solutions L, and some other properties.

It is necessary to find $2n$ for the constants $(P_1 \ldots P_n, \beta_1 \ldots \beta_n)$ by solutions of equation (11), since P_0 is known before the investigation or can be measured without any difficulty, and $\beta_0 = 1$. The solution of such an equation in a general form is rather complicated and inconvenient. Therefore, it is desirable to choose conditions under which all but one value of P become zero. In this case, the calculation of equation (11) coefficients can be determined without difficulty and with the help of various analytical and graphical methods. In the opinion of most of the Soviet scientists, the most reliable results for calculating coefficients of these equations can be obtained by using least square methods. A most peculiar property of the system is the mean number of ligands per atom of metal, $\bar{n}$, that is, the "function of formation" proposed by J. Bjerrum. In this case, all values of P_i are known and are a simple natural series of whole numbers.

The investigation of property changes of some systems is rather difficult. These difficulties can be overcome by using "competition" reactions, i.e., by studying systems containing ions M, M' and a ligand or several ligands. In our opinion, the new and most promising method of studying equilibria in solutions is that of using reactions catalysed by metal ions under investigation or by their complex compounds. This method is rather universal (catalytic reactions are known for more than 30 elements), its experimental methods are simple, and it has an especially high sensitivity (many elements can be determined in concentrations of the order of $10^{-8} - 10^{-9}$ mol./1.). Hence, by this method it is possible to study very stable coordination compounds. In addition, such phenomena as hydrolytic polymerisation and association which complicate the investigation in such low concentrations are absent.

The catalytic reactions used at present for studying complex formation may be divided into five groups:

1. Oxidation—reduction reactions are the most numerous group of catalytic reactions. The greatest number of such reactions are those in which hydrogen peroxide and anions of the type RO_3^- (ClO_3^-, BrO_3^-, NO_3^-, etc.) participate. Other such reactions are also known, in particular reactions in which particles have the same charge sign. Reactions in which H_2O_2 in an acid medium participates are catalyzed by compounds of the elements of the IV B, V B, and VI B groups of the periodic system Ti, Zr, Hf, Th, V, Nb, Ta, Cr, Mo, W) and by Fe^{3+} ions. In basic medium the catalysts are one electron oxidants and reductants with rather high redox potentials (Fe, Co, Cu, etc).

2. The reactions of isotopic exchange ($Ce^{4+} - Ce^{3+}$, $Fe^{3+} - Fe^{2+}$, $AuCl_4^- - Cl^-$, $MnO_4^- - MnO_4^{2-}$, etc.). The reactions of isotopic exchange between similarly charged particles are catalyzed by particles forming peculiar "bridges" between reacting particles (for instance, $Ce^{4+} \ldots F^- \ldots Ce^{3+}$) or by one electron oxidants-reductants (for instance, Fe^{3+} ions in the reaction of isotopic exchange between $AuCl_4^-$ and Cl^-).

3. The replacement reactions in the inner sphere of coordination compounds. As an example, it is possible to use the reaction of the replacement of cyanide in the ion $[Fe(CN)_6]^{4-}$. This reaction is catalyzed by compounds of mercury, gold and silver.

4. The reactions of the transformation of organic compounds.

5. The reactions leading to the origin of catalytic polarographic currents. The catalytic polarographic currents appear if there are small quantities of substances in solution which can be reduced more easily than the primary substance. After being reduced on the electrode, the catalyst is then oxidised by the primary substance.

The rate of catalytic reaction represented by scheme:

$$A + B = X + Y \tag{12}$$

usually can be described by the equation:

$$\frac{dx}{dt} = \chi C_K^\circ \, \Pi_c \tag{13}$$

where χ is a catalytic coefficient, C_K° is a total concentration of the catalyst and Π_c is a function of the concentrations of the reactants (usually the product of the concentrations). Usually, the values C_K° and Π_c are known from the initial conditions and $\frac{dx}{dt}$ is found from the experimental data. If there are some ligands which form coordination compounds with the catalyst, the value χ can be represented by an equation such as:

$$\bar{\chi} = \frac{\chi_0 + \chi_1 \beta_1 [L] + \ldots + \chi_i \beta_i [L]^i + \ldots + \chi_n \beta_n [L]^n}{1 + \beta_1 [L] + \ldots + \beta_i [L]^i + \ldots + \beta_n [L]^n} \tag{14}$$

where $\chi_0, \chi_1 \cdots \chi_i \cdots \chi_n$ are the coefficients which characterize the catalytic activity of $K, KL \ldots KL_i \ldots KL_n$, respectively.

Very often only a metal ion has catalytic activity, and, in this case, the stability constants can be found without difficulty. Sometimes only one coordination compound has catalytic activity. In this case the stability constants can also be found easily. If several forms of coordination compounds have catalytic activity, the determination of stability constants can be complicated.

For some years the catalytic reaction represented by the equation:

$$H_2O_2 + 2\,I^- + 2\,H^+ = 2\,H_2O + I_2 \tag{15}$$

has been used in our laboratory in studying complex formation. This reaction is catalyzed by compounds of Mo^{VI}, W^{VI}, Ta^V, Zr^{IV}, Hf^{IV}, Th^{IV}, Fe^{3+}. The coordination compounds of the elements mentioned above as a rule show no catalytic activity. However, in some cases catalytic activity is exhibited if only one particle of a ligand combines with the catalyst (tartrate, sulfate and succinate compounds of zirconium) but disappears if two particles of a ligand combine with the catalyst (the complex compound of zirconium with tartrate). The behaviour of hydroxide complexes of thorium is peculiar; only the

$ThOH^{3+}$ compound has catalytic activity but neither the Th^{4+} ion nor the $Th(OH)_2^{2+}$ ion show catalytic activity. The catalytic polorgraphic currents arising during the reduction of H_2O_2 in an acid solution[15] are suitable for studying the complex formation of molybdenum(VI) and tungsten(VI). The strength of the catalytic current is sharply reduced by the addition acids, which form coordination compounds in solution with the elements mentioned above. The strength of the catalytic current can be represented by the equation:

$$\bar{i} = \frac{i_0 + i_1 \beta_1 [L] + \ldots + i_n \beta_n [L]^n}{1 + \beta_1 [L] + \ldots + \beta_n [L]^n} \tag{14a}$$

where $i_0, i_1 \ldots i_n$ are the values of catalytic current strength which would be observed if there were no complex formation (i_0) or if there were the complete transformation of a catalyst in $KL, KL_2 \ldots KL_n$, respectively.

It is possible to determine stability constants by measuring colligative properties (cryoscopy, ebullioscopy etc.). Equations (11), (14) and (15) are true for systems in which there are only mononuclear compounds. If there are polynuclear complexes, the value of $\bar{P}$ ($\bar{\chi}$, $\bar{i}$, respectively) depends also upon the concentration of metal ions (M or K). In these cases, the calculations are more complicated. The methods of studying such systems have been worked out by L. G. Sillen and his co-workers.

The many various methods now known are not as yet sufficient to study coordination compounds reacting very slowly with a solvent or other ligands. The equilibrium in such systems is established very slowly, or is complicated by some side equilibria, or never can be established if measurable concentrations of coordination compounds are to be retained. Such coordination compounds are, in particular, compounds of cobalt(III), platinum, and some other metals. However, the stability of such coordination compounds can be found by means of well-known thermodynamic methods. The essence of these methods is the measurement of enthalpy and entropy changes in the reaction being studied. The heat of reaction is measured by means of the usual calorimetric methods. The entropy change is found from the entropy of all the substances participating in the reaction from the experimental data obtained (for instance, from the heat capacities of crystalline substances and from the entropy of phase transformations).

The stability constant is calculated from the equation:

$$\lg \beta = \frac{T \Delta S - \Delta H}{2.303 \, RT} \tag{16}$$

As an example, we can consider the determination of the equilibrium constant of the reaction:

$$[Co(NH_3)_6]_{aq}^{3+} = Co_{aq}^{3+} + 6\,NH_{3\,aq} \tag{17}$$

The heat of $[Co(NH_3)_6]^{3+}$ formation was calculated by us earlier,[16] from the heat of decomposition of luteo-salt solutions by Na_2S. For the calculation of the entropy of the luteo ion, the entropy of crystalline $[Co(NH_3)_6]Cl_3$ was determined from the measurement of the low temperature heat capacity. Since the heat of solution and solubility of $[Co(NH_3)_6]Cl_3$ are known, it is possible to calculate the entropy of solution of this salt, and, therefore, the entropy of $[Co(NH_3)_6]_{aq}^{3+}$. The standard heats and entropies of Co_{aq}^{3+} and $NH_{3\,aq}$ are known. By use of these data it is possible to find the free enthalpy change in reaction (17) and, therefore, an equilibrium constant (instability constant); it is equal to $2 \cdot 10^{-30}$, the value $2 \cdot 10^{-34}$ has been mentioned in literature.

The total thermodynamic picture of the reactions involved in the formation of coordination compounds is desirable for many reasons. From the heats of formation of coordination compounds it is possible to make some judgments about changes in the stability of coordination compounds with temperature on the basis of equations of isobars of a chemical reaction. Most of the stability constants are related to standard temperature (25°C.). However, chemists are also interested in the stability of coordination compounds at different temperatures. It is possible to estimate the values of stability constants at different temperatures with the help of the equation of isobars of a chemical reaction, but the use of this equation for the calculation of the heat of reaction from the changes of stability constants with temperature is not reliable. The use of a simple equation for the calculation of ΔH_{KS} gives a result such as:

$$\Delta H_{KS} = 40.6\,\Delta pK_{(20-30)} \tag{18}$$

where $\Delta pK_{(20-30)}$ is the difference of the logarithms of the stability constants measured at two temperatures (20° and 30°C). The heat effect equal to one Cal./mol. corresponds to a pK change equal to 0.025, the temperature change being only 10°C. Such an accuracy in determining stability constants can scarcely be obtained.

Therefore, the necessity of obtaining ΔH by a calorimetric method is evident. On the basis of using values of ΔH it is possible to make a judgment about energetic factors which influence the stability of coordination compounds. It is evident from equation (16) that the value of a stability constant is determined not only by the heat of reaction but also by the entropy change. The factors determining ΔH and ΔS are essentially different. The value ΔH is determined by bonds energies in complex particles (ML_n and MS_m), heats of their solvation, and heats of solvation of metal ions and ligands.

The entropy changes accompanying the formation of coordination compounds are determined: (1) by changes of the number in particles taking part in the reactions of complex formation (the decrease in the number of translational freedom steps and the increase in the number of vibrational and rotational ones), and (2) by desolvation of the initial particles (metal ion and ligands) and solvation of the coordination compound formed. The action of the first factor decreases entropy but the action of the second one increases it because of the setting free of the solvent molecules which solvated the metal ion and ligands.

In the reactions of complex formation in the gaseous state, the entropy change must always be negative because of the diminishing of the total number of particles. The reactions of complex formation in an aqueous solution can be accompanied by both a decrease and increase of entropy to a rather large extent. The entropy changes are determined principally by hydration of the initial particles (ligands and a metal ion). If the initial particles are weakly hydrated, ΔS is negative (for instance, in the interaction of Cu^+ with thiourea, ΔS is equal to -50 e.u.). If the initial particles are strongly hydrated, the process of complex formation is accompanied by a positive change of entropy (for instance, in the reaction between Al^{3+} and ethylendiamintetraacetate ion, $\Delta S = 112$ e.u.). Only in these two cases does the amplitude of the ΔS change exceed 160 e.u., which corresponds to a change in pK of the order of 35 units. In fact, the range of the change in ΔS values is apparently very significant and this factor is very important in the reactions involving formation of coordination compounds.

The dehydration of initial particles exerts a strong influence on the value of ΔS, and therefore the entropy changes in a series of similar reactions (i.e., reactions with the same number of the same ligands) are determined by one of two analogous equations:

$$\Delta S_{KS} = 0.1\, \Lambda_M + B \tag{19}$$

$$\Delta S_{KS} = \alpha\, \Delta S_M + \beta \tag{20}$$

where Λ_M and ΔS_M are the heat and entropy of hydration of the gaseous ion M, respectively, and B, α and β are constants. The factors determining the value ΔH_{KS} are essentially the same as the factors determining the heat of formation of gaseous complex particles, but in this case it is necessary to use the difference of the corresponding members for the complex being formed and the aquo ion. Hence:

$$-\Delta H_{KS} = \Delta W + \Delta E + \Delta C \tag{21}$$

The value ΔW is determined only from the charges and radii of the ions. The calculation of ΔW is very complicated, but in principle this calculation can always be accomplished if the necessary data are available. The numerous data analysed by us show that when central ions of coordination compounds have the structure of an inert gas atom, it is possible to use only the first member of equation (21). The ligand-field effect here is equal to zero and the value ΔC is also very small. Apparently, there is a considerable degree of covalent bonding in these coordination compounds, but here the formation of partly covalent bonds is not accompanied by a considerable energy change, owing to the small electron affinity of the central ions.

The value ΔC is determined, as was mentioned above, from the electron affinity of a central ion and from the ionisation potentials of the ligands. The value ΔC may be connected with electronegativity of the atoms coming into direct contact in coordination compounds. The importance of electronegativity in the explanation of the different stabilities of coordination compounds was emphasized by W. C. Fernelius and his co-workers. The quantity ΔC can be determined for different ligands by a comparison of the stability of analogous coordination compounds formed by ions of the same charge and radius. Examples of such pairs are: Mg^{2+} and Zn^{2+}, Ca^{2+} and Cd^{2+} and some others.

The change in entropy in the reactions examined of the type:

$$Mg L_n + Zn(H_2O)_m^{2+} = Mg(H_2O)_m^{2+} + Zn L_n \qquad (22)$$

is negligible owing to great similarity of the structures of the initial and final products. Therefore the values of ΔH for such reactions may be replaced by ΔZ or by values proportional to the differences in logarithms of stability constants of the corresponding compounds (the proportionality coefficient is equal to 2.303 RT). The contribution of different ligands to ΔC can be characterized as follows: ΔC can be characterized as follows:

$$\Delta C = 2.303\, RT\, \Delta\, pK_{Zn, Mg} \qquad (23)$$

The values of $\Delta pK_{Zn, Mg}$ are given in Table 2.

TABLE 2

Ligands	:	$\Delta pK_{Zn, Mg}$	:	Ligands	:	$\Delta pK_{Zn, Mg}$
F^-	:	-0.5	:	$P_2O_7^{4-}$	:	0.7
OH_2	:	0.0	:	OH^-	:	2.3
SO_4^{2-}	:	0.0	:	NH_3	:	2.6
$S_2O_3^{2-}$	:	0.6	:	NR_3	:	2.8 ± 0.3[†]
RCO_2^-	:	0.6 ± 0.1[*]	:		:	

[*] The mean (value) of eight values.
[†] The mean of seven values.

In this conditional method of characterizing ligand covalencies, the covalency of water is assumed to be zero. For this reason ΔC for fluoride proves to be negative.

The value ΔC depends first of all on the nature of atoms which are in direct contact with a metal atom. In the series of the ligands studied, ΔC changes in the following way: $F < O < N < C$. The values of ΔC depend also on the nature of the atoms with which the above-mentioned atom is connected in ligands. The value ΔC has a maximum for a free anion (F^- O^{2-}, N^{3-}, etc.). The more electronegative the adjacent atom, the smaller is the value ΔC. In the above-mentioned series of oxygen ligands, ΔC changes in the following way: $OH_2 \approx SO_4^{2-} < RCO_2^- \approx P_2O_7^{4-} < OH^- < O^{2-}$. These regularities are observed so strictly that the value proportional to ΔC for coordination compounds of zinc can be represented by an equation such as:

$$\Delta pK_{Zn, Mg} = 0.6n_O + 2.8n_N \qquad (24)$$

where n_O is the numbers of O atoms (connected to carbon) and n_N is the number of N atoms (connected to carbon or hydrogen) which are in direct contact with a central atom. Equation (24) can be used for calculating and specifying the stability constants of coordination compounds of zinc (or magnesium) if their structures are known. The same equation may be also used for the determination of the structures of corresponding complexes. Thus, for instance, for the oxalate and malonate complexes, $\Delta pK_{Zn, Mg}$ is 1.2, which indicates the formation of five- or six-member cycles, respectively.

For succinates and glutarates, $\Delta pK_{Zn, Mg} \approx 0.6$, which means that upon coordination, only one atom of oxygen takes part and there is no ring formation. The value of $\Delta pK_{Zn, Mg}$ for α-oxyacids approaches 1.2, and, in this case, this indicates the formation of five-member rings. The value of ΔE is the difference between extra-stabilisation energies by the fields of the ligands L and by the field of the solvent (in this particular case, H_2O). In the series of doubly-charged ions which are in the middle of the fourth period of Mendeleev's system, the sizes of the ions remain approximately constant, and, therefore, the changes of entropy during complex formation with the same ligands must be also approximately constant. In this case a similarity must exist between the change of free energy, $-\Delta Z$ (and therefore ΔpK, too) and $-\Delta H$. In the series of the ions above, the value of ΔC changes linearly with a change in the ordinal number of elements, and, therefore, the value ΔE for the ions of the given series may easily be calculated by means of the equation:

$$\Delta E_M = pK_M - pK_{Mn} - n/5\,(pK_{Zn} - pK_{Mn}) \qquad (25)$$

where M is Mn^{2+}, Fe^{2+}, Co^{2+}, Ni^{2+}, Cu^{2+}, Zn^{2+} and n for the above mentioned ions is equal to 0, 1, 2, 3, 4, 5, respectively. The energy of extra-stabilisation can be calculated by means of the equation:

$$E = \rho V \qquad (26)$$

where ρ is a factor depending upon the geometry of the coordination compound, electronic structure of the central ion, and the type of complex (high or low spin), V is a ligand-field effect, i.e., the difference between energies of two electron orbits, $d_{x^2-y^2}$ and d_{xy}. The value V depends on the nature of the ligands, the charge of the central ion, its size, and electronic structure.

The value ΔE is equal to:

$$\Delta E = \rho_L V_L - \rho_{H_2O} V_{H_2O} \qquad (27)$$

or

$$\Delta E = \Delta\rho V_L + \rho_{H_2O} \Delta V \qquad (27a)$$

where $\Delta\rho = \rho_L - \rho_{H_2O}$ and $\Delta V = V_L - V_{H_2O}$. From equations (27) and (27a), one can see that the difference of extra-stabilisation energies may be both positive and negative. The aquo-ions apparently have a configuration close to the octahedral one. On forming octahedral complexes with ligands L, $\Delta\rho$ approaches zero, but if the configuration of the complexes formed with L is quite different, then the first item of the right member of equation (27) does not go to zero. It may be shown that, on reducing the symmetry of the complex for the ions of the type d^4 and d^9 (for example, Cr^{2+}, Cu^{2+}, Mn^{3+}), the value $\Delta\rho$ is positive and for ions of the type d^1, d^2, d^3, d^6, d^7, d^8, it is slightly negative. For this reason the following series of stabilities are valid for all the complexes with non-cubic symmetry:

1. $Ca^{2+} < Ti^{2+} < V^{2+} < Cr^{2+} > Mn^{2+} < Fe^{2+} < Co^{2+} < Ni^{2+} < Cu^{2+} > Zn^{2+}$

2. $Sc^{3+} < Ti^{3+} < V^{3+} < Cr^{3+} < Mn^{3+} > Fe^{3+} < Co^{3+} < Ni^{3+} < Cu^{3+} > Ga^{3+}$.

Part of the first series (from Mn^{2+} to Zn^{2+}) was studied very carefully and the above-established sequence of the stabilities of coordination compounds was found empirically. This sequence is known as the Irving-Williams series. When octahedral complexes are formed, the first item of the right member of equation (27a) goes to zero and the sequence in the change of ΔE is the same as for aquo-ions, that is, the sequence for the coordination compounds of doubly charged ions will be as follows:

$Ca^{2+} < Ti^{2+} < V^{2+} > Cr^{2+} > Mn^{2+} < Fe^{2+} < Co^{2+} < Ni^{2+} > Cu^{2+} > Zn^{2+}$.

Such a sequence in the change of the stability of coordination compounds is really observed for hexammine, tris(ethylendiamine), tris(o-phenanthroline), and other coordination compounds with an octahedral configuration. It is possible to make a judgment about the configuration of a given compound from the ratio $\Delta E_{cu}/\Delta E_{Ni}$. The more this ratio departs from one, the more the configuration of a given compound differs from the octahedral configuration.

For coordination compounds with a tetrahedral configuration, the sequence of ΔE is different, namely:

$$Mn^{2+} < Fe^{2+} < Co^{2+} > Ni^{2+} > Cu^{2+} > Zn^{2+}$$

All of the above refers to high-spin coordination compounds. The stability of octahedral low-spin coordination compounds, because of the increase of ΔE, constantly increases in the series of: d^1, d^2, ... d^6 ions, and then sharply decreases beginning from the d^7 ion (the decrease of ρ). It is always necessary to take into account the value ΔS_{KS}, in considering the factors which determine the stability of coordination compounds. The entropy of complex formation is primarily determined by the energy of hydration of a central ion. In considering the factors which determine the stability of coordination compounds, it is expedient to classify the central ions forming the coordination compounds into three groups: (1) ions with the structure of the inert gas atoms (s^2 and s^2p^6); these ions form the elements of the first four groups of the Mendeleev's system; only for titanium is the structure d^1 (Ti^{3+}) possible; many lanthanide and actinide ions are in this group; the stability of such coordination compounds formed by these ions is determined chiefly by the electrostatic characteristics of a central ion and ligands (i.e., by charges, radii and dipole moments); (2) the ions with filled d levels (d^{10}) and ions with the electronic structure nd^{10} $(n + 1)$ s^2; these ions also form the elements of the first four groups of the periodic system (subgroups of copper, zinc, gallium and germanium, respectively); the stability of coordination compounds formed by these ions is determined not only by electrostatic characteristics, but also by the electron-affinity (electronegativity) of the central ion and the nearest atoms of ligands; in this group of coordination compounds, σ-bonds and dative π-bonds may be formed and the dative π-bonds may be formed with ligands having vacant p-orbitals ($d_\pi - d_\pi$) or d-orbitals ($d_\pi - d_\pi$); the probability of formation of such bonds increases with decreasing charge on the central ion (for example, the strength of dative π-bonds diminishes as follows: $Ag^+ > Cd^{2+} > In^{3+}$; $Cu^+ > Zn^{2+} > Ga^{3+}$; $Au^+ > Hg^{2+} > Tl^{3+} > Pb^{4+}$); (3) the ions with partly unfilled d-orbitals; these ions form the elements of the subgroups 5, 6 and 7 of the periodic system, of group 8, and several ions of the copper sub-group (Cu^{2+}, Ag^{2+}, Au^{III}); the stability of coordination compounds formed by these ions is determined not only by electrostatic characteristics and by electron affinity, but also by the energy of extra-stabilisation of a ligand field; this group of coordination compounds is characterized by a great variety of types and by maximum stability.

Some years ago, A. A. Grinberg[17] pointed out that the maximum ability of elements to coordinate is characteristic of the elements of the middle of the periodic system, i.e. for the elements forming ions with partly unfilled d-orbitals. The smooth character of a curve of pK change with change of the ordinal number for similar coordination compounds is broken. On such a curve two waves are usually observed. The form of such waves is determined by sterochemical factors and by the strength of ligand-fields as compared to the strength of the field formed by water molecules. The ligand-field effect is observed not only for ions with partly unfilled d-orbitals but also for ions with partly unfilled f-orbitals (lanthanides and actinides), though in the latter cases it is less pronounced.

The problem of mutual ligand influence is very important but it has not been studied enough. This influence of ligands can be characterized thermodynamically by changing ΔH and ΔZ in the reaction:

$$MX_p L + L' = MX_{p-n} LL' + nX \tag{28}$$

In the simplest case both ligands are the same, and X is the solvent molecule. The equilibrium constant of reaction (28) is a stepwise stability constant, and ΔH of this reaction is a stepwise heat of addition of a ligand. In the case of neutral ligands, the values of ΔH are rather constant as is seen from experiments. If the ligands are anions, ΔH decreases with an increasing number of ligands. This is true for octahedral complexes. In the case of other configurations, the relationships are different. Thus, for example, of all the complexes of mercury, the most stable compounds are those of the type HgL_2.

The stepwise stability constants have an essentially different mode of change: they continuously decrease (the values of Z become more positive). This is connected with the decrease in entropy changes during stepwise complex formation. A gradual decrease of coordination compound stability with formation is essentially an entropy effect. The character of the change in stepwise stability constants depends on the configuration of a coordination compound and is quite different for octahedral, tetrahedral, and tetragonal coordination compounds.

The question of the influence of the nature of a ligand, L', on the thermodynamic functions of reaction (28) is not yet clear enough. The experimental data for coordination compounds with different ligands are very limited. The data for inert low-spin complexes are especially interesting. One can suppose that the greatest influence occurs for ligands which are situated in transposition to ligand L, in accordance with well-known regularity of "trans-influence" discovered by I. I. Chernyaev.[18] In fact, in the cobalt coordination compounds the heat of the replacement of one and the same ligand (NH_3, Cl, NO_2) by other ligands (H_2O, Cl) is not constant, and depends on the nature of the ligand being in transposition to the ligand being replaced. The ligands placed in order of facilitating the replacement of a ligand being in transposition are in the following order:

$$NO_2^- > NH_3 > H_2O > Cl^-.$$

In recent years and in many countries, scientists have accumulated and systematized much experimental data about the stability of coordination compounds. Some regularities regarding the influence of many factors on the stability of coordination compounds have been made known.

However, it is necessary to continue accumulating experimental data on the thermodynamics of reactions of complex formation. Data about the stability of coordination compounds in a wider range of temperatures are necessary. The calorimetric investigations of complex formation reactions should be developed because only in such ways is it possible to obtain their complete thermodynamic characteristics. The only way to obtain data about the stability of most low spin coordination compounds is through calorimetric investigations together with measurements of low-temperature heat capacities.

Some groups of coordination compounds have not been sufficiently investigated. Such groups of coordination compounds are polynuclear coordination compounds and compounds with different ligands. The data about the equilibrium of coordination compounds in non-aqueous solutions are not sufficient. However, in non-aqueous solutions it is possible to observe the formation of coordination compounds which cannot exist in aqueous solution. The data about the stability of crystalline coordination compounds are also not complete.

Theoretical analyses of the extensively available experimental data and, in particular, considerations of the problems of the nature of chemical bonds in coordination compounds and the problems of mutual influence of ligands inside the molecules of coordination compounds are necessary. The methods of calculating the stability of coordination compounds in the gaseous state are also of great interest. It is necessary to study the question of the influence of the presence of foreign salts (ionic strength) on the stability of coordination compounds. It would also be very desirable to have the methods of recalculating the data obtained at any ionic strength to some definite state standardized.

REFERENCES.

1. A. F. Kapustinskii, *J. Gen. Chem. (USSR)*, **13**, 497 (1943).
2. A. F. Kapustinskii and K. B. Yatsimirskii, *J. Gen. Chem. (USSR)*, **26**, 941 (1956).
3. K. B. Yatsimirskii, *J. Gen. Chem. (USSR)*, **26**, 2376 (1956).
4. N. I. Kobozev, *J. Phys. Chem. (USSR)*, **22**, 1002 (1948).
5. K. B. Yatsimirskii, *The Thermochemistry of Complex Compounds,* Moscow, Academy of Science, USSR, 1951.
6. L. P. Mellor and L. Maley, *Nature*, **159**, 370 (1947).
7. M. Calvin and N. C. Melchior, *J. Am. Chem. Soc.*, **70**, 3270 (1948).
8. K. B. Yatsimirskii, *J. Inorg. Chem. (USSR)*, **6**, N3 (1961).
9. G. Bodländer and R. Fittig, *Z. phys. Chem.*, **39**, 597 (1902).
10. H. Morze, *Z. phys. Chem.*, **41**, 709 (1902).
11. *Stability Constants.* Part I (1957) and Part II (1958) London, The Chemical Society.
12. K. B. Yatsimirskii and V. P. Vasil'ev, "*The Instability Constants of Coordination Compounds,*" Moscow, Academy of Sciences, USSR, 1959.
13. A. Martell and M. Calvin, *Chemistry of Metal Chelate Compounds,* New York, Prentice Hall, 1952
14. F. J. C. Rossotti, "The Thermodynamics of Metal Ion Complex Formation," in *Modern Coordination Chemistry,* New York, London, 1960.
15. I. M. Kolthoff, E. P. Parry, *J. Am. Chem. Soc.*, **73**, 5315 (1951).
16. K. B. Yatsimirskii and L. L. Pankova, *J. Gen. Chem. (USSR)*, **19**, 617 (1949).
17. A. A. Grinberg, *Introduction to the Chemistry of Complex Compounds,* Moscow-Leningrad, 1951.
18. I. I. Cherniayev, *Izvestiya sectora platinyi*, **4**, 213 (1926); **5**, 118 (1927).

CONFERENCE PAPERS

THE EFFECTS OF SOME POLYFUNCTIONAL ANIONS ON ELECTRON TRANSFER BETWEEN METAL IONS IN SOLUTIONS*

CARL H. BRUBAKER, JR.

Kedzie Chemical Laboratory
Michigan State University
East Lansing, Michigan

The electron transfer process and processes which are formally equivalent to it comprise one of the largest and most important classes of chemical reactions. However, the actual mechanics of the electron transfer is rather poorly understood in many cases and it appears that no single process can account for the mechanism of all electron transfer (oxidation-reduction and isotopic electron-exchange) reactions.

In some gas phase reactions, and in reactions between large, saturated complexes (e.g., $Fe(CN)_6^{-3}$ and $Fe(CN)_6^{-4}$), it appears that direct electron transfer occurs by a tunnelling mechanism.[1,2]

In other cases in solution, considerable evidence has been presented in support of atom transfer as a mechanism for electron transfer.[3,4] For example,[3] in the exchange between Fe^{+2} and Fe^{+3} in water $FeOH^{+2}$ exchanges more rapidly than Fe^{+3}, and a large isotope effect, when the reaction is run in D_2O, suggests that a transition state complex may be $[Fe^{II}—O...H—O—Fe^{III}]^{+4}$ and that hydrogen

$$[Fe^{II}\underset{|}{—}O...H\underset{|}{—}O—Fe^{III}]^{+4}$$
$$\quad\; H \qquad\quad H$$

atom transfer may account for the electron transfer. Other systems might be explained similarly on the basis of transfer of hydrogen, halogen and other atoms.[4]

It has recently become apparent, primarily through studies by Taube and co-workers,[5] that water and other bridging groups (e.g. anions) play a very important role in many oxidation-reduction and electron exchange reactions.

---

*Part of this work has been supported financially by the U. S. Atomic Energy Commission.

In some cases the bridged transition state complexes are compatible with explanations based on atom transfer, but in many cases it seems more likely that the bridging phenomenon serves to facilitate tunnelling or may permit "electron conduction" through the bridge.

In this laboratory we have been concerned with systems in which anion bridges are indicated as important in electron transfer and have been working with the hope of obtaining information which would help distinguish among atom transfer, tunnelling and "conduction" as paths for the electron transfer. We have investigated the effects of some anions (e.g. sulfate, chloride, malonate, succinate, malate, tartrate, etc.) on exchange reactions such as Tl(I) – Tl(III),[6] Sb(III) – Sb(V)[7] and Sn(II) – Sn(IV)[8] and the Sn(II) – Ce(IV) reaction.[9] Results of these studies and work in progress on U(IV) – Tl(III) and on bridged Co(III-IV) and Co(II-III) complexes, lead us to believe that anion or other bridges are, at least often, necessary and we are inclined to believe that "conduction" and/or tunnelling can account for electron transfer in most cases. If this is indeed the case, it seems particularly important to evaluate the effects of various kinds of anion bridges on electron transfer.

The natures of the bridging groups which accelerate transfer should give some clues to the mechanics of the process. Previous studies suggest that unsaturated and symmetrical groups accelerate transfer greatly (e.g., Ball and King[10] on the Cr(II) – Cr(III) exchange). A recent, exciting study on aerobic oxidation of cytochrome C by Wang and Brinigar, shows rapid electron movement across a bridge of *1,2*-di-(*4*-pyridyl)ethylene, less with *4,4′*-dipyridyl and little when *1,2*-di-(*4*-pyridyl)ethane is used.[11] In these examples, distances seem too great for much tunnelling, as is borne out by experiments with *1,2*-di-(*4*-pyridyl)ethane, and yet electron transfer seems to occur readily through the conjugated systems. These findings agree with Taube's work on maleate and succinate[12] and some of our work on thallium exchange.[6]

Experimental Results

In our laboratory, we have studied the role of sulfate ion on the exchange between Tl(I) and Tl(III) in acid solutions and have found a two-hundredfold increase of exchange rate in passing from $HClO_4$ to H_2SO_4 of the same acidity.[6, 13, 14] The rate of reaction in sulfuric acid and sulfuric-perchloric acid mixtures is given by a rather complex rate equation, but which indicates two paths for exchange. In one path, a single $SO_4^=$ is involved, in the other, three.

These results suggest to us, symmetrical, bridged intermediates, such as;

$$I \ [Tl^1\text{—}O\text{—}\overset{\overset{\displaystyle O}{|}}{\underset{\underset{\displaystyle O}{|}}{S}}\text{—}O\text{—}Tl^m]^{+2} \text{ and}$$

$$II \ [(SO_4)Tl^1\text{—}O\text{—}\overset{\overset{\displaystyle O}{|}}{\underset{\underset{\displaystyle O}{|}}{S}}\text{—}O\text{—}Tl^m(SO_4)]^{-2}$$

If such species are indeed intermediates, then electron transfer could occur by tunnelling or by "electron conduction." If they are transition states rather than intermediates, "conduction" seems likely. Radical transfer only seems possible for hydrogen atoms in the waters of the hydration sphere and not for something like SO_4^0.

Because of the striking effect of sulfate on this exchange, we undertook to examine the effects of polyfunctional organic acids, such as the series succinic, malic, tartaric, maleic and fumaric, on the Tl(I) – Tl(III) exchange. Some of these acids reduce Tl(III) at rates comparable to the exchange, so we have now studied the effects of polyfunctional anions on the reduction of Tl(III) by U(IV).[15, 16] The reduction of Tl(III) by U(IV) is much faster than by any of the oxy-acids yet tested ($t\frac{1}{2}$ of ~ 20 min., compared to 200 hrs.).

The acids which have been studied in detail are oxalic, malonic, succinic and fumaric. Preliminary work has been carried out with malic and tartaric acids and we are preparing experiments with maleic acid.

When small amounts of oxalic acid are added to U(IV) –Tl(III) solutions in 1.76 M HClO$_4$, there is very little effect on the rate of reaction; a slight decrease in rate is observed as the ($H_2C_2O_4$) is increased. As the oxalate concentration approaches the uranium and thallium concentrations, thallium(III) oxalate separates.

In the case of succinic acid, the rate of reaction also decreases as the concentration of succinic acid increases (Table 1). These results are interpreted in terms of the complexing of Tl(III) by succinic acid and concomitant removal of the reactive Tl(III) species.

The oxidation reduction reaction is accelerated by the addition of fumaric acid until the [fumaric a.]/[Tl(III)] = 1 and then the rate falls as the fumaric acid concentration is further increased (Table 2).

Malonic acid accelerates the reaction much like fumaric, so that when [malonic a.]/Tl(III)] = 1, $k/k_0 \approx 3/2$. This work has not yet been extended to the higher concentrations of added acid.

Malic and tartaric acids accelerate the reaction but second order rate plots [log (Tl^{III})/(U^{IV}) vs. t] are not followed for more than a

TABLE 1: THE EFFECT OF SUCCINIC ACID ON THE RATE OF THE U(IV)-Tl(III) REACTION AT 25° IN 1.76 M HClO$_4$ + 1.06 M NaClO$_4$.

[U(IV)] $M \times 10^3$	[Tl(III)] $M \times 10^3$	[C$_4$H$_6$O$_4$] $M \times 10^2$	$k \times 10^2$ M^{-1} sec.$^{-1}$
5.77	9.00	0	2.20
2.88	9.00	0	2.19
3.46	9.00	0.113	2.25
3.46	9.00	0.338	1.36
3.46	9.00	0.675	1.09
3.47	9.00	1.35	0.74
3.47	9.00	2.25	0.64
3.47	9.00	4.50	0.66

small fraction of the reaction. These systems are being examined further. The effects of malic acid seem to be limited.

Studies of the electron exchange reactions between Sb(III) and Sb(V) and between Sn(II) and Sn(IV)[7,8] suggest that partially hydrolyzed species and chlorocomplexes (probably hydroxo- and chloro-bridges) are more effective in electron transfer than are the sulfate complexes. In the Sn(II) − Sn(IV) case spectrophotometry reveals an interaction dimer, which may be the intermediate in the exchange.

Discussion

The experimental results obtained in the study of thallium exchange show sulfate catalyzes exchange (as do chloride and hydrox-

TABLE 2: THE EFFECT OF FUMARIC ACID ON THE RATE OF THE U(IV)-Tl(III) REACTION AT 25° IN 1.76 M HClO$_4$ + 1.06 M NaClO$_4$.

[U(IV)] $M \times 10^3$	[Tl(III)] $M \times 10^3$	[C$_4$H$_4$O$_4$] $M \times 10^3$	$k \times 10^2$ M^{-1} sec.$^{-1}$
3.47	9.00	0	2.19
3.46	9.00	0	1.97
3.45	9.00	1.25	2.62
3.45	9.00	1.25	2.78
3.41	9.00	1.88	3.44
3.45	9.00	2.50	2.91
3.41	9.00	2.50	2.77
3.43	9.00	3.13	3.16
3.41	9.00	3.13	3.00
3.43	9.00	4.38	2.24
3.45	9.00	5.00	1.88
3.45	9.00	6.25	2.44

ide) and it seems likely that it serves as a bridge in an intermediate or activated complex. The role of sulfate as a bridge may be through its service as an "electron conductor" or simply to hold the Tl(I) and Tl(III) together long enough to permit tuneling or hydrogen atom (2 atoms) transfer; both of the latter seem rather unlikely in a two-electron transfer.

In the case of Sb(III) + Sb(V) there is no exchange in H_2SO_4 alone. In the Sn(II) − Sn(IV) case exchange occurs but sulfate does not appear to be very effective in accelerating exchange. However, this seems a good system in which to look for photochemical catalysis since the ultraviolet spectrum shows an interaction dimer; "electron conduction" may, in fact, involve excitation of the electrons to be transferred into a vacant molecular orbital (perhaps an antibonding π-orbital) of the bridged complex.

The study of the U(IV) − Tl(III) reaction shows little or no effect by oxalic acid and a retarding reaction by succinic. Oxalate probably chelates Tl(III) (and/or U(IV)) and so cannot form a bridge, and succinate, which does not seem much like an "electron conductor," probably simply ties up Tl(III) and so slows reduction (cf., the effect of succinic acid on thallium exchange[6]).

Fumaric acid first accelerates exchange and at higher concentrations loses that effectiveness. It is not difficult to explain the acceleration in terms of bridge formation and "electron conduction," but its subsequent loss of effectiveness was not expected. This may be due to the formation of higher complexes (than, say, 1:1) which are then less able to form the bridged species.

The rate increase produced by malonic acid bears further study to determine whether the effect can be attributed to a bridge mechanism. Further study is also required for tartrate and malate but the acceleration, especially noticeable with tartrate, can be justified on a basis of bridge formation and "electron conduction."

REFERENCES

1. R. J. Marcus, B. Zwolinski and H. Eyring, *J. Phys. Chem.* **58**, 432 (1954).
2. R. A. Marcus, *J. Chem. Phys.*, **24**, 966 (1956), and **26**, 867 (1957).
3. J. Hudis and R. W. Dodson, *J. Am. Chem. Soc.*, **78**, 911 (1956).
4. D. R. Stranks, Chap. 2, in *Modern Coordination Chemistry*, ed. by J. Lewis and R. G. Wilkins, Interscience, New York (1960).
5. E.g. H. Taube, *J. Am. Chem. Soc.*, **82**, 524 (1960); W. Kruse and H. Taube, *ibid.*, **82**, 526 (1960); R. T. M. Fraser and H. Taube, *ibid.*, **81**, 5514, 5000 (1959); A. Zwickel and H. Taube, *ibid.*, **81**, 2915 (1959).
6. C. H. Brubaker and J. P. Mickel, *J. Inorg. and Nuclear Chem.*, **4**, 55 (1957); C. H. Brubaker, K. O. Groves, J. P. Mickel and C. P. Knop,

J. Am. Chem. Soc., **79**, 4641 (1957) and C. H. Brubaker and C. Andrade, *ibid.,* **81**, 5282 (1959).

7. J. A. Sincius, Ph. D. Dissertation, Michigan State University (1959).
8. G. Gordon and C. H. Brubaker, *J. Am. Chem. Soc.,* **82**, 4448 (1960).
9. C. H. Brubaker and A. J. Court, *ibid.,* **78**, 5530 (1956).
10. D. L. Ball and E. L. King, *ibid.,* **80,** 1091 (1958).
11. J. H. Wang and W. S. Brinigar, *Proc. Nat. Acad. Sci.* **46**, 958 (1960).
12. H. Taube, *J. Am. Chem. Soc.,* **77**, 4481 (1955).
13. G. Harbottle and R. W. Dodson, *ibid.,* **70**, 880 (1948); R. W. Dodson, *ibid.,* **75,** 1795 (1953).
14. R. J. Prestwood and A. C. Wahl, *ibid.,* **70,** 880 (1948), and **71,** 3137 (1949).
15. A. C. Harkness and J. Halpern, *ibid.,* **81,** 3526 (1959).
16. L. P. Quinn and C. H. Brubaker, Jr., unpublished work.

THE SPECTRAL AND MAGNETIC PROPERTIES AND ELECTRONIC STRUCTURES OF SOME TETRAHEDRAL THIOCYANATO COMPLEXES OF COBALT (II)

F. A. COTTON, D. M. L. GOODGAME, M. GOODGAME, and A. SACCO

Department of Chemistry
Massachusetts Institute of Technology
Cambridge, Massachusetts

The compound $[\mathrm{Co}\{(\mathrm{C_6H_5})_3\mathrm{P}\}_2(\mathrm{SCN})_2]$ has been carefully studied magnetically and spectroscopically. The main absorption band in the visible spectrum has the high intensity and general contour which are characteristic of the visible absorption bands of tetrahedral Co(II) complexes. Moreover, the position of the band is between those for the corresponding complexes containing $\mathrm{Cl^-}$ and $\mathrm{Br^-}$ in place of $\mathrm{SCN^-}$. This shows that in this complex $\mathrm{SCN^-}$ has a place in the spectrochemical series between $\mathrm{Cl^-}$ and $\mathrm{Br^-}$. Since we know *(vide infra)* that N-coordinated $\mathrm{SCN^-}$ lies well to the strong field end of the spectrochemical series compared to $\mathrm{Cl^-}$ and $\mathrm{Br^-}$, this datum strongly suggests that the $\mathrm{SCN^-}$ ions are S-coordinated in this complex. This conclusion is supported by the magnetic moment[1] of the complex, when it is compared with those of other complexes as indicated in Table 1. These data show that for N-coordinated SCN, the complex $[\mathrm{Co(Ph_3P)_2(SCN)_2}]$ should have a far lower moment than it does, and further, that in the spectrochemical series the position of $\mathrm{SCN^-}$, which is then assumed to be S-coordinated, is between $\mathrm{Cl^-}$ and $\mathrm{Br^-}$. This conclusion with respect to the position of $-\mathrm{SCN^-}$ in the spectrochemical series is in good agreement with that reached by Schäffer from his studies of other thiocyanate complexes.[2] In addition, the

TABLE 1: MAGNETIC MOMENTS (B.M.) OF $[\mathrm{Co(Ph_3P)_2(SCN)_2}]$ AND SOME RELATED COMPLEXES

$\mathrm{X^-}$	$\mathrm{Co(Ph_3P)_2X_2}$	$[\mathrm{CoX_4}]^{2-}$
$\mathrm{I^-}$	4.62	4.88
$\mathrm{Br^-}$	4.52	4.72
$\mathrm{Cl^-}$	4.41	4.60
$\mathrm{SCN^-}$	4.46	4.40

infrared spectrum corroborates the assignment of S-coordination, since the S—C stretching band at 760 cm^{-1} is in the range (690-760 cm^{-1}) typical of S-bonded thiocyanates, but well below the range for N-bonded thiocyanates.[3-5]

The compound $[Co(Ph_3PO)_2(NCS)_2]$ has been prepared, studied magnetically and spectrally, and the data compared with corresponding data for its Cl$^-$ and Br$^-$ analogs. In this case, the relative values of the d-orbital splittings (4030, 3270, 3180 cm^{-1} for the -NCS$^-$, Cl$^-$, Br$^-$ complexes, respectively) and the magnetic moments (4.46, 4.63, 4.69 $B.M.$ for the same series) prove that the thiocyanate ions are N-coordinated. It is believed that instances of the same metal ion coordinating SCN$^-$ both ways in different compounds are quite rare.

Finally, a detailed study of the spectral and magnetic properties of the $[Co(NCS)_4]^{2-}$ ion in $[N(CH_3)_4]_2[Co(NCS)_4]$ and $HgCo(NCS)_4$ gives, *inter alia*, the results in Table 2. These results lead to the following conclusions: (1) The oscillator strengths, and particularly their ratio, show that there is considerable covalence in the metal ligand bonds when compared with the theory of Ballhausen and Liehr.[6] (2) The magnetic moments show that N-coordinated NCS$^-$ lies well toward the strong end of the spectrochemical series. (3) The differences between the Δ and μ values for the two compounds show that attachment of the outer sulfur atoms to Hg(II)[7] increases the strength of the ligand field provided by the nitrogen atoms as Schäffer had concluded[2] from his measurements on other compounds.

TABLE 2: SOME SPECTRAL AND MAGNETIC PARAMETERS OF Co(II) IN $[N(CH_3)_4]_2[Co(NCS)_4]$ AND $HgCo(NCS)_4$

	$[N(CH_3)_4]_2[Co(NCS)_4]$	$HgCo(NCS)_4$
ν_1(cm^{-1})	7,780	8,300
ν_2(cm^{-1})	16,250	16,700
Δ(cm^{-1})	4,550	4,880
$f(\nu_2)$	3.44×10^{-3}	----
$f(\nu_3)$	1.46×10^{-2}	----
$f(\nu_3)/f(\nu_2)$	4.25	----
μ(BM)	4.40	4.32
λ(cm^{-1})	149	135

REFERENCES

1. The method of computing magnetic moments has been detailed by F. A. Cotton and M. Goodgame, *J. Am. Chem. Soc.*, **83**, 1777 (1961) and by F. A. Cotton, O. D. Faut, D. M. L. Goodgame, and R. H. Holm, *ibid*, **83**, 1780 (1961).

2. C. Schäffer, *Abstracts of the Conference on Coordination Chemistry,* London, 1959, and Private Communications.
3. M. M. Chamberlain and J. C. Bailar, Jr., *J. Am. Chem. Soc.*, **81**, 6412 (1959).
4. J. Lewis, R. S. Nyholm, and P. W. Smith, to be published.
5. M. E. Baldwin, *J. Chem. Soc.*, **1961**, 471.
6. C. J. Ballhausen and A. D. Liehr, *J. Mol. Spect.*, **2**, 342 (1958); **4**, 190 (1960).
7. J. W. Jeffery, *Nature*, **159**, 610 (1947).

ON THE COMPLEX FORMATION OF DIPHENYLPHOSPHINO-BENZENE-m-SULPHONATE WITH MERCURY AND BISMUTH

JANNIK BJERRUM, BJARNE SALVESEN*, AND GRAHAM WRIGHT[†]

Department of Inorganic Chemistry
University of Copenhagen
Copenhagen, Denmark

In their studies of the complex formation of silver(I) ions with various types of ligands, Ahrland and Chatt *et al.*[1] distinguish between three main types of complex formation: (1) those (e.g., NH_3, CN^-, Cl^-, Br^-) which have a stop or inflection at $\bar{n} = 2$; (2) an intermediate type (sulphides, selenides) where the formation of complexes proceeds uniformly to $N = 4$; and (3) those (phosphines, arsines, I^-) with a stop or inflection at $\bar{n} = 1$ and $\bar{n} = 3$.

For mercury(II) ions only complex formation of type (1) with a very pronounced stop at $\bar{n} = 2$ has been examined hitherto. However, it is known that mercury seems to be unable to react with more than one ethylene molecule,[2] and that mercury dialkyl and diaryl compounds are easily converted to compounds in which mercury is attached to only one carbon atom.[3] This suggests that mercury in these compounds has the characteristic coordination number one. Ahrland and Chatt suggest for silver(I) a connection between a high stability of the mono-complex and the possibility of the ligand to accept d-electrons from the metal forming a $d\pi$-bond. With this background it was interesting to see how mercury(II) behaves towards the phosphine ligand.

In Fig. 1 our results with diphenylphosphinobenzene-m-sulphonate and mercury(II) are compared with earlier results for the ammonia system[4] and with Sillen[5] and co-workers' results for the mercury halide systems. The figure shows the distribution of the various complexes HgL_1 to HgL_4 as a function of the ligand exponent—$\log [L]$. The di-complex has in all cases a very large range of existence, but it will be seen that the range of existence of the mono-complex as

---

*Present address: Pharmaceutical Institute of the University, Blindern, Norway.

[†]Present address: Chemistry Department, University of Auckland, Auckland, New Zealand.

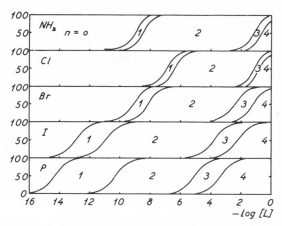

Fig. 1. Comparison of the distribution of mercury(II) between the various complexes as a function of ——log $[L]$ for the ammonia,[4] the halide[5] and the phosphine systems. The diphenylphosphinobenzene-*m*-sulphonate system was studied experimentally by Bjarne Salvesen with both mercury and platinum electrodes at low metal ion concentrations. It could be shown that mercury(I) ions do not form complexes in the region covered, and for mercury(II) only the last part of the formation curve was disturbed to a minor degree by the self-association of the ligand which begins to interfere with the complex formation for total concentrations of ligand higher than $\sim 3.10^{-3}$ M. The following values for the complexity constants were obtained in 1 M KNO_3, 0.01 M HNO_3 at 25°C: $K_1 = 10^{14.3}$ $l \cdot mole^{-1}$, $\beta_2 = 10^{24.6}$ $l^2 \cdot mole^{-2}$, $\beta_3 = 10^{29.7}$ $l^3 \cdot mole^{-3}$, $\beta_4 = 10^{33.0}$ $l^4 \cdot mole^{-4}$.

well as that of the tri-complex increases much from chloride to iodide and again from the iodide to the phosphine system. For this system it is especially the mono-complex which has a great range of existence, and the first coordination number is clearly one. It will be seen that the complex affinity increases in the series: $Cl^- < Br^- < I^- <$ phosphine.

For silver(I) Leden *et al.* have found that the coordination number two decreases in importance for ligands such as chloride and bromide,[6] and for both iodide[7] and phosphine[1] the coordination numbers one and three, instead of two, are virtually found. But also here it is remarkable that the complex affinity increases in the series: $Cl^- < Br^- < I^- <$ phosphine.

The first subgroup metal ions Cu^+, Ag^+, Au^+, and Hg^{++} all have a strong tendency to form linear complexes with ligands which cannot participate in π-bonding such as ammonia or ligands such as cyanide which only have p-orbitals available for such bonding. However, after a large range of existence of the linear di-complex, a tetrahedral complex is formed in most cases. Our data for the mercury(II)-phosphine system now seem to support the idea of Ahrland and Chatt that ligands furnished with d-orbitals capable of accepting d-electrons from the metal such as, for example, phosphines, arsines and the halide ions to an increasing extent from chloride to iodide interfere with this condition and strongly favour the coordination numbers one and three.

In case of metal ions which form tetra-coordinated and octahedral complexes the ranges of existence of the intermediary complexes are with few exceptions larger than that corresponding to the statistical distribution for the characteristic coordination number in question. However, for the same subgroup metal ions the ranges of existence of the intermediary complexes seem to decrease in the series: $Cl^- >$ $Br^- > I^- >$ phosphine.

In Fig. 2 our preliminary results with the bismuth(III)-phosphine system are compared with Ahrland and Grenthe's data[8] for the bismuth-halide systems. From the figure it will be seen that the ranges of existence of the intermediary complexes as a whole, decrease from

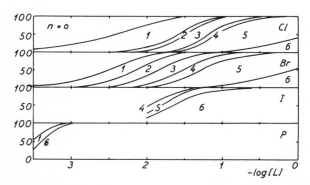

Fig. 2. Distribution of bismuth(III) complexes as a function of $-\log[L]$ for the halide[8] and the phosphine systems. The diphenylphosphinobenzene-*m*-sulphonate system was measured independently by Bjarne Salvesen and Graham Wright with a bismuth amalgam electrode. The measurements of the dilute bismuth solutions at high acid concentration were carried out with a rather high uncertainty due to a sluggish equilibrium establishment. The concentration of non-complexed ligand in a 1 M nitric acid medium at the very steep part of the formation curve was found to be approximately $1.5 \cdot 10^{-3}$ M. At this acid concentration about 80% of the "free" phosphine is protonated, and the total concentration of ligand was, in the experiments performed, so high that self-association may interfere to some extent. The results were somewhat more reproducible in nitric than in perchloric acid solutions. However, qualitatively the measurements of both investigators agree with the curves given in the figure.

chloride to iodide, and for the phosphine the ranges of existence have decreased so much that we are able to describe the system completely, neglecting the intermediary complexes between the *mono*- and the hexa-complexes. However, the average complex affinity is seen to be relatively much higher for the phosphine ligand than for the halide ions which supports the *b*-metal character of bismuth(III) in the nomenclature of Ahrland and Chatt.[1]

It is remarkable that there seems to be no steric hindrance of the formation of complexes of diphenylphosphinobenzene-*m*-sulphonate. However, it is reasonable to assume that this is connected with the relatively small value of the angles C—P—C in the phosphine molecule[9] and the relatively large size of the phosphorus atom.

Indium(III) and lead(II) ions are known to bind up to four halide ions probably forming tetrahedral complexes. However, in case of the phosphine ligand we were not able to demonstrate complex formation with indium amalgam and lead amalgam electrodes, respectively. But this is understandable when we ascribe to the intermediary phosphine complexes a high tendency to dismutation. For indium(III) ions the average complex affinity falls somewhat in the series $F^- > Cl^- > Br^- > I^-$,[10] while lead (II) as well as bismuth behave as *b*-metals. We have some reason to believe that both indium and lead ions have a not insignificant average affinity to complex with phosphine, but due to the low solubility and strong self-association of the ligand, we cannot reach the concentration range where the complex formation curve is supposed to rise. Cadmium(II) has more *b*-character but approximately the same complex affinity for the halides[11] as indium(III). For this metal ion, Ahrland and Chatt[12] have given the following values for the complexity constants: $K_1 \sim 8 \ l \cdot mole^{-1}$, $\beta_2 \sim 2500 \ l^2 \cdot mole^{-2}$. These figures point to a very steep formation curve, and the average complex affinity may well be of the same order as for the iodide system for which $\beta_4 = 3.10^6 \ l^4 \cdot mole^{-4}$.

From data for substituted phosphines[13] it can be extrapolated that PH_3 is a very weak base to be compared with $pK_{HIJ} \sim -9$ for the iodide ion. For the sulphonated triphenylphosphine

$$pK_{LH^+} = 0.13 + 0.50 \ C_{HClO_4}$$

is found here by spectrophotometric measurements in perchloric acid solutions.

In conclusion it may be said that the self-association of the aromatic phosphine molecule as well as of the corresponding phosphonium ion limits strongly the general usefulness of this ligand for complex-chemical studies.

REFERENCES

1. S. Ahrland, J. Chatt, N. R. Davies, and A. A. Williams, *J. Chem. Soc.*, 1958, 264, 276.
2. P. Brandt and O. Plum, *Acta Chem. Scand.* **7**, 97 (1953).
3. F. R. Jensen, *J. Am. Chem. Soc.* **82**, 2469 (1960).
4. J. Bjerrum, *Metal Ammine Formation in Aqueous Solution*, Haase and Son, Copenhagen 1941 and 1957.
5. L. G. Sillén, *Acta Chem. Scand.* **3**, 539 (1949).
6. E. Berne and I. Leden, *Svensk kem. Tidskr.* **65**, 88 (1953); *Z. Naturforsch.* **8a**, 719 (1953).
7. I. Leden, *Acta Chem. Scand.* **10**, 812 (1956).
8. S. Ahrland and I. Grenthe, *Acta Chem. Scand.* **11**, 1111 (1957).
9. L. S. Bartell, *J. Chem. Physics* **32**, 832 (1960).
10. N. Sundén, *Svensk kem. Tidskr.* **66**, 20, 50 (1954).
11. I. Leden, *Z. physik. Chem.* **188** A, 160 (1941).
12. S. Ahrland, J. Chatt, N. R. Davies and A. A. Williams, *J. Chem. Soc.* 1958, 1403.
13. Wm. A. Henderson, Jr. and C. A. Streuli, *J. Am. Chem. Soc.* **82**, 5791 (1960).

THE STRUCTURES OF SOME METAL-OLEFIN COMPLEXES*

N. C. BAENZIGER, J. R. DOYLE, G. F. RICHARDS

Chemistry Department
University of Iowa
Iowa City, Iowa

and

C. L. CARPENTER

Chemistry Department
Arizona State University
Tempe, Arizona

Metal-olefin complexes have been known for a long time, but only in recent years have attempts been made to explain the nature of the complexes and to determine the detailed structure of the complexes.[1,2,3] Spectroscopic evidence from both infrared and Raman has been interpreted as indicating that the C=C stretching frequency of the olefin is affected by the formation of the complex. (The shift of the stretching frequency ranges from 60 to 150 wave numbers for most complexes.) The most reasonable description of the metal-olefin bond[3] is that it arises from the overlap of a metal atomic orbital with a "pi" molecular orbital from the olefin to form the primary or "sigma" bond. An additional bond with "pi" character could be formed by overlap of some of the remaining filled d orbitals of the metal atom with some unoccupied antibonding molecular orbitals of the olefin.

The first crystal structure determinations endeavoured to determine if the orientation of the olefin relative to the metal atom was compatible with the electronic structure suggested for it. In addition, information on the *trans effect* on the binding of other groups to the metal atom was sought for platinum-olefin complexes. The results of these structural studies are accumulated in Table 1.

In all cases involving the Pt or Pd metal atoms, the structures found were compatible with the suggested electronic arrangement. The interatomic distances, however, left much to be desired. The

*This work has been supported by the Office of Ordnance Research, U. S. Army, under contract No. DA-11-022-ORD-2647.

TABLE 1: INTERATOMIC DISTANCES IN METAL-OLEFIN COMPOUNDS

Compound	R	M—C	C=C			Ref.
COT*dimer · AgNO$_3$	0.29	2.55** / 2.32	1.34 / 1.36	Other C—C distances 1.49 to 1.59 Å.		4
COT · AgNO$_3$	0.11	2.46(.03) / 2.51 / 2.78 / 2.84	1.37(.04) / 1.33	Other C—C distances 1.42 to 1.51 Å.		5
				M—Cl distances		
				cis	*trans*	
K$_2$[PtCl$_4$]				2.32	2.32	6
K[PtNH$_3$Cl$_3$]				2.35	2.32	6
K[PtC$_2$H$_4$Cl$_3$] · H$_2$O			1.5	2.26	2.40	6
"	0.14,0.19		1.5	2.33	2.38	7
[Pt(NH$_3$)$_4$][PtCl$_4$]				2.34 (±.005)	2.34	8
[Pt(Et)NH(CH$_3$)$_2$Cl$_2$] (*trans*)	0.14 / 0.08	2.21(.15)	1.47(.18)	2.30 / 2.33		9
[(EtPdCl$_2$)$_2$]	0.16	2.34 / 2.28		2.33 / 2.41	2.43 / 2.32	10
[(styrenePdCl$_2$)$_2$]	0.17	1.79(.04) / 2.29(.10)	1.32(.15)	2.32(.02) (C—C: 1.30 to 1.65 Å)	2.41(.02)	11
[norbornadiene · PdCl$_2$]	0.13	2.21(.03) / 2.22	1.51(.04) / 1.53 (C—C: 1.60 to 1.63 Å)	2.31(.01) / 2.31		12

*Cyclooctatetraene.
**To center of C=C bond.

variation of the carbon-carbon distances in the remaining portion of the olefin molecules of 0.05 to 0.35 Å emphasized the fact that the accurate location of carbon atoms in the presence of strong scatterers such as Pd, Ag, or Pt is very difficult.

The C=C distances appear to be shorter in the silver complexes (see Table 1) than in the Pd or Pt complexes. The situation is reversed for the metal-to-carbon atom distances. The standard errors in bond lengths, when reported, and the scatter in C—C bond distances indicates that the differences in the double bond distances are just on the borderline of being termed significant. (Three times the standard error is used as a criterion for significance.) In particular, the rather long distances which were found in the norbornadiene–PdCl$_2$ complex were disturbing. Although an explanation of why the C—C distances might be longer than normal could be offered and the infrared evidence supports lengthening of the double bond, the distances which were determined from the visually estimated X-ray data are perhaps too long.

Least-Squares Refinement of (Styrene-PdCl$_2$)$_2$

Some preliminary results have been obtained from a program designed to improve the accuracy of the distance determinations. Originally, the crystal structure of the styrene-PdCl$_2$ dimer was determined entirely by Fourier methods. (The unit cell dimensions are a = 13.50, b = 4.99, c = 13.69 Å, β = 90.4°, Z = 2 dimers, space group = $P2_1/n$.) At that time computing equipment which would permit the least-squares refinement of the data was not available. The interatomic distances obtained from the calculated and observed three-dimensional electron density maps gave a normal (1.32 Å) double bond distance for the double bond coordinated to the Pd atom. The Pd—C distances were 1.79 and 2.29 Å, one of which is shorter than a Pd—C single bond. The carbon-carbon distances in the ring varied from 1.30 to 1.65 Å.

Using the same visually estimated intensity data, a least squares refinement has been carried out. (The least-squares computer program had the following characteristics: individual isotropic temperature factors were determined for each atom; only diagonal terms of the least-squares matrix were evaluated; all observed reflections were given unit weight, absent reflections were given unit weight only if $|F_c| > |F_{0min}|$, zero weight otherwise.) On refinement, the discrepancy factor, $R = \Sigma \|F_0| - |F_c\| / \Sigma |F_0|$, dropped from 0.17 to 0.127 (for observed reflections only). The new distances are shown in Table 2. The standard errors, as determined from the diagonal elements of the least-squares matrix are less than in the earlier study, and the C—C distances in the ring show a smaller spread (1.30 to 1.55 Å). The short Pd—C distance has lengthened to 2.09 Å, or approximately a Pd—C single bond distance, and the C—C distance has changed to 1.45 Å. In this case, although the bond distances are not known to be much more precise than before, the bond distances are approaching more reasonable values.

Refinement of Norbornadiene-PdCl$_2$ (Norbornadiene Dichloropalladium-II)

Intensities from single crystals of norbornadiene-PdCl$_2$ have been measured at room temperature using a proportional counter with a pulse height analyzer. The crystals were mounted on a Weissenberg camera, and the counter was kept stationary at the proper angle for reflection while the crystal was slowly rocked through the reflection angle. Data were obtained from the zero through 4th layers about the b axis (size of crystal = 0.028 ×0.036 × 0.36 mm) and zero through the second layer about the c axis (0.029 × 0.038 × 0.025 mm) with Cu Kα radiation. All equivalent reflections were measured for each layer

**TABLE 2: PARAMETERS AND INTERATOMIC DISTANCES FOR
$(STYRENEPdCl_2)_2$: POSITIONS BASED ON $P2_1/n$: (x, y, z;
$\bar{x}$, $\bar{y}$, $\bar{z}$; $1/2 - x$, $1/2 + y$, $1/2 - z$; $1/2 + x$, $1/2 - y$, $1/2 + z$)**

	x	y	z
Pd	0.5826	0.3768	0.5864
Cl_1	0.585	0.669	0.448
Cl_2	0.747	0.432	0.607
C_1	0.478	0.348	0.794
C_2	0.496	0.566	0.854
C_3	0.418	0.680	0.922
C_4	0.330	0.526	0.911
C_5	0.306	0.329	0.850
C_6	0.392	0.237	0.783
C_7	0.574	0.258	0.750
C_8	0.587	0.045	0.679
Pd—Cl_1	2.324 $\pm$ 0.010 Å	C_1—C_2	1.38 $\pm$ 0.08 Å
Pd—Cl_1	2.394 0.015	C_2—C_3	1.51 0.09
Pd—Cl_2	2.252 0.010	C_3—C_4	1.42 0.09
Pd—C_8	2.09 0.05	C_4—C_5	1.33 0.09
Pd—C_7	2.32 0.05	C_5—C_6	1.55 0.08
C_8—C_7	1.45 0.07	C_6—C_1	1.30 0.07
		C_1—C_7	1.50 0.06

to serve as a check on the accuracy of alignment of the crystal, on
absorption effects, and on the reproducibility of the intensity measurements. The average deviation in intensities for equivalent reflections within a layer was 4%. Sufficient counts were recorded on both
background and reflections to give a statistical counting error in the
net intensity of 1% for the majority of the reflections. The statistical
counting error was computed for each reflection and used in the
weighting procedure to be described later. Comparison of identical
reflections obtained from the two different crystals in the two different orientations gave an unweighted average deviation of 7.7% in
F values. The strongest reflections which occurred at low angles,
though measured, were eliminated from the refinement, since no provision for correction of extinction effects was made in the least-
squares refinement program. The set of date ($hk2$) gave evidence
that partial loss of olefin from the crystal might have occurred.
Smaller reflection-to-background ratios were observed for this data,
and as a consequence the statistical counting errors are larger for
this set. Due to the weighting schemes used in the least-squares
refinement, the contribution of this data was greatly reduced in determining the final parameters.

The least-squares refinement was carried out in the same manner
as for the styrene–$PdCl_2$ dimer, except that several different weight-

ing schemes were adopted. First, almost the same weighting scheme was used as for the styrene complex, i.e., unit weights for all present reflections, 1/2 weight for absent reflections if $|F_c| > |F_0|_{min}$, zero weight for all other absent reflections. Second, weights were made proportional to $1/\% \sigma$ (σ is standard error) for observed reflections and were the same as above for absent reflections. Third, weights were chosen proportional to $1/\sigma^2(F_0)$ as an approximation to $1/\sigma^2(\Delta F)$, the proper set of weights.[13] The results obtained from these three weighting schemes are shown in Table 3.

The agreement between the calculated and observed values as expressed by the discrepancy factor, R, is considerably better for the proportional counter data (0.084) as compared to the visually estimated data (0.13). The standard deviations in bond lengths, though smaller, are not markedly so because fewer reflections were measured by the counter method. The interatomic distances are more reasona-

TABLE 3: PARAMETERS AND INTERATOMIC DISTANCES FOR NORBORNADIENE-PdCl$_2$ ($a = 9.424$, $b = 7.219$, $c = 11.712$ Å, $Z = 4$, SPACE GROUP = $Pnma$)

	Final Parameters Weight #3	Standard Deviations (in A) Weights		
		#1	#2	#3
Pd in (4c)	x: 0.6003	0.0019	0.0017	0.0013
	y: 0.2500			
	z: 0.4772	0.0023	0.0020	0.0014
Cl$_1$ in (4c)	x: 0.5324	0.0071	0.0065	0.0054
	y: 0.2500			
	z: 0.2874	0.0082	0.0074	0.0055
Cl$_2$ in (4c)	x: 0.3695	0.0064	0.0058	0.0048
	y: 0.2500			
	z: 0.5459	0.0077	0.0065	0.0054
C$_{1,4}$ in (8d)	x: 0.8391	0.019	0.015	0.014
	y: 0.4059	0.025	0.019	0.022
	z: 0.5764	0.022	0.018	0.016
C$_{2,3}$ in (8d)	x: 0.6975	0.020	0.016	0.014
	y: 0.3511	0.020	0.017	0.018
	z: 0.6330	0.023	0.019	0.014
C$_{5,6}$ in (8d)	x: 0.8147	0.018	0.014	0.013
	y: 0.1489	0.020	0.017	0.019
	z: 0.4541	0.022	0.016	0.014
C$_7$ in (4c)	x: 0.9391	0.032	0.025	0.021
	y: 0.2500			
	z: 0.6192	0.037	0.030	0.021

TABLE 3 (CONTINUED)

	Distances (in Å) Weights			Standard Deviation (in Å) Weight
	#1	#2	#3	#3
Pd—Cl$_1$	2.307	2.304	2.314	0.006
Pd—Cl$_2$	2.322	2.319	2.321	0.005
Pd—C$_{2,3}$	2.172	2.174	2.169	0.014
Pd—C$_{5,6}$	2.177	2.173	2.168	0.014
C$_1$—C$_2$	1.531	1.532	1.543	0.019
C$_1$—C$_6$	1.535	1.554	1.504	0.022
C$_1$—C$_7$	1.591	1.582	1.551	0.024
C$_2$—C$_3$	1.470	1.487	1.460	0.036
C$_5$—C$_6$	1.390	1.406	1.460	0.038

Weight # 1: Unit weights.
Weight # 2: Weight proportional to $1/\% \ \sigma$.
Weight # 3: Weight proportional to $1/\sigma^2$ (F).

ble, however. All the C—C distances could now be considered as "normal," and the C=C distances of 1.46 Å are in line with that found for the styrene complex. It is obvious that in order to make truly significant statements about interatomic distances, even better intensity data must be obtained under conditions in which the scattering of carbon is enhanced relative to the metal atom. Measurements of intensities of the norbornadiene and styrene complexes at liquid nitrogen temperatures are being undertaken.

The Structure of Dicyclopentadieneplatinum Chloride

A second way to improve the accuracy of the determination of C—C distances in the presence of a heavy atom is to find a structure in which the heavy atom is in such a special position that it does not contribute appreciably to whole classes of reflections. The intensities of these weak reflections can then be used to determine the positions of the atoms of low atomic number. Such a fortunate situation occurs in the dicyclopentadieneplatinum chloride structure.

The unit cell is orthorhombic, $a = 9.60$, $b = 12.94$, $c = 16.98$ Å, $Z = 8$. Absences establish the space group uniquely as $Pbca$. Weissenberg data were obtained with Cu Kα radiation from $(0kl)$ to $(6kl)$ and precession data were recorded with Mo Kα from $(hk0)$ and $(h0l)$ to $(h4l)$. The Pt atom has parameters of approximately 1/8, 1/4, 1/4. This makes the sets of data $(1kl)$, $(3kl)$, and $(5kl)$ weak. Therefore, these films were exposed approximately twice as long as the other films in order to obtain appreciable quantities of the weak reflection data.

The positions of the platinum atoms were immediately obvious from the appearance of the intensity data. Patterson maps evaluated in three dimensions confirmed the Pt positions and were interpreted as placing the Cl atoms at the same x level as the Pt atom. Structure factors calculated from the Pt and two Cl atoms gave excellent agreement for all strong reflections, but very poor agreement for the $(1kl)$, $(3kl)$, and $(5kl)$ sets of data and for weak reflections occurring in the remaining data sets.

Since the contribution of carbon atoms to high-angle reflections should be negligible due to the rapid decrease of scattering factor with angle, and since the $(1kl)$, $(3kl)$, and $(5kl)$ data sets did not show this characteristic decline of intensities, it was assumed that the Pt atom was slightly shifted from the ideal coordinates. By least-squares fitting the positions of the Pt and two Cl atoms to the intensity data with $1/d^2 > 0.6$, the possible deviations from the ideal arrangement were systematically explored.

From the two arrangements of Pt and Cl atoms which gave the best structure factor agreement, two bounded difference electron density projections were evaluated. The projections showed the dicyclopentadiene molecule as a rather indistinct blob of electron density, but oriented in a position which was compatible with two double bonds in the molecule coordinating with the Pt atom. From positioning the molecule approximately on these electron density maps, structure factors were calculated including all the carbon atoms. Both arrangements gave about equal agreement with the observed F values in the early stages of refinement, but one of them gave very poor agreement with the absent reflection data and, hence, was discarded.

The refinement of the structure has proceeded to an R value of 0.13, based on observed reflections. The dicyclopentadiene molecule is in the *endo* configuration with both double bonds coordinated to the Pt atom. The Pt—Cl interatomic distances are 2.28 and 2.37 Å, the Pt—C distances are 2.11, 2.16, 2.25 Å, and the C—C distances range from 1.35 to 1.63 Å.

REFERENCES

1. W. C. Zeise, *Pogg. Ann.*, **9**, 623 (1827).
2. R. N. Keller, *Chem. Reviews*, **28**, 229 (1941).
3. J. Chatt, *Cationic Polymerization and Related Complexes*, ed. P. H. Plesch, Publ. Heffer and Sons, 1953, p. 40. J. Chatt and L. A. Duncanson, *J. Chem. Soc.*, **1953**, 2939.
4. S. Nyburg and J. Hilton, *Acta Cryst.*, **12**, 116 (1959).
5. W. N. Lipscomb and F. S. Mathews, *J. Phys. Chem.*, **63**, 845 (1959).
6. G. B. Bokii and G. A. Kukina, *Kristallografiya*, **2**, 400 (1957).
7. J. A. Wunderlich and D. P. Mellor, *Acta Cryst.*, **8**, 57 (1955).

8. M. Atoji, J. W. Richardson, and R. E. Rundle, *J. Am. Chem. Soc.*, **79,** 3017 (1957).

9. P. R. H. Alderman, P. G. Owston, and J. M. Rowe, *Acta Cryst.*, **13,** 149 (1960).

10. J. N. Dempsey and N. C. Baenziger, *J. Am. Chem. Soc.*, **77,** 4984 (1955).

11. J. R. Holden and N. C. Baenziger, *J. Am. Chem. Soc.*, **77,** 4987 (1955).

12. N. C. Baenziger, J. R. Doyle and C. Carpenter, *Acta Cryst.*, **14,** 303 (1961).

13. D. W. J. Cruickshank, *International Tables of Crystallography*, Kynoch Press, 1959, Vol. II, p. 326.

THE STEREOCHEMISTRY AND MECHANISM OF SOME REACTIONS OF ETHYLENEDIAMINETETRAACETATOCOBALTATE(III) AND PROPYLENEDIAMINETETRAACETATOCOBALTATE(III)

DARYLE H. BUSCH, DEAN W. COOKE, KRISHNASAMY SWAMINATHAN, AND YONG AE IM*

Department of Chemistry
The Ohio State University
Columbus, Ohio

A substantial array of stereochemical and kinetic studies have been carried out on the cobalt(III) complexes of ethylenediaminetetraacetate (EDTA) and propylenediaminetetraacetate (PDTA). These are related to the kinetic and stereochemical studies reported here. The following reactions have been studied in varying detail: (1) conversion of pentadentate complexes into the corresponding hexadentate derivatives; (2) the electron transfer catalyzed racemization of the hexadentate cobalt(III) complexes in the presence of the cobalt(II) compounds; (3) the base hydrolysis of the hexadentate complexes; (4) the racemization of $Co^{III}EDTA^-$; and (5) the reactions of these compounds with ethylenediamine to form $Co(en)_3^{3+}$. The kinetic studies are supported by special, rotatory dispersion and synthetic investigations.

Optical Activity of Co^{III} $EDTA^-$ and Co^{III} $PDTA^-$

Concurrent with the demonstration that EDTA coordinates in both hexadentate and pentadentate fashions with cobalt(III), the complexes of $CoEDTA^-$ and $Co(EDTA)Br^{2-}$ were partially resolved into optical isomers.[1] Useful procedures for the complete resolution of the series of ions $CoEDTA^-$, $Co(EDTA)Br^{2-}$, $Co(EDTA)Cl^{2-}$, $Co(EDTA)NO_2^{2-}$, and $CoPDTA^-$ were reported by Dwyer and Garvan.[2,3,4] It has been shown that the bromo and chloro complexes convert into the hexadentate complex with complete retention of configuration.[4] The asymmetry of the second ligand, PDTA, leads to the prediction that four isomers should form; i.e., Dl, Dd, Ld, Ll. Resolution of the isomers

*The financial support of the National Science Foundation is gratefully acknowledged.

of the complex with cobalt(III), which had been prepared from racemic ligand, revealed only two enantiomers. The subsequent isolation of the ligand from the resolved complex showed it to be optically pure, suggesting an extreme stereospecificity.

Bosnick, Dwyer, and Sargeson[5] have also shown that ions which are relatively labile are rendered asymmetric upon coordination with optically active PDTA. They utilized this result to estimate the rate of ligand exchange in these systems. From these observations, it must be concluded that a substantial energy difference exists between the diastereoisomers of octahedrally coordinated PDTA. As will be shown below, this difference in energy relates to the axial vs. the equatorial orientation of the methyl group in the NCCN chelate ring. Detailed consideration of the effects of this methyl group follow from a comparison of the kinetics of a number of reactions of the cobalt(III) complexes of PDTA and EDTA.

The Formation of the Hexadentate Complex from the Acidopentadentate Complexes

The study of the rates of the reactions given in equations (1), (2), and (3) has led to the conclusion[6,7,8] that the mechanisms of these processes are most simply described as S_N1 in their rate determining steps. The observation that metal ions with high affinities for halogens (Hg^{2+}, Ag^+, Pb^{2+}) greatly accelerate the removal of Br^- and Cl^- is in accord with the view that the breaking of the Co^{III}-X bond is rate determining.

$$Co(EDTA)OH^{2-} \rightleftharpoons CoEDTA^- + OH^- \qquad (1)$$

$$Co(EDTA)Br^{2-} \rightleftharpoons CoEDTA^- + Br^- \qquad (2)$$

$$Co(EDTA)Cl^{2-} \rightleftharpoons CoEDTA^- + Cl^- \qquad (3)$$

The corresponding pentadentate complexes of PDTA have recently been prepared in this laboratory and preliminary rate data indicate that the rate of the elimination reactions are only slightly greater than those for the EDTA complexes. This observation is in keeping with the postulated mechanisms, since the relative stabilities of the ground state and a transition state of coordination number five should not be substantially altered by the structural difference in the two ligands.

The Electron Transfer Racemization of the Hexadentate Complexes

The hexadentate complexes of EDTA and PDTA with cobalt(III) should contain metal ions of essentially identical electronic arrangements and energies. This is confirmed by the near identity of their visible absorption spectra, and also by the closely similar rotatory dispersion curves we have obtained with the optically active ions. With the possible exception of slightly different solvation energies for the ions, it is difficult to see how any sizeable variations could occur between the two systems in properties and reactions which are essentially derived from the electrons of the central atom. It follows that similar electron transfer rates between the cobalt(II) and cobalt(III) complexes of PDTA and EDTA are expected.

The results of Dwyer and his co-workers,[5] however, do suggest one significant difference. In the reaction given by equation (4), the cobalt(II) complex is regarded as labile and as always present as a racemic mixture. Consequently, the reaction (4)

$$d\text{-Co}^{III}\text{EDTA}^- + \text{Co}^{II}\text{EDTA}^{2-} \rightleftharpoons l\text{-Co}^{III}\text{EDTA}^- + \text{Co}^{II}\text{EDTA} \qquad (4)$$

$$D\text{-Co}^{III} (l\text{-PDTA})^- + L\text{-Co}^{II} (d\text{-PDTA})^{2-} \rightleftharpoons$$
$$L\text{-Co}^{III} (d\text{-PDTA})^- + D\text{-Co}^{II} (l\text{-PDTA})^{2-} \qquad (5)$$

proceeds with loss of enantiomeric configuration and ultimate production of racemates. The appropriate rate equation for the electron transfer catalyzed racemization is given in equation (6).

$$-\ln (\alpha/\alpha_0) = kbt \qquad (6)$$

(α is rotation; α_0 is initial rotation; b is concentration of the cobalt(II) complex.) In contrast, the observations of Bosnick, Sargeson, and Dwyer require that one assume that the configuration of the ligand PDTA determines the configuration of the octahedral complex so that the reaction of equation (5) proceeds with complete retention of configuration. It is merely the distribution of configurations between the two oxidation states which changes with time. The rate is given by equation (7).

$$-\ln\left(\frac{\alpha - \alpha_{00}}{\alpha_0 - \alpha_{00}}\right) = k(a + b)t \qquad (7)$$

(In addition to quantities previously defined, α_{00} is rotation at equilibrium and a is the concentration of the cobalt(III) complex.) All the required parametric dependences have been confirmed and the rate laws are established. Further, two important general results have emerged. First, the two processes yield pseudo first-order rate constants k which show the same pH dependence, in accord with the scheme in equations (8), (9), and (10). Also the quantities k_1, k_2, and K are closely similar (100°).

$$Co^{III}Y^- + *Co^{II}HY^- \xrightarrow{k_1} Co^{II}HY^- + *Co^{III}Y^- \qquad (8)$$

$$Co^{II}HY^- \underset{}{\overset{K}{\rightleftharpoons}} Co^{II}Y^{2-} + H^+ \qquad (9)$$

$$Co^{III}Y^- + *Co^{II}Y^{2-} \xrightarrow{k_2} Co^{II}Y^{2-} + *Co^{III}Y^- \qquad (10)$$

Ligand	$k_1\ (M^{-1}hr^{-1})$	$k_2\ (M^{-1}hr^{-1})$	K
PDTA	2.5	0.71	2.4×10^{-3}
EDTA	2.9	0.50	2.0×10^{-3}

The corresponding enthalpies and entropies of activation are very similar. These results completely justify the expectation that the electronic processes should be quite similar.

A second major consequence of these studies is the demonstration of the extreme stereospecificity of the ligand PDTA. The synthetic experiments of Dwyer and Garvan do not obviate the possibility that small amounts of the less abundant diastereoisomer might exist (e.g., $(D-Co^{III}\ (d-PDTA)^-)$. Further, the observation that PDTA confers asymmetry on the labile cobalt(II) ion (and others) does not indicate the relative abundance of the preferred isomer since the system need only have an excess of that isomer and be at instantaneous "configurational" equilibrium to give the observed results. From our studies, it can be unequivocally stated that the less likely isomer of the cobalt(III) complex does not constitute a substantial fraction of a per cent of the equilibrium mixture of this complex. This conclusion is based on the fact that solutions containing $D-Co^{III}\ (l-PDTA)^-$ and $Co^{II}\ (l-PDTA)^{2-}$ do *not* undergo measurable mutarotation even over periods of time adequate to the establishment of an isomeric equilibrium by the electron transfer path.

As will be shown below, the stable diastereoisomer, Dl, contains an equatorial methyl group. Further, it is suggested that the repulsions giving rise to the relatively great stability of the equatorial methyl (over the axial in Ll) will increase as the several *arms* of the chelating ligand are folded back by increasing the size of the metal ion. On this basis, it is inferred that the configurationally labile cobalt(II) ion (and others) exists in essentially isomeric purity, as Ld and Dl forms.

Base Hydrolysis Reaction

A striking difference in the behavior of the EDTA and PDTA complexes is noted even in the crude rate data on the initial base hydrolysis process. As shown below, the rate of base hydrolysis of

CoEDTA$^-$ is proportional to the concentration of hydroxide ion while the corresponding reaction of CoPDTA$^-$ appears to be independent of hydroxide concentration. An appealing explanation of the behavior of the latter complex is found in the postulation of an $S_N 1$ mechanism, proceeding through a 5-coordinate intermediate (equation 11), followed by rapid acquisition of the OH$^-$ group (equation 12).

RELATIVE RATES OF BASE HYDROLYSIS (35 °C)

Co^{III}EDTA$^-$		Co^{III}PDTA$^-$	
k_{obs} (min^{-1})	(OH$^-$)	k_{obs} (min^{-1})	(OH$^-$)
3.5×10^{-2}	3.12×10^{-3}	4.1×10^{-3}	1.00×10^{-3}
1.2×10^{-2}	5.89×10^{-4}	3.8×10^{-3}	1.00×10^{-4}
7.3×10^{-3}	2.14×10^{-4}	3.6×10^{-3}	1.11×10^{-5}

$$\text{CoPDTA}^- \underset{k_{-1}}{\overset{k_1}{\rightleftharpoons}} [\text{CoPDTA}^-, \text{C.N.} = 5] \qquad (11)$$

$$[\text{CoPDTA}^-, \text{C.N.} = 5] + \text{OH}^- \xrightarrow{k_2} \text{Co(PDTA)OH}^{2-} \qquad (12)$$

If one assumes that steady state conditions apply to the five-coordinate intermediate, the pseudo first-order rate constants would have the form shown in equation (13).

$$k_{obs} = k_1 (k_2/k_{-1})(\text{OH}^-)/[1 + (k_2/k_{-1})(\text{OH}^-)] \qquad (13)$$

The data presented require that k_2/k_{-1} be at least of the order of 10^6 in order to produce the observed independence of the concentration of OH$^-$. Formulation of the reaction as an $S_N 1$ process is in agreement with current opinions on the base hydrolysis of many other cobalt(III) complexes.[9]

As indicated, the base hydrolysis of CoEDTA$^-$ is characterized by proportionality of the rate to the concentration of hydroxide. The rate constants also contain a base independent term attributable to the reverse reaction (equation 1). On the basis of other cobalt(III) systems, a scheme such as that just discussed merits consideration in this case. In order for the reaction to proceed through a five-coordinate intermediate and retain (OH$^-$) dependence, the ratio k_2/k_{-1} (equation 13) must be less than about 10^2. Since it would seem reasonable to assume that k_2 would be very similar for both CoEDTA$^-$ and CoPDTA$^-$, this suggests that the rate of conversion of the five-coordinate intermediate back into the hexadentate complex (k_{-1}) would be of the order of 10^4 times greater for CoEDTA$^-$ than for CoPDTA$^-$. There is no compelling reason to assume so great a difference in such processes. Such a conclusion would not be in agreement with the observation (see above) that the processes corresponding to equation (2) occur at similar rates for the EDTA and PDTA complexes.

A second feature of the kinetics of base hydrolysis of CoEDTA$^-$ militates against an S_N1 mechanism. It has been shown in the course of these investigations that hydroxide ion catalyzes the racemization of optically active CoEDTA$^-$ at a rate substantially in excess of the rate of appearance of the first hydrolysis product, Co(EDTA)OH^{2-}. In order for a mechanism of this kind to account for this behavior, the intermediate must be effectively symmetrical. Detailed study of the models reveals that symmetrical pentadentate intermediates are extremely unlikely; in fact, S_N1 processes should produce racemization only if the intermediate is bound to the central atom in only four positions. Further, the reactions given in equations (2) and (3) appear to undergo reaction by S_N1 mechanisms and these clearly proceed with *complete retention of enantiomorphic configuration*.

On this basis, an alternative mechanism is proposed in which bond forming is dominant in the transition state. This scheme (S_N2) is shown in equations (14) and (15), and the rate law derived from steady state considerations (in re the seven-coordinate symmetrical intermediate) is given in equation (16).

$$\text{CoEDTA}^- + \text{OH}^- \underset{k_{-3}}{\overset{k_3}{\rightleftharpoons}} [\text{Co(EDTA)OH}^{2-}, \text{ C.N.} = 7] \qquad (14)$$

$$[\text{Co(EDTA)OH}^{2-}, \text{ C.N.} = 7] \underset{k_{-4}}{\overset{k_4}{\rightleftharpoons}} \text{Co(EDTA)OH}^{2-} \qquad (15)$$

$$-d(\text{CoEDTA}^-)/dt = [k_3(k_4/k_{-3})(\text{OH}^-)(\text{CoEDTA}^-) - $$

$$k_{-4}(\text{Co(EDTA)OH}^{2-})]/(1 + k_4/k_{-3}) \quad (16)$$

The constant k_{-4} and the second term in the rate law arise from the dissociation of OH$^-$ from the product. This reaction has been studied by Shimi and Higginson.[6] The overall rate will always be OH$^-$ dependent unless the forward rate becomes vanishingly small. All the features of the base hydrolysis of CoEDTA$^-$ can be explained in terms of this mechanism. At 35 °C., $k_3 = 32.5$ M^{-1} min^{-1}, $k_4/k_{-3} = 0.435$, and $k_{-4} = 6.1 \times 10^{-3}$ min^{-1}. The equilibrium constant corresponding to equation (1) is given below (equation 17). It has the value $5.9(\pm 2.4) \times 10^{-4}$.

$$K = \frac{k_{-3}k_{-4}}{k_3k_4} \qquad (17)$$

Turning to CoPDTA$^-$, no such detailed analysis is possible with the data available to date. The apparent independence of the OH$^-$ concentration has been discussed. It is surprising that such a pronounced difference in behavior is brought about simply by placing a methyl group on the exterior of the complex ion. As will be recalled, the electron transfer process revealed a similar effect insofar as geometry is concerned but leads to almost identical behavior in aspects related to the electronic configuration of the central atom or to solvent interactions. The result of interest at the moment suggests that the presence of the methyl group militates against expansion of the coordination number so that the mechanism becomes predominantly S_N1 in character in CoPDTA$^-$ (equations 11 and 12). A critical test for this mechanism suggests itself, but has not been performed. The rate should, of course, display a pH dependence at low concentrations of OH$^-$. The success of such an experiment depends on the reverse reaction (Co(PDTA)OH^{2-} $\longrightarrow$ CoPDTA$^-$ + OH$^-$) being sufficiently slow.

Racemization of CoEDTA$^-$—The Symmetrical Intermediate

The complex ion CoEDTA$^-$ undergoes a very slow pH independent racemization, as well as the more rapid base catalyzed process. Rate constants for the processes of interest at 35° are: Thermal racemization (extrapolated) $k_r = 8.5 \times 10^{-8}$ hr^{-1}; base catalyzed racemization, $k_3 = 32.5$ M^{-1} min^{-1}; base hydrolysis, $k_h = 9.1$ M^{-1} min^{-1}. Failure of the PDTA complex of cobalt(III) to mutarotate under conditions assuring its lability indicates this to be a consequence of the relative stabilities of the possible diastereoisomers. Consequently, this result is apparently uninteresting from the standpoint of mechanism. It is of interest, however, to consider the thermal racemization of CoEDTA$^-$ in more detail. In the absence of base catalysis, this reaction proceeds very slowly, being measurable only at temperature above 75 °C. ($\Delta H^{\neq} = 40.6$ Kcal/mole; $\Delta S^{\neq} = 20.6$ cal/deg mole). The pH independence of the rate in acid solution suggests that the formation of five-coordinate intermediates is not necessary for racemization since such intermediates would be stabilized by increasing the hydrogen ion concentration. The activation energy is unusually large and suggests a process of some novelty. It is believed that this is most likely an intramolecular rearrangement (Fig. 1a) of the sort proposed by Bailar for the racemization of this compound.[10] With this idea in mind, it is easy to see why base might catalyze racemization, for the detailed structure of CoEDTA , as determined by Weakleim and Hoard,[11] nicely accommodates an incoming group on the side (actually two faces) delineated by all four carboxyl groups. The OH$^-$ group should

(a) Thermal Racemization of d—CoEDTA⁻.

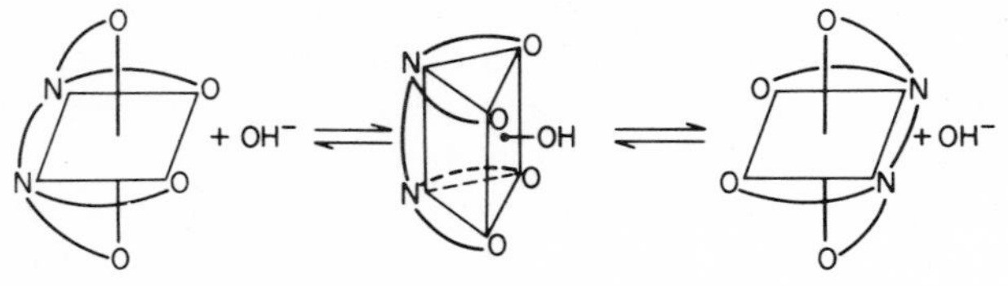

(b) Base Catalyzed Racemization of d—CoEDTA⁻.

Fig. 1

repel the carboxyl functions and promote transformation of the structure into the trigonal antiprism with the OH⁻ projecting into the rectangular face defined by the four oxygen atoms of the coordinated carboxyl groups (Fig. 1b).

As mentioned earlier, thermodynamic relationships result in such processes not being detectable in the case of D-Co(l-PDTA) since this material does not mutarotate. However, the presence of the methyl group as a substituent on the NCCN chelate ring provides an interesting situation. This relatively bulky group (as compared to hydrogen) should lead to destabilization of the type of seven-coordinate intermediate proposed here because the rotation leading to this configuration would bring the substituents on the carbon atoms into closer proximity. As mentioned before, the failure of the base hydrolysis rate of CoPDTA⁻ to exhibit a dependence on the concentration of OH⁻ supports this view. It appears, at this point, that the methyl group affects both the thermodynamics and mechanisms of substitution reactions of these compounds.

Reactions with Ethylenediamine

The most dramatic reaction observed in the chemistry of the cobalt(III) complexes of EDTA is that with ethylenediamine (equation 18).[4,12,13] Remarkably, this reaction proceeds with some retention of configuration when optically active starting material is used. In

$$CoEDTA^- + 3 \text{ en} \longrightarrow Co(en)_3^{3+} + EDTA^{4-} \tag{18}$$

50% aqueous ethylenediamine, (−)-KCoEDTA $\cdot$ 2H$_2$O produces 56.6% L-(−)-Co(en)$_3^{3+}$, the remainder being the D-(+) isomer, while the same reaction in anhydrous ethylenediamine produces 63% of the *levo* isomer of the product. Similarly, the pentadentate complexes, $Co(EDTA)Br^{2-}$ and $Co(EDTA)Cl^{2-}$, lead to about 55% of the more abundant isomer of the product. We recently ran the corresponding experiment with $(-)-Co(d-PDTA)^-$ (50% en at 25 °C.) and in the first experiment observed *complete* retention of generic configuration. The absorption spectrum of the product corresponded closely to that of an authentic sample of $K[Co(en)_3]EDTA$ and the rotatory dispersion curve was recorded and found to be similarly indicative of the identity of the product. Numerous attempts to reproduce this experiment have led to essentially random results. This is understandable. The remarkable thing is the single successful experiment. We commonly observe that extensive base hydrolysis of the PDTA and EDTA complexes of cobalt(III) produces some cobalt(II) and active $Co(en)_3^{3+}$ is catalytically racemized by electron transfer with the cobalt(II) complex. The rate of the latter process is very sensitive to surface effects and to traces of O_2.

As pointed out by Kirschner, Wei, and Bailar,[13] a highly stereospecific reaction as complicated as that given in equation (18) must occur in a series of stepwise displacements. Attempts have been made to clarify the stereochemistry and mechanisms of their reactions through kinetic measurements. In the case of $CoEDTA^-$, the competing parallel base hydrolysis reaction could be made vanishingly small by studying the process of interest at low pH in ethylenediamine-ethylenediammonium ion buffers. As anticipated, the rate behavior is extremely complex, consisting of at least two consecutive contributions, each of which clearly contains no fewer than three parallel reactions. As pointed out in preceding paragraphs, even the most elementary process (e.g., equation 1) is very complex. Because of the inherent complications of the system, attention has been confined to the initial reaction rate. Because of the limited overlap of the major consecutive processes, the initial rate was readily estimated. It was found possible to partition these rates between three parallel steps; those indicated by equation (1) and equations (19) and (20).

$$CoEDTA^- + en \longrightarrow Co(EDTA)en^- \qquad (19)$$

$$CoEDTA^- + enH^+ \longrightarrow Co(EDTA)en^- + H^+ \qquad (20)$$

As Fig. 2 shows, assuming that no rearrangements occur and that only terminal groups are replaced, permits one to predict an isomer distribution in the product $Co(en)_3^{3+}$ of 67% of the more abundant form. Further, the relationship between the configuration of the starting ma-

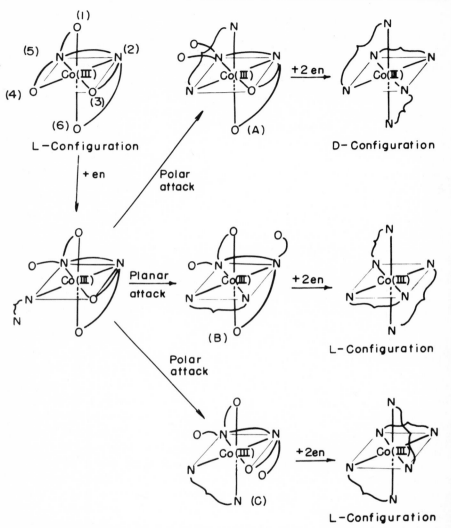

Fig. 2. Mechanism for attack of ethylenediamine on ethylenediaminetetraacetato-
cobaltate.

terial and that of the product is obvious, and the inverse relationship
could be attained only by schemes which would involve complex and
difficultly justified assumptions. Since it has already been shown that
the reaction with base leads to racemization, the yield of the excess
optical isomer will be reduced by a primary reaction with OH^-, even
if subsequent steps ultimately produce $Co(en)_3^{3+}$. One may therefore

partition the rate under the conditions utilized in the synthetic experiments of Dwyer and predict the yield of excess optical isomer. The rate equation (21)

$$-d[\ln (CoEDTA^-)]/dt = 1.38 \times 10^{-1} \text{ (en)} + 4.9 \times 10^{-3} \text{ (enH}^+) +$$
$$2.67(OH^-) \quad (21)$$

becomes

$$= 1.09 + 0.001 + 0.68 \quad (22)$$

This shows a considerable competing base hydrolysis reaction. It is calculated from these data that the excess isomer should be present to the extent of 57.6% at equilibrium. This compares much better than should be expected with the experimental value of 56.5%. It should be emphasized that the mechanism applied to this reaction attributes the stereospecificity to a favorable statistical distribution of alternate, nearly equivalent, substitution paths, rather than to steric effects of the more obvious kind.

In view of the apparent success of the concepts developed here, it appears justifiable to propose that the absolute configuration of (–)-CoEDTA$^-$ has been deduced by relating it to that of Co(en)$_3^{3+}$, for the latter has been determined by definitive experiments.[14] These configurations are given in Fig. 3. Further, since the pentadentate complexes Co(EDTA)X^{2-} form CoEDTA$^-$ without loss of optical activity, their configurations are also deduced. The configurational relationships are given below.

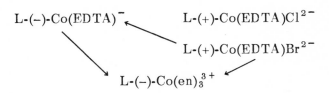

Very interesting configurational relationships relevant to the complexes of PDTA follow almost immediately. We find the absorption spectra and optical rotatory dispersion curves nearly identical for L-(–)-CoEDTA$^-$ and for (–)-Co(d-PDTA)$^-$, so it must follow that the PDTA and EDTA complexes of the same rotation have the same configuration. Further, Schnell and Karrer[15] have determined the absolute configuration of active-propylenediamine, the starting material for the preparation of PDTA, so that the absolute geometry of the optically active carbon atom is known.

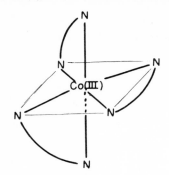

$\underline{d}$-Co(en)$_3$Cl$_3$, [α]$_{5461}$ = +440°

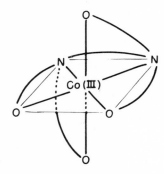

$\underline{d}$-Co(Y)$^-$, [α]$_{5461}$ = +1000°

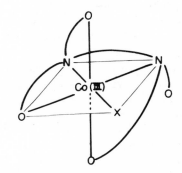

$\underline{d}$-Co(HY)X, [α]$_{5461}$ = +800° or
$\underline{d}$-Co(Y)X, [α]$_{5461}$ = +700°
where X = Br$^-$, Cl$^-$ or NO$_2^-$

Fig. 3

$$CH_2N(CH_2COOH)_2$$
$$(HOOCCH_2)_2N \triangleright \underset{|}{\overset{|}{C}} \triangleleft H$$
$$CH_3$$

L-(+)-PDTA · H$_2$O([α]$_D$ = + 47°)

It is deduced that the CH$_3$ group is equatorially oriented, in agreement with the predictions of Corey and Bailar.[16] The structure is shown in Fig. 4.

The significance of the equatorial orientation of the methyl group is apparent when one realizes that the entire stereospecificity resides in the differences in energy of the axial and equatorial locations.

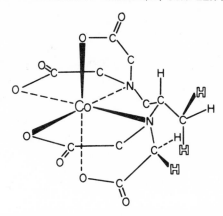

Fig. 4. Configuration of L–[Co(d–PDTA)]⁻

Clearly, the effect is steric in origin, a relationship not so plainly demonstrated in other examples of stereospecificity among complexes.

The reaction of CoPDTA⁻ with en has been investigated. In this case, measurements are more conveniently made at high pH since the competing base reaction is independent of OH⁻. The reaction appears to be surprisingly simple, giving product directly, without the mediation of detectable concentrations of intermediates. However, small corrections have to be made for the base hydrolysis reaction. The corrected pseudo first-order constants, measured under buffered and swamped conditions, obey the function given in equation (23).

$$k_{obs} = Q_1(en)(OH^-)/[1 + Q_2(OH^-)] \tag{23}$$

This rate law is readily derived for the chemical processes described in equations (24), (25), and (26), if the somewhat bizarre assumption is made that the Co(PDTA)en⁻ concentration remains small and constant (steady state).

$$\text{CoPDTA}^- + \text{en} \underset{k_{-5}}{\overset{k_5}{\rightleftharpoons}} \text{Co(PDTA)en}^- \tag{24}$$

$$\text{Co(PDTA)en}^- + \text{OH}^- \xrightarrow{-k_6} \text{C} \tag{25}$$

$$\text{C} + 2\ \text{en} \xrightarrow{\text{fast}} \text{Co(en)}_3^{3+} + \text{PDTA}^{4-} \tag{26}$$

One can understand this assumption if it is presumed that this substance (formed in equation 24) is a pentadentate PDTA complex in which only one end of the newly arrived en molecule is attached to the cobalt. The second forward step (equation 25) may then be assigned to closing of the chelate ring by an $S_N$lcb mechanism. This is shown in Fig. 5. In forming the five-coordinate intermediate the more highly strained bond at position three could break, giving complete retention of configuration (as shown above). Over the hundred-fold concentration range from pH 9.5 to 11.5, at 35 °C, the following values apply.

$$Q_1 = k_5(k_6/k_{-5}) = 2.22 \times 10^3 \tag{27}$$

$$Q_2 = k_6/k_{-5} = 1.64 \times 10^3 \tag{28}$$

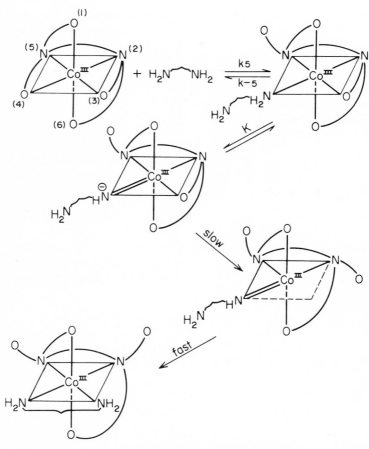

Fig. 5. Mechanism for reaction of ethylenediamine with propylenediaminetetra-acetatocobaltate.

Conclusions

1. In processes dependent on the electronic structure of the central atom and those involving substitution at the central atom by mechanisms involving bond breaking in the rate determining step, the behaviors of the complexes of PDTA and EDTA are very similar.

2. In substitution processes dependent on expansion of the coordination number in the transition state and in intramolecular rearrangements, the methyl group in PDTA sharply alters the mechanism.

3. Evidence is presented for an S_N2 mechanism in a substitution reaction of cobalt(III) (base hydrolysis of CoEDTA$^-$), while in other reactions, dissociation processes appear to occur.

4. The stereospecificity of PDTA is shown to be extreme. The more abundant isomer of Co(d-PDTA)-constitutes over 99% of an isomeric mixture at equilibrium.

5. The absolute configurations of the cobalt(III) complexes of EDTA and PDTA are strongly inferred.

6. The equatorial orientation of the methyl group in the NCCN chelate ring in CoPDTA$^-$ is inferred.

7. The stereospecificity of the reaction of ethylenediamine with optically active CoEDTA$^-$ is statistically derived, while that with CoPDTA$^-$ appears to involve more selective factors.

REFERENCES

1. D. H. Busch and J. C. Bailar, Jr., *J. Am. Chem. Soc.*, **75**, 4574 (1953); M. L. Morris and D. H. Busch, *J. Am. Chem. Soc.*, **78**, 5178 (1956).
2. F. P. Dwyer and F. L. Garvan, *Inorganic Syntheses*, **VI**, 192 (1960).
3. F. P. Dwyer and F. L. Garvan, *J. Am. Chem. Soc.*, **81**, 2955 (1959).
4. F. P. Dwyer and F. L. Garvan, *J. Am. Chem. Soc.*, **80**, 4480 (1958).
5. B. Bosnick, F. P. Dwyer, and A. M. Sargeson, *Nature*, **186**, 966 (1960).
6. I. A. Shimi and W. C. E. Higginson, *J. Chem. Soc.*, **1958**, 260.
7. M. L. Morris and D. H. Busch, *J. Phys. Chem.*, **63**, 340 (1959).
8. R. Dyke and W. C. E. Higginson, *J. Chem. Soc.*, **1960**, 1998.
9. F. Basolo and R. G. Pearson, *Mechanisms of Inorganic Reactions*, John Wiley and Sons, New York, 1958.
10. J. C. Bailar, Jr., *J. Inorg. Nucl. Chem.*, **8**, 172 (1958).
11. H. A. Weakleim and J. L. Hoard, *J. Am. Chem. Soc.*, **81**, 550 (1959).
12. F. P. Dwyer, E. C. Gyarfas, and D. P. Mellor, *J. Phys. Chem.*, **59**, 296 (1955).
13. S. Kirschner, Y. K. Wei, and J. C. Bailar, Jr., *J. Am. Chem. Soc.*, **79**, 5877 (1957).
14. Y. Saito, K. Nakatsu, M. Shiro, and H. Kuroya, *Bull. Chem. Soc., Japan*, **30**, 795 (1957); *Acta Cryst.*, **8**, 729 (1955).
15. S. Schnell and P. Karrer, *Helv. Chim. Acta*, **38**, 2036 (1955).
16. E. J. Corey and J. C. Bailar, Jr., *J. Am. Chem. Soc.*, **81**, 2620 (1959).

THE EFFECTS OF OPTICALLY INACTIVE IONS ON THE ROTATORY DISPERSION OF ASYMMETRIC COMPLEX IONS

MARVIN J. ALBINAK, DINESH C. BHATNAGAR, STANLEY KIRSCHNER, and ANTHONY J. SONNESSA*

Department of Chemistry
Wayne State University
Detroit, Michigan

It has been known since the time of Biot[1] that the rotation of the plane of polarized light by an optically active compound is a function of the wavelength of the incident light. This relationship between optical rotation and wavelength is known as rotatory dispersion and has been studied by several workers. Drude[2] has given an empirical equation which is sometimes useful in describing the optical rotatory dispersion of substances in wavelength regions outside the vicinity of optically active absorption bands. Reviews of optical rotatory dispersion have been published by Levene and Rothen,[3] Lowry,[4] Heller,[5] Klyne and Parker,[6] Moscowitz,[7] and others.[8] Cotton[9] has decribed the so-called "anomalous rotatory dispersion" of asymmetric compounds in the vicinity of their optically active absorption bands, and several workers [10,5,6,7,8,11] have studied this effect in an effort to correlate it with various structural aspects of the compounds studied.

The rotatory dispersion of asymmetric complex inorganic compounds has been studied by several investigators, including Shimura,[12] Izumiya,[13] Jaeger,[11] O'Brien and co-workers,[14] Jonassen and Bailar,[15] Martinette and Bailar,[16] Pfeiffer,[17] Mellor,[18] and others.

Kirschner and co-workers,[19,20] Albinak,[21] and Sonnessa[22] have noticed that the optical rotation and rotatory dispersion of an asymmetric complex ion change when the optically inactive ion associated

*Present address of Marvin J. Albinak: Department of Chemistry, University of Detroit, Detroit, Michigan. Present address of Anthony J. Sonnessa: Department of Chemistry, Seton Hall University, South Orange, New Jersey. The authors wish to express their sincere appreciation to the National Science Foundation for a grant without which this work could not have been carried out, to the American Cancer Society for an emergency grant which permitted the purchase of an important part of the instrument for which funds were unavailable, to Professor Wilfried Heller of Wayne State University for his helpful suggestions and comments on theory and design, and to Mr. Lee Peterson of Wayne State University for his help in the design and construction of the prism brackets and other metal parts of the instrument.

with it is changed. A further study of this effect resulted in the initiation of an investigation to determine the effects of optically inactive ions on the rotatory dispersion of asymmetric complex ions. In order to facilitate the study of rotatory dispersion of complexes, a spectrophotometric photoelectric polarimeter was constructed, the design of which is given below.

In this investigation, it was decided first to prepare and resolve several asymmetric complex cations, each with various optically inactive anions and then to do the same for several asymmetric complex anions, each with various optically inactive cations. The rotatory dispersions of all these series of complexes were measured and they were studied with a view toward determining which characteristics of the optically inactive ions contributed most to the rotatory dispersion changes and which were less important. The first series of asymmetric ions studied contained no asymmetric ligands and their asymmetry was due solely to the configuration of the optically inactive ligands about the central metal ion. Subsequent series of complexes contained asymmetric ligands, but these ions did not have the asymmetric configuration about the metal ion which is found in ions such as tris(ethylenediamine)cobalt(III), $[Co(en)_3]^{+3}$. Additional studies are underway to determine the effects of solvent polarity on rotatory dispersion changes as well as the effects of "loading" a solution containing an asymmetric complex ion with an optically inactive ion of opposite charge on the rotatory dispersion. Further studies are also underway to examine the effects of optically inactive ions on the rotatory dispersion of asymmetric inner complexes, and of the effects of absolute configuration changes on rotatory dispersion.

Experimental: A High-Precision Spectrophotometric Photoelectric Polarimeter for the Determination of Optical Rotation and Optical Rotatory Dispersion

Although photographic spectropolarimetery has certain unique advantages[5] with respect to long exposure possibilities in cases of low intensity, a relatively wide spectral range, high sensitivity, and relative ease of measuring extremely large rotations (e.g., 360°), the procedures involved are usually quite inconvenient and time-consuming. Consequently, most of the commercially available spectropolarimeters as well as those constructed by individual research investigators utilize photoelectric cells as light receptors. Some of the commercially available instruments include those manufactured by the Photovolt Corporation[23] based on an instrument described by Crumpler, Dyre, and Spell,[24] by Carl Zeiss, Inc.,[25,26] Bellingham and Stanley,[27] O. C. Rudolph and Sons, Inc.,[28,29,30,31] Perkin-Elmer

Corp.,[32,33] and others. Several interesting and unique photoelectric polarimeters, spectrophotometric polarimeters, and recording spectropolarimeters have been constructed in research laboratories throughout the world. Among these are those of Gillham,[34] Malcolm and Elliott,[35] Burer, Kohler, and Gunthard,[36] Gates,[37] Bruhat and coworkers,[38] von Halban,[39] Landt and Hirschmuller,[40] Levy,[41] Brode,[42] Gutowski,[43] Woldbye,[44] and others.[45] The foregoing instruments, however, may have one or more of the following shortcomings for many scientists engaged in research in optical rotatory dispersion today: (1) a limited wavelength range not extending into the ultraviolet region, (2) a precision no better than 0.01°, (3) a high degree of elaborateness and complexity, often making it impractical for many investigators to reconstruct such an instrument without the aid of professional technicians, (4) the need for time-consuming manipulations to operate the instrument, and (5) relatively high cost.

An interesting commercially available attachment for the Beckman DU spectrophotometer has been developed by the Standard Polarimeter Company,[46] according to a design by Keston.[47] This unit has been evaluated by Poulsen.[48] It utilizes light sources which are normally associated with the Beckman spectrophotometer, and Polaroid plates rather than polarizing prisms, which severely restrict the use of the instrument to solutions of relatively low optical density, to a limited range of wavelengths in the visible region, and sometimes to low precision.

This paper describes the construction and operation of a spectrophotometric polarimeter of high precision which can be assembled in most laboratories at relatively low cost. It has a wavelength region of 2500 Å. to 10,000 Å., a precision of 0.002° when measuring small observed angles of rotation ($< 1°$), completely variable angles between transmission planes of polarizer and analyzer prisms allowing for the measurement of observed angles of rotation greater than 1°, and requires only about thirty minutes to determine an "average" rotatory dispersion curve from 2500 Å. to 7000 Å.

Principles of Operation

The mathematical principles of operation governing this type of instrument are in the literature.[5,46,48,49] Its operation can be described qualitatively from Fig. 1 which indicates a pair of polarizing prisms placed between a source of "monochromatic" light (spectrophotometer) and a photomultiplier tube, with a polarimeter tube then being placed between these prisms. The polarizer prism is fixed and the analyzer prism may have either of two positions, A and B (e.g., located 2° on each side of total extinction). If an optically *inactive* colored or "colorless" solution is placed in the polarimeter tube with the analyzer prism in position A, and the spectrophotometer is adjusted to a given absorbance or transmittance reading (e.g., 100% transmittance), then a rotation of the analyzer prism to position B will result in no change in the transmittance because position B is at exactly the same angle from total extinction as is position A. However, if the sample is optically *active* (e.g., dextrorotatory), then less light will be transmitted through the analyzer prism upon its rotation to position B because the plane of polarized light entering the analyzer prism is no longer midway between positions A and B, but is displaced (rotated) toward A. This increase in optical density (absorbance) is directly proportional to the angle of rotation, for small angles, according to the equation:[5,46,48,49]

$$\alpha = K_1 (\Delta A) \tag{1}$$

where α is the optical rotation of the sample, K_1 is a constant, and ΔA is the absorbance difference between positions A and B. Thus, determination of the observed angle of rotation merely involves multiplication of the absorbance difference by the instrument constant (which is independent of wavelength for small angles of rotation). This procedure has the additional important advantage of automatically utilizing the actual optically active sample in its polarimeter tube as its own blank for each determination.

Construction of the Instrument

Spectrophotometer. A Beckman Model DU spectrophotometer with a line-operated (115 v. a-c) power supply, 1P-28 photomultiplier tube, and tungsten and hydrogen light sources (Beckman instruments, Inc.)[50] is used and the photocell compartment is separated from the body of the monochromator by the removal of the four large screws holding it. This separation of the phototube housing from the body of the monochromator requires that the exit lens of the monochromator be replaced by an optically inactive long-focus quartz exit beam lens.[51]

Polarizing prisms. Two polarizing prisms of the Glan-Thompson (Glazebrook) type made of calcite and cemented with butyl methacrylate to allow transmission down to 2400 Å. can be obtained already mounted and centered in divided circle plates (Gaertner Scientific Corp.[52]). The prisms used in this instrument are 10 mm square and 30 mm long. The divided circle plate assemblies are mounted separately on metal brackets which are made so that the prisms can be placed in the light path between the monochromator and the photomultiplier tube assembly, leaving room between them for a tube compartment (Fig. 1-2). Metal arms with stops are fashioned so that they

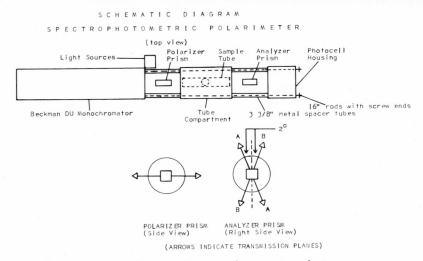

Fig. 1. Schematic diagram of spectrophotometric polarimeter.

can be fixed to the divided circle plates to allow the prisms to be rotated and stopped (e.g., at any given angle on either side of complete extinction).

Cell compartment. The cell compartment holds tubes up to 1 dm. in length and is commercially available.[53] The end-plates which are part of the standard 1 cm. cell compartment of the monochromator are also used as end-plates for the larger compartment.

Cell. The cell used is a commercially available 1 dm. center-fill polarimeter tube equipped with optically inactive fused quartz end-plates.[54, 28]

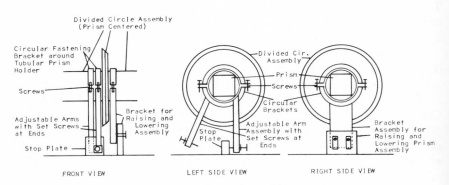

Fig. 2. Prism Assembly.

Light sources. The instrument can be used with the six-volt tungsten source provided with the DU spectrophotometer, but neither this source nor the hydrogen lamp supplied with the DU provides sufficient intensity to use the instrument below 3500 Å. Zirconium arc sources for the visible and near ultraviolet and xenon arc sources for the visible and ultraviolet regions of considerably greater intensity than the tungsten source are commercially available[55, 28] with their power supplies. The latter permits use of the instrument as a spectrophotometric polarimeter down to 2500 Å.

Construction. The components are assembled as shown in Fig. 1-3. The long focus exit beam lens should first be installed in the monochromator. Four long metal rods threaded at each end are used in place of the long screws supplied with the DU to hold the photocell and polarimeter tube compartments in place and in alignment. These components are kept apart with the aid of four cylindrical metal spacers. One polarizing prism assembly is placed between the monochromator and the tube compartment and the other between the tube compartment and the photocell housing. These assemblies are aligned (using the meter on the spectrophotometer to indicate maximum transmittance) and are clamped in place. The construction of the adjustable clamp to hold the divided circle and the adjustable arms and stop details are shown in Fig. 2. Set screws and locking nuts are located at the ends of the adjustable arms to allow for fine balancing of the two analyzer positions. After the prisms are aligned in a darkened room, the prism housing's exit and entrance tubes are wrapped and taped to the monochromator, tube compartment, and photocell housing in such a manner as to allow rotation of the prisms but to exclude external light.

Calibration and operation. After completion of alignment, the polarizer and analyzer prisms are rotated so that their transmission planes are perpendicular and parallel, respectively, to the monochromator exit slit. The arms and set screws should be set so that the analyzer prism can swing approximately 2° on either side of the vertical ("crossed" or minimum transmittance) position. Then, with a tube containing a solvent in place (the tube should be of the center-fill type and should always be placed in the same position in its compartment), the set screws are carefully adjusted so that the instrument will have exactly the same transmittance value in the two positions (e.g., 100% or 50% are most commonly used) at a given wavelength (e.g., Na_D) and slit opening. This "zero" position should be checked each time the instrument is turned on.[56]

The instrument is now ready for calibration (i.e., finding K_1 of equation (1), the slope of straight line plot of α vs. ΔA). Sucrose was chosen as a calibration standard because it is easily obtainable

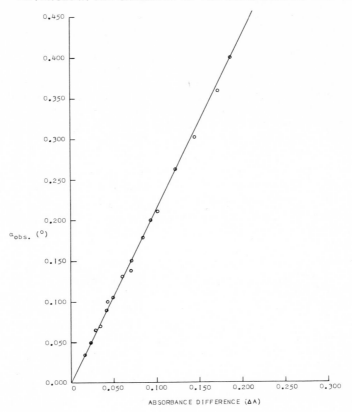

Fig. 3. Calibration curve (sucrose 25°C). $\alpha_{obs} = 2.15 \, (\Delta A)$.

in pure form, its solutions are optically stable in distilled water (exclude dust), and its rotatory dispersion formula is known.[57,58,4] Several sucrose solutions having observed rotations in a 1 dm. tube of between 0.010° and 0.500° (at the D line) on the basis of its rotatory dispersion formula are prepared. The transmittance dial is set at the chosen value (e.g., 50%, $A = 0.301$), the slit is set at the lowest value possible for use with the available light sources (usually 0.5 mm or less), and a particular wavelength is chosen. With the polarimeter tube containing the sample in place, the instrument is balanced by the sensitivity controls at the chosen absorbance value with the analyzer prism in position A (counterclockwise from extinction looking from the photocell). The analyzer prism is then turned to position B and the instrument is balanced with the absorbance control. If the absorbance is greater than the initial value (0.301), then the solution is *dextrorotatory*; if less, *levorotatory*. A plot of the A-B absorbance differences *vs.* the known optical rotation of the sucrose solutions will be a straight line for small angles of rotation ($< ca.$ 1°) and will be wavelength-independent because of the use of calcite prisms. The slope of the best straight line through the experimental points will give K_1 (Eq. 1) and may be determined graphically, or better, by the method of least squares (Fig. 3).

The determination of a rotatory dispersion curve of an unknown sample is carried out experimentally exactly as above. The optical rotation is calculated from K_1 (determined with sucrose) and the observed *A-B* absorbance difference at each wavelength. If solutions having relatively high optical densities or optical rotations greater than 1° are to be measured frequently, it is advisable to use an angle greater than 2° on either side of extinction for the sweep of the analyzer prism.[46,48]

Instrumental Results

The calibration curve with sucrose used to find K_1 is given in Fig. 4. Table 1 shows a comparison between the optical rotations of various solutions determined with a high precision visual polarimeter[59,28] equipped with a sodium lamp and filter for the *D* line, and

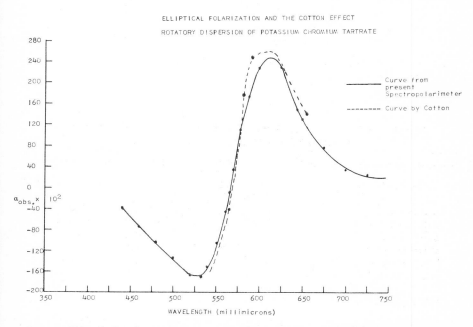

Fig. 4. Elliptical polarization and the cotton effect (rotatory dispersion of potassium chromium tartrate).

those determined with the instrument described herein at the same wavelength.

The average deviation of individual determinations of angles less than 1 ° is 0.002 ° with this instrument. Although theoretically a high degree of elliptical polarization in the region of a strong Cotton effect[9] would produce a shift in the rotatory dispersion,[5] the small angles of rotation measured and the small angle (2 ° on either side of extinction) used for the sweep of the analyzer prism minimize this effect. Actually, this effect was not observed in the optically active absorption band of potassium chromium tartrate, the very compound studied by Cotton[9] in his work on anomalous rotatory dispersion (Fig. 4).

Compounds studied. A list of the optically active complex ions studied, along with the optically inactive ions associated with them is given in Table 2.

TABLE 1: COMPARISON OF OPTICAL ROTATIONS OF SUGAR SOLUTIONS

Sample Number	Observed Rotation* (Visual Polarimeter)	Observed Rotation[†] (Spectrophotometric Polarimeter)
1	0.053 ° ± 0.003 °	0.050 ° ± 0.002 °
2	0.102 ± 0.003	0.100 ± 0.002
3	0.184 ± 0.003	0.180 ± 0.002
4	0.213 ± 0.003	0.213 ± 0.002
5	0.368 ± 0.003	0.369 ± 0.002

*Na_D line; Rudolph High Precision Visual Polarimeter, Model 80.
[†] Na_D line.

TABLE 2: OPTICALLY ACTIVE COMPLEX IONS STUDIED AND THEIR ASSOCIATED OPTICALLY INACTIVE IONS

Optically Active Complex Ion[60]	Associated Optically Inactive Ions
L-cis-$[Co(en)_2(NO_2)_2]^+$	F^-, Cl^-, Br^-, I^-, $SO_4^=$, PO_4^{-3}, ClO_4^-, ClO_3^-, NO_3^-, $(C_6H_5)_4B^-$
L-$[Co(en)_3]^{+3}$	F^- Cl^-, Br^-, I^-, $SO_4^=$, ClO_4^-, ClO_3^-, NO_3^-, PO_4^{-3}
L-$[Co(edta)]^-$	Li^+, Na^+, K^+, Rb^+, Cs^+, Mg^{++}, Ba^{++}, Al^{+3}
L-$[Cr(en)_3]^{+3}$	F^-, Cl^-, Br^-, I^-, BF_4^-, ClO_4^-, $SO_4^=$, PO_4^{-3}
D-$[Rh(ox)_3]^{-3}$	Li^+, Na^+, K^+, Rb^+, Cs^+, Mg^{++}, Ca^{++}, Ba^{++}
$[Co(NH_3)_4(d\text{-tart})]^+$	F^-, Cl^-, Br^-, I^-, BF_4^-, NO_3^-, ClO_4^-, $SO_4^=$, PO_4^{-3}
$[Pt(l\text{-alan})Cl_2]^-$	Li^+, Na^+, K^+, Rb^+, Cs^+, Mg^{++}, Ca^{++}, Ba^{++}, Al^{+3}
$[Pt(d\text{-glut})_2]^=$	Li^+, Na^+, K^+, Rb^+, Cs^+, Mg^{++}, Ca^{++}, Ba^{++}, Al^{+3}
$[Co(NH_3)_5(d\text{-tart})]^+$	F^-, Cl^-, Br^-, I^-, BF_4^-, NO_3^-, ClO_4^-, $SO_4^=$, PO_4^{-3}

Preparations. (1) *L-cis*-[Co(en)$_2$(NO$_2$)$_2$]Br was prepared and resolved according to the method of Dwyer, Gyarfas, and Mellor.[61]
(2) *L*-[Co(en)$_3$]Cl was prepared and resolved according to the method
of Werner.[62] (3) *L*-K[Co(edta)] was prepared and resolved according
to the method of Dwyer and Garvan.[63] (4) *L*-[Co(en)$_2$Cl$_2$]Cl was prepared and resolved according to the method of Bailar.[64] It was converted to *L*-[Co(en)$_2$(ox)]Cl according to the method of Werner.[65]
(5) *L*-[Cr(en)$_3$]I$_3$ was prepared and resolved by M. Albinak and co-
workers of the University of Detroit and presented as a gift to this
research group. (6) *D*-K$_3$[Rh(ox)$_3$] was prepared and resolved by F.
Dwyer.[66] (7) K[Pt(*l*-alan)Cl$_2$] was prepared according to the method
of Ley and Ficken.[67] (8) H$_2$[Pt(*d*-glut)$_2$] was prepared according to
the method of Grinberg.[68] (9) [Co(NH$_3$)$_5$(*d*-tart)]Cl was prepared according to the method of Duff.[69] (10) [Co(NH$_3$)$_4$CO$_3$]Cl was prepared
according to the method of Lamb.[70] It was converted to [Co(NH$_3$)$_4$(*d*-
tart)]Cl by treating 6.0 g. of the carbonato complex in 100 ml. of water
with 100 ml. of an aqueous solution containing 4.1 g. of *dextro*-tar-
taric acid. This solution was added dropwise with continuous stirring. After the bubbles of carbon dioxide ceased to be evolved, the
solution was evaporated almost to dryness by passing a stream of dry
air over it. The resulting dark-red, viscous semi-solid substance was
washed with 100 ml of ethanol and then ground in a mortar under
absolute ethanol (the compound is hygroscopic). It was then filtered,
washed with ether, and dried under vacuum. The yield of the dark red
powder was 5.7 g. (62%). Analysis: Calc. for [Co(NH$_3$)$_4$(*d*-tart)]Cl ·
H$_2$O: C: 14.60, H: 5.48, N: 17.02, Cl: 10.80; Found: C: 15.22, H:
5.71, N: 16.82, Cl: 11.33.

Rotatory dispersion curves. These were determined either on the
instrument described earlier or on a manual Rudolph High Precision
Photoelectric Spectropolarimeter.[30] The curves show wavelength *vs.*
"Equivalent Molecular Rotation," [α]$_E$, which is used to eliminate
nonreal differences in ion effects which may appear when molecular
rotations are used for compounds where the cation : anion ratio is
other than 1 : 1 (e.g., [Co(en)$_2$(NO$_2$)$_2$]Cl *vs.* [Co(en)$_2$(NO$_2$)$_2$]$_2$SO$_4$).
Equivalent Molecular Rotation is defined as:

$$[α]_E = [α]M/n$$

where M = molecular weight, n = number of optically active complex
ions per "molecule," and [α] = specific rotation.

Results and Discussion

A typical series of rotatory dispersion curves is shown in Fig. 5.
In general, the wavelengths of the peaks, troughs, and cross-over

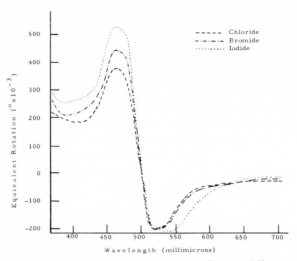

Fig. 5. Optical rotatory dispersion of $L\text{-}[Co(en)_3]^{+3}$ salts.

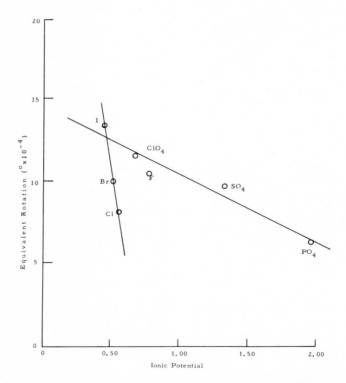

Fig. 6. Equivalent rotation vs. ionic potential for $L\text{-}[Cr(en)_3]^{+3}$ cation series.

TABLE 3: WAVELENGTHS AND MAGNITUDE OF SELECTED POINTS ON ROTATORY DISPERSION CURVES OF SALTS OF LEVO-CIS-DINITROBIS(ETHYLENEDIAMINE)COBALT(III) ION

Anion	Zero(I)* λ	First Minimum λ	First Minimum $[\alpha]_E \times 10^{-3}$	Zero(II)† λ	First Maximum λ	First Maximum $[\alpha]_E \times 10^{-3}$	Trough λ	Trough $[\alpha]_E \times 10^{-3}$	Absorption Maximum(λ)
F^-	595	490	-110	470	430	+380	375	200	440
Cl^-	600	490	-130	465	425	405	380	220	440
Br^-	...	485	-135	465	430	565	385	175	440
I^-	655	490	-140	467	425	510	390	240	440
$SO_4^=$	590	490	-135	473	435	465	395	210	440
ClO_4^-	...	490	-120	468	438	350	360	25	440
ClO_3^-	...	492	-145	463	425	360	392	90	440
NO_3^-	...	490	-160	468	428	435	387	215	440
$PO_4^{\equiv}$	685	492	-135	470	430	415	392	240	440
Ph_4B^- (I)	...	492	-150	467	430	485	380	75	440

*Zero(I): point of zero rotation above 550 millimicrons.
†Zero(II): point of zero rotation above 550 millimicrons.
All wavelengths are in millimicrons.
(I) Tetraphenylborate, $(C_6H_5)_4B^-$

TABLE 4: COMPARISON OF ROTATORY DISPERSION OF SALTS OF LEVO-TRIS(ETHYLENEDIAMINE)COBALT(III) ION

Anion	"Zero" λ	Negative Maximum λ	Negative Maximum $[\alpha]_E \times 10^{-3}$	"Zero" λ	Positive Maximum λ	Positive Maximum $[\alpha]_E \times 10^{-3}$	Trough λ	Trough $[\alpha]_E \times 10^{-3}$	Absorption Maximum λ
F^-	...	521	-250	497	463	480	380	214	420
Cl^-	...	523	-205	494	463	380	400	183	470
Br^-	645	515	-225	496	455	445	380	204	470
I^-	...	(515-530)	-250	497	455	535	380	256	470
$SO_4^=$	...	520	-220	494	470	448	390	200	470
ClO_4^-	...	515	-263	495	460	500	393	229	470
ClO_3^-	...	520	-250	497	463	490	380	223	470
NO_3^-	...	520	-220	495	460	450	395	220	470
$PO_4^{\equiv}$	...	518	-250	497	470	460	395	150	470

TABLE 5: COMPARISON OF ROTATORY DISPERSION OF SALTS OF LEVO-ETHYLENEDINITRILOTETRAACETATOCOBALTATE(III) ION

Cation	First Positive Maximum		Zero(I)	Negative Maximum		Zero(II)	Second Positive Maximum		Trough		Absorption Maximum
	λ	$[\alpha]_E \times 10^{-3}$	λ	λ	$[\alpha]_E \times 10^{-3}$	λ	λ	$[\alpha]_E \times 10^{-3}$	λ	$[\alpha]_E \times 10^{-3}$	λ
Li$^+$	625	230	585	555	−285	494	440	175	410	65	538
Na$^+$	625	212	587	545	−282	495	443	170	410	82	538
K$^+$	625	171	592	545	−350	495	462	130	410	50	537
Rb$^+$	625	218	587	545	−277	497	440	176	410	104	537
Mg^{++}	625	143	589	550	−275	495	440	124	405	67	518
Al^{+++}	625	180	587	550	−260	496	440	158	400	35	537
Ba^{+++}	625	122	588	548	−195	503	437	140	410	35	538

TABLE 6: WAVELENGTHS AND MAGNITUDE OF SELECTED POINTS ON ROTATORY DISPERSION AND ABSORPTION CURVES OF SALTS OF LEVO-CIS-OXALATO-BIS(ETHYLENEDIAMINE)COBALT(III) ION

Anion	Maximum		Zero	First Minimum		Saddle Point	Second Minimum		Absorption Maximum	
	λ	$[\alpha]_E \times 10^{-4}$	λ	λ	$[\alpha]_E \times 10^{-4}$	λ	λ	$[\alpha]_E \times 10^{-4}$	λ	σ_E
F$^-$	560	13.7	528	480	−19.0	370	305	−33.0	495	220
Cl$^-$	558	12.0	526	478	−14.6	380	305	−30.6	495	216
Br$^-$	560	10.9	526	480	−15.1	375	305	−28.2	495	210
I$^-$	560	8.5	527	480	−11.3	370	305	−22.5	495	229
BF$_4^-$	563	9.0	528	485	−13.6	375	305	−24.6	495	201
ClO$_4^-$	560	14.8	527	478	−21.2	375	305	−34.8	495	213
SO$_4^=$	560	7.0	528	480	−10.2	373	305	−16.8	495	222
PO$_4^{\equiv}$	565	10.6	527	485	−13.7	375	305	−27.8	495	162

All wavelengths are in millimicrons.

TABLE 7: WAVELENGTHS AND MAGNITUDE OF SELECTED POINTS ON ROTATORY DISPERSION AND ABSORPTION CURVES OF SALTS OF *LEVO*-TRIS(ETHYLENEDIAMINE)CHROMIUM(III) ION

Anion	Minimum		Zero	Maximum		Trough	First Absorption Maximum		Second Absorption Maximum	
	λ	$\alpha_E \times 10^{-4}$	λ	λ	$[\alpha]_E \times 10^{-4}$	λ	λ	α_E	λ	$\alpha_E \times 10^{-3}$
F⁻	490	− 10.5	464	420	21.0	355	460	115	350	4.9
Cl⁻	490	− 8.1	466	420	14.3	355	460	86.5	350	2.6
Br⁻	490	− 10.0	465	420	20.6	358	460	125	350	4.0
I⁻	490	− 13.4	463	418	24.2	355	460	136	350	2.5
BF₄⁻	490	− 6.1	464	418	11.9	355	460	114	350	3.4
ClO₄⁻	490	− 11.6	464	420	22.8	358	460	132	350	5.3
SO₄⁼	490	− 9.7	464	420	17.8	360	460	125	350	4.0
PO₄≡	490	− 6.3	464	420	11.8	360	460	110	350	2.0

All wavelengths are in millimicrons.

TABLE 8: WAVELENGTHS AND MAGNITUDE OF SELECTED POINTS ON ROTATORY DISPERSION AND ABSORPTION CURVES OF SALTS OF *DEXTRO*-TRIS(OXALATO)RHODATE(III) ION

Anion	Zero(I)	Maximum		Zero(II)	Minimum		Absorption Maximum	
	λ	λ	$[\alpha]_E \times 10^{-4}$	λ	λ	$[\alpha]_E \times 10^{-4}$	λ	α_E
Li⁺	590	460	12.0	427	360	− 48.3	400	225
Na⁺	589	460	13.7	427	360	− 52.8	400	360
K⁺	589	460	17.7	427	360	− 65.3	400	435
Rb⁺	589	460	14.4	427	360	− 59.2	400	522
Cs⁺	589	460	14.7	427	350	− 61.8	400	480
Mg⁺⁺	595	455	3.9	420	370	− 9.5	400	291
Ca⁺⁺	595	460	14.4	426	360	− 51.6	400	330
Ba⁺⁺	590	460	19.5	422	360	− 54.6	400	465

All wavelengths are in millimicrons.

TABLE 9: WAVELENGTHS AND MAGNITUDE OF SELECTED POINTS ON ROTATORY DISPERSION AND ABSORPTION CURVES OF SALTS OF d-TARTRATO-TETRAMMINECOBALT(III) ION

Anion	First Maximum (mμ)	$[\alpha]_E \times 10^{-2}$	λ Zero(I) (mμ)	λ Minimum (mμ)	$[\alpha]_E \times 10^{-2}$	λ Zero(II) (mμ)	λ Absorption Maximum (mμ)
F^-	540	+ 495	503	480	− 180	440	520
Cl^-	540	+ 305	498	480	− 65	452	520
Br^-	540	+ 310	487	480	− 65	458	520
I^-	540	+ 430	500	480	− 140	450	520
BF_4^-	540	+ 305	494	480	− 42	465	520
ClO_4^-	540	+ 215	500	480	− 65	478	520
$SO_4^=$	540	+ 245	494	480	− 80	450	520
$PO_4^{\equiv}$	540	+ 495	502	480	− 65	460	520
NO_3^-	540	+ 305	460	480	0	470	520

TABLE 10: WAVELENGTHS AND MAGNITUDE OF SELECTED POINTS ON ROTATORY DISPERSION AND ABSORPTION CURVES OF SALTS OF l-ALANINATO-DICHLOROPLATINATE(II) ION

Cation	λ Maximum^I mμ	$[\alpha]_E \times 10^{-2}$	λ Minimum mμ	$[\alpha]_E \times 10^{-2}$	λ Maximum^{II} mμ	$[\alpha]_E \times 10^{-2}$	Absorption Maximum mμ
Li^+	400	− 70	355	− 395	340	− 60	...
Na^+	400	− 80	350	− 287	320	− 200	...
K^+	400	− 50	355	− 315	340	− 185	330
Rb^+	400	− 130	350	− 425	...	...	...
Cs^+	400	− 100	355	− 427	...	...	...
Mg^{++}	400	− 100	355	− 345	...	...	...
Ca^{++}	400	− 75	355	− 375	340	...	...
Ba^{++}	400	− 70	355	− 410	...	...	...
Al^{+++}	400	− 70	355	− 305	320	− 105	...

TABLE 11: WAVELENGTHS AND MAGNITUDE OF SELECTED POINTS ON
ROTATORY DISPERSION AND ABSORPTION CURVES OF SALTS OF
d-DIGLUTAMATOPLATINATE(II) ION

Cation	$[\alpha]_E \times 10^{-2}$ $\lambda = 460$ mμ.	$[\alpha]_E \times 10^{-2}$ $\lambda = 360$ mμ.	$[\alpha]_E \times 10^{-2}$ $\lambda = 300$ mμ.
Li^+	-260	-530	-860
Na^+	-270	-530	-900
K^+	-220	-430	-680
Rb^+	-220	-465	-800
Cs^+	-250	-500	-850
Mg^{++}	-225	-475	-825
Ca^{++}	-230	-495	-855
Al^{+++}	$\ldots$	-125	-340

points (positive to negative cross-over in sign of rotation, or vice versa) are fairly constant with change of optically inactive ion, but the magnitudes of rotation at these locations often varies considerably. Data on these magnitudes are given in Tables 3–11 along with the optical absorption maxima.

It appears that the changes in magnitudes of the optical rotation are related to the degree of ion-pairing between the optically active and optically inactive ions. Illustrative of this are the plots of equivalent molecular rotation $vs.$ "ionic potential" (ionic charge/ ionic radius),[71] an example of which is given in Fig. 6. This effect is observed whether the optically active complex ions are asymmetric solely because of the configuration of optically inactive ligands about a metal ion or because of the presence of optically active ligands without this type of configuration (e.g., $[Co(NH_3)_4(d\text{-tart})]^+$).

REFERENCES

1. J. Biot, *Memoir de l'Inst.,* **13**, i, 1 (1812).
2. P. Drude, *Lehrbuch der Optik* (2nd ed.), S. Hirzel, Verlag, Leipzig, 1906.
3. P. Levene and A. Rothen, "Rotatory Dispersion," in H. Gilman, *Organic Chemistry, An Advanced Treatise,* New York, John Wiley and Sons, 1938.
4. T. Lowry, *Optical Rotatory Power,* Longmans, Green and Co., Ltd., London, 1935.
5. W. Heller and D. Fitts, "Polarimetry," in A. Weissberger, Ed., *Physical Methods of Organic Chemistry* (3rd ed.), Vol. 1, Part 3, Ch. 33, Interscience Publishers, New York, 1960.
6. W. Klyne and A. Parker, "Optical Rotatory Dispersion," in A. Weissberger, Ed., *Physical Methods of Organic Chemistry* (3rd ed.), Vol. 1, Part 3, Ch. 34, Interscience Publishers, New York, 1960.
7. A. Moscowitz, in C. Djerassi, *Optical Rotatory Dispersion,* Ch. 12, McGraw-Hill Book Co., Inc., New York, 1960.

8. W. Kauzmann, J. Walter, and H. Eyring, *Chem. Revs.*, **26**, 339 (1940); E. Condon, *Rev. Mod. Phys.*, **9**, 432 (1937); W. Kuhn, *Ann. Rev. Phys. Chem.*, **9**, 417 (1958); W. Moffitt, *J. Chem. Phys.*, **25**, 1189 (1956); H. M. Powell, *Endeavor*, **15**, 20 (1956); M. Vol'kenshtein, *Zhur. Exsptl. Teoret. Fiz. (USSR)*, **20**, 342 (1950); R. Servant, *J. Phys. Radium* [8], **3**, 90 (1942); J. Kirkwood, *J. Chem. Phys.*, **5**, 479 (1937); M. Born, *Proc. Roy. Soc.* (London), **A150**, 84 (1935); **A153**, 339 (1936); M. Betti, *Trans. Faraday Soc.*, **26**, 337 (1930); C. Djerassi, *Optical Rotatory Dispersion*, McGraw-Hill Book Co., Inc., New York (1960).

9. A. Cotton, *Compt. rend.*, **120**, 989, 1044 (1895); *Ann. Chim. Phys.*, **8**, 347 (1896).

10. C. Djerassi, *Optical Rotatory Dispersion*, McGraw-Hill Book Co., Inc., New York (1960).

11. F. Jaeger, *Optical Activity and High Temperature Measurements*, McGraw-Hill Book Co., Inc., New York, 1930.

12. Y. Shimura, *Bull. Chem. Soc. Japan*, **31**, 315 (1958).

13. N. Izumiya, *J. Am. Chem. Soc.*, **78**, 1602 (1956).

14. T. O'Brien and R. Tool, *ibid.*, **77**, 1368 (1955); T. O'Brien, J. McReynolds, and J. Bailar, Jr., *ibid.*, **70**, 749 (1948).

15. H. Jonassen and J. Bailar, Jr., *ibid.*, **70**, 756 (1948).

16. Sr. M. Martinette and J. Bailar, Jr., *ibid.*, **74**, 1054 (1952).

17. P. Pfeiffer, *J. prakt. Chem.*, **150**, 261 (1938).

18. D. P. Mellor, *Australian J. Sci.*, **3**, 99 (1941); *J. Proc. Roy. Soc. N. S. Wales*, **75**, 157 (1942).

19. S. Kirschner, A. J. Sonnessa, D. Bhatnagar, and D. Moy, *Abstr. of Papers, 14N, Division of Inorganic Chemistry, 138th Meeting, American Chemical Society*, New York, 1960.

20. S. Kirschner and D. Bhatnagar, *Abstr. of Papers, 11B, Division of Analytical Chemistry, 138th Meeting, American Chemical Society*, New York, 1960.

21. M. Albinak, Dissertation, Wayne State University, Detroit, Mich., 1958.

22. A. Sonnessa, Dissertation, Wayne State University, Detroit, Mich., 1960.

23. 95 Madison Ave., New York 16, N. Y.

24. T. Crumpler, W. Dyre, and A. Spell, *Anal. Chem.*, **27**, 1645 (1955).

25. 485 Fifth Ave., New York 17, N. Y.

26. *Zeiss Werkzeitschrift*, **26**, 103 (1957).

27. 71, Hornsey Rise, London N. 19, England; Epic, Inc., 154 Nassau St., New York 38, N. Y.

28. P. O. Box 446, Caldwell, N. J.

29. H. Rudolph, *J. Opt. Soc. Am.*, **45**, 50 (1955).

30. E. Brand, E. Washburn, B. Erlanger, E. Ellenbogen, F. Lippman, and M. Scheu, *J. Am. Chem. Soc.*, **76**, 5037 (1954).

31. Little Falls, N. J.

32. Norwalk, Conn.

33. A. Savitzky, W. Slavin, and R. Salinger, *Pittsburgh Conf. on Analyt. Chem. and Appl. Spectroscopy*, Mar. 3, 1959.

34. E. J. Gillham, *Nature*, **178**, 1412 (1956); *J. Sci. Instr.*, **34**, 435 (1957).

35. B. Malcolm and H. Elliott, *J. Sci. Instr.*, **34**, 48 (1957).

36. T. Burer, M. Kohler, and H. Gunthard, *Helv. Chim. Acta*, **41**, 2216 (1958); H. Hedriger and H. Gunthard, *ibid.*, **37**, 1125 (1954).

37. J. Gates, *Chem. and Ind.* (London), **1958**, 190.

38. G. Bruhat, A. Blanc-Lapierre, J. Schiltz, and G. Raoult, *Compt. rend.*, **214**, 615 (1942); G. Bruhat and M. Pauthenier, *Rev. opt.*, **5**, 163 (1927).

39. H. von Halban, *Nature*, 119, 86 (1927).
40. E. Landt and H. Hirschmuller, *Deut. Zuckerind.*, 62, 647 (1937).
41. G. Levy, *Anal. Chem.*, 23, 1089 (1951); G. Levy, P. Schwed, and D. Fergus, *Rev. Sci. Instr.*, 21, 693 (1950).
42. W. Brode, *J. Opt. Soc., Am.*, 41, 987 (1951).
43. H. Gutowski, *J. Chem. Phys.*, 19, 438 (1951). (Infrared region)
44. F. Woldbye, *Acta Chem. Scand.*, 13, 2137 (1959).
45. S. Mitchell and J. Veitch, *Nature*, 168, 662 (1951); D. Rank, *J. Sci. Instr.*, 27, 270 (1950); E. Willey, *ibid.*, 20, 74 (1943); G. Landegren, *Rev. Sci. Instr.*, 26, 502, 578 (1955); H. Wenking, *Z. Instrumentenk.*, 66, 1 (1958); D. Rank, J. Light, and P. Yodor, *J. Sci. Instr.*, 27, 270 (1950).
46. 6 Banta Place, Hackensack, N. J. (Bulletin No. 2).
47. A. Keston, *Abstr. of Papers, 18C, Division of Biological Chemistry, 127th Meeting, American Chemical Society*, Cincinnati, Ohio, 1955; A. Keston and J. Lospalluto, *Federation Proc.*, 12, 229 (1953).
48. K. Poulsen, *Anal. Chem.*, 32, 410 (1960).
49. P. Gallop, *Rev. Sci. Instr.*, 28, 209 (1957).
50. 2500 Fullerton Road, Fullerton, California.
51. Beckman Part No. 2950, or Gaertner Scientific Co., long focus, quartz lens.
52. 1201 Wrightwood Ave., Chicago 14, Illinois (L944-10-30 prisms mounted in L-111-PPO circles).
53. Beckman Parts No. 40854, 2120, 2504.
54. Rudolph Polarimeter Tube, Type 14, with quartz end glasses.
55. O. C. Rudolph and Sons, Inc., Xenon Compact Arc Light Source, No. 605.
56. The zero position should be determined at several widely different wavelengths, because even a slight strain in the end glasses of the polarimeter tube will produce a strain polarization which will be wavelength-dependent. If the zero positions at all wavelengths are not identical, then the difference in absorbance units between the *A-B* difference at the wavelength chosen to set the zero position of the instrument (with the cell containing solvent in place; this difference should be zero) and the *A-B* difference at another wavelength (cell containing solvent still in place) should be added (or subtracted, as the case may be) as a correction term to the *A-B* absorbance differences of samples at the latter wavelength.
57. F. J. Bates, *et al.*, "Polarimetry, Saccharimetry and the Sugars," U. S. Bureau of Standards Circular C440, Government Printing Office, Washington, D. C., 1942.
58. For sucrose at $20\,^{\circ}$C., $[\alpha] = 21.648/(\lambda^2 - 0.0213)$ (λ in microns, see Ref. 57).
59. O. C. Rudolph and Sons, Inc., Model 80.
60. Abbreviations used: en = ethylenediamine; edta = ethylenediaminetetraacetate anion; ox = oxalate anion; *d*-tart = *dextro*-tartrate anion; *l*-alan = *levo*-alaninate anion; *d*-glut = *dextro*-glutamate anion.
61. F. Dwyer, E. Gyarfas, and D. Mellor, *J. Phys. Chem.*, 59, 296 (1955); F. Dwyer and F. Garvan, *Inorganic Syntheses*, E. Rochow, Ed., 6, 195, McGraw-Hill Book Co., Inc., N. Y., 1960.
62. A. Werner, *Ber.*, 45, 121 (1912).
63. F. Dwyer and F. Garvan, *Inorganic Syntheses*, E. Rochow, Ed., 6, 192, McGraw-Hill Book Co., Inc., N. Y., 1960.

64. J. Bailar, Jr., *Inorganic Syntheses*, W. Fernelius, Ed., **2**, 222, McGraw-Hill Book Co., Inc., N. Y., 1946.
65. A. Werner, *Ber.*, **45**, 3286 (1912).
66. F. Dwyer, *J. Phys. Chem.*, **60**, 1331 (1956).
67. H. Ley and K. Ficken, *Ber.*, **45**, 380 (1912).
68. A. Grinberg, *Neorg. Khim. Akad. Nauk, SSSR*, No. 29, 37 (1955).
69. J. Duff, *J. Chem. Soc.*, **123**, 563, 569 (1923).
70. A. Lamb, *J. Am. Chem. Soc.*, **59**, 385 (1937).
71. G. Cartledge, *ibid.*, **50**, 2855, 2863 (1928); **52**, 3076 (1930).

ALKYL AND ARYL ETHYNYL DERIVATIVES OF COPPER(I) AND SILVER(I), AND THEIR COMPLEXES WITH TERTIARY PHOSPHINES

G. E. COATES and C. PARKIN*

Department of Chemistry
University of Durham
Durham, England

A few ethynyl-copper(I) and -silver(I) complexes of the type $R \cdot C : CCu-$ (Ag) $\cdot P$ (As)Et_3 (R = Ph, Me) have been reported in a preliminary note.[1] Those complexes which were sufficiently stable for cryoscopic measurements were found to be associated, and it was suggested that in the dimeric complexes, for example, the ethynyl group acts as donor towards the metal, as indicated in (I).

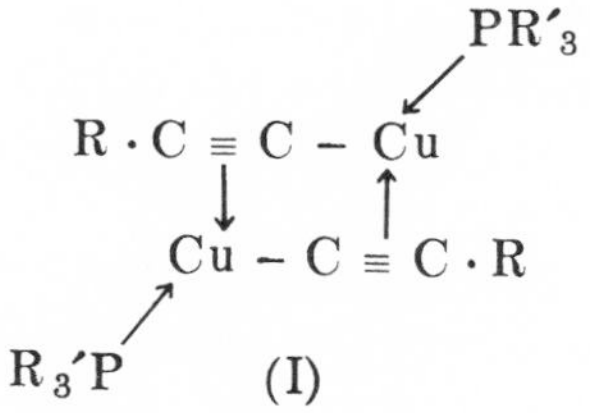

$$PR'_3$$

$$R \cdot C \equiv C - Cu$$

$$Cu - C \equiv C \cdot R$$

$$R_3'P \qquad (I)$$

Analogous compounds of gold(I), e.g., $PhC : CAuPEt_3$, are monomeric[2], since gold(I) has a relatively low tendency to raise its co-ordination number above two, in contrast to copper(I) and silver(I).

An unstable ammonia complex $(PhC : CCuNH_3)_x$ has previously been prepared by reactions in liquid ammonia. It reverts to polymeric $PhC : CCu$ in a stream of nitrogen and its molecular complexity is not known.[3] We find that phenylethynyl copper can itself be slowly extracted (in a Soxhlet apparatus) by isopropylamine; though it comes out of solution in crystalline form, the crystals so far obtained have unfortunately been too small for detailed crystallographic study.

Studies on Ethynyl Copper(I) Complexes

We now describe further studies on ethynylcopper(I) complexes,

*The authors thank the Ethyl Corporation for a research grant.

with the three principal objects, (1) to find out whether more than one molecule of tertiary phosphine would co-ordinate to each copper atom, (2) to obtain more extensive molecular weight data, and (3) to investigate the infrared absorption of the ethynyl groups in these compounds.

Difficulties due to the inconveniently high solubilities of the triethyl-phosphine complexes reported earlier have largely been overcome by the use of trimethylphosphine (the more symmetrical molecule usually resulting in higher melting points and lower solubilities).

Complexes were normally prepared by the addition of the tertiary phosphine to a suspension of the insoluble ethynyl compound in an organic solvent, followed by filtration and crystallization. Their properties are summarized in Table 1, which includes cryoscopic and infrared data..

The association of the monophosphine complexes, $RC \vdots CCuPR'_3$, is confirmed, but (X) is exceptional in being dimeric in benzene and monomeric in nitrobenzene. The nitrobenzene solutions of monophosphine complexes may well contain dimer molecules of structure (I), in which case the copper atoms have the co-ordination number *three,* but we cannot exclude the possibility that the solvent acts as donor as well as ethynyl groups, thus allowing the more usual four-co-ordination. The higher degrees of association observed in benzene are interpreted later.

In agreement with the view that ethynylcopper(I) compounds are co-ordination polymers, and that the polymerization is reduced (to structures like (I)) by tertiary phosphines successfully competing with ethynyl groups as ligands,[1] we find that when two phosphorus atoms are co-ordinated to each copper the resulting complexes, (III) and (VI), are monomeric. The bisphosphine complexes are more difficult to purify; (III) evidently dissociates in nitrobenzene solution, though partial replacement of phosphine by nitrobenzene would give the same cryoscopic result. Dissociation is probably also responsible for the bisphosphine and the one trisphosphine complex prepared melting over a range of several degrees.

Progressive addition of tertiary phosphine causes a marked lightening of colour. For example, tertiary butylethynylcopper(I), which is octameric in benzene solution both cryoscopically[4] and ebullioscopically (Found: M, 1140, 1161, 1177 in 0·73, 1·48, and 2·95% benzene solution; calc. for $(C_6H_9Cu)_8$, M, 1157) is orange-red, while its dimeric mono(trimethylphosphine) complex is yellow-green and its monomeric bisphosphine complex is colourless.

We cannot satisfactorily explain the observation that the *para-*

TABLE 1

Complex	Colour	m.p.	Degree of Association Cryoscopically in		$\nu(C\!:\!C)$* cm^{-1}
			Benzene	Nitrobenzene	
(II) $Bu^t C\!:\!:\!:\!C\cdot CuPMe_3$	yellow-green	105–106°	2·6 – 2·8	2·0	2050 vw
(III) $Bu^t C\!:\!:\!:\!C\cdot Cu(PMe_3)_2$	colourless	95–98	1·0	0·4 – 0·9	abs.
(IV) $CH_2\!:\!CMeC\!:\!:\!:\!C\cdot CuPMe_3$	yellow	82–82·5	3·3 – 3·4	2·0 – 2·2	2065 w, 2031 m
(V) $PhC\!:\!:\!:\!C\cdot CuPMe_3$	yellow	116–117	2·6 – 2·8	1·9 – 2·1	2019 w, 2045 m
(VI) $PhC\!:\!:\!:\!C\cdot Cu(PMe_3)_2$	yellow-green	94–96	1·0 – 1·4	1·0	2035 m, 2048 m
(VII) $PhC\!:\!:\!:\!C\cdot Cu(PMe_3)_3$	pale cream	88–93	unstable		2034 s, 2051 vw
(VIII) $PhC\!:\!:\!:\!C\cdot CuPEt_3$	yellow	139·5	2·5 – 2·9	1·9 – 2·0	2018 s, 2048 m
(IX) $PhC\!:\!:\!:\!C\cdot CuPPh_3$	yellow-green	212–214 (dec.)	insufficiently soluble		2043 m
(X) $p\text{--}NO_2C_6H_4C\!:\!:\!:\!C\cdot CuPPh_3$	orange	222–224 (dec.)	2·0 – 2·1	0·9 – 1·1	2015 s
(XI) $p\text{--}NO_2C_6H_4C\!:\!:\!:\!C\cdot$ $Cu(PPhEt_2)_2$	deep red	75	unstable		2025 s
(XII) $PhC\!:\!:\!:\!C\!:\!:\!:\!C\cdot CuPMe_3$	yellow	dec. >140	insufficiently soluble		2161 s, 1981 m
(XIII) $PhC\!:\!:\!:\!C\!:\!:\!:\!C\cdot CuPEt_3$	yellow	155–156 (dec.)	3·0 – 3·3	2·0 – 2·1	2159 s, 1988 m; $_b$(2167 s, 1988 m)
(XIV) $(PhC\!:\!:\!:\!C\cdot C\!:\!:\!:\!C\cdot Cu)_2$ $(PEt_3)_3$	pale yellow	95–96	0·5 – 0·7	0·9 – 1·0	$_a$2165 s, 2008 m; $_a$(2171 s, 2009 m)
(XV) $PhC\!:\!:\!:\!C\!:\!:\!:\!C\cdot CuPPr^n_3$	yellow	87	3·0 – 3·4	2·0	$_b$2164 s, 1984 m; $_b$(2166 s, 1986 m)

* Spectra measured in KBr disc, except ^{a} in benzene, ^{b} in tetrachlorethylene; vw, very weak; w, weak; m, medium; s, strong.

nitro-phenylethynyl complex *(X)* is monomeric in nitrobenzene and dimeric in benzene. It would be surprising if nitrobenzene could behave as a donor molecule of sufficient strength to split the dimer (formula (I), $R = p-NO_2C_6H_4$, $R^1 = Ph$) by co-ordination to copper. When orange crystals of *(X)*, obtained from benzene-hexane solution, are allowed to stand in contact with ethanol, in which it is insoluble, it turns into a bright red powdery material (m.p. and analysis unchanged). This red form of (X) dissolves giving an orange solution in benzene, in which it has a dimeric constitution from which the orange crystalline form can be recovered. Similarly, the orange form gives a *red* solution in nitrobenzene.

Copper(I) derivatives of alkylacetylenes (with the exception of tertiary butylacetylene) did not readily yield isolable tertiary phosphine complexes. Propynyl(triethylphosphine)copper(I) for example, at once gives a yellow precipitate of insoluble propynyl-copper(I) when added to benzene; the precipitate dissolves again if excess triethylphosphine is added.

Some diacetylene complexes $PhC\colon C\cdot C\colon C\cdot CuPR_3$ ($R = Me$, Et, Pr^n) were also prepared and unexpectedly found to be more stable to decomposition in the air than the mono-acetylenic compounds discussed earlier. In contrast, the diacetylenes (e.g., $PhC\colon C\cdot C\colon CH$) are very much less stable than the mono-acetylenes. Whereas $PhC\colon CCu\,PEt_3$ reverted to yellow amorphous $PhC\colon CCu$ after exposure to air for a day or two, the corresponding butadiynyl complex was unchanged after a week's exposure. The complex (XIV) with a $Cu\colon P$ ratio $2\colon 3$ loses triethylphosphine when it stands in the air or is heated in propanol, giving the monophosphine complex.

In general, the silver analogues, $RC\colon C\cdot AgPR_3'$, are less easy to prepare and purify than the copper compounds, and they decompose more readily on exposure to air and also to light. Since preliminary investigations[1] had shown that the copper and silver complexes are rather similar, the latter were not further studied (with the exception of the preparation of $PhC\colon C\cdot AgPMe_3$, which was found to be dimeric in boiling benzene).

Infrared Spectra

Disubstituted acetylenes absorb light in the range[5] 2190–2260 cm^{-1}. Coordination between acetylenic groups and metal atoms should result in a reduction of the stretching frequency because of electron flow from the occupied π_u-bonding orbitals to the metal and from occupied metal d orbitals to unoccupied π_g-anti-bonding orbitals of the acetylene. Both these effects should reduce the acetylenic

TABLE 2: INFRARED STRETCHING FREQUENCIES* OF THE ACETYLENIC GROUP IN RC⋮CM

R·	M = ½ Hg	Cu	Ag
Me	2156	1955	2061
Et	2165	1952	ca 2040[a,c]
Pr^n	2164[a], 2175[b]	1942	2045
Bu^t	2180, 2146 2188, 2154[b]	absent	
Ph	2149	1933	2055
p–NO$_2$C$_6$H$_4$	absent[a,c]	1929	2055
mesityl	2142	1933[c] (v. weak)	2042
p–BrC$_6$H$_4$	2160	1942	2026
PhC⋮C	2204, 2098	2180[a,c]	2048[c] 2190

*Measured in [a]KBr disc, [b]benzene solution, [c]Nujol mull.

bond order, and hence reduce the stretching frequency. For example, the acetylenic stretching frequency of ditertiary butylacetylene is reduced by about 200 cm^{-1} when it becomes π-bonded to platinum(II),[6] and similar effects have been found in heavy metal complexes of olefins.[7]

In agreement with our view that alkyl- and arylethynylcopper(I) compounds (RC⋮CCu)$_x$ are co-ordination polymers in which there is substantial back co-ordination from filled copper $3d$ orbitals to the acetylenic anti-bonding orbitals, we find that these compounds absorb in the region 1920–1960 cm^{-1} which is 270–300 cm^{-1} lower than the range characteristic of disubstituted acetylenes. This effect is less marked in corresponding silver compounds (see Table 2), whose acetylenic frequencies are in the range 2020–2060 cm^{-1}, a reduction of only 150–200 cm^{-1}. The acetylenic frequencies of some ethynyl-mercury (II) compounds are included in Table 2 for comparison as examples of disubstituted acetylenes containing ethynyl-metal bonds. Any decrease of acetylenic stretching frequency below that found in mercury derivatives should indicate some substantial electronic effect. Table 2 shows that the decrease in ν(C⋮C) on substituting copper and silver for mercury is about 200 and 100 cm^{-1} respectively. No absorption that could be due to an acetylenic vibration could be detected in tertiary butylethynylcopper(I), either in a potassium bromide disc or in solution in tetrachlorethylene; this may be connected with the mass of a copper atom being fairly near that of a butyl group.

Complex formation with a tertiary phosphine raises ν(C⋮C) by nearly 100 cm^{-1} from that observed in the corresponding ethynylcopper(I) compounds $(RC \vdots CCu)_x$. It is remarkable that the frequency of the acetylenic absorption is much the same whether the complex contains one, two, or more mols. of phosphine. Table 3 shows ν $(C \vdots C)$ for two series of complexes $RC \vdots CCu(PMe_3)_n$, $(R = Ph \cdot$ and $CH_2 : CMe \cdot)$ measured in benzene solution. Solutions containing the higher $P : Cu$ ratios were obtained by dissolving the $1 : 1$ complex in benzene and adding the appropriate amount of trimethylphosphine. Extinction co-efficients are not given since it is very likely that the solutions contain mixtures of more than one complex. It is relevant to note that in the isopropenyl series solutions for which the $P : Cu$ ratios were three and four were quite colourless, and hence could not contain appreciable amounts of the bright yellow $1 : 1$ complex.

Two or more $\nu (C \vdots C)$ bands were also observed in the spectra of some of the solid complexes pressed in a potassium bromide disc. These data are collected in Table 1. It is worth noting that $\nu (C \vdots C)$ increases in the series $PhC \vdots CMPR_3$ in the sense $M = Cu < Ag < Au$, and that the change from $(RC \vdots CCu)_x$ to $RC \vdots CCuPR_3$ (about $100\ cm^{-1}$) is much greater than that from $(RC \vdots CAg)_x$ to $RC \vdots CAgPR_3$ (about $20\ cm^{-1}$).

The observations that particularly need explanation are the cryoscopic data (apparent degree of association $2 \cdot 5 - 3 \cdot 4$ for monophosphine complexes in benzene), and the number of distinct acetylenic infrared bands. The monophosphine complex $PhC \vdots CCuPMe_3$ has been examined crystallographically by Dr. H. M. M. Shearer and Mr. P. W. R. Corfield of this Department, and the structure will be reported in detail elsewhere. The complex contains tetrameric units $(PhC \vdots CCuPMe_3)_4$, each with a zig-zag chain of four copper atoms; two phosphine molecules are bound to each of the terminal copper

TABLE 3: EFFECT OF P : Cu RATIO ON $\nu(C \vdots C)$ OF BENZENE SOLUTIONS OF $RC \vdots CCu(PMe_3)_n$

R	$n = 1$	$n = 2$	$n = 3$	$n = 4$
Ph ·	2025,m	2042,m	2041,s	2035,s
	2053,m		2061,(sh)	2061,s
	2086,w	2087,w	2087,w	2086,w
CH$_2$CMe ·	^{a}2013,m	^{b}2021,m	^{c}2017,m	^{c}2017,m
	2035,m		2039,m	2039,s
	2063,w	2064,m	2062,m	2062,s
	2089,w	2089,w		

Colour of solution: ^{a}yellow; ^{b}pale yellow; ^{c}colourless; w, weak; m, medium; s, strong; (sh), shoulder.

atoms, the central two copper atoms not being co-ordinated to phosphorus. Two of the four acetylene groups have a different environment from the other two.

The anomalous cryoscopic results are evidently due to the presence in *solution* of both tetramer and less associated species. The infra red bands are clearly due to the different types of acetylene group present in the tetramer, and again to equilibria in solution between the tetrameric and less associated species.

The mercury compound (PhC : C · C : C)$_2$Hg, has acetylenic absorptions at 2204 and 2098 cm^{-1} (KBr disc), the copper(I) and silver derivatives having single absorptions at 2180 and 2190 cm^{-1} (Table 2). Since the monophosphine complexes, PhC : C · C : C · CuPR$_3$, have two frequencies in the range 2159–2165 and 1981–1988 cm^{-1} (Table 1), it seems clear that only one of the two acetylene groups is involved to any large extent in π-bonding to copper.

Dr. Shearer and Mr. Corfield report as follows on the complex (PhC : C · C : CCu)$_2$ (PEt$_3$)$_3$ (XIV): "The space group P *bca*, $a = 14\cdot85$, $b = 20\cdot8$, $c = 26\cdot7$ A, $\alpha = \beta = \gamma = 90°$, is similar to that of PhC : CCuPMe$_3$. From these data and the observed density (1·182) the unit cell contains 16 copper atoms. These data are consistent with a structure different from that of PhC : CCuPMe$_3$ only in that three instead of two phosphine groups are bound to the terminal copper atoms of the Cu$_4$ chain." In nitrobenzene this complex evidently dissolves as dimer (two Cu atoms), and there must be extensive dissociation in benzene (see Table 1).

REFERENCES

1. D. Blake, G. Calvin, and G. E. Coates, *Proc. Chem. Soc.*, **1959**, 396.
2. G. Calvin, G. E. Coates, and P. Dixon, *Chem. & Ind. (London)* **1959**, 1628.
3. R. Nast and W. Pfab, *Chem. Ber.* **89**, 415 (1956).
4. A. Favorski and L. Morev, *J. Russ. Phys. Chem. Soc.*, **50**, 571 (1920).
5. L. J. Bellamy, *The Infra-red Spectra of Complex Molecules*, Methuen, London, 1958; N. Sheppard and D. M. Simpson, *Quart. Revs.*, **6**, 1 (1952).
6. J. Chatt, L. A. Duncanson, and R. G. Guy, *Chem. & Ind. (London)* **1959**, 430.
7. J. Chatt and L. A. Duncanson, *J. Chem. Soc.*, **1953**, 2939.

PROTON-CARBOXYLATE CATENATION EQUILIBRIA

J. D. E. CARSON and **F. J. C. ROSSOTTI**

Department of Chemistry
University of Edinburgh
Edinburgh, Scotland

Some proton-carboxylate equilibria have been reinvestigated as a preliminary to confirming whether or not polynuclear carboxylato-copper(II) complexes exist in solution. Systems studied so far include formate, acetate, propionate, butyrate,[1] valerate, isobutyrate, trimethylacetate,[2] chloroacetate, cyanoacetate, phenylacetate, glycollate, methoxyacetate, and mandelate. The general approach[3] was similar to that developed by Sillén,[4] ourselves,[5] and others[6] for rigorous studies of inorganic isopolyacids. Equilibria were investigated at $25.00 \pm 0.05\,°C.$ by potentiometric titration using cells of the type

$$\text{glass electrode} \left| \begin{array}{c} x \; M \; \text{NaA} \\ (A\text{-}x) \; M \; \text{HA} \\ (3\text{-}x) \; M \; \text{NaClO}_4 \end{array} \right| 3.00 \; M \; \text{NaClO}_4 \left| \begin{array}{c} 0.01 \; M \; \text{AgClO}_4 \\ 2.99 \; M \; \text{NaClO}_4 \end{array} \right| \text{AgCl, Ag}$$

Millivolt potentials E of these cells are related to the concentration h of free hydrogen ions by the equation

$$E = E_0 - 59.15 \log h \tag{1}$$

The term E_0 includes the difference between the standard potentials of the electrodes, the asymmetry potential of the glass electrode, and the logarithmic function of the activity coefficient of the hydrogen ions. At a constant temperature and in the presence of a 3 M sodium ionic medium, E_0 appeared to be constant within the experimental precision of ± 0.2 mv. Glass electrodes were calibrated *in situ* as concentration probes by determining E_0 in a preliminary titration of perchloric acid with sodium hydroxide or sodium hydrogen carbonate before each carboxylate run. A sodium carboxylate buffer was then added stepwise to the left-hand half-cell. Values of h derived from (1) were used to calculate the average number of protons per carboxylate ion from the relationship

$$\bar{n} = \frac{H - h + K_w h^{-1}}{A} \qquad (2)$$

where H and A are the total, analytical concentrations of hydrogen and carboxylate ions and K_w is the ionic product of water. Acid formation functions $\bar{n}(\log h)_A$ were calculated for a three- to four fold variation in $\log h$ and for a number of constant values of $A \leq 1\ M$.

Interpretation of the Data

The cyanoacetate system, for example, may be assumed to be mononuclear in the range $A \lesssim 0.05\ M$ where $\bar{n}(\log h)$ is independent of A (cf. Fig. 1). However, polynuclear association occurs at higher concentrations where $\bar{n}(\log h)$ is a function of A. The polynuclear association is comparatively slight as the dependence of A is not very marked. The sharp isohydric point $\bar{n}^*$, where all curves $\bar{n}(\log h)_A$ intersect, suggests that the polynuclear species are of a common degree of condensation.

For the possible sequence of stepwise equilibria

$$H^+ \quad + \ A^- \ \rightleftharpoons\ HA \qquad K_{11} \qquad (3)$$

$$HA \quad + \ A^- \ \rightleftharpoons\ HA_2^- \qquad K_{12} \qquad (4)$$

$$HA_2^- \ + \ H^+ \ \rightleftharpoons\ H_2A_2 \qquad K_{22} \qquad (5)$$

the mass balance equations are

$$A\bar{n} = [HA] + [HA_2^-] + 2[H_2A_2]$$

$$= K_{11}ha + K_{11}K_{12}ha^2 + 2K_{11}K_{12}K_{22}h^2a^2 \qquad (6)$$

and

$$A = a + [HA] + 2[HA_2^-] + 2[H_2A_2]$$

$$= a + K_{11}ha + 2K_{11}K_{12}ha^2 + 2K_{11}K_{12}K_{22}h^2a^2 \qquad (7)$$

where a is the concentration of free carboxylate ions. The most convenient method[4] of confirming that the experimental data conform to equations (6) and (7) and of determining the three stability constants involves a transformation of the data $\bar{n}(\log h)_A$ to the form $\log A(\log h)_{\bar{n}}$ and comparison with normalised curves $\log A (\log h)_{\bar{n}, R}$.

The dimensionless normalised variables are defined as

$$\log \mathbf{A} \;=\; \log A \;+\; \log K_{12} \tag{8}$$

$$\log \mathbf{h} \;=\; \log h \;+\; \log K_{11} \tag{9}$$

and the shape parameter is defined by

$$\log R \;=\; \log K_{22} \;-\; \log K_{11} \tag{10}$$

The normalised curves were calculated using the relationship

$$\mathbf{A} \;=\; \frac{[\mathbf{h} - \bar{n}(1 + \mathbf{h})]\,[(1 - 2R)\mathbf{h} - 1]}{\mathbf{h}\,[2\bar{n}(1 + R\mathbf{h}) - (1 + 2R\mathbf{h})]^2} \tag{11}$$

which is derived by eliminating a from (6) to (10). The appropriate value of the parameter R was calculated from the identity

$$R \;=\; \frac{2\bar{n}^{\,*} \;-\; 1}{2\bar{n}^{\,*}} \tag{12}$$

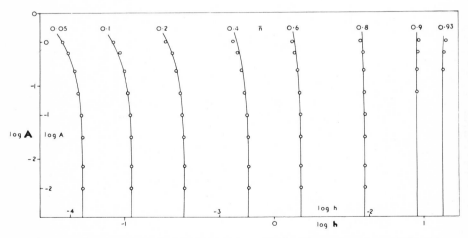

Fig. 1. Normalised curves log A (log h) $_{\bar{n},R}$, calculated using equation (11) with R = 0.425, superimposed in the position of best fit on the experimental data log A (log h)$_{\bar{n}}$ for the proton-cyanoacetate system.

for systems with an isohydric point. Otherwise, it must be found by successive approximation.

For seven of the thirteen systems studied, the hypothetical equilibria (3) to (5) are supported by the excellence of the fit of the normalised curves on to the experimental data (cf. Fig. 1). In the position of best fit, values of the stability constants are obtained by solving (8) to (10). Small deviations at high values of A between the data log A (log h)$_{\bar{n}}$ and the best families of normalised curves, calculated using (11) are consistent with the formation of trinuclear species in a few systems. Values of the stability constants for the dinuclear species, obtained by curve-fitting, were refined and stability constants for the trinuclear species $H_2A_3^-$ and H_3A_3 were obtained by successive approximation using appropriate extensions of (6) and (7).

Calculations[6] of the average number of hydrogen and carboxylate ions per polynuclear complex in a few other systems are consistent with the formation of an extensive series of polyacids H_qA_q and polyanions $H_{q-1}A_q$. As only a limited number of independent stability constants may be determined, a number of two parameter models were tested.[2] An unambiguous choice between these models proved to be impossible and only the simplest is outlined. It was assumed that q tends to very large values and that the equilibrium constants for the reactions

$$H_{q-1}A_q^- + H^+ \rightleftharpoons H_qA_q \qquad (13)$$

and

$$H_qA_q + A^- \rightleftharpoons H_qA_{q+1}^- \qquad (14)$$

are independent of q and equal to K_{11} and K_{12} respectively. It follows from (13) and (14) that the self-association constants for the reactions

$$H_{q-1}A_{q-1} + HA \rightleftharpoons H_qA_q \qquad (15)$$

are also identical[7] and equal to K_{12}. Normalised curves log A (log h)$_{\bar{n}}$ were calculated using the relationship

$$A = \frac{\bar{n}(1+h) - h}{h(1+h)(1-\bar{n})^2} \qquad (16)$$

which is derived by eliminating a from (8), (9), (13), (14) and the extended analogues of (6) and (7), and which is valid provided that

K_{12} [HA] < 1.   As these curves were superimposible within the limits of experimental error, on to the experimental data log A (log $h)_{\overline{n}}$, the model is a possible one.   Values of the association constants were obtained by solving (8) and (9) in the position of best fit.

Discussion

The association of protons and monocarboxylate ions is habitually represented by Eq. (3) only.   Nevertheless, it was suggested thirty years ago that the hydrogen diacetate[8] and hydrogen dibenzoate[9] ions exist in aqueous solution: the former to explain the acid-base catalysed enolization of acetone and the latter to explain the solubility of benzoic acid in sodium benzoate.   Several hydrogen bismonocarboxylates occur as structural units[10] in crystalline sodium and potassium salts MHA_2.   Higher acid salts (MH_2A_3 and MH_3A_4) have also been reported, but are of unknown structure. The existence of dimeric carboxylic acids in aqueous solution was first suggested[11] in 1951: dimerisation constants have since been calculated[12] from freezing point, vapour pressure, distribution, conductivity, and emf data.   Nuclear magnetic resonance, infrared and Raman spectra, dielectric behaviour, and ultrasonic absorption all indicate qualitatively that self-association occurs in aqueous solutions of carboxylic acids.   The average number of monomers per multimer in butyric acid solutions, calculated[7] from freezing point data, increases sharply from about 4 to 27 in the concentration range $2.5 \leq A \leq 17$ molal.   Infinite chains[13] exist in crystalline formic acid and acetic acids, and possibly also in one of the polymorphs of chloroacetic acid.

Although (3) suffices to explain our equilibrium data for $A \lesssim 0.05\,M$, we infer that polyacid formation is a general phenomenon at higher concentrations.   Our simultaneous identification of monomeric HA, polyacids and polyanions was made possible by the use of a constant ionic medium and rigorous methods of mathematical analysis.   In many systems, the species HA_2^- and H_2A_2 are the only polynuclear products when $A < 1\,M$.   However, there is evidence for $H_2A_3^-$ and H_3A_3 when $A \gtrsim 0.7\,M$ in the propionate, butyrate, and mandelate systems. $H_3A_4^-$, H_4A_4, and yet larger species appear to be formed in the valerate, isobutyrate, and trimethylacetate systems at concentrations where micelle formation is not apparent.   The association process may be visualised as one of alternate additions of hydrogen and carboxylate ions to a growing chain.   The latter additions are assumed to occur by hydrogen-bonding.   A catenation with alternate links identical represents an extension of the principle of stepwise equilibrium to proton-carboxylate systems.

Some of our quantitative results are summarised in Table 1. All symbols have been defined above except K_D ($= RK_{12}$) which is the dimerisation constant for the reaction

$$HA + HA \rightleftharpoons H_2A_2 \qquad K_D \qquad (17)$$

Whereas the proportions of A^- and HA in dilute solutions are functions of h and K_{11} only, the proportions of the polynuclear species are functions of H, A, and the relevant stability constants (see Fig. 2). For example, when $A = 0.7\,M$, the amount of A in the form HA_2^- is maximal at $\sim 10\%$ in 1:1 buffers of the homologous series formate to butyrate. The amount in the form H_2A_2 increases from $\sim 10\%$ in formic acid to $\sim 33\%$ in butyric acid at the same concentration.

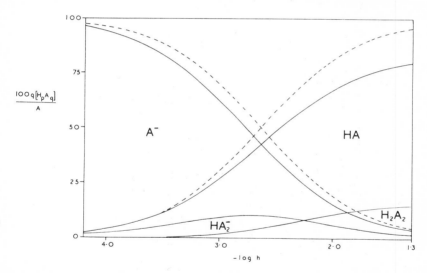

Fig. 2. The percentage distribution of cyanoacetate amongst the species formed at total concentrations $A \leq 0.05\,M$ ‒ ‒ ‒ ‒ and $A = 0.70\,M$ ——.

For the ions HA_2^-, free rotation about the central hydrogen bond is possible in solution. However, electrostatic repulsion will be expected to favour the extended form

TABLE 1: PROTON-CARBOXYLATE ASSOCIATION CONSTANTS IN A
3 M SODIUM (PERCHLORATE) IONIC MEDIUM AT 25.00 ± 0.05°C

A	$\log K_{11}$	$\log K_{12}$	$\log R$	$\log K_{22}$	$\log K_D$	Reference
Formate	3.900 ± 0.005	-0.50 ± 0.04	-0.74 ± 0.03	3.16 ± 0.04	-1.24 ± 0.07	Martin[1]
Acetate	5.014 ± 0.009	-0.34 ± 0.03	-0.38 ± 0.01	4.63 ± 0.02	-0.73 ± 0.04	Martin[1]
Propionate	5.161 ± 0.006	-0.35 ± 0.03	-0.15 ± 0.03	5.01 ± 0.04	-0.50 ± 0.06	Martin[1]
Butyrate	5.132 ± 0.007	-0.24 ± 0.03	-0.02 ± 0.02	5.11 ± 0.03	-0.26 ± 0.05	Martin[1]
Valerate	5.165 ± 0.005	-0.10 ± 0.12	0.0	5.17	-0.10	Clarke[2]
Isobutyrate	5.150 ± 0.005	-0.27 ± 0.07	0.0	5.15	-0.27	Clarke[2]
Trimethylacetate	5.325 ± 0.010	-0.14 ± 0.14	0.0	5.33	-0.14	Clarke[2]
Cyanoacetate	2.634 ± 0.005	-0.40 ± 0.02	-0.37 ± 0.01	$2.26 \pm 0.01_5$	-0.77 ± 0.03	Carson
Chloroacetate	3.018 ± 0.005	-0.36 ± 0.02	-0.35 ± 0.01	$2.67 \pm 0.01_5$	-0.71 ± 0.03	Carson
Methoxyacetate	3.728 ± 0.005	-0.28 ± 0.02	$-0.33_5 \pm 0.01_3$	3.39 ± 0.02	-0.62 ± 0.03	Carson
Phenylacetate	4.557 ± 0.008	$+0.10 \pm 0.02$	$-0.35 \pm 0.01_5$	4.21 ± 0.02	-0.25 ± 0.04	Carson
Glycollate	3.920 ± 0.005	-0.53 ± 0.02	$-0.76 \pm 0.03_5$	3.16 ± 0.04	-1.29 ± 0.06	Carson
Mandelate	3.488 ± 0.005	$-0.20 \pm 0.03_5$	-0.90 ± 0.07	2.59 ± 0.06	-1.10 ± 0.04	Carson

The dimers H_2A_2 may also exist in the open form with only one hydrogen bond; in the cyclic form, which occurs in the vapour phase and perhaps in non polar solvents; or even in an equilibrium mixture of both conformations. If the dimers were cyclic, they might be expected to be weaker acids than their monomers, i.e., $K_{22} > K_{11}$. Similarly, if the dimerisation reactions (17) were chelations, then one might expect $K_D > K_{12}$. The actual trends $K_{11} \geq K_{22} \gg K_{12} \geq K_D$ are in the expected order for ion-ion, ion-dipole, and dipole-dipole interactions and further suggest that the dimers exist predominantly in the extended form.

The free-energy argument is supported by a determination of the enthalpies and entropies of association for the acetate system. Enthalpy titrations were carried out[14] using Schlyter's adiabatic calorimeter at $25\,°C$. Concentrations of the species present in the calorimeter were calculated and the heat data solved for the enthalpies of association of HA, $HA_2{}^-$, and H_2A. Constancy of the values so calculated supports the reality of equilibria (3) to (5) and confirms the values of the stability constants obtained potentiometrically. Entropies of association ΔS were calculated[15] by combining values of the free-energy ΔG and enthalpy changes ΔH, see Table 2.

TABLE 2: THERMODYNAMIC FUNCTIONS[15] FOR PROTON-ACETATE ASSOCIATION IN A 3 M SODIUM IONIC MEDIUM AT 25°C

Reaction	ΔG(kcal/mole)	ΔH(kcal/mole)	ΔS(e.u.)
(3)	-6.839 ± 0.012	-0.721 ± 0.006	20.53 ± 0.06
(5)	-6.315 ± 0.014	-0.596 ± 0.135	19.2 ± 0.5
(4)	0.46 ± 0.04	0.300 ± 0.106	-0.5 ± 0.5
(17)	1.00 ± 0.04	0.425 ± 0.047	-1.9 ± 0.3

Values of ΔH and ΔS are similar for the pair of reactions (3) and (5): they suggest that the protonations are analogous and that (5) is not a cyclisation. Values of ΔH and ΔS for reactions (4) and (17) lead to the same conclusion for these reactions.

The values of K_{11} for acetic acid in a 3 M sodium ionic medium is in excellent agreement with independent values in the literature.[16] As would be expected, values of K_{11} valid in a 3 M sodium (perchlorate) ionic medium at $25\,°C$ are greater than the so-called thermodynamic values by a roughly constant amount (~ 0.2 log units), and the well-known trend (an increase from formate to propionate with a slight decrease to butyrate) is preserved. Values of K_{12}, K_{22}, K_D, and R also increase from formate to butyrate, the last parameter towards unity. Owing to the inter relationships

$$K_{22} = RK_{11} \quad \text{and} \quad K_D = RK_{12}$$

the pairs K_{11}, K_{22} and K_{12}, K_D each tend towards common values. This observation was the reason for our choice[2] of the two-parameter hypothesis for interpreting the more complicated equilibria in the valerate and branched-chain carboxylate systems. Stability constants for the valerate system, calculated using this model, fall into place in the sequences found for its lower homologues. Comparison of the stability constants for the propionate, isobutyrate, and trimethylacetate systems, which have carbon backbones of the same length, suggests that chain-branching slightly enhances the formation of polynuclear species. However, the effect is no more than to bring isomeric systems (butyrate and isobutyrate; valerate and trimethylacetate) roughly into line.

The trend in values of K_{11} for the straight chain acids is commonly ascribed to the inductive effect. The concomitant trends in K_{12}, K_{22}, K_D, and R might also be attributed to the same electronic effect. However, values of the parameters for substituted acetic acids do not support this hypothesis. A common value of R is found for the acetate, phenylacetate, methoxyacetate, chloroacetate, and cyanoacetate systems and values of K_{12} are equal, within experimental error, for acetate, chloroacetate, and cyanoacetate. Consequently, although values of K_{22} show the same trend as values of K_{11}, values of K_D do not, those for acetate, chloroacetate, and cyanoacetate being equal. Hence, the trends in the stability constants appear to depend mainly upon the length of the carbon skeleton.

The parameters for the glycollate and mandelate systems are unusual as compared with other substituted acetic acids. The values of R are so small as to suggest that the ions HA_2^- may be stabilised by intramolecular hydrogen bonding. However, this hypothesis may be incorrect, particularly as all the stability constants for the glycollate system are remarkably similar to those for the formate system. A further unusual feature in the mandelate system is that the trimer is a weaker acid than the dimer ($\log K_{33}/K_{22} \sim 0.5$), and may conceivably be cyclic.

Amongst the chemical consequences of the work outlined above, the following are noteworthy:

1. The hydrogen ion concentration of a monocarboxylate buffer in a constant ionic medium is a function of the total concentration of buffer A. The magnitude of the effect is indicated by the curves $\log A$ ($\log h)_{\bar{n}}$ in Fig. 1. However, in systems with an isohydric point, there will be a unique buffer, the pH of which is independent of A.

2. As a result of the identification of the hydrogen diacetate ion, there is now no unambiguous evidence for the concerted

mechanism for acid-base catalysis in aqueous solution.[17]

3. Values in the literature[18] for stability constants of weak mono-carboxylate metal-ion complexes may be slightly in error.

REFERENCES

1. D. L. Martin and F. J. C. Rossotti, *Proc. Chem. Soc.*, **1959**, 60.
2. J. J. Clarke and F. J. C. Rossotti, unpublished work.
3. F. J. C. Rossotti and H. S. Rossotti, *The Determination of Stability Constants*, McGraw-Hill Book Co., New York, 1961.
4. L. G. Sillén, *Acta Chem. Scand.*, **10**, 803 (1956).
5. F. J. C. Rossotti and H. S. Rossotti, *Acta Chem. Scand.*, **10**, 957 (1956).
6. N. Ingi, G. Lagerström, M. Frydman and L. G. Sillén, *Acta Chem. Scand.* **11**, 1034 (1957).
7. F. J. C. Rossotti and H. S. Rossotti, *J. Phys. Chem.*, **65** (1961), in press.
8. H. M. Dawson and E. Spivey, *J. Chem. Soc.*, **1930**, 2180.
9. I. M. Kolthoff and W. Bosch, *J. Phys. Chem.*, **36**, 1685 (1932).
10. J. C. Speakman, *Proc. Chem. Soc.*, **1959**, 316; **1960**, 8.
11. A. Katchalsky, H. Eisenberg and S. Lifson, *J. Am. Chem. Soc.*, **73**, 5889 (1951).
12. G. R. Nash and C. B. Monk, *J. Chem. Soc.*, **1957**, 4274, and references therein.
13. F. Holtzberg, B. Post and I. Fankuchen, *Acta Cryst.*, **6**, 127 (1953); R. E. Jones and D. H. Templeton, *Acta Cryst.*, **11**, 484 (1958); J. R. Barceló, M. P. Jorge and C. Otero, *J. Chem. Phys.*, **28**, 1230 (1958).
14. K. Schlyter and D. L. Martin, *Kgl. Tek. Högskol. Handl.*, in press.
15. D. L. Martin and F. J. C. Rossotti, *Proc. Chem. Soc.*, **1961**, 73.
16. J. Leden, *Svensk Kem. Tidskr.*, **58**, 129 (1946); A. Ellilä, *Ann. Acad. Sci. Fennicae, Ser. A*, **II**, No. 51 (1953).
17. F. J. C. Rossotti, *Nature*, **188**, 936 (1960).
18. J. Bjerrum, G. Schwarzenbach and L. G. Sillén, eds., *Stability Constants*, Part I, "Organic Ligands," The Chemical Society, London, 1957.

π-COMPLEXES FROM ACETYLENES AND METAL CARBONYLS AS INTERMEDIATES IN THE SYNTHESIS OF ORGANIC COMPOUNDS

EMILE H. BRAYE, CORNELIS HOOGZAND, WALTER HÜBEL, ULRICH KRÜERKE, ROBERT MERÉNYI, AND ERWIN WEISS

European Research Associates s.a.
95 rue Gatti de Gamond
Brussels 18, Belgium

Some years ago we started a study of the reactions of metal carbonyls with alkynes with the aims of investigating the possibilities of complex formation and of studying the chemical properties of such coordination compounds. Furthermore we hoped to isolate organometallic complexes which could throw some light on the mechanism of the "Reppe reactions"[1a] in which larger organic molecules are obtained from alkynes and metal carbonyls. At that time, apart from some iron compounds isolated by Reppe and co-workers,[1b] the only alkyne complexes known were of the type $Co_2(CO)_6(RC_2R')$ and had been prepared by Sternberg and Wender.[2]

Surprisingly, the reaction of iron carbonyls, especially $Fe_3(CO)_{12}$, with substituted acetylenes in inert solvents gave a variety of stable organo-iron compounds.[3] This reaction could also be extended to carbonyls of other transition metals; in particular, the formation of complexes of cobalt carbonyls with alkynes has been investigated in detail.[4]

The compounds obtained are penetration complexes in which an organic system is bonded to metal carbonyl groups. This organic part is formed by linking several alkynes with or without the uptake of carbon monoxide. It is of particular interest to note that this formation occurs in a single stage reaction. Compounds containing acetylenes as such, as complex ligand, are rare and it could be shown that they are generally intermediates in the formation of complexes with more complicated organic ligands. In order to study the chemical behavior of these organometallic compounds, various reactions have been carried out, leading to the elucidation of their structures as well as to new syntheses of interesting organic compounds. These complexes may be divided roughly into two groups according to the nature of the organic part.

The first group includes complexes containing a stable organic system. Representatives are tetraphenylcyclopentadienone-iron tricarbonyl (I)[3, 5] and bis-tetraphenylcyclopentadienone-nickel (II),[5] which are readily obtained by heating diphenylacetylene with iron pentacarbonyl and nickel tetracarbonyl respectively. Upon being heated to the melting point, both complexes decompose with separation of the organic ligand tetraphenylcyclopentadienone (tetracyclone). For synthetic applications, however, it is preferable to use a reagent which will remove the metal carbonyl group under milder conditions in order to reduce side reactions.

I   II   III

Thus *2,4,6*-triphenyltropone-iron tricarbonyl, $Fe(CO)_4(PhC_2H)_3$ (III),[3b] easily prepared from phenylacetylene and $Fe_3(CO)_{12}$, yields by thermal decomposition (170°) exclusively *1,3,5*-triphenylbenzene. The elimination of the ketonic group of the tropone system can be avoided by exchange of the organic ligand in III with triphenylphosphine according to the equation: III + 2PPh$_3$ ⟶ *2,4,6*-triphenyltropone (80%) + $Fe(CO)_3(PPh_3)_2$. Tropone itself is liberated in about 50% yield from tropone-iron tricarbonyl under similar conditions; the latter is formed in a 30% yield from $Fe_2(CO)_9$ and acetylene under pressure at room temperature.[6] This represents a new synthesis of tropone and substituted tropones by a two-step reaction starting from alkynes and iron carbonyls.

The formation of tetramethylhydroquinone[7] by treating tetramethylquinone-iron tricarbonyl with hydrochloric acid also illustrates this type of reaction.

The second group of organometallic complexes, readily obtained from acetylenic compounds and metal carbonyls, is characterized by the fact that the organic part forms a heterocyclic five-, six-, or seven-membered ring system (IV, V, VI, VII) with the transition metal. Stabilization of these unusual heterocycles generally occurs through π-bonding to a second metal carbonyl group. The existence of such structures was demonstrated by X-ray analysis[8] of the complex IV, first obtained by Reppe and co-workers.[1b] This structure explains the reactions of this compound as described by Jones and Whiting.[9]

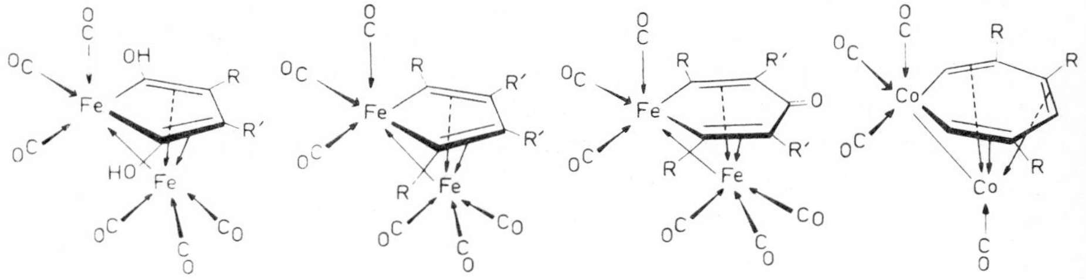

$$\text{IV} \qquad \text{V} \qquad \text{VI} \qquad \text{VII}$$

Complexes of the type $Fe_2(CO)_6(RC_2R')_2$ (V) are readily formed from iron carbonyls and substituted acetylenes.[3] The following reactions of the compound from diphenylacetylene (Table 1) suggest structure V.

The reaction products obtained indicate clearly that in the complex $Fe_2(CO)_6(PhC_2Ph)_2$ (V') two alkynes are linked forming a butadienylene group. Furthermore, it follows from the formation of tetracyclone-iron tricarbonyl that the σ-bonded iron tricarbonyl group in the ring is the more labile and is readily replaced by carbon monoxide. Thus complexes of the type $Fe_2(CO)_6(RC_2R')_2$ offer a convenient way of producing reactive butadienylene fragments, which may be used in the synthesis of furans, thiophenes, selenophenes and pyrroles. Similarly the first preparations of pentaphenylphosphole[10] and pentaphenylarsole have been achieved via the complex $Fe_2(CO)_6$-$(PhC_2Ph)_2$. The corresponding phenylacetylene complex, $Fe_2(CO)_6$-$(PhC_2H)_2$, when heated with sulfur yields exclusively 2,5-diphenyl-thiophene (80%); this shows the tendency to stereospecific linking of the alkynes during complex formation. Other examples which demonstrate the use of $Fe_2(CO)_6(RC_2R')_2$ compounds in the preparation of five-membered heterocycles are the syntheses of tetraethylthio-phene, 2,5-dimethyl-3,4-diphenylthiophene and tetracarbomethoxy-thiophene as well as the formation of tetraethylselenophene.

A similar structure (VI) is proposed for the complex $Fe_2(CO)_7$-$(PhC_2Ph)_2$ (VI'), which can be obtained from $Fe_2(CO)_9$ and diphenyl-acetylene in high yields. The following degradation reactions (Table 2) support the existence of a six-membered ring formed by two diphenylacetylenes, carbon monoxide and an iron atom.

When the iron tricarbonyl group in the ring is split off by the action of heat or u.v. light, tetracyclone-iron tricarbonyl is the main product, thus showing preferential formation of the five-membered ring from the organic skeleton of the complex. However, under other reaction

TABLE 1: REACTIONS OF $Fe_2(CO)_6(PhC_2Ph)_2$

LiAlH$_4$ / Na/NH$_3$	PhCH=CPh–CPh=CHPh PhCH=CPh–CHPh–CH$_2$Ph PhCH$_2$CHPh–CHPh–CH$_2$Ph
NaNH$_2$ / EtONa	(diene + Fe(CO)$_3$) + cyclopentadienone Fe(CO)$_3$
SO$_2$Cl$_2$ / Cl$_2$O	O=CPh–CPh=CPh–PhC=O
Δ / Br$_2$	cyclopentadienone Fe(CO)$_3$ + Fe(CO)$_3$
S, Se, PhNO / NOCl and reduc.	X=S 80%, =Se 60%, =NPh 50%, =NH 34%
PhPCl$_2$ (140°)	(64%)

conditions, replacement of the iron tricarbonyl group in the ring by carbon monoxide is also possible. The formation of tetraphenylquinone by treatment with K_2Se_x is surprising and is of preparative interest. This replacement can also occur with hetero-elements as shown by the formation of tetraphenylpyrone and -thiapyrone as well as of the hitherto unknown class of selenapyrones.

The above results suggest that in the reaction of alkynes with iron carbonyls, complexes of the type $Fe_2(CO)_7(RC_2R')_2$ (VI) and possibly $Fe_2(CO)_6(RC_2R')_2$ (V) are intermediates in the formation of cyclopentadienone-iron tricarbonyls and cyclopentadienones.

TABLE 2: REACTIONS OF $Fe_2(CO)_7(PhC_2Ph)_2$

Reagent	Products
Δ / UV light	[cyclopentadienone-Fe(CO)$_3$ complex, Ph substituted] $\longrightarrow$ Fe(CO)$_3$ + [tetraphenylcyclopentadienone]
LiAlH$_4$	[Ph-substituted cyclopentadienone-Fe complex] + [Ph-substituted dihydro cyclopentadienone] + [tetraphenyl-benzoquinone] (2–3%)
Na/NH$_3$; Na/Hg in CH$_3$OH	[tetraphenylhydroquinone, OH...OH] (21%)
Na NH$_2$/NH$_3$	PhCH$_2$–CHPh–CO–CHPh–CH$_2$Ph (90%)
K$_2$Se$_x$ / UV light	[tetraphenyl-benzoquinone] + [tetraphenylhydroquinone] + [tetraphenyl selenopyranone]
Na$_2$S$_x$ / UV light	[tetraphenyl thiopyranone] (25%)
PhNO / UV light	[tetraphenyl pyranone] (10%)

$\underline{\text{VI}'}$ [structure: $(OC)_3Fe$–Fe$(CO)_2$ with Ph-substituted ring and O]

Furthermore, it seems possible that as well as quinone-iron tricarbonyls,[7] the complex type $Fe_2(CO)_7(RC_2R')_2$ is involved in the synthesis of hydroquinones from acetylene and iron carbonyls, according to Reppe.[1]

It has been shown that neither "$FeC_{11}H_7O_5$"[1b] nor $H_2Fe_2(CO)_8$-(C_2H_2) (IV)[1b] is an intermediate in the hydroquinone synthesis. The complex formulated as "$FeC_{11}H_7O_5$" is in fact $Fe_2C_{22}H_{14}O_{10}$ and is an addition compound of two molecules of cyclopentadienone-iron tricarbonyl with one molecule of hydroquinone.[11] In this respect $Fe_2C_{22}H_{14}O_{10}$ is not directly involved in the formation of hydroquinone from acetylene and iron pentacarbonyl. The structure of IV suggests that hydroquinone might be formed by the replacement of the ring-bonded iron tricarbonyl group by acetylene.[9a] Indeed, when IV is allowed to react with acetylene under the conditions used by Reppe,[1] hydroquinone is obtained in 80% yield. However, the same reaction with dimethylacetylene yields only tetramethylhydroquinone and not the expected dimethylhydroquinone. Thus the hypothesis that IV is an intermediate in the hydroquinone synthesis can be ruled out.

Complexes of formula $Co_2(CO)_4(RC_2R')_3$ (VII) are obtained when $Co_2(CO)_6(RC_2R')$ is heated with the appropriate acetylene. These stable compounds readily react with bromine to give symmetrically substituted benzene when R = Ph and R' = COOR or CH_3.[4] Co_2-$(CO)_4[(CH_3)_3CC_2H]_3$, however, gives the unsymmetrical 1,2,4-tri-t-butylbenzene[12] which is isolated in 90% yield. This is the first synthesis of a substituted benzene bearing the bulky t-butyl groups in the ortho-position. Heat of combustion and spectroscopic measurements[13] have shown the benzene ring in this molecule to be distorted. The formation of 1,2,4-tri-t-butylbenzene can be explained on the assumption that the complex $Co_2(CO)_4[(CH_3)_3CC_2H]_3$ has the structure VII in which a cobalt atom forms a seven-membered ring with three alkynes in the appropriate sequence.

VIII   IX

Another cobalt complex of formula $Co_3(CO)_9(RC_2H)H$, first obtained by Sternberg and Wender,[14] also offers interesting preparative possibilities. Degradation with bromine yields substituted bromoforms, RCH_2-CBr_3, which are generally difficult to synthesize. This reaction seems to be of general application in the preparation of 1,1,1-trihalogenoalkanes. The formation of substituted bromoforms suggests structure VIII[15] for this complex type and explains why these compounds can be obtained only from mono-substituted acetylenes, since their formation involves migration of an acetylenic hydrogen.

$Fe_2(CO)_6(PhC_2H)_3$[3b], prepared from $Fe_3(CO)_{12}$ and phenylacetylene, has a very unusual structure. X-ray analysis by King[16] has shown the presence of two fused five-membered rings having a carbon and an iron atom in common as shown in IX. Depending on the conditions of degradation different products are obtained. In boiling benzene, the iron dicarbonyl group is eliminated yielding *2,4,6*-triphenyltropone-iron tricarbonyl. Thermal decomposition at 170° leads to the loss of all carbonyl groups with the formation of *1,3,5*-triphenylbenzene. However, oxidation with $FeCl_3$ gives *2,4,6*-triphenyltropone in 40% yield.

The formation of cyclobutadiene complexes by reacting alkynes with metal carbonyls is of particular interest. The possibility of stabilization of this hitherto unknown organic system by complex formation has been considered from a theoretical standpoint by Longuet-Higgins and Orgel.[17] Thus $Fe(CO)_3(PhC_2Ph)_2$,[3b] which is readily obtained from $Fe(CO)_5$ and diphenylacetylene, has been shown by X-ray analysis[18] to be tetraphenylcyclobutadiene-iron tricarbonyl. Good evidence has been obtained that the cyclobutadiene system is also a ligand in some cobalt[4] and molybdenum[19] complexes. However, no reaction has yet been found to confirm the presence of this ring system. The degradation products seem to depend on the nature of the transition metal.

It sometimes happens that, in the reaction of organometallic complexes with alkynes, products are formed in which the original acetylenic bond must have been broken. Thus, $Co_2(CO)_6(PhC_2Ph)$ when heated with $Me_3SiC_2SiMe_3$ gives *3,4*-diphenyl-*2,5-bis*-trimethylsilyl-cyclopentadienone as well as *2,3,5,6*-tetraphenyl-*1,4-bis*-trimethylsilyl-benzene.[4] The most plausible mechanism of this

reaction involves the intermediate formation of cyclobutadiene complexes (*X*) which then undergo ring enlargement in any position.

In the course of this work it was found that a large number of metal carbonyls and their organic derivatives[20] catalyze the cyclic trimerization of a greater variety of alkynes than does $Ni(CO)_2$-$(PPh_3)_2$.[21] Unlike Ziegler-Natta type catalysts,[22] metal carbonyls lead only to unsymmetrically substituted benzenes from asymmetric acetylenes. It is assumed that in this trimerization reaction unstable organometallic complexes are involved in which two alkynes are linked together stereospecifically.

We are now concentrating our efforts on the isolation of less stable complexes which are intermediates in the formation of the stable compounds discussed above. Thus, it has been possible to isolate relatively unstable compounds of formula $Fe_2(CO)_7(RC_2R')^{23}$ which readily react with further alkynes to give the complex type $Fe_2(CO)_7$ $(RC_2R')_2(VI)$. Other interesting compounds have the composition $Fe(CO)_4(RC_2R')^{23}$ suggesting that they are the first products of the reaction of iron pentacarbonyl with acetylenes.

REFERENCES

1. (a) W. Reppe, *Neuere Entwicklungen auf dem Gebiet der Chemie des Acetylens und Kohlenoxyds*, Springer-Verlag, 1949.
   (b) W. Reppe and H. Vetter, *Annalen*, **582**, 133 (1953).
2. H. W. Sternberg, H. Greenfield, R.A. Friedel, J. Wotiz, R. Markby and I. Wender, *J. Am. Chem. Soc.*, **76**, 1457 (1954); H. Greenfield, H. W. Sternberg, R.A. Friedel, J.H. Wotiz, R. Markby and I. Wender, *ibid.*, **78**, 120 (1956); M.R. Tirpak, C.A. Hollingworth and J.H. Wotiz, *J. Org. Chem.*, **25**, 687 (1960).
3. (a) W. Hübel, E.H. Braye, A. Clauss, E. Weiss, U. Krüerke, D.A. Brown, G.S.D. King and C. Hoogzand, *J. Inorg. Nucl. Chem.*, **9**, 204 (1959).
   (b) W. Hübel and E.H. Braye, *ibid.*, **10**, 250 (1959).
   (c) G.N. Schrauzer, *J. Am. Chem. Soc.*, **81**, 5307 (1959).
4. U. Krüerke and W. Hübel, unpublished work.
5. E. Weiss and W. Hübel, *J. Inorg. Nucl. Chem.*, **11**, 42 (1959).
6. W. Hübel and E. Weiss, *Chem. and Ind.*, 703 (1959).
7. H. W. Sternberg, R. Markby and I. Wender, *J. Am. Chem. Soc.*, **80**, 1009 (1958).
8. A.A. Hock and O.S. Mills, *Acta Cryst.*, **14**, 139 (1961).
9. (a) R. Clarkson, E.R.H. Jones, P.C. Wailes and M.C. Whiting, *J. Am. Chem. Soc.*, **78**, 6206 (1956).
   (b) J.R. Case, R. Clarkson, E.R.H. Jones and M.C. Whiting, *Proc. Chem. Soc.*, 150 (1959).
10. E.H. Braye and W. Hübel, *Chem. and Ind.*, 1250 (1959).
11. E. Weiss, R.G. Merényi and W. Hübel, *Chem. and Ind.*, 407 (1960).
12. U. Krüerke, C. Hoogzand and W. Hübel, *Chem. Ber.* (in press).
13. J. Dale, *Chem. Ber.* (in press).
14. R. Markby, I. Wender, R.A. Friedel, F.A. Cotton and H.W. Sternberg, *J. Am. Chem. Soc.*, **80**, 6529 (1958).
15. U. Krüerke and W. Hübel, *Chem. and Ind.*, 1264 (1960).
16. G.S.D. King, *Acta Cryst.*, **13**, 1028 (1960).
17. H.C. Longuet-Higgins and L.E. Orgel, *J. Chem. Soc.*, 1969 (1956).
18. R.P. Dodge and V. Schomaker, *Nature*, **186**, 798 (1960).
19. W. Hübel and R. Merényi, unpublished work.

20. W. Hübel and C. Hoogzand, *Chem. Ber.*, **93**, 103 (1960).
21. W. Reppe and W.J. Schweckendiek, *Annalen*, **560**, 104 (1948).
22. W.R. Smith, Engl. Pat. Nr. 802510 (8. 10. 1958), C.A., **53**, P8070[i] (1959);
    B. Franzus, P.C. Canterino and R.A. Wickliffe, *J. Am. Chem. Soc.*, **81**, 1514 (1959).
23. C. Hoogzand and W. Hübel, unpublished work.

CONDUCTION ELECTRONIQUE DANS LES LIAISONS DES NICKEL CARBONYLE SUBSTITUES

MICHAËL BIGORGNE

Laboratoire de Chimie minerale
Ecole Nationale Superieure de Chimie
Paris, France

Les nickel carbonyle substitués par des ligands $PX_3 X$ = F, Cl, Oϕ, OR, ϕ, R) ont été étudiés[1] spectrographiquement en faisant varier le degré de substitution pour un même ligand, et en modifiant le ligand pour un même degré de substitution. Les fréquences de vibration C—O fournissent un réseau très homogène (Fig. 1) qui permet d'observer les variations de l'ordre des liaisons C—O dans ces com-

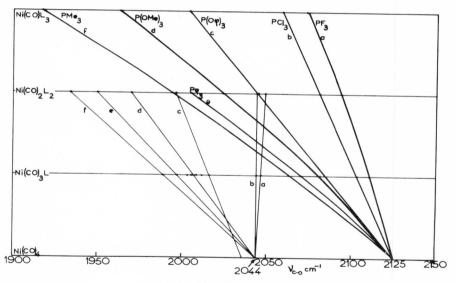

Fig. 1

posés, et de tirer des conclusions relatives au mécanisme électronique des substitutions. Ces conclusions sont confirmées par l'étude des spectres Raman des substitués où $X — R$ et OR qui permettent d'observer les variations corrélatives des ordres des liaisons Ni—C.

199

Ces conclusions sont brièvement rappelées maintenant:

1. Les fréquences des vibrations symétriques C—O des sub-stitués d'un même ligand convergent sur la fréquence de vibration symétrique C—O de Ni(CO)$_4$: 2125 cm^{-1} dans le cétane; il en est de même pour les vibrations antisymétriques.

2. Pour un même ligand, il y a décroissance régulière des fré-quences de vibration C—O et accroissement régulier des fréquences de vibration Ni—C, lorsque croît le degré de substitution.

3. Les constantes de force des liaisons C—O dans les substitués Ni(CO)$_n L_{4-n}$ ($n = 1, 2, 3$) varient linéairement avec n, pour L donné. Ainsi, pour L = PMe$_3$, les liaisons Ni—C et C—O du trisubstitué Ni(CO)(PMe$_3$)$_3$ sont approximativement des liaisons doubles (Fig. 2).

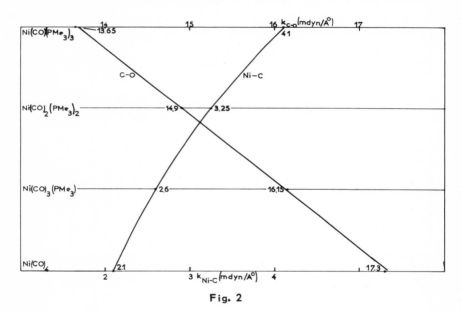

Fig. 2

Le degré de liaison π(Ni—C) de Ni(CO)$_4$ est au maximum 0, 25.

4. Lorsqu'on fait varier la nature de L, en gardant le même degré de substitution, l'ordre de classement des ligands en fonction des variations des constantes de force C—O et Ni—C suit de très près leur ordre de basicité. Plus le ligand est basique, plus la liaison Ni=C est renforcée et plus la liaison C—O est relâchée. Il se pro-duit un écoulement d'électrons du ligand vers l'atmosphère extérieure de l'oxygène à travers les atomes Ni et C.

Un examen attentif de la figure 1 fait apparaître que les atomes at-tachés à l'atome ligand sont placés dans le même ordre que celui de la classification périodique, c'est-à-dire dans l'ordre des électronégativités croissantes. En faisant abstraction de Cl, qui ne se trouve pas sur la même ligne du tableau périodique que les autres atomes, on lit la suite: C—O—F.

On peut donc se demander si l'atome lié à l'atome ligand n'est pas, en fait, l'atome responsable, par son électronégativité, de la variation des constantes de force C—O.

Par commodité d'écriture, un nickel carbonyle substitué sera représenté par:

$$r—x—l——Ni—C—O$$

l est l'atome ligand
x est l'atome attaché à l'atome ligand
r est le reste du ligand

Ainsi, dans la molécule $Ni(CO)_2(P\phi_3)_2$, l = P et x = C.

Pour vérifier l'hypothèse ci-dessus: que les atomes x reportent une partie de leur charge sur l'O des CO, il est nécessaire d'établir:

1. Que l'atome x = N se place au voisinage de C et O sur le graphique de la figure 1.

2. Que chaque liaison $l—xr$ du ligand $l(xr)_3$ contribue d'une façon égale aux variations des fréquences C—O.

1. Il existe peu de molécules stables du type PX_3 et comportant 3 liaisons P—N. La tripipéridylphosphine $P(NC_5H_{10})_3$ est l'une de celles-ci et remplace facilement, par étapes successives, 2 CO de $Ni(CO)_4$: $Ni(CO)_3[P(NC_5H_{10})_3]$ et $Ni(CO)_2[P(NC_5H_{10})_3]_2$ sont des composés solides blancs, dont les solutions dans le cétane présentent 2 bandes de vibrations d'extension C—O à 2062, $5 \pm 0,5$ cm^{-1} et 1986 ± 1 cm^{-1} pour le monosubstitué, 1992, $0 \pm 0,5$ cm^{-1} et 1932, 5 ± 1 cm^{-1} pour le di-substitué, de sorte que la courbe des fréquences (P—N) se trouve pratiquement confondue avec celle des fréquences (P—C) (Fig. 3).

Ainsi x = N se trouve bien placé au voisinage de x = C; cependant on se serait attendu à le trouver situé entre x = C et x = O, d'après la valeur de son indice d'électronégativité. Le faible décalage observé peut, sans doute, être attribué aux contraintes subies par N dans le cycle pipéridylique:

$$—N \langle 120° \rangle$$

Il aurait été préférable de faire l'examen avec des ligands du type $P(NR_2)_3$, mais ceux-ci sont d'un maniement délicat.

L'écart observé est cependant suffisamment faible pour que l'on puisse admettre que l'atome x = N a un comportement en étroite re-

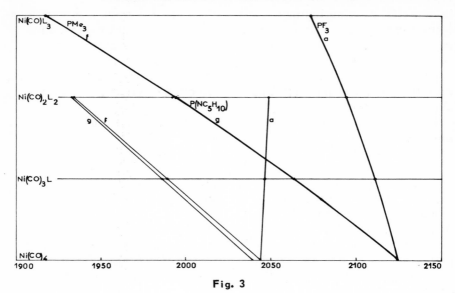

Fig. 3

lation d'électronégativité avec les atomes x voisins, C et O.

2. Pour montrer que chaque liaison l—xr du ligand $l(xr)_3$ contribue d'une façon égale aux variations des fréquences C—O, on-a observé le comportement des substitués $Ni(CO)_n(PX_3)_{4-n}$, $Ni(CO)_n(PX_2Y)_{4-n}$, $Ni(CO)_n(PXY_2)_{4-n}$, $Ni(CO)_n(PY_3)_{4-n}$,

$$\text{où } n = 1, 2, 3$$
$$X = Cl$$
$$Y = \phi \text{ ou } OBu^n$$

TABLEAU 1: FRÉQUENCES DES VIBRATIONS D'EXTENSION C—O DES COMPOSÉS $Ni(CO)_nL_{4-n}$ EN SOLUTION DANS LE CÉTANE.

$$L = P\phi_3, \ PCl\phi_2, \ PCl_2\phi, \ PCl_3$$

n	$P\phi_3$ Sym.	$P\phi_3$ Antis.	$PCl\phi_2$ Sym.	$PCl\phi_2$ Antis.	$PCl_2\phi$ Sym.	$PCl_2\phi$ Antis.	PCl_3 Sym.	PCl_3 Antis.
1	2070*	1997*	2082,0	{2017,0 / 2008,0}	2092,7	{2032* / 2023*}	2103,3	2044*
2 / 3	2005,0	1950,0	2031,3* / 1975,7*	1979,5*	2057,5 / 2018,5	2011,5*	2081,3 / 2059*	2044*

*Ces fréquences ont été déterminées à ± 1 cm⁻¹, les autres à ±0,5 cm⁻¹.

TABLEAU 2: FRÉQUENCES DES VIBRATIONS D'EXTENSION C—O DES COMPOSES $Ni(CO)_nL_{4-n}$ EN SOLUTION DANS LE CÉTANE, $L = P(OBu)_3$, $PCl(OBu)_2$, $PCl_2(OBu)$ PCl_3

n \ L	P(OBu)$_3$ Sym.	P(OBu)$_3$ Antis.	PCl(OBu)$_2$ Sym.	PCl(OBu)$_2$ Antis.	PCl$_2$(OBu) Sym.	PCl$_2$(OBu) Antis.
1	2077,0	$\begin{cases} 2000,0 \\ 2008,0 \end{cases}$	2088,7	$\begin{cases} 2024,5 \\ 2014,5 \end{cases}$	2097,5	2033,5*
2	2019*	1963,5	2047,5*	1995,5	2068,2	2023,5
3	1954,3		2004 ±2		2037*	

Le système de courbes obtenues est tout-à-fait homogène et présente les convergences habituelles sur les fréquences des vibrations symétriques et antisymétriques de $Ni(CO)_4$.

Les Fig. 4 et 5 se rapportent respectivement aux ligands P—Cl—OBu.

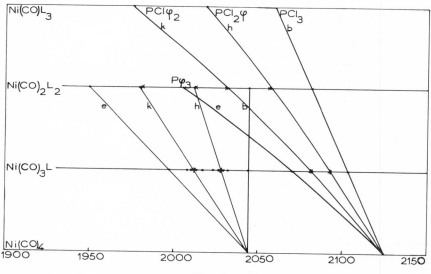

Fig. 4

La Fig. 4 montre une variation rigoureusement linéaire des fréquences C—O entre les fréquences C—O relatives à $P\phi_3$ et les fréquences C—O relatives à PCl_3. Les croix de cette figure se rapportent aux fréquences C—O calculées. En faisant la moyenne, pour chaque substitué, des fréquences des vibrations symétriques et antisymétriques, l'écart entre les valeurs observées et les valeurs calculées est 1% au maximum, c'est-à-dire inférieur à l'erreur provenant des mesures.

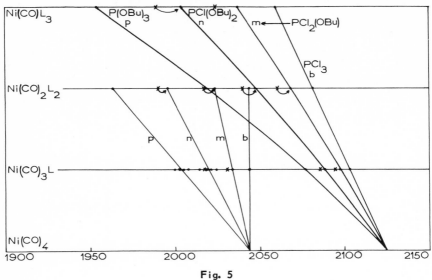

Fig. 5

On possède donc ainsi la preuve que les fréquences de vibration C—O des substitués $Ni(CO)_n(PX_3)_{4-n}$ ou $Ni(CO)_n(PX_2Y)_{4-n}$ sont directement sous l'influence de composantes liées aux groupes X et Y: en effet ces composantes, au moins pour les groupes Cl et ϕ, interviennent indépendamment les unes des autres.

Comme on a vu que l'ordre de classement des PX_3 est celui de la classification périodique pour les atomes x, il est naturel de penser que l'électronégativité des x est l'élément moteur gouvernant la conduction électronique dans ces composés.

Abel, Bennet et Wilkinson[5], examinant les spectres des trisubstitués du molybdène carbonyle avec PCl_3, $PCl_2\phi$, $PCl\phi_2$ et $P\phi_3$, ont observé une variation assez régulière des fréquences C—O. L'interprétation qu'ils en donnent est cependant différente de celle qui est présentée ici : ils pensent que l'augmentation des fréquences C—O avec les complexes-PCl_3 est dûe au plus grand pouvoir récepteur des orbitales d (capacité π) du P dans PCl_3, en raison du caractère très électronégatif de l'atome $x = Cl$. Nous pensons de préférence[(1)] que le phénomène essentiel que l'on observe est un effet purement inductif, puisque le degré de liaison π, maximum dans le métal carbonyle non substitué, reste faible dans toutes les liaisons Ni—l des nickel carbonyle substitués, et ne peut suffire à expliquer les variations considérables des ordres de liaison C—O que montrent les spectres.

Les résultats expérimentaux se révèlent plus complexes lorsque X

ou Y est constitué par OR, c'est-à-dire dans le cas des substitués-phosphites d'alkyles. La Fig. 5 montre les courbes de variation des fréquences C—O des complexes mono-, di- et tri-substitués obtenus avec PCl_3, $PCl_2(OBu)$, $PCl(OBu)_2$ et $P(OBu)_3$. Les croix indiquent les fréquences calculées que l'on devrait obtenir pour des relations linéaires, comme observé dans le cas précédent: l'écart avec les fréquences expérimentales est important.

On voit ainsi apparaître un comportement particulier des ligands $P(OR)_3$: un ligand donné, $PCl_2(OR)$ ou $PCl(OR)_2$, a un pouvoir donneur-accepteur bien déterminé pour les 3 substitués qu'il donne avec $Ni(CO)_4$, mais le pouvoir donneur-accepteur de chacun de ces ligands n'est pas seulement le résultat de composantes propres à Cl et à OR.

Ceci est sans doute à rapprocher de la position de la courbe-$P(OR)_3$ de la Fig. 1 relativement aux autres courbes: déjà on observe un écart anormal entre $P(OR)_3$ et $P(O\phi)_3$: la courbe $P(O\phi)_3$ se trouve située à peu près à la place que l'on peut déduire des indices d'électronégativité comparés de $C(PMe_3)$ et $F(PF_3)$; la courbe-$P(OR)_3$ devrait donc être placée tout près de la courbe-$P(O\phi)_3$, à l'image du couple PR_3—$P\phi_3$.

L'explication du comportement anormal des ligands $P(OR)_3$ n'a pu être déterminée. Il montre que, dans ce cas particulier, le pouvoir donneur-accepteur du ligand $P(OR)_3$ ne dépend pas uniquement de l'électronégativité de $x = 0$, bien qu'il en soit la manifestation essentielle.

Le comportement des ligands mixtes P—Cl—ϕ ne pouvant pratiquement pas résulter d'une double coïncidence, il sera admis d'une façon générale que l'électronégativité de l'atome x est l'élément déterminant des variations des fréquences C—O dans les substitués r—x—l—Ni—C—O.

3. Il reste maintenant à déterminer quel rôle jouent les atomes l, Ni et C, traversés par ce flux électronique, en autres termes quelles sont leurs conductions.

Le rôle du nickel et celui du carbone ne seront pas discutés ici: il est généralement admis que Ni conserve une charge qui varie peu d'un substitué au suivant: c'est dire qu'il présente une conduction à peu près totale. La conduction de cet atome ne pourrait être étudiée valablement qu'en observant le comportement de substitués d'un autre métal tétracarbonyle, lequel fait défaut. De la même façon, la conduction de C a été supposée totale, puisque la somme des ordres des liaisons du C, avec Ni et O, reste constante dans les divers substitués d'un même ligand: cette conduction du carbone est dûe à l'extrême mobilité de l'une des doubles liaisons C≡O.

La conduction de l a été examinée en substituant l'atome d'azote à l'atome de phosphore; les amines utilisées comportent des liaisons

N—C, ce sont le 2,2'-dipyridyle et 1'o-phénanthroline. Les éléments de comparaison avec $l = P$ sont donc les phosphines PR_3.

Les complexes $Ni(CO)_2(o$-phen) et $Ni(CO)_2(dipy)$ ont déjà été préparés par Hieber, Mühlbauer, Ehmann[2]. Ce sont des solides rouges. Nyholm et Short[3] ont examiné le spectre IR de $Ni(CO)_2(dipy)$ en dispersion dans la vaseline, en raison de son insolubilité dans les divers solvants, et annoncent les fréquences des vibrations C—O à 1950 et 1861 cm^{-1}.

L'examen de ce composé a été repris, à l'état de solide finement divisé dans la vaseline ou sous forme de pastille de KBr. On obtient, dans les 2 cas, deux bandes extrêmement larges, manifestement composées, à 1968 et 1870 cm^{-1} (KBr), en accord avec les résultats de Nyholm.

Cependant le spectre effectué sur la solution éthérée de réaction présente 2 bandes fines (Fig. 6) de même largeur environ que les

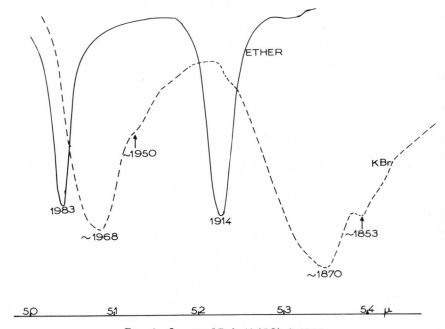

Fig. 6. Spectre IR de Ni(CO)₂(DIPY)

bandes des di-substitués-P^{III}, à 1983 et 1914 cm^{-1}. De même les cristaux rouges, isolés, puis dissous à nouveau dans l'éther, présentent ces 2 mêmes bandes.

La seule correction à effectuer sur ces fréquences provient de l'éther solvant qui abaisse quelque peu les fréquences obtenues avec les solutions dans les carbures saturés. Il n'y a pas de correction due au caractère chélate du complexe: les spectres obtenus par Chatt et Hart[4] sur les di-substitués du $Ni(CO)_4$ par des mono- et des diphosphines à liaisons P—C, sont identiques.

L'écart de fréquences observé sur $Ni(CO)_2(dipy)$, en solution et à l'état de solide, est considérable: on peut se demander si la molécule est monomère à l'état solide; la polymérisation de ce composé se justifierait également par la largeur inaccoutumée des bandes de vibration.

$Ni(CO)_2(o\text{-phen})$ a ses 2 bandes de fréquences C—O très voisines de celles du composé précédent: 1978 et 1903 cm^{-1}, dissous dans l'éther.

Il n'existe donc qu'un faible écart entre les fréquences des di-substitués à liaisons P—C et N—C: 15 cm^{-1} sur la fréquence moyenne, alors que la variation de fréquence moyenne est 120 cm^{-1} de $Ni(CO)_4$ à $Ni(CO)_2(PMe_3)_2$.

A elle seule, la différence d'électronégativité entre N(3, 0) et P(2, 1) suffit à expliquer le sens et la grandeur de cet écart. Il n'est donc pas besoin de supposer de liaisons $\pi(Ni—P)$ pour les complexes $Ni(CO)_n(PR_3)_{4-n}$, où l'atome x est le C: si elles existaient à un degré notable, les complexes homologues comportant des liaisons Ni—N devraient présenter des fréquences C—O beaucoup plus basses.

Il serait, par contre, très instructif d'examiner des complexes $Ni(CO)_n(NCl_3)_{4-n}$, à supposer qu'ils existent: on devrait observer un abaissement important des fréquences C—O par rapport aux complexes-PCl_3, puisque ces derniers comportent des liaisons $\pi(Ni—P)$ notables.

Le terme de conduction de l'atome ligand l s'introduit donc, par son indice d'électronégativité, dans la conduction totale des électrons dans le complexe: un indice d'électronégativité élevé de l abaisse les fréquences de vibration C—O, à l'inverse des indices d'électronégativité de x.

En conclusion, mis à part l'atome central de Ni, qui est très probablement un conducteur parfait, l'atome responsable des déplacements de charges le long de la chaîne $r—x—l—Ni—C—O$ est l'atome x, dont la différence d'électronégativité avec l détermine le transfert électronique: une liaison très ionique du type P—Cl, au profit de Cl, ne libère pas le doublet datif de P, tandis qu'une liaison covalente du type P—C favorise la disponibilité de ce doublet. La comparaison des spectres des complexes (x = C, l = P ou N) ne met pas en évidence de liaison $\pi(Ni—P)$.

Dans des cas particuliers, celui de $P(OR)_3$ et celui sans doute de $P(NC_5H_{10})_3$, les groupes (OR) et (NC_5H_{10}) induisent un terme de conduction supplémentaire sur l'atome de P: ceci résulte des courbes de fréquences C—O obtenues avec les mixtes P—Cl—OR, montrant que les groupes OR interagissent avec les groupes Cl, probablement par l'intermédiaire de l'atome ligand P.

Enfin le rester n'intervient que dans la mesure où il modifie la charge portée par x: on peut noter que l'extrême sensibilité des fréquences C—O aux variations de charge de x permet d'étudier comparativement les effets de charge d'un grand nombre de radicaux organiques par l'examen spectrographique des complexes nickel carbonyle-phosphine.

BIBLIOGRAPHIE

1. Bigorgne, *Bull. Soc. Chim.*, 1986 (1960).
2. Hieber, Mühlbauer and Ehmann, *Ber.*, 1932, **65B,** 1090.
3. Nyholm and Short, *J. Chem. Soc.*, 2670 (1953).
4. Chatt and Hart, *J. Chem. Soc.*, 1378 (1960).
5. Abel, Bennet, and Wilkinson, *J. Chem. Soc.*, 2323 (1959).

SOME RESULTS OF MEASUREMENTS OF EXCHANGE CURRENT DENSITIES IN ELECTRODE PROCESSES INVOLVING METAL COMPLEXES

VINCENZO CAGLIOTI, GUIDO SARTORI, CLAUDIO FURLANI, ANITA FURLANI and GIORGIO MORPURGO

Instituto di Chimica Generale di Inorganica,
Università di Roma
Rome, Italy

Whereas the equilibrium potential of a metal or redox electrode changes on formation of a complex species in solution as a function of the free energy of complex formation, and is therefore independent of the actual path through which charge transfer in the electrode reaction occurs, the rate of electron transfer, i.e. the rate of flow of a net current density (c.d.) under applied transfer overvoltage, depends strictly on the mechanism of the redox process at the electrode, and can be regarded as a kinetic manifestation of the reactivity of the complex species involved. An experimental study of the rate of electron transfer in electrode reactions of complexes requires preferably that only transfer overvoltage is operating, and this condition can be satisfied by using non-stationary polarisation techniques, such as the galvanostatic[1] or the potentiostatic method,[2] and measuring only the initial values of overvoltage and of current density (c.d.); the quantity to be determined through the experimental measurements can be the exchange current density (c.d.) only, but it is advisable to measure, if possible, also partial current densities (c.d.s.) out of equilibrium, since this allows also an investigation of possible alternative mechanisms which may take place at higher current densities (c.d.s.).

Mechanisms in Electronic Reactions of Metal Complexes

Three main types of mechanism can be encountered in electronic reactions of metal complexes. First, the soluble species undergoing reduction at the electrode is the complex species prevailingly present in solution, i.e., the complex itself without previous dissociation. Then, provided its formation constant is large enough, the cathodic c.d. is independent of the excess concentration of the free ligand C_L. If the anodic process is the dissolution of the metal or of its amalgam,

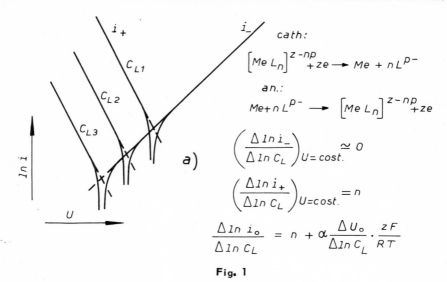

Fig. 1

then the anodic c.d. will depend on C_L (see Fig. 1). The exchange c.d. is expected to be rather high (at least higher than would correspond to a reduction mechanism via previous dissociation).

This type of behaviour can occur with all types of complexes, but is more probable with inert complexes. Electron transfer without previous dissociation is likely to occur, e.g., in redox processes, between two forms of a complex with equal c.n. and different oxidation states, such as the couple ferrocyanide-ferricyanide, and seems also to occur in the reduction of Ni^{++} in thiocyanate solutions, and of copper (II) complexes with polydentate amines. In order to compare rates of electrodic charge transfer of different complexes behaving in this general way, it is less significant to compare the exchange c.d.s, the values of which correspond to individually different equilibrium potentials, than the partial current densities (c.d.s.) at a given fixed potential. However, since the transfer coefficients may be different for different complexes, the effect of a fixed potential difference on the rate constant is not always equal. The best thing would be to compare electrodic rate constants at the null point of the electrode, but extrapolation of the partial current densities (c.d.s.) to this point would be highly uncertain, since there is no theoretical reason why the transfer coefficients should remain exactly constant throughout a wide range of overvoltages.

Second, in the other extreme case, a complex may dissociate completely down to bare metal ions before undergoing electrodic reduction.

The corresponding anodic process is then the dissolution of the metal
to bare metal ions, followed, after the transfer stage, by reaction with
the ligands. Therefore, the anodic current density (c.d.) should be
independent of C_L; furthermore, since the anodic transfer process is
the same as in the dissolution of the metal in non-complexing solutions, the Tafel plot of anodic current density (c.d.) should give the
same straight line as in non-complexing solutions, or at least its
continuation (see Fig. 2). However the equilibrium potential will be
more negative and therefore the exchange current density (c.d.) will
be lower. The cathodic current density (c.d.) will also be low, since
it is proportional to the low concentration of free metal ions in equilibrium with the complex, and at constant potential it will be inversely proportional to the nth power of C_L if n is the c.n. Although
the initial current density (c.d.) at a given overpotential depends
only on the equilibrium concentration of free metal ions, irrespective
of the lability or inertness of the complex, the successive course of
the electrolysis depends on the kinetic character of the complex: if

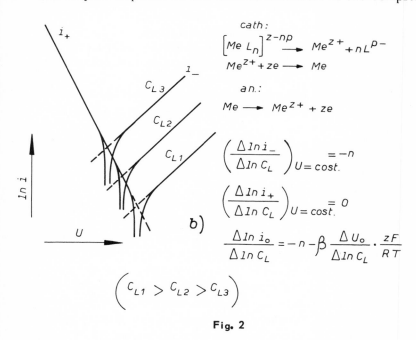

Fig. 2

the complex is labile, formation of free ions is rapid and allows the
total analytical concentration of the metal to be effective in the reduction process, just as would happen in case (1), or as happens in
the reduction of a simple salt of the metal. If however the complex

is inert, not all of the concentration of metal ion present in solution in different forms can be used up in the reduction without giving rise to additional overvoltages beyond that of charge transfer; when using a galvanostatic technique of measurement, such behaviour is revealed by a decrease of the product $i_o\sqrt{\tau}$ with increasing current density (c.d.).[3] As a limiting case, this can easily lead to practical non-reducibility of stable and inert complexes, as a consequence of the combination of low exchange current density (c.d.) and of slow formation of the active species.

Third, perhaps the most common case is intermediate between 1 and 2, i.e., the complex often undergoes partial dissociation before reduction, and the oxidation leads to dissolution of the metal with formation of a complex with c.n. lower than that of the complex form which is prevailing in solution. Both the anodic and cathodic log plots of current density (c.d.) depend now on C_L (see Fig. 3). The current densities (c.d.s.) are, in general, higher than in the case of reduction through bare metal ions, but do not yet correspond to reduction of a complex species present in a massive concentration; therefore, the current densities (c.d.s.) are expected not to be very high, and, furthermore, if the complex is inert, a decrease of $i_o\sqrt{\tau}$ in galvanostatic measurements can take place when the cathodic current density (c.d.) is increased. The occurrence of partial dissociation, so that the species which are actually active in the transfer process are complexes with low c.n., has already been presented in several cases by Gerischer.[4] We have observed numerous typical cases where this type of behaviour is verified, as, for instance, with tartrate and citrate complexes of Zn^{++}, where, at least in the presence of large excesses of free ligand, the c.n. prevailing in solution is 2, but the form actually being reduced or formed in the oxidation of Zn-amalgam is the 1:1 complex.

It can also happen that more than one complex species takes part at the same time in the electrodic process, i.e., that the reaction rates for two or more reducible or oxidizable species become comparable at a given potential. However, since two or more primary electrode processes will have, in general, different transfer coefficients, each of the possible processes will be more favoured in a definite region of overpotential. A further cause of potential dependence in the competition between two mechanisms of primary electrode processes can be selective adsorption or desorption of one of the involved species at the metallic electrode surface. As a general trend, at high cathodic current densities (c.d.s.), reduction of species with higher c.n., and at high anodic current density (c.d.), formation of species with lower c.n. will occur more easily. An example of this

cath:

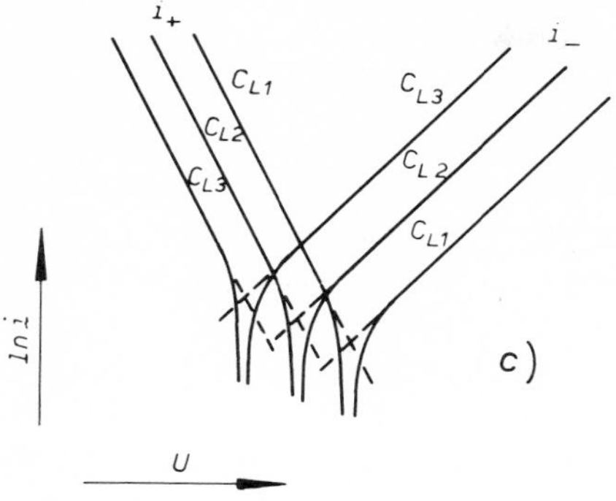

$$\left[Me\, L_n\right]^{z-np} \longrightarrow \left[Me\, L_m\right]^{z-mp} + (n-m)L^{p-}$$

$$(m < n)$$

$$\left[Me\, L_m\right]^{z-mp} + ze \longrightarrow Me + m\, L^p$$

an.:

$$Me + m\, L^{p-} \longrightarrow \left[Me\, L_m\right]^{z-mp} + ze$$

$$\left(\frac{\Delta \ln i_-}{\Delta \ln C_L}\right)_{U = cost.} = m - n$$

$$\left(\frac{\Delta \ln i_+}{\Delta \ln C_L}\right)_{U = cost.} = m$$

$$\frac{\Delta \ln i_o}{\Delta \ln C_L} = m + \alpha\, \frac{\Delta U_o}{\Delta \ln C_L} \cdot \frac{z\,F}{R\,T}$$

$$= m - n - \beta\, \frac{\Delta U_o}{\Delta \ln C_L} \cdot \frac{z\,F}{R\,T}$$

$$\left(C_{L1} > C_{L2} > C_{L3}\right)$$

Fig. 3

behaviour is offered by the ethylenediamine complexes of Cd (see below, "Experimental Results").

Among other factors which can affect the rate of electrochemical processes of complexes, mention should be made of the influence of adding certain anions, such as Cl^-, Br^-, or CNS^- to the solution; we have measured quantitatively in various instances the effect of these anions, which, as is already known, more or less enhance the rate of electrodic redox reactions.[5] A similar effect is exerted also by acetate anions in zinc solutions, although complex formation takes place in this case only to a very limited extent.

Experimental Results

Measurements have been made by the galvanostatic and by the potentiostatic method; the two methods give practically equal results, but the galvanostatic method was preferred in a number of cases, because it allows easier and more reliable corrections for the ohmic drop,[6] which is particularly large when using dropping capillary electrodes, where the internal resistance may be of the order of one hundred ohms. Measurements with amalgam electrodes were performed at dropping amalgam capillaries; a synchronizing device was used and the measurements were made directly on the drop as it issued from the capillary. Solid micro-electrodes for measurements on redox systems were made either of platinum wire or, preferably, of gold wire, with the tip freshly melted to a sphere in an inert atmosphere. Cathodic current densities (c.d.s.) in the reduction of Ni and Cu complexes were measured at a dropping mercury electrode. Complexes of Zn, Cd, Fe, Cu, Ni, Mn and Co were investigated.

Zinc complexes with tartrate and citrate are present in solutions containing a large excess of free ligands mainly as 1 : 2 complexes. The forms which actually take part in the electrode process are, however, the 1 : 1 complexes, i.e. reduction is preceded by dissociation of one ligand molecule. Addition of acetate to a solution of a simple zinc salt largely increases the reversibility of the rate of electron transfer with Zn amalgam, as had been previously reported in the case of addition of halide ions. The electrode reaction of simple *cadmium halide* salts at Cd amalgam electrodes is known to be fairly rapid[7] and measurements of their rate lie approximately around the limits of applicability of the simple galvanostatic or potentiostatic method. Complexation with tartrate or citrate does not lower appreciably the reversibility. However, the Cd-EDTA complex is reduced through previous protonation of $[CdY]^{2-}$, as had already been found polarographically by Tanaka and co-workers.[8] Its cathodic current density (c.d.) and exchange current density (c.d.) are much lower, since they correspond to the low concentration of $[CdHy]^-$ or $[HY]^{3-}$ ions in equilibrium with the complex. In solutions containing excess of ethylenediamine, Cd is present mainly as the 1 : 3 complex; in the vicinity of the equilibrium potential the form being reduced or being formed in the oxidation is the 1 : 2 complex, but at high anodic current density (c.d.). In addition, oxidation of Cd amalgam to free cadmium ions becomes increasingly favoured.

Cu and Ni complexes. Since it is difficult to have reversible electrode for these metals, we have investigated only their cathodic processes at a mercury electrode. Copper complexes with organic amines such as en, tren, and tetraen seem to be reduced with a high degree of reversibility to metal and, since their formation constants are very high, this fact points to probable reduction without previous dissociation, as had already been postulated by Delahay.[9] Copper pyrophosphate, which is present in solution mainly as the 1 : 2 complex, loses one ligand molecule and is reduced in form of the 1 : 1 complex. Among the nickel complexes, thiocyanate complexes seem to undergo reduction without previous removal of CNS   ions, whilst pyridine complexes lose, on the average, about one mole of pyridine before reduction. However no sharply integer values could be obtained by these measurements, and it is possible that several complex species are reduced at the same time.

Iron complexes, measured at solid microelectrodes, have exchange current density (c.d.) values which are often higher than those corresponding to the FeII/FeIII couple in non-complexing media,[10] thus pointing to a transfer mechanism without previous dissociation. For instance, cyanide and oxalate complexes behave much more reversibly than aquo-iron complexes; EDTA complexes have an i_0 of the same order of magnitude as in non-complexing solutions and show only minor variations with pH. A large increase of reversibility is also achieved by addition of Cl⁻ or CNS⁻ ions to solutions of simple iron salts.

Mn and Co complexes. Only a very limited number of couples II/III of complexes of these metals could be studied at a mercury electrode, owing to the high oxidizing power of the tervalent ions. Among these, the tris(ethylenediamine) complexes of cobalt(II) and the alkaline triethanolamine complexes of Mn [12] shown a rather high degree of reversibility, with slight dependence on free ligand concentration.

REFERENCES

1. P. Delahay and T. Berzins, *J. Am. Chem., Soc.,* **75,** 2486, (1953), and **77,** 6648, (1955); H. Gerischer, *Z. Elektrochem,* **59,** 604 (1955).
2. H. Gerischer and W. Vielstich, *Z. Phys Chem. N. F.* **3,** 16 (1955), and **4,** 10 (1955); H. Gerischer, *Z. Elektrochem, loc. cit.,* and *Anal. Chem.,* **31,** 33 (1955).
3. L. Gierst and A. Juliard, *Proc. Intern. CITCE,* 2nd Meeting, Tamburini, Milan, (1950) 117, 279; P. Delahay and T. Berzins, *J. Am. Chem. Soc.,* **75,** 2486 (1953).
4. H. Gerischer, *Z. Phys. Chem.* 202, 292 and 302 (1953).
5. J. E. B. Randles, *Trans. Farad. Soc.* **48,** 828, 937, 951 (1952); H. Gerischer, *loc. cit.*
6. H. Gerischer and K. E. Staubach, *Z. Elektrochem,* **61,** 789 (1957).
7. H. Gerischer and M. Krause, *Z. Phys. Chem. N. F.,* **10,** 264, (1957); W. Vielstich and P. Delahay, *J. Am. Chem. Soc.,* **79,** 1874 (1957).
8. N. Tanaka, R. Tamamushi and M. Kodama, *Z. Phys. Chem. N. F.,* **14,** 141 (1958).
9. P. Delahay and T. Berzins, *loc. cit.*
10. Previous measurements on Fe^{2+}/Fe^{3+} systems in J. E. B. Randles and K. W. Somerton, *Trans. Farad. Soc.* **48,** 937 (1952), and H. Gerischer, *Z. Elektrochem.* **54,** 362 (1950).
11. D. R. Stranks, *Discuss. Farad. Soc.* (1960), 5308 ("Electron Exchange Reactions").
12. J. Faucherre and C. Benazet, *Bull. Soc. Chim.,* 841 (1955).

ROTATORY DISPERSION OF HEMOPROTEINS

GUNTHER L. EICHHORN and ALBERT J. OSBAHR

Gerontology Branch, National Heart Institute,
National Institutes of Health, Public Health Service
Department of Health, Education and Welfare, Bethesda, Maryland,
and the Baltimore City Hospitals, Baltimore, Maryland

The existence of metal ions as an important part of the structure and function of many biological macromolecules makes the techniques of coordination chemistry an essential feature of an understanding of these substances. Frequently the metal ions are at the focal point of biological activity; at the least, they serve to modify the characteristics of the macromolecules to which they are bound. The present report is an illustration of the fact that such modification works in two directions; i.e., the presence of the metal in a macromolecular system can profoundly affect the coordination chemistry of the metal, so that the characteristics of the macromolecular metal complex can be quite different from those of a complex of smaller dimensions.

An important group of these biological macromolecular complexes is represented by the hemoproteins. These compounds consist of various proteins coordinated to the iron atom of heme, the iron complex of protoporphyrin.

The four nitrogen atoms of the porphyrin occupy the planar positions in the octahedral coordination sphere; the remaining two positions are held either by two groups from the protein, or by one group from the protein and one simple donor molecule. In cytochrome-c, for example, both positions belong to protein, and in oxyhemoglobin one position is occupied by protein and the other by a molecule of oxygen.

The hemoproteins are useful in at least three different types of biochemical processes: oxidation-reduction, peroxide degradation, and the transfer of molecular oxygen. The hemoproteins can also be classified into two groups, one of which contains four, and the other only one heme per protein, as follows (Table 1):

TABLE 1

Function	1 Heme/Protein	4 Hemes/Protein
Redox	Cytochrome-c	Cytochrome-c_1
Peroxide degradation	Peroxidase	Catalase
Oxygen carrying	Myoglobin	Hemoglobin

Metal Ion Asymmetry

Since the metal atom plays a central role in both the structure and function of all of these compounds, techniques designed to focus upon the metal atom should be useful in the study of the structure of these substances. One such technique is to make use of the possibility that the metal may be a center of asymmetry. Such a study is complicated by the fact that the hemoproteins contain two other types of asymmetry, in addition to the possible asymmetry of the iron: (1) the asymmetric carbon atoms in all individual amino acids except glycine, and (2) the macromolecular asymmetry due to the ordered structure of the protein. (It has been found, for example, that the myoglobin molecule is 70% helical and, since the helices are all of the same sense, they contribute to the optical rotation.[1] These other asymmetries are associated with absorption bands in the ultraviolet region of the spectrum; only iron atom asymmetry would lead to a Cotton effect in the visible, associated with absorption bands of the heme. Thus, by concentrating upon rotatory dispersion curves of the hemoproteins in the visible range, it should be possible to single out the metal atom asymmetry.

There are available in the literature a number of studies of rotatory dispersion curves of metal complexes with a combination of asymmetric metal atoms and asymmetric donors. One such study shows that, in the case of [Co (en) (pn) (NO$_2$)$_2$] Br, the contribution of the asymmetric cobalt and the asymmetric carbon of the propylenediamine are independent of each other.[2] The visible rotatory dispersion curve of a complex of racemic propylenediamine with optically active cobalt gives a perfectly center-symmetrical Cotton effect. The complex of active propylenediamine with racemic cobalt shows no Cotton effect, and a complex in which neither of the optically active groups is racemized yields additive rotatory dispersion. Many other cases have been noted, however, in which asymmetric donor molecules lead to visible Cotton effects, even when the metal is not itself an asymmetric center, e.g., in the complexes of copper with amino acid;[3] the vicinal effect is presumably operating in these instances.

Heme As Asymmetric Center

Examination of the structure of heme reveals that, as a consequence of the arrangement of the side chains, there can be no plane of symmetry through the heme except the plane of the porphyrin itself. Thus, the iron atom is an asymmetric center if the substituents in the 5- and 6-positions are different, or if chelation is produced; the latter result is achieved when the protein, already coordinated to the iron atom, is also attached to a side chain on the porphyrin. The iron would not be asymmetric if the 5- and 6-positions were identically substituted and there were no chelation.

Cytochrome-c

In a molecule of cytochrome-c both of the asymmetry conditions are satisfied; different amino acids are on the two sides of the porphyrin plane, and the iron is chelated. The rotatory dispersion curves of oxidized (Fe(III)) and reduced (Fe(II)) cytochrome-c are indeed anomalous, in line with the predicted metal atom asymmetry.[4]

Catalase and Peroxidase[5]

The catalase molecule is an example of the hemoproteins containing four hemes. It has been shown by Tanford and Lovrien[6] that this molecule can be split into quarters, each containing only one heme, by raising or lowering the pH. It appeared to be of interest to compare the rotatory dispersion curves of intact catalase with its four hemes and the quartered catalase with only one heme. Figure 1 shows the absorption spectra of catalase at pH 7.5, 11, and 3. All of the spectra are very similar; particularly the spectra at pH 7.5 and 11 are practically identical in the region of the 620 mμ absorption peak. Nevertheless, the rotatory dispersion curves are exceedingly different (Fig. 2 and 3). The intact catalase at pH 7.5 exhibits anomalous dispersion with an inflection at the absorption peak, but

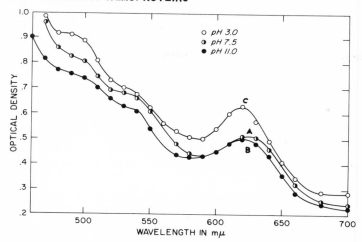

Fig. 1. Spectra of catalase (1.5% solutions). A, pH 7.5; B, pH 11.0, C, pH 3.0.

at pH 11 the rotatory dispersion is simple, with no evidence of a
Cotton effect. At pH 3 the dispersion is not quite simple, but certainly most of the Cotton effect has disappeared. It thus appears
that the intact molecule at pH 7.5 contains asymmetric iron but that
the quarter molecule at low and high pH does not.

One explanation of this phenomenon is that the heme is symmetrically surrounded by protein in each quarter molecule, but that this
symmetry is destroyed when the four quarters are associated to form
native catalase. This supposition is readily illustrated in Fig. 4.
It can be seen that a heme that is surrounded by two identical half-
protein chains on both sides in the *quarter* molecule will have one-
half protein chain on one side and three-halves protein chains and
another heme on the other side in the *whole* molecule.

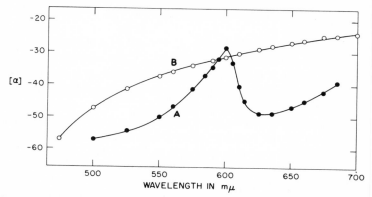

Fig. 2. Rotatory dispersion of catalase. A, pH 7.5, 3.2%; B, pH 11.0, 2.8%.

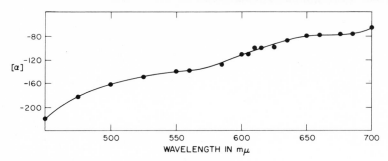

Fig. 3. Rotatory dispersion of catalase, pH 2.8, 1.5%.

There is, however, an alternative explanation for the difference in the optical behavior of catalase in neutral and basic solutions. It has been observed by Blout and Stryer[7] that solutions of proteins or polypeptides in the presence of a dye such as acridine orange exhibit a Cotton effect in the absorption band of the dye when the proteins or polypeptides are in a helical configuration. The dispersion becomes simple, however, when the polymer molecules are in the state of

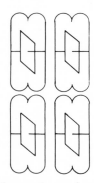

Fig. 4. Possible orientation of hemes in catalase.

random coils. Since lowering or raising the pH of catalase, in addition to splitting the molecule, brings about its denaturation (i.e., conversion of the protein from an ordered structure to a more disordered one), it is conceivable that the heme groups may behave in a manner similar to that of the dye molecules.

It is possible to differentiate between those alternative hypotheses by an investigation of the rotation properties of the peroxidase molecule. This substance contains only one heme when it is intact; raising the pH of the solution does not split the molecule, as in catalase, but it does bring about denaturation. If the effect observed with catalase is due to symmetrically placed hemes made asymmetric

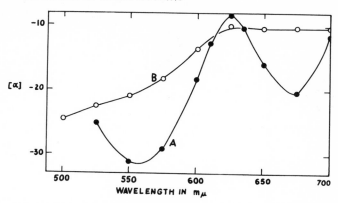

Fig. 5. Rotatory dispersion of peroxidase. A, pH 7.2, 2.5%; B, pH 11.0, 3.0%.

through association, it should not be observed with peroxidase since the latter is in the same state of association at both neutral and basic pH.

Figure 5 reveals that the rotatory dispersion curve of peroxidase in neutral solution again exhibits a Cotton effect, which is virtually eliminated at pH 11.

It is therefore concluded that anomalous dispersion in the visible spectral region of hemoproteins is associated with an ordered structure of the protein molecule, and simple dispersion results from a protein in a randomized conformation. Thus the "symmetry" or "asymmetry" of a metal in these large molecules is not a manifestation of the groups directly coordinated to the metal, but rather it is determined by the configuration of the large molecule itself. Presumably either an ordered or randomized macromolecular structure could produce optical activity in the heme band through the vicinal effect, but in the case of the randomized structure the contribution of every possible conformation would be neutralized by its mirror image.

Vitamin B$_{12}$

That the rotatory dispersion depends on gross molecular configuration, rather than specific coordinate covalent bonds, has been shown for a much smaller molecule, vitamin B$_{12}$. This molecule contains a cobalt bound to four planar nitrogen atoms in a porphyrinlike structure. The fifth and sixth coordination positions are occupied by a cyanide on one side and by a benzimidazole nitrogen on the other side; the benzimidazole is at the end of a long side-chain on the porphyrin. The cyanide can be replaced by water with virtually no change in the rotatory dispersion; the severance of the benzimidazole coordination link, however, brings about a drastic change in the curve,[8] since the chelate ring is broken in the process, and the side chain is left dangling in space.

Application to Structural Studies

If it can be said that the presence or absence of anomalous dispersion of the hemoprotein is correlated with the amount of order in the protein molecule, visible rotatory dispersion curves should be useful in investigations of chemical changes in such molecules. This notion has been applied to a reaction sequence, in which the heme is first removed from catalase and subsequently re-added to the heme-less protein. When the addition of heme to the protein is followed spectrophotometrically, it is evident that four moles of heme still react with every mole of protein (Fig. 6). This stoichiometric recombination of the components of catalase suggests that the sites to which the hemes were originally attached are still intact. However, the rotatory dispersion curve of the recombined catalase is not anomalous, suggesting that the recombined molecule as a whole has considerably less order than the original native catalase. It is concluded that the stability of the site of attachment of the heme to the protein component of catalase is considerably greater than the stability of the molecule as a whole, emphasizing the importance to the protein of maintaining its proper relationship with the coordinated metal atom.

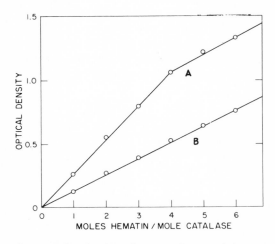

Fig. 6. Spectrophotometric titration of apocatalase with hematin. A, addition of hematin to apocatalase; B, addition of hematin to water.

Hemoglobin and Myoglobin

Investigations of the rotatory dispersion of hemoglobin and myoglobin reveal that these hemoproteins behave in the same manner that has already been described for catalase and peroxidase. These molecules are readily denatured in 8-molar urea solution. It is found, indeed, that the Cotton effect exhibited by both hemoglobin and myoglobin when they are intact[9] is lost upon treatment with urea. As in catalase, the observations with hemoglobin can be interpreted in a variety of ways, since hemoglobin contains four hemes per molecule. The observations with myoglobin, however, tend to confirm the conclusion that the Cotton effect in these macromolecular complexes is present whenever the molecule contains an ordered structure, and is lost when that ordered structure is destroyed.

REFERENCES

1. J. C. Kendrew, R. E. Dickerson, B. E. Strandberg, R. G. Hart, D. R. Davies, D. C. Phillips, and V. C. Shore, *Nature,* **185,**422 (1960).
2. J. Lifschitz, *Z. physik. Chem.,* **105,** 27 (1923).
3. P. Pfeiffer and W. Christeleit, *Z. physiol. Chem.,* **245,** 197 (1937).
4. G. L. Eichhorn and J. F. Cairns, *Nature,* **181,** 994 (1958).
5. A. J. Osbahr, Thesis, Georgetown University, 1960.
6. C. Tanford and R. E. Lovrien, *Abstracts, 135th Meeting, American Chemical Society,* p. 14-C (1959).
7. E. R. Blout and L. Stryer, *Proc. Natl. Acad. Sci.,* **45,** 1591 (1959).
8. G. L. Eichhorn, *Tetrahedron,* in press (1961).
9. Similar data have been obtained by P. Doty and associates at Harvard University (private communication).

STRUCTURAL CHEMISTRY OF METAL CARBONYL COMPLEXES

LAWRENCE F. DAHL

Department of Chemistry
University of Wisconsin
Madison, Wisconsin

In the last decade one of the most interesting and active areas of research has involved the preparation and characterization of a large number of new types of complexes, many of which are derivatives of the transition metal carbonyls. Concurrently, there has been a surge of activity concerning the mechanism of reactions of such compounds, their nature of bonding, and their use in organic syntheses and as catalysts. Unfortunately, the experimenters and theoreticians have been hampered by a lack of unambiguous structural data. Much of the voluminous literature concerning proposed structures of such complexes is wrong. It is not fair to criticize the investigators who, mainly on the basis of spectroscopic examination and chemical intuition, have proposed such structures, for in many cases the structures have turned out to be much more complicated than supposed. This confusion has hastened the use of single-crystal X-ray diffraction for obtaining the ultimate structure, since its main advantage over other structural methods is that X-ray diffraction in practically all cases provides a direct unique solution. Unfortunately, exceptions to this generalization may be found among the metal carbonyls. Once the arrangement of atoms, the interatomic distance and angles are known, one can turn to the equally fascinating problem of rationalizing these features in terms of modern theories of bonding.

The first problem and many times one of the most difficult ones encountered in structural analysis is obtaining a suitable single crystal. Crystal sizes of 0.1 to 0.2 mm in diameter are common, the optimum size of course depending on the material being studied. The acid test of a good crystal is its performance under fire in an X-ray beam as revealed by the X-ray data. The principal factor contributing to the rapid advancement of structural determinations by X-ray diffraction in the last few years has been the development of large electronic computers capable of conveniently handling the mathematical treatment of X-ray data. The development of automatic counter equipment for obtaining the X-ray data promises to make this tool even more powerful.

In illustrating the use of X-ray diffraction the results of a number of investigations which appear to provide new insight into the nature of bonding of metal carbonyls and related organometallics will be presented. At the same time, the influence of non-bonding interactions on molecular configuration in the solid state and the dangers of interpretation of structural parameters obtained by X-ray diffraction in terms of bonding interactions only will be stressed.

Consider first the metal carbonyls themselves. The mononuclear metal carbonyls have been well characterized by diffraction methods; however, until recently the structures of the polynuclear metal carbonyls have been the subject of considerable controversy. New developments concerning structural work on the polynuclear metal carbonyls will be given. These will include the three-dimensional refinement of $Mn_2(CO)_{10}$ and a detailed analysis of the final molecular configuration.

Direct structural evidence that the widely accepted metal carbonyls $Os_2(CO)_9$ and $Ru_2(CO)_9$ are, in fact, trinuclear molecular species with probable formulas $[Os(CO)_4]_3$ and $[Ru(CO)_4]_3$ will be reported. This and other evidence suggest that the metal carbonyls of the 2nd and 3rd row transition metals possess distinct structural differences from those of the 1st row transition metals.

Yellow crystals of the presumed enneacarbonyl, $Os_2(CO)_9$, were prepared by the high-pressure reaction of OsO_4 with carbon monoxide.[1] X-ray diffraction data reveal the compound to be monoclinic with $a = 8.10$ Å, $b = 14.79$ Å, $c = 14.64$ Å and $\beta = 100°27'$. The probable space group, as determined by systematic absences, is $P2_1/n$. There are 12 osmium atoms per unit cell related to one another by the four-fold positions of the space group. These data agree excellently with optical data obtained by Steinmetz and reported by Manchot and Manchot[2] for the yellow crystals of the presumed ruthenium enneacarbonyl and leave no doubt as to the isomorphism of the two compounds. The $a:b:c$ ratios and symmetry reported for the ruthenium crystals are $0.550 : 1.000 : 0.986$, $\beta = 100°46'$, point group $2/m$; from our data for the osmium compound $a : b : c = 0.548 : 1.000 : 0.990$, $\beta = 100°27'$, point group $2/m$. Even though the compound is not isomorphous with $[Fe(CO)_4]_3$,[3] the volumes per molecule are equivalent within experimental error. Further structural proof of the isomorphism of the ruthenium and osmium compounds was obtained from an X-ray examination of single crystals of ruthenium carbonyl which showed similar lattice dimensions, the same space group, and intensity data related to those of the osmium compound.

Three-dimensional Weissenberg and precession intensity data involving over 2000 reflections were obtained with MoKα radiation. The positions of the osmium atoms were located from Patterson projections of hol, hko, and okl data. Least squares refinement of the 400 observed reflections for the three zones places the osmium atoms at the corners of an equilateral triangle; the average distance between the osmium atoms in the triangle is 2.87 Å. For isotropic refinement the discrepancy factor $R_1 = 16\%$. A complete three-dimensional analysis now underway will be required to locate the positions of the carbonyl groups. The results will be presented.

Electrophilic attack of metal carbonyls by halogens and the reaction of anhydrous metal halides with carbon monoxide have resulted in the formation of a number of carbonyl halide compounds. Thus far the only structural characterization of these compounds has been the result of infrared studies[4] of $Re(CO)_5I$,[5] $Ru(CO)_2I_2$,[6] and $[Pt(CO)X_2]_2$[7] (X = Cl, Br, I). A three-dimensional X-ray study of $Mn_2(CO)_8Br_2$ has revealed dimeric molecules formed by the junction of two octahedra at an edge with bridging bromine atoms.

A heretofore unreported compound, $Ru(CO)_4I_2$, has been synthesized by high-pressure techniques. Infrared studies plus a complete X-ray examination of the compound show the ruthenium and two iodides to be cis to one another.

The compound, $Rh(CO)_2Cl$, also has been examined and its structure in the solid state is not that of a dimeric molecule indicated by freezing point depression data.[8] The structure involves a 6-fold coordination about each rhodium atom with metal-metal bonding entering in.[9]

REFERENCES

1. W. Hieber and H. Stallman, Z. $Electrochem.$, **49**, 288 (1943).
2. W. Manchot and W. J. Manchot, Z. $anorg$. $allgem$. $Chem.$, **226**, 385 (1936).
3. L. F. Dahl and R. E. Rundle, J. $Chem$. $Phys.$, **26**, 1751 (1957).
4. $Modern$ $Coordination$ $Chemistry$, J. Lewis and R. G. Wilkens, Eds., Interscience Publishers, 1960. F. A. Cotton, "The Infrared Spectra of Transitional Metal Complexes," p. 343.
5. E. O. Brimm, M. A. Lynch and W. J. Sesney. J. Am. $Chem$. $Soc.$, **76**, 3831 (1954).
6. R. J. Irving, J. $Chem$. $Soc.$, 1956, 2879.
7. R. J. Irving and E. A. Magnusses, $ibid.$, 1956, 1860.
8. W. Hieber and H. Lagally, Z. $anorg$. $allgem$. $Chemie$, **251**, 96 (1943).
9. L. F. Dahl, C. Martell and D. Wampler, J. Am. $Chem$. $Soc.$, **83**, 1761.

COMPLEX IONS IN FUSED SALTS

F. R. DUKE

Iowa State University
Ames, Iowa

Changes in activity of one salt in the presence of another in fused salt solution have been measured by a variety of techniques. These changes in activity may be interpreted in terms of equilibria of the sort:

$$M^{+n} + X^{-m} \rightleftharpoons (MX)^{+n-m}$$

$$(MX)^{+n-m} \rightleftharpoons MX_2^{(+n-2m)} \quad \text{etc.}$$

The equilibrium constants thus obtained are constant over considerable ranges of concentration of M and X. Table 1 lists some constants and the method of measurement.

An alternative explanation of such thermodynamic data is based on the "quasi-lattice" theory. No specific complex ion is assumed in this theory, but rather, specific ionic interactions are assumed with no particular structural implications of the complex ion type. Blander,[3] in particular, feels strongly that no structural conclusions should be inferred from purely thermodynamic data. He has been able to explain quantitatively activity data without assuming particular complex ion species.

Spectroscopy leads to a more direct structural interpretation.[10] It is significant that Raman spectra indicate complex ions in certain salts,[8] but that infrared spectra fail to indicate complex ions where some might be expected.[9]

REFERENCES

1. E. R. VanArtsdalen, *J. Phys. Chem.*, **60**, 172 (1956).
2. F. R. Duke and H. M. Garfinkel, *J. Phys. Chem.* (to be published).
3. M. Blander, F. F. Blankenship, and R. F. Newton, *J. Phys. Chem.*, **63**, 1259 (1959).

TABLE 1: FORMATION CONSTANTS, $K_n = \dfrac{MXn}{MXn_{-1}}$, FOR COMPLEX IONS

Complex	Solvent	T°K	Kn	Method	Ref.
$CdCl_2$	$NaNo_3$	579	$K_1K_2 = 320$	Freezing Point	1
$CdCl_4 =$	$NaNo_3$	579	$K_3K_4 = .25$	Freezing Point	1
$CdCl^+$	{ KNo_3 $NaNo_3$ Eutectic	523	20	Solubility	1
$CdBr_2$	$NaNo_3$	579	$K_1K_2 = 3000$	Freezing Point	1
$CdBr^+$	{ KNo_3 $NaNo_3$ Eutectic	523	20	Solubility	7
$CdBr^+$	{ KNo_3 $NaNo_3$ Eutectic	529	108	E.M.F.	2
$CdBr^+$	,,	547	95	E.M.F.	2
$Cd\,Br^+$	,,	571	75	E.M.F.	2
$CdBr_2$	,,	529	51	,,	2
$CdBr_2$	,,	547	47	,,	2
$CdBr_3 -$	,,	529	10	,,	2
	,,	547	2.5	,,	2
$PbCl_2$	$NaNo_3$	579	$K_1K_2 = 30$	Freezing Point	1
$PbCl^+$	{ KNo_3 $NaNo_3$ Eutectic	523	18	Solubility	7
$PbCl^+$	,,	573	11	Solubility	7
$PbCl_2$	,,	523	2	,,	7
$PbCl_2$	,,	573	3	,,	7
$PbBr^+$	,,	523	18	,,	7
$PbBr^+$	,,	548	13	,,	7
$PbBr^+$	,,	528	18	E.M.F.	2
$PbBr_2$	,,	573	2	Solubility	7
$PbBr_2$	,,	579	6	E.M.F.	2
$ZnCl_2$	$NaNo_3$	579	$K_1K_2 = 400$	Freezing Point	1
$ZnCl_4$	$NaNo_3$	579	$K_3K_4 = 0.2$	,,	1
$ZnBr^+$	{ $NaNo_3$ KNo_3 Eutectic	523	250	Kinetics	5
$ZnBro_3^+$	{ $NaNo_3$ Kno_3 Eutectic	523	1.3	Kinetics	4
$AgCl$	$NaNo_3$	647	17.7	E.M.F.	2
$AgCl_2 -$	$NaNo_3$	647	6.78	,,	2
$AgCl$	{ $NaNo_3(N=.53)$ $KNo_3(N=.47)$	647	28.0	,,	2
$AgCl_2 -$	{ $NaNo_3(N=.53)$ $KNo_3(N=.47)$	647	8.93	,,	2
$AgCl$	KNo_3	647	44.9	,,	3
$AgCl_2 -$	KNo_3	647	18.0	,,	3
$AgCl$	KNo_3	709	28.5	,,	
$AgCl_2 -$	KNo_3	709	12.5	,,	3
$AgBr$	{ KNo_3 $NaNo_3$ Eutectic	649	93.3	,,	6
$AgBr$	,,	687	72.3	,,	6
$AgBr_2 -$	,,	649	33.3	,,	6
$AgBr_2$	,,	687	18.4	,,	6

4. F. R. Duke and W. W. Lawrence, *J. Am. Chem. Soc.*, **83**, 1269 (1961).
5. F. R. Duke and W. W. Lawrence, *ibid.*, **83**, 1271 (1961).
6. F. R. Duke and H. W. Garfinkel, *J. Phys. Chem.*, **65**, 453 (1961).
7. F. R. Duke and M. L. Iverson, *ibid.*, **62**, 417 (1958).
8. W. Bues, *Z. anorg. allgem. Chem.*, **279**, 104 (1955).
9. I. Greenberg and L. J. Hallgren, *J. Chem. Phys.*, **33**, 900 (1960).
10. D. M. Grven, S. Fried, P. Graf, R. L. McBeth, *Proc. 2nd Int. Conf. on Peaceful Uses of Atomic Energy*, Pergamon Press, N.Y. V. **28** (1959).

FACTORS WHICH INFLUENCE THE STABILITY
OF ANIONIC COMPLEXES

JOHN O. EDWARDS, HERBERT R. ELLISON, CARL G. LAURO, and
JOHN P. LORAND

Department of Chemistry
Brown University
Providence, Rhode Island

There are elements in the Periodic Chart whose properties lie between those of the transition metals and those of the typical non-metals. These elements (which are called metalloids and which include boron, silicon, germanium, arsenic, antimony, selenium, tellurium and even iodine) rarely form cationic complexes. It has been long known, however, that they do form anionic complexes with hydroxide ion and that in some cases the hydroxide ion can be replaced by other anions. The present article deals with these substituted hydroxyanions and with the factors which tend to make replacement of the hydroxide ion in the coordination sphere possible.

The coordination chemistry of these hydroxyanions is quite different in some ways from the usual transition metal chemistry. For example, there is nothing akin to crystal-field effects in these complexes, and neutral ligands are very weak complexing agents. Nevertheless, there are parallels, so the subject is not out of place at a coordination compounds conference. Because of space limitations, we will not give historical or experimental details; also no references are inserted for similar reasons although our debt to previous workers is great.

Background

The symbol $R_x M(OH)_y$, where M represents the metalloid, R represents attached groups other than hydroxide ion, OH is the hydroxide ion, and x and y are numbers, will be used to represent the hydroxyanion, as will also the symbol A^-. The symbol N^- will represent the replacing anion.

In general, the reaction which is observed may be written as

$$R_x M(OH)_y + yHN \rightleftharpoons R_x MNy + yH_2O \qquad (1)$$

and it is important to note that this equation involves the conjugate acid of the ligand. The reason for this will be seen below.

Several methods for evaluation of the equilibrium constants are available, but only two are of sufficiently general usefulness to be mentioned here; these are ultraviolet spectrophotometry and pH measurement. All data presented here were obtained with these methods.

The hydroxyanions are colorless in the visible and near ultraviolet, but they generally show strong absorption in the far ultraviolet. These absorptions are characterized by high extinction coefficients and by the lack of distinct peaks. In spite of the steep variation of extinction coefficient with wavelength, reliable data (as in, for example, the rate of the glycoltellurate reaction) can be obtained.

The second method is related to the Bjerrum method for evaluation of binding constants in amine complexes. The hydroxyanion and its conjugate acid form a buffer system whose pH is governed by the equilibrium constant expression

$$K_a = \frac{[\text{H}^+][A^-]}{[\text{H}A]}$$

When a species HN is added, the reaction given above Eq. (1) occurs thus lowering the concentration of hydroxyanion in solution. As a consequence of this decrease, the hydrogen ion concentration increases and the pH decreases. For an equilibrium

$$R_x M(\text{OH}) + \text{HN} \rightleftharpoons R_x M\text{N} + \text{H}_2\text{O}$$

governed by the expression

$$K_c = \frac{R_x M\text{N}}{[R_x M(\text{OH})][\text{HN}]}$$

it can be shown that the constant K_c is related to the change in buffer pH on addition of HN by the equation

$$K_c = \frac{10^{-\Delta p\text{H}} - 1}{[\text{HN}]}$$

The Acidity Effect

The reaction of hydrogen peroxide with borate ion

$$H_2O_2 + B(OH)_4^- \rightleftharpoons B(OH)_3OOH^- + H_2O$$

has long been known, yet there is no similar reaction with boric acid. Peroxide also reacts with tellurate ion but not with telluric acid. The equilibrium constants for borate and tellurate ion complexes with peroxide are 30 and 0.68, respectively.

At first sight, one could draw the conclusion on the basis of K_c that the B—OOH link is stronger than the B—OH link, yet this conclusion is quite incorrect. What is really pertinent is the equilibrium constant for the reaction

$$OOH^- + B(OH)_4^- \rightleftharpoons B(OH)_3OOH^- + OH^-$$

and this constant K_c' may be obtained from the above value of K_c and the acidity constants for hydrogen peroxide and for water. What comes out is that K_c' is much less than one — the value is 0.15. As expected, hydroxide ion forms a stronger bond to boric acid than does perhydroxide ion.

The discrepancy between K_c and K_c' is readily pinned down for the observed reaction is driven to the right by the formation of the very stable molecule, water. Indeed, it seems possible to make a prediction that when the M—O bond is weaker than the H—O bond (as is perhaps always the case), then the hydroxide ion of the complex will usually be replaced by the anion of an acid HN. The prediction is certainly borne out in many cases such as the fluoroborates and the chloroantimonates. It presumably also is of importance in the glycol complexes for the acidities of *1,2*-diols and *1,3*-diols are greater than that of water.

Polymerization is common in solutions containing hydroxyanions such as borates, tellurates, and silicates. In the cases of the borates, it seems certain that polymerization is important only when the hydroxyanion and its conjugate acid are present. The reason for this may lie in the effect under discussion. The hydroxyanion is partially basic and its conjugate form is acidic, thus the formation of a mononegative dimer would be favored on the same grounds as peroxide complexes.

Although these cases are not neutralizations in the normal sense, the driving force (formation of water by reaction of a basic species

$R_xM(OH)_y$ with an acidic species HN) is certainly akin to that of neutralization. It is for this reason that this factor for complex stabilization is called the acidity effect here.

Statistical Effects

In trying to sort out those things which contribute to the over-all stability of a complex, it is often necessary to take into account the number of ways a complex can form and can break down. The problem can be fairly serious as in the case of pentaerythritol complexes with borate ion where, for example, the reaction

$$B(OH)_4^- + C(CH_2OH)_4 \rightleftharpoons \begin{array}{c} HO \\ \diagdown \\ HO \end{array} \underset{}{\overset{-}{B}} \begin{array}{c} O-CH_2 \\ \diagup \diagdown \\ O-CH_2 \end{array} \underset{}{C} \begin{array}{c} CH_2OH \\ \diagdown \\ CH_2OH \end{array}$$

is favored by a statistical factor of seventy-two.

It is found that the formation constants for glycerol complexes with anions are twice as large as those for *3*-methoxy-*1,2*-propanediol. Also glycerol reacts with tellurate ion twice as fast as does the monomethyl derivative. This difference of two in rate and equilibrium constants is just what is expected on statistical grounds.

We have not generally made such corrections in our data as it seems less confusing to report the observed data as such. Wherever correction is made, note will be given.

The Chelate Effect

The exceptional stability of coordination compounds formed with polydentate ligands is well known, and this stability is attributed to the entropy gain of a reaction having a larger number of product particles than reactant particles. The reaction of a glycol with tellurate ion

is such a reaction, for three molecules are formed from two. Indeed, it may be noted in Table 1 that the reaction of tellurate ion with two sugars has been found to have a positive entropy.

The driving force in the chelate effect is not the formation of a ring as such, for this is an entropy-decreasing reaction. The importance of the ring is that, if strain-less, there is no loss of bonding energy while the total number of particles increases. On such a basis, we might also expect to find the chelate effect in cases of ring compounds not involving the usual bidentate ligands. Such a case is the cyclic polymer presumably formed in borate systems. The reaction

$$B(OH)_4^- + 2B(OH)_3 \rightleftharpoons B_3O_3(OH)_4^- + 3H_2O$$

with the polyborate anion having the structure

if favored, for the equilibrium constant is 110. It would be hard to understand why such a complex is formed were it not for the fact that four product particles are formed from three reactants.

TABLE 1: THERMODYNAMIC DATA FOR TELLURATE-POLYOL COMPLEXES*

Polyol	K_c	ΔF°	ΔH°	ΔS°
Ethylene glycol	15.0	−1.60	−4.7	−10
Propylene glycol	33.5	−2.08	−4.4	−8
Glycerol	79.6	−2.59	−3.8	−4
(meso)-2,3-butanediol	16.5	−1.66	−3.2	−5
3-methoxy-1,2-propanediol	30.2	−2.02	−3.8	−5
Phenyl-1,2-ethanediol	42.0	−2.2	−4.1	−6
d-glucose	12.7	−1.51	−0.8	+2
d-galactose	46.0	−2.25	−1.5	+2
Pentaerythritol	3.1	−0.7	−4.3	−12
2,2-diethyl-1,3-propanediol	0.97	+0.2	−3.3	−12
1,1,1-tris-hydroxymethyl-ethane	0.19	+1.0	−3.9	−16

*Units of ΔH° and ΔF° are kcal mole^{-1} and of ΔS° are cal mole^{-1} deg^{-1}; data are for 25°C and aqueous solution.

The Substituent Bulk Effect

It is observed that glycol complexes are sometimes more stable if the methylene hydrogens are replaced by bulky groups. For example, *1,2*-propanediol and phenyl-*1,2*-ethanediol both complex more strongly than ethylene glycol does. It is apparent from these two cases where the groups have opposite polarity that electronic effects are secondary to a purely bulk effect.

On the *1,3*-diols the substitution of bulky groups on the middle carbon has a sizeable effect on the complexing ability. As measured by formation of cyclic acetals with aqueous acetaldehyde, the complex with *2,2*-diethyl-*1,3*-propanediol is stronger than that of *2,2*-dimethyl-*1,3* propanediol, which is in turn stronger than that of *1,3*-propanediol itself; the formation constants are 120, 72, and 22, respectively, for these complexes. Similar results were found with borate complexes.

All of these cases plus others in the literature indicate that many substituted diols complex more firmly than simple diols. Evidently, the substituent groups hold the two hydroxyl groups in close proximity to each other for polyol configurations with hydroxyl groups *trans* to each other are less likely to occur when substituents are present. Alternatively a simple diol has a larger rotational entropy to be lost in complexing than does a substituted diol.

Nature of the Hydroxyanion

In Table 2, equilibrium constants for the formation of glycol complexes are presented. It may be noted therein that the strength of the complex is markedly dependent on the nature of the hydroxyanion. With borate ion (and also with phenylboronate ion and arsenite ion), the strengths of *1,2*-diol complexes are about the same as those of *1,3*-diol complexes. With tellurate ion, the *1,2*-diols bond more strongly, while with the hydrated form of acetaldehyde the *1,3*-diols bond more tightly.

At least, in part, the differences are related to different $O-M-O$ bond angles, with a smaller angle being expected to favor the smaller 5-membered ring of a complex with a *1,2*-diol. The angle of 90° and the discrimination between diols in the tellurate case is certainly consistent with this idea. On the other hand, there is a tetrahedral angle in both the borate and the aldehyde hydrate, yet there is a significant difference between these two hydroxycompounds in their reaction with diols.

From the acidity effect mentioned earlier, it is predicted that the weaker the $M-O$ bond, the higher will be for formation constant for the complex. There is yet to be investigated experimentally.

Stoichiometry

It should be pointed out that the bondings in anionic complexes can

TABLE 2: POLYOL COMPLEXING CONSTANTS FOR VARIOUS HYDROXYCOMPOUNDS*

Polyol	Borate	Arsenite	Tellurate	Acetaldehyde
Ethylene glycol	1.85	(0.07)	13.9	0.7
Propylene glycol	3.10	(0.10)	33.4	1.2
2,3-butanediol	3.45	(0.13)	21.3	—
Pinacol	5.1	—	1.15	—
Glycerol	16.0	1.15	79.6	8.
3-methoxy-*1,2*-propanediol	7.50	0.66	30.2	0.8
Phenyl-1,*2*-ethanediol	7.45	(0.23)	42.0	—
1,3-propanediol	1.15	—	1.78	22
Pentaerythritol	240.	1.00	2.24	Large
2,2-dimethyl-*1,3*-propanediol	8.1	—	—	72
2,2-diethyl-*1,3*-propanediol	10.6	—	0.97	ca 120
2-hydroxymethyl-*1-2*-methyl-*1,3*-propanediol	74	—	—	Large
d-(+)-galactose	127	1.95	46.0	—
Fructose	650	5.90	214	—
l-(+)-arabinose	130	1.60	46.9	—
d-glucose	80	1.45	12.7	—
d-mannose	50	2.30	106	—
Mannitol	2100	—	1680	26

*Data are for 25°C and aqueous solution.

be quite variable. Most of the time, one finds complexes containing one molecule of hydroxyanion and one molecule of ligand, but this is by no means always true. It is therefore important that the equilibrium constant be checked over ranges of reactant concentration in order to be sure of the stoichiometry, and even then one still has problems of formation of bicyclic systems, etc., as will be seen in the next section.

We have found, for example, complexes of three different types just between borate ion and pentaerythritol. The main complex in dilute solution contains one boron and one polyol, but in higher concentration ranges are found other complexes with ratios of one boron to two polyols and of two borons to one polyol.

Discussion

One reason why we have been investigating these factors that stabilize anionic complexes is that one finds quite specific reactions having large formation constants. A couple of such specific reactions will be briefly discussed here in order to illustrate two points: (1) that strong complexing often involves a unique structure and (2) that several factors rather than one are combined in the stabilization of such a complex.

The first case is that of the predominant polyanion found in boric acid and borate ion solutions. This polyanion contains three boron atoms, and it has one negative charge and an indeterminate number of oxygen and hydrogen atoms. In view of the occurrence in several borate salts of the anion with ring structure previously mentioned, it seems reasonable to suppose that this same configuration is present in the polyanion in solution. The acidity factor explains why the polyanion should have more boron atoms than negative charges. The chelate factor would certainly contribute to the stability of a ring structure, particularly where the ring can be formed without intramolecular repulsion as is probably true here. Thus in this case, at least two factors must be considered in any discussion of the magnitude of the formation constant.

An interesting problem arose in our study of the complexes of *1,3*-diols with borate ion and with phenylboronate ion. As may be seen in Table 2, pentaerythritol binds several orders of magnitude more strongly than does *1,3*-propanediol. Although a final explanation of this large difference cannot be given here, three factors at least must be considered. Statistical arguments predict that pentaerythritol should be intrinsically better by a factor of six, and this constitutes a portion, albeit small, of the difference. The bulk properties of pentaerythritol are similar to those of *2,2*-diethyl-*1,3*-propanediol, thus the substituent bulk effect should contribute to the stability of the pentaerythritol complex although probably to a lesser extent than an order of magnitude (see Table 2). Finally, a fraction of the complexes present may well have a bicyclic structure as

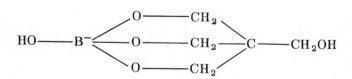

and this also would make the formation constant observed for pentaerythritol extra large. At the present time we are looking for ways to prove the existence of such a bicyclic complex.

PHYSICO-CHEMICAL INVESTIGATIONS ON π-COMPLEXES

HEINZ P. FRITZ

Anorganisch-chemisches Institut der Universität München
München, Germany

This report is concerned with the results of our measurements of the UV-, IR-, and NMR-spectra, dipole moments, and debyeograms of substances prepared in the Munich group of Prof. E. O. Fischer. Therefore, in several cases, additional details of the syntheses will be given.

One of the most promising techniques applied in our laboratory during the last year was the use of UV-irradiation, mostly in the presence of mercury.[1] By this method obviously highly reactive molecular fragments as intermediates of the syntheses of olefin complexes are obtained. Thus, starting from cyclopentadienyl-metal-carbonyl derivatives, e.g., $C_5H_5V(CO)_4$ or $C_5H_5Mn(CO)_3$, or carbonyls, e.g., $[Co(CO)_4]_2$, compounds of the types $C_5H_5VC_4H_6(CO)_2$, $C_5H_5MnC_2H_4(CO)_2$ or $[C_4H_6Co(Co)_2]_2$ can be isolated. A different and widely applicable way leads to cationic species like $[C_5H_5FeC_2H_4(CO)_2]^+$ and related ones.[2]

The isolation of butadiene and ethylene complexes of a number of transition metals, V, Cr, Mo, W, Mn, Fe, Co, and Os, enabled us to reach a more thorough understanding of the long-known shift of the $C{=}C$ stretching frequencies to lower values in π-complexes, since until now mainly compounds of noble metals were described. As a rule, this shift ranges from at least 70/cm in Ag^+ complexes to *ca.* 120/cm for the great part of the transition metal complexes. As was to be expected, conjugation lowers this still further.

The identification of butadiene complexes is greatly facilitated by the fact that in the $7\,\mu$ region three characteristic bands appear, one of which is the $C{=}C$ stretching and two of which are CH deformation frequencies.[3] On the basis of these bands for $C_8H_8[Fe(CO_3]_2$ a "butadiene-type" ligand can be confirmed, as it has been found to exist very recently.[4] In connection with our work[5] on $[C_8H_8]^{-2}$ several complexes of cyclo-octatetraene have been studied IR-spectroscopically and in some cases the NMR- and UV-spectra have been determined also. The results will be discussed shortly.

Reactions of allyl alcohol or allylhalides with metal halides,[6] metal carbonylates[7,8] or metal carbonyls[9] yield π-allyl complexes. Thus, by treating $Ni(CO)_4$ with allyl bromide or iodide the corresponding $[\pi-C_3H_5NiX]_2$ compounds have been isolated.[9] In several cases reactions of cyclic dienes on certain metal compounds do not lead to previously assumed diene complexes, but to cyclic "en-yl" compounds,[10] e.g., cyclopentenyl-Ni-cyclopentadienyl. The IR-spectra of such compounds have been investigated thoroughly and the NMR-spectra of some of the cyclic derivatives will be discussed. They clearly show the existence of π-bonded, non-classical "en-yl" systems, contrary to recently reported classical structures for allyl-Grignard compounds.[11]

During the last year several approaches to the substitution of $[Co(C_5H_5)_2]^+$ have been tried. They all led to the formation of derivatives of $C_5H_5CoC_5H_6$. In every case the *endo*-proton of the methylene group has been substituted.[12] The reaction with cyclopentadienyl anion yielded some information on the long known $Co_2(C_5H_5)_5$. A structure with a σ-bonded C_5H_4 ring situated between two $C_5H_5CoC_5H_5$ parts seemed most probable from the preparative side. However, there is no evidence in the IR-spectrum for the assumption of two π-bonded cyclopentadiene systems in the compound, although the colour might suggest it. Preliminary results of a three-dimensional Fourier-analysis point to two $[Co(C_5H_5)_2]$ parts and one C_5H_5 ring between them without any form of stronger bonds to the two sandwich structures.[13] On using the indenyl- instead of cyclopentadienyl-anion this "bridging" does not occur, but a $C_5H_5CoC_5H_5-C_9H_7$ is obtained. Successful substitution reactions on chromium complexes still under study will be described in detail.[14]

The structure of di-benzene-chromium was found recently to have D_{3d}-symmetry,[15] as had been postulated earlier on the basis of the IR-spectrum.[16] An approximately fixed Kekulé-structure can be visualized. The IR-spectra of di-benzene-Mo, -W, and -V would conform to a different molecular symmetry. Therefore, the debyeograms of these three compounds have been measured and, in fact, instead of the cubic symmetry of $Cr(C_6H_6)_2$, rhombic ones have been found for the Mo and W derivatives and a monoclinic one for $V(C_6H_6)_2$. In comparison to the situation with the di-cyclopentadienyls of Fe, Ru and Os[17], these results suggest an eclipsed position of the rings in $Mo(C_6H_6)_2$ and $W(C_6H_6)_2$. The unit cell dimensions are not of the same size for these two compounds, as was expected on the basis of the radii of the central atoms.

Finally, for the $[Cr(C_6H_6)_2]^+$ cation the IR- and Raman-spectra show a six-fold symmetry of the ion. This is readily understood using the theoretical picture of Ruch.

REFERENCES

1. E. O. Fischer and H. P. Kögler, *Z. Naturforschg.*, **15b,** 676 (1960).
2. E. O. Fischer and K. Fichtl, *Chem. Ber.*, **94,** 200 (1961).
3. E. O. Fischer, P. Kuzel and H. P. Fritz, *Z. Naturforschg.*, **16b,** 138, (1961).
4. B. Dickens and W. N. Lipscomb, *J. Am. Chem. Soc.*, **83,** 489 (1961).
5. H. P. Fritz and H. Keller, *Z. Naturforschg.*, **16b,** 231 (1961).
6. J. Smidt and W. Hafner, *Z. Angew. Chem.*, **71,** 284 (1959).
7. D. W. Moore, H. B. Jonassen, T. B. Joyner and A. J. Bertrand, *Chem. & Ind.*, **1960,** 1304.
8. H. D. Kaesz, R. B. King and F. G. A. Stone, *Z. Naturforschg.*, **15b,** 682 (1960).
9. E. O. Fischer and G. Bürger, *ibid 16b*, 77 (1961).
10. E. O. Fischer and H. Werner, *Tetrahedron Letters*, No. 1, 17 (1961).
11. J. E. Nordlander, W. G. Young and J. D. Roberts, *J. Am. Chem. Soc.*, **83,** 494 (1961).
12. E. O. Fischer and G. Herberich, *Chem. Ber.*, in press.
13. Personal communication to Prof. E. O. Fischer by O. V. Starovskii, Inst. Elementorganic Compounds, Moscow, USSR.
14. E. O. Fischer and H. Brunner, *Z. Naturforschg.*, in press.
15. F. Jellinek, *Nature*, **187,** 871 (1960).
16. H. P. Fritz and W. Lüttke, *V. Intern. Conf. Coord. Chem.* (London), 1959, *Special Publ. No. 13,* 123, The Chemical Society, London, (1959).
17. E. O. Fischer and W. Pfab, *Z. Naturforschg.*, **7b,** 377 (1952).
    J. D. Dunitz and L. E. Orgel, *Nature*, **1953,** 121.
    Ph. F. Eiland and R. Pepinsky, *J. Am. Chem. Soc.*, **74,** 4971 (1952).
    G. L. Hardgrove and D. H. Templeton, *Acta Cryst.*, **12,** 28 (1959).
    F. Jellinek, *Z. Naturforschg.*, **14b,** 737 (1959).

ON THE MECHANISM OF OLEFIN POLYMERIZATION WITH ZIEGLER-NATTA CATALYSTS

P. COSSEE*

*Koninklijke/Shell-Laboratorium, Amsterdam
(Shell Internationale Research Maatschappij N. V.)
Amsterdam-N., Holland*

Ziegler's discovery that ethylene could be polymerized at low pressure under the influence of a mixture of a transition-metal compound and a metal alkyl derived from a strongly electro-positive metal, opened a completely new field of catalysis. In particular, Natta[2] and his co-workers have extended the possibilities of this peculiar reaction.

Several investigators have contributed to provide a suitable mechanism.[3-10] With one exception,[3] they agree that the monomer molecule is interposed between a metal atom and a carbon atom of an organometallic compound. There is, however, still disagreement concerning the nature of the active centres. According to most theories at least two metal ions bound in a complex are required; one to accommodate the monomer molecule, the other bearing the alkyl group. A further point of discussion is whether the growing polymer chain is attached to the transition metal or to the non-transition metal. The results of recent investigations strongly support the view that the growth reaction takes place at the transition-metal ion.[10-21]

In the literature on Ziegler-Natta catalysis little attention has been given to theoretical concepts such as ligand-field theory and molecular-orbital methods, in order to obtain a more detailed picture of the specific role of the transition element.

In the present paper we will try to approach Ziegler-Natta catalysis using such concepts as π-bonding of olefins to transition elements and strength of transition metal-to-carbon bonds, which will be treated in the next section. Next a reaction mechanism will be proposed which may account for the driving force of the propagation reaction, the specificity of particular transition metal compounds, and the stereospecificity of a number of these catalysts in the polymerization of α-olefins.

---

*The author is much indebted to Drs. E. J. Arlman, E. W. Duck and E. L. Mackor, and to Prof. G. C. A. Schuit for many valuable discussions.

THEORETICAL CONCEPTS

π-Bonding of Olefins with Transition Elements

This kind of bonding, schematically indicated in Fig. 1, was proposed by Chatt and Duncanson[22] for complexes of ethylene with platinum compounds. A recent X-ray structure analysis of *trans-* $[Pt \{C_2H_4\} \{NH(CH_3)_2\} Cl_2]$ by Alderman *et al.*[23] showed that the C—C distance is considerably stretched from 1.34 Å in the free olefin to 1.47 Å in the complex, whilst the distance between Pt and the centre of the C—C bond appears to be 2.09 Å. Almost the same parameters were found recently in the butadiene-ion tricarbonyl.[24] The long C—C distance, which comes very close to what may be expected for a single bond between two trigonally-hybridized C-atoms (1.48 Å), shows that the electrons from the third p-orbital of each carbon atom are indeed highly delocalized.

The revelant orbitals* in such a π-bond are given below in order of increasing energy:

$$\psi_1 = a d_{x^2 - y^2} + \sqrt{\frac{1 - a^2}{2}}\, \{p_A + p_B\}$$

$$\psi_2 = b\, d_{yz} + \sqrt{\frac{1 - b^2}{2}}\, \{p_A - p_B\}$$

$$\psi_3 = \sqrt{1 - a^2}\; d_{x^2 - y^2} - \frac{a}{\sqrt{2}} \{p_A + p_B\}$$

$$\psi_4 = \sqrt{1 - b^2}\; d_{yz} - \frac{b}{\sqrt{2}} \{p_A - p_B\}\,.$$

Two of these, ψ_1 and ψ_2, are bonding (cf. Fig. 2b). This molecular-orbital energy diagram by no means pretends to be quantitative,

---

*For convenience the formulae have been given for the case where bonds with the other ligands are 100% ionic. Since, as a rule, they are not, $d_{x^2-y^2}$ and d_{yz} ought to be replaced by linear combinations with ligand orbitals having the same symmetry. As a further simplification, interaction of the metal 4s- and 4p-orbitals has been omitted.

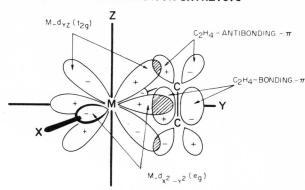

Fig. 1. Schematic picture showing spatial arrangement of the relevant orbitals in a "π-bond" between a transition metal and C_2H_4.

but is based on the generally adopted ideas on the relative positions of metal and ligand orbitals. In Fig. 2 the octahedral arrangement was chosen to demonstrate the effect of π-bonding, since this will serve our purpose better. The experimentally known metal-olefin complexes are square planar. In such complexes, however, the effect of the olefin on the energy-level scheme is quite similar, the only difference being the $d_z{}^2$-orbital, which is now a very low-lying one.

In Pt^{2+} compounds, for example, d_{xy}, d_{xz}, $d_z{}^2$, and ψ_2 are occupied by pairs of electrons. Because of the occupation of ψ_2 we may say that a kind of double bonding exists between Pt^{2+} and the olefin, giving rise to a reasonably stable complex.

For transition elements with no or only a few d-electrons, ψ_2 will be empty or only half-filled. Therefore no great stabilization due to double bonding may be expected. However, the rearrangement of the energy-level scheme, resulting from coordination of an olefin to such a transition element, will still apply (cf. Fig. 2a and 2b).

When we accept as a logical first step in Ziegler-Natta catalysis the coordination of a monomer molecule to a transition metal-alkyl compound, [12,13,19,20] we may assume that this will be through a π-complex, a suggestion made earlier by Fischer.[25] The resulting rearrangement among the energy levels will prove to be an important feature in the discussion of catalytic activity.

The Strength of Transition Metal-Alkyl Bonds

Jeffé and Doak[26] made a first attempt to explain the apparent instability of transition metal-to-carbon bonds. Their theoretical calculations were based on a simple model, but they found a significant

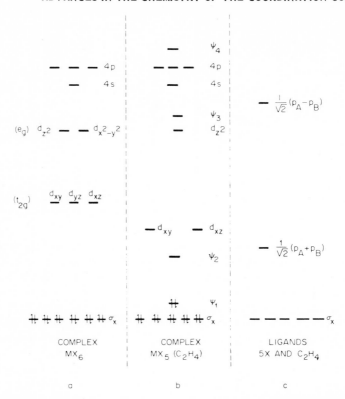

Fig. 2. Tentative M.O. energy diagram for complexes MX_6 and MX_5 (C_2H_4), respectively, showing the effect of "π-bonded" C_2H_4 on t_{2g}-level (for simplicity: $4s$ and $4p$ do not interact; MX-bond is 100% ionic).

difference between transition- and non-transition metals. They concluded that the electro-negativity difference between transition elements and carbon is not large enough for strong ionic bonds, whilst covalent effects are weak.

Recently Chatt and Shaw[27] proposed that the difficulty in preparing simple transition metal-alkyl compounds may be related to the ease with which transition metal-to-carbon bonds are broken into radicals. They assume that in a molecular orbital diagram more than a certain minimum energy difference, ΔE, between the highest filled and the first empty orbital is required to obtain stable organometallic compounds. The presence in transition metal compounds of a non-σ-bonding t_{2g}-level* would be the reason that this minimum energy

---

*Throughout this paper the group of orbitals d_{xy}, d_{xz} and d_{yz} is designated by t_{2g}-orbitals even when the symmetry is not strictly cubic.

difference is very often not attained. Thus, according to the authors, when the t_{2g}-levels are filled (for example in Pt^{2+}) an electron from this level might easily be promoted by thermal excitation into one of the anti-bonding levels, followed by a radical decomposition of the corresponding metal-to-carbon bond. In the alternative case, where the t_{2g}-levels are empty or nearly so, thermal excitation would bring an electron from one of the bonding orbitals into one of the t_{2g}-orbitals, with the same result for the corresponding metal-to-carbon bond.

Chatt and Shaw succeeded in demonstrating that by increasing the distance between the filled t_{2g}-level of Pt^{2+} and the anti-bonding level through coordination with tertiary organic phosphines, stable alkyl compounds of platinum could indeed be obtained.

If we apply their arguments to ions of transition elements with empty or nearly empty t_{2g}-orbitals, it appears that in order to stabilize metal-alkyl bonds, one needs ligands having enough electrons available to fill all bonding combinations with t_{2g}-metal orbitals (cf. alkyls and aryls of $(C_5H_5)_2Ti^{2+}$).

On the other hand, one must expect that ligands with empty orbitals of the right symmetry to give a bonding combination with partly filled t_{2g}-orbitals of the metal ion will favour radical decomposition of weak metal-alkyl bonds.

This is illustrated in Fig. 3b for the combination of ethylene with a transition metal-alkyl complex having no d-electrons.

The difference $\Delta E'$ between the energies of the orbital:

$$\phi_{RM} = a \cdot d_{z^2} + \sqrt{1 - a^2} \cdot (sp_3)_R$$

representing the metal-to-carbon bond (the bonds MX are, for simplicity, assumed to be 100% ionic) and of the orbital:

$$\psi_2 = b \cdot d_{yz} + \sqrt{\frac{1 - b^2}{2}} \cdot \{p_A - p_B\}$$

has become small, thus facilitating the expulsion of a radical R.

The example already illustrates the importance of the "Chatt and Shaw model" for the discussion of Ziegler-Natta catalysis.

MECHANISM OF THE PROPAGATION REACTION

The propagation step in Ziegler-Natta polymerizations, which is now generally taken to be the interposition of an olefin molecule

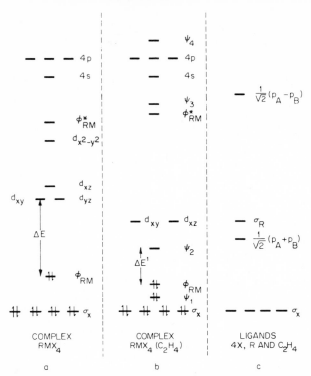

Fig. 3. Tentative M.O. energy diagram for complexes RMX_4 and RMX_4 (C_2H_4), respectively, showing reduced distance between ϕ_{RM} and t_{2g}-level (same simplifications as for Fig. 2).

between a metal atom and an alkyl group:

$$M\text{---}R + CH_2\!\!=\!\!CH_2 \longrightarrow M\text{---}CH_2\text{---}CH_2\text{---}R,$$

requires, as pointed out by several authors,[12,13,19,20] a transition metal-alkyl bond and the possibility of coordinating the monomer to the transition element. The simplest configuration meeting these requirements is shown in Fig. 4, which represents an essentially octahedrally coordinated transition metal ion of which one of the octahedral positions is vacant whilst another is substituted by an alkyl group. In many of the currently used catalysts X_1 to X_4 are halogen ions.

Such a situation is most easily visualized at the surface of halogenides with layer structures, which are components of the most satisfactory catalyst systems (for example α-TiCl$_3$ + Al (C_2H_5)$_3$).

Then R, X_1 and the vacant position are to be found in the close-packed surface layer of anions, whereas X_2, X_3 and X_4 are anions in the second layer of the lattice of the solid compound.[28]

In solution the composition and structure of the active complexes are not very well known. The transition element is very probably part of a larger complex system with other metal compounds.[12,18] When X_1 to X_4 are regarded as bridging groups, the configuration as shown in Fig. 4 is a feasible one also in homogeneous systems.

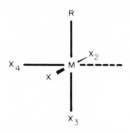

Fig. 4. Configuration supposed to be the active centre in a Ziegler-Natta catalyst. M = transition metal ion, R = alkyl (growing polymer chain), $X_1 - X_4$ are anions.

The propagation reaction may now proceed as follows:

The olefin is coordinated to the transition metal ion at the vacant octahedral position through π-bonding, as outlined on page 242. When the metal ion is one with no or only a few electrons in the t_{2g}-orbitals, this complex formation is accompanied by a rearrangement of the energy levels, which is schematically indicated in Fig. 3a and 3b.

If ΔE is larger and $\Delta E'$ smaller than the critical energy difference in the Chatt and Shaw model (see page 243), it is seen that the metal-alkyl bond becomes susceptible to radical breaking at the very moment the monomer molecule is coordinated to the metal ion.

In this way the activation energy for a rearrangement in which the alkyl group moves from the transition metal towards the nearest C-atom of the olefin is reduced.

After this first step the transition metal ion under consideration still has its alkyl group (two C-atoms longer) and its vacant position, which have, however, changed places. The process may thus be repeated and the growing polymer chain oscillates between two octahedral positions of one transition metal ion.

DISCUSSION

A comparison of the present theory with a number of the existing ones shows that there are two main features:

1. Specific use is made of a transition element in essentially octahedral surroundings. This is obvious in all those cases where a solid catalyst with a layer structure (e.g., α-$TiCl_3$) is used. In homogeneous systems, when complexes of lower-valency transition elements with non transition metal compounds are probably the active species, it seems a much more realistic picture.

2. The growing polymer chain oscillates between two octahedral positions of *the same* metal ion, whereas in the theories based on binuclear complexes it moves between two metal ions.

When these concepts are used, together with the theoretical ones outlined in the previous sections, the proposed mechanism permits explanation of a number of facts not covered by the existing ones:

1. Only slight nuclear displacements are involved in the propagation step. The process is to a first approximation of an electronic rearrangement: an initial electron jump from the bond between metal and alkyl into the depressed t_{2g}-level, followed by the formation of a new bond between an alkyl radical and the nearest C-atom of the olefin. At the moment of the migration of the alkyl radical the latter already contains, at least partly, an extra electron in its anti-bonding orbital.

Figure 5 demonstrates that the relative positions of alkyl group and olefin molecule are very favourable for such a process. When the centre of the olefin is placed at the same distance as the negative ions, it is seen that the van der Waals radii are at least touching each other. The R-group approaches from the right angle. When the parameters used in Fig. 5[29] are adopted, the distance between R and the nearest C-atom must only contract from about 3.3 Å to 1.54 Å.

We feel that this is perhaps the explanation of the low activation energy (≈ 10 kcal/mole)[2] of the propagation, which is very difficult to reconcile with large nuclear displacements.

2. The proposed mechanism provides an explanation for the driving force of the propagation reaction and is at the same time well in keeping with the known kinetics. The very thorough investigations by Natta[2] of the polymerization of C_3H_6 with an α-$TiCl_3$-Al $(C_2H_5)_3$-

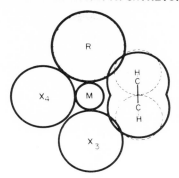

Fig. 5. Diagram of transition state; drawn to scale; radii are used which may be considered representative: $R = 2.0$ Å, $X_3 = X_4 = 1.8$ Å, $M = 0.75$ Å, C (in

$$C_2H_4) = 1.7 \text{ Å, distance } M \longrightarrow \overset{C}{\underset{C}{||}} = MX.$$

system as a catalyst show that the rate of propagation is proportional to the total amount of α-$TiCl_3$ and the pressure of the olefin and is independent of the Al-alkyl concentration.

In our mechanism the Al-alkyl indeed plays no essential role in the propagation step. Nevertheless, its presence is very important and in many instances indispensable, as it may play a role in alkylating and reducing the transition element, in chain transfer and as a scavenger. All the mechanisms of termination and chain transfer proposed by Natta[2] remain equally valid in our mechanism.

3. The theoretical arguments indicate that the process of interposition of olefins is a subtle one. The isolated transition metal-alkyl bonds must be sufficiently stable in the absence of coordinated olefin, which requires an electronegativity of the metal ion that is not too high. This same bond must become sufficiently destabilized when an olefin molecule is coordinated in the vacant position. Therefore the d-orbitals of the t_{2g}-type must be sufficiently extended but not too diffuse in order to be influenced by combination with the anti-bonding olefin orbital. This also requires ions with a relatively low effective nuclear charge. It is a condition practically equivalent to Natta's statement[30] that transition elements with an ionization potential for the first electron <7 ev are particularly active.

Considering that the sizes of d-orbitals are highly dependent on atomic number and valency of the metal and also on the kind of negative ions surrounding it,[31] one may understand the high sensitivity of Ziegler-Natta catalysis to so many parameters.

Unfortunately, very little is known of the theoretical parameters required for a more quantitative treatment than could be given in the present contribution.

4. The fact that in our mechanism the growing polymer chain oscillates between two positions of the same metal ion provides a simple and logical explanation for the isotacticity of the polypropylene formed when we specialize our arguments for the catalyst system α-$TiCl_3/Al(C_2H_5)_3$.[32]

We hope that this theoretical approach will not only be of importance in Ziegler-Natta catalysis, but may contain useful ideas for application in a much wider field of catalysed reactions.

REFERENCES

1. K. Ziegler, E. Holzkamp, H. Breil and H. Martin, *Angew. Chem.*, **67**, 541 (1955).
2. Review by: G. Natta and I. Pasquon, *Adv. in Catalysis*, **11**, 1 (1959).
3. C. D. Nenitzescu and A. H. Ciresicahuch, *Angew. Chem.*, **68**, 438 (1956).
4. F. Eirich and H. Mark, *J. Coll. Sci.*, **11**, 748 (1956).
5. G. Bier, *Kunststoffe*, **48**, 354 (1958).
6. G. Natta, *J. Inorg. Nuclear Chem.*, **8**, 589 (1958).
7. H. Uelzmann, *J. Pol. Sci.*, **32**, 457 (1958).
8. F. Patat and H. Sinn, *Angew. Chem.*, **70**, 496 (1958).
9. A. Gumboldt, H. Schmidt, *Chem. Ztg.*, **83**, 636 (1959).
10. P. H. de Bruyn, *Chem. Weekbl.*, **56**, 161 (1960).
11. C. Beermann and H. Bestian, *Angew. Chem.*, **71**, 618 (1959).
12. W. L. Carrick, *J. Am. Chem. Soc.*, **80**, 6455 (1958).
13. D. B. Ludlum, A. W. Anderson and C. E. Ashby, *ibid.*, **80**, 1380 (1958).
14. W. P. Long, *ibid.*, **81**, 5312 (1959).
15. K. Ziegler, Int. Conf. on Coordination Chemistry, London (1959). *The Chem. Soc., Spec. Publ.*, **13**, 1 (1959).
16. K. Oita, *J. Pol. Sci.*, **43**, 585 (1960).
17. W. L. Carrick, F. J. Karol, C. L. Karapinka and J. J. Smith, *J. Am. Chem. Soc.*, **82**, 1502,(1960).
18. W. P. Long and D. S. Breslow, *ibid.*, **82**, 1953 (1960).
19. W. L. Carrick, R. W. Kluiber, E. F. Bonner, L. H. Wartman, F. M. Rugg and J. J. Smith, *ibid.*, **82**, 3883 (1960).
20. W. L. Carrick, W. T. Reichle, F. Pennella and J. J. Smith, *ibid.*, **82**, 3887 (1960).
21. W. L. Carrick, A. B. Chasar and J. J. Smith, *ibid.*, **82**, 5319 (1960).
22. J. Chatt and L. A. Duncanson, *J. Chem. Soc.*[1953], 2939.
23. P. R. H. Alderman, P. G. Owston and J. M. Rowe, *Acta Cryst.*, **13**, 149 (1960).
24. O. S. Mills and G. Robinson, *Proc. Chem. Soc.* [1960], 421.
25. E. O. Fischer, Int. Conf. on Coordination Chemistry, London (1959). *The Chem. Soc., Spec. Publ.*, **13**, 73 (1959).
26. H. H. Jaffé and G. O. Doak, *J. Chem. Phys.*, **21**, 196 (1953).
27. J. Chatt and B. L. Shaw, *J. Chem. Soc.* [1959], 705.
28. P. Cossee, *Tetrahedron Letters*, **17**, 12 (1960).
29. L. Pauling, *The Nature of the Chemical Bond* (3rd ed.), New York, 260 (1960).
30. G. Natta, *Angew. Chem.*, **68**, 393 (1956).
31. D. P. Craig and E. A. Magnusson, *Disc. Far. Soc.*, **26**, 116 (1958).
32. P. Cossee, *Tetrahedron Letters*, **17**, 17 (1960).

THE PARAMAGNETIC RESONANCE SPECTRA OF CHROMIUM(III) AND MANGANESE(IV) HEXAFLUORIDE IONS*

LINDSAY HELMHOLZ, ANTHONY GUZZO, and ROBERT N. SANDERS

Department of Chemistry
Washington University
St. Louis, Missouri

The paramagnetic resonance spectrum of the fluoroferrate ion, $FeF_6^=$, in dilute solid solution has been discussed[1,2] in terms of the coefficients of the atomic orbitals making up the molecular orbitals occupied by the five unpaired electrons in this ion. This discussion led to the values of the coefficients of the individual fluorine $2s$ orbitals, $N_{eg}^2 a^3/3$, equal to 0.008 and for each of the fluorine p orbitals, $(N_{eg}^2 b^2/3 - N_{t_{2g}}^2 c^2/4)$, equal to 0.035. In the expression for the p-orbital coefficient, the first term gives the $p\sigma$ contribution and the second the contribution of the $p\pi$ electrons. It has generally been assumed that N_{eg}^2 and $N_{t_{2g}}^2$ have values close to unity and that $c^2/4$ is small compared to $b^2/3$, that is, σ-bonding predominates. In order to investigate this latter point and to obtain some idea of the magnitude of the π-orbital contribution we have observed the spectra of $CrF_6^=$ and $MnF_6^=$ in dilute solid solution in K_2NaGaF_6 and Cs_2GeF_6 respectively. Each of these ions has three unpaired electrons, presumably in t_{2g} orbitals, and, if this is an exact description of the situation, $N_{eg}^2 a^2/3$ and $N_{eg}^2 b^2/3$ should be zero. The spectra indicate that the fluorine s contribution is not zero, but is much smaller than in the $FeF_6^=$ and that the anisotropic p-contribution is of the same order of magnitude as in $FeF_6^=$. The sign of the p coupling constant, moreover, has been shown by Shulman and Knox[3] to be negative, whereas the value of A_p for $FeF_6^=$ is positive. Internal consistency of our data also indicates this difference in sign. This result indicates a considerable amount of π-bonding, which in turn means the σ-bonding in $FeF_6^=$ has been underestimated. Consequently

---

*This work has been carried out with the assistance of the National Science Foundation through their grant, NSF-G 7381. This report is abstracted from the thesis submitted by A. V. Guzzo and R. N. Sanders in partial fulfillment of the requirements for the Degree of Doctor of Philosophy (A.V.G.) and Degree of Master of Arts (R.N.S.).

the extent of "covalency" must be considerable and assumptions mentioned above must be re-examined.

Procedure

Solid solutions of $CrF_6^=$ and MnF_6^- in the diamagnetic solids K_2NaGeF_6 and Cs_2GeF_6 were prepared by allowing concentrated HF solutions of the solvent solids with traces of the paramagnetic ions to evaporate slowly. This procedure yielded octahedra approximately 1 to 1.5 mm on an edge, with the cube faces more prominently developed in the case of the cesium salt. X-ray examination showed no evidence of deviation from the symmetry O_h for the environment of the chromium and manganese ions.[4] The metal to fluorine distances in these compounds are:

$$Ga—F = 1.90 \overset{o}{A}\,^4$$
$$Ge—F = 1.77 \overset{o}{A}\,^5$$
$$Cr—F = 1.91 \overset{o}{A}\,^3$$
$$Mn—F = 1.74 \overset{o}{A}\,^6$$

The concentrations of paramagnetic ions were in the range of 1.0 to 0.1 per cent.

The spectra were observed at 77° K or slightly below using the same techniques employed in Ref. 2.

The complex ions in the solid solvents used are all in parallel

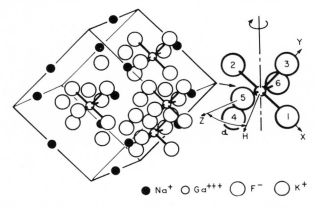

● Na⁺   ○ Ga⁺⁺⁺   ◯ F⁻   ◯ K⁺

Fig. 1. A portion of the unit cell of K_2NaGaF_6 is shown with only the octahedra at the origin and three face centers. The octahedron at the right shows the central atom coordinate system and the position of the axis of rotation of the crystal relative to the axes of the crystal and the octahedra. In the case of $CrF_6^≡$ it is assumed that the paramagnetic ion replaces the $GaF_6^≡$ ion. The Cs_2GeF_6 structure is similar to this, differing only in that the sodium ions are absent, and the potassium and $GaF_6^≡$ ions are replaced by cesium and GeF_6^- ions respectively. The orientations are the same.

orientation. Figure 1 shows this orientation with respect to the crystal axis and the applied magnetic field; it is given by a single angular parameter α, the angle between the magnetic field direction and the line between fluorine atoms 5 and 6. The rotation axis is taken in the [110] direction referred to the axial system of the octahedron.

Results

The spectra are shown in Fig. 2 and 3. They show anisotropic behavior but not such large fluorine hyperfine splittings as in the case of $FeF_6^{\equiv}$. The spectra can be accounted for on the basis of the energy levels of the following Hamiltonian:

$$\mathcal{H} = g\beta H \cdot S + A_s \sum_1^6 S \cdot I + A_p \sum_1^6 \{f(\alpha)S_z I_z + f^1(\alpha)S_z I_x + f^1(\alpha)S_z I_y\} + B \sum_1^6 I_z$$

to which a term $A_{sMn} S \cdot I_{Mn}$ must be added for the $MnF_6^{=}$ case. The last term gives the fluorine nuclear Zeeman energy. The coupling constants $(A_s A_p)$ have the same significance as in reference 1 and 2 and the values of the $f(\alpha)$ are:

$$f(\alpha) = 1/2\ (3 \cos^2 \alpha - 1) \quad \text{for atom 1-4}$$
$$f(\alpha) = +(3 \cos^2 \alpha - 1) \qquad\qquad 5\text{-}6$$
$$f'(\alpha) = -3/2 \sin \alpha \qquad\qquad\quad 1\text{-}2$$
$$f'(\alpha) = +3/2 \sin \alpha \qquad\qquad\quad 3\text{-}4$$
$$f'(\alpha) = 0 \qquad\qquad\qquad\qquad 5\text{-}6$$
$$f''(\alpha) = -3/2 \sin \alpha \cos \alpha \qquad\quad 1\text{-}2$$
$$f''(\alpha) = -3/2 \sin \alpha \cos \alpha \qquad\quad 3\text{-}4$$
$$f''(\alpha) = -3 \sin \alpha \cos \alpha \qquad\qquad 5\text{-}6$$

The magnetic axes for this evaluation of the function $f(\alpha)$ have been chosen with z along the field direction, x along the axis of rotation and y perpendicular to these directions.

Discussion of the Spectra

$CrF_6^{\equiv}$. For this case the [100] spectrum, which should be relatively simple since $f'(\alpha)$ and $f''(\alpha)$ are zero, is not particularly helpful since the resolution is very poor even at 77° K. Contributing to this difficulty is the fact that the $S = 3/2 \longrightarrow S = 1/2$ absorptions fall on top of the $S = 1/2 \longrightarrow S = 1/2$ lines and are considerably less well resolved. It seems to be the case that the relaxation time for this particular orientation is shorter than for the other directions observed.

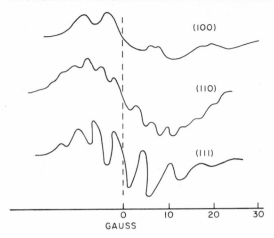

Fig. 2. The derivative curves for $CrF_6^{\equiv}$ dissolved in K_2NaGaF_6 with the magnetic field in the indicated directions.

Using the [111] spectrum as a starting point two sets of parameters appear to be possibilities. (1) $A_p = \pm6.7$, $A_s = \mp7.2$ (2) $A_p = \pm4.0$, $A_s = \pm1$. In order to decide between these, the derivative curves were calculated for the spectra in the three principal directions. Gaussian line shapes were used as is suggested by the $FeF_6^{\equiv}$ spectra.[7] The comparison of the [100] spectra for the two possibilities leaves little doubt that the second set is the proper choice. The parameters were refined by adjusting them to give a reasonable fit be-

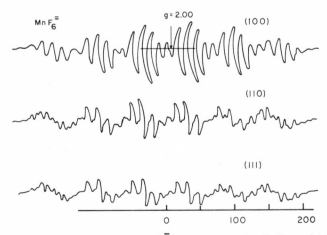

Fig. 3. The derivative curves for $MnF_6^{=}$ dissolved in Cs_2GeF_6 with the magnetic field in the indicated directions.

tween observed and calculated derivative curves for the [110] and
[111] spectra (shown in Fig. 4). The experimental data are not very
satisfactory, and we have not attempted to obtain a closer fit by varying the values of A_s and A_p and the Gaussian half-widths, but have
attributed rather large limits of error to the parameters. The final,
"best" values are:

$$A_s = \pm 1.1 \pm 0.5$$
$$A_p = \pm 4.5 \pm 1.0$$

$MnF_6^=$: In this case the [100] spectrum shows the best resolution and
may be accounted for by the assumptions (1) $A_s = \pm 15$ $A_p = 0$ or
(2) $A_p = \pm 10$ $A_s = + 5$. The possibility, so far as positions of lines
are concerned, $A_s = 20$ $A_p = 5$, can be eliminated by intensity considerations. The overlaping of the spectra for the various values of
I_{Mn} cause some trouble, but the peaks at the extreme ends of the
spectrum show the seven lines expected and the intensity relationships (the same for either choice) are qualitatively what is predicted.
The choice between the two sets can be made readily from a consideration of the [111] spectrum which shows about twice as many
lines as are observed when the magnetic field is in the [100] direction. The values $A_s = 15$, $A_p = 0$ are ruled out by this observation
since they should give a spectrum identical with the [100] spectrum.

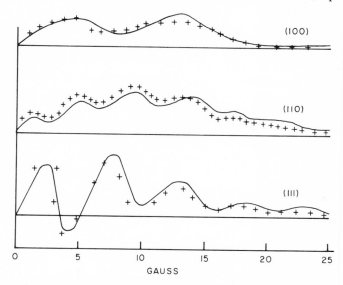

Fig. 4. The calculated and observed derivative curves for $CrF_6^=$. The solid curves
indicate the observed, and the crosses the calculated values of the derivatives at 1 gauss intervals for [100] and [111] and at 0.5 gauss intervals for
the [110] spectra.

The parameters were refined by adjusting them to give a better fit with the experimental line positions and intensities. The final values are:

$$A_p = \mp 9.5 \pm 1.0$$
$$A_s = \pm 5.5 \pm 1.0$$
$$A_{sMn} = 77.0 \pm 1.0$$

The improved resolution, observed in Fig. 3 with decreasing value of I_{Mn} is caused by the second order terms of the $S \cdot I_{Mn}$ term in the Hamiltonian. This results in a displacement of the $3/2 \rightarrow 1/2$ and $1/2 \rightarrow 1/2$ spectra relative to one another by amounts which increase with I_{Mn}.

Discussion of Results

$CrF_6^=$. A discussion of the significance of these results depends on a decision as to the sign of the coupling constants, which can be obtained only indirectly from these data. Fortunately, the fluorine nuclear resonance in K_2NaCrF_6 has been investigated by Shulman and Knox[3] who find the values $A_p = -7.2 \pm 1.2$ and $A_s = -1.0 \pm 0.5$. The discrepancy between the results of these authors and ours is fairly large in the case of A_p, perhaps too large to be explained by the difference in environment and needs further investigation, but the sign is almost certainly correct. Internal consistency of our data leads to this same result by the following argument: if A_p for chromium were positive, its value would be very closely equal to the direct dipolar contribution, the effect of the unpaired electrons on the central atom and one would anticipate an increase of at most of 30% in going from $CrF_6^{\equiv}$ to $MnF_6^=$, whereas the effect of increased π-overlap would tend to decrease this difference so that the overall effect would be a small one or perhaps even a decrease in the absolute value of A_p. The fact that the magnitude of A_p is more than twice as large for manganese as for chromium would then be difficult to explain if the values were positive. We have consequently chosen the negative signs for A_p in the cases of both ions.

We have no simple explanation for the fact that the A_s parameters have opposite signs. That these quantities are not zero as required by the simple molecular orbital considerations means that they result in all probability from contributions of higher lying states through configurational interaction, and it is difficult to predict what these effects should be.

Assuming that the effect of configurational interaction on the molecular orbital coefficients is small the expression for A_p is:

$$A_p = \frac{2}{5}\frac{\mu_n}{3I_n}\{-N_{t_{2g}}^2 c^2/4\} \left\langle \frac{1}{r^3} \right\rangle_{F_{2p}} + \mu_n/I_n CN_{t_{2g}}^2 \qquad (1)$$

The first term gives the contribution of the unpaired electron on the fluorine atoms and the second term takes into account the direct interaction of the central atom electrons with the fluorine nuclei. The quantity C is discussed in the appendix and has a value of approximately $0.75/R^3$ for the cases discussed here. The value of $N_{t_{2g}}$ is estimated by assuming it to be 1.00, with a value of the group overlap 0.1, solving for c, and then finding $N_{t_{2g}}$ by successive approximations. The expression for $N_{t_{2g}}$ is

$$N_{t_{2g}} = 1/(1 + c^2 - 2cG)^{1/2}$$

where G (the group overlap integral) $\int d_{xy} \cdot c/2(\pi_y^1 - \pi_y^2 + \pi_x^3 - \pi_x^4)d\tau$. It is assumed also in these calculations that the molecular orbitals are antibonding. The values obtained are

$$CrF_6^{\equiv} \quad N_{t_{2g}}^2 (-c^2/4) = -0.06 \pm .01$$

$$N_{t_{2g}}^2 = 0.875$$

$$MnF_6^{=} \quad N_{t_{2g}}^2 (-c^2/4) = -0.095 \pm .01$$

$$N_{t_{2g}}^2 = 0.735$$

$$FeF_6^{\equiv} \quad N_{t_{2g}}^2 (-c^2/4) = -0.04 \pm .01 \text{ (estimated)}$$

$$N_{eg}^2 (+b^2/3) = 0.076$$

The value of $N_{t_{2g}}^2 c^2/4$ for $FeF_6^{\equiv}$ is estimated from the trend with bond distance and central atom charge and may be in error by 50%. Since the values of $N_{t_{2g}}^2$ are derived on the basis of the assumptions mentioned, limits of error for these quantities would have no real significance.

The values of the orbital coefficients are, at best, only of qualitative significance. The present data do not permit accurate determination of the parameters and, further, the non-zero values of A_s and A_{sMn} indicate that configurational interaction must be important. It is difficult to say how this latter effect would influence the coupling constants, A_p, but because of the qualitative correspondence between the experimental facts and the conclusions drawn from the simple molecular orbital scheme we are inclined to attribute no more than 20% of the magnitudes of the A_p's to this configurational interaction.

The relatively great importance of σ- and π-bonding in these fluoride complexes indicated by our results suggests that the energy separation ot the anti bonding eg and t_{2g} orbitals may be influenced to a considerable extent by the type of bonding. This energy difference is important, in turn, in the determination of the multiplicity of the ground states of complex ions of the transition elements, for example, the sextet state for $FeF_6^{\equiv}$ and the doublet for $Fe(CN)_6^{\equiv}$. If the π-bonding is limited for some reason—as in the cyanides because the π orbitals are already used, or as in the heavier elements because of increased interatomic distances—then the anti-bonding t_{2g} orbital may be an almost pure d-function and have a lower energy than in the case where strong π-bonds are formed by the lower lying d-π combination. The eg-t_{2g} energy separation will then be larger favoring the pairing of the valence electrons.

APPENDIX

The value of the direct dipolar interaction, the magnetic interaction of the electrons located on the central atom with the fluorine nuclei, can be written in terms of the functions of α, $f(\alpha)$, $f'(\alpha)$ and $f''(\alpha)$ and the coordinates of the electron on the central atom and R, the interatomic distance. After integration over the central atom coordinate the expression becomes:

$$f(\alpha)/(r')^3 \{1-3/2(r/r')^2 \sin^2 \theta\}$$

where r is the distance from the central atom to the electron and r' the distance from that electron to the fluorine nucleus in question. The angle θ is the angle between r and the line between the central atom and the fluorine atom being considered, and R the X-F distance

$$(r')^2 = (r^2 + R^2 - 2rR \cos \theta)$$

What is desired, the quantity C of equation 1, is the function $f(\alpha)/(r')^3 \, 1-3/2(r/r')^2 \sin^2 \theta$ averaged over the central atom d functions. $f(\alpha)$ depends only on the angle of orientation of the crystal. The remainder of the expression is:

$$\frac{1}{r^3}\left\{1 - \frac{3}{2}\left(\frac{r}{r'}\right)^2 \sin^2 \theta\right\} = \frac{1}{2r^3}\frac{\partial^2}{\partial h_1^2}\left\{1 + \left(\frac{R}{r}\right)^2 - 2\frac{R}{r}\cos \theta\right\}^{-\frac{1}{2}} =$$

$$\frac{1}{2r^3}\frac{\partial}{\partial h_1^2}\left(\frac{r}{R}\right)\left\{1 + \left(\frac{r}{R}\right)^2 - \frac{2r}{R}\cos \theta\right\}^{-\frac{1}{2}} \quad (2)$$

Where $h_1 = (R/r)$ and $h = (r/R)$. The second derivatives of the terms in brackets give series in h_1, and h with Legendre polynomials as coefficients. When multiplied by $1/2r^3 = h_1^3/R^3$ these give series expansions of the desired functions. Since the θ dependence of the central atom d functions can be expressed as function of Legendre polynomials, the orthogonality and normalization properties of these functions reduce the calculations to a relatively few evaluations of average values of $(1/r^3)$. The first term in these series is just $1/R^3$ and is a good approximation for the Fe^{+++} case. For the case that only the $3d_{t_{2g}}$ orbitals are occupied a calculation using orbitals which approximate the self consistent field orbitals gives a value of $0.75/R^3$ for c. For $FeF_6^{\equiv}$ the value of C is $0.975/R^3$ for the same approximate type of radical wave function.

REFERENCES

1. L. Helmholz, *J. Chem. Phys.*, **31**, 172 (1959).
2. L. Helmholz and A. V. Guzzo, *ibid.*, **32**, 302 (1960).
3. R. G. Shulman and K. Knox, *Phys. Rev. Letters*, **4**, 603 (1960).
4. A. V. Guzzo, Thesis, Washington University, St. Louis, Mo., 1960.
5. J. L. Hoard and W. B. Vincent, *J. Am. Chem. Soc.*, **61**, 2849 (1939).
6. H. Bode and W. Wendt, *Z. Anorg. Allgem. Chem.*, **269,** 165 (1952).
7. S. Geschwind, Bell Telephone Laboratories, Private communication.

SPECTROSCOPIC STUDIES OF REACTIONS OF COORDINATION COMPOUNDS WITH CYANIDE AND THIOCYANATE IONS IN THE SOLID STATE*

SISTER M. DENNIS GLONEK, SISTER M. ROSARIA PETRA, and
COLUMBA CURRAN

*Department of Chemistry
University of Notre Dame
Notre Dame, Indiana*

Reactions of coordination compounds in the solid state previously studied in this Laboratory include the displacement of methyl anthranilate from its complexes with zinc chloride by halide ions;[1] halogen exchange involving palladium(II) and platinum(II) complexes,[2] and palladium(IV) and platinum(IV) complexes;[3] and the displacement of *para*-substituted anilines from metal complexes by such organic solids as hexamethylenetetramine, lysine, and thiourea.[4] Both ultraviolet and infrared spectra were utilized in these investigations, chiefly the former. Halogen exchange in complexes of the type L_2MeCl_2 and L_2MeCl_4 were observed to proceed more extensively the greater the electron releasing property of the ligand, indicating that exchange involved essentially S_N1 replacement rather than S_N2 displacement reactions.

Solid state reactions of complexes with cyanide and thiocyanate ions are revealed in many instances by shifts to higher frequencies of the absorption peaks associated with the $C{\equiv}N$ stretching vibration at 2080 and 2050 cm^{-1}, respectively. These shifts in a variety of complexes have been summarized by Mitchell and Williams. The present investigation is concerned with the interaction of these ions with complexes containing halogen atoms.

Experimental

Potassium cyanide, potassium thiocyanate, cupric chloride, palladous chloride, potassium tetrachloroplatinate(II), potassium hexachloroplatinate(IV), potassium tetrachloropalladate(II) and potassium hexachloropalladate(IV) were reagent grade materials. Potassium

---

*This work was supported in part under A.E.C. Contract AT(11-1)-38 with the Radiation Laboratory of the University of Notre Dame.

trichlorocuprate(II) was prepared by dissolving equivalent portions of potassium chloride and cupric chloride in water and evaporating the solution. The preparation of all other compounds will be reported elsewhere; they were analyzed for metal or halogen or both, or for carbon and hydrogen.

Equivalent portions (one thiocyanate ion per halogen atom) of reactants were mixed by agitating in a Wig-L-Bug in polystyrene vials for 25 sec at room temperature, 22 °. The reactants were carefully dried before mixing. Spectra were obtained of the mixtures in potassium bromide disks shortly after mixing. The absorption patterns of the thiocyanate groups in the great majority of these disks did not change appreciably over a period of a month. The cobalt complexes were notable exceptions; the extent of reactions in disks of these complexes increased as much as three-fold over a period of three months. Reactions in aged disks were undoubtedly catalyzed by moisture in the potassium bromide.

Infrared spectra were obtained with a Perkin-Elmer Model 21 spectrophotometer. Absorption maxima marked "a" were obtained with a sodium chloride prism; all other spectra were obtained with a calcium fluoride prism. The absorbance ratios listed in Table 1 are the ratios of the peak heights ($\log I_0/I$) of the shifted and unshifted thiocyanate absorption maxima. The last column of Table 1 lists the absorbance per milligram of cyanide ion. The value of this quantity for potassium cyanide is 0.07.

Abbreviations used in Table 1 are *py* for pyridine, *dipy* for α, α'-dipyridyl, *en* for ethylenediamine, and *bmte* for *1,2*-bis(methylthio)-ethane. All square and tetragonal compounds with monodentate ligands are *trans*.

Discussion of Results

Reactions with Thiocyanate Ions. The date in Table 1 can best be analyzed in the light of the crystal structures of the complexes. Unfortunately, X-ray diffraction studies have been made for only a few of these compounds. Zannetti and Serra[6] have determined the structure of some complexes of the type Me py_2Cl_2 and have summarized the results of other investigators in this field. The complexes of manganese, iron, α-cobalt, nickel, copper, cadmium and mercury have a *trans* tetragonal configuration, with bridging chlorine atoms. The chlorine bridges are known to be symmetrical (all Co—Cl distances equal) in the cobalt complex and unsymmetrical in the copper, cadmium, and mercury complexes. The absorbance ratios listed in Table 1 reveal that the order of ease of replacement of bridged chlorine atoms in these tetragonal chains by thiocyanate ions is: Cd > Cu =

TABLE 1: INFRARED ABSORPTION BY COORDINATED THIOCYANATO AND CYANO GROUPS

	SCN		CN	
	ν_{max} cm^{-1}	Absorbance Ratio	ν_{max} cm^{-1}	Absorbance mg CN$^-$
1. Mn py$_2$Cl$_2$	2090	0.30	2105	0.10
2. Mn py$_2$Br$_2$	2092	1.0	2105	0.12
3. Fe py$_2$Cl$_2$	2101	0.45	2070	0.28
			2050	0.28
4. α-Co py$_2$Cl$_2$	2126	0.16	2128	0.23
5. β-Co py$_2$Cl$_2$	2124	5.3	2123	0.59
6. Co py$_2$Br$_2$	2124	1.06	2123	0.05
7. Co py$_2$I$_2$	2124	0.36	2123	0.27
8. Ni py$_2$Cl$_2$	2110	0.20	2128	0.56
9. Ni py$_2$Br$_2$	2110	0.40	2119	0.32
10. Ni py$_2$I$_2$	2110	0.28	2119	0.90
11. Ni py$_4$Cl$_2$	unresolved		2119	0.19
12. Ni py$_4$I$_2$	2070	0.55	2119	0.56
13. Cu py$_2$Cl$_2$	2096	0.43	2089^a	2.5
14. Cu py$_2$Br$_2$	2095	1.86	2119^a	1.33
			2088	0.6
15. Cd py$_2$Cl$_2$	2096	0.55	2141	0.09
16. Cd py$_2$Br$_2$	2096	0.25	2145	0.07
17. Cd py$_2$I$_2$	2104	0.50	2141	0.15
18. Zn py$_2$Cl$_2$	2077	> 10.	2155	0.08
19. Zn py$_2$Br$_2$	2077	1.0	2151	0.10
20. Zn py$_2$I$_2$	2077	0.8	2146	0.12
21. Pt py$_2$Cl$_2$	2110	0.10	pyridine displaced	
22. Pt py$_2$Cl$_4$	2119	0.33		
23. Pd py$_2$Cl$_2$	2114	0.25	2114	0.173
	2101	0.19		
24. Pd py$_2$Br$_2$	2114	0.32		
	2101	0.28		
25. Cu en Cl$_2$	2138	0.21	2088^a	0.56
	2113	0.43		
26. [Cu en$_2$]Cl$_2$	no reaction		2083^a	
27. [Cu(NH$_3$)$_4$]Cl$_2$	2119	4.2	NH$_3$ displaced	
28. Pt en Cl$_2$	2117	0.33		
29. [Pt en$_2$]Cl$_2$	2076	0.87	ligand displaced	
30. [Pd en$_2$]Cl$_2$	2076	0.46	ligand displaced	
31. Pd en Cl$_2$	2114	0.12		
32. Cu dipy Cl$_2$	2088	0.55	2092^a	0.39
33. Cu bmte Cl$_2$	2083	0.73	2079^a	0.92
34. Zn bmte Cl$_2$	2092	1.87		
35. Zn bmte I$_2$	2085	1.54		
36. Pt bmte Cl$_2$	2105	0.04	2132^a	0.22
37. PtCl$_2$(*iso*-Bu$_2$S)$_2$	2128	0.47	2088^a	0.7
38. PdCl$_2$(*iso*-Bu$_2$S)$_2$	2118	0.36	no reaction	
39. CuCl$_2$	2153	1.47		
40. KCuCl$_3$	2158	1.5	2088^a	0.23

TABLE 1 (continued)

	SCN		CN	
	ν_{max} cm^{-1}	Absorbance Ratio	ν_{max} cm^{-1}	Absorbance mg CN$^-$
41. K_2PtCl_4	2092	0.26		
42. K_2PtCl_6	2110	0.83		
43. $PdCl_2$	2119	1.02		
	2092	1.20		
44. K_2PdCl_4	2119	1.43		
	2092	1.58		
45. K_2PdCl_6	2119	1.03		
	2092	0.95		
46. K_2PdBr_6	2119	3.40		
	2092	2.95		

Fe > Mn > Ni > Co. (In the reaction with the mercury complex, spectra revealed that the thiocyanate ion displaced the pyridine.) This order appears to be related to the strengths of the chlorine bridges.

The only X-ray evidence for the crystal structure of dibromobispyridine complexes known to the authors is that for Cu py_2Br_2,[7] indicating a configuration similar to the dichloro compound. We have noted[8] a splitting of the absorption peak at 750 cm^{-1}, associated with coupling between C—H out-of-plane vibrations, in tetrahedral bispyridine complexes, and more recently a correlation between the frequency of the in-plane C—H bending vibration and configuration, about 1080 cm^{-1} for tetragonal and 1067 cm^{-1} for tetrahedral. On this basis we have assigned a tetragonal configuration to the dibromo complexes of manganese, nickel and cadmium. The order of absorbance ratios for these complexes is: Cu > Mn > Ni > Cd (compounds 14,2,9,17). The larger values for the first three complexes relative to the corresponding dichloro compounds indicates, as expected, weaker bridging by bromine than by chlorine. The low reactivity of Cd py_2Br_2 is surprising.

Spectral data indicate a tetrahedral configuration for the complexes of zinc, cobalt (excepting α-Co py_2Cl_2) and CdI_2. These are the most reactive of the bispyridine complexes and the order of reactivity is: Cl >> Br > I. The spectra of the reaction mixtures of the zinc complexes indicate the formation of nitrogen-to-zinc bonds. In all other reactions (of complexes of the above metals) the formation of —SCN— bridges is indicated, resulting in tetragonal Me $py_2(SCN)_2$ complexes. X-ray data have revealed this configuration for the complexes of cobalt(II) and copper(II).[9] It is rather surprising that in the partially reacted mixtures there is no spectral evidence for any un-bridged Me—NCS groups.

Ni py_4Cl_2 and $Cu(NH_3)_4Cl_2$ are examples of tetragonal compounds in which the chlorine atoms are not bridged; these complexes react more readily with the thiocyanate ion than do the bispyridine complexes. Cu en_2Cl_2 is anomalous in this regard. It is to be expected that tetrahedral complexes of copper(II) with no halogen atoms in the inner coordination sphere would react only slowly with thiocyanate ions to form octahedral compounds. We await X-ray data before as-signing tetrahedral configurations on the basis of reactivity.

Pt py_2Cl_2 is the least reactive of all the bispyridine complexes studied. Octahedral Pt py_2Cl_4 is about three times as reactive as the Pt(II) complex. A similar increase in absorbance ratio is noted from K_2PtCl_4 to K_2PtCl_6. On the contrary, K_2PdCl_6 is slightly less reactive than K_2PdCl_4 and K_2PdBr_6 is more reactive than the former.

An interesting reaction is that between bis(ethylenediamine) Pt(II) dichloride (compound 29) and the thiocyanate ion. A strong shifted peak is observed and the spectrum reveals that the ethylenediamine is not displaced. This indicates five- or six-covalent Pt(II). The shifted peak at 2076 cm^{-1} is lower than that for the reaction mixture of Pt $enCl_2$, 2117 cm^{-1}, indicating a weaker sulfur-to-platinum bond. Significant changes occur in the regions of the N—H stretching and deformation vibrations of the spectrum, indicating weaker hydrogen bonding in the thiocyanato complex than in the dichloride. Bis(ethyl-enediamine) palladium(II) dichloride reacts in a similar manner but less extensively to form a five- or six-covalent palladium(II) complex. A similar compound of the thiocyanato group with the bis(o-phenylene-bisdimethylarsine)palladium(II) ion has been reported by Harris and Nyholm. [10]

Table 1 reveals no uniformity in the comparative effects of the presence of the mono- and bidentate ligands on the extent of replace-ment of a halogen atom by a thiocyanato group. Replacement of two pyridine ligands by *1,2*-bis(methylthio)ethane decreases the reac-tivity of the zinc chloride complex and increases the reactivity of the zinc iodide complex. Pt $enCl_2$ is more reactive than Pt py_2Cl_2, whereas Pt $bmteCl_2$ is much less reactive than $PtCl_2(iso\text{-}Bu_2S)_2$. Cu $dipyCl_2$ and Cu py_2Cl_2 have similar reactivities despite the dif-ferences (*cis* and *trans*) in the positions of the chlorine atoms.

Just as palladous chloride and the tetrachloropalladate ion are the most reactive palladium(II) complexes, so cupric chloride and the tri-chlorocuprate anion contain the most reactive chlorine atoms of the copper(II) complexes studied. This reactivity is probably due in part to the greater ease of diffusion of the thiocyanate ion in these crystal lattices compared to those of complexes with organic ligands. These high reactivities along with those of tetrahedral complexes, octahedral platinum(IV) complexes and the low reactivity of square platinum(II) compounds indicate, although they do not definitely establish, that these reactions are S_N1 replacements rather than S_N2 displacements.

Reactions of Cyanide Ions. The absorbance per milligram of cyanide ion is a rather good indication of the relative extent of reaction of various complexes (if the organic ligand is not displaced) of any one metal. However absorption by the cyano group increases sharply on coordination, and to a different extent with different metals, thus preventing a comparison of the extent of reaction of complexes of different metals.

Zinc complexes react weakly with cyanide ions as is evident from the absorbance of the unshifted CN peak. This ion often displaces the organic ligand. It is particularly effective in removing pyridine and ethylenediamine from square planar complexes, suggesting that it exerts a displacing action.

The most interesting reaction of the cyanide ion is with copper(II) complexes. In solution this interaction results in reduction to Cu(I); we have not found any report in the literature of a compound containing the NC-Cu(II) linkage. Evidence for the formation of this bond in solid state reactions is the very strong absorption by the reaction mixtures in the 2083 cm^{-1} region without loss of color and, except for the ammonia complex, without displacement of the donor ligand. In the ultraviolet region, the 262mμ band characteristic of dibromo complexes is shifted to 259mμ in the spectrum of the reaction mixture without decrease in total absorption.

REFERENCES

1. M. A. G. Hill and C. Curran, *Abstracts of 132nd Meeting of the American Chemical Society,* New York (1957).
2. M. Q. Ryan and C. Curran, *Spectrochimica Acta,* 12, 373 (1958).
3. M. A. G. Hill and C. Curran, *Abstracts of 137th Meeting of the American Chemical Society,* Cleveland (1960), p. 24R.
4. M. St. A. Radzikowski, F. R. Klebacher, and C. Curran, *Abstracts of the 138th Meeting of the American Chemical Society,* New York (1960).
5. P. C. H. Mitchell and R. J. P. Williams, *J. Chem. Soc.,* 1912 (1960).
6. R. Zannetti and R. Serra, *Gazz. Chim. Ital.* 90, 328 (1960).
7. V. Kupcik, Czech. *J. of Physics,* B10, 182 (1960).
8. C. Curran and S. Mizushima, *Abstracts of the Fourth International Meeting on Molecular Spectroscopy,* Bologna, Italy (1959).
9. M. A. Porai-Koshits and G. N. Tischenko, *Soviet Physics Crystallography,* 4, 239 (1959).
10. C. M. Harris and R. S. Nyholm, *J. Chem. Soc.,* 4375 (1956).

PRODUCTS AND KINETICS OF PRIMARY AND SECONDARY AQUATION OF DICHLOROBIS (ETHYLENEDIAMINE)-CHROMIUM (III) CATIONS IN ACIDIC AQUEOUS SOLUTION*

CLIFFORD S. GARNER

Department of Chemistry
University of California
Los Angeles, California

and

DAVID J. MAC DONALD

California Research Corporation
Richmond, California

In connection with a program of comparing the reaction kinetics of analogous chromium(III) and cobalt(III) coordination complexes, we have determined under a variety of conditions the pseudo first-order rate constant and activation energy for production of ionic (i.e., uncoordinated) chloride by the primary aquation of *trans*-$[Cr(en)_2Cl_2]^+$ in HNO_3 solution in the absence of light.[1] At 25.00 ± 0.03 °C the rate constant was found to be $(2.25 \pm 0.03) \times 10^{-5}$ sec^{-1}, independent of initial concentration of complex over the range 1.6-11.3 mf, of pH from 0.14 to 2.9, and of ionic strength (adjusted with $LiNO_3$) from 0.016 to 1.0. The apparent rate constant increased *ca.* 1.9-fold at pH 4.9, an effect which cannot be attributed to base hydrolysis if the base hydrolysis rate constant is 3.7×10^{-2} M^{-1} sec^{-1} as reported.[2] Over the range 0-0.392 f sulfate (H_2SO_4 + Na_2SO_4), $10^5 k = 2.25 + 3.4 (SO_4^=)$, where $(SO_4^=)$ is the molar concentration of $SO_4^=$ calculated from the data of Baes,[3] catalysis by sulfate can be explained by assuming an S_N1 dissociation mechanism in which ion-pair formation with SO_4^- electrostatically facilitates the dissociation of Cl^- from the complex. The Arrhenius activation energy in the absence of sulfate is 23.23 ± 0.17 kcal/mole over the range 15-35°C. The other molar thermodynamic data at 25.0°C are:

---

*Work done at the University of California, Los Angeles, partly under Contract AT(11-1)-34, Project No. 12, between the U.S. Atomic Energy Commission and the University.

$\Delta H^{\circ\ddagger} = 22.64 \pm 0.17$ kcal, $\Delta F^{\circ\ddagger} = 23.79 \pm 0.01$ kcal, $\Delta S^{\circ\ddagger} = -3.86 \pm 0.57$ cal deg^{-1}, and $\log_{10} pZ$ (sec^{-1}) = 12.70 ± 0.20. Visible light accelerates the reaction rate. The above value of the rate constant is 1.7-fold lower than a previously reported value[2] based on exploratory measurements at a single initial concentration of complex (2 mf) in 0.1 f HNO$_3$ at an ionic strength of 0.1 (absence of light unreported).

Preliminary study of the secondary aquation (release of second chloro ligand) of $trans$-[Cr(en)$_2$Cl$_2$]$^+$ indicated that a simple two-step process such as

$$trans\text{-}[Cr(en)_2Cl_2]^+ + H_2O \;\rightarrow\; cis\text{- or } trans\text{-}$$
$$[Cr(en)_2(OH_2)Cl]^{+2} + Cl^-$$
$$[Cr(en)_2(OH_2)Cl]^{+2} + H_2O \;\rightarrow\; cis\text{- or } trans\text{-}$$
$$[Cr(en)_2(OH_2)_2]^{+3} + Cl^-$$

could not account for the observations. Consequently we undertook to separate and identify the reaction products at varying reaction times during the aquation of $trans$- and cis-[Cr(en)$_2$Cl$_2$]$^+$ and of $trans$- and cis-[Cr(en)$_2$(OH$_2$)Cl]$^{+2}$. The earlier exploratory study[2] of aquation of $trans$-[Cr(en)$_2$Cl$_2$]$^+$ and the extensive investigation[4] of aquation of cis-[Cr(en)$_2$Cl$_2$]$^+$ were based solely on measurements of the rate of chloride-ion release, and like the majority of previous kinetic studies of aquation of coordination complexes, had not included identification of the reaction products. Such characterization of products, including their geometrical configuration, is required for a full understanding of the reaction mechanisms, and can result in discovery of reaction paths not revealed by studies of the rate of formation of ionic chloride alone.

Separations of the above chromium(III) species were achieved with 40-mm × 9-mm columns of Dowex AG50W-X8 cation-exchange resin (100–200 mesh, in H$^+$ form). Reaction solutions, usually 0.1 f in H$^+$, were forced down a column at 5–50 ml per minute with complete adsorption of the chromium species on the resin. The various cationic complexes were selectively eluted, the progress of the variously colored bands down the column being followed visually. Typical volumes and concentrations of HNO$_3$ eluent found satisfactory for elution of the following complexes are: $trans$-[Cr(en)$_2$Cl$_2$]$^+$, 200 ml, 0.3f; cis-[Cr(en)$_2$Cl$_2$]$^+$ (and also a species formed in aquation of $trans$-[Cr(en)$_2$Cl$_2$]$^+$ and tentatively identified as a $trans$-dichloro-cis-diaquomonoethylenediamine cation, hereinafter referred to as $trans$-[Cr(en)(OH$_2$)$_2$Cl$_2$]$^+$), 250 ml, 0.6 f; $trans$-[Cr(en)$_2$(OH$_2$)Cl]$^{+2}$, 200 ml, 1.4 f; cis-[Cr(en)$_2$(OH$_2$)Cl]$^{+2}$ and one or more chloride-free complexes formed in increasing proportions at later reaction times in the aquation of $trans$-$[Cr(en)_2Cl_2]^{+2}$, <10% at 4 hrs, 250 ml, 2.0 f; chloride-free complexes (perhaps cis- and $trans$- $[Cr(en)_2(OH_2)_2]^{+3}$, $[Cr(en)(OH_2)_4]^{+3}$, etc.), 50 ml, 10 f. Separations were normally good, except that the tail of the third-fraction band usually overlapped the head of the fourth-fraction band, especially in $trans$-$[Cr(en)_2Cl_2]^{+}$ aquation at later reaction times. The identity of the complexes in these chromatographic fractions, including species not previously characterized, was established by determinations of the Cl/Cr atom ratios (plus N/Cr atom ratio in $trans$-$[Cr(en)(OH_2)_2Cl_2]^+$), coupled with the visible absorption spectra of the complexes (see Fig. 1) determined at 25°C with a Cary Model 11 recording spectrophotometer, and by the order of elution from the cation-exchange resin, from which it is generally found that the $trans$ isomer of complexes of these types is more easily eluted than the cis isomer (which has the larger electric dipole moment for interaction with the resin). These separations permitted the isolation and characterization for the first time of cis- and $trans$-$[Cr(en)_2(OH_2)Cl]^{+2}$ in solution for determination of their visible absorption spectra and for use in the aquation studies of these two complexes. Contact of reaction mixtures with the resin in chromatographic separations was shown not to affect the course or rate of the reactions being studied.

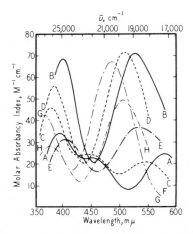

Fig. 1. Visible absorption spectra of chromium(III) complexes at 25°: A, $trans$-$[Cr(en)_2Cl_2]^+$, 0.1 f HNO$_3$; B, cis-$[Cr(en)_2Cl_2]^+$, 0.1 f HCl; C, $trans$-$[Cr(en)_2$-$(OH_2)Cl]^{+2}$, 0.2 f HNO$_3$ or 1.2 f HCl; D, cis-$[Cr(en)_2(OH_2)Cl]^{+2}$, 2 f HCl; E, $trans$-$[Cr(en)(OH_2)_2Cl_2]^+$(?), 3 f HClO$_4$; F, $trans$-$[Cr(en)_2(OH_2)_2]^{+3}$, 0.02 f HNO$_3$ + 1 f NaNO$_3$, ref. 5; G, cis-$[Cr(en)_2(OH_2)_2]^{+3}$, 0.02 f HNO$_3$ + 1 f NaNO$_3$, ref. 5; H, $[Cr(en)(OH_2)_4]^{+3}$, 0.1 f HClO$_4$, ref. 6; the molar absorbancy index a_M is defined by the relation $\log_{10}(I_0/I) = a_M c l$.

By combining chromatographic separation data with measurements of the total rate of loss of reactant complex ion (usually present at initial concentrations of 1–10 mf) and rate of production of ionic chloride, together with spectrophotometric observations, we have been able to evaluate or place upper limits on thirteen rate constants for reactions occurring at 35.00 ± 0.05°C in the primary and secondary aquation of *trans*- and *cis*-[Cr(en)$_2$Cl$_2$]$^+$ and the rearrangements of these two cations and their first-stage aquation products in the absence of light. These rate constants are given in Table 1, which includes comparative data on the analogous cobalt(III) complexes where such data are available. Figure 2 summarizes the essential kinetic relationships in a more readable form. The total rate constant for disappearance of the starting material was found from the slope of linear plots of the natural logarithm of the ratio of initial concentration of the reactant species to its concentration at reaction time t (as found from chromatography) *vs.* t. For *trans*-[Cr(en)$_2$Cl$_2$]$^+$ the plotted points did not significantly deviate from a straight line even after 95% reaction, showing that the reactions involved are not measurably reversible under the experimental conditions; for *cis*-[Cr(en)$_2$Cl$_2$]$^+$ the plot is less precise because of the much shorter reaction half-time (*ca.* 10 min *vs.* 132 min for the *trans* isomer). Rate constants for production of individual reaction products were determined by extrapolating to $t = 0$ the chromatographic separation data obtained at short reaction times, and using the relation that $k_{ij} = dX_j/dt$ in the limit $t = 0$, where k_{ij} is the first-order rate constant for formation of product j from reactant i, and X_j is the mole-fraction of

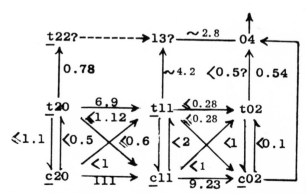

Fig. 2. $10^5 k$ (sec.$^{-1}$) for primary and secondary reactions of [Cr(en)$_2$Cl$_2$]$^+$ cations in 0.1 f HNO$_3$ (HCl or HClO in a few cases) at 35.0°C in the dark; first and second digits of code number for complex gives, respectively, the number of Cl and H$_2$O ligands per Cr.

TABLE 1: AQUATION AND REARRANGEMENT RATE CONSTANTS AT 35.0° C IN THE DARK

$(2')tr.-[\mathrm{Cr(en)(OH_2)_2Cl_2}]^+$ (?) $\dashrightarrow$ (7) $[\mathrm{Cr(en)(OH_2)_3Cl}]^{+2}$ (?) $\xrightarrow{k_{78}}$ (8) $[\mathrm{Cr(en)(OH_2)_4}]^{+3}$ $\xleftarrow{k_{68}}$

$\Big\uparrow k_{12}'$ $\qquad\qquad\qquad \uparrow k_{37}$ $\qquad\qquad\qquad \downarrow k_{58}$

(1)$tr.-[\mathrm{Cr(en)_2Cl_2}]^+$ $\underset{k_{14}}{\overset{k_{13}}{\rightleftarrows}}$ (3)$tr.-[\mathrm{Cr(en)_2(OH_2)Cl}]^{+2}$ $\underset{k_{36}}{\overset{k_{35}}{\rightleftarrows}}$ (5)$tr.-[\mathrm{Cr(en)_2(OH_2)_2}]^{+3}$

$k_{12}\updownarrow k_{21}$ $\qquad\qquad k_{34}\updownarrow k_{43}$ $\qquad\qquad k_{56}\updownarrow k_{65}$

(2)$cis-[\mathrm{Cr(en)_2Cl_2}]^+$ $\underset{k_{24}}{\overset{k_{23}}{\rightleftarrows}}$ (4)$cis-[\mathrm{Cr(en)_2(OH_2)Cl}]^{+2}$ $\underset{k_{46}}{\overset{k_{45}}{\rightleftarrows}}$ (6)$cis-[\mathrm{Cr(en)_2(OH_2)_2}]^{+3}$

Reaction	Acid	Method[a]	10⁵ × Rate constant[b], sec⁻¹	
			Cr complexes[b]	Co complexes
$k_{12} + k_{13} + k_{14} + k_{12}$	0.1 f HNO₃	Chr. sep. (1)	8.75 ± 0.05	
$k_{12} + k_{13} + k_{14}$	0.1 f HNO₃	Cl⁻ titr. (1)	8.02 ± 0.07[c]	16[k]
$k_{12} + k_{13} + k_{14}$	0.1 f HNO₃	Cl⁻ titr. (1)	(14)[d]	
k_{12}'	0.1 f HNO₃	Chr. sep. (1)	0.78 ± 0.05	
k_{12}'	0.1 f HNO₃	Subtraction	(0.73 ± 0.09)	
$k_{12} + k_{14}$	0.1 f HNO₃ or HCl	Chr. sep. (1)	1.12 ± 0.40	
k_{13}	0.1 f HNO₃	Subtraction	6.90 ± 0.41	
k_{13}	0.1 f HNO₃			
k_{24}	0.1 f HCl or HClO₄	Chr. sep. (1)	(7.2 ± 0.6)	
k_{24}	0.1 f HCl	Chr. sep. (2)	111 ± 2	
k_{24}	0.1 f HCl	Cl⁻ titr. (2)	104[e]	
k_{24}	0.1 f HClO₄	Cl⁻ titr. (2)	(109 ± 6)	
		Spectro. (2)	(100 ± 10)	85[l]

Rate constant	Medium	Method	Value	Alt.
k_{28}	0.1 f $HClO_4$	Spectro. (2)	<1	
k_{21}	0.1 f $HClO_4$	Spectro. (2)	<0.5	
$k_{34}+k_{35}+k_{36}+k_{37}$	0.1 f HNO_3	Chr. sep. (1)	~5	12(?)[m]
$k_{34}+k_{35}+k_{36}$	0.1 – 0.27 f HNO_3	Cl⁻ titr. (3)	0.28 ± 0.14	
k_{34}	0.1 f HNO_3	Spectro. (3)	$\lesssim 0.6$	~34[n]
k_{37}	0.1 f HNO_3	Cl⁻ titr. (3)	~4.2 ± 1.4	
k_{46}	0.1 f HNO_3	Cl⁻ titr. (4)	9.23 ± 0.02	~5[o]
k_{46}	0.1 f HNO_3	Cl⁻ titr. (2)	(~20)[g]	
k_{46}	0.1 f HNO_3	Chr. sep. (4)	(9.7 ± 1.1)	
k_{46}	1.3 f HNO_3	Spectro. (4)	22 ± 2	
k_{45}	1.3 f HNO_3	Spectro. (3)	<1	
k_{43}	1.3 f HNO_3	Spectro. (3)	<2	<9[q]
k_{56}	0.02 f HNO_3, 2 f $NaNO_3$	Spectro. (5)	<1[h]	
k_{58}	0.1 f $HClO_4$	Estimate	<0.5(?)[i]	~4[p]
k_{65}	0.02 f HNO_3, 2 f $NaNO_3$	Spectro. (5;6)	<0.1[h]	<0.1[p]
k_{68}	0.1 f $HClO_4$	Spectro. (6)	0.541[j]	
k_{78}	0.1 f HNO_3	Cl⁻ titr. (3)	~2.8 ± 0.6	

[a]Chr. sep. refers to chromatographic separations; numbers inside parentheses indicate chromium complex initially present. [b]Errors given are standard deviations, usually from a least-squares treatment; where two or more values of a given k appear, values inside parentheses are considered less reliable. [c]Rate constant for production of ionic chloride from $trans$-$[Cr(en)_2Cl_2]^+$, ref. 1 [d]Calc. from 25° k of ref. 2, using our E_a. [e]Calc. from 30° k of ref. 4, using their E_a. [f]Numerical integration by IBM-709 computer of differential equations representing hypothesized reaction path. [g]Extrapolated from rough 20° and 25° ks, ref. 4. [h]Estimated from data of refs. 5 and 6. [i]Estimated from data of ref. 6 assuming $trans$-$[Cr(en)_2(OH_2)_2]^{+3}$ aquates less rapidly than the cis isomer. [j]Calc. from 30° k of ref. 6, using their E_a. [k]Ref. 7. [l]Calc. from 25° spectrophotometric k in 0.1 f HNO_3, ref. 8, using E_a of ref. 9. [m]Ref. 11; value appears not to have been corrected for competing aquation and base hydrolysis, and may have been done in presence of light—no added acid? [n]Actually ($k_{34} + k_{43}$), estimated from results of Tobe reported in ref. 12; acid unknown. [o]Estimated from 30° k given in ref. 13 from analysis of data of ref. 9. [p]Estimated from 25° k in 0.10 f HNO and cis-$trans$ equilibrium quotient of ref. 14. [q]Based on rate of loss of optical activity of l-cis-$[Co(en)_2Cl_2]^+$ in 0.01 f acid at 30°, ref. 10, which has been shown, ref. 13, to involve cis-to-trans isomerization of the l-cis-$[Co(en)_2(OH_2)Cl]^{+2}$ product.

total Cr found as product j. The rate of production of the postulated $trans$-[Cr(en) (OH$_2$)$_2$Cl$_2$]$^+$ from $trans$-[Cr(en)$_2$Cl$_2$]$^+$ was obtained from chromatographic data at long reaction times by numerical integration of the set of differential rate equations representing this reaction scheme, with the aid of a FORTRAN program devised for the IBM-709 electronic computer of the Western Data Processing Center at U.C.L.A. Certain other rate constants were similarly evaluated with the computer.

Figure 3 shows the rate of growth and decay of the various chromium species produced in the aquation of $trans$-[Cr(en)$_2$Cl$_2$]$^+$ in 0.10 f HNO$_3$ at 35.0 °C in the dark. At one half-life ($ca.$ 2 hrs) for the disappearance of $trans$-[Cr(en)$_2$Cl$_2$]$^+$, $ca.$ 66% of the reacted complex has gone to $trans$-[Cr(en)$_2$(OH$_2$)Cl]$^{+2}$, $ca.$ 20% to cis-[Cr(en)$_2$(OH$_2$)-Cl]$^{+2}$, $ca.$ 10% to the species tentatively characterized as $trans$-[Cr(en)(OH$_2$)$_2$Cl$_2$]$^+$, and $ca.$ 4% to chloride-free complexes (diaquobis(en) and tetraquomono(en) species). Production of some or all of the cis-[Cr(en)$_2$(OH$_2$)Cl]$^{+2}$ may be the result of $trans$-to-cis isomerization of $trans$-[Cr(en)$_2$Cl$_2$]$^+$ (neither this rearrangement nor

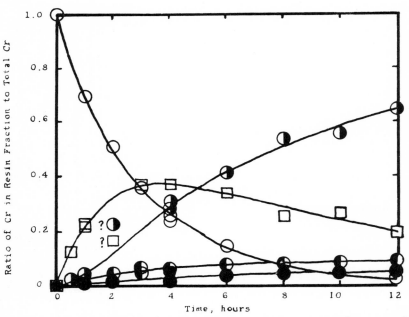

Fig. 3. Chromatographically separated products of aquation of $trans$-[Cr(en)$_2$Cl$_2$]NO$_3$ in 0.10 f HNO$_3$ at 35.0 °C: ○, $trans$-[Cr(en)$_2$Cl$_2$]$^+$; ◐, $trans$-[Cr(en)(OH$_2$)$_2$Cl$_2$]$^+$ (?); □, $trans$-[Cr(en)$_2$(OH$_2$)Cl]$^{+2}$; ◑, cis-[Cr(en)$_2$(OH$_2$)Cl]$^{+2}$ (fraction becomes increasingly impure after ca. 2 hrs., probably from formation of chloride-free complexes); ● all other chloride-free complexes.

its reverse could be detected), inasmuch as the rate of aquation of cis-$[Cr(en)_2Cl_2]^+$ is so much faster than the $trans$-to-cis rearrangement that the latter could easily provide an important reaction path without the concentration of the cis intermediate reaching a detectable level. Preliminary experiments of Baldwin and Tobe[15] on aquation of $trans$-$[Co(en)_2Cl_2]^+$ show considerable change of configuration occurs; in the chromium case it therefore seems probable that at least some of the cis-$[Cr(en)_2(OH_2)Cl]^{+2}$ product of $trans$-$[Cr(en)_2Cl_2]^+$ aquation is formed directly.

The distribution of products in aquation of $trans$-$[Cr(en)_2(OH_2)Cl]^{+2}$ could not be ascertained, since we were unable to separate chromatographically the cis- and $trans$-diaquo products. Moreover, the spectrophotometric observations were not useful for this purpose inasmuch as they indicated the presence of some chromium species in addition to the expected cis- and $trans$-$[Cr(en)_2(OH_2)_2]^{+3}$ and $[Cr(en)(OH_2)_4]^{+3}$. The unknown species may be an intermediate such as the $[Cr(en)(OH_2)_3Cl]^{+3}$ (of unknown configuration) postulated as component 7 (see Table 1) in order to account for the observed production of ionic chloride in aquation of $trans$-$[Cr(en)_2(OH_2)_2]^{+3}$, attempts to isolate a component 7 species chromatographically were unsuccessful. Even if it were possible to separate the product cis- and $trans$-diaquo species, presence of cis-diaquo product would be inconclusive evidence on the steric course of the aquation inasmuch as this product could readily be accounted for by the path $trans$-chloroaquo → cis-chloroaquo → cis-diaquo (this isomerization and its reverse were not detected experimentally).

On the other hand, the steric course of the primary and secondary aquation of cis-$[Cr(en)_2Cl_2]^+$ is essentially unequivocal. The only product detected in the primary aquation is cis-$[Cr(en)_2(OH_2)Cl]^{+2}$. The aquation rate constants determined by chloride titration, by chromatographic separation, and spectrophotometrically assuming cis-chloroaquo as sole product of the primary aquation, all agree within experimental error (see Table 1). Moreover, cis-$trans$ rearrangements of $[Cr(en)_2Cl_2]^+$ and $[Cr(en)_2(OH_2)Cl]^{+2}$ cations are too slow to play a significant role in affecting the configuration of the chloroaquo product. Consequently, cis-$[Cr(en)_2Cl_2]^+ + H_2O \rightarrow \sim 100\%$ cis-$[Cr(en)_2(OH_2)Cl]^{+2} + Cl^-$ accounts for the primary aquation. Similar statements can be made regarding the aquation of cis-$[Cr(en)_2(OH_2)-Cl]^{+2}$. Although the aquation rate constant determined spectrophotometrically (based on measurements at 385, 510 and 520 mμ, and assuming cis-diaquo as sole initial product) is $ca.$ twice the rate constants found by chromatography and by chloride titration, the spectrophotometric measurements were made in 1.3 f HNO$_3$, where the high concentration of nitrate (and the high ionic strength) might be expected to give a rate increase from ion-pair effects, rather than in $0.1\ f\ HNO_3$ as was used in the other determinations. The spectrum changed with time in accord with the scheme *cis*-chloroaquo $\longrightarrow$ *cis*-diaquo $\longrightarrow$ tetraquomono(en), without evidence of formation of *trans*-chloroaquo or *trans*-diaquo species. All the evidence indicates that the aquation of *cis*-$[Cr(en)_2(OH_2)Cl]^{+2}$ yields *ca.* 100% of *cis* product.

These stereochemical results for *cis*-$[Cr(en)_2Cl_2]^{+2}$ and *cis*-$[Cr(en)_2(OH_2)Cl]^{+2}$ are in accord with the observation of Ingold[16] and of Ingold, Nyholm and Tobe[17] that in aquation of all *cis* cobalt(III) octahedral complexes studied there is apparently total retention of configuration. Whether this stereokinetic rule is generally applicable to chromium(III) octahedral complexes and to cases where the outgoing group is not chloride remains for further research to demonstrate.

Other comparisons between chromium(III) and cobalt(III) dichlorobis(en) and chloroaquobis(en) complexes are not readily made since these cobalt complexes have not yet been investigated in the detailed way reported here for these chromium complexes. On the basis of the limited comparative data available, there appear to be no striking differences in kinetic behavior in acid solution. If the influence of solvent water is ignored, crystal-field theory predicts lower activation energies for aquation of the d^3 chromium(III) complexes than for the d^6 cobalt(III) complexes, in agreement with the experimental values in $0.1\ f\ HNO_3$ at $25.0\,^\circ C$ below:

	10^5k, sec^{-1}	Ea, kcal	$\Delta S^{\circ\,\ddagger}$, cal/deg
cis-$[Cr(en)_2Cl_2]^+$	33.0[4]	21.1[4]	−5.72[4]
cis-$[Co(en)_2Cl_2]^+$	25[8]	22.3[9]	−11
trans-$[Cr(en)_2Cl_2]^+$	2.25±0.03[1]	23.23±0.17[1]	−3.86±0.57
trans-$[Co(en)_2Cl_2]^+$	3.2[7]	24.2[9], 28[7]	0, +10

That the aquation of *trans*-$[Co(en)_2Cl_2]^+$ is faster than that of *trans*-$[Cr(en)_2Cl_2]^+$, despite the lower activation energy of the latter, is evidently associated with the greater activation entropy of the latter.

Much more research, including determinations of E_a and $\Delta S^{\circ\ddagger}$ and resolution of over-all rate constants into rate constants of individual characterized reactions, is required for an understanding of the mechanisms of aquation reactions of cobalt(III) and chromium(III) complexes.

REFERENCES

1. D. J. MacDonald and C. S. Garner, *J. Inorg. Nuclear Chem.*, **18**, 219 (1961).

2. R. G. Pearson, R. A. Munson and F. Basolo, *J. Am. Chem. Soc.*, **80**, 504 (1958).
3. C. F. Baes, *ibid.*, **79**, 5611 (1957).
4. J. Selbin and J. C. Bailar, Jr., *ibid.*, **79**, 4285 (1957).
5. F. Woldbye, *Acta Chem. Scand.*, **12**, 1079 (1958).
6. H. L. Schläfer and R. Kollrack, *Z. physik. Chem.*, *N. F.*, **18**, 22 (1958).
7. R. G. Pearson, C. R. Boston and F. Basolo, *J. Am. Chem. Soc.*, **75**, 3089 (1953).
8. R. G. Pearson, C. R. Boston and F. Basolo, *J. Phys. Chem.*, **59**, 304 (1955).
9. J. P. Mathieu, *Bull. soc. chim. (France)*, **3**, 2121, 2152 (1936).
10. J. P. Mathieu, *ibid.*, **4**, 683 (1937).
11. D. T. Haworth, E. F. Neuzil and S. L. Kittsley, *J. Am. Chem. Soc.*, **77**, 6198 (1955); *Experientia*, **12**, 335 (1956). See also A. G. Sharpe and D. B. Wakefield, *ibid.*, **13**, 460 (1957) and reply of S. L. Kittsley, *ibid.*, **13**, 460 (1957).
12. P. J. Staples and M. L. Tobe, *J. Chem. Soc.*, 4803 (1960).
13. R. G. Pearson, R. E. Meeker and F. Basolo, *J. Am. Chem. Soc.*, **78**, 2673 (1956).
14. J. Bjerrum and S. E. Rasmussen, *Acta Chem. Scand.*, **6**, 1265 (1952).
15. M. E. Baldwin and M. L. Tobe, *J. Chem. Soc.*, 4275 (1960).
16. C. K. Ingold, *Theoretical Organic Chemistry*, Butterworths Scientific Publications, London, 1959, pages 84–102.
17. C. Ingold, R. S. Nyholm and M. L. Tobe, *Nature*, **187**, 477 (1960).

KINETICS AND MECHANISM OF THE SUBSTITUTION OF WATER IN $Co(CN)_5OH_2^{-2}$ BY VARIOUS LIGANDS

ROBERT J. GRASSI, ALBERT HAIM, and W. K. WILMARTH

Department of Chemistry
University of Southern California
Los Angeles, California

Attempts to distinguish S_N1 and S_N2 mechanisms for anation reactions by comparing the rate of water exchange with the rate of anation have not been successful because of outer-sphere association between the reactants [1,2] or because of slow rate of anation as compared to water exchange.[3,4] One approach to avoid outer-sphere association between the reactants involves the use of anionic complexes. The aquopentacyanocobaltate (III) ion[5] was chosen for a combined study of anation and water exchange.

The rates of substitution of H_2O in $Co(CN)_5OH_2^{--}$ by N_3^-, SCN^-, Br^-, I^-, NH_3, $S_2O_3^{--}$ CNO^- and $SC(NH_2)_2$ have been measured spectrophotometrically at appropriate wavelengths. Since the ligand concentrations were in large excess, the slopes of the linear plots of log $(D_\infty - D)$ versus time yielded pseudo-first-order rate constants (reported in sec^{-1}).

The pseudo-first-order rate constant k for reaction (1), which proceeds to completion

$$Co(CN)_5OH_2^{--} + N_3^- \qquad Co(CN)_5N_3^{-3} + H_2O \qquad (1)$$

even at the lowest azide ion concentration used, is first-order in (N_3^-) at low values of (N_3^-), but becomes less than first-order as (N_3^-) increases. At $40°$, ionic strength 1.0 and pH 6.4, the dependence of k upon (N_3^-) is given by equation(2), where (N_3^-) varies from $0.0355\ M$ to $0.90\ M$.

$$k = \frac{1.6 \times 10^{-3}\,(N_3^-)}{1.9 + (N_3^-)} \qquad (2)$$

At $20°$, ionic strength 5.0 and pH 6.4, the dependence of k upon (N_3^-) is given by equation 3, where (N_3^-) varies from $0.5\ M$ to $5.0\ M$.

$$k = \frac{5.1 \times 10^{-4}\,(N_3^-)}{3.0 + (N_3^-)} \qquad (3)$$

The first-order rate constant for the reverse of reaction (1) is 4.56×10^{-7} sec^{-1} at $40°$, ionic strength 1.0 and pH 6.4. At $60°$ and ionic strength 1.0, the rate of aquation of Co(CN)$_5$N$_3$$^{-3}$ is pH independent between pH 6.0 and 0.1 M hydroxide ion concentration, with a first-order rate constant 8.0×10^{-6} sec^{-1}. The aquation of Co(CN)$_3$N$_3$$^{-3}$ in 0.04 M HClO$_4$ is complete in 1 hour at $60°$.

The rate of reaction (1) is pH dependent. At $40°$, ionic strength 1.0 and (N$_3$$^-$) = 0.90 M, the pseudo-first-order rate constant decreases by 6% from pH 6.7 to pH 8.65, by 12% from pH 6.7 to pH 9.05, and by a factor of 280 from pH 6.7 to 0.10 M OH.$^-$ The dependence of k upon (N$_3$$^-$) varies with pH. As indicated by equation (2), at pH 6.4 k becomes less than first-order in (N$_3$$^-$) as (N$_3$$^-$) increases. At 0.009 M OH$^-$ k is first-order in (N$_3$$^-$) for (N$_3$$^-$) varying between 0.18 M and 0.90 M. At pH 10.1 there is curvature in plots of k versus (N$_3$$^-$), but the curvature is not so pronounced as that observed at pH 6.4. The complete dependence of k upon (N$_3$$^-$) and pH is given by equation (4), where the pH varies between 6.4 and 0.10 M OH$^-$, and (N$_3$$^-$) varies between 0.18 M and 0.90 M.*

$$k = \frac{[1.6 \times 10^{-3}(H^+) + 6.5 \times 10^{-4} \times 2 \times 10^{-10}](N_3^-)}{[1.9 + 3 \times 10^3(OH^-) + (N_3^-)][2 \times 10^{-10} + (H^+)]} \tag{4}$$

At $40°$, ionic strength 1.0 and pH 3.4,† the pseudo-first-order rate constant for reaction (5), which proceeds to completion even at the lowest thiocyanate ion concentration

$$Co(CN)_5OH_2^{--} + SCN^- \longrightarrow Co(CN)_5NCS^{-3} + H_2O \tag{5}$$

used, depends upon (SCN$^-$) according to equation (6), where (SCN$^-$) varies between 0.10 M and 0.80 M.

$$k = \frac{1.6 \times 10^{-3}(SCN^-)}{2.9 + (SCN^-)} \tag{6}$$

At $20°$ and ionic strength 5.0 the dependence of k upon (SCN$^-$) is given by equation (7), where (SCN$^-$) varies between 0.50 M and 5.0 M.

$$k = \frac{5.1 \times 10^{-4}(SCN^-)}{5.0 + (SCN^-)} \tag{7}$$

Again k approaches zero-order dependence upon (SCN$^-$) as (SCN$^-$) increases.

---

*At the highest hydroxide concentrations used, formation of Co(CN)$_5$ N$_3$$^{-3}$ does not proceed to completion; under these conditions, initial rates were used to obtain the rate of the forward reaction.

†Preliminary experiments indicated that the rate of reaction (5) is pH independent from 0.01 M HClO$_4$ to pH 6.7.

Reaction (8) does not proceed to completion even at the highest bromide ion concentration used. Therefore, the pseudo-first-order

$$Co(CN)_5OH_2^{--} + Br^- \rightleftharpoons Co(CN)_5Br^{-3} + H_2O \qquad (8)$$

rate constants k obtained from the slopes of plots of log $(D_\infty - D)$ *versus* time measure the rate of approach to equilibrium. The measurements, carried out at 40°, ionic strength 1.0 and pH 6.4, with Co(III) initially present either as $Co(CN)_5Br^{-3}$ or $Co(CN)_5OH_2^{--}$, conform to equation (9), where (Br^-) varies between 0.00 M and 0.80 M.

$$k = \frac{1.6 \times 10^{-3} \ (Br^-) + 1.68 \times 10^{-3}}{10 + (Br^-)} \qquad (9)$$

Experimentally, k is first-order in (Br^-). Although equation (9) does not predict a first-order dependence of k upon (Br^-), the deviation from linearity is very small and within the scatter of the experimental points. The rate of aquation of $Co(CN)_5Br^{-3}$ at 40° and ionic strength 1.0 is pH independent between 0.01 M $HClO_4$ and 0.10 M NaOH, with a first-order rate constant $1.68 \times 10^{-4} sec^{-1}$. The equilibrium constant for reaction (8), measured independently by spectrophotometry, is 0.88.

A quantitative measurement of the rate of water exchange between $Co(CN)_5OH_2^{--}$ and solvent has not yet been obtained because of induced exchange during separation. However, it has been possible to set the following tentative limits on the first-order rate constant k_{ex} for the exchange: $1.3 \times 10^{-3} sec^{-1} > k_{ex} > 1.0 \times 10^{-3} sec^{-1}$, at 40°, ionic strength 1.0 and pH 6.4.

Preliminary rate experiments with various ligands yield the following order of reactivity: $OH^- > N_3^- > SCN^- > SC(NH_2)_2 > I^- > NH_3 > Br^- > S_2O_3^{--} > CNO^- > H_2O$. In this series, the position of H_2O is that calculated for H_2O at a concentration equal to that of the other ligands.

The results obtained in the study of the substitution of water in $Co(CN)_5OH_2^{--}$ by azide and thiocyanate ions conform to the predictions of an S_N1 mechanism:

$$Co(CN)_5OH_2^{--} \underset{k_2}{\overset{k_1}{\rightleftharpoons}} Co(CN)_5^{--} + H_2O \qquad (10)$$

$$Co(CN)_5^{--} + ^- \overset{k_3}{\longrightarrow} Co(CN)_5X^{-3} \qquad (11)$$

In terms of this mechanism, the pseudo-first-order rate constant should depend upon (X^-), the azide or thiocyanate concentration, according to equation (12).

$$k = \frac{k_1(X^-)}{(X^-) + k_2/k_3} \tag{12}$$

Comparison of equation (12) with equations (2, 4, 6 and 7) yields these results: at $40°$, ionic strength 1.0: $k_1 = 1.6 \times 10^{-3}$ sec^{-1}, $k_2/k_3 = 1.9$ for N$_3^-$, $k_2/k_3 = 2.9$ for SCN$^-$; at $20°$, ionic strength 5.0: $k_1 = 5.1 \times 10^{-4}$ sec^{-1}, $k_2/k_3 = 3.0$ for N$_3^-$, $k_2/k_3 = 5.0$ for SCN$^-$.

For the bromide system, reaction (13), the reverse of reaction (11) must be included

$$Co(CN)_5 X^{-3} \xrightarrow{k_4} Co(CN)_5^{--} + X^- \tag{13}$$

in the mechanism. The pseudo-first-order rate constant for approach to equilibrium is then given by equation (14).

$$k = \frac{k_1(X^-) + k_2 k_4/k_3}{(X^-) + k_2/k_3} \tag{14}$$

Comparison of equation (14) with equation (9) yields the results: $k_2/k_3 = 10$, $k_4 = 1.68 \times 10^{-4}$ sec^{-1}. The equilibrium constant for reaction (8) calculated from the kinetic parameters is $k_1 k_3/k_2 k_4 = 0.95$, a value in good agreement with the value 0.88 measured directly.

According to the $S_N 1$ mechanism, the limiting rate of substitution at sufficiently high anion concentration should equal the rate of water exchange between Co(CN)$_5$OH$_2^{--}$ and solvent. This requirement is fulfilled as seen by comparing the value of k_1 obtained in the azide and thiocyanate studies with the limits set on k_{ex}.

The pH independence of the rates of aquation of Co(CN)$_5$Br^{-3} and Co(CN)$_5$N$_3^{-3}$ also conforms to the requirements of the $S_N 1$ mechanism. This result further indicates the absence of an $S_N 2$ path for reaction between Co(CN)$_5$OH^{-3} and N$_3^-$, and simplifies the interpretation of the dependence of k upon pH. For an $S_N 1$ mechanism according to equations (10, 11, and 15), the dependence of k upon (N$_3^-$) and pH is given by equation (16).

$$Co(CN)_5 OH^{-3} \underset{k_2'}{\overset{k_1'}{\rightleftharpoons}} Co(CN)_5^{--} + OH^- \tag{15}$$

$$k = \frac{[k_1(H^+) + k_1' Ka](N_3^-)}{[(k_2/k_3) + (k_2'/k_3)(OH^-) + (N_3^-)][Ka + (H^-)]} \tag{16}$$

Ka, the concentration equilibrium constant for reaction (17), has a value 2×10^{-10} at $40°$ and ionic strength 1.0.

$$Co(CN)_5 OH_2^{--} \rightleftharpoons Co(CN)_5 OH^{-3} + H^+ \tag{17}$$

Comparison of equation (16) with equation (4) yields the results: $k_1' = 6.5 \times 10^{-4} \sec^{-1}$ and $k_2'/k_3 = 3 \times 10^3$. Therefore $k_1'/(k_2'/k_3) = 2.17 \times 10^{-7} \sec^{-1}$. From microscopic reversibility considerations it can be shown that $k_1'/(k_2'/k_3) = k_1 K_w/K_a \, (k_2/k_3)$. Using $k_1 = 1.6 \times 10^{-3} \sec^{-1}$, $k_2/k_3 = 1.9$, $Ka_a = 2 \times 10^{-10}$ and $K_w = 5.65 \times 10^{-14}$ (the product $m_H + m_{OH} -$ for 1 M NaCl at 40°), $k_1 K_w/K_a (k_2/k_3) = 2.37 \times 10^{-7} \sec^{-1}$, in good agreement with the value $2.17 \times 10^{-7} \sec^{-1}$ for $k_1'/(k_2'/k_3)$.

REFERENCES

1. A. C. Rutenberg and H. Taube, *J. Chem. Phys.*, **20**, 823 (1952).
2. F. A. Posey and H. Taube, *J. Am. Chem. Soc.*, **79**, 255 (1957).
3. C. Postmus and E. L. King, *J. Phys. Chem.*, **59**, 1208 (1955).
4. J. F. Below, R. E. Connick and C. P. Coppel, *J. Am. Chem. Soc.*, **80**, 2961 (1958).
5. A. Haim and W. K. Wilmarth, *ibid.*, **83**, 509 (1961).

THE CHEMISTRY OF ALKYL- AND ACYL-COBALT CARBONYLS

RICHARD F. HECK AND DAVID S. BRESLOW

Research Center
Hercules Powder Company
Wilmington, Delaware

The preparation of a number of alkyl- and acyl-cobalt carbonyls was investigated because of their possible relationship with the hydroformylation or oxo reaction.[1]

Alkylcobalt carbonyls have been prepared by reacting sodium cobalt tetracarbonyl with alkylating agents according to the procedure first described by Hieber and co-workers.[2]

$$RX + NaCo(CO)_4 \xrightarrow{Et_2O} RCo(CO)_4 + NaX$$

The procedure is useful only with active alkylating agents because of the instability of the alkylcobalt compounds. Acylcobalt carbonyls have been prepared by three procedures: reaction of alkylcobalt carbonyls with CO, acyl halides with sodium cobalt tetracarbonyl, and olefins with cobalt hydrotetracarbonyl and CO, all at 0°.

$$RCo(CO)_4 + CO \longrightarrow RCOCo(CO)_4$$

$$RCOX + NaCo(CO)_4 \longrightarrow RCOCo(CO)_4 + NaX$$

$$RCH{=\!=}CH_2 + HCo(CO)_4 + CO \longrightarrow RCH_2CH_2COCo(CO)_4 +$$

$$\overset{\displaystyle CH_3}{\underset{\displaystyle }{R\overset{|}{C}HCOCo(CO)_4}}$$

The first method is more conveniently carried out by alkylating sodium cobalt tetracarbonyl in the presence of CO. The third method is not a good synthetic procedure because a mixture of isomers is formed and several side reactions are possible.

It was of interest to determine the direction of addition of cobalt hydrotetracarbonyl to olefins at low temperatures. In the presence of CO, both *1*-pentene and *2*-pentene yield products derived from the addition of cobalt to C_1 and to C_2, somewhat more of the terminal addition product being obtained from *1*-pentene. It is known that double-bond isomerization occurs both at low temperatures[3] and under the usual oxo conditions,[4,5] and the products obtained at low temperatures are roughly comparable to those obtained under oxo conditions.[6,7] With a branched terminal olefin, such as isobutylene, however, the results are quite different. At $0°$ the product is exclusively that derived from cobalt addition to the tertiary carbon atom, whereas under oxo conditions only about 5% of the addition takes this course, the major product resulting from addition to the terminal carbon atom.[8]

$$(CH_3)_2C\!\!=\!\!CH_2 + HCo(CO)_4 + CO \xrightarrow{0°} (CH_3)_3CCOCo(CO)_4$$

A similar reversal has been found with methyl acrylate. Under oxo conditions, only addition to the terminal carbon atom takes place,[9] whereas at $0°$ the major product results from addition to the secondary carbon atom, although some of the other is also formed.

$$CH_2\!\!=\!\!CHCOOCH_3 + HCo(CO)_4 + CO \longrightarrow CH_3OOC\overset{\displaystyle CH_3}{\overset{\displaystyle |}{C}}HCOCo(CO)_4 +$$

$$\text{major}$$

$$CH_3OOCCH_2CH_2COCo(CO)_4$$

$$\text{minor}$$

It appears, therefore, that the direction of addition of cobalt hydrocarbonyl to double bonds is a function of electron availability, electron-rich double bonds resulting in acid-type addition and electron-deficient double bonds in hydride-type addition. Straight-chain olefins appear to fall between these two extremes. The difference in the direction of addition at low and at elevated temperatures could be explained if the addition were reversible, and evidence for the reversibility has been obtained. Injection of ethylcobalt tetracarbonyl into the heated inlet of a gas chromatographic apparatus at $200°$ gave a 90% yield of ethylene.

$$(C_2H_5O)_3^+BF_4^- + NaCo(CO)_4 \xrightarrow[0°]{Et_2O} C_2H_5Co(CO)_4 \xrightarrow{200°}$$

$$C_2H_4 + HCo(CO)_4$$

Alkylcobalt tetracarbonyls are air-sensitive, thermally unstable materials. Acylcobalt tetracarbonyls are also air sensitive, but are more stable thermally than the corresponding alkyl compounds. Thus, acetylcobalt tetracarbonyl[1] is a yellow, crystalline solid melting at $-33°$; it decomposes at $-20°$, but can be handled in solution at room temperature. Its structure was assigned on the basis of its analysis, the fact that one CO was absorbed in the reaction of methyl iodide with sodium cobalt tetracarbonyl, and the fact that the same compound was obtained from acetyl bromide and sodium cobalt tetracarbonyl:

$$CH_3I + NaCo(CO)_4 + CO \longrightarrow CH_3COCo(CO)_4 \longleftarrow CH_3COBr +$$

$$NaCo(CO)_4$$

Hieber and co-workers[2] reported a band at 5.8μ in the gas phase infrared spectrum of methylcobalt tetracarbonyl, which they attributed to decomposition of the compound to acetone. The same band is present in the solution spectrum, but it is too intense to be attributed to acetone. The discovery that acetylcobalt tetracarbonyl and other acylcobalt compounds show the same band, but with greater intensity, has led to the conclusion that an equilibrium exists between alkyl tetracarbonyl and acyl tricarbonyl.[1]

$$RCo(CO)_4 \rightleftharpoons RCOCo(CO)_3$$

This interpretation helps to explain many puzzling results. Thus, it has been known for some time that the rate of the oxo reaction is inversely proportional to the CO pressure,[10,11] and that CO inhibits the conversion of dicobalt octacarbonyl to cobalt hydrotetracarbonyl with hydrogen.[12] We have found that the addition of cobalt hydrotetracarbonyl to olefins and the reduction of acylcobalt tetracarbonyls by either hydrogen or cobalt hydrotetracarbonyl are all inhibited by CO. The most reasonable explanation is that all these reactions involve coordinately unsaturated cobalt species, such as cobalt hydrotricarbonyl, acylcobalt tricarbonyl, dicobalt heptacarbonyl, etc. Reaction is preceded by complex formation between these species and substrate—olefin, hydrogen, etc.—and competition between substrate and CO for the vacant position on the cobalt accounts for the CO inhibition.

Alkyl- and acyl-cobalt tetracarbonyls react with triphenylphosphine to form acylcobalt tricarbonyl monotriphenylphosphine adducts, the former with no gas evolution and the latter with evolution of one mole of CO.[13] Since the latter reaction is zero order in phosphine, it must involve prior formation of acylcobalt tricarbonyl.

$$RCOCo(CO)_4 \rightleftharpoons RCOCo(CO)_3 + CO \qquad \text{slow}$$

$$RCOCo(CO)_3 + (C_6H_5)_3P \longrightarrow RCOCo(CO)_3P(C_6H_5)_3 \qquad \text{fast}$$

These compounds are thermally stable, relatively air-insensitive, crystalline substances and a considerable number have been prepared (Table 1) either by reacting an alkyl halide with sodium cobalt tetracarbonyl in the presence of triphenylphosphine, or by addition of tri-

TABLE 1: ACYLCOBALT TRICARBONYL TRIPHENYLPHOSPHINE COMPLEXES
$$RCOCo(CO)_3P(C_6H_5)_3$$

R =	Prepd. from	M.P. (dec.)
CH_3—	CH_3I, CH_3COBr	123
C_2H_5—	C_2H_5I	98–100
$(CH_3)_2CH$—	$(CH_3)_2CHCOCl$	101
$CH_3(CH_2)_4$—	$CH_3(CH_2)_4COCl$	95–98
C_6H_5—	C_6H_5COCl	119–122
—⟨benzene ring⟩—	$ClOC$—⟨benzene ring⟩—$COCl$	
CH_3OCH_2—	CH_3OCH_2Cl	150
$C_2H_5OOCCH_2$—	$BrCH_2COOC_2H_5$	63.5–65.5
$CH_3OOCCH_2CH_2$—	$CH_3OOCCH_2CH_2COCl$	115–117

phenylphosphine to acylcobalt tetracarbonyl made from acyl halide and sodium cobalt tetracarbonyl.

Acylcobalt carbonyls and their triphenylphosphine adducts react with several nucleophilic reagents to displace the cobalt moiety.

$$RCOOCH_3 + NaCo(CO)_4$$

$$RCOCo(CO)_4 \nearrow^{CH_3ONa} \searrow_{C_6H_5NH_2}$$

$$RCONHC_6H_5 + HCo(CO)_4$$

These reactions have been very useful in determining the structure of the various cobalt complexes investigated.

An investigation of the reaction of unsaturated halides has led to the discovery of a new class of complex compounds.[14] The reaction of allyl bromide with sodium cobalt tetracarbonyl at 0° resulted in the evolution of one mole of CO. From the reaction mixture was isolated an air-sensitive but thermally stable, yellow, crystalline compound which melted at − 33 to − 32°. Treatment with iodine in methanol liberated three moles of CO, indicating that the compound is allyl-cobalt tricarbonyl rather than the expected tetracarbonyl.

$$CH_2{=}CHCH_2Br + NaCo(CO)_4 \xrightarrow[0°]{Et_2O} C_3H_5Co(CO)_3 + CO$$

Proton magnetic resonance showed three different types of hydrogen in a 2 : 2 : 1 ratio. Since a simple π-bonded structure (I) should have four different kinds of hydrogen, the molecule was formulated as possessing a nonclassical, symmetrical structure (II), with the carbons and hydrogens in one plane and the cobalt either above or below.

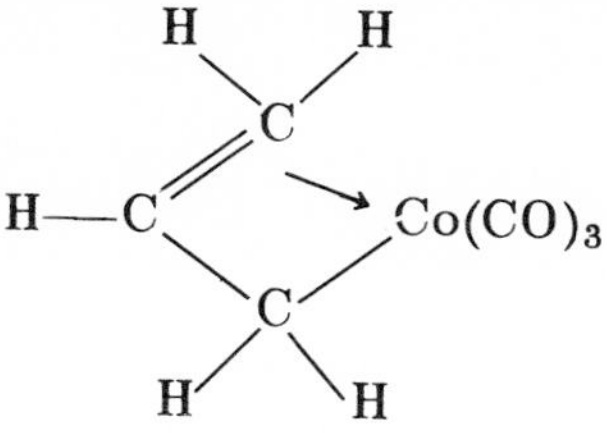

I

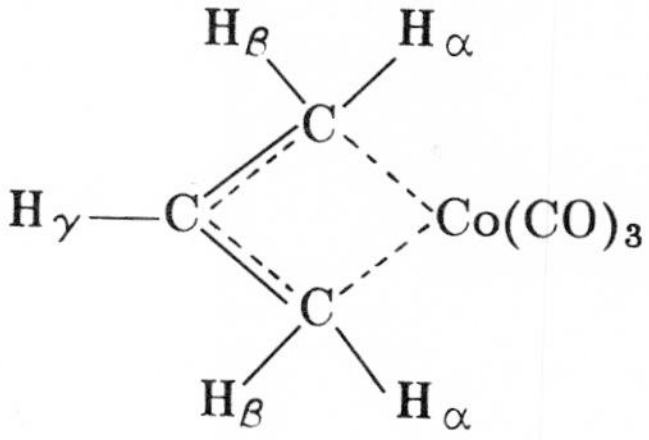

II

Treatment of II with triphenylphosphine displaced CO and yielded allylcobalt dicarbonyl triphenylphosphine. Similarly, crotyl bromide yielded 2-butenylcobalt tricarbonyl, which was assigned the same type of structure (III).[14] This was shown to be identical with the previously reported[15] butadiene-cobalt hydrotetracarbonyl adduct. Structure III has been recently confirmed by proton magnetic resonance.[16]

$$CH_3CH{=}CHCH_2Br + NaCo(CO)_4 \longrightarrow$$

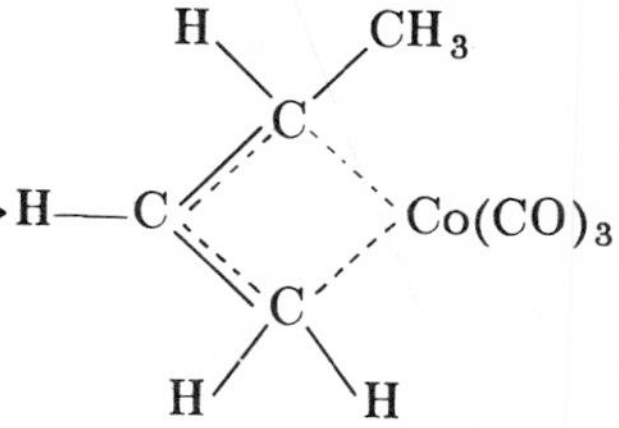

III

$$\longleftarrow CH_2{=}CHCH{=}CH_2 + HCo(CO)_4$$

Symmetrical π-allyl bonding of a number of metals is now known. Thus, allylpalladium chloride dimer[17] and allylmanganese tetracarbonyl[18] have been shown to have this structure. Recently we prepared a nickel compound by a different synthesis, and showed it to have the symmetrical structure.

$$CH_2{=}CHCH_2Cl + Ni(CO)_3P(C_6H_5)_3 \xrightarrow[40°]{MeOH}$$

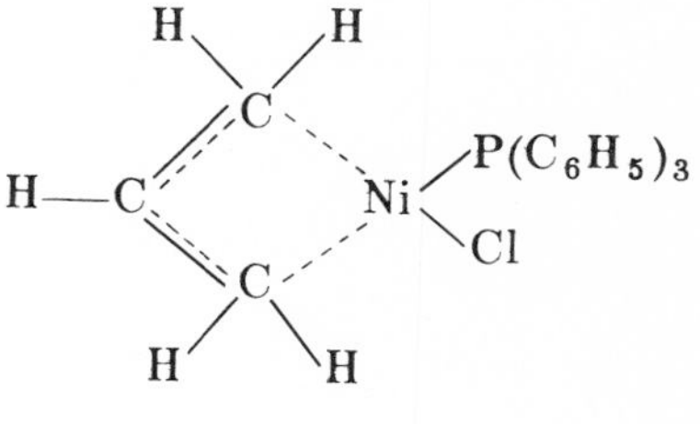

It is clear, therefore, that π-allyl bonding is a general phenomenon, and other transition metals will very likely yield similar complexes.

REFERENCES

1. R. F. Heck and D. S. Breslow, *Chem. & Ind. (London)*, 467 (1960).
2. W. Hieber, O. Vohler and G. Braun, *Z. Naturforsch.*, **13b**, 192 (1958).
3. G. Karapinka and M. Orchin, *Abstracts 137th Meeting, American Chemical Society*, Cleveland, April 5–14, 1960, p. 92–0.
4. G. Natta, R. Ercoli and S. Castellano, *Chim. e ind. (Milan)*, **37**, 6 (1955).
5. I. Wender, S. Metlin, H. W. Sternberg, S. Ergun and H. Greenfield, *J. Am. Chem. Soc.*, **78**, 5401 (1956).
6. A. I. M. Keulemans, A. Kwantes and T. van Bavel, *Rec. trav. chim.*, **67**, 298 (1948).
7. I. J. Goldfarb and M. Orchin, *Advances in Catalysis*, Vol. IX, Academic Press, Inc., New York, 1957, p. 609.
8. I. Wender, J. Feldman, S. Metlin, B. H. Gwynn and M. Orchin, *J. Am. Chem. Soc.*, **77**, 5760 (1955).
9. H. Adkins and G. Kresek, *ibid.*, **71**, 3051 (1949).
10. G. Natta, R. Ercoli, S. Castellano and F. H. Barbieri, *ibid.*, **76**, 4049 (1954).
11. A. R. Martin, *Chem. & Ind. (London)*, 1536 (1954).
12. P. Pino, R. Ercoli and F. Calderazzo, *Chim. e ind. (Milan)*, **37**, 783 (1955).
13. R. F. Heck and D. S. Breslow, *J. Am. Chem. Soc.*, **82**, 4438 (1960).
14. R. F. Heck and D. S. Breslow, *ibid.*, **82**, 750 (1960).
15. H. B. Jonassen, R. I. Stearns, J. Kenttämaa, D. W. Moore and A. G. Whittacker, *ibid.*, **80**, 2586 (1958).
16. D. W. Moore, H. B. Jonassen and T. B. Joyner, *Chem. & Ind. (London)*, 1304 (1960).
17. H. C. Dehm and J. C. W. Chien, *J. Am. Chem. Soc.*, **82**, 4429 (1960).
18. H. D. Kaesz, R. B. King and F. G. A. Stone, *Z. Naturforsch.*, **15b**, 682 (1960).

RATE COMPARISONS FOR ELECTRON TRANSFER BETWEEN PENTAMMINECOBALT(III) COMPLEXES AND CHROMOUS, VANADOUS AND EUROPOUS IONS*

ROBIN T. M. FRASER

The University of Ottawa
Ottawa Ontario, Canada

It has recently been demonstrated [1,2] that electron transfer between Cr^{++} aq. and pentamminecarboxylatocobalt(III) complexes takes place through organic acid as the bridging group. With monobasic or aliphatic dibasic acids, the chromium attacks the ligand at the carboxyl group adjacent to the cobalt centre, and the electron is transferred through the path $Cr..O \overline{\cdots} C \overline{\cdots} O$—Co. When the ligand is fumaric or terephthalic acid, there exists the possibility of a conjugated system extending through the ligand from the carboxyl group remote from the cobalt, and attack by chromous ion does take place at both carboxyl groups. The two paths for the reaction can be distinguished since the rate of remote attack[†] varies linearly with the acid content of the solutions,[3] and, further, remote attack induces hydrolysis in ester ligands, whereas adjacent attack does not.[4,5]

With ligands such as acetate or butyrate, then, the overall rate of reaction is first order in both chromous ion and cobalt complex, independent of acid concentration, and the specific rate constants are almost identical. Apparently the rest of the ligand does not influence the rate very much, and in particular it has been pointed out[6] that the carboxyl group at the remote end of the succinate ligand does not increase the rate of reaction; no chelation of the chromous ion takes place. With all complexes, but particularly with conjugated ligands, the over-all rate of the reaction

$$(NH_3)_5CoL^{++} + 5H^+ + Cr^{++} \rightarrow 5NH_4^+ + Co^{++} + CrL^{++}$$

---

*The europium oxide used in the experiments was purchased with a grant from the Chemical Society (London). Other funds were made available by the National Research Council of Canada.

[†]The terms *remote attack* and *adjacent attack* refer respectively to attack by the chromous ion at the carboxyl group situated on the ligand some distance from the cobalt or to attack at the carboxyl bound to the cobalt centre.

does not depend solely on the rate of the electron transfer process; the rearrangements of the ligand to form a path suitable for transfer and the rate of substitution giving rise to the bridged (binuclear) complex will be of some importance. To make the systems more amenable to investigation, the ligand can be varied systematically, either keeping the same terminal groups and varying the length of the path through which electron transfer must occur, or by keeping the path for transfer constant and varying the terminal group or the rest of the ligand not associated with the transfer. In the present investigation, the ligands have been chosen so that the attack by the reductant takes place at a carboxyl oxygen adjacent to the cobalt(III) centre with subsequent electron transfer Red $..$ O$\overline{}$C—C—Co(III), and the effect of vary-
$$\overset{|}{R}$$
ing the substituent R determined.

Experimental

The method of preparing the cobalt(III) complexes has been described elsewhere. [5] The reducing solutions containing chromous, vanadous or europous ion were prepared and stored under nitrogen in Machlett burettes converted to Jones reductors. The stock solution of vanadyl perchlorate was prepared from vanadyl sulphate and barium perchlorate. The sodium perchlorate solution used to adjust the ionic strength of the solutions to 1.0 was prepared by mixing equivalent amounts of A.R. sodium hydroxide and perchloric acid. All specific rate constants were determined spectrophotometrically by following the disappearance of the absorption maximum of the cobalt complex. The reactant solutions were mixed under nitrogen and forced into 10 cm silica cells freed from oxygen. A Beckman DK 1 recording spectrophotometer was used to measure the absorbance change with time.

Results

Reactions Independent of Hydrogen Ion Concentration. Most of the reactions studied followed the rate law $-d(\text{Co}L^{++})/dt = k(\text{Co}L^{++})$ (reductant) where $\text{Co}L^{++}$ represents the pentamminecobalt complex, and showed no dependence upon the acidity of the solutions. The free energies, heats and entropies of activation were determined from the usual expressions,

$$k \text{ (specific rate constant)} = (kT/h)e^{-\Delta F^{\ddagger}/RT}$$
$$= (kT/h)e^{\Delta S^{\ddagger}/R}e^{-\Delta H^{\ddagger}/RT},$$

and the first three tables list the values found for k, $\Delta S^{\ddagger}$, $\Delta H^{\ddagger}$.

TABLE 1: SPECIFIC RATE CONSTANTS ($\mu = 1.0$, $25.0\,^\circ$C)

Complex	$k_{Cr^{++}}^{*}$	$k_{V^{++}}$	$k_{Eu^{++}}$
Acetato	0.18[2]	0.43	0.18
Chloroacetato	0.10	1.25	3.16
Cyanoacetato	0.11	1.13	
Dichloroacetato	0.074	1.03	2.08
Benzoato	0.14	0.52	0.24
o-chlorobenzoato	0.074	0.57	0.39
o-iodobenzoato	0.082	0.90	0.28
o-phthalato	0.075[2]	1.01	2.16
m-phthalato	0.093[2]	0.60	0.64
p-chlorobenzoato	0.21	0.60	
p-iodobenzoato		0.37	0.27
p-hydroxybenzoato	0.13	0.53	
p-cyanobenzoato	0.18	0.88	
p-sulfobenzoato	0.16[7]		

$* k = 1.\ mol^{-1}\ sec^{-1}$.

Changing the nature of the substituent R in the ligand has only a small effect on the $\Delta F^{\ddagger}$ value. At $25\,^\circ$C with chromous ion as reductant, the change is from 18.5 kcal/mol (acetate) to 18.7–18.9 (α-substituted acetates) or from 18.7 kcal/mol (benzoate) to 18.9–19.1 (*ortho*-substituted) or 18.4–18.6 (*para*-substituted benzoates); thus α- or o-substitution decreases the rate of reaction slightly, p-substitution causes a slight increase. In general, with vanadous ion, any

TABLE 2: ENTROPIES OF ACTIVATION (CAL/MOL DEGREE)

Complex	$\Delta S_{Cr^{++}}^{\ddagger}$	$\Delta S_{V^{++}}^{\ddagger}$	$\Delta S_{Eu^{++}}^{\ddagger}$
Acetato	-50[2]	-41	-47
Chloroacetato	-37	-27	-25
Cyanoacetato	-49	-27	
Dichloroacetato	-55	-26	-35
Benzoato	-46	-37	-40
o-chlorobenzoato	-43	-24	-50
o-iodobenzoato	-54	-5	-51
Salicylato		-27	
o-phthalato	-45[2]	-24	-30
m-phthalato	-56[2]	-29	-33
p-chlorobenzoato	-28	-33	
p-iodobenzoato		-30	
p-hydroxybenzoato	-30	-28	
p-cyanobenzoato	-37	-24	
p-sulfobenzoato	-34[7]		

substitution tends to lower $\Delta F^{\ddagger}$, and rates increase; the effect is more marked for α-substitution ($\Delta F^{\ddagger}$ changes from 18.1 to 17.4–17.5 kcal/mol) and o-substitution (17.8 to 17.3–17.7 kcal/mol). In p-substitution, the nature of the group determines whether the rate is decreased very slightly (Cl—, I—: $\Delta F^{\ddagger}$ 17.9, 18.0 kcal/mol) or increased (HO—, CN—: $\Delta F^{\ddagger}$ 17.7, 17.4 kcal/mol). The largest

TABLE 3:   HEATS OF ACTIVATION (KCAL/MOL)

Complex	$\Delta H^{\ddagger}_{Cr^{++}}$	$\Delta H^{\ddagger}_{V^{++}}$	$\Delta H^{\ddagger}_{Eu^{++}}$
Acetato	3.5[2]	5.8	4.4
Chloroacetato	7.9	9.4	9.3
Cyanoacetato	4.0	9.4	
Dichloroacetato	2.5	9.6	6.9
Benzoato	4.9	6.7	6.2
o-chlorobenzoato	6.0	10.5	3.2
o-iodobenzoato	2.8	15.8	3.3
Salicylato		9.3	
o-phthalato	5.1[2]	10.2	8.2
m-phthalato	2.6[2]	9.0	7.9
p-chlorobenzoato	10.0	8.0	
p-iodobenzoato		9.0	2.1
p-hydroxybenzoato	9.6	9.3	
p-cyanobenzoato	7.5	10.2	
p-sulfobenzoato	8.3[7]		

change in $\Delta F^{\ddagger}$ with substitution is found in the reaction of europous ion with the acetates (18.5 to 16.8 kcal/mol); with substituted benzoates the effect is much less.

    Dibasic or Hydroxy Acids As Ligands. It has already been pointed out[6] that the substitution of succinic acid for acetic makes little difference to the rate of reaction when chromous ion is reductant. With europous and vanadous ion, however, the rate increases when the acetate is replaced with either succinate or methyl succinate (that is, the half-ester). Table 4 shows the specific rate constants for the reaction.

    Further, when the solution containing the vanadium, cobalt and methyl succinate is taken immediately after reaction and extracted with ether, the organic product is found to be succinic acid, not the half-ester. Apparently chelation of the reductant by the ligand plays some part in these reactions.

    An interesting possibility arises with an unsymmetrical ligand such as malic acid: The conditions for formation of the pentamminocobalt(III) complexes are non-specific, so that two different complexes may be formed:

$$[(NH_3)_5Co\text{---}O_2CCH_2CH(OH)CO_2H]^{++} \quad and$$

$$[(NH_3)_5Co\text{---}O_2CC(OH)HCH_2CO_2H]^{++}$$

TABLE 4: SPECIFIC RATE CONSTANTS (L MOL^{-1} SEC^{-1}) AT 25°C

Complex	V^{++}	Eu^{++}
Acetato	0.43	0.18
Succinato	0.89	2.6
Methylsuccinato	1.0	2.5

Titration of the free carboxyl group with base showed that the preparation of malato complex was at least 98% pure (that is, free from the pentammineaquo complex), but with each of the three reductants the rate of disappearance of the cobalt complex showed that two different species were present in approximately equal proportions. Table 5 lists the values found for the specific rate constants for some hydroxy acids.

With vanadium, all the reactions are independent of the acid content of the solutions, but this is not the case with the chromium re-

TABLE 5: SPECIFIC RATE CONSTANTS FOR HYDROXY ACIDS

Complex	$k^*_{Cr^{++}}$	$k_{V^{++}}$	Temp (°C)
Malato (slow)	0.17		19.0
		0.15	22.0
Malato (fast)		2.4	22.0
	1.2 (H$^+$ = 0.65M)		19.0
	1.3 (H$^+$ = 0.40M)		19.0
	2.1 (H$^+$ = 0.20M)		19.0
	> 2.7 (H$^+$ = 0.10M)		19.0
Lactato		0.58	24.8
	0.98 (H$^+$ = 0.65M)		
	2.2 (H$^+$ = 0.2M)		
Salicylato		0.64	29.3
	0.08 (H$^+$ = 0.6M)		17.0
	0.09 (H$^+$ = 0.2M)		17.0
	0.12 (H$^+$ = 0.15M)		17.0
	0.15 (H$^+$ = 0.1M)		17.0

$^*k = 1$ mol^{-1} sec^{-1}.

sults; here the variation of k (observed) is given by the expression

$$k(\text{obs}) = k + k^1/(\text{H}^+).$$

Only α- or o-hydroxy acids give this result; the slow form of the malato (which is presumably $[(\text{NH}_3)_5\text{CoO}_2\text{CCH}_2\text{CH(OH)CO}_2\text{H}]^{++}$) does not, and neither does the p-hydroxybenzoato complex.

Discussion

Two problems arise in assembling a closely related set of complexes for a comparative study. One is the difficulty of preparing the complexes themselves; for instance, with halogenated benzoic acids, particularly *para*-substituted, it is found that the rate of substitution of the ligand into the complex is fairly slow, while the rate of decomposition of the reaction mixture to cobaltic oxide is rapid. The second is the difficulty in interpreting results when more than one reaction path operates. It would be of great interest to examine the effect on k, $\Delta F^{\ddagger}$, ΔS and $\Delta H^{\ddagger}$ of moving the second carboxyl group in the phthalic acids. This can be done for the *ortho* and *meta* acids, since steric reasons prevent conjugation in the first, and conjugation is not possible between the two carboxyls in the second.[2] With the *para* acid, however, attack can take place at either carboxyl group, and, further, remote attack can lead to electron transfer by either a protonated or non-protonated path. The specific rate constant observed will be of the form $[k + k^1(\text{H}^+)]^{(2)}$, and it is not possible to determine how much of k refers to adjacent attack alone. An estimate can be made if the remote carboxyl is esterified, but experiments show[5] that the nature of the ester group has a strong influence on the resulting electron transfer, so that the effect of the remote carboxyl group can still not be determined.

Some generalizations are possible, however, for the reactions of the complexes listed in Table 1. In all cases, reaction occurs by attack at the adjacent carboxyl group with subsequent electron transfer Red...O⠿C—O—Co, and the nature of the substituent R does not

$$\underset{R}{\text{Red}...\text{O}⠿\overset{|}{\text{C}}—\text{O}—\text{Co}}$$

affect the rate of reaction very much. On the other hand, the values for $\Delta S^{\ddagger}$ and $\Delta H^{\ddagger}$ (Tables 2, 3) show large variations, more or less systematically. In all cases there is a linear relationship[8] between $\Delta S^{\ddagger}$ (or $T\Delta S^{\ddagger}$) and $\Delta H^{\ddagger}$, of the form $T\Delta S^{\ddagger} = \alpha\Delta H^{\ddagger} + \beta$ as shown in Figures 1, 2. For chromous ion, $\alpha = 0.94$, $\beta = 18.0$ kcal/mol; for vanadous the values are 0.97 and 17.5. With europous a similar relation holds. Included in Fig. 1 are the values of $\Delta H^{\ddagger}$ and $\Delta S^{\ddagger}$ for a

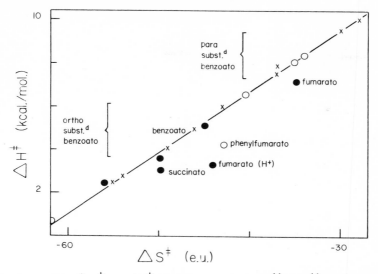

Fig. 1. Variation of $\Delta H^{\ddagger}$ and $\Delta S^{\ddagger}$ for the reactions $CoL^{++} + Cr^{++}$: **(X)** this investigation, **(●)** Taube, Ref. 2, **(O)** Fraser and Taube, Ref. 7.

series of reactions (such as fumarate) known to proceed by both adjacent and remote attack. The fact that these values do not fall near the line is important; it confirms that the reactions with Cr^{++} listed in Table 1 occur by adjacent attack only, and from the close similarity of the α and β values for Cr^{++} and V^{++} supports the earlier view that labile reductants such as V^{++} and Eu^{++} may also react through inner-sphere bridged complexes.[9]

With chromous ion, the $\Delta H^{\ddagger}$ and $\Delta S^{\ddagger}$ values fall into two fairly distinct groups: those with high $\Delta H^{\ddagger}$ but less negative $\Delta S^{\ddagger}$ (*para*-substituted), and those with low $\Delta H^{\ddagger}$ but less negative $\Delta S^{\ddagger}$ (*ortho*- or *un*-substituted); this distinction does not appear with the vanadous results.

The $\Delta S^{\ddagger}$ values for vanadous are less negative and show less spread (-41 to -24 cal/mol degree) than do the values for chromous (-56 to -28 cal/mol degree), if we except the *o*-iodobenzoato complex. The $\Delta S^{\ddagger}$ values for the *ortho*-substituted complexes are interesting. As the size of the group increases, the entropy of activation becomes much more favourable for vanadous: $-H(-37$ cal/mol degree$) < -OH(-27)$ $< -Cl$ or $-CO_2H(-24) < -I(-5)$, while the reverse trend is observed for chromous ion. On the one hand, we are proceeding from two substitution-inert ions (CoL^{++}, V^{++}) to two labile (Co^{++}, V^{+++}); on the other, from one inert (CoL^{++}) to another substitution-inert ion (CrL^{++}), and the trends in entropy are just what might be expected.

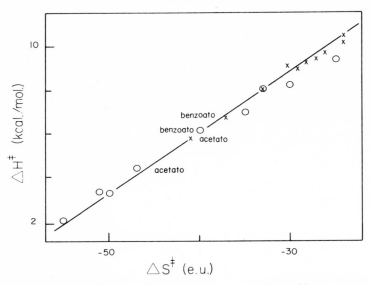

Fig. 2. Variation of $\Delta H^{\ddagger}$ and $\Delta S^{\ddagger}$ for the reaction $CoL^{++} + V^{++}$ (X) and $CoL^{++} + Eu^{++}$ (O).

The forms of the rate laws for reactions of hydroxy acids with chromium are:

$$-d(CoL^{++})/dt = (0.80 + 0.23/[H^+])(Cr^{++})(CoL^{++})(\text{malato, } 19.0\,^{\circ}C)$$
$$= (0.050 + 0.24/[H^+])(Cr^{++})(CoL^{++})(\text{salicylato, } 23.0\,^{\circ}C)$$
$$= (0.60 + 0.31/[H^+])(Cr^{++})(CoL^{++})(\text{lactato, } 19.0\,^{\circ}C)$$

A similar inverse dependence of the rate constant is not found with vanadous ion. Certainly for the salicylato complex, and probably for the other two, the acid-independent term in the rate law refers to normal adjacent attack. The suggestion has recently been made[10] that electron transfer may take place through hydrogen-bonded systems such as occurs between amide and carboxyl groups. If such a mechanism were to operate with these three complexes, it would be reasonable to expect vanadous ion to show similar behaviour, while the fact that the acid-inverse path occurs only with chromous ion implies that some characteristic property of the reductant is involved. It should also be noted that this acid-inverse path occurs with monobasic as well as dibasic hydroxy acids. It is a different effect from that observed by Sebera and Taube[6], who find a rate law such as

$$-d(CoL^{++})/dt = (k_1 + k_2[H^+] + k_3/[H^+])(CoL^{++})(Cr^{++})$$

operates in the reduction of the fumarato complex with the third term in the rate constant due to reaction by the anion path $[(NH_3)_5CoO_2CCH{=}CH{-}CO_2^-]^+$. Their k_3 is important only at very low acidities; it is characteristic of dibasic acids, whereas the inverse effect discussed above is characteristic of hydroxy acids.

Examination of the reaction mixture immediately after electron transfer is complete shows that only one of the carboxyl groups remains free (presumably both $[CrO_2CCH_2CH(OH)CO_2H]^{++}$ and $[CrO_2CCH(OH)CH_2CO_2H]^{++}$ are present) in the case of the malato reaction; there does not appear to be any such Cr(III) complex as $[Cr{-}O{-}CH(CO_2H){-}CH_2CO_2H]^{++}$, although this is not too surprising. Rather than postulating electron transfer through a hydrogen-bonded system such as

$$
\begin{array}{c}
\text{O---H}{-}\text{O---Cr}^{++}\\
\parallel \qquad \diagup\\
\text{Co}{-}\text{O}{-}\text{C}{-}\text{C}
\end{array}
$$

perhaps the effect can be explained as chelation of the chromous ion by the ligand

$$
\begin{array}{c}
\text{Cr}^{++}\\
\diagup \quad \diagdown\\
\text{O} \qquad \text{O}\\
\parallel \qquad |\\
\text{Co}{-}\text{O}{-}\text{C}{-}\text{C}{-}
\end{array}
$$

requiring prior loss of the hydroxyl hydrogen.

With vanadous ion as reductant, the specific rate constant for the reaction with the lactato complex is greater than for acetato, showing that the α-hydroxyl group is lowering the $\Delta F^{\ddagger}$ value. With the malato (fast) complex the rate constant is further increased, due to the combined effects of the hydroxyl and additional carboxyl group.

REFERENCES

1. H. Taube, *J. Am. Chem. Soc.*, **77**, 4481 (1955).
2. H. Taube, *Can. J. Chem.*, **37**, 129 (1959).
3. D. K. Sebera, Ph.D. Dissertation, University of Chicago, 1959.
4. R. T. M. Fraser, D. K. Sebera, H. Taube, *J. Am. Chem. Soc.*, **81**, 2906 (1959).
5. R. T. M. Fraser, *ibid.*, **83**, 564 (1961).
6. D. K. Sebera and H. Taube, *ibid.* (to be published).
7. R. T. M. Fraser and H. Taube, *ibid.* (to be published).
8. K. J. Laidler and H. Eyring, *Ann. N.Y. Acad. Sci.*, **39**, 303 (1940).
9. R. T. M. Fraser and H. Taube, *J. Am. Chem. Soc.*, **81**, 5514 (1959).
10. K. D. Kopple and G. F. Svartos, *ibid.* **82**, 3227 (1960).

ON THE STEREOCHEMISTRY OF ETHYLENEDIAMINETETRA-ACETATO COMPLEXES OF THE IRON GROUP AND RELATED CATIONS

J. L. HOARD, GORDON S. SMITH,* and **MAURICE LIND** †

Department of Chemistry
Cornell University
Ithaca, New York

The stereochemical considerations to be presented deal mostly with discrete complexes formed through reaction of ethylenediaminetetra-acetic acid (EDTA; H_4Y) with cations of the first transition period. We are primarily concerned with the synthesis of quite varied bits of structural evidence into a stereochemical pattern which, fragmentary though it be, has some striking features. We wish, for example, to present our a priori case of more than two years' standing[1] for a fully chelated but *seven*-coordinate formulation, $[Fe(OH_2)Y]^-$, of the commonly prepared EDTA complex of ferric iron. The verdict of direct structural results, returned at the eleventh hour, is favorable for the most part to our case (*vide infra*).

In view of space limitations, our presentation is organized as follows: Data of structural significance, classified according to experimental method, are presented, and their import noted, in a series of appropriately headed sections. There follows the attempted synthesis of these data into a coherent stereochemical pattern for discrete EDTA complexes.

I. The Data of Stereochemical Import

A. Data from Complete Structure Analysis. In the isomorphous crystals, $A[CoY] \cdot 2\,H_2O$, $A = NH_4^+$, Rb^+, the CoY^- anion is sexadentate

† We are particularly indebted to the National Science Foundation for continuous support since inception of our studies of EDTA complexes. To the U. S. Army Research Office (Durham) we owe thanks through the contribution of J. V. Silverton to structural results (cf., Ref. 14) cited prior to publication. Support during the past year from the Advanced Research Projects Agency is also gratefully acknowledged. Machine computations have been carried out at the Cornell Computing Center through the courtesy of Mr. Richard C. Lesser, Director. Thanks are due the Monsanto Chemical Company for the grant of an academic year (1960–61) fellowship to Maurice Lind.
*Present address: Mellon Institute, 4400 Fifth Ave., Pittsburgh, Pa.

with two nitrogen and four oxygen atoms attached to cobalt in quite distorted octahedral configuration.[2] Two of the glycinate rings—the pair for which the closing Co—O bonds would ideally be coplanar with the Co—N bonds—are highly strained, the inevitable consequence of maintaining the integrity of the ethylenediamine ring and approximately (ca. ±5°) regular tetrahedral bond angles at nitrogen, a common junction for three rings. Strain in the complex increases rapidly with increasing size of the central atom, and we estimate that a bond distance of about 2.10 Å, 10% longer than the average in CoY^-, will surely require any sexadentate octahedral complex to be unstable. Two additional factors of importance are: (1) the intrinsic strength of the bonds formed by other central atoms will not often approach that of Co(III); (2) protonation of the uncomplexed oxygen atom of carboxylate in a glycinate ring (to give a glycine ring) must be strongly destabilizing.

The structure established[3] for crystalline $Ni(OH_2)H_2Y$, with which the complex Cu(II) acid is isostructural, strengthens the preceding analysis. In partial compensation for increases in bond lengths ($\gtrless 0.15$ Å) as compared with CoY^-, the quinquedentate $Ni(OH_2)H_2Y$ utilizes a water molecule instead of one of the strained rings to complete the octahedral coordination. The strained ring which is present is apparently protonated, none too securely anchored, and may owe its existence in the crystal to the strong network of hydrogen bonding. The orientation of the observed small quasi-tetragonal distortion is in agreement with the analysis of strain.[3] (A truly four-coordinate square coplanar configuration is singularly unsuited to take advantage of the complexing power of EDTA; the wrong pair of glycinate rings must be used.) The stereoisomer studied, the only one to be obtained, is stereochemically much superior to the three others of chemically equivalent a priori probability.[3]

B. Infrared Absorption Spectra of Crystalline Complex Acids. The infrared absorption spectra recorded for various crystalline EDTA complex acids are used here to decide just one essential point: whether uncomplexed · COOH exists in the crystals. Morris and Busch[4] studied seven crystalline quinquedentate complexes of Co(III): $CoYX^-$, $CoHYX^-$, $Co(YOH)X^-$, in which the blocking ligand X^- was NO_2^-, Br^-, or Cl^-, and the uncomplexed free arms were $\cdot CH_2COO^-$, $\cdot CH_2COOH$, $\cdot CH_2CH_2OH$, respectively. We are interested in their convincing assignment of two well-resolved medium intensity bands at about 1750 and 1228 cm^{-1} to · COOH of an uncomplexed arm. In interpreting the spectra for complex acids we are occasionally uncertain whether the 1750 cm^{-1} band (attributed to carbonyl stretching in · COOH) is absent or whether there is merging with the most prominent band of the spectrum at about 1650 cm^{-1} (also attributed to carbonyl stretching, but in · COOM of a ring); the pattern is surely much influenced by hydrogen bonding. The 1228 cm^{-1} band is rather better behaved. The conclusions given by our studies are:

Uncomplexed · COOH is pretty certainly absent in CoHY · 8 H$_2$O, FeHY · 5/2 H$_2$O, and Mn[MnHY]$_2$ · 10 H$_2$O. Uncomplexed · COOH is surely present in CrHY · H$_2$O, and the isomorphous Ni(II) and Cu(II) complex acids (cf., I-A). Uncomplexed · COOH probably exists in AlHY · XH$_2$O, MgH$_2Y$ · 6 H$_2$O, BaH$_2Y$ · 4 H$_2$O, and CdH$_2Y$ · 3 H$_2$O.

C. **Acid-Base Titration Curves in Aqueous Solution.** Schwarzenbach *et al.* suggest that the complex acids of Co(III)[5] and Fe(III)[6] are both sexadentate in consequence of pK values characteristic of strong mineral acids. The somewhat smaller promotion of acid strength attending formation of the Cr(III) acid led Schwarzenbach and Biedermann[7] to the formulation Cr(OH$_2$)HY, i.e., to a quinquedentate complex with a coordinated water molecule and a free arm. A second titratable hydrogen (pK = 7.15) in the Cr(III) complex was reasonably ascribed to[7]

$$\text{Cr(OH}_2)\text{Y}^- + \text{OH}^- \longrightarrow \text{Cr(OH)Y}^- + \text{H}_2\text{O}$$

(violet)   (blue)

The similar behavior displayed by the Fe(III) complex received a much less convincing explanation.[6] Because FeY^- was considered to be both sexadentate and six-coordinate, it was assumed that starting at a pH just above 5, the rupture of glycinate rings to permit entrance of OH$^-$ is the significant process occurring.

The behavior of our solutions of the Fe(III) complex, including the pH range around 5 where the 1 : 1 salts crystallized, closely paralleled the description of Schwarzenbach and Heller.

D. **X-Ray Studies of Isomorphism.** From unit cell, density, and space group data for some twenty crystalline EDTA complexes, a few conclusions of special import are noted. Table 1 contains cell data for five isomorphous compounds crystallizing with four-molecule units in the distinctive orthorhombic space group, P2$_1$2$_1$2$_1$.

TABLE 1: CELL DATA FOR THE ISOMORPHOUS SERIES, AMY · 2H$_2$O

Compound	Lattice Constants			Density, g/cc	
	a, Å	b, Å	c, Å	Calc.	Obs.
NH$_4$CoY · 2H$_2$O	6.46	23.16	10.09	1.765	1.75
RbCoY · 2H$_2$O	6.43	23.08	10.18	2.06	2.07
NH$_4$CrY · 2H$_2$O	6.54	23.48	10.17	1.68	1.68
RbCrY · 2H$_2$O	6.50	23.22	10.15	2.00	1.96
NH$_4$AlY · 2H$_2$O	6.55	23.31	10.12	1.59	1.58

Being isostructural with CoY^- (I-A), the sexadentate and octahedral character of CrY^- and AlY^- is firmly established.

Neither $RbFeY \cdot 2H_2O$ nor $NH_4FeY \cdot 3/2H_2O$ appears in the isomorphous series of Table 1. Both are monoclinic, but with different space groups; neither displays any similarity of lattice translation with the data of Table 1. A similarly complete failure of isomorphism between $NaFeY \cdot 3H_2O$ and $NaCoY \cdot 4H_2O$, and among the complex acids, $FeHY \cdot 5/2H_2O$, $CoHY \cdot 8H_2O$, and $CrHY \cdot H_2O$ is observed.

One would normally expect the sexadentate species, $FeHY$ and FeY^-, to be not merely isostructural, but virtually isodimensional with the corresponding $CoHY$ and CoY^-. This expectation, however, is justified only if Fe(III) is in the doublet spectroscopic state, i.e., with one unpaired electron, and thus able to form d^2sp^3 bonds.

E. Magnetic Susceptibility Data. Klemm and Raddatz[8,9] report magnetic susceptibilities for a few crystalline EDTA complexes. $NaCoY \cdot 4H_2O$ is diamagnetic. The indicated number of unpaired electrons per central atom is three and two, respectively, for Cr(III) and Ni(II) in the complex acids, and five for Fe(III) in both the acid and the ammonium salt.

There is no doubt that the effective size of Fe(III) and the isoelectronic Mn(II) is substantially larger in the sextet than in the doublet spectroscopic state. From Pauling's discussion[10] of this general matter (cf., *The Anomalous Manganese Radius*, p. 254 of Ref. 10), we estimate the increase in bond length, doublet to sextet state, as about 0.35 Å.

II. Stereochemical Synthesis of the Data

Synthesis of the evidence set forth in the preceding section into a partial stereochemical pattern for EDTA complexes is presented roughly in the order of increasing complication. For any given central atom, the acidic and anionic forms may require individual treatment. Some direct evidence on configuration from X-ray structure analyses in progress is cited for Fe(III) and Mn(II) complexes.

A. Cobalt(III) Complexes. The complex anion CoY^- is sexadentate and octahedral in a pair of isomorphous crystals[2] and no evidence exists for an alternative configuration in any other environment. The infrared data (I-B) and the titration curve (I-C) for the complex acid would have it sexadentate in the crystal and in solution, the absence of a second titratable hydrogen[5] would have it six-coordinate, and it is hard to believe that it is not also octahedral. More exciting, perhaps, is the realization that $CoHY$ is likely to remain the sole example of a complex EDTA acid which is both sexadentate and octahedral.

B. Nickel(II) and Copper(II) Complexes. Direct analysis[3] of the isomorphous crystals, $Ni(OH_2)H_2Y$ and $Cu(OH_2)H_2Y$, gives the quinquedentate octahedral configuration of I-A. The infrared data (I-B) subscribe to the presence of uncomplexed $\cdot COOH$. We surmise that a quadridentate octahedral form with two coordinated water molecules may be significant in solution (cf., I-A). The possibility that the anion $MY^=$ exists in sexadentate octahedral configuration may not be entirely ruled out by the earlier analysis (I-A); some significance may attach to our lack of success in obtaining a crystalline salt suitable for X-ray study.

C. Chromium(III) and Aluminum(III) Complexes. A quinquedentate six-coordinate formulation, $Cr(OH_2)HY$, for the molecule in the crystal emerges from joint consideration of the infrared data (I-B), the empirical formula, and the fact that the water molecule is so tightly bound that its presence was not recognized during the original analysis[11] for water of crystallization. (The crystalline Cu(II) and Ni(II) acids were similarly reported[12] as anhydrous.) The solution data have been interpreted[7] (I-C) in similar terms. The configuration of $Cr(OH_2)HY$ is almost certainly a more stable, more compact, and less distorted version of that established[3] (I-A) for NiH_2Y; the strained ring in $Cr(OH_2)HY$, being unprotonated and not subject to *quasi*-tetragonal distortion, stands to gain the most.

The complex Al(III) acid, obtained as a powder for which cell data and precise water content are lacking, very probably contains uncomplexed $\cdot COOH$ (I-B). Isomorphism of the Cr(III) and Al(III) acids is a reasonable expectation.

The sexadentate octahedral configuration for CrY^- and AlY^- is established by the data of Table 1. It is probable that in an intermediate pH range (5–9?), both $Cr(OH_2)Y^-$ and $Cr(OH)Y^=$ are converted, though perhaps slowly, into sexadentate CrY^-. We were unable to prepare a salt containing either of the quinquedentate species.

D. Iron(III) Complexes. The infrared (I-B) and the solution[6] (I-C) studies agree that the complex ferric acid is sexadentate. The failure of isomorphism (I-D) between chemically analogous Co(III) and Fe(III) complexes, both acidic and anionic, is attributed to the larger effective size (I-E) of sextet Fe(III) as compared with singlet Co(III) or doublet Fe(III). If the estimated increase of 0.35 Å in bond length be at all realistic, the probability that the ferric complex is both sexadentate and octahedral becomes negligible (I-A). Once the well-founded predilection for the octahedron is abandoned, it becomes apparent, e.g., from a Fisher-Taylor-Hirschfelder model, that a trigonal prismatic arrangement of the six atoms attached to iron involves practically no strain in any of the five chelated rings. And, moreover, with a bond distance approaching 2.2 A, there is adequate room to attach a water molecule to iron along the normal to the open square face opposite the nitrogen atoms. The resulting configuration, of maximum symmetry C_{2v}-mm, is that assumed by $NbF_7^=$, sterically of the first quality for the coordination of seven monodentate ligands of comparable size.[13] The model thus obtained for $Fe(OH_2)Y^-$ is so flexible that probably the twofold axis passing through H_2O, Fe, and the midpoint of the line joining the nitrogen atoms, is the only symmetry element which the complex can profitably retain. This, or any other sexadentate seven-coordinate configuration implying the species, $Fe(OH_2)HY$, $Fe(OH_2)Y^-$, $F(OH)Y^=$, accounts more convincingly for the acid-base titration curve than does the explanation offered by Schwarzenbach and Heller.[6] Using just the solution and magnetic data (and an open mind), this model was tentatively suggested in our first EDTA research proposal of five years past.

Our structure analysis of $Rb[Fe(OH_2)Y] \cdot H_2O$, using three-dimensional Fourier analysis of *hkl* data, is now far enough along to give configuration, but only approximate bond data. The $Fe(OH_2)Y^-$ is sexadentate and seven-coordinate with the water molecule firmly attached to iron. The Fe—N bond distances, *ca.* 2.3 Å, are fully as large as predicted, but the Fe—O distances, averaging about 2.05 Å, correspond to an increase of about half that estimated for transition from doublet to sextet Fe(III). Disregarding symmetry, the configuration is very crudely pentagonal bipyramidal; in fact, however, only the twofold axis specified earlier can be present. We think that we see why this configuration is preferred to that of $NbF_7^=$ for this multidentate complex, but we need more dependable bond data to make a convincing case, even to ourselves. A preliminary announcement of results[14] should appear prior to the Conference.

E. **Manganese(II) Complexes.** Knowing that Mn(II) is even more likely than the isoelectronic Fe(III) to be in the sextet state, and having obtained infrared evidence (I-B) against uncomplexed · COOH in a preparation thought to be the complex acid, $MnH_2Y \cdot XH_2O$, we have suggested[1] that the acid complex is sexadentate but not octahedral. The preparation used turns out to be the acid salt, $Mn[Mn(HY)]_2 \cdot 10H_2O$, to which, provided discrete complexes are present, the prediction is transferable. Structure analysis[15] of this material, though less advanced than for $Rb[Fe(OH_2)Y] \cdot H_2O$, provides some conclusions which probably cannot be changed. Four sexadentate seven-coordinate $[Mn(OH_2)HY]^-$ anions in general positions of $P2_1/n$ are "almost discrete." Two manganous ions in centers of inversion show octahedral coordination, with four water molecules and two carbonyl oxygen atoms from glycinate rings of two neighboring complexes as near neighbors. There are, additionally, eight bridging water molecules. All bond distances promise to be large, $ca. \geq 2.2$ Å, corresponding throughout, we predict, to sextet Mn(II). The configuration of the complex anion is quite asymmetric, but perhaps is more like that of $NbF_7^=$ than of any other simple polyhedron. The position of the acid hydrogen (when later inferred) promises special interest.

F. **Rare Earth Complexes.** In view of the electronic structure and relatively large ionic radii ($> r_{Fe^{+++}}$) of the rare earths, we suggest that EDTA complexes of rare earth ions will prove to be sexadentate and seven-coordinate, $[M(OH_2)Y]^-$, in salts crystallizing from aqueous solution (cf., 16). We suggest further that in the crystalline acetylacetonates of the rare earths [16], $M(acac)_3 \cdot H_2O$, the ubiquitous water molecule will turn out to be attached to the rare earth atom. The configuration proposed [17] for ZrF_7^{3-} is perhaps the best a priori choice for a seven-coordinate $M(OH_2)$ $(acac)_3$ molecule. The only obvious alternative to seven-coordination is to place water molecules in a hydrocarbon environment; we do not think that seven-coordinate complexes need be all that rare.

REFERENCES

1. Unpublished. Complete exposition in Research Proposal to National Science Foundation, Feb., 1960. Presented earlier in various lectures.
2. H. A. Weakliem and J. L. Hoard, *J. Am. Chem. Soc.*, **81**, 549 (1959).
3. Gordon S. Smith and J. L. Hoard, *ibid.*, **81**, 556 (1959).
4. M. L. Morris and D. H. Busch, *ibid.*, **78**, 5178 (1956).
5. G. Schwarzenbach, *Helv. Chim. Acta*, **32**, 839 (1949).
6. G. Schwarzenbach and J. Heller, *ibid.*, **34**, 576 (1951).
7. G. Schwarzenbach and W. Biedermann, *ibid.*, **31**, 459 (1948).
8. W. Klemm, *Z. anorg. allg. Chem.*, **252**, 225 (1944).
9. W. Klemm and K. Raddatz, *ibid.*, **250**, 204 (1942).
10. L. Pauling, *The Nature of the Chemical Bond* (3rd ed.), Cornell University Press, Ithaca, (1960).
11. H. Brintzinger, H. Thiele, and U. Müller, *Z. anorg. allgem. Chem.*, **251**, 285 (1943).
12. H. Brintzinger and G. Hesse, *ibid.*, **249**, 113 (1942).
13. J. L. Hoard, *J. Am. Chem., Soc.*, **61**, 1252 (1939).
14. J. L. Hoard, M. Lind, and J. V. Silverton, *ibid.*, **83**, 2770 (1961).
15. J. L. Hoard, B. Pedersen, S. Richards, and J. V. Silverton, *ibid.*, "Communications to the Editor," submitted July, 1961.
16. J. J. Fritz, I. Grenthe, P. E. Field, and W. C. Fernelius, *ibid.*, **82**, 6199 (1960).
17. G. C. Hampson and L. Pauling, *ibid.*, **60**, 2702 (1938).

HEATS AND ENTROPIES OF REACTION OF TRANSITION METAL IONS WITH POLYAMINES

M. CIAMPOLINI, P. PAOLETTI and L. SACCONI

Department of General and Inorganic Chemistry
University of Florence
Florence, Italy

One of the present trends in the field of coordination chemistry is to determine the heats of formation of metal complexes by direct calorimetric methods. By combining these data with published values of free energy changes, the entropy changes are then obtained. In the present paper the results of calorimetric investigations of the equilibria between bivalent ions from Mn^{2+} to Zn^{2+} and polyamines ethylenediamine[1] (en), diethylenetriamine[2] (dien), 2, 2', 2''-triamino-triethylamine (tren), triethylenetetramine (trien), and N, N', N''-tetrakis-(2-aminoethyl)ethylenediamine (penten) in aqueous solutions are reported. The ionic media used were the same as those employed for determining the values of the stability constants.[3]

Table I lists the heat change values for the reactions

$$[M(H_2O)_6]^{2+}_{aq} + nL_{aq} \rightleftharpoons [M(H_2O)_{6-x}L_n]^{2+}_{aq} + xH_2O \tag{1}$$

TABLE 1: $-\Delta H$ VALUES (IN KCAL/MOLE) FOR THE REACTIONS
$$[M(H_2O)_6]^{2+}_{aq} + nL_{aq} \rightleftharpoons [M(H_2O)_{6-x}L_n]^{2+}_{aq} + xH_2O$$

nL	Mn^{2+}	Fe^{2+}	Co^{2+}	Ni^{2+}	Cu^{2+}	Zn^{2+}	Ref.
1 en	2.80	5.05	6.90	8.90	13.05[b]	6.65[c]	a
2 en	6.00	10.40	13.95	18.25	25.40[b]	13.75[c]	a
3 en	11.05	15.85	22.15	28.35		20.70[c]	a
1 dien			8.15	11.85	18.00	6.45	d, e
2 dien	6.95	12.95	18.40	25.30	26.15	16.60	d, e
1 tren	3.00	6.30	10.65	15.15	20.40	13.75	e
1 trien	2.30	6.05	10.65	14.00	21.55	8.90	e
1 penten	8.85	9.65	14.75	20.25	24.50	14.50	e

[a] Cf. Ref. 1; ionic medium 1 M KCl.
[b] I. Poulsen and J. Bjerrum, Acta Chem. Scand., 9, 1407 (1955); ionic medium 1M KNO₃.
[c] The values in 1 M KNO₃ (cf. ref. 1) are the following: $-\Delta H_1 = 7.00$; $-\Delta H_{1-2} = 11.90$; $-\Delta H_{1-3} = 17.10$.
[d] Cf. Ref. 2.
[e] Ionic medium 0.1 M KCl.

The ΔH values for the complexes of Mn(II) and Fe(II) with dien were not determined, as the values of the relative formation constants were lacking.

With en and den complexes the ΔH values for successive steps generally increase slightly. The $Zn^{2+}-$en and $Cu^{2+}-$den systems are exceptions. For Zn(II) it is admitted that in the second step a structural change with endothermic release of two more water molecules and the formation of a tetrahedral $[Znen_2]^{2+}$ ion takes place.[1] This has been already admitted for the $[Zn(NH_3)_4]^{2+}$ and $[Zn(NH_3)_3]^{2+}$ complexes as well.[4] With Cu(II) the $-\Delta H_2$ value (8.15 kcal/mole) which is lower than the value of $-\Delta H_1$ (18.00 kcal/mole) is explained by the formation of only two bonds between the copper and the second dien molecule. Besides, the lower tetragonality of the $[Cudien_2]^{2+}$ ion reflects a crystal field stabilization energy lower than that of the $[Cudien]^{2+}$ ion.[5]

The plots of the heat changes vs. the atomic number are reported in Figs. 1 and 2. The values of the enthalpies of formation increase

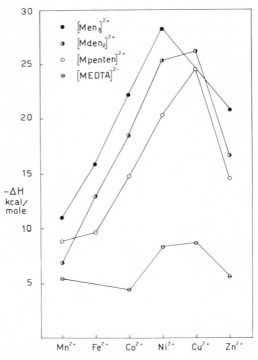

Fig. 1. Plots of the heats of formation of hexacoordinated polyamine metal ions vs. the atomic number.

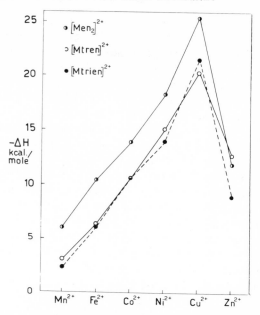

Fig. 2. Plots of the heats of formation of tetracoordinated polyamine metal ions vs. the atomic number.

from Mn(II) to Cu(II) and then diminish at Zn(II) in agreement with the well-known Irving-Williams order. The curves run roughly parallel. The heat change values decrease by 3-4 kcal/mole going from the $[M\text{en}_3]^{2+}$ to the $[M\text{dien}_2]^{2+}$ complex ions and from the $[M\text{dien}_2]^{2+}$ to the $[M\text{penten}]^{2+}$ complex ions (Fig. 1 and Table 1); the same occurs going from the $[M\text{en}_2]^{2+}$ to the $[M\text{tren}]^{2+}$ and/or $[M\text{trien}]^{2+}$ complexes (Fig. 2 and Table 1). This could be due either to a strain within the chelate rings[6] or to the fact that the bonds between the metal and the secondary or tertiary nitrogen atoms of the amines are weaker than those of the primary or secondary nitrogen atoms. Confirmation of this hypothesis can be found in the fact that the heats of reaction of di- and trialkylamines with different acceptors like hydrogen ion,[7] trimethylboron,[8] NiDBH,[9] etc., are lower than those of monoalkylamines.

In the diagram in Fig. 1 the ΔH value for the $[\text{Mnpenten}]^{2+}$ ion is anomalous, being higher than even that of the $[\text{Mndien}_2]^{2+}$ ion. A roughly similar behavior is found in the ΔH values of reaction of metal ions with EDTA[10] which are shown in the same figure. This anomaly poses the problem of the number of amine groups of the penten coordinated to the metal. In the Fe(II), Co(II) and probably

Ni(II) complexes the penten acts as a hexadentate ligand. On the other hand, the heats of reaction of Cu^{2+} and Zn^{2+} with penten are found to be equal to those with the monoprotonated ligand Hpenten$^+$, 24.80 and 14.65 kcal/mole respectively. We conclude, therefore, that in the [Cupenten]$^{2+}$ and [Znpenten]$^{2+}$ complexes there are only five metal-to-nitrogen bonds. It is not easy to explain the unusually high value of ΔH for the [Mnpenten]$^{2+}$ complex, but one can admit that the penten is bound with six nitrogen atoms and that furthermore the relatively larger radius of the manganese ion allows some water molecules to get closer to the metal.

The curves in Fig. 2, with the exception of Zn(II), run, as we have said, roughly parallel; the second two curves, referring to the [Mtren]$^{2+}$ and [Mtrien]$^{2+}$ complexes, almost coincide. An octahedral structure with two molecules of water in the first coordination sphere should be attributed to all these complexes. In the complexes with tren, owing to the steric requirements of this ligand, the two water molecules have to be in *cis* positions.

The $-\Delta H$ value for the [Zntren]$^{2+}$ complex (13.75 kcal/mole) is much higher than that for the [Zntrien]$^{2+}$ complex (8.90 kcal/mole) and even higher than that for [Znen$_2$]$^{2+}$ (11.90 kcal/mole) complex. As a tetrahedral structure was attributed to the last complex, the same structure must be postulated for the [Zntrien]$^{2+}$ complex whose $-\Delta H$ value differs from the preceding one by the same 3-4 kcal/mole. To the [Zntren]$^{2+}$ ion, as to the other [Mtren]$^{2+}$ ions, a *cis*-octahedral configuration is to be assigned.

Fig. 3 shows the heats of formation of the [Men$_3$]$^{2+}$ and [Mdien$_2$]$^{2+}$ complexes plotted vs. the atomic number; the upper curves refer to the experimental values, while the others refer to the heats corrected for the crystal-field stabilization energy. The value for the [Cuen$_3$]$^{2+}$ ion is not known owing to its low stability. The value for the [Cudien$_2$]$^{2+}$ ion was not corrected because of the Jahn-Teller effect and because the number of copper-nitrogen bonds which exist in this complex is not known with certainty.

Table 2 shows the values of the entropies of reaction of the bivalent metal ions from Mn^{2+} to Zn^{2+} with the polyamines. These data generally confirm the hypotheses on the stereochemistry of these complexes drawn from the enthalpy values. The ΔS values for the formation of [Zndien]$^{2+}$, [Znen$_2$]$^{2+}$ and [Zntrien]$^{2+}$ complexes are larger than the values for the other complex ions and are in accordance with the hypothesis of a tetrahedral arrangement with the consequent release of a greater number of water molecules and the increase in the translational entropy. The entropy of formation for [Zntren]$^{2+}$ ion, on the other hand, is approximately equal to that of

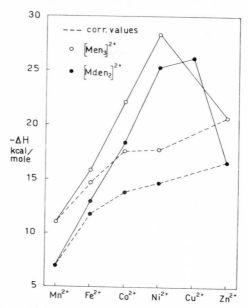

Fig. 3. Plots of experimental and corrected (crystal-field stabilization energy) heats of formation of $[Men_3]^{2+}$ and $[Mdien_2]^{2+}$ ions.

the other $[Mtren]^{2+}$ ions, which confirms the already suggested octahedral configuration. The fact that the ΔS values for $[Znen_3]^{2+}$, $[Zndien_2]^{2+}$ and $[Znpenten]^{2+}$ complexes are markedly higher than the corresponding ones with Mn^{2+}, Fe^{2+}, Co^{2+} and Ni^{2+}, may be ex-

TABLE 2: ΔS **VALUES (IN E.U.) FOR THE REACTIONS**

$$[M(H_2O)_6]^{2+}_{aq} + nL \rightleftharpoons [M(H_2O)_{6-x}L_n]^{2+}_{aq} + x H_2O$$

nL	Mn^{2+}	Fe^{2+}	Co^{2+}	Ni^{2+}	Cu^{2+}	Zn^{2+}	Ref.
1 en	3.0	3.0	4.0	5.5	5.5[b]	3.5[c]	a
2 en	2.0	0.0	2.0	3.0	1.0[b]	10.5[c]	a
3 en	−10.5	−8.5	−12.0	−11.0		2.0[c]	a
1 dien			9.0	8.5	12.0	18.5	d, e
2 dien			1.5	0.0	8.5	9.5	d, e
1 tren	16.5	18.5	22.0	16.0	18.0	20.0	e
1 trien	15.0	15.0	14.5	16.0	19.5	25.0	e
1 penten	12.5	18.5	21.5	19.5	19.0	25.0	e

[a] Cf. ref. 1; ionic medium 1 M KCl.
[b] I. Poulsen and J. Bjerrum, *Acta Chem. Scand.*, **9**, 1407 (1955); ionic medium 1 M KNO₃.
[c] Cf. ref. 1; ionic medium 1 M KNO₃.
[d] Cf. ref. 2.
[e] Ionic medium 0.1 M KCl.

plained by a lower rigidity of the complexes formed, possibly due to a coordination lower than six and the consequent freedom of movement of the $-CH_2-CH_2-NH_2$ chain.

The ΔS values for the formation of the $[Cudien]^{2+}$ and $[Cutrien]^{2+}$ ions are also notably high. Jörgensen admits that in these ions, as opposed to other ions with the same ligands, the polyamine tends to place itself in an equatorial plane rather than in a non-planar position.[5] The former arrangement, while more strained, is stabilized by a higher value of the crystal-field stabilization energy. The dipole moment of this planar form is lower than that of the non-planar, so that the planar $[Cudien]^{2+}$ and $[Cutrien]^{2+}$ ions will be able to orientate fewer water molecules than the corresponding $[Nidien]^{2+}$, $[Nitrien]^{2+}$, etc., ions. Therefore the entropy of the final state will be higher.[11] For the $[Cudien]^{2+}$ complex the high entropy of formation is, just as for the $[Zndien]^{2+}$ complex, in accordance with the hypothesis of a number of metal-to-nitrogen bonds fewer than six. The low ΔS value for the $[Mnpenten]^{2+}$ complex may be related to the above hypothesis of a greater hydration to this complex ion.

Table 2 shows that, for an equal number of nitrogen atoms bound to an ion, the ΔS values become more and more positive as the number of chelate rings increases. The enthalpy and the entropy changes here collected allow the study of the chelate effect. From various sources the hypothesis has been advanced that the chelate effect, estimated from the free energy differences, is only an entropy effect.[6,12] In other words, this means that the heat of formation is approximately constant for all the complexes of the same ion having an identical number of metal-nitrogen bonds. From our measurements it appears, on the contrary, that the heats evolved in the formation of the polyamines complexes with a higher number of chelate rings are lower, but that the higher entropy changes generally outweigh this opposite effect.

From equation (1) it follows that

$$\bar{S}'_{[M(H_2O)_{6-x}L_n]^{2+}_{aq}} = \bar{S}'_{[M(H_2O)_6]^{2+}_{aq}} + nS^0_{L_{aq}} + \Delta S - xS^0_{H_2O}$$

where $\bar{S}'$ represents the "corrected" partial molal entropies[13]

$$\bar{S}'_{[M(H_2O)_6]^{2+}_{aq}} = \bar{S}^0_{M^{2+}_{aq}} + 6\,S^0_{H_2O}$$

$$\bar{S}'_{[M(H_2O)_{6-x}L_n]^{2+}_{aq}} = \overline{\overline{S^0}}_{[ML_n]^{2+}_{aq}} + (6-x)S^0_{H_2O}$$

$S^0_{H_2O}$ is the absolute molal entropy for water and $S^0_{L_{aq}}$ is the partial molal entropy of the ligands.

This equation has been used to calculate the partial molal entropies for complex ions of polyamines and of other ligands. The entropies of the ligands were calculated by using the Cobble equation,[13] except for H_2O and NH_3 whose experimental values are reported in the literature.[14]

The values of $S'_{[M(H_2O)_{6-x}L_n]^{2+}_{aq}}$ are presented in Table 3. In the first row the type and number of ligands coordinated to each metal ion are listed. The columns present the values of partial molal entropies of the corresponding complex ions. The values indicated with an asterisk were calculated by assuming the formation of only five metal-nitrogen bonds, a $—CH_2—CH_2—NH_2$ group of the ligand still being free in a way that the sixth coordination position is taken up by one water molecule. No value is listed for the Zn(II) complexes with 3 NH_3, dien, 2 en, 4 NH_3 and trien, which are assumed to be tetrahedral since number of water molecules released in the course of the reaction (1) is uncertain.

From an inspection of the Table 3 it appears:

1. The values in each column, i. e., the partial molar entropies for complexes of the $[M(H_2O)_{6-x}L_n]^{2+}_{aq}$ type fall into a narrow range. The starred values need not be considered as they have a different configuration.

2. The entropy values of the aquo-ions (first column) are the lowest of all.

3. The $\bar{S}'$ values tend to increase: (a) with an increasing number of amino groups coordinated to the metal. This increase in entropy, however, drops rapidly after the first amino groups are taken up; (b) with an increasing number of ethylene groups.

Table 3 shows that the substitution of one molecule of water by one of ammonia in the aquo-ions $[M(H_2O)_6]^{2+}$ (M = Ni, Cu, Zn) produces an entropy increase of 9–12 e.u. The introduction of a second molecule of ammonia increases the $\bar{S}'$ value by an additional 6–11 e.u. Successive engagements of ammonia show the same less-pronounced tendency. The higher entropy of the ammonia complex ions with respect to that of the aquo-ions is to be attributed mainly to the lower second sphere hydration of the former. The water molecule, indeed, is more "hydrated" than ammonia (hydration entropy of NH_3 = − 19.7 e.u.; entropy of condensation of H_2O = −28.4 e.u.).[14] It may be admitted that this difference in hydration persists even in the complexes, so that aquo-ions will be surrounded by more "frozen" water molecules. The higher attractive power of the aquo-ions toward polar molecules is proved also by the lower absorption on alumina, in aqueous solution, of the hexammine ion

TABLE 3: PARTIAL MOLAL ENTROPIES $\bar{S}_{[M(H_2O)_{6-x}L_n]^{2+}_{aq}}$ (IN E.U.) OF SOME AMINE COMPLEXES

	6H₂O^a	NH₃^b	2NH₃^b	en	tn^c	3NH₃^b	dien	4NH₃^b	2en	2tn^c	trien	tren	6NH₃^b	3en	3tn^c	2den	penten
Mn²⁺	82			96					106		114	113		104			112
Fe²⁺	73			87					95		105	106		97			109
Co²⁺	78			93			101		102		110	114		99		109	117
Ni²⁺	77	86	93	93	97	97	101	99	102	110	110	107	93	99	111	106	114
Cu²⁺	76	86	94	93^c		98	103	100	99^c	112	113	109				131*	129*
Zn²⁺	74	86	97	89								109		109		119*	133*
No. nitrogen atoms	–	1	2	2	2	3	3	4	4	4	4	4	6	6	6	6	6
No. chelate rings	–	–	–	1	1	–	2	–	2	2	3	3	–	3	3	(4)	(5)

* Calculated on the hypothesis of the formation of five M-N bonds.
^a Calculated $\bar{S}^o_{M,aq}$ values taken from L. A. K. Staveley and T. Randall, *Disc. Far. Soc.*, **26**, 157 (1958) and W. M. Latimer, *Oxidation Potentials*, Prentice-Hall, Inc., Englewood Cliffs, N.J., 1952.
^b Calculated from ΔS values taken from ref. 4. ^c Calculated from ΔS values by I. Poulsen and J. Bjerrum, *Acta Chem. Scand.*, **9**, 1407 (1955).

$[Co(NH_3)_6]^{3+}$ as compared to $[Co(NH_3)_4 (H_2O)_2]^{3+}$, $[Co(NH_3)_3(H_2O)_3]^{3+}$ and even to the aquo-ion $[Co(H_2O)_6]^{2+}$, in spite of the fact that the latter has an ionic potential Z/r of about one-half that of the $[Co(NH_3)_6]^{+3}$ ion. [15]

Few S' values can be obtained for the ammonia complexes and only one for the hexammine ion. The S' values become pretty well stabilized after the first few ammonia molecules have been introduced. With ethylenediamine the S' values stop increasing after only two molecules of en have been taken up. These conclusions are preliminary since they rest on scanty data.

The number of coordinated nitrogen atoms being equal, the $\bar{S}'$ values increase with an increasing number of methylene groups. Thus we have the following sequence of $\bar{S}'$ values: 3 nitrogen atoms: 3 NH_3 << dien; 4 nitrogen atoms: 4 NH_3 < 2 en < tren —trien; 6 nitrogen atoms: 6 NH_3 < 3 en < 2 dien < penten; 3 en < 3 tn.

Let us consider now the replacement reaction:

$$ML_n' + mL'' = ML_m'' + nL'$$

in which the ligand L'' is more dentate than the L' ligand. The ML_m'' complex, therefore, contains $(n-m)$ more chelate rings than ML'. The ΔS value for this reaction is:

$$\Delta S = (\bar{S}'_{ML_m''} - \bar{S}'_{ML_n'}) + (n\bar{S}^0_{L'} - n\bar{S}^0_{L''}) \tag{2}$$

Table 4 presents data relative to a series of chelating reactions. The ΔS values of the chelating processes are always positive, from 11–20 e.u. when the two complexes differ by one chelate ring, to 62 e.u. when the difference is five rings. The two terms at the right

TABLE 4: CONTRIBUTIONS OF THE TERMS

$\bar{S}'_{ML_m''} - \bar{S}'_{ML_n'}$ AND $n\bar{S}^0_{L'} - m\bar{S}^0_{L''}$ TO $\Delta S_{replacement}$ (IN E.U.)

nL'	mL''	Δ (No. rings)	$\Delta S_{replacement}$	$\bar{S}'_{ML_m''} - \bar{S}'_{ML_n'}$	$n\bar{S}^0_{L'} - m\bar{S}^0_{L''}$
2 en	1 tren	1	14 18 20 13 17	7 11 13 6 10	7
2 en	1 trien	1	13 15 12 13 3	9 11 8 9 19	4
2 dien	1 penten	1	20 20	8 8	12
3 en	2 dien	1	14 11	10 7	4
3 en	1 penten	2	23 27 33 30	8 12 18 15	15
3 NH_3	1 dien	2	18 19	4 5	14
4 NH_3	2 en	2	20	3	17
6 NH_3	3 en	3	31	6	25
6 NH_3	1 penten	5	62	21	41

of equation (2) are positive. The first goes from 3 to 21 e.u., the second from 4 to 41 e.u.

On the basis of scanty available data about ammonia and chelate amine complexes, Rasmussen[16] has concluded that the entropy changes of these chelating processes are due, for the most part, to the entropy difference between ligands of different dentate character. The data here presented, however, allow us to state that the entropy difference between complex metal ions of different chelate character also contributes to a comparable degree.

According to the Cobble approach, the entropy of the ligands may be expressed by the equation

$$\overline{S}^0{}_{ligand} = S^0{}_{internal} + S^0{}_{translational} + \Delta S^0{}_{solution}$$

where:

$S^0{}_{internal} = 9.2(N) - S^0{}_{structural}$, is the internal entropy of the molecule;

$S^0{}_{translat.} = 3/2\, R \ln M + 26.00$, is the translational entropy, and $\Delta S^0{}_{solut.} = -16.00 - 0.22\, Vm$, is the entropy of solution of the gaseous molecule.

Table 5 presents the value of $S^0{}_{ligand}$, $S^0{}_{internal}$, $S^0{}_{translational}$ and $\Delta S^0{}_{solution}$ for the various ligands from NH_3 to penten. By proceeding along the series of increasing dentate character, 6 NH_3, 3 en, 2 dien, penten (six nitrogen atoms) and 4 NH_3, 2 en, tren, trien (four nitrogen atoms), we notice that, while the internal entropy as well as the entropy of solution increases, the entropy of translation decreases. For

TABLE 5: CONTRIBUTION OF THE $S^\circ{}_{internal}$, $S^\circ{}_{translational}$ AND $\Delta S^\circ{}_{solution}$

TO THE PARTIAL MOLAL ENTROPIES S° OF SOME AMINES

L	S°	$S^\circ{}_{internal}$	$S^\circ{}_{translational}$	$\Delta S^\circ{}_{solution}$
6 NH_3	158	74	204	− 120
3 en	133	110	115	− 92
3 tn	151	138	116	− 103
2 dien	129	129	80	− 80
1 penten	117	141	42	− 66
4 NH_3	105	49	136	− 80
2 en	88	74	77	− 61
2 tn	101	92	78	− 69
1 tren	81	89	41	− 49
1 trien	84	92	41	− 49
3 NH_3	79	37	102	− 60
1 den	65	65	40	− 40

instance, in the reaction

$$[Nien_3]^{2+} + penten = [Nipenten]^{2+} + 3\ en,$$

$$\Delta S = (\overline{S}'_{[Nipenten]^{2+}} - \overline{S}'_{[Nien_3]^{2+}}) + (3\overline{S}^0_{en} - \overline{S}^0_{penten}) = 30\ e.u.$$

This first term on the right is equal to 9 e.u., while the second is 21 e.u. For the two ligands in question we also have

$$(3\overline{S}^0_{en} - \overline{S}^0_{penten}) = (3S^0_{en} - S^0_{penten})_{internal} + (3S^0_{en} -$$

$$S^0_{penten})_{translational} - (3\Delta S^0_{en} - \Delta S^0_{penten})_{solution} = -30 + 72 -$$

$$21 = 21\ e.u.$$

In conclusion, the increase in the entropy change value, which stabilises the complex having a greater number of chelate rings, must be ascribed: (1) to the increase in the number of $-CH_2-$ groups in the metal complex; (2) to the increase in the number of free particles which occurs on complex formation with a consequent increase in translational entropy.

REFERENCES

1. M. Ciampolini, P. Paoletti and L. Sacconi, *J. Chem. Soc.*, 4553 (1960).
2. M. Ciampolini, P. Paoletti and L. Sacconi, *ibid.*, in press.
3. J. Bjerrum, G. Schwarzenbach and L. G. Sillén, *Stability Constants*, Part I, Chem. Soc. Special Publ. No. 6, 1957.
4. K. B. Yatsimirskii and P. M. Milyukov, *Zh. neorg. khim.*, **2**, 1046 (1957); *Zh. fiz. khim.*, **31**, 842 (1957).
5. C. K. Jörgensen, *Acta Chem. Scand.*, **10**, 887 (1956).
6. G. Schwarzenbach, *Helv. Chim. Acta*, **35**, 2344 (1952).
7. D. H. Everett and W. F. K. Wynne-Jones, *Trans. Faraday Soc.*, **35**, 1380 (1939).
8. H. C. Brown, D. H. McDaniel, and O. Häfliger, in Braude and Nachod, *Determination of Organic Structures by Physical Methods*, Academic Press Inc. Publ., New York, N. Y., 1955, p. 642.
9. L. Sacconi, G. Lombardo and R. Ciofalo, *J. Am. Chem. Soc.*, **82**, 4182 (1960); L. Sacconi and G. Lombardo, *ibid.*, **82**, 6266 (1960).
10. R. G. Charles, *ibid.*, **76**, 5854 (1954); R. A. Care and L. A. K. Staveley, *J. Chem. Soc.*, 4571 (1956).
11. J. Chatt and R. G. Wilkins, *ibid.*, 4300 (1952); 526 (1956).
12. M. Calvin and R. H. Bailes, *J. Am. Chem. Soc.*, **68**, 949 (1946); R. J. P. Williams, *J. Phys. Chem.*, **58**, 121 (1954).
13. J. W. Cobble, *J. Chem. Phys.*, **21**, 1446, 1451 (1953).
14. National Bureau of Standards, "Selected Values of Chemical Thermodinamic Properties," Washington, D. C., Circular 500.
15. L. Sacconi, *Disc. Far. Soc.*, **7**, 173 (1949).
16. S. E. Rasmussen, *Acta Chem. Scand.*, **10**, 1279 (1956).

THE CRYSTAL STRUCTURES OF SOME POLYMERIC THIO-CARBAMATES OF THE COINAGE METALS AND THEIR INTERPRETATION

ROLF HESSE*

Department of Chemistry
University of Uppsala
Uppsala, Sweden

The dialkyldithiocarbamates of the monovalent coinage metals form polymeric molecules in the solid state and in solutions of different organic solvents. Their formula can be written

$$[R_2NCS_2M]_P$$

where R = alkyl, M = Cu, Ag or Au, P = degree of polymerity, and P has different values, mainly 2, 4, and 6.

Simultaneous investigations on these compounds have been carried out in Uppsala by R. Hesse and S. Åkerström. Åkerström[1] has made preparative and physical studies and the present author is working on the crystal structures by X-ray methods.

A brief description of the structures of $[(n\text{-}C_3H_7)_2NCS_2Au]_2$, $[(C_2H_5)_2NCS_2Cu]_4$ and $[(C_2H_5)_2NCS_2Ag]_6$ will be given below, followed by a short discussion of their main features. A detailed account of the determination and interpretation of the structures will be published elsewhere.[2]

Structures

The structures of the molecules are seen in Fig. 1, 2, and 4. The metal-sulphur coordination in the copper and silver compounds is given in Fig. 3 and 5. The central silver group is visualized in Fig. 6. The molecular symmetries are, respectively, 22, $\overline{4}$, and $\overline{1}$ for the gold, copper, and silver compounds.

A characteristic feature of the molecules is that they all contain a central metal group with short metal-metal distances, comparable with those in the corresponding metallic elements. In the gold com-

---

*I wish to thank the Head of this Institute, Professor G. Hägg, for his kind interest in my work and for the facilities he has put at my disposal.

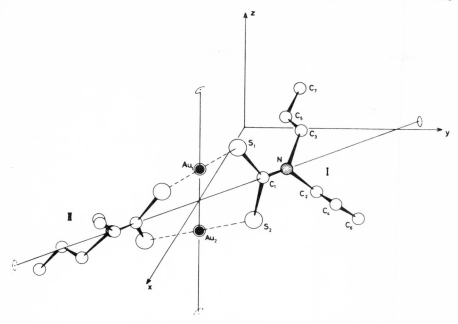

Fig. 1. $[(n\text{-}C_3H_7)_2NCS_2Au]_2$-molecule.

pound the Au-Au-distance (2.76 Å) is even markedly shorter than in the metal. The metal group may be described as, respectively, an Au_2-pair, a slightly distorted Cu_4-tetrahedron, a doubly bent Ag_6-chain.

The metal-sulphur coordination is linear in the gold compound and almost triangular in the copper and silver compounds, the distance from the metal atom to the plane of the sulphur triangle being short. The sulphur atoms always coordinate one or two metal atoms. The coordination distances correspond to covalent bonding. One distance $(Ag_I\text{-}S_{III\ 1} = 2.70$ Å) in the silver compound is, however, somewhat longer.

The inner part $S_1S_2C_1NC_2C_3$ (notation, see Fig. 1) is almost planar in all thiocarbamate molecules. This indicates double-bond character of the C_1—N bond and thus an electron displacement in the thiocarbamate molecules in a direction towards the sulphur atoms.

The interaction between different polymeric molecules is weak in the gold and copper compounds and they are easily dissolved in organic solvents. The studied silver compound is, however, very sparingly soluble, which may be explained by the fact that the distance from the atom Ag_I to a sulphur atom in an adjacent hexameric

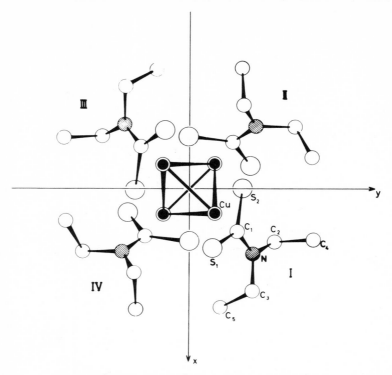

Fig. 2. $[(C_2H_5)_2NCS_2Cu]_2$-molecule. xy projection.

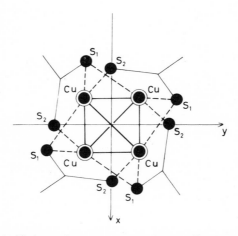

Fig. 3. Copper diethyldithiocarbamate. xy projection. Copper-sulfer coordination.

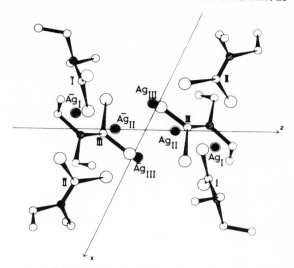

Fig. 4. $[(C_2H_5)_2NCS_2Ag]_6$-molecule. xz projection.

molecule is not longer than 2.99 Å. This may be looked upon as a tendency of the compound to form a chain polymer. It may, however, be noticed that silver (I) di-*n*-propyl dithiocarbamate and higher homologs, which also seem to be hexameric, are readily dissolved.

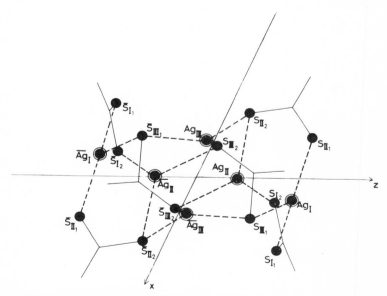

Fig. 5. Silver diethyldithiocarbamate. xz-projection. Silver-sulfer coordination.

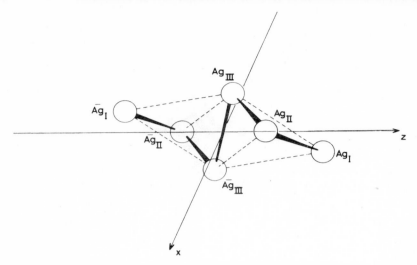

Fig. 6. Arrangement of silver atoms in a $[(C_2H_5)_2NCS_2Ag]_6$-molecule. xz projection.

Discussion

It is evident that the structures described are rather unorthodox, at least at first sight, and a number of points might be brought under consideration for explanation. The following could be mentioned:

1. Polymerity of molecules.
2. Different degrees ($P = 2, 4, 6$) of polymerity.
3. Three-fold coordination of copper and silver.
4. Short metal-metal distances.
5. Configuration of the central metal groups.

When looking for explanations one has to regard several factors, some of which may determine or at least influence the structures:

1. Coordinating properties of metal atoms.
2. Coordinating properties of sulphur atoms.
3. Interaction between metal atoms.
4. Interaction between sulphur atoms (in different dithiocarbamate molecules).
5. Steric coupling (in the same dithiocarbamate molecule) between sulphur atoms.
6. Mesomeric effects in dithiocarbamate molecules.
7. Other collective electron interactions.
8. Space demand of dithiocarbamate molecules.
9. Interaction between different (polymeric) molecules.

This list of factors is rather long and may seem discouraging. Yet a systematic discussion has been attempted with the object of elucidating this complex of structural problems. A full-length account of the discussion, which is still not completed, cannot be given here. Only some points should be mentioned.

A compound containing metal (A) and ligand (X), where both A and X have demands and possibilities of high symmetric linking, is most often built up as a three-dimensional, periodic high polymer (e.g., CuCl, AgI, ZnS). If, however, the linking from the X-ligands has to be very unsymmetric, other arrangements may be formed, e.g., aperiodic polymers, two- or one-dimensional periodic arrangements or low polymers. If, in addition to that, the space demand of X is high compared to that of A, it will be still more difficult to realize a three-dimensional periodic polymer and even two- or one-dimensional arrangements. This is probably the situation for a great number of organic AX-compounds, e.g., thiocarbamates, xantates, mercaptides and other "salts" of monobasic organic acids with "complex-forming" univalent metals.

The thiocarbamates reported above are low polymers. (The silver compound might perhaps be regarded as a borderline case.) It could, however, be mentioned that the di*methyl*dithiocarbamates of copper-(I) and silver (I) are practically insoluble in all common organic solvents. In these compounds the space demand of the X-groups is lower than in the higher homologs and it seems probable that they are built up as high polymers. It is possible that some gold (I) dialkyldithiocarbamates, which are under investigation, are chain polymers. Some silver(I) mercaptides studied by Åkerström[1] are probably hexamers.

One could then ask the question: Are there any reasonable simpler alternatives to the structures found? A systematic investigation of such alternatives based on some assumptions as to the metal-sulphur linking is in progress. Some of it can be mentioned here.

In the monomers the metal-sulphur coordination would be very unsymmetric and thus they are not very probable. The simplest low polymer is the dimer, met with in the gold compound.

If it is assumed that there is a trend for the metal atoms to coordinate more than two sulphur atoms, and that these coordinated sulphur atoms should be situated in different thiocarbamate molecules, then it is found that the degree of polymerity has to be at least four. The simplest type of molecule is, under these conditions, that represented by the copper compound.

One will find that no tetramer is likely in which all metal atoms coordinate four sulphur atoms. It seems very probable that a coordination of four or higher around the metal atoms is sterically unlikely in other low polymers. Then, assuming a trend of the metal atoms to link more than two sulphur atoms, threefold coordination would be the remaining alternative. Threefold copper-sulphur coordination has been found in some complicated sulphide structures, e.g., CuS^3 and $(Cu, Fe)_2As_4S_{13}$.[4]

Concerning the short metal-metal distances one might discuss the possibilities:

1. There are attractive forces acting between the metal atoms.
2. The metal atoms are forced together as a result of other forces in the structure, e.g., those between metal and sulphur atoms. The steric coupling between sulphur atoms (sulphur-sulphur distance about 3.05 Å) in the thiocarbamate molecules is of special importance in this case.

The situation is least complicated in the gold compound. Assuming linear S-Au-S coordination and fixed Au-S distances, the Au-Au distance could have values up to about 3.05 Å. It seems most reasonable to explain the short distance (2.76 Å) actually found, as due to Au-Au attraction of some kind. An alternative explanation would be that the C_1-S-Au angle for some reason (apart from Au-Au-interaction) should have a certain fixed value. It is finally not very probable that the short metal-metal distance would be a result of Van der Waals forces between different molecules, the gold-gold distance in the metallic phase of the element being 2.88 Å.

It seems probable that the general shape of the central metal groups in the copper and silver compounds is determined by the sterically possible ways of metal-sulphur linking. The actual metal-metal distances may, however, be influenced by attractive forces between the metal atoms.

Metal aggregates in monovalent coinage metal complexes have been found by Wells[5] in $[(C_2H_5)_3AsCuI]_4$ and by Brown and Dunitz[6] in DAB $\cdot$ Cu(I). In the former compound there is a central regular Cu_4-tetrahedron in which each of the Cu atoms is coordinated by three iodine atoms and one arsenic. If the copper-copper contacts are not considered, the coordination around the copper atoms is tetrahedral. In DAB $\cdot$ Cu(I) there is a central Cu_2-pair. Each copper coordinates two nitrogens. This compound is dimeric. Higher polymers are perhaps less likely in this case.

REFERENCES

1. S. Åkerström, *Arkiv Kemi*, **14**, 387 (1959).
2. R. Hesse, (to be published).
3. I. Oftedal, *Z. Krist*, **90**, 120 (1935).
4. L. Pauling and E. W. Neumann, *Z. Krist*, **88**, 54 (1934).
5. A. F. Wells, *Z. Krist*, **94**, 447 (1937).
6. I. D. Brown and J. D. Dunitz, Acta Cryst. **14**, 480 (1961).

SYNTHESIS AND REACTIONS OF A NEW CLASS OF IRON ISONITRILE COMPLEXES, (RCH$_2$NC)$_5$FeCNX

WALTER Z. HELDT

E. I. du Pont de Nemours and Company
Explosives Department
Experimental Station Laboratory
Wilmington, Delaware

Iron isonitrile complexes are prepared by: (1) addition of isonitriles to iron(II) salts such as Fe(ClO$_4$)$_2$,[1] (2) addition of isonitriles to iron carbonyls,[2] and (3) alkylation of ferro- or ferricyanides with alkyl halides.[3]

Synthesis of Isonitrile Complexes

We have found that if the alkyl halide to alkali ferrocyanide ratio is 4-8 and if the alkyl halide is activated in the α-position by a carbon-carbon double bond, as in C$_6$H$_5$CH$_2$Br, a new class of isonitrile complexes is formed:

$$5\ C_6H_5CH_2Br + K_4Fe(CN)_6 \longrightarrow (C_6H_5CH_2NC)_5FeCNBr\ (I) + 4\ KBr$$

Compound I has a M. W. of 729 ±9 (calcd. 765.5) in bromoform but a M. W. of 380 in nitrobenzene, indicating a dissociation into two particles in the latter solvent. The I.R. spectrum of I shows two peaks in the triple-bond region at 2115 cm^{-1} and at 2195 cm^{-1}, which are assigned to inorganic cyanide and to complexed organic isonitrile, respectively (Fig. 1).

Addition of an anion to I dissolved in a methanolwater mixture yields metathetical products of I (Fig. 2). The replacement of the bromide ion in I by the anion added indicates that the bromide is the anion for the monopositive cation [(C$_6$H$_5$CH$_2$NC)$_5$FeCN]$^+$.

The structure of I was confirmed (Fig. 2) by conversion of I to (C$_6$H$_5$CN$_2$NC)$_6$FeBr$_2$ (II) and (C$_6$H$_5$CH$_2$NC)$_4$Fe(CN)$_2$ (IV) whose I.R. spectra are included in Fig. 1; by oxidation of I with permanganate to benzoic acid; by reduction to benzyl- and N-methyl benzylamine; and by hydrolysis to benzylamine.

The most probable mechanism of the alkylation reaction of K$_4$Fe(CN)$_6$ is the displacement of halide from the alkyl halide by the isocyano groups of the ferrocyanide anion or of the partially alkylated

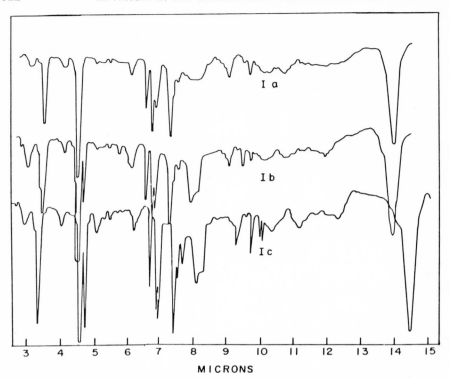

Fig. 1. Infrared spectra in $CHCl_3$ of $(C_6H_5CH_2NC)_6FeBr_2$(a); $(C_6H_5CH_2NC)_5$-$FeCNBrH_2O$(b); $(C_6H_5CH_2NC)_4Fe(CN)_2$(c).

ferrocyanide anion. This is in agreement with the observations that both the ionization of the alkyl halide and the nucleophilicity of the anion influence the rate of reaction:

1. In the following series the alkylation of $Fe(CN)_6^{-4}$ is fastest with $(C_6H_5)_3CBr$:

$$(C_6H_5)_3CBr > (C_6H_5)_2CHBr > p\text{-}CH_3C_6H_4CH_2Br \cong o\text{-}CH_3C_6H_4CHBr >$$

$$C_6H_5CH_2Br \cong CH_2 = CHCH_2Br > p\text{-}ClC_6H_4CH_2Br >$$

$$p\text{-}CH_3CO_2C_6H_4CH_2Br > p\text{-}O_2NC_6H_4CH_2Br \cong (CH_3)_3CBr$$

2. The rate of alkylation of $K_3Fe(CN)_6$, a weak nucleophile, with $(C_6H_5)_3CBr$ is slower than the rate of alkylation of $K_4Fe(CN)_6$, a stronger nucleophile. This evidence suggests a concerted mechanism. Since $(C_6H_5)_3CBr$ forms the most stable carbonium ion in the series quoted, the reaction of alkyl bromides yielding carbonium ions of

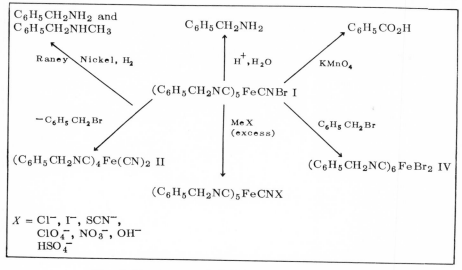

Fig. 2. Structure proof of $(C_6H_5CH_2NC)_5FeCNBr$ (I).

lesser stability must therefore also proceed by a similar mechanism depending on the nucleophilicity of the anion employed.

Reaction of $(RCH_2NC)_5FeCNX$ with Nucleophiles

Nucleophilic agents react with I in three different fashions:

1. If the nucleophile is a strong base such as sodium hydroxide, the reaction with I in an aqueous system at 100–150 °C yields decomposition or polymerization products of I which still contain complexed iron.

2. If the nucleophile employed forms stable iron(II) complexes, for example, KCN, then benzylisonitrile can be isolated in up to 62% conversion, if the reaction is performed in an anhydrous medium such as ethylene glycole dimethyl ether.

3. If the nucleophile is a weak base and is not known to form stable complexes of iron(II), e.g., methanol or ethyl mercaptan, then alkylation of the nucleophile takes place. Methanol yields methyl benzyl ether when heated with I at 150°C and 700 atm N_2 pressure, and ethyl mercaptan similarly yields ethyl thiobenzylether.

The "Transalkylation" Reaction

When I is heated with an alkyl halide, $R'X$, a "transalkylation" of I may take place (Fig. 3). The "transalkylation" reaction is best

$$(RNC)_5 FeCNBr + R'Br \longrightarrow \begin{cases} (a) \left(\begin{matrix}(RNC)_4 \\ R'NC\end{matrix}\right) FeCNBr \\[2ex] (b) \left(\begin{matrix}(RNC)_3 \\ (R'NC)_2\end{matrix}\right) FeCNBr \\[2ex] (c) \left(\begin{matrix}(RNC)_2 \\ (R'NC)_3\end{matrix}\right) FeCNBr \\[2ex] (d) \left(\begin{matrix}RNC \\ (R'NC)_4\end{matrix}\right) FeCNBr \\[2ex] (e) \ (R'NC)_5 FeCNBr \end{cases} + RBr$$

$R' = $ (o, m, p)-$H_3CC_6H_4CH_2Br$, β-naphthyl methyl Br, $C_6H_5COCH_2Br$
$CH_3(CH_2)_{14}CH_2Br$, $HO_2C(CH_2)_{10}CH_2Br$, etc.
The halogen in $R'Br$ may be also Cl or I.

Fig. 3. Transalkylation of $(C_6H_5CH_2NC)_5FeCNBr$.

performed by heating I with an $R'X$ which boils higher than $C_6H_5CH_2$-Br (X) and by continuously removing by distillation under vacuum the $C_6H_5CH_2Br$ (X) formed in the reaction.

The reaction of I with most $R'X$ is quite rapid at 100–150°C, 60–90% conversions to transalkylated products, $(R'NC)_5FeCNBr$ (X), are usually achieved after 30–120 minutes. As expected, a high ratio of $R'X/I = 8$ favors e (in Fig. 3), a lower ratio of $R'X/I = 4$ c,d (in Fig. 3).

The rate-determining step in the reaction is apparently the elimination of one mole of benzyl bromide to yield cis-$(C_6H_5CH_2NC)_4$Fe-$(CN)_2$ (Fig. 4). The following evidence substantiates this statement:

1. The "transalkylation" of II, the *"trans"* isomer, with p-CH_3C_6-H_4CH_2Br and p-$NO_2C_6H_4CH_2Br$ is much slower than the transalkylation of I with the same reagents.

2. The alkylation of the remaining CN in I, a mono-positive ion, is much slower than the total transalkylation of I with p-$NO_2C_6H_4CH_2Br$ or with p-$CH_3O_2CC_6H_4CH_2Br$. Furthermore, when IV was heated with p-$NO_2C_6H_4CH_2Br$ only a trace of "transalkylated" product, $(R'NC)_5FeCNBr$, was isolated and much decomposition occurred.

Reaction of $(C_6H_5CH_2NC)_5FeCNHSO_4$ with Electrophiles

It was of interest to investigate the reactivity of the mono-positive cationic complex, $[(C_6H_5CH_2NC)_5FeCN]^+$, toward electrophilic reagents and compare its reactivity to the neutral complex $(C_6H_5CH_2-(NC)_4Fe(CN)_2$ and to the noncoordinated ligand.

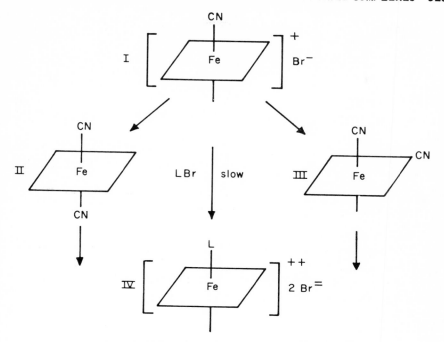

Fig. 4. The stereochemistry of the transalkylation reaction.

Attempted acylation of $[(C_6H_5CH_2NC)_5FeCN]^+$ with benzoyl chloride, either in an excess of the acyl halide or nitrobenzene as the solvent using $AlCl_3$ as the catalyst, failed, even under rigorous conditions.[4] Similarly, no acylation of the neutral complex $(C_6H_5CH_2-NC)_4Fe(CN)_2$ (II) could be effected. On the other hand, both I and II could be nitrated, sulfonated, or alkylated with propylene when concentrated sulfuric acid was used as the reaction medium (Fig. 5). Perhaps $AlCl_3$, a stronger Lewis acid than concentrated sulfuric acid, forms a complex with I and II which resists attack by a cationic species such as $C_6H_5CO.^+$

The substituted products given in Fig. 5 were oxidized with permanganate to the corresponding acids which were then esterified with diazomethane. Each mixture of esters was separated into its components by chromatography on alumina or by vapor-phase chromatography on celite. Nitration and bromination of I and II yielded iron isonitrile complexes in which only one benzene ring was substituted, apparently only in a para-position. Sulfonation of I and II yielded iron isonitrile complexes in which every ring was sulfonated in the *para*- and *meta*-positions. Propylation of I introduced seven propyl groups

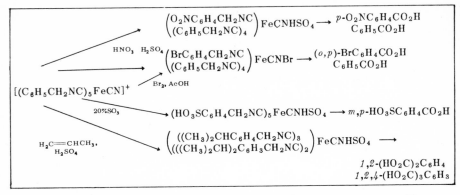

Fig. 5. Electrophilic aromatic substitutions in $[(C_6H_5CH_2NC)_5FeCN]^+$.

into the complex. Upon oxidation this material yielded terephthalic and trimellitic acids.

As evidenced from the I.R. spectrum the main structure of the iron isonitrile complex is V:

$$\langle\!\!\!\bigcirc\!\!\!\rangle - CH_2 : \overset{(+)}{N} : :: C : \overline{Fe} \longleftrightarrow \langle\!\!\!\bigcirc\!\!\!\rangle - CH_2 : \overset{\cdot\cdot}{N} : : C : Fe$$

$$V \qquad\qquad\qquad\qquad VI$$

The onium form of the isonitrile group in V would be expected to show a strong negative inductive effect, hence be *meta*-directing similarly to trimethyl benzylammonium chloride, which yields upon nitration 88% of the *meta*-nitrated product.[5] Although materials accounting in the two degradative steps was only 50–80%, no *meta*-substituted products were identified in the reaction mixtures of the mono-nitrated complex. Hence, the inductive effect of the complexed isonitrile group is much weaker than the inductive effect of the ammonium ion.

Competition reactions of an equimolar large excess of I and toluene for the nitronium ion (NO_2^+) in a homogeneous solution indicated that the reactivity of I toward the nitronium ion approximates the reactivity of toluene toward the nitronium ion. No noticeable differences in reactivity under the reaction conditions investigated for nitration, sulfonation, bromination, and alkylation were noted between I, the cationic species, and II, the neutral species.

REFERENCES

1. (a) L. Malatesta, "Isocyanide Complexes of Metals", In *Progress in Inorganic Chemistry*, F. A. Cotton, Ed., Interscience Publ. Inc., New York, 1960.
   (b) L. Malatesta, A. Sacco, *An. Chim. (Rome)*, **43,** 622 (1953).

2. W. Hieber and D. von Pigenot, *Ber.*, **89,** 193, 610, 616 (1956).
3. E. G. J. Hartley and H. M. Powell, *J. Chem. Soc. (London)*, **101** (1933).
4. H. C. Brown and F. R. Jensen, *J. Am. Chem. Soc.*, **80,** 2291 (1958).
5. (a) C. K. Ingold, F. R. Shaw, and I. S. Wilson, *J. Chem. Soc.*, **1928,** 1280. (b) C. K. Ingold, *Structure and Mechanism in Organic Chemistry*, Cornell University Press, 1953, p. 233.

DETERMINATION OF MOLECULAR WEIGHTS OF POLYNUCLEAR METAL CHELATES BY NON-EQUILIBRIUM ULTRACENTRIFUGATION

RICHARD L. GUSTAFSON and ARTHUR E. MARTELL

Department of Chemistry
Clark University
Worcester, Massachusetts

The studies of polymeric reactions of metal chelates have been hindered because the applications of potentiometric, spectrophotometric and polarographic techniques have not been adaptable, in many cases, to the determination of the degree of aggregation of these chelates. It seemed quite natural that the methods of determination of molecular weights by ultracentrifugation techniques should be applied to polynuclear chelate systems.

In 1954 Johnson, Kraus and Scatchard[1] published the derivation of equations necessary to describe the distribution of charged polymers in a centrifugal field under equilibrium conditions. Subsequently Johnson, Kraus and co-workers calculated the degrees of aggregation of $Zr(IV)$,[2,3] $Hf(IV)$,[3,4] $Bi(III)$,[5] $In(III)$,[6] $Au(III)$,[6] $Hg(I)$,[6] $Hg(II)$,[6] $Pb(II)$,[7] and $Sn(IV)$[7,8] ions under various pH conditions.

The chief disadvantage of the experiments carried out by the above workers is that quite long centrifugation times, often as long as a week, are required. We have applied the Archibald[9] non-equilibrium method of determining molecular weights, as described by Klainer and Kegeles,[10] to the methods of dealing with charged polymers, as outlined by Johnson and co-workers.[1] In this way centrifugation times of a half hour or less are employed with little loss in accuracy relative to results obtained by the use of the equilibrium technique.

In a previous publication,[11] the present authors described the results of the first experiments involving polyelectrolytes carried out by the use of the non-equilibrium ultracentrifugation technique. The systems studied were 1:1 $Th(IV)$-diethylenetriaminepentaacetate (DTPA) and 1:1.5 $Th(IV)$-pyrocatechol-*3,5*-disulfonate (Tiron) chelates. The former compound was shown to be monomeric, whereas the latter chelate was shown to be binuclear at pH 5; the latter conclusion agreeing with the results of solvent extraction studies of Bogucki *et al.*[12] The discussion of ultracentrifugation studies outlined in this paper will be concerned with the results obtained in the investigation mentioned above as well as with more recent studies involving mononuclear and polynuclear chelates of Th(IV) and Zr(IV) ions.

Experimental

The experimental techniques were exactly as described previously by Klainer and Kegeles [10] and by Gustafson and Martell. [11] Each experiment required three centrifugations, two of which were carried out in a cell containing a four-degree sector-shaped centerpiece as shown in Fig. 1. The first centrifugation was carried out on a solution containing the metal chelate at a suitable supporting electrolyte concentration, while the second involved the supporting electrolyte alone. The degree of sedimentation was recorded photographically (Fig. 1) wherein the refractive index gradient, dn/dx, was plotted as a function of the distance, x, from the center of rotation. Since, according to Archibald,[9] equilibrium is maintained at all times at the

(a) Four-degree centerpiece

(b) Two-degree boundary-forming centerpiece

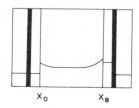

X_0 X_B

(c) Diagram obtained using four-degree cell

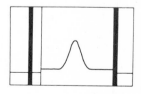

(d) Diagram obtained using boundary-forming cell

Fig. 1. Cells employed and corresponding sedimentation diagrams obtained in ultracentrifugation.

phase boundaries, x_0 and x_b, the values of dn/dx obtained at these points, even after only several minutes of spinning, may be used in the calculation of the molecular weight of the sedimenting species. The quantities $dn*/dx$ for the polymeric component alone are obtained by subtracting the values of dn/dx obtained in the second centrifugation from those of the first.

A third centrifugation, in which solvent is layered over the polymeric solution in a boundary-forming cell described by Kegeles,[18] permits the determination of the initial concentration of the polymeric component in terms of refractive index units. The result of such an experiment is a Gaussian curve (Fig. 1), under which the area is proportional to the concentration of polymeric species.

Mathematical Treatment of Data

In the determination of molecular weights of polyelectrolytes, it is necessary that the following conditions be approximately satisfied: (1) only a single polymeric component may be present; (2) the partial specific volumes of the polymeric component and the supporting electrolyte must be constant; (3) the solution density must be constant; (4) the activity coefficients of all species must be constant throughout the cell; (5) the supporting electrolyte must sediment in the same manner both in the presence of and in the absence of the polymeric species.

The distribution of a component in a centrifugal field under equilibrium conditions may be defined, using the notation of Johnson et al.[1] by the equation

$$\frac{d \ln a}{d(x^2)} = \frac{M(1 - \overline{v}\rho)\omega^2}{2RT} = \frac{L\omega^2}{2RT} = A \tag{1}$$

where a is the activity of the polymer, x the distance from the center of rotation, M the molecular weight, $\overline{v}$ the partial specific volume, ρ the solution density, ω the angular velocity, R the molar gas constant and T the absolute temperature.

Johnson et al.[1] have defined the polymeric component (component 2) as having the formula $PX_{z/2}B_{-z/2}$ where P is the polymeric ion, X is the counter ion, BX is the supporting electrolyte and z is the charge of the polymeric ion. The polymeric component has a molecular weight represented by the relationship

$$M_2 = M_{PX_z} - \frac{z}{2}M_{BX}$$

where M_{PX_z} is the molecular weight of the polymeric component and M_{BX} that of the supporting electrolyte. The concentration, c_3, of the supporting electrolyte, BX, may be expressed by the equations

$$c_3 = c_B + (z/2)c_2 \tag{2a}$$

$$c_3 = c_X - (z/2)c_2 \tag{2b}$$

If constancy of activity coefficients is assumed, combination of equations (1), (2a) and (2b) leads to the equation

$$\frac{d \ln a_2}{d(x^2)} = \frac{d \ln c_P c_X^{z/2} c_B^{-z/2}}{d(x^2)} =$$

$$\frac{d \ln c_2 + [z\eta/(1 - \eta^2)](d \ln c_2 - d \ln c_3)}{d(x^2)} \tag{3}$$

where $\eta = zc_2/2c_3$.

If it is assumed that $1 - \eta^2 = 1$, equation (3) may be modified to give

$$N = \frac{d \ln c_2'/d(x^2)}{A_2' - z'\eta[d \ln c_2'/d(x^2) - d \ln c_3/d(x^2)]} \tag{4}$$

where

$$A_2' = L_2' \omega^2/2RT$$

$$L_2' = M_{PX_z}'(1 - \overline{v}_{PX_z}\rho) - \frac{z'}{2}M_{BX}(1 - \overline{v}_{BX}\rho)$$

and

$$\eta = z'c_2'/2c_3 = 1/(1 + 2c_B/z'c_2')$$

The primed symbols refer to the monomer units according to the relationships $NM_{PX_z}' = M_{PX_z}$ and $z' = z/N$. M_{PX_z}' and $\overline{v}_{PX_z}$ represent the molecular weight and partial specific volume of the monomer unit, PX_z, and M_{BX} and $\overline{v}_{BX}$ represent the same quantities for the supporting electrolyte, BX.

Rearrangement of equation (4) leads to the more useful expression

$$N = \frac{(dc_2'/dx)/2c_2'x}{A_2' - z'\eta\{[(dc_2'/dx)/dx]/2c_2'x - (dc_3/dx)/2c_3x\}} \tag{5}$$

If it is assumed that neglect of the quantity $(dc_3/dx)/2c_3x$ results in a small change in N, equation (5) reduces to

$$N = \frac{1}{2A_2' c_2' x/(dc_2'/dx) - z'\eta} \tag{6}$$

In order to evaluate the quantity c_2' in equation (6), Klainer and Kegeles have derived the equations

$$c_2' \text{ (top)} = c_0 - \frac{1}{x_0^2} \int_{x_0}^{X} x^2 (dc_2'/dx) dx \tag{7}$$

and

$$c_2' \text{ (bottom)} = c_0 + \frac{1}{x_b^2} \int_{X}^{x_b} x^2 (dc_2'/dx) dx \tag{8}$$

where c_2' (top) and c_2' (bottom) represent the concentrations of polymeric solute at the top and bottom phase boundaries, respectively, x_0 and x_b are the distances of the top and bottom phase boundaries from the center of rotation and X is the coordinate in the x direction at which dc_2'/dx is equal to zero. The quantity c_0 of equations (7) and (8) is determined by integration of the curve obtained using the two-degree boundary-forming cell according to the equation

$$c_0 = \int_{x_0}^{x_b} (dc_2'/dx) dx \tag{9}$$

Results and Discussion

Th(IV) Chelates. Th(IV)-Diethylenetriaminepentaacetic Acid (DTPA). Calculation of the degree of aggregation for Th(IV)-DTPA, in which the chelate concentration was varied over more than an eight-fold range while the sodium nitrate concentration was maintained at 1.000 M, gave an average value of $N = 0.90 \pm 0.03$ when the charge per monomer unit was assumed to be -1. If the effects of charge were neglected in the calculations an average value of 0.83 ± 0.03 was obtained. The latter results showed that the addition of large quantities of neutral salt failed to mask charge effects in this case. It seemed somewhat surprising, however, that such low values of N would be found when the actual charge of the chelate was accounted for in the calculations.

Pedersen[14] has discussed the effects of charge upon sedimentation of polyelectrolytes and has shown that two types of salt effects must be considered. A primary charge effect is produced as a result of the different sedimentation tendencies of the heavier polymeric ion and the lighter counter ion, the net result being an increased degree of sedimentation for the counter ion and a lesser degree for the macro ion. The addition of supporting electrolyte reduces the intensity of the electric field about the sedimenting species such that as the ratio PX_z/BX approaches zero, the value of the calculated molecular weight approaches that of the actual molecular weight, M_{PX_z}. This effect has been called by Pedersen the primary salt effect.

The addition of neutral salt in order to neutralize the primary charge effect leads to the secondary salt effect, which is observed when the supporting electrolyte is composed of ions which have different sedimentation coefficients, s. The calculated value of the molecular weight will be equal to the actual value only if B^+ and X^- (or B^- and X^+) have equivalent sedimentation constants. The degree of disparity has been shown to be proportional to the absolute value of the difference between the s values of anion and cation of the supporting electrolyte.

Consideration of the sedimentation constants listed in Table 1 suggests a qualitative explanation for the low values of N obtained for

TABLE 1: SEDIMENTATION CONSTANTS FOR MONOVALENT IONS AT $25°$C.[14]

Ion	$s_{25}0$(Svedberg Units)
Li^+	0.033
Na^+	0.131
K^+	0.239
Cl^-	0.144
NO_3^-	0.252
Br^-	0.462
I^-	0.747

the Th(IV)-DTPA system. In the $NaNO_3$ medium employed, the NO_3^- ion tends to sediment faster than does the Na^+ ion. This produces a microscopic charge separation such that a slight net positive charge exists at the upper phase boundary and a net negative charge exists at the lower boundary. This superposition of an electrophoretic field upon the centrifugal field results in an inhibition of the tendency of the negatively charged Th(IV)-DTPA ion to sediment, thus giving rise to low values of the molecular weight. When Th(IV)-DTPA was centrifuged in a more nearly ideal 1.00 M KNO_3 electrolyte ($\Delta s = 0.013$), an average value of N of 0.97 ± 0.05 was calculated at $z' = 1$.

The results of experiments carried out at various $NaNO_3$ concentrations are summarized in Table 2. Here it may be seen that as the salt concentration is increased from 0.135 to 2.00 M, the calculated values of N decrease, presumably because of an increased contribution by the secondary salt effect.

TABLE 2: CALCULATED VALUES OF N FOR Th(IV)-DTPA CHELATES AT VARIOUS $NaNO_3$ CONCENTRATIONS AT 25° C

Conc Th(IV)-DTPA	Conc NaNO3	$N(z'=1)$
3.37×10^{-2} M	0.135 M	0.99 ± 0.03
3.59×10^{-2} M	0.250 M	0.94 ± 0.01
3.28×10^{-2} M	0.500 M	0.94 ± 0.02
3.54×10^{-2} M	1.000 M	0.89 ± 0.02
3.42×10^{-2} M	2.000 M	0.87 ± 0.01

Th(IV)-pyrocatechol-3,5-disulfonate (Tiron). Murakami and Martell[15] have shown that at pH 5 a stable chelate is formed containing 1.5 Tiron molecules per Th(IV) atom. Ultracentrifugation of 1:1.5 Th(IV)-Tiron chelates in 1.0 M NaCl ($\Delta s = 0.013$) resulted in the data shown in Table 3. Although the deviations are quite large, the results clearly show that the predominant species present in solution is binuclear. Solvent extraction experiments by Bogucki *et al.*[12] demonstrated a polynuclearity of 2.0 for the 1:1.5 Th(IV)-Tiron system, thus giving strong support to the ultracentrifugation results.

Th(IV)-N-hydroxyethylethylenediaminetriacetate (HEDTA). Bogucki and Martell[16] have attempted to elucidate the structure of the polynuclear chelate formed when a solution containing equimolar amounts of Th(IV) and N-hydroxyethylethylenediaminetriacetic acid (HEDTA) is adjusted to pH 7 by addition of $4\frac{2}{3}$ moles of base per mole of metal

TABLE 3: CALCULATED VALUES OF N FOR 1:1.5 Th(IV)-TIRON CHELATES IN 1 M NaCl AT 25° C

Conc Th(IV)		$N(z'=2)$
0.53×10^{-2} M		2.19 ± 0.29
1.28×10^{-2} M		2.11 ± 0.09
1.72×10^{-2} M		1.91 ± 0.11
2.46×10^{-2} M		1.91 ± 0.25
3.56×10^{-2} M		2.01 ± 0.03
4.20×10^{-2} M		1.81 ± 0.14
6.23×10^{-2} M		2.14 ± 0.06
	Average	2.01 ± 0.17

chelate. Mathematical analysis of their potentiometric data indicated that a polymer was formed having the general formula $ThA(Th[OH]_2A)_n$, where A represents the ligand molecule and [OH] represents either a coordinated hydroxo or dissociated hydroxyethyl group. Although the most probable value of n in this case is 5, theoretical plots based on the assumption of a hexamer disagreed markedly with plots based on experimental data. More recent attempts to determine equilibrium constants, assuming the final product to be a trimer, have also been unsatisfactory.

The results of ultracentrifugation of Th(IV)-HEDTA samples containing $4\frac{2}{3}$ moles of hydroxide ion per mole of metal chelate are shown in Fig. 2, where the assumed charge per monomer unit is plotted against the degree of aggregation, N. It may be seen that for a z' value of 0.67 an average of 5.2 monomer units are bound per polymer. The small random distribution of results over a wide concentration range (average deviation of N at $z' = 0.67$, based on 30 pieces of experimental data, is ±4%) is evidence that the system is not polydisperse. The presence of a single polymeric species containing an average of two thirds of a hydroxo group per monomer unit requires that the degree of aggregation be some multiple of three. The results suggest that the Th-HEDTA chelate polymer is most probably a hexamer.

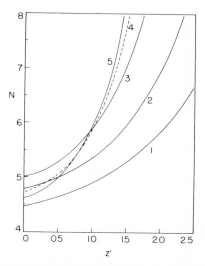

Fig. 2. Ultracentrifugation of 1:1 Th(IV)-HEDTA chelate at pH 7 in 1 M NaCl at 25°. Initial chelate concentrations: (1) 1.08×10^{-2} M; (2) 1.98×10^{-2} M; (3) 3.97×10^{-2} M; (4) 7.29×10^{-2} M; (5) 9.51×10^{-2} M.

It is impossible to decide on the basis of potentiometric or spectrophotometric evidence whether or not the hydroxyethyl group is bound to the metal ion. The value of the molecular weight per monomer unit was based on the assumption that the alkoxyl group is involved in coordination. If the alkoxyl group were not bound in this way, M'_{PX_z} would be increased from 533 to 551, or by a difference of the molecular weight of one water molecule. This would also result in a lower value of $(1 - \overline{v}_{PX_z}\rho)$, the net result being a slight change in the calculation of the degree of polymerization. Calculations have shown that the assumption that $M'_{PX_z} = 551$ rather than 533 results in a change of less than 0.2 percent in the calculated value of N.

Th(IV)-HEDTA-Tiron (1:1:1). Potentiometric titrations of solutions containing equimolar mixtures of thorium ion, N-hydroxyethylethylenediaminetriacetic acid and pyrocatechol-*3,5*-disulfonate produced inflections after the addition of $4\frac{2}{3}$ and 6.0 moles of sodium hydroxide per mole of metal ion.[16] Attempts at mathematical solution of the various equilibria involved were prevented because of the complexity of the system. However, it appeared that determination of the degree of polymerization by means of ultracentrifugation might be successful in the case of this mixed chelate.

A summary of values of N as a function of z' for solutions containing $4\frac{2}{3}$ moles of base per mole of Th(IV)-HEDTA-Tiron is shown in Fig. 3. The upward trend of values of N with increasing metal che-

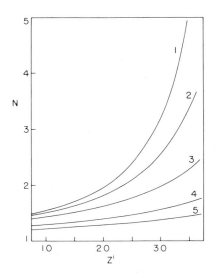

Fig. 3. Ultracentrifugation of 1:1:1 Th(IV)-HEDTA-Tiron chelate at $m = 4.67$ in 1.2 M NaCl at 25°. Initial chelate concentrations: (1) 1.15×10^{-1} M; (2) 8.02×10^{-2} M; (3) 4.86×10^{-2} M; (4) 2.29×10^{-2} M; (5) 1.15×10^{-2} M.

late concentration strongly suggests that the system is polydisperse. The average value of N at $z' = 2.67$ (which would be the actual charge per monomer unit if the system were monodisperse) is 1.9 ± 0.4, suggesting that the average degree of polymerization corresponds to a preponderance of binuclear species. From the inflection at $m = 4\frac{2}{3}$ (where m is equal to the number of moles of hydroxide added per mole of metal ion), it was expected that the value obtained for the degree of polymerization, N, would be some multiple of 3. While the over-all picture is not clear, it appears that the largest polymers present in solution under the conditions described are trimers.

The results of ultracentrifugations of Th(IV)-HEDTA-Tiron solutions containing six moles of hydroxide ion per mole of metal ion are shown graphically in Fig. 4. The crossovers of the curves suggest that the mixed chelate is binuclear with a charge of -2. However, the fact that a mixed chelate of Th(IV)-HEDTA-Tiron must have a charge of -4 indicates that the system is highly polydisperse, the degree of polynuclearity ranging from 2 to 6 or more. It is possible that the steepness of the majority of the plots of Fig. 4 may be caused by the fact that the $z'\eta$ terms employed in the calculations are exceedingly large in the cases of the most concentrated solutions.

At high z' values, small errors in $A_2' c_2' x / (d c_2' / d x)$ result in extremely large errors in the calculated values of N. Data from addi-

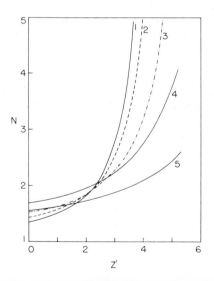

Fig. 4. Ultracentrifugation of 1:1:1 Th(IV)-HEDTA-Tiron chelate at $m = 6.0$ in 1.2 M NaCl at 25°. Initial chelate concentrations: (1) 1.06×10^{-1} M; (2) 7.41×10^{-2} M; (3) 4.23×10^{-2} M; (4) 2.12×10^{-2} M; (5) 1.06×10^{-2} M.

tional experiments carried out in 3–4 molar neutral salt solutions will
be required before definite conclusions may be reached with respect
to the degree of polymerization of Th(IV)-HFDTA-Tiron mixed
chelates.

Zr(IV)-Chelates. Because of the marked tendency of the Zr(IV) ion
and its chelates to hydrolyze and polymerize, relatively few Zr(IV)
chelate systems have been studied in detail to date. Intorre and
Martell[17] have shown that the Zr(IV)-ethylenediaminetetraacetate
(FDTA) chelate hydrolyzes and dimerizes under neutral pH conditions,
and equilibrium constants have been calculated from potentiometric
data for the various reactions involved. However, the details of the
interaction of two other soluble chelate systems, $1:1$ Zr(IV)-HEDTA
and $1:1:1$ Zr(IV)-EDTA-Tiron have not been elucidated. It was
hoped that ultracentrifugation of these systems could at least determine the nature of the chelates produced.

Zr(IV)-HEDTA. Potentiometric titration of a $1:1$ mixture of Zr(IV)
and *N*-hydroxyethylethylenediaminetriacetic acid produces a single
steep inflection after the addition of four moles of hydroxide per mole
of Zr(IV).[16] This behavior is quite different from that of the Th(IV)-
HEDTA system which exhibits a slight inflection at $m = 3$ and a steep
inflection at $m = 4\frac{2}{3}$. The results of ultracentrifugation of the neutral
Zr(IV)-HEDTA chelate are shown in Table 4. Here it may be seen
that there is a systematic increase in the values of N as the chelate
concentration is increased. This suggests that the system is polydisperse since an opposite trend would normally be expected for a
monodisperse system, due to increased non-ideality with corresponding increases in polymer concentrations.

TABLE 4: RESULTS OF ULTRACENTRIFUGATION OF 1:1 Zr(IV)-HEDTA CHELATES IN 1.2 M NaCl AT 25° C

Conc Zr(IV)	$N(z' = 0)$	K_D
9.23×10^{-2} M	1.72	1.71×10^2
9.13×10^{-2} M	1.70	1.45×10^2
9.06×10^{-2} M	1.70	1.46×10^2
6.33×10^{-2} M	1.61	1.02×10^2
6.22×10^{-2} M	1.63	1.21×10^2
6.11×10^{-2} M	1.67	1.68×10^2
3.40×10^{-2} M	1.59	1.64×10^2
3.32×10^{-2} M	1.60	1.81×10^2
3.26×10^{-2} M	1.59	1.71×10^2
1.71×10^{-2} M	1.37	0.75×10^2
1.65×10^{-2} M	1.39	0.88×10^2
1.59×10^{-2} M	1.42	1.11×10^2
		Average $K_D = (1.4 \pm 0.3) \times 10^2$

If the assumption is made that the Zr(IV)-HEDTA system is composed of a mixture of monomers and dimers, the following equations represent the solution equilibria:

$$K_D = \frac{[D]}{[M]^2}$$

$$T_M = [M] + 2[D]$$

$$N = \frac{T_M}{[M] + [D]} .$$

Here K_D represents the equilibrium constant for reaction of monomers $[M]$ to form binuclear chelates, $[D]$. T_M represents the molar concentration of metal ion in both forms as calculated from ultracentrifugation data obtained at the upper phase boundaries. The relative constancy of the values of K_D over a six-fold range of chelate concentration is consistent with the assumption that a mixture of mononuclear and binuclear chelates exists in the concentration range studied.

Zr(IV)-EDTA-Tiron. In Table 5 are presented data obtained upon centrifugation of solutions containing equimolar amounts of Zr(IV), disodium EDTA and Tiron to which four moles of NaOH per mole of metal ion have been added.

The upward trend of N values at $z' = 4$, which is the charge per monomer unit of this mixed chelate, suggests that the system contains a mixture of mononuclear and binuclear species. Calculation of dimerization constants in this case produced values of K_D which drifted upward over a wide range as the chelate concentration increased. In order to clarify the nature of the species present it would appear to be advisable to repeat the experiments at a higher supporting electrolyte concentration in order to reduce activity coefficient variations in the

TABLE 5: CALCULATED VALUES OF N AS A FUNCTION OF z' FOR Zr(IV)-EDTA-TIRON CHELATES IN 1.2 M NaCl AT 25° C

Conc Zr(IV)	$N(z' = 3)$	$N(z' = 4)$	$N(z' = 5)$
8.53×10^{-2} M	1.07	1.41	2.29
5.87×10^{-2} M	1.06	1.32	1.84
4.29×10^{-2} M	1.00	1.19	1.51
2.39×10^{-2} M	0.98	1.10	1.28
1.19×10^{-2} M	0.94	1.02	1.13
Av. values	1.01 ± 0.04	1.2 ± 0.1	1.6 ± 0.4

various solutions and to reduce the magnitudes of the $z'\eta$ terms in the calculations of N.

REFERENCES

1. J. S. Johnson, K. A. Kraus and G. Scatchard, *J. Phys. Chem.*, **58**, 1034 (1954).
2. K. A. Kraus and J. S. Johnson, *J. Am. Chem. Soc.*, **75**, 5769 (1953).
3. J. S. Johnson and K. A. Kraus, *ibid.*, **78**, 3937 (1956).
4. J. S. Johnson, K. A. Kraus and R. W. Holmberg, *ibid.*, **78**, (1956).
5. R. W. Holmberg, K. A. Kraus and J. S. Johnson, *ibid.*, **78**, 5506 (1956).
6. J. S. Johnson and K. A. Kraus, *ibid.*, **79**, 2034 (1957).
7. J. S. Johnson and K. A. Kraus, *ibid.*, **81**, 1569 (1959).
8. J. S. Johnson and K. A. Kraus, *J. Phys. Chem.*, **63**, 440 (1959).
9. W. J. Archibald, *J. Phys. Coll. Chem.*, **51**, 1204 (1947).
10. S. M. Klainer and G. Kegeles, *J. Phys. Chem.*, **59**, 952 (1955).
11. R. L. Gustafson and A. E. Martell, *J. Am. Chem. Soc.*, **82**, 5610 (1960).
12. R. F. Bogucki, Y. Murakami and A. E. Martell, *ibid.*, **82**, 5608 (1960).
13. G. Kegeles, *ibid.*, **74**, 5532 (1952).
14. K. O. Pedersen, *J. Phys. Chem.*, **62**, 1282 (1958).
15. Y. Murakami and A. E. Martell, *J. Am. Chem. Soc.*, **82**, 5605 (1960).
16. R. F. Bogucki and A. E. Martell (unpublished results).
17. B. J. Intorre and A. E. Martell (unpublished results).

SPECTRAL AND MAGNETIC STUDIES OF SUBSTITUTED Ni(II) SALICYLALDIMINE COMPLEXES*

R. H. HOLM*

Department of Chemistry
Harvard University
Cambridge, Massachusetts

It is now well recognized that there exists a small group of chemically well-characterized complexes of bivalent nickel which may be termed "magnetically anomalous" in the sense that their magnetic moments do not always correspond to an integral number of unpaired electrons per nickel ion, i.e., $0 < \mu_{eff} \lesssim 3.1$ B.M. This partial paramagnetism has been found nearly always in solutions in either coordinating or essentially noncoordinating solvents prepared by dissolving complexes diamagnetic as solids. The first such example of this behavior was that of bis(formylcamphor)-ethylenediimine-nickel (II), which was found to have a magnetic moment of 1.9 B.M. in methanol.[1] Later Lifschitz[2] and Basolo and Matoush[3] found this complex to be partially paramagnetic in other media. Willis and Mellor[4] in 1947 reported the results of a more extensive survey of the magnetic moments of other quadri-coordinate Ni(II) complexes in solution and discovered a number of cases of partial paramagnetism. In recent years Clark and Odell[5] and Sacconi *et al.*[6,7] have made more intensive studies of the magnetism and spectra of these anomalous complexes.

Except for one rather unique class of four-coordinate Ni(II) complexes of aminotroponeimines[8,9] all of the magnetically anomalous behavior at this writing has been found in the Schiff base complexes of Ni(II) with various salicylaldimines. In this paper the investigations and discussion will be confined to the complexes of general type I. The spectra and magnetism of the analogous tricyclic *cis* complexes have recently been discussed.[11]†

---

*The author wishes to acknowledge the financial support of the National Science Foundation under research grant NSF G–12312.

†A complete summary of four-coordinate Ni(II) complexes will form part of a forthcoming review (cf. Ref. 13).

Bis(N-methylsalicylaldimine)Ni(II) (I, R$=$CH$_3$) is the outstanding example of anomalous complexes of type I. A diamagnetic solid, it has been reported to give the following moments at or near room temperature: chloroform 1.9–2.2,[4–6, 12] benzene 1.8–2.4;[4–6] toluene 1.4–1.7,[5,12] xylene 0.9,[5] 1.9,[12] dioxane 2.1–2.3,[4–6] and ethanol 2.4, 2–6[4,5] B.M.

Two explanations have been proposed to account for the peculiar magnetism. The first, a temperature and concentration dependent conformational equilibrium between planar (diamagnetic) and tetrahedral (paramagnetic) forms,[1,3–5,12] may be safely discarded for reasons previously mentioned.[14] The second explanation, based on either the weak[15] or strong[10] ligand-field model, assumes a planar structure and involves a temperature-dependent population of a singlet ground state and a thermally accessible upper triplet state separated by an energy Δ. Analysis of the existing data on the temperature dependence of the magnetic moment of the N-methyl compound and several other related complexes in inert solvents[5, 12] indicate that these data cannot reasonably be fitted to the proposed[10] Boltzman function describing the temperature variation of the susceptibility with changing population of ions over the low-lying singlet and triplet states.

Assuming a planar structure in solution, it seems reasonably certain that the solution paramagnetism of the N-methyl compound is intimately related to the in-plane ligand-field strength of the O$_2$N$_2$ donor set which is such as to place the nickel ion near to, but slightly on the strong-field side of, the triplet-singlet ground state cross-over point. Hence, removal of crystalline forces[10] or perturbation by solvent[15] or solute[14] might substantially enhance the triplet character of the Ni(II) ground state. In addition, substitution on the basic salicylaldimine ligand skeleton by appropriate groups, so as to alter the molecular steric requirements and/or the in-plane ligand-field-strength might conceivably induce a large change in solution paramagnetism. Therefore, a wide variety of substituted Ni(II) salicylaldimine complexes was characterized and their spectral and magnetic properties investigated. The complexes are most conveniently discussed according to the general structure of the substituent R appended to the nitrogen. In this work R = methyl and n-alkyl, aryl, sec-alkyl.

R = Methyl and n-Alkyl

The fact that the N-methyl complex exhibits appreciable paramagnetism in solution, whereas the homologous n-alkyl complexes are essentially diamagnetic (cf. Table 1 and Ref. 6), is clearly not accountable in terms of a significant change in the in-plane ligand-field strengths. Rather, some more specific cause must be sought. Maki[15] has shown that weak tetragonal perturbation of the ligand field along the z-axis destabilizes the singlet relative to the triplet state, and has proposed that in solvents such as chloroform weak solvent inter-

TABLE 1: SPECTRAL AND MAGNETIC DATA FOR
BIS(R-N SALICYLALDIMINE) Ni(II) COMPLEXES,
R = METHYL AND n-ALKYL

R	μ_{eff} (solid)	Solvent	Conc (mmolal)	T (°K)	μ_{eff}	λ_{max} (ε_{max})
CH_3	diamagnetic	$CHCl_3$	25.13–91.04	297	1.13–1.86	610 (67)
		C_6H_6	28.37–96.79	297	1.27–2.23	
		$CHCl_3/MeOH*$	29.57	297	2.92	610 (25)
CH_3 $X = 3CH_3$	diamagnetic	$CHCl_3$	23.88–90.75	297	0	614 (73)
CH_3 $X = 5CH_3$	diamagnetic	$CHCl_3$	27.98–54.14	297	0.79–1.23	619 (53)
CH_3 $X = 3$-i-Pr	diamagnetic	$CHCl_3$	25.09–90.00	298	0	625 (89)
CH_3 $X = 5$-i-Pr	diamagnetic	$CHCl_3$	24.92–48.91	297	0–0.87	618 (87)
C_2H_5	diamagnetic	$CHCl_3$	90.10	300	0.51	615 (70)
		$CHCl_3/MeOH*$	27.29	297	1.97	612 (45)
n-C_3H_7	diamagnetic	$CHCl_3$	99.12	298	0.42	615 (70)
		$CHCl_3/MeOH*$	27.23	298	1.86	613 (47)
n-C_4H_9	diamagnetic	$CHCl_3$	97.73	297	0.52	615 (70)
		$CHCl_3/MeOH*$	29.56	296	1.94	615 (47)

*50% v/v.

action with the nickel ion is responsible for the partial paramagnetism of the N-methyl complex. This proposal, which undoubtedly explains the full paramagnetism of many dihydrates and dipyridinates of Ni(II) complexes which when de-solvated are diamagnetic solids, is rather difficult to test in this class of complexes whose low solubilities in hydrocarbon solvents preclude magnetic measurements in such media. If in the N-methyl and related complexes the situation is one involving a temperature-dependent single-triplet population of nickel ions in monomeric complexes with or without a solvent perturbation of Λ, then at a fixed temperature the magnetism and spectra should be concentration-independent. Reference to Table 1 shows that, contrary to previous reports,[4,5] the solution magnetism as measured by the Gouy method and by nuclear resonance[16] is dependent on concentration. In chloroform (0.037–0.130 M) and benzene (0.025–0.083 M) the molar susceptibility of the N-methyl compound increases by factors of ~ 2.7 and ~ 3.1, respectively. Further, the intensity of the broad band in the near infrared, centering at ~ 1160 mμ and assigned as the $^3B_{3g} - {}^3B_{1g}$ transition,[15] does not follow Beer's Law; e.g., ε_{1160} varies by a factor of ~ 2 in the range 0.04–0.11 M.

The foregoing observations are not consonant with only monomeric species in solution, but are indicative of solute association. This is particularly likely since it was recently shown the N-ethyl, -n-propyl, and -n-butyl complexes are monomeric and essentially diamagnetic in benzene, whereas several sec-alkyl complexes are associated and partially paramagnetic.[14] One possible mode of association is shown in II in which the nickel ion in one molecule is bonded weakly to an oxygen in another molecule, thus becoming five- or six-coordinate depending on the molecular complexity. Harris, Lenzer, and Martin[17] have proposed a similar polymeric octahedral structure for the fully paramagnetic bull-colored solid modification of the N-methyl compound. Examination of scale models indicates

that with R groups larger than methyl, rotational motion of the groups will introduce a definite steric barrier to association as depicted in

II. Additional evidence for association of the N-methyl compound is deduced from the magnetic behavior in solution of various derivatives substituted on the aromatic ring by the groups X (III). Substitutions of methyl or isopropyl groups at the 3- and 5-position of the ring greatly reduce or eliminate solution paramagnetism. In accord with magnetic data (cf. Table 1), models show the 3-positions to be the more critical sterically, and all these compounds are diamagnetic in solution. Although small changes in the in-plane ligand-field strengths are produced by ring substitution, it seems very likely that steric resistance to association is dominant.

That tetragonal perturbation of the ligand field of otherwise diamagnetic complexes by oxygen interaction with nickel can produce triplet character in the ground state is indicated by the partial paramagnetism of all of the complexes in this group in chloroform-methanol. The energy of the visible ligand-field band is essentially unchanged, but the intensity is strongly decreased. An interaction of this type was, however, not observed for the R = methyl-butyl complexes in pure dioxane.[6]

R = Aryl

All of the complexes prepared bearing aromatic substituents on the nitrogen superficially resemble the methyl and n-alkyl derivatives, being green crystalline solids and fairly soluble in chloroform and benzene. However, reference to Table 2 shows that with two exceptions the complexes are strongly paramagnetic in solution. Four of them are paramagnetic solids and, together with some α-branched derivatives (discussed in the following section), represent the first examples of solid-phase paramagnetism in Ni(II) salicylaldimine complexes.

Replacement of an n-alkyl by an aromatic substituent makes no important change in the in-plane ligand-field strength, as judged from

TABLE 2: SPECTRAL AND MAGNETIC DATA FOR BIS(R-N SALICYLALDIMINE)Ni(II) COMPLEXES, R = ARYL

R	μ_{eff} (solid)	Solvent	Conc (mmolal)	T (°K)	μ_{eff}	λ max (ε_{max})
C_6H_5	diamagnetic	$CHCl_3$	23.89	300	2.92	617 (27)
		C_6H_6	23.10	299	3.08	
p-C_6H_4F	diamagnetic	$CHCl_3$	24.42	301	2.88	615 (30)
		C_6H_6	22.57	298	2.93	
p-C_6H_4Cl	3.34	$CHCl_3$	26.61	301	2.91	615 (27)
		C_6H_6	19.02	298	3.09	
m-C_4H_4Cl	3.37	$CHCl_3$	24.91	297	3.20	615 (15)
		C_6H_6	24.93	297	3.21	
o-$C_6H_4CH_3$	diamagnetic	$CHCl_3$	28.81	300	1.00	617 (85)
		C_6H_6	21.32	299	0.80	
m-$C_6H_4CH_3$	3.34	$CHCl_3$	28.20	302	3.25	612 (20)
		C_6H_6	26.43	300	3.26	
p-$C_6H_4CH_3$	3.46	$CHCl_3$	27.18	298	3.03	614 (23)
		C_6H_6	20.36	299	3.14	
$1,5$-$C_6H_3(CH_3)_2$	diamagnetic	$CHCl_3$	41.02	298	0	617 (86)
		C_6H_6	36.00	297	0	

the constancy of the frequency of the "615 mμ" bands assigned to the $^1A_{1g}$ – $^1B_{3g}$ or $^1B_{1g}$ transition.[15,18] However, in the cases of strong solution paramagnetism the intensities of these bands are markedly lower, due to the decreased singlet character of the hybrid ground state. In these cases two other weaker bands appear in the very near infrared at 775 and 1000 mμ ($\varepsilon_{max} \sim 9$), both of which are absent in the o-tolyl and 1,5-dimethylphenyl derivatives and, hence, are transitions involving a triplet ground state. The assignments of these bands are, however, still uncertain.

On the basis of the data presented thus far, it is seen that by varying the group R it is possible in certain instances to transform the Ni(II) ground state from essentially triplet to predominantly singlet in relatively inert solvents. As with the n-alkyl derivatives solute association is possible, though not necessarily by the same means, so that the magnetic measurements were made on rather dilute solutions. Similar to the observations on the n-alkyl derivations, the two very weakly paramagnetic aryl-substituted complexes are monomeric in freezing benzene. Both the m- and p-tolyl complexes are monomeric and represent two of the very few examples of spin-free monomeric Ni(II) which are very possibly planar or nearly planar.

Investigations of the aryl-substituted complexes is continuing. Of obvious importance is the temperature dependence of the magnetism and spectra. Another important point, which might account for the enhanced magnetism of these complexes, is the extent of mesomeric interaction between the basic ligand system and the aromatic substituent. Steric difficulties preclude coplanarity of the two moieties but some π-overlap might be possible. In the two cases in which *ortho* substitution prevents this interaction, it is not known whether the diamagnetic behavior is due to a purely electronic effect or steric inhibition to association.

R = sec-Alkyl

A number of new complexes of Ni(II) were investigated in which the alkyl substituent was branched at the α-carbon directly bonded to nitrogen. Some of these complexes are dark brownish-green paramagnetic solids, whereas others are green and diamagnetic and resemble the *n*-alkyl derivatives mentioned previously. Regardless of the nature of the solid phase, all of these complexes dissolve in chloroform and benzene to give brown solutions containing partially paramagnetic complexes (cf. Table 3). This behavior in solution occurs only when the complex bears the local $N-C\begin{smallmatrix} C \\ C \end{smallmatrix}$ structure, and does not occur when one has the structure $N-C-C\begin{smallmatrix} C \\ C \end{smallmatrix}$ as in the *N*-isobutyl complex, which is monomeric and possesses magnetic and spectral properties completely similar to the *n*-alkyl derivatives.

Without exception, the *sec*-alkyl complexes are associated in freezing benzene[14] and possess ligand-field spectra markedly dissimilar to other complexes previously discussed. The spectra consist of two poorly resolved bands appearing usually as shoulders at ~ 580 and ~ 690 mμ and two bands in the near infrared at 905 (ε_{max} 4–6) and 1470 mμ (ε_{max} ~ 20). The association can be broken down in pyridine and spectra and magnetism (μ_{eff} = 3.1–3.2 B.M.) normally found in this solvent are obtained.

In these complexes the connection between partial paramagnetism and association in solution is clearly established. The solubility of several of the ring-substituted derivatives permits measurements in cyclohexane in which the possibility of weak solvent interaction with the metal and its related effect on the magnetism is completely removed. In this solvent the spectra are identical with those in chloroform and benzene and only a small change in magnetic moment is observed. These observations rule out solvent participation as the only means of effecting paramagnetic behavior in solutions of complexes diamagnetic as solids.

The association of the α-branched complexes must occur by a substantially different mode of interaction than is the case for bis(N-methylsalicylaldimine)Ni(II). In these cases the association as measured by the paramagnetism is only very weakly dependent on concentration (cf. Table 3), whereas in the same solvents and over the same concentration ranges the magnetism of the N-methyl complex is markedly concentration-dependent. Further, the substitution of methyl and isopropyl groups in the 3-position of the aromatic ring slightly enhance, rather than strongly diminish, the magnetic moments in solution. Substitution in the 5-position also does not greatly decrease the paramagnetism.

It seems clear that the magnetism of the solid complexes is due largely to the exigencies of crystal packing, and that upon removal

TABLE 3: SPECTRAL AND MAGNETIC DATA FOR BIS(R-N SALICYLALDIMINE)Ni(II) COMPLEXES, R = BRANCHED ALKYL

R	μ_{eff} (solid)	Solvent	Conc (mmolal)	T(°K)	μ_{eff}	λ max (ε_{max})*
i-C$_3$H$_7$	3.28	CHCl$_3$	25.16	297	2.22	~ 580(81), ~ 690(37)
			99.63	297	2.31	
		C$_6$H$_6$	25.00	298	2.18	
			107.8	298	2.17	
S-C$_4$H$_9$	3.36	CHCl$_3$	26.56	297	2.23	~ 590(80), ~ 710(32)
			102.6	297	2.34	
		C$_6$H$_6$	23.11	297	2.14	
			102.8	297	2.11	
C$_5$H$_9$	diamagnetic	CHCl$_3$	24.94	296	2.52	~ 580(85), ~ 700(38)
			75.67	297	2.67	
		C$_6$H$_6$	29.46	298	2.58	
C$_6$H$_{11}$	diamagnetic	CHCl$_3$	22.43	298	1.84	~ 580(71), ~ 700(23)
i-C$_3$H$_7$	diamagnetic	CHCl$_3$	23.77	297	2.09	~ 590(83), ~ 670(57)
X = 3CH$_3$		C$_6$H$_6$	28.81	297	2.27	
			110.5	298	2.36	
		C$_6$H$_{12}$	32.16	297	2.19	
i-C$_3$H$_7$	3.28	CHCl$_3$	24.72	297	2.40	~ 660(69), ~ 690(65)
X = 3-		C$_6$H$_6$	24.57	297	2.60	
			63.25	297	2.68	
i-C$_3$H$_7$		C$_6$H$_{12}$	31.33	297	2.47	

*Spectra in chloroform, ~0.02M.

of crystalline constraints the solid diamagnetic complexes may then associate in solution. In the absence of definite structural information on the solid paramagnetic complexes, one may speculate that they are associated to some extent, if not infinitely polymerized, and that upon dissolution are dissociated to some degree. The small differences in paramagnetism in relatively inert solvents may then be dependent, at least in part, on the extent of dissociation rather than solely by weak solvent interactions with the nickel ion.

The results of this investigation, together with the important findings of Fackler and Cotton on Ni(II) bis(β-diketone) complexes,[19] emphasize the necessity for the consideration of solute association among these factors which may lessen the tetragonal character of the ligand field and hence promote the relative stability of a triplet ground state.

REFERENCES

1. H. S. French, M. Z. Magee, E. Sheffield, *J. Am. Chem. Soc.*, **64**, 1924 (1942).
2. Lifschitz, *Rec. Trav. Chim.*, **66**, 401 (1947).
3. F. Basolo and W. R. Matoush, *J. Am. Chem. Soc.*, **75**, 5663 (1953).
4. J. B. Willis and D. P. Mellor, *ibid.*, **69**, 1237 (1947).
5. H. C. Clark and A. L. Odell, *J. Chem. Soc.*, 3431 (1955).
6. L. Sacconi, P. Paoletti, G. Del Re, *J. Am. Chem. Soc.*, **79**, 4092 (1957).
7. L. Sacconi, R. Cini, M. Ciampolini, and F. Maggio, *ibid.*, **82**, 3487 (1960).
8. W. R. Brasen, H. E. Holmquist, and R. E. Benson, *ibid.*, **82**, 995 (1960).
9. W. D. Phillips and R. E. Benson, *J. Chem. Phys.*, **33**, 607 (1960).
10. C. J. Ballhausen and A. D. Liehr, *J. Am. Chem. Soc.*, **81**, 538 (1959).
11. R. H. Holm, *ibid.*, **82**, 5632 (1960).
12. S. Fujii and M. Sumitani, *Sci. Repts. Tohoku Univ.*, 1st Ser., **37**, 49 (1953).
13. F. A. Cotton, D. M. L. Goodgame, and R. H. Holm, *Prog. Inorg. Chem.*, to be published.
14. R. H. Holm and T. M. McKinney, *J. Am. Chem. Soc.*, **82**, 5506 (1960).
15. G. Maki, *J. Chem. Phys.*, **28**, 651 (1958); **29**, 162 (1958); **29**, 1129 (1958).
16. D. F. Evans, *J. Chem. Soc.*, 2003 (1959).
17. C. M. Harris, S. L. Lenzer, and R. L. Martin, *Austr. J. Chem.*, **11**, 331 (1958).
18. J. Ferguson, *J. Chem. Phys.*, **34**, 611 (1961).
19. J. P. Fackler, Jr. and F. A. Cotton, *J. Am. Chem. Soc.*, **82**, 5005 (1960); *idem.*, *ibid.*, **83**, (1961), in press.

FURTHER STUDIES ON THE METAL COMPLEXES OF N,N'-DISUBSTITUTED DITHIOOXAMIDES

RICHARD N. HURD, GEORGE DeLaMATER, GEORGE C. McELHENY, and JOHN P. McDERMOTT*

Chemical Research Department
Medicinal Division
Mallinckrodt Chemical Works
St. Louis, Missouri

Studies of the metal complexes of dithiooxamide[1] and its N,N'-disubstituted derivatives[3] constitute an area of research in which only a modest number of papers[2] have appeared in the 33 years that have elapsed since the first of these complexes was reported.[1] The first publication[1] described the relatively high decomposition points, vivid colors, and insolubility characteristics of several dithiooxamidometal complexes, and its authors, Rây and Ray, proposed that these properties were due to the chelation of the metal atoms to dithiooxamide molecules. However, they visualized these complexes as monomeric chelates in which a metal atom had four coordinate bonds with a single-ligand molecule as shown in Fig. 1. In the light of modern knowledge, this strained structure seems unlikely.

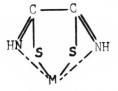

Figure 1

Recent X-ray studies indicate that the dithiooxamide molecule is planar with a center of symmetry.[4] Barceló used this information in the interpretation of the infrared spectra of dithiooxamidocopper(II), -nickel(II) and -cobalt(III), and suggested that structure 2 represented

*We are particularly indebted to Miss Ella M. Bettinger, Mallinckrodt Chemical Works, for obtaining and interpreting the infrared spectra.

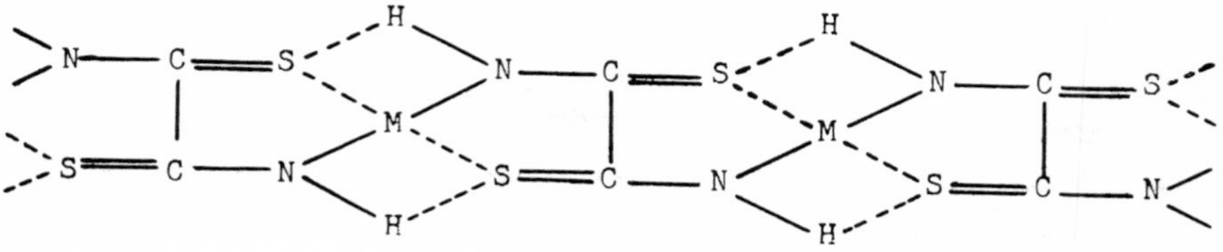

Figure 2

these complexes.[5] Since Barceló observed no absorption due to S—H groups in the spectrum of dithiooxamide or its complexes and saw strong absorption due to the thiocarbonyl group in the spectra of its metal complexes, he depicted the ligands in their keto resonance forms (Fig. 2). However, Jensen,[6] as well as Xaviar and Rây,[7] speculated that in these complexes the dithiooxamide ligands might exist primarily in the *trans enol* form. The latter authors pictured the dithiooxamidometal complexes as shown in Fig. 3. Here no hydrogen-bonding is shown.

Miller and Brody observed that the pharmacological activity of several *N,N'*-disubstituted dithiooxamides was related to their formation of zinc complexes in biological systems.[8] Their ultraviolet spectroscopic evidence indicated that Zn(II) atoms and ligand molecules were combining in a 2:1 ratio to form the complexes. On this basis they proposed the structure shown in Fig. 4.

Chelated monomeric structures with dithiooxamide ligands in the *trans enol* form have been proposed for the Ru(III) complexes of dithiooxamide[9] (Fig. 5) and the Pd(II) complex of *N,N'*-bis[*3*-(dimethylamino)propyl]-dithiooxamide[10] (Fig. 6).

Results and Discussion

Solid nickel(II),[11] cobalt(III), copper(II), cadmium(II), zinc(II) and platinum(IV) complexes of *N,N'*-disubstituted dithiooxamides result from reaction of the appropriate dithiooxamide and metal ion under

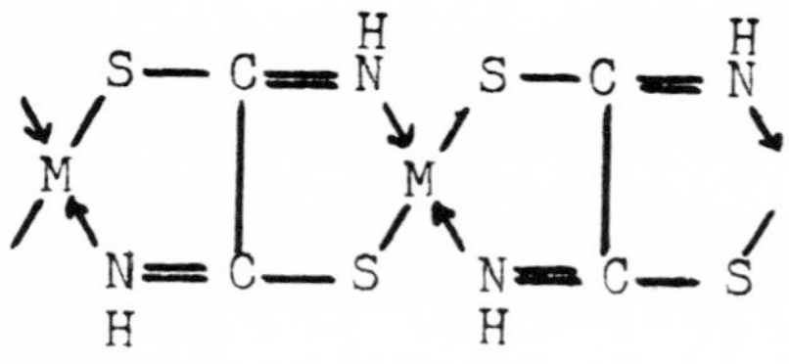

Figure 3

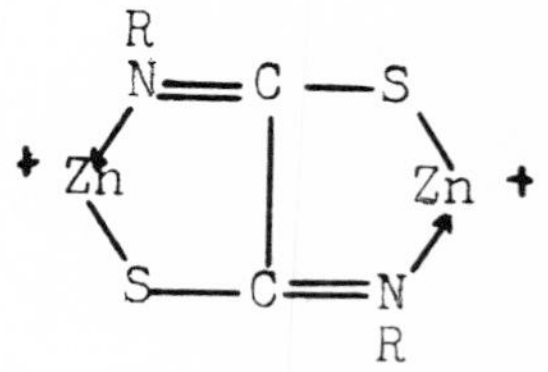

Figure 4

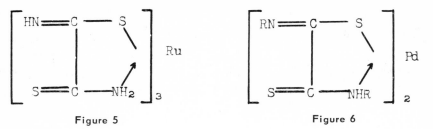

Figure 5   Figure 6

mildly basic conditions. Formation of all of the Ni(II), Co(III), Cu(II) and Cd(II) complexes, as well as several Zn(II) complexes, is represented by the following general reaction:

$$2nM^{+a} + anR\text{NH} \cdot \text{CS} \cdot \text{CS} \cdot \text{NH}R \longrightarrow [(RN \cdot \text{CS} \cdot \text{CS} \cdot NR)_a M_2]_n + 2an\text{H}^+.$$

In this generalization M^{+a} represents a metal cation of charge $+a$, and R stands for the organic substituent of the ligand.

All of the complexes have infrared spectra showing strong absorptions of the N—C=S group. Absorption characteristic of S-H bonds is not found in any of the spectra. Thus, for the complexes formed by the general reaction stated above we may write structure 7, analogous to the work of Barceló. Each complex depicted by Fig. 7 consists of neutral, coordinated metal atoms that are bridged by dithiooxamide or N,N' disubstituted dithiooxamide ligands in the keto form. In each complex electroneutrality is achieved and covalent metal-nitrogen bonds are formed by the displacement of a proton from each amido nitrogen of every bridging dithiooxamide ligand.

Strong absorptions due to N-H bonds, that are characteristic of the spectra of all the parent ligands, are either completely absent or reduced to much weaker absorptions in the spectra of all the complexes here reported, except those of dithiooxamide itself. Explanation for the appearance of strong N-H absorption in the dithiooxamide complexes is obvious. The appearance of weak N-H absorption in the

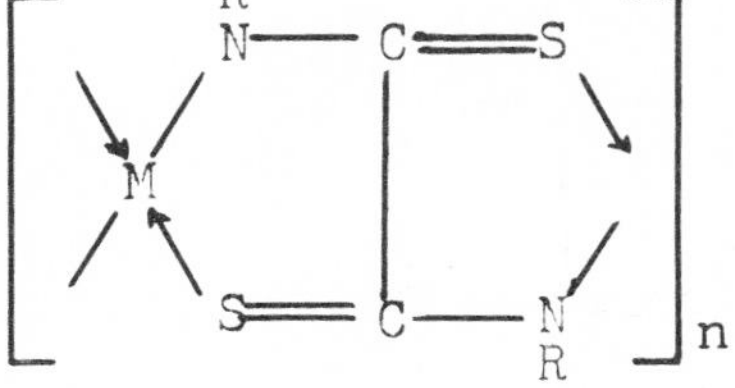

Figure 7

spectra of some of the metal complexes can be explained in terms of the structures proposed for these complexes. For example, three of the Cd(II) complexes, XX, XXI, and XXII-A, have weak spectral N-H absorptions. The structures proposed for these complexes on the basis of analyses (Table 3) are fairly short chains that terminate in molecules of the ligands. In order for the structures to be uncharged, one of the terminal ligand molecules of each chain must retain its amido hydrogen atoms. Since one out of every five to seven molecules of ligand retains its hydrogens, N-H absorption would be expected to be weakly retained in the complex spectra.

The Preparation and Structures of Dithiooxamidonickel(II) Complexes.[11] These complexes, listed in Table 1, are readily prepared in quantitative yields by admixture of aqueous, alcoholic solutions of equimolar amounts of a Ni(II) salt, a dithiooxamide, and two equivalents of a base at room temperature. Reaction is always instantaneous, but the reaction temperature never rises appreciably. The crude products can be purified by Soxhlet extraction with alcohol and water, in which they are insoluble.

Evidence that the formation of the Ni(II) complexes is represented by the general reaction given earlier, and that the products have the structure given in Fig. 7, is furnished by the infrared spectra of the pure complexes. Except for I, the N-H absorption characteristic of the parent ligands is absent in the spectra of the complexes. Further, the spectra of all of the Ni(II) complexes exhibit characteristic —N—C≡S absorption but not —SH absorption.

Further evidence in support of these concepts was reported last year for the Ni(II) complexes.[11] This evidence may be summarized here into three points: Tetraethyldithiooxamide does not react with Ni(II) ion. This result is as predicted from the general reaction and the structure shown in Fig. 7, both of which require that an amido hydrogen be available for replacement by the coordinating metal. Secondly, it was shown that for each equivalent of ligand consumed in complex formation nearly two equivalents of acid were formed. Finally, the analyses of the complexes agreed well with the structure given in Fig. 7.

Complexes IV-XII (incl.) are represented as polymeric, although the analytical data fit equally well for the monomeric case of $n = 1$. The polyfunctional nature of the parent dithiooxamides, analytical evidence that complexes I, II, III and XIII are polymers, and a consideration of the properties of these complexes (such as their insolubility in aqueous and organic solvents and their thermal stability), strongly suggest that n has a value considerably greater than unity in the structure given for complexes IV-XII (incl.).

TABLE 1: DITHIOOXAMIDONICKEL(II) COMPLEXES

No.	Nickel(II) Complex of a Dithiooxamide, RNH·CS·CS·NHR, where R is:	Structures $DTO = RNH \cdot CS \cdot CS \cdot NHR$ $DTO - H = RNH \cdot CS \cdot CS \cdot NR$ $DTO - 2H = RN \cdot CS \cdot CS \cdot NR$	Color
I	H	$(DTO)[(DTO - 2H)Ni]_{15}$	Blue-Black
II[11]	CH_3-	$a.\ (DTO)[Ni(DTO - 2H)]_4Ni(DTO)$ $b.\ [(DTO - 2H)Ni]_{6-8}(DTO - H)Na$ $c.\ Na(LTO - H)[(DTO - 2H)Ni]_{18}(DTO - H)Na$	Purple
III	$CH_3(CH_2)_{11}-$	$[(DTO - 2H)Ni]_8(DTO)$	Purple-Violet
IV[11]	$CH_3(CH_2)_{17}-$	$[(DTO - 2H)Ni]_n$	Violet
V[11]	(benzyl) $-CH_2$	$[(DTO - 2H)Ni]_n$	Dark Blue
VI	(2-chlorobenzyl) $-CH_2$ Cl	$[(DTO - 2H)Ni]_n$	Dark Purple
VII	(4-chlorobenzyl) Cl $-CH_2$	$[(DTO - 2H)Ni]_n$	Blue-Purple
VIII[11]	$(CH_3)_2NCH_2CH_2CH_2-$	$[(DTO - 2H)Ni]_n$	Red-Brown
IX[11]	$HOCH_2CH_2-$	$[(DTO - 2H)Ni]_n$	Brown
X	$HOCH_2CH_2OCH_2CH_2OCH_2CH_2CH_2-$	$[(DTO - 2H)Ni]_n$	Brown
XI	$CH_3COCH_2CH_2-$ $\parallel O$	$[(DTO - 2H)Ni]_n$	Dark Blue
XII	$CH_3(CH_2)_{11}OCCH_2-$ $\parallel O$	$[(DTO - 2H)Ni]_n$	Dark Brown
XIII	$HOOCCH_2-$	See Fig. 1	Red-Brown

The complete analyses of N,N'-dimethyldithiooxamidonickel(II) show that the size and terminal structure of the polymer chain depend on the conditions of preparation and purification.[11] In order for good agreement to exist between the analyses and a structure, $[(CH_3NCSCSNCH_3)Ni]_n$, that is homologous with the general structure (Fig. 7), the complex chains would have to be long enough so that heterogeneous terminal groups would not appreciably change the empirical formula. Such was not the case with II. When II was prepared in the absence of base and purified by extraction with both alcohol and water, its analyses were in good agreement with structure II-a (Table 1), a complex chain of alternating ligands and tetra-coordinate Ni(II) atoms terminating in ligands at both ends.

This structure is in accord with the principle that greatest complex stability is achieved when a given metal atom is involved in the maximum number of chelate rings. Nickel coordinated at a terminal position in II can be involved in only one chelate ring.

When II is prepared in the presence of two equivalents of base (sodium hydroxide), and purified by extraction with alcohol only, a residual amount of sodium remains. This sodium may be bound to the complex by chelate formation at the terminal positions as shown in Fig. 8. This hypothesis leads to the formulation of structures II-b or II-c for II prepared in this manner. These structures are in good agreement with the analyses of the complex. It is not likely that Na(I) has replaced Ni(II) in the complex chain since this involves sodium in an abnormal coordination number.

Further evidence for the polymeric nature of II was shown by comparison of the analyses of a number of samples of II, prepared under identical conditions except with respect to the relative amount of base used. The nickel content of the samples increases with use of increasing amounts of base when two equivalents or less of base are employed. Such an increase is explained by the analyses in terms of structures such as II-a, II-b and II-c, in which there are one or two more molecules of ligand than there are nickel atoms. In such

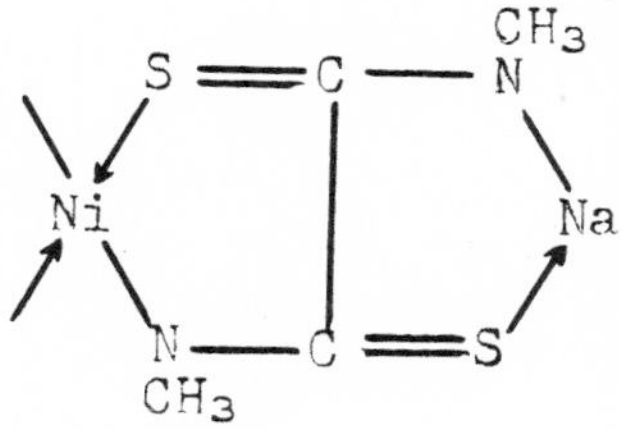

Figure 8

structures, the ratio of atoms of Ni(II) to molecules of ligand is always less than unity, but approaches it with increasing length of the complex chains.

The structures shown for complexes I and III follow from similar considerations.

N,N -Bis(carboxymethyl)-dithiooxamidonickel(II) differed from the other Ni(II) complexes in that it contained a large amount of water (9.6%) that could not be removed by exposure of the complex to phosphorus pentoxide for two days at 65° (0.01 mm). The infrared spectrum of complex XIII, in addition to the absorptions characteristic of the other Ni(II) complexes, shows absorptions that are characteristic of both the carboxylic group and carboxylate salt as well as water. These observations and the analyses suggest that XIII is a complex similar to the other Ni(II) complexes with respect to its chelated chain, but involving about half of the carboxyl groups in salt formation with Ni(II) cations. The unremovable water may be coordinated with Ni(II) cations. Figure 9 depicts one structure that accounts for the observed facts although it should be noted that there is no evidence available upon which to decide whether the carboxylic groups are neutralized in a regular or a random manner.

The magnetic susceptibility of one of the nickel(II) complexes, N,N'-dimethyldithiooxamidonickel(II), was found to be 2.4 Bohr magnetons.[11] This value is more than 0.4 Bohr magneton smaller than that often associated with paramagnetic tetra-coordinate nickel(II) complexes.[12] The depressed value may be explained on the basis that both planar and tetrahedral configurations about nickel(II) occur in II, with the latter heavily favored.

Preparation and Structure of Other Metal Complexes of Dithiooxamides. N,N'-Dimethyldithiooxamidocopper(II), XIV, was prepared in the same manner as its nickel analogue, II. Its analyses and infrared spectrum were in agreement with a structure, $[(CH_3N \cdot CS \cdot$

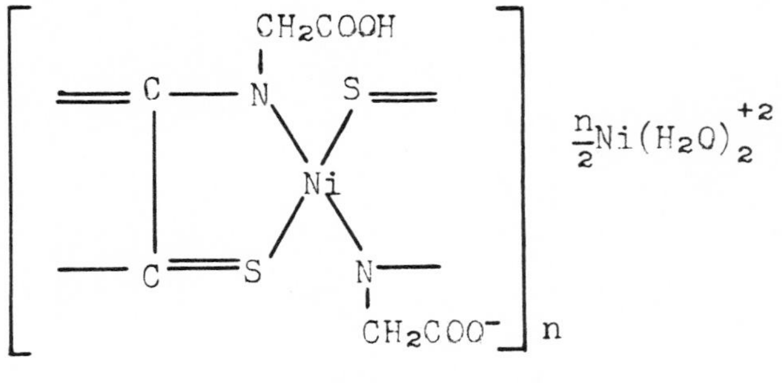

Figure 9

$CS \cdot NCH_3)Cu]_n$, analogous to that proposed by Barceló for dithiooxamidocopper(II), which is consistent with the observations that copper(II) salts and either dithiooxamide[13] or N,N'-bis[3-(dimethylamino)-propyl]-dithiooxamide[14] react in equimolar proportions.

Zinc(II) salts gave rise to the complexes listed in Table 2. These complexes were prepared and purified in 70–85% yields by the same methods described earlier for nickel(II) complexes. Reactions between zinc(II) ions and the dithiooxamides were noticeably slower than those-with nickel(II) or copper(II) ions.

N,N'-Dioctadecyldithiooxamidozinc(II), XV, was prepared using a 2:1 molar ratio of zinc salt to ligand with two equivalents of triethylamine as the base. Figure 7 ($R = CH_3(CH_2)_{17}$-) represents a possible structure for this complex that agrees closely with its analyses, and is consistent with its infrared spectrum and properties. Preparation of this N,N'-dialkyldithiooxamidozinc(II) is in contrast with the recent report[15] that N,N'-dimethyldithiooxamide is unreactive towards Zn(II) ions.

The infrared spectra of complexes XVI and XVII show absorptions due to both carboxyl groups and carboxylate salts. These results, supported by the analyses, suggest that in the carboxyalkyl complexes zinc participates in two ways—by chelation with the dithiooxamide ligands as it does in complex XV, and by salt formation with part of the carboxyl groups. It may be significant that in complex XVI, which contains a large amount of water that cannot be removed by the usual drying techniques, there exists the possibility of chelation of the Zn(II) cation with the ligand group, $(-\overset{|}{N}-CH_2-COO-)^-$. In complex XVII, which contains only trace amounts of water, chelation of Zn(II) cations with the ligand, $(-\overset{|}{N}-(CH_2)_5-COO-)^=$, is unlikely. This hypothesis is supported by the fact that in the infrared spectrum of XVI no N-H absorption can be detected, whereas in the spectrum of XVII there is high N-H absorption.

N,N'-bis[3-(dimethylamino)-propyl]-dithiooxamidozinc(II) retained an irreducible amount of chloride ion (Table 2) that could not be removed by techniques that were successful for the purification of the other zinc complexes, which were also prepared from zinc chloride. A structure that accounts for this fact, agrees with the analyses, and is compatible with the infrared spectrum of complex XVIII, is shown in Fig. 10.

One further zinc complex, (XIX), has been prepared from the polymeric product of reaction of dithiooxamide and 1,4-cyclohexane-bis-(methylamine). The low zinc content of XIX suggests that under the

TABLE 2: DITHIOOXAMIDOZINC(II) COMPLEXES

No.	Zinc Complexes of a Dithiooxamide, $RNH \cdot CS \cdot CS \cdot NHR$, where R is:	Color	Analyses Calcd. Found or (Found)							
			C	H	N	S	Zn	H$_2$O	Cl
XV	$CH_3(CH_2)_{17}$—	Tan			4.07	9.30	9.51		
					4.50	8.58	9.76	0.2	
XVI	$HOOCCH_2$—	Light Gray			7.22	16.98	29.18	8.6	
XVII	$HOOC(CH_2)_5$—	Pale Yellow			5.98	14.87	17.78	0.5	
XVIII	$(CH_3)_2NCH_2CH_2CH_2$—	Cream	38.30	6.40	14.81	16.95	20.60	1.06	2.08
			38.96	6.04	14.88	17.44	20.40	1.0	1.79
XIX	—$NHCH_2$—[cyclohexyl]—CH_2—	Pale Yellow			12.18	21.32	9.90		

TABLE 3: DITHIOOXAMIDOCADMIUM(II) COMPLEXES

No.	Cadmium Complexes of Dithiooxamides, RNH·CS·CS·NHR, where R is:	Color	Structure
XX	CH₃—	Yellow	$[(CH_3NCSCSNCH_3)Cd]_4$, $CH_3NHCSCSNHCH_3$
XXI	(cyclohexyl)	Yellow	$[\text{(cyclohexyl)}-NCSCSN-\text{(cyclohexyl)}-Cd]_4$, (cyclohexyl)$-NHCSCSNH-$(cyclohexyl)
XXII-A	(furfuryl)$-CH_2-$	Yellow	$[\text{(furyl)}-CH_2NCSCSNCH_2-\text{(furyl)}-Cd]_7$, (furyl)$-CH_2NHCSCSNHCH_2-$(furyl)
XXII-B	(furfuryl)$-CH_2-$	Yellow	$[\text{(furyl)}-CH_2NCSCSNCH_2-\text{(furyl)}-Cd]_n$

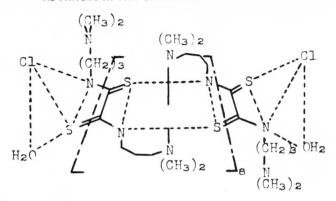

Figure 10

experimental conditions used, some of the chelating ligands were rendered inaccessible to Zn(II) ions by enclosure within particles of the polymeric starting material.

Four dithiooxamidocadmium(II) complexes have been prepared, three of which are listed in Table 3. The fourth complex, that of dithiooxamide itself, slowly decomposes on standing at room temper ature[1] to yield, among other products, cadmium sulfide and hydrogen sulfide. These complexes were prepared by admixture of hot alcohol or acetone solutions of equimolar amounts of the reactants and two equivalents of sodium acetate. Reaction took place immediately. Complexes XX, XXI and XXII-*A* were isolated as soon as addition of the reactants was complete, but complex XXII-*B* was not separated for a day.

The structures given in Table 3 are in close agreement with the results of analyses and the infrared spectra of the complexes. The differences in analyses of XXII-*A* and XXII-*B* suggest that formation of longer complex chains is favored by a longer reaction time. The structure given for XXII-*B* implies that the polymer is long enough so that a deviation from unity of the ratio of the number of dithiooxamide molecules to cadmium atoms cannot be detected.

Two cobalt complexes were made by the same procedures used for nickel(II) complexes. The formulas given in Table 4 are in agreement with the analyses and infrared spectra. A structure that would conform to these formula is shown on page 361.

These results are in agreement with the recent report by Jacobs and Yoe[14] that *N,N′*-bis[3-(dimethylamino)propyl]-dithiooxamide and cobalt(II) salts react in 3 : 2 molar proportions to give a cobalt(III) complex.

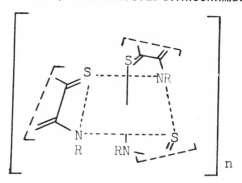

Figure 11

TABLE 4: DITHIOOXAMIDOCOBALT(III) COMPLEXES

No.	Cobalt(III) Complexes of Dithiooxamides, RNH·CS·CS·NHR, where R is:	Color	Formula
XXIII	CH_3—	Olive-Brown	$[(CH_3NCSCSNCH_3)_2Co]_n$
XXIV	$CH_3(CH_2)_{11}$—	Red-Brown	$[(C_{12}H_{25}NCSCSNC_{12}H_{25})_{3/2}Co]_n$

Two platinum(IV) complexes of N,N'-dioctadecyldithiooxamide were obtained by reaction of chloroplatinic acid, the dithiooxamide and sodium acetate in the molar ratios shown in Table 5. The products precipitated from refluxing, aqueous, alcoholic solutions of the reactants were purified by several recrystallizations from alcoholic benzene.

Although the low melting points and appreciable solubility in benzene are evidence that these complexes, unlike all of the others re-

TABLE 5: N,N'-DIOCTADECYLDITHIOOXAMIDOPLATINUM(IV) COMPLEXES

No.	H_2PtCl_6 :	Molar Ratio $\dfrac{C_{18}H_{37}NHCS}{C_{18}H_{37}NHCS}$: CH_3COONa		M.P.	Color	Analyses			
						N	S	Pt	Cl
XXV	1 :	2 :	4	87–89°	Red-Brown	4.86	8.12	12.59	0.3
XXVI*	1 :	1 :	2	90–92°	Dark Red		7.56	15.28	0.5

*XXVI contains 0.34% water.

TABLE 6: SOLUBILITIES OF DITHIOOXAMIDOMETAL COMPLEXES AT 25°C

Metal	Solvent Complex	5% HCl	5% NaOH	Conc. H$_2$SO$_4$	Conc. HNO$_3$	Dimethyl-formamide	Ethanol, Acetone, Benzene, CCl$_4$
Zn(II)	XV	i.	i	i.-sol. on warming	sl.s	i	i
	XVI	sl.s	s.	s.		i	i
	XVII	i	s.(slowly)	s.(slowly)		i	i
	XVIII	s.	i	s.		i	i
	XIX	i	i	s.	s.	i	i
Cu(II)	XIV	i	i	s. (yellow solution that turns green)	s.(yellow solution that turns green)	i	i
Cd(II)	XX	i	i	s.(slowly)	s., gas evol.	i	i
	XXI	i	i	s.(slowly)	s.	i	i
	XXII-A	i	i	s. black tar	s.	i	i
Co(III)	XXIII	i	i	s. black tar with yellow solution turning red	sl.s.-only after 45 min.	i	i
Pt(IV)	XXIV	i	i	i	sl.s.	i	i
	XXV						s
	XXVI						s

ported here, are probably not polymeric, the analytical and spectral data are not sufficient to permit the assignment of exact structures. There is spectral evidence that substantial chelation of Pt(IV) with the ligand has taken place, with Pt-N bonds replacing N-H bonds. The weak N-H absorption visible in the spectra of both XXV and XXVI is further evidence that these complexes are not composed of large polymeric structures, since such absorption would be associated with molecules of ligand that are chelated to only one Pt(IV) atom.

Properties of the Metal Complexes of Dithiooxamides. Properties of the Ni(II) complexes have previously been described in detail.[11] It is sufficient to say here that they are all solids with high decomposition points and are insoluble in water, moderately strong acids and most organic solvents. They are decomposed by concentrated sulfuric acid, and are slightly soluble in a few organic solvents, such as pyridine and dimethylformamide. These properties are, of course, modified by changes in the N-substituents. N,N'-Bis-(carboxymethyl)-dithiooxamidionickel(II), (XIII), for example, readily dissolves in 5% alkali and is slightly soluble in 5% hydrochloric acid.

Qualitative observations of the solubility characteristics of other metal complexes are summarized in Table 6. The Pt(IV) complexes were the only ones observed to be appreciably soluble in organic solvents. The alkaline solutions of the two Zn(II) complexes with carboxyl groups, XVI and XVII, can be acidified and the uncomplexed dithiooxamides recovered therefrom.

In addition to N,N'-dimethyldithiooxamidonickel(II),[11] all of the Cd(II) and Pt(IV) complexes have X-ray diffraction patterns which indicate crystallinity. The other complexes have not been examined in this respect.

The melting or decomposition points of a number of the complexes have been observed and are summarized in Table 7. The Ni(II) complexes, which were reported earlier,[11] are not included. Only the Pt(IV) complexes are found to melt without decomposition. The difference in decomposition points of XXII-A and XXII-B supports the hypothesis advanced earlier on their relative molecular size.

Recently, two spectral ranges, 6.51–6.70μ and 11.09–11.51μ, were found to be characteristic for N——C=S absorptions in the infrared spectra of N,N'-disubstituted dithiooxamides.[16] In several of these compounds N——C=S absorptions were absent in the 11.09–11.51μ range, but appeared instead in the range, 8.30–9.10μ. All of the complexes reported here exhibit N——C=S absorption in the 6.51–6.70μ range. In addition, all of the Pt(IV) and Cd(II) complexes, a majority

TABLE 7: DECOMPOSITION* AND MELTING POINTS OF COMPLEXES

Metal	Complex	M.P. or Dec. Pt.	Observations
Cu(II)	XIV	290–292°	Color of solid darkens and amber liquid distills at 290°.
Zn(II)	XV	108–125°, 134°	Solid decomposes to opaque amber glass at 108–125°, particularly at 124–125°. Glass becomes clear at 134°.
	XVI	>350°	
	XVII	230–255°	Material turns dark brown over this range.
	XVIII	240–242°	Decomposes to black tar with gas evolution.
	XIX	468°	Decomposes to black tar. Color darkens at 220°
Cd(II)	XX	>300°	Color of solid lightens above 200°.
	XXI	309–310°	Decomposes to brown tar.
	XXII-A	190–191°	Decomposes to black tar.
	XXII-B	199–203°	Decomposes to black tar.
Co(III)	XXIII	300–550°	The color of the material darkens over a wide range of lower temperatures, becoming black by 550°. No liquefaction.
	XXIV	291°	Decomposes to black tar.
Pt(IV)	XXV	87–89°	Red melt. No decomposition.
	XXVI	90–92°	Red melt. No decomposition.

*All decomposition points are observed on samples heated from room temperature at the approximate rate of 2–3°/min.

of the Ni(II) complexes, and all but one Zn(II) complex show N—C=S absorptions in the 11.09–11.51μ range. Three Ni(II) complexes have long wave length N—C=S absorptions just outside of this range: II (11.57μ), III (11.55μ), and V (11.52μ). One Ni(II) complex, XII, shows a shift in absorption of the N—C=S group from this range to the 8.30–9.10μ range. The Cu(II) and Co(III) complexes, as well as one Zn(II) complex, XV, have their lower-energy N—C=S absorptions at longer wave lengths than 11.51μ.

A sufficient number of Ni(II) complexes have been studied to permit observation of a family spectral characteristic. Ni(II) complexes with aliphatic or aralkyl substituents have spectra in which both N—C=S absorptions are at longer wave lengths than in the parent ligands. In the case of Ni(II) complexes that have substituents with functional groups, the $\Delta\lambda_{NCS}$ values are irregular—some shifts are to shorter and some to longer wave lengths.

REFERENCES

1. P. Rây and R. M. Ray, *J. Indian Chem. Soc.*, **3**, 118 (1926).
2. R. N. Hurd and G. DeLaMater, *Chem. Revs.*, **61**, 45 (1961).
3. A. J. Chalk and J. F. Smith, *Nature*, **174**, 802 (1954).

4. B. Long, P. Markey, and P. Wheatley, *Acta Cryst.*, **7**, 140 (1954); cf. T. A. Scott, Jr., Ph.D. dissertation, State College of Washington, 1957 (*Dissertation Abstr.*, **18**, 90 (1958)).
5. J. Barceló, *Spectrochim. Acta*, **10**, 245 (1958).
6. R. A. Jensen, *Z. anorg. Chem.*, **252**, 227 (1944).
7. J. Xaviar and P. Ray, *J. Indian Chem. Soc.*, **35**, 432 (1958).
8. J. G. Miller and T. M. Brody, *J. Pharmacol. Exptl. Therap.*, **121**, 43 (1957).
9. R. P. Yaffe and A. F. Voight, *J. Am. Chem. Soc.*, **74**, 3163 (1952).
10. W. D. Jacobs, *Anal. Chem.*, **32**, 512 (1960).
11. R. N. Hurd, G. DeLaMater, G. McElheny, and L. V. Peiffer, *J. Am. Chem. Soc.*, **82**, 4454 (1960).
12. J. C. Bailar, Jr., *The Chemistry of the Coordination Compounds*, Reinhold Publishing Co., New York, 1956, pp. 360, 602.
13. I. V. Tananaev and S. Y. Levitman, *Zhur. Anal. Khim.*, **4**, 212 (1949).
14. W. D. Jacobs and J. H. Yoe, *Anal. Chim. Acta*, **20**, 435 (1959).
15. J. Xaviar and P. Ray, *J. Indian Chem. Soc.*, **35**, 590 (1958).
16. R. N. Hurd, G. DeLaMater, G. McElheny, R. Turner, and V. H. Wallingford, *J. Org. Chem.*, **26**, in press.

THE INERT GASES AS POTENTIAL LIGANDS

N. N. GREENWOOD and A. J. OSBORN

Department of Chemistry
The University
Nottingham, England

The inert gases form moderately stable clathrate compounds,[1,2] but all attempts to involve the outer electrons in true chemical bonding have so far been unsuccessful. Thus, earlier claims to have produced compounds with metals in a glow discharge have been refuted,[2] though there is spectroscopic evidence for unstable ionic species such as He_2^+ and HeH^+. The latter compound suggests that, under favourable circumstances, the inert gases might be able to function as ligands to particularly powerful electron acceptors. Moreover, the inert gases are isoelectronic with the halide ions which are known to form a variety of coordination compounds.

Boron trifluoride was at one time reported to form a series of adducts with argon at low temperatures and high pressures,[3] but a reinvestigation of the system showed that the liquids were, in fact, immiscible and formed no compounds.[4] Krypton and xenon have lower ionization potentials than argon but these, too, were immiscible with boron trifluoride.[4] At the time these measurements were made, boron trifluoride was regarded as the strongest electron acceptor available, but more recent thermochemical measurements have shown that boron trichloride and tribromide are stronger acceptors, the sequence being $BF_3 < BCl_3 < BBr_3$.[5,6] A preliminary investigation showed that xenon was completely miscible with an equimolar amount of either boron trichloride or tribromide and it was therefore decided to study these systems more fully to see whether this increased miscibility implied some chemical interaction.

The phase diagram of the system boron tribromide-xenon shows a simple eutectic at $-116°$ and 97.5% of xenon. The melting points of the components were boron tribromide $-46.4°$, xenon $-112.6°$. As the vapour pressure of xenon is 13 atm at the melting point of boron tribromide, it was necessary, over most of the composition range, to seal individual mixtures of appropriate composition into high-pressure glass tubes for observation, and to correct for the amount of xenon in the gas phase. Points on the liquidus curve when plotted as log

366

(mole fraction of BBr_3) against $1/T\,^{\circ}K$ showed that the heat of solution of solid boron tribromide in liquid xenon was 4.06 kcal mole^{-1} in the range 3–20 mole % of boron tribromide. When allowance is made for the heat of fusion of boron tribromide and its heat of dilution, this low value indicates very little chemical interaction. Liquid-liquid immiscibility was not observed under any conditions of temperature or pressure studied.

The phase diagram of the system boron trichloride-xenon had a eutectic at $-137.5\,^{\circ}$ and 73.7% of xenon. Points on the liquidus indicated that the partial molal heats of solution of boron trichloride was in the eutectic melt 2.5 kcal mole^{-1} (cf. heat of fusion of xenon, 0.55 kcal mole^{-1}; heat of fusion of boron trifluoride, 1.0 kcal mole^{-1}).[7]

An interesting phenomenon was observed in the boron trichloride-xenon system at compositions above 65% of xenon. The solid-mixture first melted at the solidus temperature and the amount of liquid continued to increase as the temperature was raised until all the solid had just melted (freezing point). At this stage the system consisted of two liquid phases separated by a flat meniscus which disappeared about $0.1\,^{\circ}$ above the freezing point. There is thus incipient formation of two liquid phases with a critical solution temperature just above the freezing point of the mixture. The limited mutual solubility of liquid and solid boron trichloride in liquid xenon was further shown by the fact that, although successive small additions of boron trichloride to xenon rapidly lowered the melting point of the solvent ($-112.6\,^{\circ}$), the mixture could not be liquified completely until the melting point of boron trichloride ($-108\,^{\circ}$) was approached. As a result, the phase diagram showed a spurious maximum at 93% of xenon ($-107.5\,^{\circ}$), but this does not imply the existence of a compound $BCl_3 \cdot 13Xe$ melting at the same temperature as pure boron trichloride.

The preceding phase studies give fairly conclusive evidence for the lack of chemical interaction between xenon and the heavier boron trihalides. However, the most direct evidence for the incipient formation of chemical bonds would come from Raman spectra. The boron trihalides are planar molecules, point group D_{3h}, with three Raman-active fundamentals, viz., the totally symmetric stretching mode $\nu_1(A_1')$ and two doubly degenerate modes $\nu_3(E')$ and $\nu_4(E')$. A tetrahedral molecule of the type $Xe \longrightarrow BX_3$, point group C_{3v}, would have six Raman-active modes: ν_1, ν_2, ν_3, all totally symmetric (A_1), and ν_4, ν_5, ν_6, all doubly degenerate (E). Accordingly spectra were taken of liquid boron trichloride and tribromide, and of liquid 1:1 mixtures of xenon with boron trichloride (at $-100\,^{\circ}$) and boron tribromide (at $-65\,^{\circ}$). There was no detectable difference in the spectra when xenon was added and no new lines were observed, implying negligible tendency for xenon to coordinate. Indeed, the Raman experiments provide an even more sensitive method of detecting incipient bond formation since any tendency of the boron atom to move out of the plane of the three halogen atoms would result in a splitting of the ν_1 mode due to the differing masses of the two boron isotopes. No such splitting of the boron trichloride line at 471 cm^{-1} or the boron tribromide line at 279 cm^{-1} was detected. This result, incidentally, also implies that there is no detectable tendency for the boron trihalides to dimerize in the liquid state at low temperatures.

Discussion

The immiscibility of xenon with boron trifluoride over a large range of composition,[4] the tendency towards immiscibility with boron trichloride at low concentrations near the freezing point, and the complete miscibility of xenon with boron tribromide over the whole composition range calls for some comment. Using the Hildebrand Theory[8] it is possible to calculate the critical solution temperature, T_c, of two liquids from the relation

$$2RT_c \simeq \tfrac{1}{2}(V_1 + V_2)(\delta_1 - \delta_2)^2 \tag{1}$$

where R is the gas constant, V_1 and V_2 are the molar volumes, and δ_1 and δ_2 are solubility parameters defined by the relations

$$\delta \simeq [(\Delta H_{vap} - RT/V]^{\frac{1}{2}} \tag{2}$$

and

$$d|\ln|\delta/dt \simeq -1.25 \ \alpha \tag{3}$$

where ΔH_{vap} is the heat of vapourization at low pressures and α is the coefficient of expansion of the liquid. Values of solubility parameters calculated in this way are given in Table 1. Application of equation (1) then shows that an equimolar mixture of boron trifluoride and xenon is expected to be miscible at 170°K whereas, in fact, it is immiscible.* Likewise, the other boron trihalides would be expected to form a one-phase equimolar mixture with xenon. The reason for this "anomalous" immiscibility is not clear, but it is interesting to note that boron trifluoride and boron tribromide themselves have been reported to form a two-phase liquid system[9] despite the similarity in their solubility parameters (see Table 1).

---

*This observation[4] was confirmed. A 1:1 mixture was sealed in a pressure tube and allowed to warm slowly. At $-100°$ there was a well-defined convex liquid-liquid interface; this became flatter as the temperature was raised and disappeared at $-79.8°$.

TABLE 1: SOLUBILITY PARAMETERS, δ, AT $T\,^{\circ}K$

Liquid	Kr	Xe	Xe	BF$_3$	BCl$_3$	BCl$_3$	BBr$_3$
$T\,^{\circ}K$	121	170	210	170	170	210	210
δ	7.5	7.9	6.8	7.9	9.2	8.5	9.8
V ml	34	43	48	43	72	76	87

In discussing reasons for the non-existence of coordination complexes of the inert gas with boron trihalides several factors must be considered. These include (1) steric effects, (2) electronegativity of the ligand, (3) influence of bond length on bond energy, and (4) lattice energies. It can be said at once that steric effects play little part. A simple radius ratio calculation shows that there is ample room even for four iodine atoms around boron (cf. carbon tetraiodide) and a scale model indicates that the molecule XeBBr$_3$ would be in no way strained (cf. the isoelectronic molecule ICBr$_3$, which is a yellow solid melting at $35\,^{\circ}$ with decomposition).[10]

In a general way, ease of complex formation via a σ bond decreases with increasing electronegativity of the ligand, e.g., $N > O > F > Ne$, and substituents which increase the availability of electrons at the donor atom increase the strength of the ligand. Thus, the halide ions are much stronger electron pair donors than are the isoelectronic inert gases because of the effect of the negative charge in increasing the electron availability (decreasing the electronegativity). This can be seen by comparing the energy, in e.v., required to remove two electrons from the halide ions and from the neutral inert gas atoms.

$$F^- \quad 3.62 + 17.42 = 21.04 \qquad Ne \quad 21.56 + 41.07 = 62.63$$
$$Cl^- \quad 3.83 + 13.01 = 16.84 \qquad Ar \quad 15.76 + 27.62 = 43.38$$
$$Br^- \quad 3.54 + 11.84 = 15.38 \qquad Kr \quad 14.00 + 26.4 \;\; = 40.4$$
$$I^- \quad 3.24 + 10.44 = 13.68 \qquad Xe \quad 12.13 + 21.1 \;\; = 33.2$$

On this measure of donor strength xenon is some 50% weaker than the fluoride ion, but two other factors intervene to reduce the donor strength still further, viz., the decrease of bond strength with increase in bond distance, and the decrease in coulomb lattice energy. These factors ensure, for example, that potassium tetrafluoroborate is more stable than the tetrachloroborate or tetrabromoborate: $K^+BF_4^- > K^+BCl_4^- > K^+BBr_4^-$. The absence of ionic lattice forces in a compound such as XeBCl$_3$ would reduce its stability still further. A relevant comparison can be made here with the hydrogen halides in which ionic forces are also absent. Thus, hydrogen fluoride does not coordinate with boron trifluoride,[11] nor does hydrogen chloride with boron trichloride.[12]

In summary we may say that the absence of complexes of xenon with boron trichloride and tribromide is not surprising, but that the experiments outlined above serve as a useful test of the donor ability of xenon to electron acceptors which are more powerful than boron trifluoride.

Experimental

Xenon was 99-100% pure, the main impurity being krypton. The boron trihalides were commercial samples which were purified by treatment with mercury and followed by repeated low-temperature fractionation in a vacuum line. Mixtures of appropriate composition were synthesized gas-volumetrically and condensed into glass pressure-vessels of known volume. Temperatures were measured with a 10-junction copper-constantan thermocouple and Pye-vernier potentiometer. Readings were precise to 0.005° but thermostatic control at low temperatures and reproducibility of readings were $\pm 0.1°$.

Samples for Raman spectra were sealed in round-ended tubes capable of withstanding high pressures. Exposures were made in Dr. L. A. Woodward's laboratory[13] by Dr. R. A. Plane and we would like to express our appreciation of their help and interest.

REFERENCES

1. H. M. Powell and M. Guter, *Nature,* **164,** 240 (1949); H. M. Powell, *J. Chem. Soc.,* **1950,** 298, 300, 468.
2. J. G. Waller, *Nature,* **186,** 429, (1960), and refs. therein.
3. H. S. Booth and K. S. Willson, *J. Am. Chem. Soc.,* **57,** 2273 (1935).
4. E. Wiberg and K. Karbe, *Z. anorg. Chem.,* **256,** 307 (1948).
5. H. C. Brown and R. R. Holmes, *J. Am. Chem. Soc.,* **78,** 2173 (1956).
6. N. N. Greenwood and P. G. Perkins, *J. Chem. Soc.,* **1960,** 1141.
7. N. B. S. Circular 500, "Selected Values of Chemical Thermodynamic Properties."
8. J. H. Hildebrand and R. L. Scott, *The Solubility of Nonelectrolytes,* (3rd. ed), Reinhold Publishing Co., 1950.
9. B. A. Cooke and H. A. E. MacKenzie, *J. South African Chem. Inst.,* **6,** 4 (1953).
10. W. M. Dehn, *J. Am. Chem. Soc.,* **31,** 1221 (1909).
11. D. A. McCaulay and D. P. Lien, *ibid.,* **73,** 2013, (1951).
12. D. R. Martin, *J. Phys. Colloid Chem.,* **51,** 1400 (1947).
13. L. A. Woodward, J. R. Hall, R. N. Dixon, and N. Shepherd, *Spectrochem. Acta,* **15,** 249 (1959).

THE KINETICS OF FAST SOLVENT SUBSTITUTION IN METAL COMPLEX FORMATION

M. EIGEN

Max Planck Institut für physikalische Chemie
Göttingen, Germany

In recent years new techniques for the investigation of very rapid reactions in solution have become available. As a consequence, a detailed study of a number of important reaction mechanisms has been possible. In the present paper, applications with respect to the problem of metal complex formation are reported. The experimental information has been obtained by means of relaxation techniques, which are described elsewhere.[1] The studies cover the time range between 1 second and fractions of a millimicrosecond. They led to a detailed analysis of the substitution mechanism in metal-ligand recombination.

The maximum speed by which two partners in solution can recombine is limited by the rate of diffusive encounters. This process can approximately be expressed by a second order rate constant which has the order of magnitude of 10^9 to 10^{10} M^{-1} sec^{-1}.[2] According to our present knowledge, the rates of metal-ligand recombination are usually appreciably below this limit. Only the solvent ions H^+ and OH^- (excess and defect protons) are exceptions because of their special kinetic properties in H-bonded media.[3] These ions are able to penetrate the ordered solvent structure in the coordination spheres of their reaction partners by a special jump mechanism. In all other cases, any recombination mechanism in aqueous solution requires the substitution of water molecules from the coordination spheres of the reacting partners. Since the water molecules in the inner coordination spheres of metal ions usually are bound quite tightly, this step of substitution may be slow with respect to the elementary step of diffusion and thus may represent the rate-limiting step of the total reaction. Evidence for this conclusion has been obtained from studies of a variety of metal ions and ligands with quite different tendencies of complex formations. The reaction mechanism shows certain features which will allow us to draw some general conclusions.

Experimental

The following measurements have been carried out:

1. Sound absorption measurements[4] in the frequency range of ω (= $2\pi\nu$) = 10^5 to 2×10^9 c/s (corresponding to a time range of 10^{-5} to 5×10^{-10} sec). Complete relaxation spectra, caused by perturbation of metal complex equilibria in the sound wave, have been recorded. If the populations of ligands in the different coordination spheres of the metal ion show almost an equipartition—which is the case for some week aquo-complexes—the relaxation spectrum is representative of the coupled mechanism of stepwise substitution and yields the rate constants of all individual reaction steps.

2. Fast spectrophotometric rate measurements in the time range between 1 and 10^{-6} sec, using the temperature jump method.[5] This method has been employed throughout in the investigation of stronger complexes having chelate structures, where the final step of complex formation (spectral change) is dominant.

3. Measurements of the dispersion of the dissociation field effect in the time range of 10^{-4} to 10^{-7} sec, using a high electric-field pulse technique.[6] This method has been applied only to electrolytes of simple type, such as $HgCl_2$.

The following systems have been studied:

1. Phosphate and uramil-diacetate complexes of alkaline ions (Li^+, Na^+, K^+).[7]

2. Sulfate-, thiosulfate-, chromate-, phosphate-, (ATP, ADP)-, acetate-, EDTA (or similar)-complexes of alkaline earth and earth metal ions (Be^{2+}, Mg^{2+}, Ca^{2+}, Al^{3+}; ref. cf. Table 1).

3. Complexes of divalent transition metal ions (Mn^{2+}, Fe^{2+}, Co^{2+} Ni^{2+}, Cu^{2+}, Zn^{2+}) with some ligands listed under (2) (ref. cf. Table 1) halide complexes of Fe^{3+} (ref. cf., Table 2) and Hg^{2+}.[8]

Since these studies are still under way, the complete tables of data will be completed currently. The following results, however, already allow some general conclusions.

Results

Empirically, two groups of mechanisms (with intermediates) have been found so far.

1. In the first group, the rate-limiting step of complex formation for a given metal ion is fairly independent of the nature of the entering ligand, even if the complex stabilities for the different ligands vary over many orders of magnitude. The ligand specificity, as expressed by the stability constant, then occurs only in the rate of dis-

TABLE 1: RATE CONSTANTS OF H_2O SUBSTITUTION $[\vec{k}$ in $(sec^{-1})]$

$$Me(H_2O)_x \cdots L \; \rightleftharpoons \; MeL \cdot (H_2O)_{x-1} \cdots H_2O$$

(Refs. 9 to 16)

	SO_4^{2-}	$S_2O_3^{2-}$	CrO_4^{2-}	ATP^{4-}	ADP^{4-}	Y^{n-} *
Al^{3+}	~ 1					
Be^{2+}	$1 \cdot 10^2$					
Mg^{2+}	$1 \cdot 10^5$	$1 \cdot 10^5$	$1 \cdot 10^5$	$\sim 10^5$	$\sim 10^5$	$\sim 10^5$
Ca^{2+}			$1 - 2 \cdot 10^7$	$\gtrsim 10^7$	$\gtrsim 10^7$	$\sim 10^7$
Mn^{2+}	$3 \cdot 10^6$					
Fe^{2+}	$\sim 1 \cdot 10^6$					
Co^{2+}	$2 \cdot 10^5$					$\sim 2 \cdot 10^5$
Ni^{2+}	$1 \cdot 10^4$					$1 \cdot 10^4$
Cu^{2+}	$\gtrsim 10^7$					

* Y = protonated metal-phthaleine[17] for Mg^{2+} and Ca^{2+};
Y = $HEDTA^{3-}$ for Ni^{2+} and Co^{2+};
T = 298°K, ionic strength 0.1 M.

sociation (apart from some influences of general ionic interaction according to the respective charge type). Table 1 shows some first-order rate constants (related to the rate-limiting step of substitution) for a number of examples belonging to this group. For weak complexes these values have been directly measured; for strong complexes they have been obtained from overall rates corrected for the electrostatic interaction in the encounter complex. For comparison, the ions Be^{2+} and Al^{3+} are included in Table 1, although they do not belong to this group (cf. below). However, only a few studies have been conducted so far with these ions. All ions show another discrete reaction step with a rate constant around 10^8 to 10^9 sec^{-1}. This step is less characteristic for the different metal ions of the same charge type. It is due to the substitution in the outer coordination sphere. The rate of this substitution step still differs by a factor of about 10 from those of the elementary steps of diffusion, which cause a broad continuous relaxation spectrum with $\tau < 10^{-9}$ sec. For the alkaline ions the substitution in the inner sphere occurs so rapidly that a discrimination of two steps is not possible any more.[7]

The second group contains ions showing strong hydrolysis, such as Fe^{3+} (and also Be^{2+} and Al^{3+}). For these ions, the rate is strongly dependent on the acidity of the entering ligand, as is shown for some Fe^{3+} complexes in Table 2. Furthermore, there are several rate phenomena due to reactions of the hydroxo compounds. For Be^{2+} the effects of two higher nuclear complexes could be observed.[10] The feature of this group of ions is that the rate of hydrolysis (e.g.,

TABLE 2: OVERALL RATES OF Fe^{3+} – COMPLEX FORMATION

(Refs. 9, 18, 18, 20)

$\vec{k}$ in $[M^{-1} sec^{-1}]$

	Br^{-*}	$Cl^{-\dagger}$	SCN^-	$SO_4^{2-\ddagger}$	F^-
Fe^{3+}	1 ± 0.5	9.4 ± 1	127 ± 10	$(3 \pm 2) \cdot 10^3$	$4 \cdot 10^3$
$FeOH^{2+}$	$3 \cdot 10^4$	$\sim 10^4$	$\sim 10^4$	$\sim 3 \cdot 10^5$	—

* I = 1.6 M.
† I = 0.6 M.
‡ I = 1 M.

splitting of a H_2O molecule in the encounter complex) exceeds appreciably the possible rate of substitution in the unhydrolyzed complex.

Discussion

Let us consider the first-mentioned group of reactions. It can be shown that the rate constants listed in Table 1 refer to the step of substitution of water molecules from the inner coordination sphere of the metal ions. It may be mentioned that these data, which are characteristic of the metal ion only—even if the stability constants for the different ligands range over many orders of magnitude—are also in general agreement with the NMR data for the exchange of labeled water molecules from metal ion coordination spheres obtained by Connick and co-workers.[21] These facts may throw some light on the mechanism.

For nucleophilic substitution two general mechanisms are commonly discussed, classified as S_N1 and S_N2, according to Hughes and Ingold (cf., Basolo and Pearson[22]). In the first mechanism (S_N1) substitution occurs via intermediate reduction of the coordination number with subsequent replacement by the ligand. In the other mechanism (S_N2), a second order process is involved consisting of the attack of the ligand with intermediate increase of the coordination number and subsequent loss of a water molecule. Both mechanisms, of course, represent only limiting cases and the actual process may be intermediate. It seems, however, that the data favour somewhat an S_N1-type of mechanism. Since the complex stability differs appreciably for the different ligands and since some of the ligands are even more weakly bound than water molecules,* one should expect

---

* This amounts in some cases to 1 order of magnitude.

for a pure S_N2 mechanism a much stronger ligand specificity than has actually been found. A clear decision, however, will require more precise data with a variety of different ligands. Small differences seem to be present, but these may be due also to steric effects, chelation, etc. It should be emphasized again, that the above classification is only a formal one; one may well expect some differences.

More information about the mechanism may be obtained by considering the individual values for different metal ions. At a first glance there is some proportionality to the radius of the metal ion, and a great deal of the activation energy involved in the substitution process will be of electrostatic nature. A quantitative comparison shows that there is no simple relationship between rate constant and ionic charge and radius as due to a simple ion-dipole interaction term of the form $ze_0\bar{\mu}/r^2$, where ze_0 is the charge, r the distance of H_2O from the metal ion, and $\bar{\mu}$ the effective (static and induced) dipole moment of the water molecule. At least three more terms have to be considered, as there are dipole-dipole interactions ($\sim \bar{\mu}^2/r^3$) causing fixed positions of H_2O in the coordination spheres, polarization work ($\sim \mu_i^2/\alpha$, with α = polarizability of the metal ion and μ_i induced dipole moment of H_2O) and van der Waals repulsion ($\sim 1/r^9$) (cf. the literature quoted in Ref. 22). The presence of these latter terms follows directly from comparing metal ions such as Al^{3+}, Be^{2+}, and Mg^{2+}.

If these details are taken into consideration, most divalent ions fit very well into the expected order according to their radius. This group includes the ions with the noble gas configuration and also some ions of the transition series: Co^{2+}, Fe^{2+}, Mn^{2+}. However, there are some exceptions.

Ni^{++} has the same (or slightly larger) radius as Mg^{2+}, but is one order of magnitude slower. From a classical point of view, such a difference could not be understood. It was however predicted by Pearson,[22] that among the series of divalent transition metals the spin-free d^8 system of Ni^{2+} should show an appreciable crystal-field stabilization in the transition state, regardless of whether the intermediate is a square pyramid complex (S_N1 mechanism) or pentagonal bipyramid complex (S_N2 mechanism). In contrast, the spin-free d^5, d^6 and d^7 systems of Mn^{2+}, Fe^{2+} and Co^{2+} should not show such a stabilization in the transition state and therefore should behave more analogously to ions with closed electron shells, as in fact is shown by the data in Table 1.

Another exception is presented by the Cu^{2+} ion (and probably also by Zn^{2+}, though more data still have to be collected). Cu^{2+} is known to form square planar rather than octahedral complexes as in the case of the ions mentioned above. Since it is possible to arrange 6 water molecules around a copper ion, there are two H_2O molecules (one above and one below the plane) which are less tightly bound and may be replaced even more easily than in a homogeneous spherical charge distribution. Cu^{2+} ions therefore react very rapidly. A slower reaction effect which previously was found[23] turned out to be due to hydrolysis.

In general, the rate data are more specific for the metal ion properties than are stability constants. This is due to the fact that the stability constant yields information about the competition between ligand and solvent molecule in the coordination sphere. It is well known that the stability constants do not always show a parallelism with the metal ion radius. For instance, Ca^{2+} forms some complexes which are more stable than Mg^{2+} complexes (e.g., EDTA), but other complexes which are less stable (metalphthaleine).[17] The phosphate complexes, on the other hand, which are of importance in certain enzymatic reactions, do not differ appreciably in their stability constants, although it is known that Ca^{2+} and Mg^{2+} show antagonistic activation effects. These may be of kinetic nature, since the rate constants differ by several orders of magnitude. Mechanisms for such activation processes in which either Ca^{2+} (consecutive process) or Mg^{2+} (competition process) is more active have been proposed.[12]

Another point may deserve some mention. It has been found that the exchange of labeled metal ions from strong complexes (such as Ni-EDTA[16]) is a quite slow process which can be followed by classical techniques. In these cases, the slowness of the process is not due to a slow exchange of water molecules, but to the slow dissociation of the chelate complex. The high value for the complex formation, as reported in Table 1, was obtained from such studies. The close agreement with the values from relaxation measurements strengthens the above argument: the rate of complex formation from hydrated divalent ions is a very rapid process which is mostly characteristic of the metal-aquo ion. The reverse reaction, the dissociation of the complex, contains then, in addition, the specific influences of the ligands.

The second group, represented by Fe^{3+} in Table 2, shows quite different behaviour. Here a strong dependence on the nature of the ligand is found also for the rates of complex formation. This dependence shows some parallelism to the acidity of the ligand which decreases in the order given in Table 2. Apparently, the rate-limiting step in these cases is a hydrolysis process. The rate of substitution for small and highly charged ions such as Fe^{3+} is relatively small. It is exceeded by many orders of magnitude by the rate of hydrolysis. From measurements in a larger pH-range it is known that hydroxo-complexes (such as $FeOH^{2+}$, cf. Table 2) show appreciably higher substitution rates. These, of course, have to be taken into consideration if the values for the substitution rates for unhydrolyzed species are determined. The values for Fe^{3+} in Table 2 are corrected in this way. Even then, they show the influence of ligand acidity. This dependence can be understood in the following way. The encounter complex includes configurations where metal ion and ligand are separated by just one water molecule. This molecule is split into H^+ (accepted by the ligand) and OH^- (accepted by the metal) much more rapidly than its substitution by the ligand can occur. This hydrolysis process is not expressed in the pH-dependence, since it involves both H^+ and OH^-. The substitution rate then corresponds to that of the hydroxocompound, but after completion H^+ and OH^- recombine again to a water molecule. It is obvious that such a "catalytic" substitution can occur only if the rate of hydrolysis is high with respect to the rate of normal substitution, which is not the case for most of the examples quoted in Table 1. Usually, the reaction mechanism in the latter group is further complicated by formation of higher nuclear hydroxo-complexes, of which only some have been identified.

It is hoped that further studies of this kind will help to clarify our picture of the mechanism of metal complex formation as well as of other reactions in solution.

REFERENCES

1. M. Eigen, L. DeMaeyer in *Technique of Organic Chemistry*, Vol. VIII (2nd ed.), New York, 1961, cf. also papers of L. DeMaeyer, M. Eigen, K. Tamm in *Z. Elektrochem.*, **64**, No. 1 (1960).
2. P. Debye, *Trans. Electrochem. Soc.*, **82**, 265 (1942).
3. M. Eigen and L. DeMaeyer, *Proc. Roy. Soc.*, **A 247**, 505 (1958).
4. M. Eigen and K. Tamm, *Z. Elektrochem.* (1961) (in press).
5. G. Czerlinski and M. Eigen, *Z. Elektrochem.*, **63**, 652 (1959) (cf. ref. 1).
6. M. Eigen, L. DeMaeyer and J. Schoen, *Z. Elektrochem.*, **59**, 483, 986 (1955).
7. M. Eigen, W. Kruse, G. Maass (to be published).
8. M. Eigen, E. Eyring (to be published).
9. H. Wendt, Dissertation, Göttingen, 1960.
10. H. Diebler and M. Eigen, *Z. phys. Chem. N.F.*, **20**, 299 (1959).
11. M. Eigen, *Z. Elektrochem.*, **64**, 115 (1960).
12. H. Diebler, M. Eigen and G. G. Hammes, *Z. Naturforschg.*, **15b**, 554 (1960).
13. M. Eigen and G. G. Hammes, *J. Am. Chem. Soc.*, **82**, 5951 (1960).

14. G. Czerlinski, H. Diebler and M. Eigen, *Z. phys. Chem. N.F.*, **19**, 246 (1959).
15. M. Eigen, G. Schwarz and G. Maass (to be published).
16. C. M. Cook and F. A. Long, *J. Am. Chem. Soc.*, **80**, 33 (1958).
17. G. Schwarzenbach, *Die komplexometrische Titration*, Stuttgart, 1957.
18. P. Matthies, H. Wendt (to be published).
19. J. F. Below, R. E. Connick and C. F. Coppel, *J. Am. Chem. Soc.*, **80**, 2961 (1958).
20. D. Pauli, W. Mac and F. Smith, *Canad. J. Chem.*, **38**, 567 (1960).
21. R. E. Connick and R. E. Poulson, *J. Chem. Phys.*, **30**, 759 (1959).
22. F. Basolo, G. G. Pearson, *Mechanisms of Inorganic Reactions*, New York, 1958.
23. M. Eigen, G. Kurtze, K. Tamm, *Z. Elektrochem.*, **57**, 103 (1953).

HIGH-SPEED DIGITAL COMPUTATIONS RELATING TO THE COMPLEXING OF A METAL ION[*]

Z. ZIMMERMAN HUGUS, JR.

Department of Chemistry
University of Minnesota
Minneapolis, Minnesota

The use of graphical methods[1] in the quantitative treatment of systems containing complexes has been extensive. While such methods admirably serve to summarize a large quantity of data or are useful in the estimation of concentrations of species present in interdependent chemical equilibria, they also possess distinct disadvantages.

First, while the derivation of equilibrium constants by graphical methods can be carried out on a wide variety of types of experimental data, such derivation is not unique; in fact, even ardent enthusiasts of graphical techniques scarcely can fail to admit the subjective nature of the treatment and, thus also, the subjective nature of the results. In addition, graphical methods yield no dependable measure of the reliability of derived parameters, e.g., equilibrium constants.

Thus, in a case where two or more investigators have studied the same system with divergent results or conclusions, the selection of the "best" parameters, e.g., equilibrium constants, relating to the system to be used in another connection is left to the personal judgement, or perhaps prejudice, of the selector. An objective measure of reliability would be useful even to an experienced person of considered judgement in such a process of selection.

Second, although graphical techniques can be profitably used in the estimation of interdependent equilibria, one can by only modestly increasing the number of such equilibria devise cases in which the use of graphical methods becomes excessively tedious.

The relatively recent expansion in the availability, size and speed of digital computing machinery offers, in principle at least, a most useful adjunct for the investigator in the field of the quantitative description of systems containing complexes. In the expectation that

---

[*]Grateful acknowledgment is made to Professor M. L. Stein, director, and to the staff of the Numerical Analysis Center of the University of Minnesota for their many kindnesses.

379

in the future many investigators of complexation will find occasion to employ digital computers, and particularly in view of the fact that the programming of such machinery is increasingly being couched in problem-oriented language, we present here some of our experiences in the use of a large-scale digital computer.

The computer we have used in our work is the Univac Scientific (ERA 1103) Computer of the University of Minnesota. This macnine employs a high-speed memory of 1024 cells and a magnetic drum memory of 16,384 cells. We have used throughout a floating-point interpretive routine for arithmetic, which restricts the number of significant decimal digits in a stored number to seven, but has not, we feel, affected our results due to round-off.

The problems discussed here are of twn types:

1. The computation of the species' concentrations in simultaneous interdependent chemical equilibria.

2. The reduction of experimental data so as to derive the most probable values of certain parameters including equilibrium constants, as well as the standard errors in these parameters.

Computation of Simultaneous Interdependent Chemical Equilibria

In conjunction with several studies in our laboratory it became necessary to carry out a number of computations of this type for homogeneous systems differing only in stoichiometry. For example, in a calorimetric investigation of the iron(III)-fluoride system by Dr. Paul Scott[2] it was necessary to compute in a number of cases the concentrations of ten species (*vide infra*). While such computations were tedious but tractable by hand computation, similar more complicated computations were apparent in our projected study of other systems. It was therefore decided to write a computer program that would relieve the burden of hand computation in those cases as well as to check the calculations of Dr. Scott for the iron(III)-fluoride system.

One can always choose a set of "components" (in the sense of the Phase Rule) from the reactions of which the remaining species can be derived. If m is the number of such components and n the total number of species in the system, then there are $n - m$ such reactions and these reactions are quantitatively described by $n - m$ equilibrium constants. In addition one has m stoichiometric mole balance conditions, which together with the $n - m$ equilibrium quotient conditions comprise a total of n equations in the n species concentrations. These equations are, however, non-linear in general and, moreover, elimination of the unknowns cannot in general be carried out systematically.

Since the many-fold repetition of a low-order process can readily be carried out on a computer, whereas a person by hand computation might prefer to use a high-order method with a minimum of repetition of the process, we chose to iterate a set of conditions common to all equilibria in homogeneous systems, namely, the mole balance conditions.

Denoting the concentration of components A, B and C by A, B and C and the concentration of the derived species $A_iB_jC_k$ by $A_iB_jC_k$ and the total or stoichiometric concentration of A, B and C by ΣA, ΣB and ΣC, we have then for the reaction forming $A_iB_jC_k$,

$$iA + jB + kC = A_iB_jC_k,$$

the equilibrium constant expression,

$$A_iB_jC_k = K_{ijk}A^iB^jC^k.$$

Here K_{ijk} is the usual concentration equilibrium constant and throughout we presume activity coefficient corrections to be unnecessary. There are $n - m$ such equilibrium constant expressions and these may be substituted into the mole balance relationships,

$$\Sigma A = A + \Sigma \, iA_iB_jC_k, \tag{1}$$

$$\Sigma B = B + \Sigma \, jA_iB_jC_k, \tag{2}$$

$$\Sigma C = C + \Sigma kA_iB_jC_k, \tag{3}$$

thus giving

$$\Sigma A = A + \Sigma \, i\,K_{ijk}A^iB^jC^k, \tag{1a}$$

$$\Sigma B = B + \Sigma \, j\,K_{ijk}A^iB^jC^k, \tag{2a}$$

$$\Sigma C = C + \Sigma k\,K_{ijk}A^iB^jC^k. \tag{3a}$$

The correct values of A, B and C will satisfy these relationships and having these correct values of the concentrations of A, B and C one can readily compute the concentrations of the derived species, viz., $A_iB_jC_k$.

All that need be done is to iteratively solve the equations (1a), (2a) and (3a). This can be accomplished, we have found, by the Newton-Raphson method[3] with certain modifications.

Denote by F_1, F_2 and F_3 the expressions:

$$F_1 = -\Sigma A + A + \Sigma \, i\,K_{ijk}A^iB^jC^k, \tag{1b}$$

$$F_2 = -\Sigma B + B + \Sigma \, j\,K_{ijk}A^iB^jC^k, \tag{2b}$$

$$F_3 = -\Sigma C + C + \Sigma k\,K_{ijk}A^iB^jC^k, \tag{3b}$$

and expanding each of these expressions about a value A_0, B_0, C_0 we have

$$F_1(A_0 + \delta A, B_0 + \delta B, C_0 + \delta C) = F_1(A_0, B_0, C_0) + (F_{1A}) \delta A + \quad (1d)$$

$$+ (F_{1B}) \delta B + (F_{1C}) \delta C + \dots$$

and so on, where (F_{1A}), etc., are the derivatives of F_1 with respect to A, etc., evaluated at A_0, B_0, C_0. If the higher-order terms quadratic in δA, δB and δC can be neglected, then the left side of equation $1d$ can be made arbitrarily small and we have an equation for δA, δB, δC resulting from (1d) and two more equations from the similar equations involving F_2 and F_3.

Written out the equations are:

$$(1 + \Sigma i^2 K_{ijk} A^i B^j C^k) \frac{\delta A}{A} + (\Sigma ij K_{ijk} A^i B^j C^k) \frac{\delta B}{B} +$$
$$(\Sigma ik K_{ijk} A^i B^j C^k) \frac{\delta C}{C} = -F_1, \quad (1e)$$

$$(\Sigma ij K_{ijk} A^i B^j C^k) \frac{\delta A}{A} + (1 + \Sigma j^2 K_{ijk} A^i B^j C^k) \frac{\delta B}{B} +$$
$$(\Sigma jk K_{ijk} A^i B^j C^k) \frac{\delta C}{C} = -F_2, \quad (2e)$$

$$(\Sigma ik K_{ijk} A^i B^j C^k) \frac{\delta A}{A} + (\Sigma jk K_{ijk} A^i B^j C^k) \frac{\delta B}{B} +$$
$$(1 + \Sigma k^2 K_{ijk} A^i B^j C^k) \frac{\delta C}{C} = -F_3. \quad (3e)$$

F_1, F_2 and F_3 are to be evaluated at A_0, B_0, C_0, some approximate value for the solution, and then the above set of linear algebraic equations (1e), (2e), (3e) can readily be solved for the fractional shifts in A, B and C, that is, $\frac{\delta A}{A}$, etc. From an initial set of values of A, B, C, namely A_0, B_0, C_0, one thus obtains a new set of values A_1, B_1, C_1 which, subject to certain restrictions, are an improvement in terms of decreasing F_1, F_2 and F_3, and using A_1, B_1, C_1 computes a new set of A_2, B_2, C_2 and so on. When the largest of the fractional shifts has become suitably small, the final set of values of A, B and C are used to compute the concentration of the other $n - m$ species.

In connection with a specific problem one must decide which species to choose as components. Ideally these should be major species, but this is not necessary; for example, in the Iron(III)-fluoride system we chose Fe^{+++}, F^- and H^+. In no case is F^- a major species, nor is Fe^{+++} in most of our cases.

In Table 1 are listed the coefficients for the various species in terms of the components, Fe^{+++}, F^- and H^+. It should be pointed out in particular that negative values of the coefficients are allowable and here, since water is present in abundance, the formation of $Fe(OH)^{++}$ is regarded as occurring by the reaction:

$$Fe^{+++} - H^+ = Fe(OH)^{++},$$

which is the formal equivalent of the commonly written reaction,

$$Fe(H_2O)_6^{+++} = Fe(H_2O)_5(OH)^{++} + H^+.$$

We find that starting with the total stoichiometric concentrations of iron, fluorine and hydrogen as the initial concentrations of Fe^{+++}, F^- and H^+, we converge to better than 1 part in 10^6 in no more than sixteen iterations. The actual computer time per stoichiometry is approximately two minutes. This time is increased over an optimum

TABLE 1: COEFFICIENTS IN THE EQUILIBRIA INVOLVED IN THE IRON(III)-FLUORIDE SYSTEM

Species	Component		
	Fe^{+++}	F^-	H^+
Fe^{+++}	1	0	0
$Fe(OH)^{++}$	1	0	-1
$Fe_2(OH)_2^{+4}$	2	0	-2
FeF^{++}	1	1	0
FeF_2^+	1	2	0
FeF_3	1	3	0
F^-	0	1	0
HF	0	1	1
HF_2^-	0	2	1
H^+	0	0	1

time by at least an order of magnitude since we use a floating-point routine for all arithmetic on our fixed-point machine and also because we must guard in difficult cases (and therefore in the general program) against both overflow and underflow (a number too large or too small to be properly stored in the machine). In the latter connection we compute $K_{ijk}A^iB^jC^k$ as

$$\exp\{\ln K_{ijk} + i\ln A + j\ln B + k\ln C\},$$

which necessitates then taking three logarithms ($\ln K_{ijk}$ is stored internally rather than K_{ijk}), one exponential and three additions instead of $(i + j + k)$ multiplications (or divisions).

The modifications to the usual Newton-Raphson process which we have found necessary are as follows:

1. If one starts with an incredibly poor guess for, say, A, then within the precision of the machine the value of $\dfrac{\delta A}{A}$ obtained in the first iteration may be -1, in which case the second value of A would be zero. This is not allowable in our process, however, since we compute ln A in the next iteration. We therefore limit the maximum possible fractional decrease in a component concentration to a specifiable value; -0.9 appears to work well.

2. In certain exceptional cases, the Newton-Raphson procedure leads to an oscillatory approach to the correct values, or possibly to non-convergence. This was discovered in the use of our program by chance, and probably corresponds to the existence of an m-dimensional analogue of an inflection point.[3] At any rate, by reducing the size of the shifts in A, B and C it is possible to overcome such difficulties, and we have included a test for oscillatory behavior in our program.

The computer storage requirements for the program and for data are very modest, hence this program seems adaptable to smaller computers for the computation of a wide variety of systems with interdependent equilibria. If one has a very large number of stoichiometries involving a given set of equilibria, it would doubtless be time-saving to write a computer program for that specific set of equilibria. However, this would not appear to be the usual case for workers in the field of complexation, and a single program capable of treating many different systems is, in our opinion, more useful.

Our program, as now operative, will treat cases of up to 24 species formed from up to 4 components. Although an increase in these numbers presents no real problem, we have found this adequate up to the present. For example, one can readily treat the case of a metal ion, M^{+s}, with hydrolysis, being complexed by two weak acid ligands, H_pL_1 and H_qL_2; components in such a case might be M^{+s}, H^+, L_1^{-p}, L_2^{-q}.

Data Reduction of Complexometric Measurements

Apparently the first application of least squares methods to complexometric data was by Roughton, Otis and Lyster,[4] who thereby treated the oxygen absorption by sheep haemoglobin. These workers did not use a computer but did use unequal weights for different data points, a refinement which van Eck,[5] who recalculated, using a computer, some of the ammine complexing data of Spike,[6] ignored (justi-fiably, we believe).

More recently Rydberg and Sullivan,[7] as well as Rabideau and Moore,[8] have applied least squares methods to other types of complex-ing data.

We have written programs suitable for the reduction of complexo-metric data derived from spectrophotometric, polarographic, calori-metric and potentiometric measurements. To illustrate such data-re-duction procedures, we shall here consider a program appropriate for the treatment of a certain type of potentiometric data.

Potentiometric data relating to the complexing of a metal ion, M, by a ligand, A, leads to one of the following situations, in all of which ΣM, the stoichiometric metal concentration, and ΣA, the stoi-chiometric ligand concentration are known:

1. M, the free metal ion concentration, measured.
2. A, the free ligand concentration, measured.
3. Both M and A measured.

Case 1 comprises the systems investigated by Leden,[9] for ex-ample. We shall consider at length the treatment of such data.

Case 2 is exemplified by the ammine systems investigated by Bjerrum[10] and by the systems treated by least squares techniques by Roughton, et al., and by van Eck.

Case 3 has, to our knowledge, not yet been treated by least squares methods, although a substantial body of data of this type relating to hydrolytic polymerization has been obtained by Sillén and his co-workers[11] at Stockholm.

In Case 1, which we shall now further consider, one has a number of triads of data: ΣM_i, ΣA_i, E_i. In addition, from experience, one can presumably specify variances in each of these quantities. E_i is the potential of a suitable concentration cell and is related to M_i by the relation,

$$M_i = \Sigma M_i \exp(-\alpha E_i), \tag{4}$$

$$\text{where } \alpha = \frac{n\mathfrak{F}}{RT}, \tag{5}$$

the latter symbols having their usual meanings.

In addition one has two stoichiometric mole balance conditions:

$$0 = -\Sigma A_i + A_i + M_i \Sigma n\beta_n A_i^n, \tag{6}$$

and

$$0 = -\Sigma M_i + M_i + M_i \Sigma \beta_n A_i^n, \tag{7}$$

where β_n is the usual cumulative formation constant for MA_n.

Now although one knows ΣM_i and ΣA_i and can derive from E_i and ΣM_i a value of M_i, there is not available a value of A_i.

There is, however, a possibility of computing A_i which is quite straightforward: One solves one of the two expressions (6) or (7) for A_i using provisional values for the β_n and the experimental values of ΣA_i or ΣM_i and M_i. The usual Newton-Raphson method suffices in solving for A_i. This value of A_i is then substituted back into the other expression, (7) or (6), and the residual, that is, the value of the right side of (7) or (6), computed. Adjustment of the β_n is then carried out so that the properly weighted sum of the squared residuals is minimized, and this process is iterated until convergence of the values of the β_n's is achieved.

In this method of computation, which is relatively simple, there are several questions which occur and the answers to which are of prime importance if the technique is to be employed.

First, does the process converge? Empirically, the answer to this question seems to be yes, provided that the provisional values of the β_n's are reasonably close to the "true" values and provided that the data are reasonably good. However, in systems where the β_n are very large and therefore where A_i is much smaller than ΣA_i, convergence of the β_n values can be exceedingly slow. In such cases convergence is not, in our experience, oscillatory. Consequently, by deliberately overshifting the corrections, convergence can be greatly accelerated.

Second, should one choose to solve (6) *or* (7) for the value of A_i? The answer to this question is not certain, although it probably is as follows: choose (6) if the formation constants for the higher complexes are relatively more uncertain and (7) if the formation constants of the lower complexes are relatively more uncertain. Such a choice is based on the occurrence of n in the summation in equation (6) but not in equation (7).

Third, is this procedure at least squares method? The answer to this, strictly speaking, is no, since one does not know A_i from measurement but computes its value by a procedure which is an addition to the usual least squares method. Strictly, least squares methods are applicable only to systems in which the variables are normally distributed, however, and since in many applications of least squares methods one does not investigate the validity of assuming normal distributions, we do not feel that the prodedure described above is more suspect than many other conventional applications of least squares methods. This evidently cannot serve as a justification for the use of the method; rather the relative simplicity of the method and the ease of usefully applying it to various cases do commend it to the attention and possible use of complexometric investigators.

Fourth and finally, how does one choose the proper weights for the residuals? The answer to this question is of considerable importance since weighting can, for example, appreciably alter the results of polynomial curve fitting by least squares,[12] and would be expected to be important in the present method as well.

The quantity which should be minimized is

$$\frac{\Sigma \, w_i r_i^2}{\Sigma \, w_i} \tag{8}$$

where w_i is the weight of the ith residual, r_i. Division by Σw_i is necessary since only the relative weights of the points can have significance and since decreasing $\Sigma w_i r_i^2$ by merely reducing each w_i does not change the goodness of fit.

One must then choose the relative weights of different data points in order to carry out the least squares regression analysis. To do this the least squares method precribes that w_i should be inversely proportional to the variance, σ_i^2, of the data point.[13] While other weighting schemes have been used, often without justification,[14] if one does use weighting according to the inverse variance, how is the variance of a data point to be determined?

There are two possibilities other than arbitrary assignment: determination by the replication of an experiment, and assignment on the basis of experience. The first possibility is much more difficult in practice than might be apparent, for if errors in several quantities are contributing to the variance of the quantity in which r_i is the residual, then replication must be carried out a large number of times for each data point, in order to satisfactorily determine the variance of the point. This is not common practice in complexometric measurements, although if there were no alternative method it should become such.

The second method, which we recommend, is as follows:

1. Assign variances to the experimentally measured quantities in accordance with the errors known or presumed to be associated with the measurement of each of these quantities.

2. From the formula for the propagation of variance then compute the resulting variance in the quantity whose residuals appear in (8).

3. Use the inverse of this variance in weighting. The relative weights will depend algebraically on the β_n's; neglect this dependence and substitute the provisional values of the β_n's in w_i in applying the usual least squares method to expression (8).[13]

As an example of the application of this weighting procedure, consider the case in which we solve equation (6) for A_i and then seek to minimize the sum of the weighted squared residuals of the right side of equation (7). Denote the right side of equation (7) by G.

Then

$$\sigma_G^2 = \left(\frac{\delta G}{\delta \Sigma M}\right)^2 \sigma_{\Sigma M}^2 + \left(\frac{\delta G}{\delta E}\right)^2 \sigma_E^2 + \left(\frac{\delta G}{\delta A}\right)^2 \left[\left(\frac{\delta A}{\delta \Sigma A}\right)^2 \sigma_{\Sigma A}^2 + \left(\frac{\delta A}{\delta \Sigma M}\right)^2 \sigma_{\Sigma M}^2 + \left(\frac{\delta A}{\delta E}\right)^2 \sigma_E^2\right] \quad (9)$$

In equation (9), $\left(\frac{\delta G}{\delta \Sigma M}\right)$, $\left(\frac{\delta G}{\delta E}\right)$, and $\left(\frac{\delta G}{\delta A}\right)$ are directly evaluated from equation (7) whereas $\left(\frac{\delta A}{\delta \Sigma A}\right)$, etc. are evaluated from equation (6). Thus, from the substitution of educated guesses for $\sigma_{\Sigma M}$, σ_E, and $\sigma_{\Sigma A}$ in equation (9) one can derive the corresponding variance in G, that is, σ_G^2, and, from its inverse, the relative weight of each data point.

It should be pointed out that we have not been constrained to linearize our function, G, nor to seek some non-linear form which gives equal weight for all data points by the existence of least squares subroutines suitable for those cases only; all our subroutines were written *ab initio*. Rabideau and Moore treating similar data apparently used a code involving equal weights and justify this essentially by the assumption that only the variance in Σ_i is of importance. Strictly, of course, this cannot be so, although it is in their cases doubtless a good approximation.

We have analyzed a number of sets of data using the above-described computer program which will treat as many as 800 data points and fit up to six constants. In the analysis of data for systems with relatively weak complexes such as Cd^{++}-CNS^-[9], or Sn^{++}-Cl^-[15] convergence to one part in 10^5 in a set of β_n's takes no more than five cycles of least squares regression. The computation time per data point per cycle in these cases is approximately six seconds.

Thus, for example, a least squares analysis of 171 data points relating to chloride complexing of tin(II) in acid medium[15] was carried out with each cycle of regression requiring about 15 minutes. After convergence has been achieved, the complete inverse matrix of the coefficients of the least squares normal equations is printed out as well as the stepwise complexing constants and their variances. Finally, each data point is "back-calculated" using the final set of β_n's, so as to provide an indication of the point-by-point goodness-of-fit.

The final constants with their standard errors are for Tobias' data[15] on the system, Sn^{++}-Cl^-:

$\beta_1 = 15.12 \pm 0.25,$

$\beta_2 = 54.88 \pm 2.08,$ $\qquad K_2 = 3.63 \pm 0.19$

$\beta_3 = 47.15 \pm 4.25,$ $\qquad K_3 = 0.86 \pm 0.11.$

At the time of writing this paper, the process of data reduction for a system involving robust complexes has not yet yielded a final set of constants.

Professor Edward L. King[16] has kindly made available to us an extensive set of potentiometric measurements relating to the complexing of thallium(III) by chloride ion. The approximate values of β_1 and β_2 for this system are 10^7 and 10^{13}, and thus at $\bar{n}$ values less than 2 the free chloride ion concentration is very low. This leads, as indicated above, to a very slow convergence on a final set of the β_n's.

Furthermore, because the Newton-Raphson method must be iterated a large number of times for satisfactory convergence with robust complexes, the computation time per data point per cycle of regression rises to approximately 13 seconds.

From a least squares regression analysis of two sets of Professor King's data: 106 data points for solutions with $\mu = 0.5$ and 96 data points for solutions with $\mu = 3.0$, we have derived the constants given in Table 2. These values should be regarded as provisional rather than final values and no errors are assigned therefore.

In arriving at these values we have, from time to time, when a particular constant showed a continuing drift, printed out a back calculation of the data points and examined the residuals for runs of positive or negative values. Upon finding such a run, the value of the appropriate stepwise complexity constant is adjusted by hand calculation to reduce these residuals in magnitude, and the recomputed cumulative constants used as input for the next cycle of regression.

TABLE 2

$\mu = 0.5$	Input Constants	Output after 8 Cycles of Least Squares Regression
β_1	$6.0 \cdot 10^6$	$11.2 \cdot 10^6$
β_2	$1.08 \cdot 10^{12}$	$1.05 \cdot 10^{12}$
β_3	$3.56 \cdot 10^{14}$	$2.68 \cdot 10^{14}$
β_4	$1.89 \cdot 10^{16}$	$2.08 \cdot 10^{16}$

$\mu = 3.0$	Input Constants	Output after 13 Cycles of Least Squares Regression
β_1	$1.5 \cdot 10^7$	$6.00 \cdot 10^7$
β_2	$8.55 \cdot 10^{12}$	$7.34 \cdot 10^{12}$
β_3	$1.20 \cdot 10^{15}$	$14.62 \cdot 10^{15}$
β_4	$2.00 \cdot 10^{17}$	$20.75 \cdot 10^{17}$

In particular, such correction is desirable in this case for β_1 which is very poorly determined by the data.

Final results for the Tl^{+++}-Cl^- system will be presented at the Coordination Chemistry Conference and we plan to publish the results in a joint paper with Professor E. L. King.

REFERENCES

1. See, for example, G. Hägg, *Die theoretischen Grundlagen der analytischen Chemie*, Birkhäuser, Basel, 1950.
2. Paul C. Scott, Ph.D. Thesis, University of Minnesota, 1959.
3. E. Whittaker and G. Robinson, *The Calculus of Observations* (4th ed.), Blackie & Son, Glasgow, 1944, pp. 84–87.
4. F. J. W. Roughton, A. B. Otis, and R. L. J. Lyster, *Proc. Roy. Soc.* **144B**, 29 (1955).
5. C. L. van P. van Eck, Ph.D. Thesis, University of Leiden, 1958.
6. C. G. Spike, Ph.D. Thesis, University of Michigan, 1953.
7. J. Rydberg and J. C. Sullivan, *Acta Chem. Scand.* **13**, 2057 (1959).
8. S. W. Rabideau and R. H. Moore, *J. Phys. Chem.* **65**, 371 (1961).
9. I. Leden, *Z. Phys. Chem.* **A188**, 160 (1941).
10. J. Bjerrum, *Metal Ammine Formation in Aqueous Solution*, P. Haase and Son, Copenhagen (1941).
11. For example, A. Olin, *Acta Chem. Scand.*, **11**, 1445 (1957); F. Granér, Å. Olin, and L. G. Sillén, *ibid.*, **10**, 476 (1956); R. S. Tobias, *ibid.*, **12**, 198 (1958).
12. Z Z. Hugus, Jr., unpublished work.
13. W. E. Deming, *Statistical Adjustment of Data*, John Wiley and Sons, New York, 1943.
14. R. L. Kay, *J. Am. Chem. Soc.* **82**, 2099 (1960).
15. Data of R. S. Tobias; R. S. Tobias and Z Z. Hugus, Jr. (to be published).
16. E. L. King, private communication.

THE MECHANISM OF FORMATION AND DISSOCIATION OF CERTAIN METAL CHELATE COMPOUNDS

ROBERT HOGG, GORDON A. MELSON, and RALPH G. WILKINS*

Department of Chemistry
The University
Sheffield, England

There has been little systematic investigation of the factors influencing the rate of dissociation (hydrolysis or aquation) of metal chelates. In this paper the important factors will be discussed and illustrated with both detailed and fragmentary information from researches on complexes of elements of the first transition period with aliphatic polyamines and polypyridyls.

Ligand Characteristics

Multidentate Character. It might be expected that the kinetic stability of a chelate towards complete dissociation to metal ion and ligand would increase with the number of donor atoms in the ligand, i.e., with the number of interlinked rings present in the complex. Considering the dissociation of $[Ni A]^{2+}$[†] in neutral solution from exchange studies (Table 1) we find that although the rate decreases markedly in going from bidentate ethylenediamine to higher dentate complexes, there is only a slight difference between the dissociation of complexes of the terdentate ligand (dien) and the sexadentate ligand [1] (penten). With the quadridentate ligands, trien and tren, geometrical shape is important, models indicating that the latter fits more neatly about octahedral nickel. These dissociation rates will be a complicated function of several stepwise dissociative and formation rate constants, especially for the more complicated amines, so that other considerations, e.g., basicity of complexed ligand, will be important as well as ring formation. Examination of the detailed

---

*We thank the University of Sheffield and the United States Department of the Army, through its European Research Office, for maintenance grants (to R. H. and G. A. M., respectively) during the tenure of which most of this work was performed. We are also grateful to Dr. A. Jubb and Imperial Chemical Industries Ltd., for a gift of tripyridyl.

†Probable coordinated water will be ignored in this paper.

TABLE 1: DISSOCIATION OF NICKEL POLYAMINE COMPLEXES, $[Ni A]^{2+}$, AT $0°$

A	Dissociation Half-Life (sec)	
	pH = 7	pH = 3.5
$H_2N \cdot CH_2 \cdot CH_2 \cdot NH_2$ (en)[11]	840	60
$(H_2N \cdot CH_2 \cdot CH_2)_2NH$ (dien)	6×10^4	7
$(H_2N \cdot CH_2 \cdot CH_2 \cdot NH \cdot CH_2-)_2$ (trien)	4×10^4	~ 1 sec (one NH_2); 300 sec
$(H_2N \cdot CH_2 \cdot CH_2)_3N$ (tren)	$\gg 9 \times 10^4$	~ 1 sec (one NH_2); 300 sec
$[(H_2N \cdot CH_2 \cdot CH_2)_2N \cdot CH_2-]_2$ (penten)	3×10^4	~ 1 sec (two NH_2); 6000 sec

data with the iron(II) and nickel(II) complexes of $2,2'$-bipyridyl (bipy) and $2,2',2''$-tripyridyl (tripy) shows that the reduced rate of exchange of the terdentate-containing complex resides mainly in a decreased entropy (with little attendant change in energy) of activation. This is seen from a comparison of both higher and lower complexes (Table 2; compounds 1 and 2, 6 and 8, 7 and 9). The cobalt-dipyridyl complexes exchange too rapidly for their rates to be measured by conventional techniques.

The situation with regard to multidentate character and stability changes in acid solution. Once a donor nitrogen atom becomes free it has a good chance of being protonated, re-formation rates are slower and further ligand atom-metal breakage now becomes more effective. Examination of models shows that the terminal primary amine group of dien and (even more) of trien and penten is strained when complexed to the metal, so that it dissociates in acid solution

TABLE 2: DISSOCIATION OF POLYPYRIDYL COMPLEXES AT pH $\sim$ 7 AT $25°C$

	Complex	10^3k (min^{-1})	log A	E_{act}
1[a]	$[Fe\ dipy_3]^{2+}$	8.0	18.8	28.4
2	$[Fe\ trpy_2]^{2+}$	0.01	16.1	28.7
3	$[Fe\ trpy]^{2+}$	398	12.8	18.0
4	$[Co\ trpy_2]^{2+}$	40	9.5	14.8
5	$[Co\ trpy]^{2+}$	6.3	12.6	20.2
6[a]	$[Ni\ dipy_3]^{2+}$	186	15.6	22.2
7[b]	$[Ni\ dipy]^{2+}$	3.7	15.0	23.7
8	$[Ni\ trpy_2]^{2+}$	0.1	11.3	20.8
9	$[Ni\ trpy]^2$	0.0016	12.0	24.2

[a] Ellis and Wilkins, unpublished observations.
[b] Reference 3.

more readily than ethylenediamine or the remaining coordinated amine groups (Table 1). There are significant spectral changes accompanying these successive dissociative stages and we have obtained quantitative data for these steps using rapid-flow techniques.

The Arrhenius parameters for the limiting rate of dissociation of $[Fe\ dipy_3]^{2+}$ and $[Fe\ tripy_2]^{2+}$ in acid solution resemble one another, $k = 10^{18.6} \exp(-27,400/RT)$ and $10^{18.3} \exp(-27,400/RT)$ min^{-1}, respectively, and if in acid solution we are measuring the rate of first bond rupture,[2a] the processes are remarkably similar kinetic-wise for the two complexes. The rates of dissociation of $[Ni\ dipy_3]^{2+}$ and $[Ni\ tripy_2]^{2+}$ also approach one another as the acidity increases (in 1.0-2.0 M HCl at $1°C$, $k_{diss} = 0.03$ and 0.3 min^{-1}). It is clear then that the pH has a more marked effect with the more complicated chelates and that for these it is the most important medium factor influencing rate.

Substitution of Ligand. One of the interests in complexes containing aromatic ligands such as dipyridyl and phenanthroline is examining the effect of ring substitution on the rate of dissociation of the complex. By far the most sensitive position is the one adjacent to the site of coordination, substitution of which markedly enhances dissociation.[3] It would be expected from an examination of models and from stability measurements[4] that $2,2',2'',2'''$-tetrapyridyl (tetrapy) would coordinate only through three of the four nitrogen atoms. It will therefore behave on coordination as a 2-substituted tripyridyl, and the relatively rapid rate of reaction of $[Ni\ tetrapy]^{2+}$ in neutral solution ($k_{25°} \sim 4 \times 10^{-3}$ min^{-1}) is thus readily understandable.

Number and Type of Ligand. On the basis of data so far available, the majority of nickel higher species, $Ni\ A_n$, dissociate more rapidly than the lower ones, $Ni A_{n-1}$, etc. Since in a "normal" system the lower species is relatively more stable thermodynamically, the consequence of this behaviour is that the successive formation rate constants, $Ni \longrightarrow Ni\ A_{n-1} \longrightarrow Ni A_n$, are approximately equal.[5] Apart from the rapidity of many formation reactions, this fact may present additional difficulties in their measurement. In addition, formation rates appear less sensitive to structural factors than dissociation. Very little information is available on the behaviour of mixed chelate compounds. A simple experiment is illuminating: when a freshly prepared solution of solid[6] $[Ni\ phen\ (H_2O)_4](NO_3)_2$ dissolved in water is treated with one equivalent of $2,3$-diamino-$2,3$-dimethylbutane (tetraMeen), a greyish, blue solid quickly separates. This compound, $[Ni\ phen\ (tetraMeen)\ (H_2O)_2](NO_3)_2$, when dissolved in water at room temperature, disproportionates rapidly and completely. The aliphatic diamine thus labilises the coordinated phenanthroline, which in its absence only very slowly dissociates from the nickel.[6]

Metal Characteristics

Octahedral Complexes. Basolo and Pearson[2b] have stimulated a good deal of interest in the effect of the electronic configuration of the metal on the rate of reaction of its complexes. The difference, ΔE, in crystal-field stabilisation energy (C.F.S.E.) is calculated for the octahedral (reactant) and square-pyramid (transition state) configurations for various d^n systems. It is then expected that the greater the loss of C.F.S.E. in the change, the slower the reaction proceeds (higher energy of activation). Some data on phenanthroline complexes have already been used to show the general validity of this idea[7,8] and the present results offer further evidence (Table 3). For the bis(tripyridyl) metal complexes, the rate sequence is Co > Ni > Fe, accompanied by increasing energies of activation (increments about 6-8 kcal/mole) and increasing calculated C.F.S.E. losses (ΔE increments $2Dq$, i.e., about 6 kcal/mole). For the mono (tripyridyl) metal complexes the rate now decreases in the order Fe > Co > Ni with increasing energies of activation, although the values are closer than in the *bis* series in agreement with the calculated C.F.S.E. ΔE changes of 0, 0 and 2, respectively. The really striking difference is between the low-spin $[Fe\ tripy_2]^{2+}$ and the high-spin $[Fe\ tripy]^{2+}$, with a difference of 11 kcal/mole in their energies of activation, in most satisfying agreement with prediction. On either a displacement or a dissociation mechanism for reaction,

TABLE 3: ENERGIES OF ACTIVATION AND C.F.S.E. CHANGES FOR THE REACTIONS OF TRIPYRIDYL COMPLEXES

Electronic System	Complex Ion	E_{act} (kcal/mole)	$\Delta E\ (Dq)^{2(b)}$	Magnetic Moment (μ) (20-24 °C)
$d_\varepsilon^6 d_\gamma^0$	$[Fe\ tripy_2]^{2+}$	29	4	0.0
d^7	$[Co\ tripy_2]^{2+}$	15	0	2.6
d^8	$[Ni\ tripy_2]^{2+}$	21	2	3.1
d^5	$[Mn\ tripy]^{2+}$	fast	0	5.7
$d_\varepsilon^4 d_\gamma^2$	$[Fe\ tripy]^{2+}$	18	0	5.1
d^7	$[Co\ tripy]^{2+}$	20	0	4.9
d^8	$[Ni\ tripy]^{2+}$	24	2	3.2
d^9	$[Cu\ tripy]^{2+}$	fast	0	...
d^{10}	$[Zn\ tripy]^{2+}$	fast	0	...

a much larger C.F.S.E. loss would be expected for the diamagnetic than for the paramagnetic iron complex.[2b] The entropies of activation for the two iron-tripyridyl complexes are also interesting. The *positive* value for the *bis* species contrasts sharply with the highly negative value for the *mono*, and for the other four tripyridyl complexes (Table 2). This positive value can be explained in terms of the diamagnetic *bis* ⟶ paramagnetic *mono* change,[2c] and the more usual value for the paramagnetic *mono* ⟶ paramagnetic metal ion is evidence that this is the correct interpretation.

These results relate to neutral exchange, where the rate constant almost certainly is a composite one. However, the important parameter for these arguments is the energy of activation, and this is similar to that obtained in acid dissociation where the data may refer to the more appropriate and simple single-bond breakage process.

The diversity of rate behaviour observed with tripyridyl complexes disappears with highly multidentate ligands, for the half-lives of neutral exchange of $[M \text{ penten}]^{2+}$, M = Mn, Co, Cu and Zn are all similar, with values 1-15 min at $0°$ much faster, once again, than the corresponding nickel complex (Table 1).

Four-coordinate Complexes. At present, we must rely on highly-substituted ethylenediamine complexes to give slow enough dissociation rates in acid solution for measurement. For planar bis (diethyldiMeen*) complexes, Cu > Ni, the respective rate constants being $k = 10^{15.4} \exp(-19,400/RT)$ and $k = 10^{14.8} \exp(-22,500/RT)$ min.$^{-1}$ Once again the differences in energy of activation can be correlated with C.F.S.E. changes.[2d] The corresponding cobalt and zinc complexes dissociate rapidly; this would be expected for planar zinc but not for cobalt, although the stereochemistry of these two complexes is not known.

The Measurement of Chelate Dissociation

Exchange Experiments. The dissociation of the tris(dipyridyl), bis(tripyridyl) and mono(penten) complexes was measured using labelled ligand. ^{14}C-dipyridyl was synthesised from ^{14}C-glycerol and ^{14}C-penten from ^{14}C-ethylenediamine according to the method described by Gauss, Moser and Schwarzenbach.[9] Because of the difficulty of synthesis of labelled tripyridyl from simple radiochemicals, ^{3}H-tripyridyl was prepared by mixing tripyridyl with 1-2 Curies of T_2 for several days, and then extensively purifying, *via* complex

---

*DiethyldiMeen = *3,4*-diamino-*3,4*-dimethylhexane.

formation, from radiation decomposition impurities. The equilibria involved with the tripyridyl complexes can be represented thus:

$$MA_2 \rightleftarrows MA + A \quad (R_2)$$
$$MA \rightleftarrows M + A \quad (R_1).$$

Exchange of M with MA_2 (M = Fe, Co or Ni) can be examined because small concentrations of M can co-exist with MA_2 without the production of substantial amounts of MA. For the cobalt and nickel complexes, $R_1 \ll R_2$ and the exchange rate is thus a measure of the rate of dissociation of the *mono* species. For the iron complexes, $R_1 \gg R_2$ and both metal and ligand exchange with MA_2 measure the dissociation of this species. The dissociation of [Fe tripy]$^{2+}$ was therefore obtained from its disproportionation rate:

$$2 \,[\text{Fe tripy}]^{2+} \longrightarrow \text{Fe}^{2+} + [\text{Fe tripy}_2]^{2+}$$

which occurred quantitatively when solid Fe tripy Br$_2$ was dissolved in water. Since the extinction coefficient of the *bis* (ε_M^{max} = 1.15 × 10^4 at 552 mμ.) is much higher than the *mono* (ε_M^{max} = 860 at 555 mμ), the rate can be followed spectrally. The same is substantially true for the cobalt-tripyridyl system, the *bis* having two maxima in the visible (ε_M^{max} = 1.4 × 10^3 at 505 mμ and 1600 at 450 mμ), whereas the *mono* has featureless low absorption (ε_M = 21.0 at 440 mμ). Disproportionation in this case was incomplete as it was also with [Ni tripy]$^{2+}$, and since the spectral change involved in the latter case was very small the disproportionation was not so accurate (or so unequivocal) a measure of its dissociation as the exchange result. The agreement between the exchange and disproportionation methods for cobalt and nickel was good.

The dissociation of [Ni dipy]$^{2+}$, [Ni tetrapy]$^{2+}$ and the remaining nickel polyamine complexes was measured from metal exchange. In the case of the dien, trien and tren complexes this rate will probably include terms involving nickel ion concentration[10] but will yield a *measure* of the "spontaneous" lability for qualitative comparative purposes.

Net Dissociation. The polyamine complexes dissociate completely at pH < 4 and in the region pH 2-4, the pH-stat[11] can be used effectively to differentiate the various stages in the dissociation. In more acidic solutions, spectrophotometry is the most effective method for following the rates, but for the polyamine and even certain tripyridyl complexes of the first transition period, rapid methods, e.g., stopped-flow,[5] must be used. It is proposed to report on some results of this kind at the Conference.

REFERENCES

1. G. Schwarzenbach and P. Moser, *Helv. Chim. Acta*, **36**, 581 (1953).
2. F. Basolo and R. G. Pearson, *Mechanisms of Inorganic Reactions*, John Wiley and Sons, Inc., New York, N.Y., 1958. (*a*) p. 152, (*b*) p. 108, (*c*) p. 269, (*d*) p. 203.
3. Peter Ellis, R. Hogg, and R. G. Wilkins, *J. Chem. Soc.*, **1959**, 3308.
4. Arpad A. Bergh, Gilbert P. Haight, and Philip George, *Abstracts of Papers, 136th Meeting, American Chemical Society*, September 1959, p. 43N.
5. A. K. Shamsuddin Ahmed and R. G. Wilkins, *J. Chem. Soc.*, **1960**, 2901.
6. R. G. Wilkins and M. J. G. Williams, *J. Chem. Soc.*, **1957**, 4514.
7. R. G. Pearson, *J. Phys. Chem.*, **63**, 321 (1959).
8. Peter Ellis and R. G. Wilkins, *J. Chem. Soc.*, **1959**, 299.
9. W. Gauss, P. Moser, and G. Schwarzenbach, *Helv. Chim. Acta*, **35**, 2359 (1952).
10. D. W. Margerum and J. F. Gates Clarke, Jr., *Abstracts of Papers, 138th Meeting, American Chemical Society*, September 1960, p. 8N.
11. A. K. Shamsuddin Ahmed and R. G. Wilkins, *J. Chem. Soc.*, **1959**, 3700.

TRACTABLE POTENTIAL FUNCTIONS AS DERIVED FROM THEORIES OF BONDING FOR METAL CARBONYLS AND METAL CYANIDE COMPLEXES*

LLEWELLYN H. JONES

Los Alamos Scientific Laboratory
University of California
Los Alamos, New Mexico

An important contribution to coordination chemistry would be an understanding of the forces holding the ligands to the central atom, and the perturbations these forces induce in the coordinating groups. To gain such an understanding we must determine such forces in many different specific coordination compounds and be able to explain the differences from one compound to another in accord with theories of bonding. The vibrational spectrum of a molecule is actually a display of such interatomic forces and thus should be an important revelation to the coordination chemist.

From the infrared absorption spectra and the Raman spectra of molecules and complex ions one can determine the frequencies of many of the fundamental normal vibrations of the molecules (or ions). If most of the vibrational frequencies are known and properly assigned, it may be possible to calculate some of the bond force constants and bond angle force constants which inform us about the resistance to distortion of the various bonds and bond angles. For these force constants to be completely meaningful the interaction constants in the potential function must be known. These cross terms tell us how distortion of one internal coordinate affects another internal coordinate. (By internal coordinate we mean a bond length or bond angle or some other coordinate specifying the atomic arrangement in the compound.) Aside from being necessary for calculation of the primary force constants, the interaction constants give, in themselves, important information about bonding in molecules and complex ions.

Though a large amount of spectral data has been obtained, there exist relatively few molecules for which sufficient data are available from which to determine reliable force constants. It is the purpose of this paper to outline some of the difficulties and to describe how we

*Work performed under the auspices of the USAEC.

can use our knowledge of the chemical bond to make the problem solvable for some cases of metal carbonyls and metal-cyanide complexes.

We are going to consider especially the hexacarbonyls, $M(CO)_6$, of octahedral symmetry. A schematic representation of the molecule is shown in Fig. 1. Our approach will be to force a displacement of one coordinate and estimate qualitatively what effect this will have

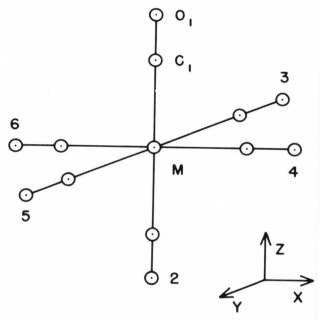

Fig. 1. Schematic diagram of $M(CO)_6$ molecule.

on the other coordinates. This will lead to relationships among the various interaction constants in the potential function, thus reducing the number of unknowns to calculate from the observed frequencies.

POTENTIAL FUNCTIONS

Since the forces are approximately harmonic, a suitable potential function is made up primarily of quadratic terms. The molecular system can be defined by a certain number of internal coordinates (such as bond distances, bond angles, non-bonded distances, etc.).

If we define a set of internal coordinates, q_i, and their displacements, S_i, we can write a general quadratic potential function

$$2V = \sum_{ij} k_{ij} S_i S_j \tag{1}$$

The problem is to determine what set of coordinates, q_i, is most convenient to use and which k_{ij} are important, as there are generally more k_{ij} to determine than there are data available.

For example, a molecule requires $3N - 6$ internal coordinates ($3N - 5$, if linear) to describe the relative positions of the nuclei. For a molecule with no symmetry there are $3N - 6$ vibrational frequencies but there are $(3N - 6)(3N - 5)/2$ different k_{ij}. Thus for a 4 atomic molecule with no symmetry there are 6 vibrational frequencies and 21 general quadratic force constants, k_{ij}, and there would be no hope of determining all the k_{ij}. By use of isotopic substitution one can often gain additional data—but generally not enough to make the problem solvable. There is a third type of data to consider; namely, amplitudes of motion of the various internal coordinates associated with the vibrations of known frequency. These amplitudes are functions of the force constants, k_{ij}. Theoretically they can be determined from electron diffraction studies; however, this has been done in only a very few cases and with rather insufficient accuracy.

If the molecule has symmetry, the problem is not so formidable. The secular determinant can be broken up into the various symmetry blocks. Linear combinations of the internal coordinates are chosen to have the proper symmetry and there are no cross terms between coordinates of different symmetry. Though this reduces the number of k_{ij} values to be determined, in general there remain many more k_{ij} than there are fundamental vibrational frequencies.

Simple Force Fields

One method of making the problem solvable is to assume all cross terms are 0 ($k_{ij} = 0$ for $i \neq j$). Then for an unsymmetrical molecule there are $3N - 6$ force constants to determine from $3N - 6$ frequencies. If symmetry is present there will be more frequencies than force constants and we have a check on the suitability of the potential function.

Simple Central Force Field. The main assumption of central forces is that the S_i are displacements of the bonded and non-bonded distances. A simple central force field includes the assumption that $k_{ij} = 0$ for $i \neq j$. This is a crude approximation as indicated by the comparison of calculations with observations.

Simple Valence Force Field. This rests on the assumption that the only forces of importance are those between bonded atoms and those which fix the bond angles. Thus, we let the S_i be changes of bond lengths and of bond angles, and let all $k_{ij} = 0$ for $i \neq j$. This approximation appears to be better than that of central forces but is generally quite inadequate to fit the data.

Urey-Bradley Force Field

This is a combination of the simple valence force field with the simple central force field. That is, we have three types of internal coordinates: changes in bond lengths, changes in bond angles, and changes in distances between non-bonded atoms. For molecules with symmetry the Urey-Bradley Force Field in general requires fewer force constants than there are fundamental frequencies and is therefore quite tractable. In many cases it appears to give excellent results. However, there are cases in which the Urey-Bradley Field is definitely inadequate; this seems to be true especially where "resonance structures" can be anticipated. For example, in metal carbonyls the Urey-Bradley Force Field would predict no appreciable interaction between the different C—O bond stretches. However, this is not the case. We feel it is because of possible changes in π bonding during the vibrations.

A π Electron Interaction Potential Function

In order to derive a suitable potential function for metal carbonyls and related species we start with a general quadratic valence force field. Then from theories of chemical bonding we attempt to relate many of the interaction force constants and thus reduce the number of unknowns necessary to determine from the observed frequencies. The following treatment is similar to that used by the author for $Ni(CO)_4$.[1] Let us write the potential function

$$2V = \sum_i F_i S_i^2 + 2 \sum_{j > i} \sum_i F_{ij} S_i S_j. \tag{2}$$

The F_i are valence type force constants, the F_{ij} are the interaction constants, and the S_i are valence type internal displacement coordinates (changes in the q_i, which are bond lengths and bond angles). Let us now make a small unit positive displacement of q_k ($S_k = +1$). This will result in the other q_i changing so as to minimize the potential energy, which is now expressed by

$$2V = F_k + \sum_{i \neq k} F_i S_i^2 + 2 \sum_{i \neq k} F_{ik} S_i + 2 \sum_{\substack{j > k \\ j \neq k}} \sum_{i \neq k} F_{ij} S_i S_j. \tag{3}$$

In order to determine how the various q_l change when $S_k = +1$ for nonredundant coordinates we minimize the potential energy with respect to S_l

$$\frac{\partial V}{\partial S_l} = 0 = F_{kl} + F_l(S_l)_k + \sum_{i = k = l} F_{il}(S_i)_k. \tag{4}$$

If we can predict the various $(S_i)_k$, even qualitatively, we arrive at a set of relations among the F_{ij}. However, these simultaneous equations are rather unmanageable. Therefore, we turn to a simplifying approximation. If the F_{ij} are small compared to the F_i and F_j, as is usually found to be true, we can achieve a good approximation by neglecting the sum term in equation 3 and we find for $S_k = +1$

$$F_{kl} = -F_l(S_l)_k \tag{5}$$

in which $(S_l)_k$ = the displacement of coordinate q_l resulting from unit positive displacement of q_k.

Our procedure will be to use our knowledge of the chemical bond to predict relations among the $(S_l)_k$. In particular, we shall apply this to the 13 atomic molecules of octahedral symmetry such as $Cr(CO)_6$, $Cr(CN)_6^{-3}$, etc. Rather than attempt to derive a general potential function we shall first treat the special case of the hexacarbonyls, $M(CO)_6$, where M is Cr, Mo, or W. Later we can modify this treatment to cover the hexacyanides and possibly the recently reported $V(CO)_6$.[2]

CONSIDERATION OF BONDING IN M(CO)₆

The neutral atoms Cr, Mo, and W each have 6 outer d electrons. When the six CO ligands arrange themselves in octahedral symmetry about the central metal atom, they split the five-fold degenerate d orbitals into two groups: the d_ε orbitals of T_{2g} symmetry (d_{xy}, d_{xz}, and d_{yz}) and the d_γ orbitals (d_{z^2}, $d_{x^2-y^2}$). The d_ε orbitals are much more stable then d_γ and the six d electrons collect in these three orbitals leading to the observed diamagnetism of the hexacarbonyls of chromium, molybdenum, and tungsten. The six ligands will each donate a pair of electrons to the metal atom, forming a strong σ bond. This will lead to a high negative charge on the metal atom. As a result there is a strong tendency for the metal atom to donate its d_ε electron pairs to the p orbitals of the carbon atoms forming π bonds of the type $d_\pi(M) - p_\pi(C)$ However, this pi-bonding is in competition with $p_\pi(C) - p_\pi(O)$ bonding. In such cases, with considerable metal-carbon π bonding, such bonding must play an important role in the interactions. We shall thus treat the problem as though the interactions between the d_π electrons of the metal and the p_π electrons of the carbon atoms are the main contribution to the interaction constants.

In order to make the problem tractable we make the following hypotheses:

1. Stretching a C—O bond results in decreased overlap of the $C(\pi)$—$O(\pi)$ orbitals, and vice versa. We shall go further and assume that for small displacements (small with respect to the first order displacements occurring during a vibration) the change in overlap is proportional to the change in bond length as stated in the following equation:

$$(S_l)_k = -K_l(\Delta\pi)_{l,k} \tag{6}$$

K_l is a proportionality constant for coordinate q_l. $(\Delta\pi)_{l,k}$ is the change in π bonding in coordinate q_l as a result of unit displacement of q_k ($S_k = +1$).

2. The carbon p_π orbitals will π-bond 100% at all times (partly with the oxygen p_π orbitals and partly with the metal d_π orbitals). This assumption states that a change in C_iO_i π bonding is accompanied by an equal change in opposite sign in MC_i π bonding. $(\Delta\pi)_{C_iO_i} = -(\Delta\pi)_{C_iM}$

3. The total amount of $d_\pi(M) - p_\pi(C)$ bonding remains constant so that the metal atom can keep its negative charge low. $\Sigma (\Delta\pi)_{C_iM} = 0$.

4. The interactions are small enough so that Eq. (5) is a good approximation.

Hypotheses (1), (2), and (4) appear to be quite reasonable. For metal carbonyls, hypothesis (3) is probably pretty good because of the strong tendency to form M—C π bonds. For other cases it may require modification.

In order to discuss the interactions we use the model given in Fig. 1. The d_{z^2} and $d_{x^2-y^2}$ orbitals are concentrated along the bonds. They do not contain electrons and will not be considered here. The d_{xy}, d_{xz}, and d_{yz} orbitals are concentrated along the bisectors of the 12 CMC angles. They each contain two electrons.

STRETCH-STRETCH INTERACTION

We shall first force a small unit positive displacement of C_1O_1 ($S_{C_1O_1} = +1$). This will result in a decrease in the overlap of $p_x(C_1)$ with $p_x(O_1)$ and of $p_y(C_1)$ with $p_y(O_1)$. Thus the p_x and p_y orbitals of C_1 will be more available for bonding with the d_{xz} and d_{yz} orbitals of M. This increase in C_1M π-bonding will cause a contraction in the C_1M distance. Now that the d_{xz} and d_{yz} orbitals are π bonding more with C_1, they shall π bond less with the other C atoms. By hypothesis (3) the total decrease in π bonding of M to C_2, C_3, C_4, C_5, and C_6 will equal the total increase of π bonding in C_1M. It seems appropriate to make a table of the change in π bonding. (See Table 1.)

Now by hypothesis (2) a change in π bonding of C_iM is accompanied by an equal change of opposite sign in π bonding of C_iO_i. This is set down in Table 2.

We now make use of equation (6).

$$(S_l)_k = -K_l(\Delta\pi)_{l,k}.$$

Letting

$$K_{CM} = d/a$$
$$K_{CO} = 3b/a$$

TABLE 1: CHANGE IN π BONDING FOR S_{C_iM} WHEN $S_{C_1O_1} = +1$

	$\Delta\pi(d_{xz})$	$\Delta\pi(d_{yz})$	$\Delta\pi(d_{xy})$	$\Sigma\Delta\pi$
C_1M	$+a/2$	$+a/2$	0	$+a$
C_2M	$-a/6$	$-a/6$	0	$-a/3$
C_3M	0	$-a/6$	0	$-a/6$
C_4M	$-a/6$	0	0	$-a/6$
C_5M	0	$-a/6$	0	$-a/6$
C_6M	$-a/6$	0	0	$-a/6$
$\Sigma\Delta\pi$	0	0	0	0

we arrive at the results of Table 3.

We still require expressions such as $(S_{C_iM})_{C_jM}$. For this we shall let $S_{C_2M} = +1$. From equation (5), since $F_{kl} = F_{lk}$, we can write

$$F_{C_2M,C_1O_1} = -(S_{C_2M})_{C_1O_1}F_{CM} = -(S_{C_1O_1})_{C_2M}F_{CO}$$

and

$$(S_{C_1O_1})_{C_2M} = (S_{C_2M})_{C_1O_1}F_{CM}/F_{CO}.$$

From hypotheses (1) and (2)

$$\frac{(S_{C_1M})_{C_2M}}{(S_{C_1O_1})_{C_2M}} = -K_{CM}/K_{CO} = -d/3b.$$

Thus, $(S_{C_1M})_{C_2M} = -d(S_{C_2M})_{C_1O_1}F_{CM}/3bF_{CO} = -d^2F_{CM}/9bF_{CO}.$

Similarly,

$$(S_{C_3M})_{C_2M} = -d^2F_{CM}/18bF_{CO}.$$

TABLE 2: CHANGE IN π BONDING FOR $S_{C_iO_i}$ WHEN $S_{C_1O_1} = +1$

	$\Delta\pi(p_x)$	$\Delta\pi(p_y)$	$\Sigma\Delta\pi$
C_2O_2	$a/6$	$a/6$	$a/3$
C_3O_3	0	$a/6$	$a/6$
C_4O_4	$a/6$	0	$a/6$
C_5O_5	0	$a/6$	$a/6$
C_6O_6	$a/6$	0	$a/6$

For simplicity we now let $dF_{CM} = D$ and $bF_{CO} = B$. Then, by using equation (5) and the expressions for the various $(S_l)_k$ we can write the expressions for the stretch-stretch F_{ij} as in Table 4.

Thus we have reduced 7 interaction constants to only 2.

The above treatment takes care of all the stretch-stretch interaction terms. In order to complete the problem we must have expressions for the bend-bend and stretch-bend interaction terms.

BEND-BEND INTERACTIONS

For a consideration of the bend-bend interaction, let us make use of Fig. 2.

If we bend the bond O_1—C_1 towards 4, the p_x orbital of C_1 will overlap the 1, 4 lobe of d_{xz} more. This will tend to rotate the d_{xz} orbital in the clockwise direction to equalize $d_\pi - p_\pi$ overlap, as in the principle of orbital following.[3] It follows that the C_4O_4 bond will bend away from C_1O_1. Thus we will favor a structure such as shown in Fig. 3A. This explains why the inactive frequency which involves this particular motion has a much lower force constant than the other M—C—O bending frequencies. We consider this the only important M—C—O bend-bend interaction for $M(CO)_6$.

Next we shall consider the interaction of MCO bending with CMC bending. If we increase the C_1MC_4 angle, the p_x orbital of C_1 shows increased overlap with the 1, 6 lobe of d_{xz}, and the p_z orbital of C_4 shows increased overlap with the 2, 4 lobe of d_{xz}. In order to equalize $d_\pi - p_\pi$ bonding, C_1O_1 will bend toward 4 and C_4O_4 will bend toward 1, as seen in Fig. 3B.

TABLE 3: CHANGES IN q_l FOR $S_{C_1O_1} = +1$

$$(S_{C_1M})_{C_1O_1} = -d$$
$$(S_{C_2M})_{C_1O_1} = d/3$$
$$(S_{C_iM})_{C_1O_1} = d/6 \qquad i = 3, 4, 5, \text{ and } 6$$
$$(S_{C_2O_2})_{C_1O_1} = -b$$
$$(S_{C_iO_i})_{C_1O_1} = -b/2 \qquad i = 3, 4, 5, \text{ and } 6$$

TABLE 4: STRETCH-STRETCH INTERACTION CONSTANTS FOR M(CO)$_6$ UNDER πIVFF

$$F_{C_1M,C_1O_1} = D$$
$$F_{C_2M,C_1O_1} = -D/3$$
$$F_{C_3M,C_1O_1} = -D/6$$
$$F_{C_2O_2,C_1O_1} = B$$
$$F_{C_3O_3,C_1O_1} = B/2$$
$$F_{C_2M,C_1M} = D^2/9B$$
$$F_{C_3M,C_1M} = D^2/18B$$

Now let us consider the mutual interaction of the CMC angles. If $\alpha_{ij} = \Delta C_i M C_j$, we see that $\alpha_{14} + \alpha_{24} + \alpha_{26} + \alpha_{16} = 0$. This redundancy requires a slightly different treatment and we won't go into it here more than to say that a reasonable assumption appears to be that the coplanar α-α interaction constants are all equal and the others are negligible.

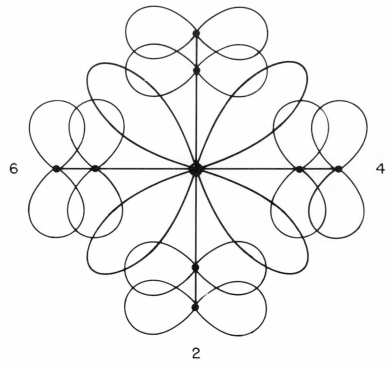

Fig. 2. Schematic diagram of π orbitals for M(CO)$_6$.

STRETCH-BEND INTERACTIONS

Stretch of C_iO_i should have only higher order effects on the various angles so we shall assume all $F_{C_iO_i,\beta}$ and $F_{C_iO_i,\alpha} = 0$.

If we stretch C_1M ($S_{C_1M} = +1$) there may be a slight tendency for the C atoms to repel each other, which would make α_{13}, α_{14}, α_{15}, and α_{16} decrease. By the previous argument this would, in turn, cause the C_iO_i bonds ($i = 3$, 4, 5, and 6) to bend away from C_1O_1. This is indicated schematically in Fig. 3C.

SYMMETRY FORCE CONSTANTS FOR M(CO)$_6$ UNDER πIVFF

We can now write out all the force constants and interaction constants in terms of 10 constants. In the general case there are 23

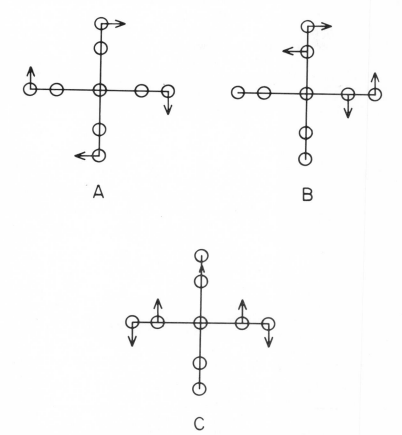

Fig. 3. Schematic displacements of bending coordinates.

symmetry force constants, thus we have quite a reduction. Combining these in the proper symmetry we have the symmetry force constants of Table 5. Thus, we have reduced the problem to determining 10 force constants from a possible 13 fundamental vibrational frequencies.

APPLICATION OF πIVFF TO Mo(CO)$_6$

We shall now briefly discuss the application of this force field to the experimental observations on the vibrational spectrum of Mo(CO)$_6$. At this time we feel we can assign 12 of the thirteen fundamental frequencies though many of the assignments are inconclusive. However, there is enough evidence to allow us to examine the force field as related to the bonding in Mo(CO)$_6$.

Only four of the 13 fundamental frequencies are infrared active. However, some of the others can be assigned with near certainty from combination bands observed in the infrared. There is apparently no appreciable anharmonicity except for the CN stretching vibrations. With the aid of combination bands we have assigned approximate values to the anharmonic constants in an attempt to improve the accuracy of the quadratic potential function.

TABLE 5: SYMMETRY FORCE CONSTANTS FOR M(CO)$_6$ UNDER πIVFF

A_{1g}	F_{11}	$F_{CO} + 3B$
	F_{22}	$F_{MC} + D^2/3B$
	F_{12}	0
E_g	F_{33}	F_{CO}
	F_{44}	F_{MC}
	F_{34}	D
F_{1g}	F_{55}	$F_\beta - 3P$
F_{1u}	F_{66}	$F_{CO} - B$
	F_{77}	$F_\beta + P$
	F_{88}	$F_{MC} - D^2/9B$
	F_{99}	$4f_\alpha/3$
	F_{67}	0
	F_{68}	$4D/3$
	F_{69}	0
	F_{78}	$-(2\sqrt{2})K$
	F_{79}	$(\sqrt{2})T$
	F_{89}	$4H$
F_{2g}	$F_{10,10}$	$F_\beta + P$
	$F_{11,11}$	$4f_\alpha/3$
	$F_{10,11}$	T
F_{2u}	$F_{12,12}$	$F_\beta + P$
	$F_{13,13}$	$4f_\alpha/3$
	$F_{12,13}$	$\sqrt{2}\,T$

Let us look again at our force constant matrix (see Table 5). We are fairly certain of the A_{1g} and F_{1u} frequencies. From these frequencies we can arrive at fairly good values for F_{CO}, F_{MC}, B, and D by making assumptions about K, T, and H. In first approximation we let K and H equal zero. We are left with a set of force constants to calculate all the frequencies. These are given in Table 6.

The E_g frequencies, ω_3 and ν_4, were not used in the calculation. The agreement of calculated and observed ω_3 is quite good. The agreement for ν_4 is less good; however, it is certainly tolerable considering the approximations involved, and serves to substantiate the derivation of the potential function. The agreement can easily be made even closer by adding other parameters in the derivation. How-

TABLE 6: FORCE CONSTANTS AND FREQUENCIES FOR Mo(CO)$_6$

F_{CO}	18.040	$4f\alpha/3$	0.251
F_{MC}	1.742	P	0.076
B	0.107	K	0
D	0.536	T	0.045
F_β	0.915	H	0

	Calc.	Obs.		Calc.	Obs.
ω_1	2183	[2183][a]	ν_8	368	368
ν_2	390	390	ν_9	80	80
ω_3	2111	[2104][a]	ν_{10}	587	
ν_4	324	(343)[b]	ν_{11}	86	80
ν_5	482	482	ν_{12}	576	(575)[b]
ω_6	2086	[2086][a]	ν_{13}	62	(62)[b]
ν_7	594	593			

[a] These frequencies have been corrected for anharmonicity.
[b] These frequencies are quite uncertain.

ever, it does not appear desirable to do this until the doubtful frequency assignments are more firmly established.

It is interesting to compare these results with those on Ni(CO)$_4$ (see Ref. 1). The comparison is given in Table 7.

The higher F_{MC} and lower F_{CO} for Ni(CO)$_4$ indicate greater MC double-bond character. The interactions, B and D, are somewhat greater for Mo(CO)$_6$. The most striking difference is in the M—C—O bending constant, F_β, which is almost $2\frac{1}{2}$ times greater for Mo(CO)$_6$ than Ni(CO)$_4$. At present we do not understand the reason for this great difference.

It is of interest to compare the above results with a Urey-Bradley treatment. For the stretching frequencies the best fit we can obtain with such a treatment is given in Table 8.

TABLE 7: COMPARISON OF FORCE CONSTANTS OF Mo(CO)$_6$
WITH THOSE OF Ni(CO)$_4$

	Ni(CO)$_4$	Mo(CO)$_6$
F_{CO}	17.55[a]	18.04
F_{MC}	2.09	1.74
B	0.086	0.107
D	0.33	0.536
F_β	0.38	0.915
F_α	0.23	0.25
P	0.08	0.076
K	0.017	0[b]
T	0	0.045[b]
H	0	0[b]

[a]In Ref. 1 the anharmonicity relations were incorrectly applied, so F_{CO} should be 17.55, instead of 17.31. The other constants are not affected by this change.

[b]Quite arbitrary until ν_{10} and ν_{12} are better known.

CYANIDE COMPLEXES

A similar treatment can be applied to cyanide complexes, such as Co(CN)$_6^{-3}$. However, from the observed frequencies of this complex as well as other cyanide complexes, there is immediately apparent a big difference from the hexacarbonyls. That is, the three CN frequencies (A_{1g}, E_g, and F_{1u}) lie close together indicating very little CN, CN interaction. Let us glance again at the stretching force constants under the πIVFF, as seen in Table 9.

Since it is apparent from the observed frequencies that $B \approx 0$, in order that $D^2/3B$ not go to infinity, it must be true that $D \approx 0$. This suggests that the off-diagonal stretch-stretch interaction terms can be neglected for cyanide complexes, thus greatly simplifying the solution as well as giving support to some of the earlier work in which the off-diagonal terms were neglected arbitrarily. However, if the π bonding

TABLE 8: UREY-BRADLEY TREATMENT FOR Mo(CO)$_6$

	Cal.	Observed
ω_1	2109	2183
ν_2	390	390[a]
ω_3	2079	2104
ν_4	261	(343)
ω_6	2086	2086[a]
ν_8	368	368[a]

[a]These three frequencies were used to derive the force constants. It is apparent that this treatment is unsatisfactory.

TABLE 9: πIVFF STRETCHING FORCE CONSTANTS FOR M(CN)$_6$

$$F_{CN}{}^{A_{1g}} = F_{CN} + 3B$$
$$F_{MC}{}^{A_{1g}} = F_{MC} + (D^2/3B)$$
$$F_{CN,MC}{}^{A_{1g}} = 0$$

$$F_{CN}{}^{E_g} = F_{CN}$$
$$F_{MC}{}^{E_g} = F_{MC}$$
$$F_{CN,MC}{}^{E_g} = D$$

$$F_{CN}{}^{F_{1u}} = F_{CO} - B$$
$$F_{MC}{}^{F_{1u}} = F_{MC} - D^2/9B$$
$$F_{CN,MC}{}^{F_{1u}} = 4D/3$$

is less important, other interactions become more important. Nevertheless, it appears that neglect of the off-diagonal stretch-stretch interactions may still be justified. If a displacement of C_1O_1 does not affect the other C_iO_i while displacement of C_1M causes a considerable change of the other C_iM, this would indicate that increasing C_1O_1 does not cause much change in C_1M.

In conclusion, we wish to point out that the pi interaction valence force field described herein appears to fit the vibrational spectra of metal carbonyls. The results support the idea that $M(d_\pi) - C(p_\pi)$ bonding plays an important role in the interactions among the various internal coordinates.

For cyanide complexes there appears to be a fundamental difference from carbonyls. M—C pi-bonding is apparently less important and the solution of the vibrational problem is simplified.

REFERENCES

1. L. H. Jones, *J. Mol. Spec.*, **5**, 133 (1960).
2. R. Ercoli, F. Calderazzo, A. Alberola, *J. Am. Chem. Soc.*, **82**, 2966 (1960).
3. J. W. Linnett and P. J. Wheatley, *Trans. Faraday Soc.*, **45**, 33 (1949).

A COMPARISON OF THE STABILITIES OF METAL CHELATES CONTAINING N, P, AND As AS DONOR ATOMS

HARRY IRVING and D. L. PETTIT

Department of Inorganic and Structural Chemistry
The University
Leeds, England

From the point of view of metal complex formation it is generally recognised that acceptor atoms can be classified according to one of two types: (1) those which form their most stable complexes with the first member of each vertical group in the Periodic Table (viz., N, O, and F), and (2) those which form their most stable complexes with the second (*viz.*, P, S, and Cl) or subsequent members.[1,2] Class (2) character is displayed most strongly in a group of elements lying at the centre of the Periodic Table bordered on the right-hand side by copper, cadmium, and thallium. In this context every oxidation state must be considered as a different acceptor atom, e.g., Cu(I) belongs definitely to class (2), whereas Cu(II) shows weak class (1) character towards halide ions[3] but may behave as a class (2) metal towards ligand atoms from Groups V and VI.

Most of the metals of class (2) form inert, non-volatile complexes which are usually very insoluble in water and do not lend themselves to investigation by equilibrium studies in homogeneous solution. Indeed the only published results in this field refer to complexes of silver with certain unidentate ligands which have been rendered water-soluble by the introduction of one or more sulphonic acid groups into the phenyl groups attached to the donor atoms.[4] In the present paper a wider range of metals has been studied and an attempt has been made to study ligands capable of forming chelate rings in which nitrogen has been replaced in turn by phosphorus and arsenic.

Owing to preparative difficulties a full range of suitable compounds could not be obtained. Others were tried but had to be abandoned on account of the insolubility of their metal derivatives, their susceptibility to oxidation, or their ease of hydrolysis or decarboxylation. The final choice was restricted to the following compounds:

$$C_6H_5As\Big\langle\begin{array}{l}CH_2 \cdot COOH \\ CH_2 \cdot COOH\end{array}\qquad (I)\qquad\qquad p\text{-}Cl \cdot C_6H_4As\Big\langle\begin{array}{l}C_2H_4 \cdot COOH \\ C_2H_4 \cdot COOH\end{array}\qquad (II)$$

$$C_6H_5N\begin{array}{c} {}^{CH_2 \cdot COOH} \\ {}_{CH_2 \cdot COOH} \end{array} \quad (IV) \qquad C_6H_{11}N\begin{array}{c} {}^{CH_2 \cdot COOH} \\ {}_{CH_2 \cdot COOH} \end{array} \quad (III)$$

and $(C_6H_5)X \cdot C_2H_4 \cdot COOH$ (V) $X = N$;   (VI) $X = P$;   (VII) $X = As$

A comparison of (I) and (IV) will show the effect of replacing nitrogen by arsenic; the compound (III) was included to obtain additional data for complexones of type (IV). Comparison of (I) and (II) would permit an assessment of the effect of an increase in the size of the chelate rings. Since it was very unlikely that six-member chelate rings would form at all with the compounds (V), (VI), and (VII), they should show the effects of replacing nitrogen successively by a phosphorus or arsenic atom. Owing to their lower solubility all measurements with these three ligands had to be carried out in 20% aqueous dioxan, but no difficulty was experienced with the other ligands in working with solutions at least 0.002 M. In all cases a constant salt background of 0.1 M potassium nitrate was employed.

Acid dissociation constants were all determined by potentiometric titration using a glass electrode and a calomel reference electrode. Attempts to use a hydrogen electrode with the arsine derivative (I) were unsuccessful, for above $pH = 7$ it became poisoned and had to be completely replated before it could be used again.

Acid dissociation constants were calculated from the titration curves by the usual methods,[5] but a graphical method had to be employed with (I) and (II) whose dissociation constants were similar in magnitude causing the buffer regions to overlap considerably. Simultaneously with the removal of the first proton from cyclohexylamine-diacetic acid (III; H_2L), the second proton must migrate to the nitrogen atom for the value of $pK_2 = 10.61$ is characteristic of the ionisation of an ammonium ion. Despite the much lower value of $pK_2 = 4.96$ for phenyliminodiacetic acid (IV), it seems probable that the second proton is located on nitrogen also, for the aromatic ring will stabilise the basic ion L^{2-} relative to its conjugate acid, HL^- so that the dissociation of the anilinium ion, $C_6H_5 \cdot NH_2^{(+)} \cdot CH_2 \cdot COO^{(-)}$, occurs at a relatively low pH. The site of the remaining proton in the ion HL^- of the arsine-acids (I) and (II) is not certain. In the former acid the difference between $pK_1 = 3.60$ and $pK_2 = 5.03$ is larger than can be attributed to purely statistical factors (about 0.6 log units). The difference for the corresponding carbon acid (glutaric acid $pK_1 = 4.21$, $pK_2 = 5.06$) is of this order. In the chlorophenyl-arsine (II) the carboxyl groups are separated from the arsenic atom by a longer chain and the dissociation of the protons will be less influenced by inductive effects from the arsenic or by the attached aromatic system. In fact the values $pK_1 = 4.17$ and $pK_2 = 5.08$ are not far from those of propionic acid itself ($pK = 4.88$) and their difference is largely explicable on statistical grounds.

The dissociation constants of the acids (V)-(VII) are very similar and there is little doubt that the dissociation is that of a proton from the carboxyl group. Since the addition of 20% dioxan generally results in an increase in the pK value of about 0.3 units, the values for the three acids $(C_6H_5)X \cdot C_2H_4 \cdot COOH$ ($pK_1 = 5.06, 5.03,$ and $5.21,$ respectively, in 20% dioxan; see Table 1) are close to the value for propionic acid itself ($pK = 4.71, \mu = 0.2, T = 20\,^\circ C$).

The stability of complexes formed with divalent ions was investigated by conventional methods. Since complexes higher than 1:1 were not encountered with copper, nickel, zinc, and cadmium, and contributions due to protonated or hydroxylated species were negligible over the pH range 3-10, the calculation of stability constants was simple (see Table 1). The 1:1 copper complex of phenylarsine diacetic acid (I) formed as a bright green precipitate at pH 4.6. Its composition was confirmed by ultimate analysis and by the method of continuous variations by following the absorbancy of the complex at 322 and 350 mμ. No evidence was obtained for any complex formation between the arsenic-containing ligands (I) and (II) and alkaline earth metals.

The determination of stability constants for complexes of the arsines with type (2) metals such as silver proved more difficult. The results of potentiometric titrations of mixtures of phenylarsinediacetic acid and silver ions in which only the change in pH was recorded for several different concentration ratios, [total silver]/ [total ligand acid], proved difficult to interpret although they demonstrated the occurrence of the protonated species AgHL and the simple 1:1 complex AgL^-. Titrations in the presence of a large excess of silver ions were also tried and Schwarzenbach's methof of "temporary constants" was employed.[7] Other titrations were carried out with a constant concentration of silver ions achieved by working with an ionic background of 0.1 M KBrO$_3$ to which a calculated amount of AgNO$_3$ had been added, sufficient to produce a slight permanent precipitate of AgBrO$_3$.[8] From such titrations constants about 0.5 log units lower than those finally shown in Table 1 were obtained. Since [Ag$^+$] was calculated from published solubility products for AgBrO$_3$ rather than from direct measurements, a constant error may have been introduced.

Finally, solutions of (I) in aceticacid-sodium acetate buffers were titrated with silver ions. [Ag$^+$] was measured with a silver/silver iodide electrode and [H$^+$] measured simultaneously by using a glass

TABLE 1

Ligand	I	II	III	IV	V[b]	VI[b]	VII[b]
pK_1	3.60	4.17	2.25	2.40[a]	5.06	5.03	5.21
pK_1	5.03	5.08	10.61	4.96[a]			
Copper(II)							
$\log K_1$	2.51	~1.5	11.04	6.57[a]	n.m.	n.m.	n.m.
Nickel							
$\log K_1$	1.49	n.m.	8.08	3.53[a]	n.m.	n.m.	n.m.
Zinc							
$\log K_1$	1.4	n.m.	7.60	3.22[a]	n.m.	n.m.	n.m.
Cadmium							
$\log K_1$	~1	n.m.	6.94	2.16[a]	n.m.	n.m.	n.m.
Silver							
$\log K_1$	5.37	5.00	4.60	1	n.m.	3.80	3.87
$\log K_2$	...	...	...	...	...	2.70	...
$\log K^M_{MHL}$	4.02	3.98	...	...	...	2.7	2.3
$\log K^H_{MHL}$	3.68	4.06	...	...	...	3.93	3.64
Mercury(II)							
$\log K_1$	14.7[c]	...	13.8	8.26	...	...	...
$\log K_2$	5.22	...	9.0	3.65	...	...	...
$\log \beta_2$	19.92	24.4	22.8	12.91	(20.9)	16.9	(22.5)
Copper(I)							
$\log K_1$	5.6	...	...	...	...	...	...
$\log K^H_{MHL}$	4.0	...	...	...	...	...	...

[a]Schwarzenbach, G., Anderegg, G., Schneider, W., and Senn, H., *Helv. Chim. Acta*, **38**, 1147 (1955).
[b]Measurements in 20% aqueous dioxan. [c]From a potentiometric determination of mixtures of HgCl$_2$ and the ligand (I), the values log K_1 = 13.4 and log K_2 = 19.2 were obtained.

electrode and pH-meter. Titrations were carried out at pH 5.92 and at 4.48 using three different concentrations of silver ion in each case. Stability constants were then calculated by Leden's method as modified by Fronaeus,[4] employing graphical integration to obtain the free ligand concentration. Values of $\bar{n}$ tended to go just above unity at high ligand concentrations, but the predominant complexes were clearly AgL$^-$ and AgHL and there was no evidence of the participation of AgH$_2$L$^+$ or of bimetallic species. An alternate method of calculation is as follows: if C_L and C_M are the total concentrations of ligand and metal, respectively, and [H] and [M] the hydrogen- and metal-ion concentrations when the degree of neutralisation is a, it can be shown that

$$\frac{(2 - R) + (1 - R)[H]/K_2 - [H]^2 R/K_1 K_2}{[M](R - 2)} = \frac{[H](R - 1)K^M_{MHL} + K_{ML}}{(R - 2)K_2}$$

where $R = (aC_L + [H] - [OH])C_L$, $K_{ML} = [ML]/[M][L]$, $K^M_{MHL} = [MHL]/[M][HL]$, $K_1 = [H][HL]/[HL]$, $K_2 = [H][L]/[HL]$, and charges have been omitted for simplicity. A plot of the left-hand term against the expression $[H](R - 1)/(R - 2)K_2$ gave excellent straight lines (not reproduced) from which K_{ML} was calculated from the intercept and K^M_{MHL} from the slope.

Measurements of the stabilities of mercury(II) complexes were made entirely by Schwarzenbach's "p[Hg]" method[9] which permits adequate time for the equilibria to be established and involves simultaneous measurements of pH and pHg. The calculations become difficult when more than one complex is present. They also depend upon the assumption that mercurous ions do not enter competitively into complex formation.

Discussion

The effect of replacing N by As is shown by a comparison of the stability of complexes formed by the ligands (IV) and (I). Since the value of pK_2 for (I) (5.03) and (IV) (4.96) do not differ much from that of glutaric acid ($pK_2 = 5.08$) where a non-coordinating methylene group has replaced N or As, any increase above the values $K_{CuL} = 2.40$ or $K_{ZnL} = 1.60$ reported for glutaric acid would indicate that bonding through nitrogen or arsenic had occurred. It is clear from Table 1 that bonding through nitrogen does occur in (IV), but bonding through arsenic in (I) is negligible. This is in accordance with expectation if only sigma-bonds are involved. Since comparable data for phenyliminodipropionic acid and pimelic acid are not available, a similar discussion cannot be applied to ligand (II), but comparison with results for (I) demonstrate the effect of increasing ring size in lowering stability.

The stability order $Cu^{2+} > Ni^{2+} > Zn^{2+} > Cd^{2+} > Ag^+$ which holds for most nitrogen-donors is illustrated by the new data for cyclohexylaminediacetic acid (III). Comparison with data for phenyliminodiacetic acid (IV) demonstrates the effect of the aromatic ring attached to nitrogen, for by participation in its pi-bonding system, its lone pair is less available for donor bond formation. The still greater weakness of an arsenic-containing analogue would be predicted for class (1) metals.

With silver, however, which is a typical class (2) metal, the situation is clearly reversed for now the Ag = As bond is strengthened by $d\pi$ bonding involving electrons from the filled 4d shell of the silver ion and the unoccupied d-orbitals of the arsenic. This effect cannot, of course, occur with nitrogen. Experiment shows that (I) and (II) form stronger bonds with Ag^+ than even the aliphatic amine (III). That there is so little difference in the stability of the silver complexes of (I) and (II) might suggest that bonding through the carboxylic oxygen atoms was negligible in both cases so that changes in the sizes of the chelate rings from 5- to 6- membered has become of secondary importance. However, the inductive effect of the p-chlorine atom in (II) could weaken the sigma bond aht the mesomeric effect might somewhat reduce the $d\pi$ bonding; this could account for the lower value of K_{AgL} observed. Yet at the pH of measurement the carboxyl groups in both (I) and (II) are fully ionised, and if they were not chelated their inductive effect on the arsenic atoms would be less in (II) than in (I) owing to the interposition of the additional methylene groups. These effects taken together may explain the similarity in the values of K_{AgL} for the two ligands. It is noteworthy that with both ligands there is a marked tendency for the 1:1 complex to take up a proton (log k^H_{AgHL} = 3.68 and 4.06, respectively), that of the longer chain ligand being the greater.

The stabilities of complexes of mercury with arsenic or phosphorus as donor atoms have not previously been reported. Since Hg(II) has quite pronounced class (2) character,[1,2] very stable complexes would be expected. This is borne out by the preset results (Table 1). The mercury complexes of (I) and (II) are far stabler than that of phenyliminodiacetic acid. The greater reclutance to form a bis-complex with the arsine acid (K_1/K_2 = $10^{9.5}$) as compared with the nitrogen anologue (K_1/K_2 = $10^{3.6}$) is particularly interesting.

In view of the poor donor character of ligands of the type $(C_6H_5)_2XCH_3$ (where X = N, P, and As) towards class (1) metals, and the further weakening consequent upon replacing CH_3 by $CH_2 \cdot COO^{(-)}$, the failure to detect any complex formation with the ligands (V), (VI) and (VII) is not unexpected. Even a small entropy gain from the formation of a six-membered chelate ring cannot be expected to overcome the unfavourable enthalpy terms. However, with class (2) metals the effect of $d\pi$ bonding is strikingly obvious. The arsine is reluctant to form more than a 1:1 complex; but two molecules of the phosphine are coordinated with approximately equal ease so that there is no marked "step" at $\bar{n}$ = 1. One very striking result is that the measured stabilities are so much lower than for silver complexes of the ligands m-$Ph_2P \cdot C_6H_4 \cdot SO_3^{(-)}$ (log K_1 = 8.15, log K_2 = 8.15) or $As(C_6H_4 \cdot SO_3^{(-)}-m)_3$ (log K_1 = 5.36).[4] Owing to the low solubilities of the complexes with mercury, too much reliance cannot be placed on the values of stability constants with (V) and (VII); there is no doubt, however, that the complexes are extraordinarily stable.

REFERENCES

1. S. Ahrland, J. Chatt, and N. R. Davies, *Quart. Reviews*, **12**, 265, (1958).
2. H. Irving, *Fifth Internat. Conf. on Coordination Compounds, Chem. Soc. Special Publication No. 13* (1959).
3. B. G. Carleson and H. Irving, *J. Chem. Soc.*, **1954**, 4390.
4. S. Ahrland, J. Chatt, N. R. Davies, and A. A. Williams, *ibid.*, **1958**, 276.
5. H. Irving, R. Shelton, and R. Evans, *ibid.*, **1958**, 3540.
6. H. Rossott, Ph.D. Thesis, Oxford, 1954.
7. G. Schwarzenbach and H. Ackermann, *Helv. Chim. Acta*, **31**, 1034 (1948).
8. J. Prue and G. Schwarzenbach, *ibid.*, **33**, 963 (1950).
9. G. Schwarzenbach and G. Anderegg, *ibid.* **40**, 1894 (1957).

SOME METAL PYRAZINE COMPLEXES

A. B. P. LEVER, J. LEWIS, and R. S. NYHOLM

William Ramsay and Ralph Forster Laboratories of Chemistry
University College London
London, England

The compounds formed between pyridine and metallic salts have been well investigated, but little is known of the corresponding pyrazine compounds. Pyrazines have a second potential donor nitrogen atom in the 4 position and are much weaker bases than the pyridines. The pyrazine nucleus appears to protonate or quaternize at only one of the nitrogen atoms, the second atom being deactivated. It is of obvious interest to investigate the reactivity of this group of compounds towards transition metal ions. We have recently studied the reaction of pyrazine and methyl substituted pyrazines with copper(I) and (II), nickel(II) and cobalt(II) and the work reported here is concerned with the cobalt(II) complexes.

Pyrazine and its derivatives react with cobalt halides to give two main classes of compounds, $LCoX_2$ and L_2CoX_2. Each of these groups appears to give compounds with octahedral and tetrahedral structures, depending on the halogen and the pyrazine used. Table 1 gives the various compounds and classes observed, with the stereochemistry of the solids.

The stereochemistry of the solids has been assigned on the basis of the magnetic moment and the visible and ultra-violet spectra of the compounds. Octahedral compounds normally have moments in the range 4.8–5.3 B.M. whilst tetrahedral complexes have lower moments in the range 4.3–5.0 B.M. In the case of the majority of tetrahedral compounds, there is strong absorption in the region 600 to 750 mμ of the spectrum with extinction coefficient of the bands of the order of 10^2, whilst octahedral compounds absorb in the region 450 to 630 mμ with extinction coefficients of the order of 10.

The magnetic moments of all the compounds classified as octahedral are greater than 4.90 B.M., and the reflection spectra of the pyrazine adducts show no adsorption in the 600–750 mμ region. The remaining "octahedral'' compounds have magnetic moments well outside the

TABLE 1

Class	Octahedral	Colour	μ_{eff}B.M.	Tetrahedral	Colour	μ_{eff}B.M.
	$MPCoCl_2$	Violet-pink	5.36			
				$MPCoBr_2$	Blue	4.68
				$MPCoI_2$	Green	4.59
$L\,CoX_2$	$2:5$-$DMPCoCl_2$	Violet-pink	5.4			
				$2:5\,DMPCoBr_2$	Blue	4.65
				$2:5\,DMPCoI_2$	Green	4.54
	P_2CoCl_2	Pink	4.92			
	P_2CoBr_2	Pink	5.04			
	P_2CoI_2	Orange	5.26			
L_2CoX_2	$(2:6\,DMP_2)_2$ $CoCl_2$	Violet-pink	5.46			
	$(2:6\,DMP)_2$ $CoBr_2$	Violet-pink	5.34			
				$(2:6\,DMP)_2CoI_2$	Green	4.76

P = Pyrazine; MP = Methylpyrazine; 2:5-DMP = 2.5 Dimethylpyrazine; 2:6-DMP = 2.6 Dimethylpyrazine.

tetrahedral range but do show some absorption in the region 600–750 mμ. The compounds considered to be tetrahedral all have reflection spectra showing intense absorption in the 600–750 mμ region and moments in the range anticipated for tetrahedral compounds.

As with the corresponding pyridine complexes, some of the compounds appear to produce in solution a number of species in equilibrium with each other. In certain cases this equilibrium is markedly dependent on the solvent, the concentration of the added complex and/or the temperature. Thus, in the case of methylpyrazine cobalt iodise, ($MPCoI_2$), the molecular weight in camphor favours a dimeric structure (Table 2), whilst in acetone the molecular weight data imply a dissociation of the complex.

The chloride and bromide complexes of 2:6-dimethylpyrazine may be used further to illustrate this point. The chloride, ($2:6$-DMP_2CoCl_2), is a violet-pink solid, with a magnetic moment, $\mu = 5.46$ B.M., indicating an octahedral structure in the solid. The compound dissolves in nitromethane and acetone to give blue solutions with spectra typical of tetrahedral complexes. The compound is a non-electrolyte in acetone and the molecular weight data would indicate that the compound exists in these solutions as a monomeric tetrahedral complex $(2:6$-$DMP)_2CoCl_2$. The corresponding bromide, also, ap-

TABLE 2

Compound	Solvent	Molecular Weight	
		Observed	Calculated
$(2:6\text{-DMP})_2CoCl_2$	Acetone	351	346
$(2:6\text{-DMP})_2CoBr_2$	Acetone	297	435
$(2:6\text{-DMP})_2CoI_2$	Camphor	490	529
$(MP)CoI_2$	Acetone	272	407
	Camphor	840	
$(2:5\,DMP)CoBr_2$	$2:5\,DMP$	672	327
$(2:5\,DMP)CoI_2$	$2:5\,DMP$	860	421

2:6-DMP =2:6 Dimethylpyrazine; 2:5-DMP =2:5 Dimethylpyrazine; MP =
Methylpyrazine.

pears to be octahedral in the solid state, and gives in nitromethane
and acetone blue solutions with spectra characteristic of tetrahedral
species. In agreement with this tetrahedral-octahedral conversion
the magnetic moment in acetone solution is reduced from the value of
5.34 B.M. observed for the solid to $\sim$ 4.2 B.M. The complex is a non-
electrolyte in acetone, but the molecular weight data in acetone now
excludes the formulation of the compound as a simple monomeric
species $(2:6\text{-DMP})_2CoBr_2$. In agreement with this, the solutions in
acetone do not obey Beer's Law, and a marked variation in spectra
is observed on addition of 2:6 dimethylpyrazine. A possible explanation of this system involves an equilibrium between the complexes $(2:6\text{-DMP})_2CoBr_2$ and $(2:6\text{-DMPCoBr}_2)_2$.

OPTICAL ACTIVITY IN RARE-EARTH AND TRANSITION METAL COMPLEXES

ANDREW D. LIEHR

Bell Telephone Laboratories, Inc.
Murray Hill, New Jersey

A substance is said to be optically active if it will rotate the plane of polarization of electromagnetic radiation which impinges upon it. There exist two general types of optical activity: (1) natural and (2) forced. A substance is said to be naturally optically active if in its *natural* state it exhibits the phenomenon of optical activity. A substance is said to exhibit *forced* optical activity if it will only rotate the plane of polarization of the incident radiation when under external duress—such as is supplied by the application of (screw-shear) pressure, electrical fields, magnetic fields, and extremes of temperature conditions. Fortunately, both the natural and forced optical rotatory power of material media can be discussed quite simply on a macroscopic and microscopic basis if one confines oneself to a phenomenological description of the phenomenon. The detailed evaluation of the parameters occurring in such a description, though extremely interesting, is quite difficult. We shall, therefore, confine ourselves solely to the phenomenological discussion of optical rotatory power and shall only quote the results of the more fundamental quantum-mechanical theory of Rosenfeld.

The characteristic feature of propagation in an optically active medium which is responsible for the rotation of the plane of polarization is *circular double refraction*. This was first recognized by Fresnel. A substance is said to be *double refracting* if, in a given direction the index of refraction, m, and hence the (phase) velocity, $v = \dfrac{c}{n}$ for the propagation of electromagnetic waves, is different for two different states of polarization. In the case of optical activity the index of refraction (or velocity) is different for right and left circularly polarized waves, respectively.*

---

*This circumstance implies than an optically active medium is also *circularly dichroic* that is, that it possesses a different coefficient of absorption, κ, for right and left circularly polarized light.

To see just how natural or forced circular double refraction will account for optical rotatory power, we must invoke the electromagnetic theory of Maxwell. According to it there are two vectors associated with an electromagnetic wave which are transverse to the direction of propagation. These are the electric induction, $\vec{D}$, and the magnetic induction, $\vec{B}$. Suppose the wave is traveling in the direction of the unit vector $\vec{k}$ with a velocity of $\frac{c}{n}$, where n is the index of refraction of the medium and c is the velocity of light. If we introduce unit vectors $\vec{i}$ and $\vec{j}$, mutually orthogonal to $\vec{k}$, in such a way that $(\vec{i}, \vec{j}, \vec{k})$ form the basis of a right-handed coordinate system, then $\vec{D}$ and $\vec{B}$ may be written in the shorthand form $\vec{D} = \text{Real}\left[\vec{D}_0 \exp\left[i\left(\omega t - \frac{2\pi n z}{\lambda}\right)\right]\right]$;

$$\vec{B} = \text{Real}\left[\vec{B}_0 \exp\left[i\left(\omega t \frac{2\pi n z}{\lambda}\right)\right]\right] \quad (1)$$

where $\vec{D}_0$ and $\vec{B}_0$ are constant vectors in the $(\vec{i}, \vec{j})$ plane, ω is the angular frequency of the wave, and λ is the wavelength *in vacuo*. For a right circularly polarized wave the constant amplitude $\vec{D}_0$ will be of the form

$$\vec{D}_0 = D(\vec{i} + i\vec{j}), \quad (2)$$

for taking the real part of the expression for $\vec{D}$ we obtain

$$\vec{D}_r = D\left[\vec{i} \cos\left(\omega t - \frac{2\pi n z}{\lambda}\right) - \vec{j} \sin\left(\omega t - \frac{2\pi n z}{\lambda}\right)\right]. \quad (3)$$

We see that at $t = 0$, $z = 0$, $\vec{D}_r$ is parallel to $\vec{i}$, and as time goes on the direction of $\vec{D}_r$ at $z = 0$ rotates in a *clockwise* sense as viewed by an observer faced in the $-\vec{k}$ direction—that is, faced so that the radiation enters his eyes. Similarly a left circularly polarized wave is represented by

$$\vec{D}_0 = D(\vec{i} - i\vec{j}) \quad (4)$$

so that

$$\vec{D}_l = D\left[\vec{i} \cos\left(\omega t - \frac{2\pi n z}{\lambda}\right) + \vec{j} \sin\left(\omega t - \frac{2\pi n z}{\lambda}\right)\right]. \quad (5)$$

These results express the fact that circularly polarized electromagnetic radiation may be regarded as the superposition of two perpendicular plane polarized waves, out of phase by 90°. Similarly, we see that linearly polarized radiation may be likewise regarded as arising from the superposition of two circularly polarized waves, e.g.,

$$\vec{D} = \vec{D}_l + \vec{D}_r = 2D\,\vec{i}\,\cos\left(\omega t - \frac{2\pi n z}{\lambda}\right) \tag{6}$$

Now consider that the wave is made up of a superposition of a right circularly polarized wave with phase δ and a left circularly polarized wave with phase $-\delta$. Then

$$\vec{D} = \vec{D}_r(\delta) + \vec{D}_l(-\delta) = D\left[\begin{array}{c} \vec{i}\left\{\begin{array}{l}\cos\left(\omega t - \frac{2\pi n z}{\lambda} + \delta\right)\\ + \cos\left(\omega t - \frac{2\pi n z}{\lambda} - \delta\right)\end{array}\right\}\\ -\vec{j}\left\{\begin{array}{l}\sin\left(\omega t - \frac{2\pi n z}{\lambda} + \delta\right)\\ - \sin\left(\omega t - \frac{2\pi n z}{\lambda} - \delta\right)\end{array}\right\}\end{array}\right] \tag{7}$$

or using the trigonometric expansion formulae $\cos(a + b) = \cos a \cos b - \sin a \sin b$, etc., we have

$$\vec{D} = 2D\left[\vec{i}\,\cos\left(\omega t - \frac{2\pi n z}{\lambda}\right)\cos\delta - \vec{j}\,\cos\left(\omega t - \frac{2\pi n z}{\lambda}\right)\sin\delta\right] \tag{8}$$

or

$$\vec{D} = 2D\cos\left(\omega t - \frac{2\pi n z}{\lambda}\right)\vec{s}\,(\delta),\ \vec{s}\,(\delta) = \vec{i}\,\cos\delta - \vec{j}\,\sin\delta \tag{9}$$

Thus for $\delta = 0$ we have linear polarization along the $\vec{i}$ axis, as was demonstrated previously in Eq. (6), and if $\delta > 0$ the plane of polarization is turned *clockwise* with respect to the $\vec{i}$ axis:

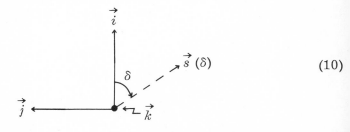

$$\tag{10}$$

Now let us suppose that the medium has different indices of refraction n_r and n_l for right and left circularly polarized radiation, respectively. Suppose at $t = t_1$ and $z = 0$ the radiation is polarized along $\vec{i}$. After traversing a distance d along the z axis, the two circular components of $\vec{D}$ will be:

$$(1) \quad t = t_1, \quad z = 0: \vec{D} = \vec{D}_r + \vec{D}_l = 2D\,\vec{i}\,\cos\,\omega t_1 \tag{11}$$

$$(2) \quad t = t_2, \quad z = d: \vec{D} = D\,\vec{i}\left[\cos\left(\omega t_2 - \frac{2\pi n_r d}{\lambda}\right) + \cos\left(\omega t_2 - \frac{2\pi n_l d}{\lambda}\right)\right]$$

$$- D\,\vec{j}\left[\sin\left(\omega t_2 - \frac{2\pi n_r d}{\lambda}\right) - \sin\left(\omega t_2 - \frac{2\pi n_l d}{\lambda}\right)\right] \tag{12}$$

Since

$$n_{(r)\atop(l)} = \frac{1}{2}(n_r + n_l) \mp \frac{1}{2}(n_l - n_r) = \bar{n} \mp n' \tag{13}$$

we may write

$$\vec{D} = \vec{i}D\left[\cos\left(\omega t_2 - \frac{2\pi\bar{n}d}{\lambda} + \frac{2\pi n'd}{\lambda}\right) + \cos\left(\omega t_2 - \frac{2\pi\bar{n}d}{\lambda} - \frac{2\pi n'd}{\lambda}\right)\right]$$

$$- \vec{j}D\left[\sin\left(\omega t_2 - \frac{2\pi\bar{n}d}{\lambda} + \frac{2\pi n'd}{\lambda}\right) - \sin\left(\omega t_2 - \frac{2\pi\bar{n}d}{\lambda} - \frac{2\pi n'd}{\lambda}\right)\right] \tag{14}$$

Thus we see that if we set

$$\delta = \frac{2\pi n'd}{\lambda} = \frac{\pi(n_l - n_r)d}{\lambda} \tag{15}$$

in equation (14) it reduces to equation (7) which was studied previously. Hence, we have shown that the plane of $\vec{D}$ is rotated clockwise by the angle δ at $z = d$, by comparison with our previous example, Eq. (7). Therefore, the rotatory power, φ which equals the rotation per unit length, is

$$\varphi = \frac{\delta}{d} = \frac{\pi}{\lambda}(n_l - n_r) \tag{16}$$

As λ is usually very small compared with d, the path length (except for microwaves), one can obtain appreciable rotations despite the fact that the difference in the two phenomenological parameters n_l and n_r may be quite small.

The question now arises as to how Maxwell's equations must be generalized in order that we may get circular double refraction. As optical activity is a property of the medium, this generalization must be made in the material connections between $\vec{D}$ and $\vec{E}$, and $\vec{B}$ and $\vec{H}$.

It has been found that an appropriate generalization is

$$\vec{D} = \varepsilon\vec{E} - g\dot{\vec{H}}$$
$$\vec{B} = \mu\vec{H} + g\dot{\vec{E}} .$$

$$(17)$$

Setting g equal to zero in (17) yields the usual defining equations for the dielectric constant ε and the magnetic permeability μ, as well as that of the index of refraction $n = (\varepsilon\mu)^{1/2}$. In most cases μ may be set equal to unity, and circular double refraction may be attributed to a change in ε due to the phenomenological parameter g. However, in the important case of the *ferromagnetic Faraday effect*, that is, the appearance of (forced) optical activity due to an external magnetic field in ferromagnetics, it is the change in the permeability μ which causes circular double refraction; the change in ε usually being of much smaller magnitudes. We shall not pursue this case further in today's lecture. Thus we set $\mu = 1$ in the above equations and derive from the Maxwell field equations

$$\operatorname{div} \vec{D} = 0 \qquad\qquad \operatorname{div} \vec{B} = 0$$

$$\operatorname{curl} \vec{E} = \frac{-1}{c}\dot{\vec{B}} \qquad\qquad \operatorname{curl} \vec{H} = \frac{1}{c}\dot{\vec{D}} \qquad (18)$$

the following equations for n_l and n_r

$$n_r = \varepsilon^{1/2} - \omega g, \qquad\qquad n_l - n_r = 2\omega g$$
$$n_l = \varepsilon^{1/2} + \omega g,$$

$$(19)$$

ω being the common angular frequency of $\vec{D}$ and $\vec{B}$. This result, combined with our previous equation, yields for the optical rotatory power φ, the connection

$$\varphi = \left(\frac{2\pi}{\lambda}\right)^2 cg \qquad\qquad (20)$$

The next problem is to see what kind of response the individual molecules must exhibit in response to the impressed electromagnetic fields—that is, what kind of *microscopic material connections* will produce the proposed macroscopic material equations. A suitable choice of such reaction has been found to be (for the case $\mu = 1$)*

---

*The quantum-mechanical theory of Rosenfeld leads to microscopic equations of the form:

$$\vec{p} = \alpha\vec{E}_{\text{eff}} - \frac{\beta}{c}\dot{\vec{H}}_{\text{eff}} + \gamma\vec{H}_{\text{eff}}$$

$$\vec{m} = \chi\vec{H}_{\text{eff}} + \frac{\beta}{c}\dot{\vec{E}}_{\text{eff}} + \gamma\vec{E}_{\text{eff}}$$

$$\vec{p} = \alpha \, \vec{E}_{\text{eff}} - \frac{\beta}{c} \, \vec{H},$$

$$\vec{E}_{\text{eff}} = \vec{E} + \frac{4\pi}{3} \, \vec{P}, \quad \text{the Lorentz field.} \tag{21}$$

$$\vec{m} = \chi \vec{H}_{\text{eff}} + \frac{\beta}{c} \, \dot{\vec{E}}_{\text{eff}},$$

where $\vec{p}$ and $\vec{m}$ are the induced electric and magnetic dipole moments of the molecule. The essential point here is the introduction of the parameter β. The quantities α and χ are the usual electric and diamagnetic polarizability terms. These microscopic equations, together with the macroscopic identities

$$\vec{P} = N_1 \vec{p}, \qquad \vec{M} = N_1 \vec{m} \tag{22}$$

for the electric and magnetic moments per unit volume, yield, in addition to the well-known equation of ordinary dispersion theory

$$\frac{4\pi}{3} N_1 \alpha = \frac{\varepsilon - 1}{\varepsilon + 2} \tag{23}$$

an analogous expression for rotatory dispersion

$$\frac{4\pi}{3} N_1 \frac{\beta}{c} = \frac{g}{\varepsilon + 2}. \tag{24}$$

Then using the relation $n^2 = \varepsilon$, we have the rotatory power in terms of the molecular parameter β as

$$\varphi = \frac{16\pi^3 N_1 \beta}{\lambda^2} \cdot \frac{n^2 + 2}{3} . \tag{25}$$

It is this parameter β which must be determined either classically, or more preferably, quantum-mechanically, in order to understand the relation between molecular structure and optical activity. The phenomenological extension of Maxwell's equation along the lines indicated above was apparently first given by Cauchy and Gibbs.

The quantum-mechanical theory of Rosenfeld shows that

$$N_1 \beta = \sum_{\text{states } a} N_1(a) \beta_a \tag{26}$$

where

$$\beta_a = \frac{c}{3\pi h} \sum_b \frac{R_{ba}}{\nu_{ba}^2 - \nu^2}, \tag{27}$$

and where R_{ba} is the rotational strength of the absorption line, ν_{ba}, for the quantum jump $a \longrightarrow b$:

$$R_{ba} = \text{Imaginary } [(a \mid \vec{p} \mid b) \cdot (b \mid \vec{m} \mid a)]. \tag{28}$$

The similarity of these equations for rotatory dispersion and the usual expressions for ordinary dispersion (polarization) is quite striking:

$$N_1 \alpha = \sum_a N_1(a) \, \alpha_a \tag{29}$$

$$\alpha_a = \frac{e^2}{4\pi^2 m_{\text{electron}}} \sum_b \frac{f_{ba}}{\nu_{ba}^2 - \nu^2} \tag{30}$$

where f_{ba} is the so-called oscillator strength (a measure of the intensity) of the absorption line ν_{ba}:

$$f_{ba} \sim \nu_{ba} \mid (a \mid \vec{p} \mid b) \mid^2. \tag{31}$$

Rosenfeld has also derived a similar equation for Faraday rotations (and the Kerr double refraction—this is not circular, however—under applied electric fields) under applied magnetic fields. The Faraday rotation is found to depend approximately linearly on the magnetic field and on the oscillator strengths f_{ba}. The frequency dependence is given by $\beta_a = \beta_a' + \beta_a''$, β_a' giving a *paramagnetic* Faraday effect and β_a'' the diamagnetic Faraday effect, where

$$\beta_a' \sim \text{const } f\left(\frac{H}{kT}\right) \cdot \sum_b \frac{\nu f_{ba}}{\nu_{ba}(\nu_{ba}^2 - \nu^2)} \tag{32}$$

$$\beta_a'' \sim \text{const } H \sum_b \frac{\nu f_{ba}}{(\nu_{ba}^2 - \nu^2)^2} \tag{33}$$

In equation (32) and (33), the sum over states a, b is only over quantum numbers such as the "principal quantum number n" and "the total angular momentum j." The sum over the "azimuthal quantum number m_j" is taken care of in the function $f\left(\frac{H}{kt}\right)$:

$$f\left(\frac{H}{kT}\right) = \tanh\left(\frac{m j \mu H}{kT}\right) \text{(Kramers function)}..$$ for strong crystal fields in rare-earth crystals

$$f\left(\frac{H}{kT}\right) = \text{Brillouin function} \ldots\ldots\ldots$$ for weak crystal fields in rare-earth complexes   (34) and at low temperatures

$$f\left(\frac{H}{kT}\right) \approx \frac{H}{kT} \text{ (Curie function)} \ldots\ldots\ldots$$ for weak crystal fields in rare-earth complexes at high temperatures

We can now see which crystals of rare-earth and transition metal complexes may exhibit natural and the forced optical activity of the Faraday effect.*

1. *Natural optical activity*: The crystal must be such that there exists at least one transition which is *both* electric dipole and magnetic dipole allowed—see Eqs. (27) and (28). This implies that the point group symmetry of the crystal may contain *only axes of rotation—no reflection or inversion elements are allowed*. Also the observation frequency ν must be sufficiently close to one of the allowed transition frequencies ν_{ba}.

2. *Faraday rotations*: The crystal must have allowed electric dipole transitions, ν_{ba}, in the region of the observation frequency ν. In particular, for the paramagnetic rotation, as the contribution to β_a' of the state $+ m_j$ is equal and opposite to that of the state $- m_j$, we see that the population numbers of these two states must be sufficiently different for an observable effect.[1] It is also to be noted here that if the crystal field is sufficiently asymmetric so that the transitions within a given multiplet (i.e., within a given j value) are weakly electric dipole allowed, one might hope to see a paramagnetic Faraday rotation in the microwave region. This, to my knowledge, has not as yet been reported experimentally and might be worthwhile looking for.

REFERENCES

1. J. M. Daniels and H. Wesemeyer, *Canad. J. Physics*, **36**, 405 (1958).
2. M. Born and P. Jordan, *Elementare Quantummechanik*, Berlin, Julius Springer, 1930.
3. J. P. Mathieu, "Les Théories Moléculaires du Pouvoir Rotatoire Naturel," *C.N.R.S.*, Paris, 1946.
4. W. Kanzmahn, *Quantum Chemistry*, New York, Academic Press, 1957.
5. A. J. Moscowitz in C. Djerassi, *Optical Rotatory Dispersion*, New York, McGraw-Hill, 1960, Chapter 12.
6. A. D. Liehr (to be published).

---

*The Faraday effect is not to be confused with the inverse Zeeman effect.

STRUCTURE AND REACTIVITY OF THE OXYANIONS OF TRANSITION METALS: ELECTRONIC SPECTRA

M. C. R. SYMONS

Department of Chemistry
The University
Leicester, England

As a probe to study electronically excited states of ''closed-shell'' oxyanions such as permanganate and chromate, we have prepared corresponding ions with one or two ''outer'' electrons such as manganate and hypomanganate. In particular, electron-spin resonance studies have shown that these outer electrons are held in a doubly degenerate e-level which uses the d-orbitals of the metal atom with relatively small π-type overlap with oxygen $2p$-orbitals.[1] Less conclusively these studies have revealed that the next level is a trebly degenerate t_2-level spread over the whole molecule and some 15,000 cm^{-1} above the e-level.[2]

Spectra of Closed-Shell Ions

It is thus reasonable to assume that the two intense absorption bands found in the visible and near ultraviolet regions for closed-shell ions are, in order of increasing energy, caused by transitions $t_1 \longrightarrow e$ and $t_1 \longrightarrow t_2$, where t_1 is a trebly degenerate non-bonding level located entirely on oxygen.[3] This assignment is different from that derived from a molecular-orbital treatment of the energy levels by Wolfsberg and Helmholz,[4] but was assumed by Ballhausen and Liehr[5] and Carrington and Schonland[6] as a basis for calculations of intensities.

That this assignment is reasonable may be seen from the following considerations. On going from vanadate to chromate, the first transition is displaced by about 10,000 cm^{-1} to lower energies. There is a slightly smaller shift of 8,500 cm^{-1} on going from chromate to permanganate. These large shifts are of the correct magnitude for an electron-transfer from an orbital largely located on oxygen to an orbital largely concentrated on the metal atom, and would be hard to explain in any other way.

We would expect a similar trend for the $t_1 \rightarrow t_2$ transition, but the shifts should be smaller since the t_2 level is less concentrated on the central metal. The difference between the energies of the second bands for chromate and permanganate is 4,400 cm^{-1}; that for the second bands of vanadate and chromate is not known because the second maximum for vanadate cannot be estimated accurately, but it is certainly considerably smaller than the energy difference between the bands of lowest energy. Thus these assignments seem reasonable.

Spectra of Ions with One or Two Outer Electrons

These spectra were discussed earlier[7] in terms of the level-scheme of Wolfsberg and Helmholz[4], but have recently been re-interpreted[6] in the light of results obtained from electron-spin resonance studies.[1] The basis of this re-interpretation is that only the transitions thought to be important for closed-shell ions, namely $t_1 \rightarrow e$ and $t_1 \rightarrow t_2$, contribute appreciably to the observed spectra. It was shown by group-theoretical arguments that, for ions with one outer electron, both these transitions have four components, which could well be clearly separated from each other by coulomb effects. The spectra of such ions should, therefore, be complicated and difficult to interpret.

However, for ions having two outer electrons, there is but one allowed component for either transition and hence only two intense bands of low energy should be observed. It was assumed[6] that the lowest energy band for hypomanganate was due to the $t_1 \rightarrow e$ transition, and a molecular-orbital calculation of intensities based on the measured intensities for the first bands of permanganate and hypomanganate, and the fact that the first band for manganate lies mid-way between these (see Fig. 1), gave a calculated intensity for manganate exactly equal to that measured for its first band. A similar calculation based on the assumption that the second band in the spectrum of hypomanganate is due to the $t_1 \rightarrow t_2$ transition, gave an intensity for the $t_1 \rightarrow t_2$ transition for manganate roughly equal to the sum of the intensities for the second, third and fourth bands. Accordingly, it was concluded that these three bands represent separate components for this transition.

It was concluded that the $e \rightarrow t_2$ transition for these ions would be very weak and consequently hard to detect.

The purpose of this note is to re-examine these assignments. It is felt that the number of hidden approximations in molecular-orbital calculations of the type used,[4,5,6] together with the considerable complexity of the ions under consideration render deductions drawn from quantitative calculations either of transition energies or intensities open to question. The same conclusion has recently been

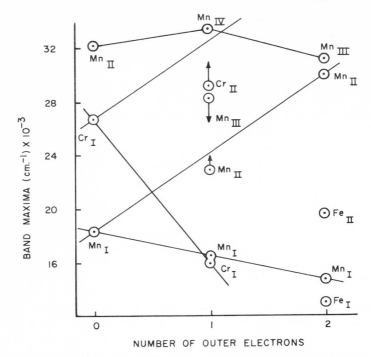

Fig. 1. Energies of band maxima from the ultraviolet and visible spectra of oxyanions as a function of the number of "outer" electrons (X_I, X_{II}, and X_{III} designate the maxima for the first, second and third bands for the relevant oxyanions, XO_4).

reached in a smiliar context.[8] In this contribution arguments based on observed trends in spectra for related ions are used to derive a new assignment which is examined critically in relation to that referred to above.[6]

A variety of qualitative conclusions about the spectra to be expected for ions with outer electrons can be drawn, if the interpretation of the spectra of closed-shell ions given in the first section is accepted.

1. Since the $t_1 \longrightarrow e$ transition is an electron-transfer from oxygen towards the metal atom, and since there are, for the series permanganate, manganate, hypomanganate zero, one, and two electrons in the acceptor e-level respectively, we predict a steady increase in the energy of the $t_1 \longrightarrow e$ transition for this series. Trends are depicted in the figure, from which we tentatively conclude that the second band in the spectrum of hypomanganate is the $t_1 \longrightarrow e$ transition, and that probably the second and third together comprise this

transition for manganate. Similarly, the second band for hypo-chromate[9] is probably only the first component of the $t_1 \longrightarrow e$ transition.

The first bands for these ions follow a trend which is strongly in the reverse direction for all the ions whose spectra have been record-ed, so the alternative assignment[6] is not in accord with these con-siderations. (It might also be thought somewhat surprising that the four possible components of the $t_1 \longrightarrow e$ transition for manganate should combine to give a single narrow band with very well-resolved fine-structure characteristic of a single electronic transition.[10])

2. For isoelectronic ions, the trends in $t_1 \longrightarrow e$ transitions on going across the Periodic Table should be comparable with those for closed-shell ions. Thus for hypochromate and manganate, and hypomanganate and ferrate, there should be shifts to lower energies of about $10,000$ cm^{-1}. All one can say for the former pair is that on the assignment of (1) above, there *is* a strong shift to lower energies, but for the latter pair this shift turns out to be about $11,000$ cm^{-1} for the second bands but only $2,000$ cm^{-1} for the first bands. Thus these considerations are in good accord with the as-signment made in (1) above, rather than that based on calculations of intensities.[6]

3. The mean energy for the $t_1 \longrightarrow t_2$ transitions, in contrast with that for the $t_1 \longrightarrow e$ transitions, should not be greatly altered by the presence of electrons in the e-level. Therefore, other things being equal, they should be found in the same spectral region as those for the parent closed-shell ions. The $t_1 \longrightarrow t_2$ band for permanganate has a maximum at about $32,200$ cm^{-1}. For manganate, therefore, it seems reasonable to identify the band at $33,440$ cm^{-1} with at least one component of this transition for manganate. A careful examin-ation of the broad second band for hypomanganate revealed double maxima in the $30,650$ cm^{-1} region,[7] and it is possible that the second of these is the expected $t_1 \longrightarrow t_2$ transition.

This transition is predicted, on the reasoning given above, to lie beyond the range of measurement for all other ions studies,[7,9] because of the high optical density of the media.

4. Calculations of the expected intensities for $e \longrightarrow t_2$ trans-itions for ions with outer electrons suggest that they should be very weak relative to the $t_1 \longrightarrow e$ and $t_1 \longrightarrow t_2$ transitions.[6] However, although this transition bears a close resemblance to the familiar $d \longrightarrow d$ transitions of complex compounds, there are a variety of reasons why they could have considerable intensity. In contrast to those for octahedral complexes, such transitions are fully allowed by symmetry, and mixing of the appropriate d-orbitals with

metal p-orbitals, and ligand orbitals, as well as the close proximity of intense charge-transfer bands, can all combine to give intensities of the magnitude found for the lowest energy transitions for manganate, hypomanganate or ferrate.

It is significant that it was not possible, in terms of the earlier assignment,[6] to identify positively the $e \longrightarrow t_2$ transition in the spectra of any of the oxyanions with outer electrons. However, if the analysis given in (1) and (3) above is accepted, then it is possible to identify the lowest energy bands for these ions with the $e \longrightarrow t_2$ transition. Various factors which favour this concept will now be listed.

5. An approximate value for the energy of the $e \longrightarrow t_2$ transition for a given ion can be derived from the difference between the energies of the first and second bands for the corresponding closed-shell ions. This difference, for permanganate, is about $14,000$ cm^{-1}. A more detailed comparison suggests that for manganate, the energy required for the $e \longrightarrow t_2$ transition should be slightly greater than this since the electron in the t_2 level is partly located close to oxygens with their full quota of six non-bonding electrons, whereas for excited permanganate there are only five. For hypomanganate the latter effect will be counterbalanced by the presence of another electron in the e-level, which should facilitate an electronic transition from this into the t_2 level.

These qualitative expectations are fulfilled, in terms of the present hypothesis, the first bands for manganate and hypomanganate having maxima at $16,530$ and $14,800$ cm^{-1} respectively. Similarly, for chromate, the gap between the e and t_2 levels is about $10,000$ cm^{-1}, whilst the first band in the spectrum of hypochromate has a maximum at about $15,900$ cm^{-1}.

6. Since the $e \longrightarrow t_2$ transition probably involves slight movement of negative charge away from the metal atom, other things being equal, there should be a small shift to *higher* energies with increase in the charge of the metal nucleus, for isoelectronic ions. There is, in fact, hardly any change if the first bands are assigned to this transition. For hypochromate and manganate there is a shift of 530 cm^{-1} in the predicted sense, and for hypomanganate and ferrate the shift is about $2,000$ cm^{-1} in the opposite sense. These small shifts are reasonable in terms of our assignment, but would be hard to understand if these transitions are $t_1 \longrightarrow e$.

Discussion

We conclude that a new assignment for the spectra of transition metal oxyanions having one or two outer electrons should be made, in which the lowest energy band in their spectra is identified with an $e \longrightarrow t_2$ transition. The second, or second and third bands together, are now identified with the $t_1 \longrightarrow e$ transition, and the $t_1 \longrightarrow t_2$ transition is thought to occur in about the same spectral region as for the parent closed-shell ions.

Some other properties of these ions are more in accord with this than the previous assignment.

Vibrational Fine-Structure. The symmetrical breathing mode, ν_1, for permanganate is about 835 cm^{-1}.[11] That for the first excited state lies between 750 and 780 cm^{-1} depending upon the environment.[10] This marked decrease of 70 cm^{-1} clearly reflects a weakening of the metal-oxygen bonds when an electron is placed in the anti-banding e-level. However, ν_1 for the first excited state of maganate is about 790 cm^{-1} as measured from the spectrum of manganate in single crystals of potassium sulphate.[12] In a less restricting environment this would be slightly reduced, so it seems that ν_1 for the excited states for permanganate and manganate are very similar. If the first excited state for manganate is $(t_1)^6 (t_2)$, as predicted in this note, then there should be little change in ν_1. (This is supported by the fact that ν_1 for permanganate in the $(t_1)^5 (t_2)$ configuration is about 760 cm^{-1}.[10])

However, ν for the second excited state of manganate should be smaller if this state is $(t_1)^5(e)^2$. Teltow's results for the second band are very ill-defined. However the average value for ν_1 calculated for the third band is about 720 cm^{-1} for one orientation of the host crystal.[12] These trends are all consistent with the present assignment. It would be interesting to compare ν_1 for the ground states of manganate and hypomanganate with these values, but unfortunately it is difficult to measure the Raman spectra of these ions because of their instability and intense colours throughout the visible and near ultraviolet region.

Reactivity. Finally, it may be significant that there is a steady decrease in the electron-accepting power of oxyanions as the number of outer electrons increases. This is clear from measurements of electrode potentials, and several other considerations of reactivity.[13] Comparisons of this sort of information with data from electronic spectra are complicated by the operation of the Franck-Condon principle with respect to solvation and bond-lengths. Nevertheless, these effects must cancel to a considerable extent when trends in reactivity are compared.

Acceptance of an external electron into the e-level may be compared with movement of a non-bonding t_1 electron into this level. Thus by comparison with reactivity trends, one would expect a strong shift of the $t_1 \longrightarrow e$ transition to higher energies as the number of outer electrons increases. This conclusion is in accord with the present, but directly opposed to the earlier assignments.

One use of these correlations may be illustrated by reference to the unknown tetroxide of iron. One can predict the energy for the $t_1 \longrightarrow e$ transition for this oxide by three different approaches: First, from the plot correlating ionic radius with absorption maxima, we obtain 8,000 cm^{-1} [7]. Second, from the plot given in the figure, we predict 7,000 cm^{-1} by extending a line through the value for the second ferrate transition. Finally, we can deduce a value of 9,500 cm^{-1} by subtracting 17,000 cm^{-1} from the energy for the first transition of ruthenium tetroxide. This figure is the mean of the differences between the band maxima of permanganate and pertechnitate on the one hand, and chromate and molybdate on the other. Thus, iron tetroxide should be an extremely powerful oxidizing agent, far stronger than permanganate, which is one of the most powerful known. It is therefore not surprising that all attempts to prepare this oxide have failed. Even perferrate, FeO_4^-, should, on the correlation shown, be a more powerful oxidizing agent than permanganate so, again, that our attempts to prepare this ion have been fruitless is understandable.

REFERENCES

1. A. Carrington, D. J. E. Ingram, K. A. K. Lott, D. S. Schonland, and M. C. R. Symons, *Proc. Roy. Soc.*, **A,254**, 101 (1960).
2. D. S. Schonland, *Proc. Roy. Soc.*, **A,254**, 110 (1960).
3. A. Carrington, and M. C. R. Symons, *J. Chem. Soc.*, **889** (1960).
4. M. Wolfsberg and L. Helmholz, *J. Chem. Phys.* **20**, 837 (1952).
5. C. J. Ballhausen and A. D. Liehr, *J. Mol. Spectros*, **2**, 342 (1958).
6. A. Carrington and D. S. Schonland, *Mol. Phys.*, **3**, 331 (1960).
7. A. Carrington, D. S. Schonland, and M. C. R. Symons, *J. Chem. Soc.*, 659 (1957).
8. U. Kläning and M. C. R. Symons, *J. Chem. Soc.*, in press.
9. N. Bailey and M. C. R. Symons, *J. Chem. Soc.*, 203 (1957).
10. J. Teltow, *Z, Phys. Chem.*, **B40**, 397 (1938).
11. A. M. Taylor, *Trans. Faraday Soc.*, **25**, 856 (1929).
12. J. Teltow, *Z. Phys. Chem.*, **B43**, 198 (1939)..
13. A. Carrington and M. C. R. Symons, *J. Chem. Soc.*, 3373 (1956).

INFRARED SPECTRA AND STRUCTURES OF α-DIIMINE METAL CHELATE COMPOUNDS

KAZUO NAKAMOTO*

Jeppson Laboratory of Chemistry
Clark University
Worcester, Massachusetts

The nature of the metal-nitrogen bond in the metal chelate compounds of *2,2′*-bipyridine (BIPY), *2,2′,2″*-terpyridine (TRPY) and related compounds has been a subject of considerable interest in past years because of their relatively high stability. It has been postulated that the metal-nitrogen bonds in these compounds are strengthened by the resonance such as shown below: [1]

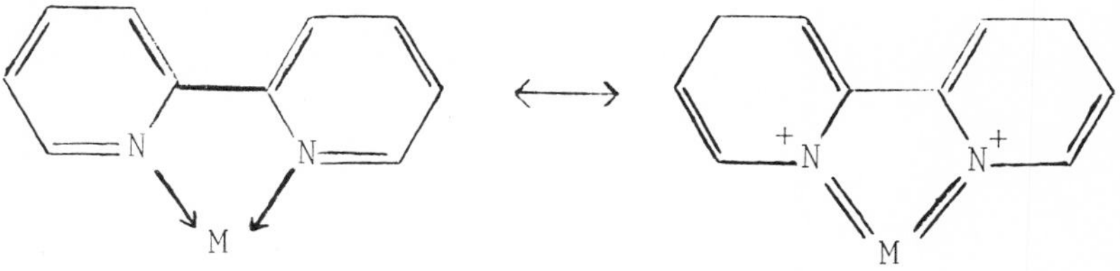

This paper is to report observations and theoretical analyses of the infrared spectra of the metal chelate compounds of α-diimines with Fe(II), Co(II) and Ni(II), and to provide direct evidence for the un- usually high stability of the Fe(II) complexes.

Experimental

The metal chelate compounds of glyoxal-bis-methylimine (GMI) with Fe(II) and Ni(II) and of biacetyl-bis-methylimine (BMI) with Fe(II), Co(II) and Ni(II) have been prepared according to methods described in the literature.[2,3] The Ni(II) complex of GMI was prepared for the first time during this investigation. The infrared spectra were ob-

*The author wishes to express his sincere appreciation to the U.S. Army Research Office (Durham) who supported this investigation under contract DA-19-020-ORD-5119, and to the Massachusetts Institute of Technology Computation Center for the use of an IBM 709 computer for the calculations.

437

tained by using a Perkin-Elmer Model 21 infrared spectrophotometer equipped with NaCl, KBr, and CsBr optics. The KBr disk method was employed in the NaCl and KBr regions, whereas the Nujol mull technique was used in the CsBr region. Calibration of the frequency reading was made with polystyrene film (NaCl region), *1,2,4*-trichlorobenzene (KBr region) and water vapor for all regions.

Results and Discussion

It has been shown previously[4] that among various vibrational modes of the metal chelate compound, the metal-ligand vibration affords the most direct information on the strength of the coordinate bond. In order to assign the metal-ligand vibration, however, it is necessary to carry out a normal coordinate treatment on a chelate ring system. For this purpose, the metal chelate compounds of α-diimines, such as shown below, were selected, since they are the most simple systems which maintain the properties of the BIPY and TRPY metal chelates.

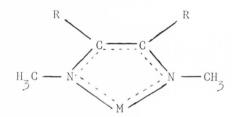

R = H, Glyoxal-bis-methylimine (GMI)

R = CH_3, Biacetyl-bis-methylimine (BMI)

In doing a normal coordinate treatment, an octahedral model containing $1:3$ ratio of metal to ligand was employed so as to take into account all the interactions between ligands. As will be seen later, a simple $1:1$ model calculation does not give satisfactory results since strong interaction exists between ligands. Figure 1 indicates the molecular model of the $1:3$ complex of D_3 symmetry together with the 75 internal coordinates involved. Using these internal coordinates, the 75th order **G** and **F** matrices were constructed. By the use of the redundant conditions (5 for each chelate ring and 3 around the central metal), the order of these matrices was reduced to 57th order. From symmetry considerations they were further resolved into component matrices involving $a_1 (10) + a_2 (9) + e (19)$. It should be noted that 6 redundant coordinates still remain in these resolved matrices (1 in a_1, 1 in a_2 and 2 in e). Therefore, the number of genuine vibrations is 51. After applying high-frequency separation for the CH stretching mode, the matrix secular equation of the form, $|\mathbf{GF} - \mathbf{E}\lambda| = 0$, was solved for each species using an IBM 709 computer.

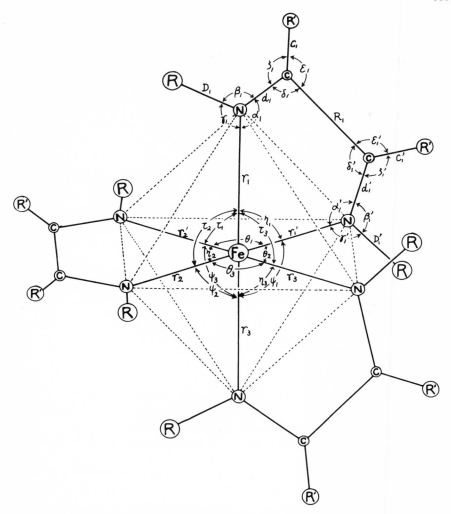

Fig. 1. Molecular model and internal coordinates of the 1 : 3 complex.

The potential energy was expressed by using a Urey-Bradley type field:[5]

$$V = \sum_i [K_i' r_{i0} (\Delta r_i) + \tfrac{1}{2} K_i (\Delta r_i)^2] + \sum_i [H_i' \tau_{i\alpha}^2 (\Delta \alpha_i) +$$

$$\tfrac{1}{2} H_i \tau_{i\alpha}^2 (\Delta \alpha_i)^2] + \sum_i [F_i' q_{i0} (\Delta q_i) + \tfrac{1}{2} F_i (\Delta q_i)^2]$$

Here, Δr_i, $\Delta \alpha_i$, and Δq_i are the changes of the bond length, bond angles, and the distances between non-bonded atoms. The symbols K_i, K_i', H_i, H_i', F_i and F_i' represent the stretching, bending, and repulsive force constants, respectively. Furthermore, r_{i0}, $r_{i\alpha}$ and q_{i0} are the values of the distances at the equilibrium positions, and are inserted to make the force constants dimensionally similar. The quantities K_i' and H_i' vanish in the final result, since they can be expressed in terms of F' by the equilibrium condition. F' was taken as $-\frac{1}{10} F$ by assuming that the repulsive energy between non-bonded atoms is proportional to $1/r^9$. The set of the force constants used in the calculation of $[Fe(GMI)_3]^{2+}$ is given in Table 1. Most of the

TABLE 1: FORCE CONSTANTS IN $[Fe(GMI)_3]$ I_2 (10^5 dyne/cm)

Stretching	Bending	Repulsive
$K(C \cdots N) = 6.5$	$H_\alpha = 0.05$	$F_1(C \cdots M) = 0.1$
$K(C \cdots C) = 4.4$	$H_\beta = 0.25$	$F_2(CH_3 \cdots M) = 0.1$
$K(Fe \cdots N) = 4.7$	$H_\gamma = 0.10$	$F_3(N \cdots N) = 0.1$
$K(CH_3 {-} N) = 3.9$	$H_\delta = 0.05$	$F_4(C \cdots N) = 0.1$
	$H_\epsilon = 0.20$	$F_5(H \cdots N) = 0.6$
	$H_\zeta = 0.20$	$F_6(C \cdots CH_3) = 0.5$
	$H_\eta = 0.05$	$F_7(H \cdots C) = 0.1$

values were taken from the force constants of other compounds having similar bonds. The force constants related to the Fe—N bonds were determined so as to obtain the best fit between the calculated and observed frequencies. As is seen in Table 2, the agreements between the calculated and observed values are satisfactory in view of the complexity of the system. However, the separation between two frequencies calculated as 750 and 630 cm^{-1} is not sufficient to fit the observed spectrum. A similar calculation on a simple 1:1 complex model gives only a slight separation between these two bands. Therefore, such an approximation cannot be applicable to the Fe(II) complex.

Table 1 indicates that the C—N and C—C stretching force constants are much smaller than those of pure double bonds, whereas the Fe—N stretching force constant is much larger than those of other coordinate bonds. For example, the Pt—C stretching force constant in $[Pt(CN)_4]^{2-}$ is reported to be 3.43×10^5 dyne/cm.[6] Thus these results provide direct evidence for the proposed strong resonance in the chelate ring of the Fe(II) complex. As is seen in Fig. 2, however, the infrared spectra of $[Ni(GMI)_3]^{2+}$ and $[Ni(BMI)_3]^{2+}$ are markedly dif-

TABLE 2: COMPARISON OF CALCULATED AND OBSERVED FREQUENCIES OF $[Fe(GMI)_3]I_2$ (cm^{-1})

Obs.*	Calc.	Predominant Mode†
1530(s)	1549(a_1), 1547(e)	ν(C$\cdots$N) + ν(C$\cdots$C)
	1530(a_2), 1525(e)	ν(C$\cdots$N) + δ(C——H)
1438(s)	$\cdots$	CH$_3$ deg. def.
1407(s)	$\cdots$	CH$_3$ sym. def.
1305(s)	1323(a_1), 1335(e)	δ(C——H) + ν(C$\cdots$N)
	1290(a_2), 1261(e)	δ(C——H) + ν(C$\cdots$N)
1149(s)	1123(a_2), 1142(e)	ν(N——CH$_3$) + ν(Fe$\cdots$N)
1084(s)	1104(a_1), 1087(e)	ν(N——CH$_3$) + ν(Fe$\cdots$N)
1057(s)	1057(a_1), 1071(e)	ν(C$\cdots$C)
847,829(s)	$\cdots$	π(C——H)
745(w)	756(a_2), 742(e)	ν(Fe——N) + ν(N——CH$_3$)
515,501(m)	631(a_1), 655(e)	ν(Fe——N) + ν(N——CH$_3$)
470,461(s)	482(a_2), 448(e)	ring def. + δ(N——CH$_3$)
372(s)	352(a_2), 325(e)	ring def. + δ(N——CH$_3$)
306(s)	303(a_1), 260(e)	δ(N——CH$_3$) + ring def.
$\cdots$	188(a_1), 218(e)	δ(N——CH$_3$) + ring def.
$\cdots$	142(a_2), 174(e)	δ(N——Fe——N)
$\cdots$	92(a_1), 130(e)	δ(N——Fe——N)

*s, m, and w denote strong, medium, and weak bands, respectively.
†ν, δ, and π represent stretching, in-plane bending, and out-of-plane bending modes, respectively.

ferent from those of the corresponding Fe(II) complexes.* Although calculations have not yet been made on the Co(II) and Ni(II) complexes, it is evident from the observed spectra that strong resonances such as seen in the Fe(II) complex do not exist in other transition metal chelates.

It is anticipated that usual empirical band assignments based on the concept of "group frequency" may not be applicable to such a chelate ring system because strong coupling occurs between various vibrational modes. In order to know the nature of the observed bands, it is therefore necessary to determine the mixing ratio of various modes in each band. The **L** matrix defined by the following relation:

$$S = LQ \quad \text{or} \quad Q = L^{-1}S$$

expresses the relative amplitude of each symmetry coordinate in a given normal vibration. (Here, **S** denotes the internal symmetry coordinates, and **Q** represents the normal coordinates.) It should be noted, however, that the dimension of L for the stretching coordinates is different from those for the deformation coordinates. In such a case, it is better to calculate the distribution of potential energy in

---

*The infrared spectrum of $[Co(BMI)_3]^{2+}$ is similar to that of $[Ni(BMI)_3]^{2+}$.

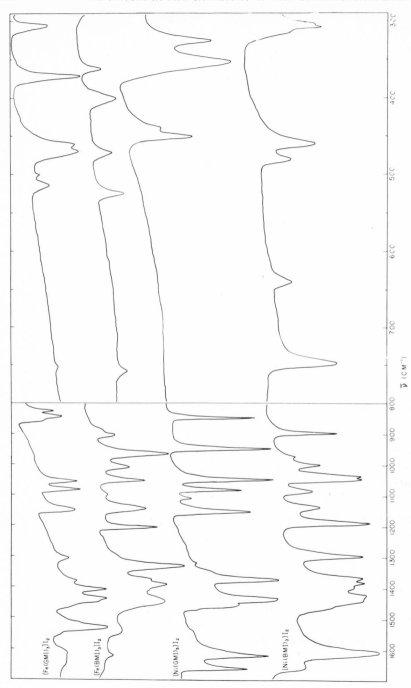

Fig. 2. Infrared spectra of α-diimine chelate compounds with Fe(II) and Ni(II).

the internal symmetry coordinates of each normal vibration. The potential energy of the whole molecule for a given normal vibration (Q_λ) is given by

$$V = \tfrac{1}{2} \ Q_\lambda^2 \Sigma F_{kl} L_{k\lambda} L_{l\lambda}$$

where $F_{ii}L^2_{i\lambda}$ are the distributions of energies in the coordinate, S_i, in the normal vibration, Q_λ.[6] Therefore, the potential energy distributions, $F_{ii}L^2_{i\lambda}$ have been calculated for all the vibrations. The predominant modes listed in Table 2 are based on the results of such calculations. It is seen that the Fe—N stretching mode couples strongly with the N—CH$_3$ stretching vibration. Thus no pure metal-ligand vibration exists in the Fe(II) complex. Similar strong coupling is seen between the C⋯N, and C⋯C stretching and C—H in-plane bending modes.

REFERENCES

1. F. H. Burstall and R. S. Nyholm, *J. Chem. Soc.*, 3570 (1952); R. S. Nyholm and L. N. Short, *ibid.*, 2670 (1953).
2. P. Krumholtz, *J. Am. Chem. Soc.*, **75**, 2163 (1953).
3. P. E. Figgins and D. H. Busch, *ibid.*, **82**, 820 (1960).
4. K. Nakamoto and A. E. Martell, *J. Chem. Phys.*, **32**, 588 (1960).
5. T. Shimanouchi, *J. Chem. Phys.*, **17**, 245, 734 and 848 (1949).
6. D. M. Sweeny, I. Nakagawa, S. Mizushima, and J. V. Quagliano, *J. Am. Chem. Soc.*, **78**, 889 (1956).

THE COMPLEXES OF NIOBIUM AND TANTALUM WITH ETHYLENEDIAMINETETRAACETIC ACID

ROBERT E. KIRBY and HENRY FREISER*

Department of Chemistry
University of Arizona
Tucson, Arizona

Niobium(V) forms a stable, soluble EDTA complex which can be reversibly reduced at the dropping mercury electrode to niobium(IV) and niobium(III) in stepwise fashion.[1] This behavior makes it possible to study the nature of the complex-forming reaction and the reduction.

In order to apply polarographic observations to the quantitative study of the electrode reactions involving the reduction of Nb(V), it was found necessary to (1) buffer carefully the solutions, and (2) to heat the reaction mixtures to boiling in order to obtain complete reaction in a short time and then cooling to the desired temperature before the polarogram is obtained. Under these conditions, the following information about the reduction of Nb(V) to Nb(IV) was obtained:

1. The wave is a one electron reversible wave. Typical values of n obtained by the usual log $i/i_d - i$ vs. $E_{1/2}$ plot in several runs were: 0.98, 1.00, 1.01, 0.96, 0.96, 0.95. Also the change of half-wave potential with temperature was -1.3 mv per degree.

2. The half-wave potential varied linearly with the pH in a manner which depended on the pH. That is, in the region pH 0.5 to 2, the slope of the $E_{1/2}$ vs. pH line was indicative of the participation 1.0 H^+ in the region pH 2-3, the slope of 2.0 H^+, and, from pH 3-6, the slope showed involvement of 2.5 H^+. The concentration of EDTA did not effect $E_{1/2}$ values.

3. The diffusion current also varied with the pH. In the range pH 1 to 4 it remained essentially constant, but decreased significantly at higher pH values and reduced to insignificant values at pH values of 6 and above. Similarly, the wave height decreases markedly at pH values under 1. The diffusion current changed in a completely linear manner with Nb concentration. Changes in the EDTA concentration had no effect on the diffusion current.

From these observations it is possible to conclude that the reducible species is a mononuclear Nb(V) EDTA complex which, upon re-

---

*Financial assistance from the Wright Air Force Development Division in this work is gratefully acknowledged.

duction, retains the same number of EDTA molecules. This probably means that the reducible complex contains only one EDTA molecule. The pH dependence of the half-wave potential probably reflects the presence of oxo or hydroxo coordinating groups in the Nb complex. Thus in the range pH 2-3,

$$NbOY^- + 2H^+ + \rightleftharpoons Nb(IV)Y + H_2O \qquad (1a)$$

or

$$Nb(OH)_2Y^- + 2H^+ + \rightleftharpoons NbY^- + 2H_2O, \text{ etc.} \qquad (1b)$$

Alternatively, the Nb(IV) EDTA complex could be a protonated complex but this seems less likely:

$$NbY^+ + 2H^+ + \rightleftharpoons Nb(H_2Y)^{++}. \qquad (2)$$

The variation of diffusion current with niobium concentration was found to be sufficiently linear to provide the basis for a polarographic estimation of niobium in solutions containing from 0.5 μg. Nb/ml to 1 mg Nb/ml.[2]

The observation that the height of the polarographic reduction wave was time-dependent prompted a study of the kinetics of the reaction. In this study, the diffusion current was taken to be a measure of the concentration of the reducible species which, from work outlined above, is mononuclear and probably contains one EDTA moiety per niobium.

It was found possible to initiate measurements of i_d thirty seconds after mixing reactants. Within this time, enough reducible species had formed to give a measurable diffusion current. This quantity amounted to approximately 20% of the total final level. This amount was essentially independent of pH (between 3 and 4 but not at higher pH values), EDTA (0.05 to 0.2 M), and niobium (at least between 0.4 mM and 4.0 mM) concentrations. The rate at which the remaining 80% of the reducible species formed was studied as a function of niobium, EDTA, and pH levels at 25°C.

The rate data indicated the presence of two parallel reactions, both first-order, in niobium, and fractional orders in both EDTA and H$^+$.

These data indicate the presence of at least two Nb(V)-EDTA complexes which transform at different rates to give a reducible NbOY$^-$ or Nb(OH)$_2$Y$^-$ species. A possible reaction path consistent with these findings will be discussed.

Tantalum(V) was also found to form a stable soluble EDTA complex which exhibited a reversible one-electron reduction at the dropping mercury electrode.[3] Further studies are being conducted.

REFERENCES

1. Ferrett and Milner, *J. Chem. Soc.*, 1186–1192 (1956).
2. Kirby and Freiser, in press, presented at the Pittsburgh Conference on Analytical Chemistry and Applied Spectroscopy, Feb. 28, 1961.
3. Kirby and Freiser, *J. Phys. Chem.*, **65,** 191 (1961).

THE ROLE OF THE SOLVENT IN CHEMICAL EQUILIBRIA; ELECTRODE POTENTIALS AND COMPLEX-ION FORMATION IN ANHYDROUS ETHYLENEDIAMINE*

WARD B. SCHAAP, RICHARD E. BAYER, JOSEPH R. SIEFKER, and FREDERIC C. SCHMIDT

Department of Chemistry
Indiana University
Bloomington, Indiana

Because the use of water as a solvent medium for carrying out chemical reactions and studies is so predominant, the influences that the extraordinary properties of water exert on interactions among dissolved species are easily overlooked. Chemistry in other solvents, particularly those not having oxygen donor atoms, can be very different, and it is only when this non-aqueous chemistry is compared with aqueous chemistry that the role of the solvent in chemical equilibria is delineated.

Studies of acid-base equilibria in non-aqueous systems have contributed much to understanding the role of the solvent.[1] Relative proton affinities of solvent and solute species and the dielectric constant of the solvent are important factors determining the extent of ionization and dissociation.[2]

Considerable data on solubilities of salts in various solvents have been accumulated and the factors that influence solubility are quite well understood, though the necessary thermodynamic data for predicting these solubilities are seldom available for non-aqueous systems.

The chemical nature of the solvent is also important in other types of reactions, but, in general, these have not been investigated nearly so much as neutralization reactions or solubilities. Two such solvent-influenced reaction types are discussed in this paper. These are (1) electrode potentials of metal ions and (2) complex ion formation. Experimental data are presented which allow comparison of electrode potentials (relative) and stability constants of complex ions measured in the two dissimilar solvents ethylenediamine and

*Contribution No. 993.

447

water. Ethylenediamine differs from water in the identity of its donor atoms, its greater basicity, its chelate-forming structure and its much lower dielectric constant (about 12.5).

Electrode Potentials

That the solvation energy of an ion is directly involved in determining the magnitude of its electrode potential can be seen from the following reaction which represents the electro-deposition of a solvated cation:

$$M \text{ (solvent)}_x^{+n} + ne^- \rightleftharpoons M_s + x \text{ solvent.}$$

In this reaction the metal-solvent bonds must be broken for the reaction to proceed as written. Other factors being constant, such as the ionization potential and sublimation energy, the stronger the bonds between the cation and the solvent molecule, the more reactive (less noble) the metal.

A number of polarographic half-wave potentials for the reduction of cations in ethylenediamine as solvent and some $E^{\circ\prime}$ values for metal-metal ion electrodes have been measured in this laboratory. These are given in Table 1 along with the half-wave potentials or $E^{\circ\prime}$ values for the same ions in water and the over-all stability constants of the ethylenediamine complexes, measured in aqueous solution, of some of the cations. The relative potentials in the two solvents are represented graphically in Fig. 1 along with data from liquid ammonia.[3,4]

RELATIVE   REDUCTION   POTENTIALS

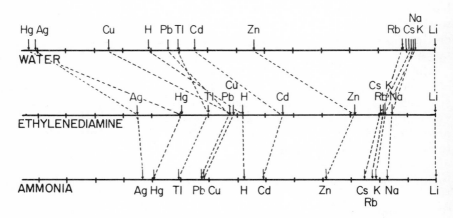

Fig. 1. Relative reduction potentials.

TABLE 1: REDUCTION POTENTIALS OF SOME CATIONS IN WATER AND IN ANHYDROUS ETHYLENEDIAMINE

Ion	$E_{1/2}$ in Ethylene-diamine* (vs. Zn Ref. Elect.)	$E_{1/2}$ in Aqueous Soln.[6] (vs. S.C.E.)	Relative Shifts, $E_{1/2}en - E_{1/2}aq$	log K_n of Metal-Ethylene-diamine Complex[7]
	v.	v.	v.	
Cs^+	-0.176	-2.10	$+1.92$	—
Rb^+	-0.199	-2.03	1.83	—
K^+	-0.207	-2.13	1.92	—
Na^+	-0.246	-2.11	1.86	—
Li^+	(-0.56)	-2.27	1.78	—
Tl^+	$+1.039$	-0.459	1.50	0.3
Pb^{++}	$+0.896$	-0.388	1.28	(8)§
Cd^{++}	$+0.530$	-0.578	1.28	12.2
Zn^{++}	$+0.10$	-0.997	1.11	13.0
Cu^{++} ($\rightarrow$ Cu)	$(+0.937)$	$+0.02$	1.10	20.1
Hg^{++}	$(+1.226)$†	$(+0.47)$	0.92	23.3
	$(E^{o\prime} = 1.39)$	$(E^o = 0.60)$	0.76	
Ag^+	$(E^{o\prime} = 1.53)$	$(E^o = 0.55)$	0.79	7.7
H^+	$(E^{o\prime} = 0.8)$‡	$(E^o = -0.246)$	0.98	10.0
			1.0	

*Potentials measured vs. the zinc amalgam-zinc chloride reference electrode in ethylenediamine. $E_{1/2}$ values refer to solutions containing 0.25 M LiCl as supporting electrolyte. $E_{1/2}$ values in parentheses are calculated or estimated from other experimental data.

†Potential of mercury pool (vs. zinc reference electrode) in en containing 0.25 M LiCl.

‡Estimated on basis of preliminary data using Pt (H$_2$) electrode in en.

§Based on unpublished data of R. E. Bayer, Carroll College, Waukesha, Wis.

It should be remembered that polarographic reduction potentials are approximately equal to standard potentials of amalgam electrodes E_a^o. Also, because the effect of amalgam formation is independent of the solvent, the relative changes in half-wave potentials correspond approximately to relative changes in the E^o values of the metal-metal ion electrodes in the two solvents.

Half-wave potentials measured in ethylenediamine include the effects of ion-pairing by both the supporting electrolyte and the reducible ion[5] and are estimated to be from 0.1 to 0.2 volts more negative than the true E_a^o values. Nevertheless, because all cations are compared under identical conditions, the effects of ion-pairing remain fairly constant throughout the series and are not expected to cause errors of more than 0.1 volt in the *relative* values reported.

The last three values in Table 1 were measured by conventional potentiometric methods and are corrected for ion-pair formation. These $E^{o\prime}$ values are compared with E^o values in aqueous solution versus the S.C.E. to make the shifts comparable.

The horizontal voltage scales used in Fig. 1 are the same for all solvents. Since the values are relative, the identities of the reference electrodes used are immaterial. Also, the vertical relationship of the scales is arbitrary. We have chosen to position the scales so that the potentials of lithium in the solvents are connected by a vertical line. This implies that the absolute potentials of the Li, Li^+ electrodes in the solvents are the same.* Several lines of evidence indicate that this is a reasonable first approximation.

Examination of Fig. 1 reveals some interesting changes in relative electrode potentials. The elements which form stable ethylenediamine complexes become less noble, while the alkali metals become more noble. For example, whereas the potential of cesium amalgam is about 1.1 volts different from that of zinc amalgam in water, in ethylenediamine the difference decreases to only about 0.2 volt. Moreover, the electromotive series is different in the two solvents. Thallium, for example, is more noble than both copper and lead in ethylenediamine, whereas in water the opposite is true. Also, the potentials of the alkali metal amalgam electrodes change regularly from cesium to lithium in ethylenediamine, whereas in water the order is scrambled. Potentials in liquid ammonia (at $-36\,^\circ C$) are similar to those in ethylenediamine, except for some differences attributable to the chelate structure of the latter.

In a previous publication in this series[8] it was shown that relative changes in the reduction potentials of a series of ions in the two solvents, en and H_2O, can be correlated very well with the relative stabilities of the metal-ethylenediamine complexes in aqueous solution. The correlation, which relates the shift in half-wave potential between the two solvents, $E_{\frac{1}{2}en} - E_{\frac{1}{2}aq}$, with the logarithm of the over-all stability constant, is shown in Fig. 2 using all available data. The greater the stability constant of the aqueous metal-ethylenediamine complex, the greater its relative shift in the negative direction.

In his discussion of the thermodynamics of chemistry in liquid ammonia solutions, Jolly[4] makes use of the assumption that the stability constant of the ammonia complex of a cation in aqueous solu-

---

*Other methods for comparing electrode potentials in different solvents have been proposed. Pleskov [*Fortschr. d. Chemie* (Russ.) **16**, 254 (1947)] assumed that the energy of solvation (and the E°) of Rb^+ was constant in various solvents. Strehlow [*Z. Elektrochem.*, **56**, 827 (1952)] attempted to improve this assumption by calculating the small ΔF changes for Rb^+ in various solvents using the Born equation. He also applied Hammett's indicator method and obtained relative E values agreeing farily well with those of Pleskov. Ethylenediamine was not included.

tion is a quantitative measure of the free-energy change involved
when an ion is transferred from water to liquid ammonia (ΔF_t). These
free-energy changes are then used, together with aqueous $E°$ values,
to estimate electrode potentials in liquid ammonia.

It can be shown that Jolly's procedure actually amounts to assuming a linear relationship such as the one observed experimentally
in ethylenediamine and shown in Fig. 2. The equation of the straight
line shown in Fig. 2 is

$$\left| E_{\frac{1}{2}} \right|_{en} - \left| E_{\frac{1}{2}} \right|_{aq} = E' - \frac{RT}{nF} \ln K_N$$

where E' is the intercept, the value of which depends on the reference electrodes used and the liquid-junction potential between the
two solvents. Rearranging, and assuming that changes in $E_{\frac{1}{2}}$ values

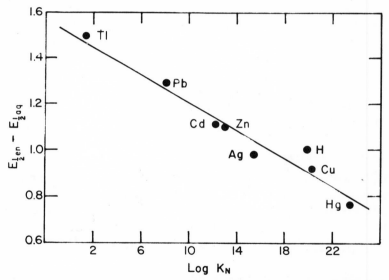

Fig. 2. Plot of difference in reduction potentials for ions in ethylenediamine and
water *versus* the logarithm of the stability constant of the aqueous metal-
ethylenediamine complex (for $n = 2$). (Potentials in en are *vs.* the zinc
amalgam-zinc chloride-lithium chloride reference electrode and potentials
in water are *vs.* the S.C.E.)

parallel changes in $E°$ values when the solvent is changed (and
changing signs to conform to the Latimer electrode potential sign
convention),

$$-nF \left(E°_{en} - E°_{aq} \right) = -RT \ln K_N + E'$$

and

$$\Delta F^{0}_{f\,en} - \Delta F^{0}_{f\,aq} = \Delta F^{0}_{K} + C$$

where ΔF^{0}_{K} is the standard free-energy change for the complex-forming reaction in aqueous solution. Jolly's analogous equation for liquid ammonia solutions is

$$\Delta F^{0}_{K} = \Delta F^{0}_{transfer} = \Delta F^{0}_{f\,NH_3} - \Delta F^{0}_{f\,H_2O} - 16\,Z$$

where Z is the charge of the ion. The last two equations can be seen to be equivalent.

It is possible, therefore, with a knowledge of relative electrode potentials in aqueous solution and a knowledge of stability constants of aqueous metal complexes with a ligand, to predict approximate relative electrode potentials and free energies if the pure ligand is made the solvent at the same temperature. This generalization has also been found to hold true in this laboratory with other amine ligands, such as butylamine, diethylenetriamine and liquid ammonia (at 25 °C). It is planned to test it also in liquid solvents with other strongly coordinating donor atoms, e.g., sulfur.

Furthermore, stability constants of hypothetical ethylenediamine complexes of species that may not exist in aqueous solution, e.g., Cu^{+}, may be estimated from potentials observed in the anhydrous solvent.

Complex-Ion Formation

The formation of coordination complexes is another type of reaction in which the solvent is directly involved and would be expected to influence the magnitude of the equilibrium constant. Such equilibria may be represented, in general, by the reaction,

$$M(\text{solvent})^{+n}_{x} + y\,\text{ligand}^{-b} \rightleftharpoons M(\text{ligand})^{+(n-yb)}_{y} + x\,\text{solvent}.$$

In this reaction all species are regarded as solvated; however, the solvent molecules in the innermost coordination sphere of the cation, which are replaced by the ligands, are specially designated. It is obvious that the stronger the cation-solvent bonds, the smaller will be the tendency for a given ligand to complex a given cation.

Consideration of the relative electrode potentials in water and in ethylenediamine, shown in Fig. 1, leads one to expect that water molecules solvate the alkali metal cations more strongly than do ethylenediamine molecules, and thus the possibility exists that complexes of the alkali metals with water would be stable in ethylenediamine solutions. Conversely, water would not be expected to form stable complexes with the transition metal cations in ethylenediamine solution.

To test these expectations, changes in the half-wave potentials for the polarographic reduction, in ethylenediamine, of Cd^{++}, Na^+, K^+ and Rb^+ upon addition of water were measured. In an ethylenediamine solution containing about 2.6 M water, the shift in half-wave potential of Cd^{++}, compared to the anhydrous solution, was negligible (2 to 3 mv) as expected. The $E_{1/2}$ values of the alkali metals, however, shifted in the direction expected for complex formation and by amounts of 25, 32 and 34 mv, respectively, for Na^+, K^+ and Rb^+. Because of the small $E_{1/2}$ shifts and the difficulty in getting precise, reproducible data at the negative potentials involved, the study of the alkali metal-water complexes was not carried further.

The complexes of cadmium with cyanide were chosen for study in ethylenediamine because the aqueous stability constants for these ligands show that cyanide forms appreciably more stable complexes with cadmium than does en (in water) and may reasonably be expected to form stable complexes in ethylenediamine as solvent also. The equilibrium constants reported for aqueous solutions are as follows:[7]

$$Cd^{++} \cdot aq + 4\ CN^- \cdot aq \rightleftharpoons Cd(CN)_4^{-2} \cdot aq \qquad (K_{CN})_{aq} = 10^{18.8}$$

$$Cd^{++} \cdot aq + 2\ en \cdot aq \rightleftharpoons Cd(en)_2^{+2} \cdot aq \qquad (K_{en})_{aq} = 10^{10.3}.$$

From these two reactions the constant for the replacement of the two en molecules by four CN^- ions *in water* can be calculated, i.e.,

$$Cd(en)_2^{+2} \cdot aq + 4\ CN^- \cdot aq \rightleftharpoons Cd(CN)_4^{-2} \cdot aq + 2\ en \cdot aq$$

$$(K_{CN/en})_{aq} = 10^{18.8}/10^{10.3} = 10^{8.5}\ (moles \cdot liter^{-1})^{-2}.$$

The equilibrium constants above are calculated in the usual manner, i.e., with the activity of the solvent taken as unity and all other concentrations expressed in moles $\cdot$ liter^{-1}. Such units are not suitable for comparing the last reaction above with the analogous reaction carried out in ethylenediamine as solvent because of the changes in choices of standard states. Equilibrium constants on a mole fraction basis can be compared, however. These "unitary," dimensionless constants for the above reactions are:

$$(K'_{CN})_{aq} = 10^{18.8}(55)^4 = 10^{25.8}$$
$$(K'_{en})_{aq} = 10^{10.3}(55)^2 = 10^{13.8}$$
$$(K'_{CN/en})_{aq} = 10^{8.5}(55)^2 = 10^{12.0}.$$

The consecutive formation constants of the cadmium cyanide complexes were measured experimentally at $25\,°C$ in ethylenediamine as solvent using the DeFord and Hume polarographic method.[9] NaCN was used as the source of CN^- and 0.25 M $NaNO_3$ was used as supporting electrolyte. The equilibrium constants calculated in the usual manner, i.e., taking the activity of the solvent to be unity and assuming that $[CN^-]$ is given by the stoichiometric concentration of NaCN present, are as follows:

$$Cd^{++} \cdot en + \ \ CN^- \cdot en \rightleftharpoons Cd(CN)^+ \cdot en \quad K_1 = 360$$

$$Cd^{++} \cdot en + 2\ CN^- \cdot en \rightleftharpoons Cd(CN)_2 \cdot en \quad K_2 = 7.4 \times 10^4$$

$$Cd^{++} \cdot en + 3\ CN^- \cdot en \rightleftharpoons Cd(CN)_3^- \cdot en \quad K_3 = 7.4 \times 10^6$$

$$Cd^{++} \cdot en + 4\ CN^- \cdot en \rightleftharpoons Cd(CN)_4^{-2} \cdot en \quad K_4 = 4 \times 10^8 \ (\text{moles} \cdot \text{liter}^{-1})^{-4}.$$

The unitary, mole fraction constant for the over-all reaction may be compared with $(K'_{CN/en})_{aq}$ and is

$$(K'_4)_{en} = 10^{8.6}(15)^4 = 10^{13.3}$$

The value of $(K'_4)_{en}$ is apparently only slightly larger than the value calculated for the replacement of en by CN^- around Cd^{++} in aqueous solution.

Actually, since the dielectric constant of ethylenediamine is only 12.5, and since the reaction was studied in the presence of 0.25 M sodium nitrate, the reaction may involve, at least to some extent, neutral ion-paired species. Such a reaction would be represented as follows (neutral ion-paired species are enclosed in braces):

$$\{Cd^{++}, 2\ NO_3^-\} \cdot en + 4\ \{Na^+, CN^-\} \cdot en \rightleftharpoons \{2\ Na^+, Cd(CN)_4^{-2}\} \cdot en$$
$$+ 2\ \{Na^+, NO_3^-\} \cdot en.$$

It can be shown that the equilibrium constant for this reaction, $(K''_4)_{en}$, is related to that of the ionic reaction above, $(K'_4)_{en}$, by the expression

$$K''_4 = K'_4\ \frac{k_a k_b k_c^2}{k_d k_e k_f^4}$$

where k_a and k_b are the successive ion-pair association constants of $Cd(CN)_4^{-2}$ with Na^+, k_c is the association constant for Na^+ and NO_3^-, k_d and k_e are the successive constants for Cd^{++} with NO_3^-, and k_f is the constant for Na^+ and CN^-. As an approximation, if the constants for the divalent species are assumed to be equal, i.e., $k_a k_b \cong k_d k_e$, and if the association constants for Na^+ with NO_3^- and CN^- are about equal, $k_c \cong k_f$, then the above relation reduces to

$$K_4'' = K_4'/k_f^2.$$

Thus, the probable effect of ion-pairing is to *decrease* the value of the experimentally observed equilibrium constant below what it would have been if the reaction had actually occurred between dissociated ions. It may be concluded, then, that the replacement of ethylenediamine in the innermost coordination sphere of Cd^{++} by cyanide ion proceeds much more readily in ethylenediamine as solvent than in aqueous solution.

The values of the observed stepwise constants for the cadmium cyanide complexes in ethylenediamine are $k_1 = 360$, $k_2 = 205$, $k_3 = 100$, and $k_4 = 55$. The chelate structure of the solvent leads to the expectation that pairs of cyanide ions should tend to add to cadmium, causing the ratios between the stepwise constants to vary as follows: $k_1/k_2 = $ (small); $k_2/k_3 = $ (large); and $k_3/k_4 = $ (small). The observed ratios are $k_1/k_2 = 1.8$, $k_2/k_3 = 2.1$, and $k_3/k_4 = 1.8$. The differences in these ratios are not large, but it is surprising that the effect is observed at all, because the effects of both the relative charges of the species in each stepwise reaction and the statistical factor cause the successive stepwise constants to decrease sharply throughout the series. (Stepwise constants obtained with a neutral ligand should show up the effect of the chelate structure of the solvent more clearly.)

Formation constants for several simpler systems were also determined in ethylenediamine as solvent, using conductometric or potentiometric methods. In the cases of the silver halides, the potentiometric measurements were made using dilute solutions with only a single salt present, and limiting law activity coefficient corrections were applied in the calculations. The silver cyanide sys-

TABLE 2: FORMATION CONSTANTS OF SOME SIMPLE SILVER COMPLEXES IN ETHYLENEDIAMINE

Reaction	$(K_{AgX})_{en}$	Method
$Ag^+ + Cl^- \rightleftharpoons AgCl$	$10^{3.54}$	E (Ag wire)
$Ag^+ + Br^- \rightleftharpoons AgBr$	$10^{4.08}$	Conduct.
$Ag^+ + Br^- \rightleftharpoons AgBr$	$10^{4.05}$	E_{Ag}
$Ag^+ + I^- \rightleftharpoons AgI$	$10^{4.79}$	E_{Ag}
$Ag^+ + CN^- \rightleftharpoons AgCN$	$(10^{7.7})^a$	E_{Ag}
$Ag^+ + 2CN^- \rightleftharpoons Ag(CN)_2^-$	$(10^{13.3})^a$	E_{Ag}

[a]Concentration constants, not corrected for ion pairing or activity coefficients.

tem contained 6×10^{-4} M silver nitrate and sodium cyanide concentrations up to about 3×10^{-3} M. Ion-pair corrections were *not* made, so that even though the solutions are quite dilute, the constants reported for Ag^+ with CN^- may be low. The constants are reported on the usual molarity scale.

REFERENCES

1. L. F. Audrieth and J. Kleinberg, *Non-Aqueous Solvents*, John Wiley and Sons, Inc., New York (1953).
2. I. M. Kolthoff and P. J. Elving, *Treatise on Analytical Chemistry*, Interscience Encyclopedia, Inc., New York (1959), Chapt. 11 and 13.
3. H. A. Laitinen and C. J. Nyman, *J. Am. Chem. Soc.*, **70**, 2241 (1948); H. A. Laitinen and C. E. Shoemaker, *ibid.*, **72**, 663 (1950); *ibid.*, **72**, 4975 (1950); H. A. Laitinen and A. B. McElroy, *J. Phys. Chem.*, **57**, 564 (1953).
4. W. L. Jolly, *J. Chem. Educ.*, **33**, 512 (1956).
5. W. B. Schaap, *J. Am. Chem. Soc.*, **82**, 1837 (1960).
6. I. M. Kolthoff and J. J. Lingane, *Polarography* (2nd ed.), Interscience Publishers, Inc., New York (1952).
7. J. Bjerrum, G. Schwarzenbach, and L. Sillén, *Stability Constants*, The Chemical Society, London (1958).
8. W. B. Schaap, A. E. Messner, and F. C. Schmidt, *J. Am. Chem. Soc.*, **77**, 2683 (1955).
9. D. D. DeFord and D. N. Hume, *ibid.*, **73**, 5321 (1951).

ON THE INTERACTION OF MERCURY(II) WITH PURINE AND PYRIMIDINES*

RICARDO FERREIRA,[†] EPHRAIM BEN-ZVI, TETSUO YAMANE,[†]
JANIS VASILEVSKIS, and NORMAN DAVIDSON

California Institute of Technology[‡]
Pasadena, California

The study of the binding of Hg^{II} by DNA shows that Hg^{++} adds to the base moieties of the nucleic acids.[1] It was therefore of interest to investigate the complexing of Hg^{II} by various purine and pyrimidine derivatives.

Hg^{++} characteristically forms linear complexes of the type L-Hg-L, where L is the ligand. The $2:1$ complexes with several purine and pyrimidine derivatives are formed in the presence of an excess of the complexing ligand, according to the equation

$$Hg^{++} + 2HL^{+m} = HgL_2^{+2m} + 2H^+, \qquad K = \beta_2 K_a^2 \qquad (1)$$

where m (the charge on HL) = 1 for the adenosine, adenine, and cytosine cations, and $m = 0$ for thymine and thymidine; β_2 is the conventional formation constant for the binding of two L^{m-1} units by Hg^{++} and K_a is the acid constant of HL^{+m}.

Reaction (1) was studied potentiometrically by the procedure described earlier,[2] at an ionic strength of 0.1 M ($NaClO_4$). The potential of a mercury electrode varied with the several concentrations as expected from Eq. (1). The results are displayed in Table 1; there is a correlation between the proton affinity of L and its affinity for Hg^{++} and the values of $\log K$ for Eq. (1) are in the range of 1.5–3.0.

The values of $\log \beta_2 K_a^2$ are comparable to that for imidazolium, 2.4, and greater than that of ammonium, -1.

We have been interested in the $1:1$ complexes formed in the presence of excess metal ion. These cannot be investigated potentio-

*Research supported by the U. S. Atomic Energy Commission, under Contract AT(11-1)-188.
†Present address: Centro Brasil. Pesq. Fisicas, Av. Wenceslau Braz 71, Rio de Janeiro, Brazil.
‡Contribution No. 2695 from the Gates and Crellin Laboratories of Chemistry.

TABLE 1: FORMATION CONSTANTS OF HgL_2 COMPLEXES

HL*	pK_a	$\log \beta_2$	$\log K = \log \beta_2 K_a^2$
HAs^+	3.5	8.5	1.5
HAd^+	4.2	11.5	3.1
HCs^+	4.5	10.9	1.9
HTd	9.6	21.2	2.0
HTh	9.8	21.2	1.6

*As = adenosine, Ad = adenine, Cs = cytosine, HTd = thymidine, HTh = thymine.

metrically because of the equilibrium[3]

$$Hg^{++} + Hg \rightleftharpoons Hg_2^{++}, \qquad K = 130 \tag{3}$$

The uv absorption of the nucleic acid bases is altered by the addition of Hg^{++}, and we have endeavored to investigate the 1:1 complexes by a spectrophotometric method.

The characteristic reaction may be written as

$$Hg^{++} + H_nL^{+m} \rightleftharpoons HgL^{2+m-n} + nH^+ \tag{2}$$

(As we shall see, the number of protons released, n, was different for different cases, so it is expedient to denote the uncomplexed ligand as H_nL^{+m}.) The equilibrium constant for reaction (2) and the value of n was deduced from the variation of absorbance with the concentrations of H^+ and Hg^{++}, using the relation

$$\frac{1}{\bar{\varepsilon} - \varepsilon_0} = \frac{1}{\varepsilon_1 - \varepsilon_0} + \frac{1}{(\varepsilon_1 - \varepsilon_0)K} \frac{(H^+)^n}{(Hg^{++})} \tag{3}$$

where K is the equilibrium constant for reaction (2). The quantities ε_0, ε_1, and ε are the extinction coefficients of H_nL, the extinction coefficient of the complex, and the formal extinction coefficient per mole of ligand, respectively.

The measurements were carried out with base concentrations of the order of 10^{-4} M, Hg^{II} concentrations of $10^{-2} - 10^{-3}$ M, and pH in the range of 1-3. The value of n ($n = 1$ or $n = 2$ usually), the number of protons released, was selected as that integral value which gave the best straight line plot of Eq. (3). We realize that there is some uncertainty in this procedure, but we have analyzed our results as carefully as possible and believe that they are reliable.

The results may be summarized by the following statements:

1. Neutral thymidine (HTd) releases one proton on reaction with Hg^{++}:

$$HTd + Hg^{++} \rightleftharpoons Hg\text{-}Td^+ + H^+, \qquad K = 19 \tag{4}$$

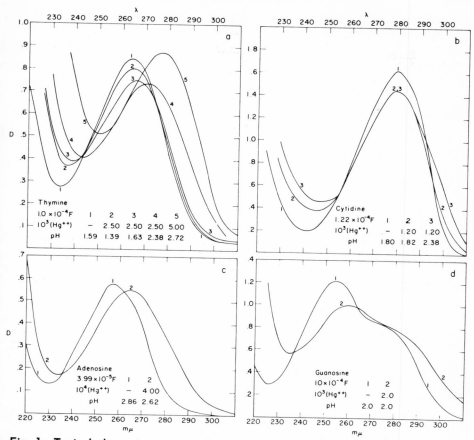

Fig. 1. Typical absorption spectra of some purine and pyrimidine derivatives in the absence and presence of Hg^{++}.

The uv absorbance of the complex is less than that of the thymidine.

A similar result is observed with neutral thymine, but at high ratios of $(Hg^{++})/(H^{+})$ there is evidently a second complex with a light absorption maximum shifted to longer wave lengths. The spectra are displayed in Fig. 1a. A quantitative analysis of the data for the second complex was not feasible. We assume that in thymidine, where $N - 1$ is blocked by the sugar, Hg^{++} replaces the H on $N - 3$; in thymine ($R = H$), Hg^{++} can also replace the H on $N - 1$. The methyl and ethyl mercury cations also form complexes with thymidine:[4]

$$HTd + RHg^+ \rightleftharpoons TdHgR + H^+, \qquad K = 0.5(Me),\ 0.3(Et) \qquad (5)$$

The spectra are similar to that of $TdHg^+$.

2. With the cytidine cation, HCd^+,

(R = sugar), the spectra (Fig. 1b) indicate the two reactions

$$HCd^+ + Hg^{++} \rightleftharpoons HgCd^{++} + H^+, \qquad K = 21 \qquad (6)$$

$$HgCd^{++} + H_2O \rightleftharpoons HOHgCd^+ + H^+, \qquad K_a = 6.0 \times 10^{-3}\ M \qquad (7)$$

3. Our most surprising result is that the addition of Hg^{++} to the adenosine cation (HAs^+) results in the displacement of *two* protons. The structure of the adenosine cation is believed to be

with R = sugar, and with the acid proton shown on the N-1 nitrogen (although the site of protonation is neither certain nor important for our arguments). For reasons to be explained shortly, we shall write this reaction as

$$HAs^+ + Hg^{++} + H_2O \rightleftharpoons HOHg(As)^+ + 2H^+, \qquad K = 0.02\ M \qquad (8)$$

Spectral data are shown in Fig. 1c.

With the adenine cation itself ($R = H$), a similar reaction is observed, and the same is the case for the cations of 6-dimethylaminopurine (HDMeAd$^+$), 7-methyl adenine (H7MeAd$^+$), and 9-methyl adenine (H9MeAd$^+$).

$$HAd^+ + Hg^{++} + H_2O \rightleftharpoons HOHg(Ad)^+ + 2H^+, \qquad K = 7\ M \qquad (9)$$

$$HDMeAd^+ + Hg^{++} + H_2O \rightleftharpoons HOHg(DMeAd)^+ + 2H^+, \quad K = 7\ M \qquad (10)$$

$$H7MeAd^+ + Hg^{++} + H_2O \rightleftharpoons HOHg(7MeAd)^+ + 2H^+, \quad K = 6.3\ M \qquad (11)$$

$$H9MeAd^+ + Hg^{++} + H_2O \rightleftharpoons HOHg(9MeAd)^+ + 2H^+, \quad K = 0.025\ M \quad (12)$$

With the methyl mercury cations, only one proton is released from the adenine and adenosine cations.

$$HAd^+ + MeHg^+ \rightleftharpoons AdHgMe^+ + H^+, \qquad K = 1.67 \qquad (13)$$

$$HAs^+ + MeHg^+ \rightleftharpoons AsHgMe^+ + H^+, \qquad K = 0.035 \qquad (14)$$

The protonated form of guanosine (HGs$^+$, $pK_a = 2.17$) also reacts with Hg^{++} to release two protons.

$$HGs^+ + Hg^{++} + H_2O \rightleftharpoons HOHgGs^+ + 2H^+, \qquad K = 0.7\ M \qquad (15)$$

(spectra in Fig. 1d)

The release of two protons upon addition of Hg^{II} has been verified by pH-stat titration experiments, at pH's of 2.0–2.5, for adenosine, guanosine, and 6-dimethylaminopurine.

The puzzling question is where does the second proton that is released into the solution upon addition of Hg^{++} to a purine cation come from? For adenine, one might propose that both the $N-1$ and $N-9$ protons are displaced. But this explanation will not work for adenosine, or 7-methyl adenine, or 9-methyl adenine. The amino hydrogens cannot be involved because a similar result is obtained with 6-dimethylamino purine. In all cases, the spectral shifts are very similar to that displayed in Fig. 1c, so it is not reasonable to say that the $N-9$ hydrogen is being displaced in adenine and 6-dimethylamino-purine, whereas an amino hydrogen is displaced from the methyl adenines or adenosine.

The facts are most consistent with the proposal that the R—Hg—OH$_2^{++}$ group is a rather strong acid when R is a purine and ionizes according to the equation

$$R-Hg-OH_2^{++} \longrightarrow R-Hg-OH^+ + H^+$$

with a pK_a of less than 1.5. This result is rather unexpected, in view of the fact that the pK_a of H_2O—Hg—OH_2^{++} is 3.7, and the pK_a of H_2O—Hg—OH^+ is 2.6 (the decrease in pK_a between Hg^{++} and $HgOH^+$ is itself surprising),[5] and the pK_a of CH_3—Hg—OH_2 is 4.5.[6]

In the data reported above, large binding constants are observed when the $N - 9$ nitrogen is not blocked, and smaller constants when it is. We therefore suspect that this is the strongest binding site for the $HgOH^+$ grouping.

Preliminary evidence favors the hypothesis that the acidity of the H—OH_2^{++} group is enhanced when it is attached to an imidazole-type nitrogen. Thus, in a pH-stat titration of imidazolium at pH 2 in the presence of excess Hg^{++}, ($\sim 10^{-2} M$), there were four protons released per $C_3N_2H_5^+$ added, corresponding, we believe, to the product

whereas with the pyridine cation, only one proton is released.

REFERENCES

1. T. Yamane and N. Davidson, *J. Am. Chem. Soc.*, **83,** May or June (1961).
2. P. Brooks and N. Davidson, *ibid.*, **82,** 2118 (1960).
3. A. Jonsson, I. Qvarfort and L. G. Sillén, *Acta Chem. Scand.*, **1,** 461 (1947).
4. CH₃HgOH was kindly donated as a 2% aqueous solution by Mr. D. Katsaros of the Agricultural Division, Morton Chemical Co., Woodstock, Illinois.
5. *Stability Constants*, Part II, "Inorganic Ligands," compiled by J. Bjerrum, G. Schwarzenbach and L. Sillén (The Chemical Society, London, 1958), p. 19.
6. W. L. Hughes, *Annals N. Y. Acad. Sci.*, **65,** 454 (1957); T. D. Waugh, H. S. Walton, and J. A. Lasvick, *J. Phys. Chem.*, **59,** 395 (1955).

STABILITY OF COORDINATION COMPOUNDS IN DEUTERIUM OXIDE*

NORMAN C. LI AND PHILOMENA TANG

Department of Chemistry
Duquesne University
Pittsburgh, Pennsylvania

A survey of the literature shows that kinetic deuterium isotope effects have been extensively studied and that a few data exist for the isotope effect on acid dissociation constants; however, very little has been published on the stability of coordination compounds in deuterium oxide. This situation is not surprising because isotope effects on reaction velocities and on acid dissociation constants are more pronounced than on formation constants of metal complexes.

Several papers have appeared recently on the use of ordinary glass-calomel electrode for measurement of acidity in D_2O solutions.[1] These authors have studied the relation between true and apparent pH of solutions in deuterium oxide and found the correction for DCl solutions and $DClO_4$ solutions in D_2O to be $+0.4$ pH unit. In this paper we report the use of this method for the determination of formation constants of six coordination compounds in deuterium oxide. The formation constants of the Mn(II) complexes of tricarballylate and of adenosine mononphosphate have also been determined by an ion-exchange method, using Mn^{54} as tracer.

Experimental

Materials. Deuterium oxide, 99.8% D_2O, was purchased from Bio-Rad Laboratories and used without further purification. Adenosine-5'-monophosphate and glutathione in the reduced state were obtained from the Sigma Chemical Co. and Pfanstiehl Co., respectively. Potentiometric titrations show that the purity of these preparations was better than 99%. The glycine peptides were purchased from Nutritional Biochemicals Corp. The metal salts were recrystallized from deuterium oxide and analyzed by conventional means. NaOD was

*This investigation was supported by the U.S. Atomic Energy Commission through Contract No. AT(30-1)-1922 and by Research Grant NSF G7447 from the National Science Foundation.

prepared by diluting CO_2-free saturated solution of sodium hydroxide with deuterium oxide. For the low concentrations used, this did not alter the deuterium content by a significant amount.

Carrier-free Mn^{54} was obtained from the Nuclear Science and Engineering Corp. For the cation-exchanger, Dowex-50, 8% crosslinked, 100-200 mesh, was used.[2] The capacity of this type of resin has been found to be independent of pH over a wide pH range.[3]

Procedure. pH measurements were made at 25° using a conventional calomel-glass electrode couple with a Beckman Model G pH meter, in both protium oxide and deuterium oxide systems. The pD of a solution in deuterium oxide is determined by use of the equation

$$pD = pH + 0.40 \tag{1}$$

where pH is the apparent pH meter reading in D_2O medium. Equation (1) has been previously obtained by Hyman, *et al.*,[1] Glasoe and Long,[1] and Li *et al.*[1]

In aqueous systems, pH is defined as $-\log C_{H_3O^+} - \log f_\pm$, where $f_\pm$ is the activity coefficient, and at a total ionic strength of 0.1, $-\log f_\pm$ is assumed to be 0.10.[4] We have assumed this value of the activity coefficient for all solutions in deuterium oxide studied in this investigation.

In the ion-exchange method, the Dowex-50 resin is treated with a Veronal buffer solution, pH 7.2, consisting of 0.009 M sodium diethyl barbiturate, 0.008 M HCl and 0.09 M NaCl, and equilibrated with H_2O or D_2O for two days, filtered by suction and air-dried overnight. The flasks containing resin and solutions were agitated at $25 \pm 1°$. After a three-hour shaking period, a 4 ml sample of supernate was removed from each flask for radiochemical analysis. Mn^{54} was counted directly as liquid samples in a scintillation counter.

Results

pH **Titration of 1:1 (Ligand:Metal Ion) Molar Mixtures in Deuterium Oxide.** The formation constants of the 1:1 citrate complexes have been determined by pH titration of solutions containing 0.005 M citric acid, 0.005 M metal(II) chloride and 0.085 M NaCl with standard solutions of NaOD. The titration data for the Ni- and Mn- complexes of citrate are given in Table 1. The symbols (A^{-3}) and $\bar{n}$ represent the total concentration of free citrate ion and the average number of moles of citrate anion bound per mole of the divalent metal ion, respectively, and are calculated by means of equations (2) and (3).

$$(A^{-3}) = \frac{(3T - (\text{NaOD}) - (D^+)) K_1 K_2 K_3}{K_1 K_2 (D^+) + 2K_1 (D^+)^2 + 3(D^+)^3} \tag{2}$$

$$\bar{n} = \frac{T - (A^{-3})(K_1K_2K_3 + K_1K_2(D^+) + K_1(D^+)^2 + (D^+)^3)/K_1K_2K_3}{T_m}. \quad (3)$$

In these equations, T and T_m are the total concentrations of citric acid and metal salt, respectively, and K_1, K_2, K_3 are the three acid dissociation constants of citric acid, the values of which in D_2O are taken from the paper of Li, *et al.*[1] Equations (2) and (3) are similar to equations (12a) and (12b) given by Li *et al.*[5]

TABLE 1: TITRATION OF METAL(II)-CITRATE MIXTURES, 25°

25 ml Solution Containing 0.0050 M $NiCl_2$, 0.0050 M Citric Acid, 0.0085 M NaCl; plus v ml of 0.1169 M NaOD

v, ml	pD	pA^{-3}	$\bar{n}$	$\log k_1$
0.00	2.99			
1.25	3.88	6.38	0.187	5.74
1.50	4.02	6.12	0.259	5.66
1.75	4.19	5.82	0.336	5.52
2.00	3.92	5.63	0.428	5.51
			Ave.	5.61

30 ml Solution Containing 0.0050 M $MnCl_2$, 0.0050 M Citric Acid, 0.085 M NaCl; plus v ml of 0.1169 M NaOD

v, ml	pD	pA^{-3}	$\bar{n}$	$\log k_1$
1.20	4.28	5.47	0.04	4.09
1.40	4.44	5.19	0.088	4.17
1.60	4.60	4.92	0.137	4.12
1.80	4.78	4.64	0.193	4.02
2.05	4.92	4.47	0.280	4.06
2.30	5.12	4.23	0.371	4.00
2.55	5.37	3.97	0.462	3.90
			Ave.	4.05

The formation constants of the nickel complexes of the glycine peptides were determined by titrating solutions containing 0.01 M glycine peptide, 0.01 M $NiCl_2$, 0.07 M NaCl with NaOD, in D_2O in the manner described by Li and Chen[5] for the H_2O system. The pK_{2,D_2O} of the glycine peptides were determined to be glycylglycine, 8.76; triglycine, 8.58; tetraglycine, 8.57. The titration curves of the nickel complexes show that additional ionizations, ascribed to amide hydrogen ionizations, must be taken into account. Table 2 gives a summary of the constants obtained in D_2O, together with literature values obtained in H_2O system.[6] The term pK_1 refers to the reaction

$$NiA^+ = NiA + H^+$$

in which a proton or deuteron is ionized from an amide nitrogen.

TABLE 2: TITRATION OF NiCl$_2$-GLYCINE PEPTIDE MIXTURES, 25°*

| | Glycylglycinate | | Triglycinate | | Tetraglycinate | |
	In D$_2$O	In H$_2$O	In D$_2$O	In H$_2$O	In D$_2$O	In H$_2$O
log k_1	4.13	3.93	3.80	3.70	3.77	3.65
pK_1	†	9.35	8.87	8.25	8.7	8.10

*Values in H$_2$O are taken from Ref. (6).
†pK_1 not calculated because of precipitation.

pH Titration of 2 : 1 (Ligand : Metal Ion) Molar Mixtures in Deuterium Oxide. Table 3 lists the results obtained with nickel complex of glutathione. In the study of zinc complex with glutathione, Li *et al.*,[7] assume that the chelating agent is the species from which all ionizable protons have been removed, A^{-3}. For the nickel complex, this does not lead to a constant value of the formation constant. We therefore assume that A^{-2} is the chelating species, as has been done by Martin and Edsall.[8]

TABLE 3: TITRATION OF NICKEL CHLORIDE-GLUTATHIONE MIXTURES, 25°

10 ml solution containing 0.010 M glutathione, 0.085 M NaCl and 0.0050 M NiCl$_2$, plus v ml. of 0.1191 M NaOD

v, ml	pD	$A^-\times 10^3$	pA^{-2}	$\overline{n}$	log Q
1.10	6.51	6.21	5.13	0.619	4.78
1.20	6.71	5.10	5.01	0.856	4.88
1.40	7.21	2.91	4.76	1.332	5.06
1.50	7.65	1.85	4.51	1.566	5.08

Glutathione in deuterium oxide: pK_2 = 4.15; pK_3 = 9.43; pK_4 = 10.34
Glutathione in H$_2$O:[7] pK_2 = 3.59; pK_3 = 8.75; pK_4 = 9.65.

In Table 3, the pK's of glutathione were determined in deuterium oxide in the manner described by Li *et al.*,[7] for glutathione in protium oxide. The values of A^-, A^{-2}, $\overline{n}$ and Q are calculated by means of the following equations:

$$(A^-) = 2T - (NaOD) - (D^+) \tag{5}$$

$$(A^{-2}) = (A^-)(D^+)/K_3 \tag{6}$$

$$\overline{n} = \frac{T - (A^-) - (A^{-2})}{T_m} \tag{7}$$

$$Q = \frac{\overline{n}}{(2 - \overline{n})(A^{-2})} \tag{8}$$

A plot of log Q *vs.* $\overline{n}$ yields a straight line. The extrapolated value of log Q at $\overline{n} = 0$ is 4.57. According to the Scatchard method,[10] this limiting value of log Q is equal to log k_1 − log N, where N is the number of sites available for binding of the ligand. Since we have chosen $N = 2$, log k_1 is calculated to be 4.87, where k_1 refers to the reaction

$$Ni^{+2} + A^{-2} = NiA. \tag{9}$$

Ion-exchange experiments with Mn(II)-complexes. Results obtained with Mn-complexes of adenosine-5-monophosphate, AMP, are summarized in Table 4. K_d is the distribution coefficient of the Mn^{54} isotope between resin and solution phases. In each flask 20 ml of solution containing a Veronal buffer, Mn^{54} and AMP, were equilibrated with 60 mg resin, which had been treated with the Veronal buffer.

TABLE 4: ION-EXCHANGE EXPERIMENTS WITH Mn(II-ADENOSINE-5-PHOSPHATE MIXTURES AT 25°, $u = 0.10$

In H₂O			In D₂O		
Conc AMP $T \times 10^3$	$1/K_d$	pH	Conc AMP $T \times 10^3$	$1/K_d$	pH meter reading
0.00	0.65	7.02	0.00	0.70	6.89
4.07	1.37	6.89	3.71	1.42	6.96
8.14	2.34	6.89	7.72	2.79	7.03
16.27	6.02	6.89	13.90	5.37	7.09
24.41	12.39	6.89	18.07	8.52	7.11

From the data of Table 4, plots of $[(K_d^0/K_d) - 1]/T$ vs T were made in the manner described by Li et al.[2] Straight lines were obtained, from which the values of the formation constants have been calculated and are summarized in Table 5. The value of log k_1 in H₂O, obtained by the ion-exchange method, is in excellent agreement with that found by Smith and Alberty,[10] who report $k_1 = 156 \pm 20$, in H₂O, $\mu = 0.2$.

TABLE 5: FORMATION CONSTANTS OF Mn(II)-AMP COMPLEXES, 25°, $u = 0.10$

In H₂O			In D₂O	
log k_1	log k_2	log k_1 (literature value)	log k_1	log k_2
2.19	2.14	2.19[10]	2.24	2.15

The Mn(II)-tricarballylate complex was studied by the same ion-exchange method. At pH 7.0–7.1, and in the range of concentration of tricarballylate ion from 0.004 to 0.02 M, $u = 0.16$, $1/K_d$ is a linear function of the concentration. Therefore only a 1:1 complex is

formed. The formation constant in deuterium oxide is found to be
$\log k_1 = 1.93$.

Discussion

Li *et al.*,[2] by a similar ion-exchange method in H_2O, report log
$k_1 = 1.99$ for Mn(II)-tricarballylate complex. The stability of this coordination compound is therefore the same in deuterium oxide as in
protium oxide. This is as expected because the complexing agent is
taken to be the anion A^{-3}, the species from which all ionizable protons have been removed. If the complexation reaction is written

$$M^{++} + H_3A = MA^- + 3\,H^+ \qquad K'$$

then $K' = k_1 K_3^3$, where K_3 is the third acid dissociation constant of
tricarballylic acid. The deuterium isotope effect on K' would then
correspond to the third power of the isotope effect on the third acid
dissociation constant, which has been found by Li *et al.*,[1] to be
$10^{-2.40}$.

Citrate differs from tricarballylate in that an additional —OH
group is present, adjacent to a carboxylate group. In deuterium oxide, the —OH group would be replaced by —OD, and if this is a
binding site, an appreciable deuterium isotope effect would be expected for the citrate complex. The values of $\log k_1$ in protium oxide
of the Ni and Mn-complexes of citrate have been reported to be 5.11[5]
and 3.54,[2] respectively. Comparison of these values in H_2O with the
values listed in Table 1 shows that the deuterium isotope effect is
indeed appreciable, amounting to 0.5 log unit.

Table 5 shows that the formation constants of the Mn-*AMP* complexes are practically the same in H_2O as in D_2O. Although Smith
and Alberty[10] demonstrate that sodium complexes with *AMP*, and in
the ion-exchange experiment sodium ion was used, the complexation
was so weak (k of Na-*AMP* equals three[10]), that its presence does not
affect the calculation for the Mn-*AMP* complex. Li *et al.*,[2] have already
shown that the complexing action of the Veronal buffer is also negligible under the conditions employed. The absence of any deuterium
isotope effect on the formation constant of the Mn-*AMP* complexes
indicates that the binding site is in the 5-phosphate position. In
deuterium oxide, all the hydroxyl hydrogens in the sugar moiety of
AMP would be replaced by deuterium, so that if any of these act as a
binding site, some difference would be found between the formation
constants in protium oxide and deuterium oxide.

As seen in Table 2, the formation constants of the Ni-glycine peptide complexes in D_2O are only slightly higher than in H_2O. The
values of pK_1 in D_2O, however, are about 0.6 log unit higher than in

H_2O. Since the pK refers to acid dissociation from the amide nitrogen, considerable isotope effect is expected. Li *et al.*,[1] found that $pK_D - pK_H$ is a linear function of pK_H for acid dissociation from specific groups, and that the equations are:

$$—COOH: pK_D - pK_H = 0.086 + 0.124\, pK_H \qquad (10)$$

$$—NH_3^+ \text{ and } —ImH^+: pK_D - pK_H = 0.243 + 0.0417\, pK_H \qquad (11)$$

The values of $pK_D - pK_H$ for the pK_1's listed in Table 2 are in good agreement with the values calculated from equation (11).

The isotope effects on the acid dissociation constants of glutathione can be seen in Table 3. The effect on pK_2 agrees with that calculated from equation (10) within 0.03 log unit, so that K_2 refers to acid dissociation from —COOH group. For pK_3 and pK_4, the deviation from the value calculated from Eq. (11) is 0.08 log unit. The considerable deviation may be accounted for by the supposition that K_3 and K_4 are a mixture of the sulfhydryl and amino ionizations.[8]

For the Ni-glutathione complex in H_2O system, Martin *et al.*,[8] report $\log Q_2$ at $\bar{n} = 0$ to be 4.70. Q_2 is defined by the equation

$$Q_2 = \bar{n}/(2 - \bar{n})\,(HG^{--})$$

where (HG^{--}) represents a glutathione molecule with both carboxyl groups and the sulfhydryl groups ionized, the ammonium group being still positively charged. If we let A^{-2} be the chelating species, as is done in equation (8), the limiting value of $\log Q_2$ at $\bar{n} = 0$ in H_2O can be shown to be equal to 4.53, from which $\log k_1$ of Ni-glutathione in H_2O is calculated to be 4.83. As mentioned above, the corresponding value of $\log k_1$ in D_2O is 4.87, so that the stability in deuterium oxide is about the same as in protium oxide. This is reasonable if we assume Ni is bound to the amino and carboxylate groups of the glutamyl residue in glutathione.

In summary, we have shown in this paper that the determination of the presence and absence of deuterium isotope effect, and the magnitude of the effect, can be of great aid in elucidating the groups from which acid dissociation take place, and the binding sites of ligands toward metal ions.

REFERENCES

1. K. Mikkelsen and S. O. Nielsen, *J. Phys. Chem.*, **64**, 632 (1960); H. H. Hyman, A. Kaganove, and J. J. Katz, *ibid.*, **64**, 653 (1960); P. K. Glasoe and F. A. Long, *ibid.*, **64**, 188 (1960); N. C. Li, P. Tang, and R. Mathur, *ibid.*, **65**, 1074 (1961).
2. N. C. Li, W. M. Westfall, A. Lindenbaum, J. M. White, and J. Schubert, *J. Am. Chem. Soc.*, **79**, 5864 (1957).
3. W. C. Baumann and J. Eichborn, *ibid.*, **69**, 2830 (1947).

4. *Symposium on pH Measurement*, ASTM Special Technical Publication No. 190 (1956).
5. N. C. Li, A. Lindenbaum, and J. M. White, *J. Inorg. & Nucl. Chem.*, **12**, 122 (1959); N. C. Li and M. C. M. Chen, *J. Am. Chem. Soc.*, **80**, 5678 (1958).
6. R. B. Martin, M. Chamberlin, and J. T. Edsall, *ibid.*, **82**, 495 (1960).
7. N. C. Li, G. Gawron, and G. Bascuas, *ibid.*, **76**, 225 (1934).
8. R. B. Martin and J. T. Edsall, *ibid.*, **81**, 4044 (1959).
9. J. T. Edsall, G. Felsenfeld, D. S. Goodman, and F. R. N. Gurd, *ibid.*, **76**, 3054 (1954).
10. R. M. Smith and R. A. Alberty, *J. Phys. Chem.*, **78**, 2376 (1956).

PROTON EXCHANGE RATES IN DILUTE SOLUTIONS OF PARAMAGNETIC COMPLEX IONS; AQUEOUS Ti(H$_2$O)$_4$ F$_2^+$ SOLUTIONS*

L. O. MORGAN

Department of Chemistry
University of Texas
Austin 12, Texas

Under appropriate conditions the exchange rate for protons between paramagnetic complex ions and surrounding bulk solvent may be measured by nuclear magnetic resonance techniques. Dipolar and spin-exchange interactions between the central ion and near neighbor protons are much larger than those with more remote protons so that a proton entering the complex is subjected to enhanced relaxation. If the residence time, τ_h, of a proton in the complex ion is long compared to the relaxation time, T_{1c} or T_{2c}, of the ligand protons, the over-all proton relaxation times are given by:

$$1/T_1 = p/\tau_h \quad \text{and} \quad 1/T_2 = p/\tau_h$$

assuming that proton relaxation in the bulk solvent is negligible. The quantity p is the fraction of the total protons occupying equivalent positions in the complex ions. For more than one kind of exchangeable proton in the complex the appropriate relations are summations of the (p/τ_h) values. It is possible in principle to observe several relaxation rates independently, if T_{1c}, T_{2c}, and τ_h are sufficiently long relative to experimental times.

Pearson, Palmer, Anderson, and Allred[1] have developed an expression for the transverse proton relaxation rate, following the methods of McConnell and Berger[2] and McConnell[3]:

$$1/T_2 = (1/T_{2w}) + [p/(T_{2c} + \tau_h)]$$

in which T_{2w} is the relaxation time for protons not in the complex.

---

*Supported by the Robert A. Welch Foundation.

An equivalent relation holds for the longitudinal relaxation rate, $1/T_1$. These equations meet the necessary boundary conditions and are useful in the interpretation of intermediate cases. In general, the condition that τ_h be long compared to T_{1c} and T_{2c} is more frequently met in the latter case, so that measurements of T_2 are more often fruitful for determination of proton exchange rates than are those of T_1. The results of line width measurements have been reported for a number of chromium(III) complexes[1] and spin-echo T_2 determinations have been used to obtain exchange rates in solutions of several copper(II) diamine complexes.[4,5] (Details of the theory and methods employed in the work reported in this paper are given in ref. 4 and 5.) The exchange effect in T_1 has been shown to be of importance in the case of hexaquochromium(III) ion solutions[6] using the data of Hausser and Laukien,[7] which were obtained for a wide range of temperatures.

Transverse relaxation of protons in paramagnetic complexes occurs as a result of electron-proton dipole-dipole interaction with a correlation time determined by tumbling of the microscrystalline unit or by the electron spin relaxation time, whichever is shorter, and, in many cases, through electron-proton spin exchange with a time dependence determined by τ_h and τ_s, the electron spin relaxation time:

$$1/\tau_e = (1/\tau_h) + (1/\tau_s)$$

For ions with $S > 1/2$ there may be more than one relaxation time, in which case the shortest appears first and is of the greatest importance. It should be pointed out that most proton relaxation measurements in paramagnetic ion solutions are done in very dilute solutions and that a great many of the published electron spin line width and relaxation measurements are for more concentrated solutions. Generally speaking, interionic interactions are of considerable importance for electron spin relaxation in solutions more concentrated than about 0.05 M. At lower concentrations the electron spin relaxation times are usually independent of ionic concentration. In magnetic fields corresponding to proton resonance frequencies greater than about 1 mc-spin-exchange has little or no effect on longitudinal proton relaxation. Thus, it is a relatively straightforward matter to separate dipolar and exchange terms in transverse relaxation.

In hexaquomanganese(II) ion solutions T_2 is much shorter than T_1, the exact amount depending upon the frequency at which observations are made. An analysis of relaxation data as a function of temperature in such solutions was done by Bernheim, Brown,

Gutowsky, and Woessner,[8] using the equations of Solomon[9] and Bloembergen[10] for calculations of the dipolar and isotropic spin-exchange contributions, respectively. Results indicated that at high temperatures the appropriate correlation time is τ_h, and at low temperatures (room temperature and below), τ_s. These results were later confirmed by Bloembergen and Morgan,[6] and extended to demonstrate and explain the field dependence of τ_s. This is the only case so far reported in which the proton residence time in the complex has been shown to be of importance in defining the correlation time for transverse proton relaxation.

The work to be reported here comprises an investigation of the proton relaxation behavior in aqueous $Ti(H_2O)_4F_2^+$ (hereafter, B) solutions at a number of temperatures and resonance frequencies.* The narrow electron spin resonance line of this ion in aqueous solution was first observed by R. V. Jones in an unpublished investigation and has recently been studied in D_2O by Maki and Waters.[11] In that medium the ESR line is a triplet, each component of which is several times narrower than the single, unresolved line observed in ordinary water. Upon adding HF or NaF to titanium(III) sulfate or choride, the line character changes markedly until two equivalents of fluoride have been added, and is essentially unchanged thereafter. On the basis of the observed hyperfine interaction and the ESR titration behavior it has been concluded that B has unique stability among the possible fluoride complexes of titanium(III).[11]

The ESR line of B in aqueous solution has been looked at in this laboratory[12] as a function of temperature at 9 and 24 kmc. The over-all derivative peak-to-peak width at 9 kmc increases exponentially from 15.4 oersteds at 300°K to 22.0 oersteds at 360°K, corresponding to minimum transverse electron spin relaxation times of 4.3×10^{-9} and 3.0×10^{-9} sec, respectively. At 24 kmc the over-all line width is essentially constant over the same temperature range at 16.2 oersteds; the minimum transverse relaxation time is 4.1×10^{-9} sec.

With electron spin relaxation times of that order of magnitude it is to be expected that very short proton T_2 values will be observed in solutions of B, if proton exchange is sufficiently rapid and the ion proton coupling in the complex is sufficiently great. The observed values are indeed shorter than the corresponding values of T_1, and decrease markedly with increasing temperature. The increase in the spin-exchange contribution to transverse relaxation at pH 2 corresponds to an apparent activation energy of ca 8.5 kcal/mole and

---

*Much of the experimental work reported here was done by Miss Joye Murphy.

τ_h (300°K) $= 4 \times 10^{-5}$ sec. At higher acid concentrations T_2 is less at low temperatures (<320°K) and essentially the same at high temperatures. In either case, T_2 is independent of resonance frequency in the range 2.8 to 60 mc. These facts all suggest that the transverse relaxation process is controlled by the proton exchange rate, rather than by electron spin relaxation rate.

The behavior of T_1 at all frequencies is that expected for a correlation time of 2×10^{-11} sec and an apparent activation energy of ca 4 kcal/mole. These values correspond closely to those for hexaquocopper(II) ion solutions of comparable concentration, in which tumbling of the microcrystalline ion controls longitudinal relaxation. The absolute values of T_1 in the two cases are those predicted on the basis of the relative numbers of water molecules in the two ions.

It is suggested that the [H⁺] independent proton exchange process is the exchange of water molecules:

$$\text{Ti}(\text{H}_2\text{O})_4\text{F}_2^+ = \text{Ti}(\text{H}_2\text{O})_3\text{F}_2^+ + \text{H}_2\text{O}$$

The observed activation energy is very close to that obtained for the similar proposed process in hexaquomanganese(II) ion solutions.[1,7,13] However, the τ_h for B is 1800 times greater.

The [H⁺]-dependent process may involve association of protons with fluoro groups in the complex:

$$\text{Ti}(\text{H}_2\text{O})_4\text{F}_2^+ + \text{H}_3\text{O}^+ = \text{Ti}(\text{H}_2\text{O})_4(\text{HF})\text{F}^{++} + \text{H}_2\text{O}$$

At a given low temperature, the process exhibits first-order dependence on [H⁺] and a complex temperature dependence which is not quantitatively accounted for at this writing.

REFERENCES

1. R. G. Pearson, J. Palmer, M. M. Anderson, and A. L. Allred, *Z. Electrochem.*, **64**, 110 (1960).
2. H. M. McConnell and S. B. Berger, *J. Chem. Phys.* **27**, 230 (1957).
3. H. M. McConnell, *ibid.*, **28**, 430 (1958).
4. L. O. Morgan, J. Murphy, and P. F. Cox, *J. Am. Chem. Soc.* **81**, 5043 (1959).
5. P. F. Cox and L. O. Morgan, *ibid.* **81**, 6409 (1959).
6. N. Bloembergen and L. O. Morgan, *J. Chem. Phys.* **34**, 842 (1961).
7. R. Hausser and G. Laukien, *Z. Physik.*, **153**, 394 (1959).
8. R. A. Bernheim, T. H. Brown, H. S. Gutowsky, and D. E. Woessner, *ibid.*, **30**, 950 (1959).
9. I. Solomon, *Phys. Rev.* **99**, 559 (1955).
10. N. Bloembergen, *J. Chem. Phys.* **27**, 572, 595 (1957).
11. A. H. Maki and E. Waters, private communication (to be published).
12. L. O. Morgan and A. W. Nolle (to be published).
13. R. E. Connick and R. E. Poulson, *J. Chem. Phys.* **30**, 759 (1959).

SOME NEW HYDRIDO COMPOUNDS OF RHENIUM AND IRIDIUM

LAMBERTO MALATESTA

*Istituto di Chimica Generale
della Universita di Milano
Milano, Italy*

The research on the coordination compounds of rhenium and iridium, recently carried out in the Institute of Chimica Generale of the University of Milan, showed that these elements form very stable phosphine derivatives[1]. Since it had been found by Chatt[2] that many phosphine complexes of transition metals can be hydrogenated to give stable hydrides, for instance $PdClH(Et_3P)_2$ and $PtXH(Ph_3P)_2$, we investigated the reaction of the phosphine derivatives of rhenium and iridium with several hydrogenating agents. In this paper we shall report the results obtained with sodium boro-hydride.

Rhenium Derivatives

The reaction of $ReI_2(Ph_3P)_2$ with sodium boro-hydride in ethanol gives in rather poor yields a red crystalline diamagnetic substance, m.p. 155°, which on the basis of the following evidence has to be considered as a complex hydride of rhenium(III). The compound does not contain iodine; it contains ''hydride'' hydrogen as shown both by chemical and spectroscopic evidence; the analytical figures correspond to the formula $ReH_x(Ph_3P)_2 \cdot 2 C_2H_5OH$, in which, for the moment, x is left undetermined (found: C, 62.5; H, 5.34; P, 7.84; Re, 23.3%. $C_{40}N_{42}O_2P_2Re$ requires C, 59.6; H, 5.58; P, 7.7; Re, 23.1%). The compound is remarkably stable in air in the solid state; in organic solvents it is either very sparingly soluble or it decomposes; the only solvent in which it can be dissolved to an appreciable extent without decomposition is benzene. On recrystallization from benzene it loses the two molecules of ethanol and gives the unsolvated $ReH_x(Ph_3P)_2$ as red crystals, m.p. 178°, stable in air in the solid state and having the same solubility as the ethanol solvate (found: C, 59.5; H, 4.9; P, 8.9; Re, 25.9%. $C_{36}H_{30}P_2Re$ requires C, 60.6; H, 4.6; P, 8.7; Re, 26.1%). The presence of the hydride hydrogen was quantitatively proved, and the hydride hydrogen content quantitatively determined, by treating the compound with a solution of iodine in xylene and adsorbing the evolved gas on palladium black. Under these conditions, exactly three hydrogen atoms per rhenium atom are evolved, so that the compounds may be formulated as $ReH_3(Ph_3P)_2 \cdot 2 C_2H_5OH$ and $ReH_3(Ph_3P)_2$ respectively, in satisfactory agreement with the analytical data. The hydride hydrogen can also be evolved by thermal decomposition of the compounds at 200°, using molten triphenylphosphine as a solvent, but this method gives rather erratic results ranging from 2.5 to 3.5 hydrogen atoms per rhenium atom.

The compound $ReH_3(Ph_3P)_2$ is coordinately unsaturated and it would be expected that, as it binds two molecules of ethanol in $ReH_3(Ph_3P)_2 \cdot 2C_2H_5OH$, it could also take on two other molecules of phosphine to give $ReH_3(Ph_3P)_4$. The seven-coordinated $ReH_3(Ph_3P)_4$, together with the known $FeH_2[oC_6H_4(PEt_2)_2]_2$[3] and the $IrH_3(Ph_3P)_3$ described in the next section, form a series of complex hydrides: ReH_3L_4, FeH_2L_4, and IrH_3L_3 (where L is a ligand containing a phosphorus donor atom) in which all metals reach the inert gas structure, and it could be expected to be more stable than the penta-coordinated compound. It is therefore surprising that all attempts to make it react with phosphine failed, especially so because the seven-coordinated $ReH_3(Ph_3P)_4$ is easily obtained in good yield when carrying on the reduction of $ReI_2(Ph_3P)_2$ with $NaBH_4$ in ethanol in the presence of an excess of triphenylphosphine. Under these conditions the reaction proceeds almost quantitatively according to the scheme:

$$2 ReI_2(Ph_3P)_2 + 4 Ph_3P + 5 NaBH_4 + H_2O =$$
$$2 ReH_3(Ph_3P)_4 + 4 NaI + NaOH + 5 BH_3.$$

$ReH_3(Ph_3P)_4$ is a yellow crystalline diamagnetic substance, m.p. 144°, which in the solid state and in the dark is indefinitely stable, while it darkens slowly when exposed to light. It is very sparingly soluble in organic solvents, and in solution it decomposes very rapidly. The hydride content of this compound was quantitatively determined, as in the diphosphine derivatives, by reaction with iodine in xylene solution (found: C, 69.9; H, 5.4; P, 10.0; Re, 15.5%. $C_{72}H_{60}P_4Re$ requires C, 69.8; H, 5.1; P, 10.0; Re, 15.0%).

Both $ReH_3(Ph_3P)_2$ and $ReH_3(Ph_3P)_4$ are transformed by halogenated solvents, such as chloroform and methylene chloride, into compounds of the type $ReX_4(Ph_3P)_2$, (X = Cl, Br). These are red, crystalline substances, sparingly soluble in organic solvents and remarkably stable. They are paramagnetic with μ = 3.8 B.M. These halogen derivatives of rhenium(IV) are also formed when the hydrides react with elemental chlorine and bromine or with hydrochloric and hydrobromic acids, the latter either as dry gases or in benzene solution. The reaction with hydrochloric and hydrobromic acid proceeds very neatly with the evolution of exactly 3.5 moles of hydrogen per mole of the hydride. However, it cannot be considered to be an exchange reaction of the type observed for other metal hydrides:

$$\text{MeH}_m + n\text{HX} = \text{MeH}_{m-n}X_n = n/2\ \text{H}_2$$

because there is not direct relationship between the number of hydrogen atoms in the starting compound and that of the halogen atoms in the product. In fact, if the hydrides are first heated at 180° *in vacuo* so that about two thirds of the hydride hydrogens are eliminated, and the decomposed mass is then treated with hydrochloric acid, the product is again the tetrachloride, $\text{ReCl}_4(\text{Ph}_3\text{P})_2$.

The reactions between the hydrides and hydrochloric and hydrobromic acid may therefore be written:

$$\text{ReH}_3(\text{Ph}_3\text{P})_2 + 4\ \text{HX} = \text{Re}X_4(\text{Ph}_3\text{P})_2 + 3.5\ \text{H}_2$$

and

$$\text{ReH}_3(\text{Ph}_3\text{P})_4 + 4\ \text{HX} = \text{Re}X_4(\text{Ph}_3\text{P})_2 + 3.5\ \text{H}_2 + 2\ \text{Ph}_3\text{P}$$

It is evident that the hydrogen evolved is not all of "hydride" origin. It may be noted here that the reaction with iodine in xylene solution proceeds in quite a different way, yielding the diiododiphosphine-rhenium(II):

$$\text{ReH}_3(\text{Ph}_3\text{P})_2 + \text{I}_2 = \text{ReI}_2(\text{Ph}_3\text{P})_2 + 1.5\ \text{H}_2$$

$$\text{ReH}_3(\text{Ph}_3\text{P})_4 + \text{I}_2 = \text{ReI}_2(\text{Ph}_3\text{P})_2 + 1.5\ \text{H}_2 + 2\ \text{Ph}_3\text{P}$$

In this case, the hydrogen evolved is all "hydride" hydrogen, so that this reaction may be used in its quantitative determination.

Very little could be done in the investigation of the two described rhenium hydrides by physical methods, mainly because of their low solubility in those organic solvents which do not cause decomposition. In particular, it was not possible to obtain any information from N.M.R. studies. The I.R. spectra of the Nujol mulls shows one single rather broad band, at about 2000 cm^{-1} for both compounds, which has to be attributed to the Re-H stretching. The intensity of this absorption is unexpectedly lower than usually observed for the metal-hydrogen stretching of other hydrides, for instance of the ruthenium, palladium and platinum derivatives investigated by Chatt,[4] and of the iridium compound prepared in our Institute and described in the next section. The presence of a single band in the metal-hydrogen stretching region would agree with a trigonal bipyramid structure for the five-coordinated $\text{ReH}_3(\text{Ph}_3\text{P})_2$, with the three hydrogens in the equatorial plane. However, the validity of this conclusion is somewhat impaired by the fact that only one absorption is present in the spectrum of the seven-coordinated compound, for which more bands would be expected because of the lower symmetry.

Iridium Derivatives

The reaction between the soluble iridium bromide, triphenyl phosphine and sodium boro-hydride in ethanol yields a mixture of two substances, which, on the basis of the following evidence, can be considered to be the two isomeric forms of the complex hydride $IrH_3(Ph_3P)_3$. These compounds are white, crystalline, diamagnetic substances which in the solid state and in the dark are indefinitely stable to air but discolour when exposed to light. They are insoluble in ethanol and hexane and moderately soluble in benzene, methylene chloride and tetrahydrofurane, giving colourless stable solutions. The two compounds, which we have called α and β, are present in the crude reaction product in a fairly constant ratio (α/β = 5/1 approximately), and can be separated by repeated fractional crystallization from benzene-ethanol.

The compounds α and β have identical composition, corresponding to a 1/3 ratio between iridium and triphenylphosphine (α found: C, 66.5; H, 5.1; P, 9.6; Ir, 19.5%; β found: C, 66.2; H, 5.2; P, 9.7; Ir, 19.8%. $C_{54}H_{45}P_3Ir$ requires C, 66.0; H, 4.9; P, 9.48; Ir, 19.7%), but differ in their physical properties. The α compound has a m.p. of 176°, dipole moment μ = 2.7 D in dilute benzene solution at 20°, and its I.R. spectrum (as a Nujol mull) shows two bands at 2124 and 1745 cm,$^{-1}$, respectively. The band at 2124 cm^{-1} is rather broad and of medium intensity, while that at 1745 cm^{-1} is extremely sharp and strong. The β compound has a m.p. of 149–152°, dipole moment μ = 4.3 D in dilute benzene solution at 20°, and the I.R. spectrum of the Nujol mull shows a single band at 2083 cm^{-1}, sharp but of medium intensity. As the bands at 2124, 2083 and 1745 cm^{-1} can only be attributed to the iridium-hydrogen stretching, the I.R. spectra show that both the α and β compounds are complex hydrides. The number of hydride hydrogen atoms cannot be deduced from the micro-analytical figures and the direct determination of the hydride hydrogen, in a way similar to that described for the rhenium derivatives, could not be satisfactorily carried out. Besides, no information was obtained from the N.M.R. spectra, because of the limited solubility of the compounds in suitable solvents. However, their chemical behaviour and, in particular, the following reactions, are consistent with the presence of three hydride hydrogens in both compounds.

1. The α and β compounds react with hydrochloric and hydrobromic acids in tetrahydrofurane, with the evolution of two moles of hydrogen per mole of hydride, and the formation of dichlorohydridotris(triphenyl-phosphine)iridium:

$$IrH_3(PH_3P)_3 + 2\ HX = IrHX_2(Ph_3P)_3 + 2\ H_2$$

The product obtained in this reaction, a white crystalline substance stable to air both in the solid state and in solution, is very similar to the triethylphosphine derivative $IrHCl_2(Et_3P)_3$ prepared by Chatt[5] in another way. In particular the I.R. spectrum in Nujol shows a single peak at 2220 cm^{-1}, very sharp, though of medium intensity, which must be attributed to the Ir—H stretching (Chatt reports 2114 and 2213 cm^{-1} for the isomeric forms of his compounds). It is interesting to note that in this reaction the α and β compounds yield the same product. On treatment with sodium borohydride in tetrahydrofurane, $IrHCl_2(Ph_3P)_3$ undergoes a reverse reaction, reforming the tri-hydride as a mixture of α and β, having approximately the usual 5/1 ratio.

2. With carboxylic acids, both α and β evolve one molecule of hydrogen per mole of hydride, and yield compounds of composition corresponding to $IrH_2(OCOR)(Ph_3P)_3$. These are white crystalline substances, fairly soluble in organic solvents, non-electrolytes and monomeric in solution. Their I.R. spectra show two bands of medium intensity in the metal-hydrogen stretching region (2220, 2150 cm^{-1} in Nujol mull), which in connection with chemical evidence indicate the presence of two hydrogen atoms. Moreover the carboxylate ion can easily be replaced by simple univalent coordinating anions such as bromide and iodide, to give compounds which can only be formulated as $IrH_2X(Ph_3P)_3$.

3. With a dilute solution of perchloric acid in alcohol, the α and β hydrides give a stable compound, which, in benzene solution, is undissociated and monomeric (electric moment $\mu = 13\ D$), and, in acetone, behaves as a uni-univalent electrolyte. This compound must therefore be formulated as the salt of a complex hydride cation in which the iridium atom is five-coordinated: $[IrH_2(Ph_3P)_3][ClO_4]$. (I.R. spectrum in Nujol: 2140 and 2249 cm^{-1}).

The above experimental facts prove the presence of three hydride hydrogen atoms in both α and β, which therefore must be considered the geometric isomers of $IrH_3(Ph_3P)_3$. On the other hand it may be noted that the existence of a compound of formula $IrH_3(Ph_3P)_3$ is not at all surprising, once the formula of a compound like Chatt's $IrHCl_2(Et_3P)_3$ has been undoubtedly established. From the dipole measurements ($\mu_\alpha = 2.7\ D$; $\mu_\beta = 4.3\ D$), it appears that the α compound, which has the higher melting point and the lower solubility, is the *trans* isomer, while the low-melting, more soluble β is the *cis*-isomer. The ratio between the experimental values of the dipole moments is 1.6 while the calculated ratio is 1.71 for the *cis* and *trans* isomers of an octahedral MA_3B_3 compound. The agreement is very good, considering the inevitable distortion of the octahedron. A satisfactory interpretation of the I.R. spectra has not yet been possible to achieve. However, it is interesting to note that between the two bands of the α (*trans*) isomer there is an unusually high separation of 380 cm^{-1}. It may be also observed that it is always the lower and more intense band that disappears on substituting one or two hydrogen atoms of a with other anionic ligands.

Concluding, our research on the hydrogenation of the rhenium and iridium phosphine derivatives has proved that these elements form stable hydride complexes containing three hydrogen atoms, which is the highest number yet reported. The chemical behaviour of these compounds, and in particular the fact that iridium forms the series $IrH_3(Ph_3P)_3$, $IrH_2X(Ph_3P)_3$, $IrHX_2(Ph_3P)_3$ and $IrX_3(Ph_3P)_3$, the terms of which are very similar, is indeed good evidence for the fact that in these complex hydrides, the hydrogen atoms have a halogenoid character.

TABLE 1: HYDRIDE-PHOSPHINE COMPLEXES OF RHENIUM AND IRIDIUM

Compound	Colour and Crystal Form	m.p.		I.R. Absorption Frequencies (cm−1) in Nujol
$ReH_3(Ph_3P)_2$	red	178°	193*	2000
$ReH_3(Ph_3P)_4$	yellow	144°		2050
$\alpha\text{-}IrH_3(Ph_3P)_3$	white prisms	174°	225*	2124,1745
$\beta\text{-}IrH_3(Ph_3P)_3$	white needles	153°	217*	2083
$IrH_2(OCOCH_3)(Ph_3P)_3$	white prisms	167°		2200,2150
$IrH_2(OCOCH_2COOH)$ (Ph_3P)_3$	white prisms	157°		2180,2160
$IrH_2Br(Ph_3P)_3$	ivory prisms	168°		2220,2065
$IrH_2(Ph_3P)_3$	pale yellow tablets	152/159°		2210,2083
$IrH_2(Ph_3P)_3ClO_4$	white prisms	139/143°		2140,2249
$IrHBr_2(Ph_3P)_3.C_6H_6$	yellow prisms	167°		2220

*m.p. (dec. in vacuum)

REFERENCES

1. M. Angoletta, *Gazz. Chim. It.*, **90**, 1021, (1960); M. Freni and V. Valenti, *J. Inorg. Nuclear Chem.*, **16**, 240,1961; *Idem, Gazz. Chim. It.*, *90* 1436 and 1445 (1960).
2. J. Chatt and B.L. Shaw, *Sonderdruck aus XVII international Congress of Pure and Applied Chemistry*, Butterwoth, London, 1960, p. 147 and following.
3. J. Chatt, F.A. Hart, and R.G. Hayter, *Nature*, **187**, 55, (1960).
4. J. Chatt, L.A. Duncanson, and B.L. Shaw, *Chem. Ind.*, 859 (1958).
5. J. Chatt and B.L. Shaw, *ibid.* 1931 (1960).

NUCLEOPHILIC SUBSTITUTION REACTIONS OF TRIS(1,10-PHENANTHROLINE)NICKEL(II) AND TRIS(1,10-PHENANTHROLINE)IRON(II)

D. W. MARGERUM and L. P. MORGENTHALER*†

Department of Chemistry
Purdue University
Lafayette, Indiana

The rate of dissociation of tris($1,10$-phenanthroline)Iron(II) (abbreviated $FePh_3^{+2}$) is greatly increased in the presence of hydroxide ion,[1] while the rate of dissociation or racemization of $NiPh_3^{+2}$ is only slightly increased in basic solution up to about 0.1M hydroxide ion.[2,3] This difference in behavior is examined over an extended range of hydroxide ion concentration and is also examined in the presence of cyanide ion and azide ion. The pronounced effect of these nucleophiles on the rate of the substitution reactions of $FePh_3^{+2}$ is of particular interest because the lack of acidic protons on $1,10$-phenanthroline rules out an S_N1CB mechanism. In view of the interest concerning S_N1CB or S_N2 mechanisms for Co(III) reactions,[4-8] it is worthwhile to examine this Fe(II) system which is isoelectronic with Co(III). The hydroxide ion behavior with $FePh_3^{+2}$ is not a specific effect as both cyanide and azide ions also accelerate the Ph dissociation.[9] This is in striking contrast to the lack of kinetic effect of these nucleophiles in their $NiPh_3^{+2}$ substitution reactions.[10] The mixed ligand complexes which are products of some of these substitution reactions are of thermodynamic and kinetic interest themselves. Experimental evidence for the various complexes and for their kinetic behavior is presented elsewhere as are the experimental details for the data cited.[9,10]

---

*The authors wish to express their thanks to the Research Corporation and to the Purdue Research Foundation for their support of this work.

†Western Electric Engineering Research Center, Princeton, New Jersey.

NUCLEOPHILIC SUBSTITUTION OF $FePh_3^{+2}$

Hydroxide Ion

The reaction sequence proposed[1] for the dissociation of $FePh_3^{+2}$ up to 1 to 2 M base is

$$FePh_3^{+2} \quad \begin{cases} \xrightarrow{k_d} \\ \xrightarrow{k_1[OH^-]} \\ \xrightarrow{k_2[OH^-]^2} \end{cases} \qquad FePh_2^{+2} \overset{rapid}{\rightleftharpoons} FePh^{+2} \overset{rapid}{\rightleftharpoons} Fe^{+2}$$

$$+ \qquad\qquad + \qquad\qquad +$$

$$Ph \qquad\qquad Ph \qquad\qquad Ph$$

where the hydroxide ion complexes of the products are omitted. This reaction system was re-examined to be sure that no colored intermediate complexes such as $FePh_2(OH)_2$ existed because such a complex was found with $FePh_2(CN)_2$ and $NiPh_2(OH)_2$. The disappearance of $FePh_3^{+2}$ was again followed spectrophotometrically but now at all wavelengths between 410 and 540 mμ. All wavelengths gave identical rate constants which were first order in $FePh_3^{+2}$ up to 85% dissociation. The reaction was also followed by the extraction and analysis of the Ph released. The same rate constant was obtained assuming the release of 3Ph per $FePh_3^{+2}$ dissociated. These experiments confirm the initial assumption that there are no colored products of appreciable absorbance in this region and that there are no inert complexes formed after the initial dissociation.

The effect of hydroxide ion on the observed first-order rate constant, k_0, is shown in Fig. 1 ($k_0 = k_d + k_1[OH^-] + k_2[OH^-]^2$; the rate is first-order due to excess hydroxide ion).

Cyanide Ion

Contrary to one report[11] we found a stable $FePh_2(CN)_2$ complex in aqueous solution as the reaction product of $FePh_3^{+2}$ and cyanide ion. The sharp color change of $FePh_2(CN)_2$ from orange-red to purple when it is extracted into chloroform is apparently due to a solvent interaction.[12,13]

The rate of the cyanide reaction with $FePh_3^{+2}$ was followed spectrophotometrically in aqueous solution, taking the absorbance of the product into account. The reaction gave excellent first-order rates in the presence of excess $[CN^-]$ for 85% dissociation of $FePh_3^{+2}$. The reaction was also followed by chloroform extraction and analysis of $FePh_2(CN)_2$, giving identical rate constants.

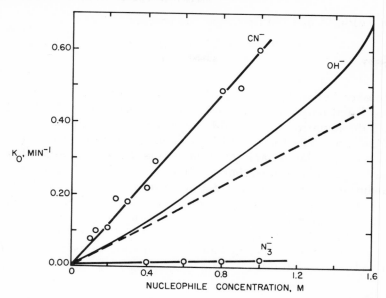

Fig. 1. Observed first-order rate constant, k_0, for the dissociation of $FePh_3^{+2}$. (The solid curve for OH^- is taken from previous data and the dashed line indicates the slope for k_1 only.)

The mechanism postulated proceeds by two paths

$$FePh_3^{+2} \xrightarrow{k_d} \begin{array}{c} FePh_2^{+2} + 2CN^- \\ + \\ Ph \end{array} \xrightarrow{rapid} FePh_2(CN)_2$$

and

$$FePh_3^{+2} + CN^- \xrightarrow{k_1} \begin{array}{c} FePh_2CN^+ + CN^- \\ + \\ Ph \end{array} \xrightarrow{rapid}$$

The observed first-order rate constant (excess CN^-) is $k_0 = k_d + k_1$ [CN^-] up to 1.0 M cyanide ion. The values of $\Delta H^{\ddagger} = 20$ kcal and $\Delta S^{\ddagger} = -3$ e.u. were obtained from k_1 values between $10°$ and $35°$ at an ionic strength maintained at 2.0 M with KCl. The average kinetic results are summarized in Fig. 1 and Table 1.

Azide Ion

The dissociation of $FePh_3^{+2}$ in the presence of N_3^- was followed spectrophotometrically, but, unlike the cyanide system, the products of the reaction were essentially colorless. However, some type of intermediate complex did cause a metastable equilibrium to be established between $FePh_3^{+2}$ and the first reaction product

$$FePh_3^{+2} + N_3^- \rightleftharpoons A \longrightarrow B$$
$$+$$
$$Ph$$

The rate expression, $k_0 = k_d + k_1[N_3^-]$, was again obtained in excess $[N_3^-]$, but only for about 10–15% dissociation of $FePh_3^{+2}$. Beyond 15% dissociation a noticeable back reaction from product A slowed the rate. The final equilibrium position for the system (B) predicts no appreciable back reaction at this stage. Since neither A nor B have appreciable absorbance relative to $FePh_3^{+2}$ at 510 mμ, these undefined products do not detract from the kinetic conclusions regarding the disappearance of the characteristic red $FePh_3^{+2}$ complex. The average rate constants at high ionic strength are given in Table 1 and the effectiveness of N_3^- relative to CN^- and OH^- is seen in Fig. 1. The values of k_1 in Table 1 were used to calculate $\Delta H^{\ddagger}$ = 21 kcal and $\Delta S^{\ddagger}$ = –10 e.u.

TABLE 1: SECOND-ORDER RATE CONSTANTS FOR THE REACTION OF $FePh_3^{+2}$ WITH CYANIDE AND AZIDE IONS

Nucleophile	Temp, $^{\circ}$C	Ionic Strength		k_1 (min^{-1}l.mole^{-1})
		μ	Added Salt	
CN^-	10.0	0.01	Na_2SO_4	0.11
CN^-	10.0	2.00	KC1	0.073
CN^-	25.0	0.01	Na_2SO_4	1.6 .
CN^-	25.0	0.10	Na_2SO_4	0.48
CN^-	25.0	1.00	Na_2SO_4	0.28
CN^-	25.0	2.00	KCl	0.60
CN^-	35.0	2.00	KCl	1.5
N_3^-	10.0	2.00	KCl	0.00091
N_3^-	25.0	2.00	KCl	0.0099
N_3^-	35.0	2.00	KCl	0.024

NUCLEOPHILIC SUBSTITUTION OF $NiPh_3^{+2}$

Hydroxide and Ethylenediaminetetraacetate Ions

Unlike the $FePh_3^{+2}$ system, the aqueous dissociation of $NiPh_3^{+2}$ has bis- and mono-*1,10*-phenanthroline complexes which are stable and sluggish. The reactions of the bis and mono complexes must be taken into account in studying the loss of the first Ph from $NiPh_3^{++}$.

This dissociation

$$NiPh_3{}^{+2} \xrightleftharpoons[k_{3f}]{k_{3d}} \begin{array}{c} NiPh_2{}^{+2} \\ + \\ Ph \end{array} \xrightleftharpoons[k_{2f}]{k_{2d}} \begin{array}{c} NiPh^{+2} \\ + \\ Ph \end{array} \xrightleftharpoons[k_{1f}]{k_{1d}} \begin{array}{c} Ni^{+2} \\ + \\ Ph \end{array}$$

rate in the presence of high [OH⁻] was determined by three different methods:

1. The rate of reaction

$$NiPh_3{}^{+2} + 2OH^- \rightleftharpoons NiPh_2(OH)_2 + Ph$$

was followed by the analysis of free Ph after its extraction into dichloromethane. However, this reaction does not proceed very far to the right, and even at very low concentrations of $NiPh_3{}^{+2}$ an early correction for the back reaction is necessary.

2. The racemization of $NiPh_3(ClO_4)_2$ and $NiPh_3I_2$ was followed in NaOH and gave rate constants which were in agreement with those from the above method. The ionic strength could not be kept constant as the [OH⁻] varied because of the insolubility of most salts of $NiPh_3{}^{++}$. The racemization rates are given in Table 2.

TABLE 2: RACEMIZATION OF NiPh₃⁺⁺ IN THE PRESENCE OF HYDROXIDE ION (25.00 ± .05°)

[OH⁻]	k_{rac}, min⁻¹ × 10⁴
1.0	9.8[a]
1.0	8.7[a]
2.0	11[a]
3.0	12[a]
pH 5.8	6.62
0.40	7.00
0.60	7.20
0.60	7.99
0.70	8.01
0.80	8.10
1.00	8.38
1.20	8.68
1.50	8.66
1.00	8.30
1.00	8.36[b]
1.00	7.21[c]

[a] $NiPh_3(ClO_4)_2$ was used in these rates: $NiPh_3I_2$ was used for all others.
[b] 5.0×10^3 M EDTA present.
[c] 0.10 M EDTA present.

The racemization and dissociation rates of $NiPh_3^{+2}$ are equal in weakly basic solutions[2,3] and to confirm this fact in strongly basic solutions the dissociation rate was checked by another method.

3. The reaction

$$NiPh_3^{+2} + Y^{-4} \longrightarrow NiPhY^{-2} + 2\ Ph$$

where Y^{-4} is the EDTA anion, which was present in excess, was followed by Ph extraction. The rate constants from this reaction were in agreement with those obtained by the other two methods. The EDTA did not affect the rate of loss of the first Ph. It has been shown that the mixed complex, $NiPhY^{-2}$, is stable and that $NiPh_2(OH)_2$ and $NiPh_2Y^{-2}$ rapidly lose a Ph compared to $NiPh_3^{+2}$ or compared to $NiPh_2(H_2O)_2^{+2}$.[10]

Concentrated hydroxide ion increases the rate of dissociation of $NiPh_3^{+2}$ by a factor of almost two, while under similar conditions the $FePh_3^{+2}$ dissociation rate increases by a factor greater than 200.

Cyanide Ion

The reaction

$$NiPh_3^{+2} + 4\ CN^- \longrightarrow Ni(CN)_4^{-2} + 3\ Ph$$

in excess cyanide ion gave no evidence of intermediates of appreciable concentration. The reaction was followed spectrophotometrically at 343 mμ where bonded and unbonded Ph can be distinguished. In order to confirm the fact that the bis Ph complex was not present during the reaction, the compound $NiPh_2(CN)_2 \cdot 2\ H_2O$ was prepared separately. This compound is quite insoluble in water but rapidly dissolves in NaCN to give $Ni(CN)_4^{-2}$ and free Ph. Thus the mixed cyanide, 1,10-phenanthroline complexes like the hydroxide intermediates lose Ph much faster than the corresponding aquo complexes. However, cyanide ion has no appreciable effect on the rate of dissociation of $NiPh_3^{+2}$ as seen in Table 3.

TABLE 3: EFFECT OF CYANIDE AND AZIDE IONS ON THE DISSOCIATION RATE OF $NiPh_3^{+2}$ (25.00 $\pm$ 0.05°)

Nucleophile	$k_{3d} \times 10^4$, min^{-1}
0.60 M NaCN	7.0
0.80 M NaCN	6.3
1.00 M NaCN	6.6
1.20 M NaCN	6.9
1.40 M NaCN	6.8
0.80 M NaN$_3$	7.0[a]
1.00 M NaN$_3$	6.8[a]
1.20 M NaN$_3$	7.1[a]

[a] EDTA present.

Azide Ion with EDTA

A 20-fold excess of EDTA was added to $NiPh_3^{+2}$ and NaN_3 in order to displace the reaction to form $NiPhY^{-2}$. Table 3 shows that the N_3^- did not affect this dissociation rate.

DISCUSSION

The fact that $NiPh_3^{+2}$ is not subject to attack by OH^-, CN^- or N_3^- while $FePh_3^{+2}$ is attacked by all three, eliminates a number of otherwise plausible mechanisms for these reactions. Thus, the stepwise rupture of the chelate previously suggested,[1] while very important for some systems, does not seem to apply in this case. The iron(II) complex might be more sensitive to hydroxide or cyanide intermediates in a stepwise rupture of Ph, but the nickel(II) complex ought to show some dependence on these ions if this path were important. Nor is the ion pair mechanism $(S_N 1IP)$ [14] reasonable since both complexes have the same charge and size. In fact, increased ionic strength represses these reactions in aqueous solution. As mentioned previously, the $S_N 1CB$ mechanism is not possible since there are no ionizable protons.

Another mechanism previously discussed for the hydroxide ion effect necessitated the formation of some unique intermediate species between $FePh_3^{+2}$ and OH^-, which is not a mere ion-pair.[1] The present data now suggest that this may well be the case if interaction occurs directly between the nucleophile and the metal ion in the complex. [15] The geometry of the Ph complexes creates three major holes or pockets near the metal ion between the Ph molecules. It has been suggested [16] that each of these holes contains two water molecules. Therefore, moderately close approach of a small negative nucleophile to the metal ion is possible. The nucelophile is inside the face of the octahedral complex. Richardson suggests that the π orbitals of the nucleophile could interact with the antibonding molecular orbitals involving the metal $3d$ atomic orbitals. In the iron(II) complex such interaction would weaken the octahedral bonds, giving a more labile complex. On the other hand, the two additional $3d$ electrons in nickel(II) would greatly diminish this type of interaction. This can explain the nucleophilic attack on $FePh_3^{+2}$ but not $NiPh_3^{+2}$. The proposed mechanism for $FePh_3^{+2}$ is the rapid formation of a weak ion-pair with the anion as close to the metal as steric hindrance permits without deforming any Ph bonds. Interaction then occurs when the nucleophile and the metal ion come closer together (with steric strain for larger nucleophiles but still without breaking any Ph bonds). This interaction weakens the octahedral Fe—N bonds and gives a more labile species which then dissociates much faster than the initial complex. The mechanism is

$$FePh_3^{+2} + L^{-x} \underset{k_d}{\overset{K_L}{\rightleftharpoons}} (FePh_3L)^{+2-x} \xrightarrow{kL'} \text{Products}$$

where L^{-x} is the nucleophile (OH^-, CN^-, N_3^-) and the k_1 values in Table 1 and Fig. 1 are equal to $k_L'K_L$. According to this mechanism the coordination of the metal ion expands to seven before dissociation. After dissociation the attacking nucleophile could rapidly move to the initial octahedral coordination site. However, the seventh coordination via the antibonding orbitals is always much weaker than the octahedral bonds. Thus the mechanism is different from either typical S_N2 or S_N1 reactions. The effectiveness of the nucleophile in this reaction would depend upon its ability to approach the metal ion and upon the closed-shell repulsion as well as its π-stabilization. Since K_{OH} ought to be greater than K_{CN} due to the size of the ions, k'_{CN} is greater than k'_{OH} in agreement with their nucleophilic character. However, N_3^- may have a considerably lower K_{N_3} than CN^- due to steric factors so that the k_1 for N_3^- may not reflect its nucleophility. The $\Delta H^{\ddagger}$ and $\Delta S^{\ddagger}$ values tend to support this.

If the $[OH^-]^2$ term found before is not due to activity effects, then another ion-pair intermediate, $FePh_3(OH)_2$, could be postulated which dissociates even faster than $FePh_3OH^+$ by a similar mechanism.

An interesting prediction based on this mechanism is that the dissociation of $FePh_3^{+2}$ in non-aqueous solvents should be much greater for these nucleophiles because of favored ion-pair formation. In fact, this effect has already been reported [17] for $Fe(bipy)_3^{+2}$ in methanol where the effectiveness of Cl^-, Br^-, HSO_4^-, NO_3^- and ClO_4^- are compared. These ions cause changes in the dissociation rate of $Fe(bipy)_3^{+2}$ which are very small compared to the effect of NaCN or $NaOCH_3$ on the dissociation rate of $FePh_3(ClO_4)_2$ in methanol. For example, the cyanide reaction proceeds 400 times faster in methanol than it does for the same $[CN^-]$ in water.

This mechanism also offers an explanation for the intramolecular racemization of $FePh_3^{+2}$ and $FePh_3^{+3}$ compared to the dissociative racemization of $NiPh_3^{+2}$. In this case water is the nucleophile which interacts with Fe(II) or Fe(III) (both of low spin), weakening and expanding their Ph bonds and giving a fast rate of racemization without dissociation. Hydroxide ion should accelerate these racemizations, but the dissociation is also very fast in base. However, both complexes racemize faster in water than in acid. [18]

Another prediction based on this mechanism is that Co(III) complexes should behave like the $FePh_3^{+2}$ complex. Unfortunately

$CoPh_3^{+3}$ cannot be studied due to its catalysis by rapid exchange with $CoPh_2^{+2}$. However, the racemization of *1,9*-bis(salicylidene-amine)-3,7-dithiamonanecobalt(III) complex has been reported to have a first-order cyanide ion and hydroxide ion attack.[19] This complex does not have ionizable protons and should have solvent pockets similar to the Ph complexes according to the structure proposed for similar complexes.[20] In general, positively charged complexes of Co(III) and Cr(III) which are not sterically blocked from approach at the octahedral face ought to be subject to nucleophilic attack by negative ligands according to this mechanism. A small ligand like OH^- should be particularly effective .

REFERENCES

1. D. W. Margerum, *J. Am. Chem. Soc.*, **79**, 2728 (1957).
2. N. R. Davis and F. P. Dwyer, *Trans. Faraday Soc.*, **48**, 244 (1952).
3. R. G. Wilkins and M. J. G. Williams, *J. Chem. Soc.*, 1763 (1957).
4. F. Basolo, H. H. Schmidtke, and R. G. Pearson, *J. Am. Chem. Soc.*, **82**, 4434 (1960).
5. F. Basolo and R. G. Pearson, *Mechanisms of Inorganic Reactions*, John Wiley and Sons, Inc., New York, 1958.
6. C. K. Ingold, R. S. Nyholm, and M. L. Tobe, *Nature*, **187**, 447 (1960).
7. D. D. Brown, C. K. Ingold, and R. S. Nyholm, *J. Chem. Soc.*, 2678 (1953).
8. C. K. Ingold, *Fifth Weizmann Memorial Lecture Series*, The Weizmann Science Press of Israel, 1959.
9. D. W. Margerum and L. P. Morgenthaler (to be published).
10. L. P. Morgenthaler and D. W. Margerum (to be published).
11. A. A. Schilt, *J. Am. Chem. Soc.*, **79**, 5421 (1957).
12. A. A. Schilt, *ibid.*, **82**, 3000 (1960).
13. A. A. Schilt, *ibid.*, **82**, 5779 (1960).
14. R. G. Basolo, P. M. Henry, and F. Basolo, *J. Am. Chem. Soc.*, **79**, 5382 (1957).
15. J. W. Richardson, D. W. Margerum, and L. P. Morgenthaler (to be published).
16. A. Jensen, F. Basolo, and H. M. Neumann, *J. Am. Chem. Soc.*, **80**, 2354 (1958).
17. L. Seiden, F. Basolo, and H. M. Neumann, *ibid.*, **81**, 3808 (1959).
18. N. R. Davis and F. P. Dwyer, *Trans. Faraday Soc.*, **49**, 180 (1953); *ibid.*, **50**, 820 (1954).
19. A. L. Hope and J. E. Pure, *J. Chem. Soc.*, 2782 (1960).
20. F. P. Dwyer and F. Lions, *J. Am. Chem. Soc.*, **72**, 1545 (1950).

THE KINETICS OF THE REACTION OF SOME PLANAR NICKEL(II) COMPLEXES WITH EDTA

R. KENT MURMANN

Department of Chemistry
University of Missouri
Columbia, Missouri

Of the ions which commonly form planar complexes (Pt^{+2}, Pd^{+2}, Au^{+3}, Ag^{+2}, Ni^{+2}, Cu^{+2}), platinum(II) has been most extensively studied both with regard to the stereochemistry and the kinetics of reactions. The mechanisms of platinum(II) complex reactions have been reviewed and discussed recently by Basolo and Pearson.[1] The reaction kinetics of most of the planar molecule ions are potentially complicated by oxidation-reduction and often inconvenient for study due to either their extreme rapidity or slowness. Many of the nickel(II) complexes have more favorable characteristics. Furthermore in all cases there is a marked tendency to coordinate a fifth and sixth group weakly.

The study by Wilkins[2] of the acid dissociation, coupled with the metal and ligand exchange of [Ni(C-substituted ethylenediamine)$_2$]$^{+2}$, provides information about the kinetic nature of the planar state of nickel(II). An extension of this work to other planar-forming ligands and to more complicated reactants is important for the light it may shed on the whole mechanistic picture.

The ligands which form planar complexes with nickel(II)[3,4], chosen for study, are tetraMeAO, AO, N-alkylAO and ENAO.* The latter three complex ions have a +1 charge due to the formation of a single hydrogen bond between *cis*-oxime groups. The formation constants of these species have been determined[3,4] as well as the rates of formation and dissociation.[2,5] The reactant EDTA seemed especially suited for a study of this type in view of its hexadentate nature, large formation constant and acid-base characteristics.

In the pH range 6−11 the primary reactant species are EDTA^{-2}, EDTA^{-3}, EDTA^{-4}, [Ni(AO)$_2$ − H]$^+$ and [Ni(AO)$_2$ − 2 H]$^\circ$, while the product is the same regardless of the reactant complex and is

---

*(AO) = *2*-amino-*2*-methyl-*3*-butanone oxime, (N-alkylAO) = *2*-alkylamino-*2*-methyl-*3*-butanone oxime, (ENAO) = *2, 2′*-ethylenediamino-bis-*2*(methyl-butanone) dioxime, (TetraMeEn) = *2,3* dimethyl-*2,3*-diamino butane.

described by the formula [Ni (EDTA)]$^{-2}$. A simple consideration of the relative formation constants shows that the reactions will go essentially to completion with only a slight excess of EDTA.

The planar Ni(II) complexes have relatively high molar absorption compared to [Ni (EDTA)]$^{-2}$ in the 400 mμ region and the rates of reaction were followed by absorption measurements at A_{max}. for each complex. The reactions were initiated by injection of small amounts of concentrated complex ion solutions to pre-thermostated, buffered EDTA solutions. Preliminary experiments indicated that the rate of reaction was dependent on the concentration of complex, EDTA$_T$, negative ions and ionic strength while being independent of type of positive ion and the products (NiEDTA^{-2} and AO). In most of the measurements EDTA was used as its own buffer. This was entirely satisfactory because the reaction does not liberate large quantities of acid and the ligands replaced counteract this through their basic character. All of the measurements reported were carried out with a large excess of EDTA$_T$ and treated as pseudo first-order reactions in order to reduce the reactant ratio error and to assure completion of the reaction. Under these conditions the dissociation of [Ni(AO)$_2$ – H]$^+$, [Ni(N-alkylAO)$_2$ – H]$^+$, [Ni(EnAO) – H]$^+$, and [Ni(tetraMeEn)$_2$]$^{+2}$ followed first-order kinetics over at least five half-lives. At constant pH and approximately constant ionic strength the pseudo first-order rate constant increased with EDTA$_T$ in the manner shown by Fig. 1.

With the N-MeAO complex two paths are operative corresponding to the expression rate = k [complex]$_t$ + k' [complex]$_t$ [EDTA]$_t$ while the expression for the unsubstituted complex has only one term, rate = k' [complex]$_t$ [EDTA]$_t$. In the latter case, due to the higher value of k' for the parent complex, an EDTA independent term, equal in magnitude to that of the N-MeAO complex, would not be observable. The complexes of both tetraMeEn and N-i-prAO behave similarly with N-MeAO. The magnitude of the rate varies considerably on changing the ligand and this is more apparent in Fig. 2.

Since the rate has a term dependent on the total concentration of EDTA to the first power, it seemed plausible to attempt a selection of the EDTA reacting species on the basis of pH dependency. At constant [EDTA] and ionic strength the rate was very sensitive to pH as shown in Fig. 2. The general form of all α-amineoxime complexes is identical with the unsubstituted AO complex. [Ni(AO)$_2$ – H]$^+$ ion is about 200 times faster than the N-alkyl derivatives and increasing the alkyl size only straightens out the shoulder. The isopropyl derivative shows an inverse first-order dependency on [H]$^+$ while in the tetraMeEn complex, hydrogen ion dependence is slight.

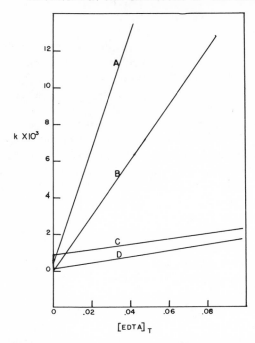

Fig. 1. Pseudo first-order rate constant (min.$^{-1}$) vs concentration of EDTA (total) (25.3°C, pH-9.50). For *bis*-complexes of nickel(II) and A, tetraMeEn; B, AO; C, N-MeAO; and D, i-prAO. K × 10^2 for AO and teTraMeEn.

A comparison of the pseudo first-order rate constant at constant pH and [EDTA]$_t$ as a function of salt concentration showed, for simple salts, a decrease in rate with increasing salt concentration. Although the concentrations were too high for a precise theoretical description, this is the general form for a reaction involving ions of unlike charge. The rate was unaffected by changes in positive ions Na$^+$, Li$^+$, K$^+$, Ni^{+2} but was quite strongly dependent on the negative ion. Figures 3 and 4 compare the pseudo first-order rate constants for several negative ions with [Ni(AO)$_2$ − H]$^+$ and [Ni(N − MeAO)$_2$ − H]$^+$, respectively. Negative ions which are capable of spanning two coordination positions show abnormal behavior and increase the rate markedly for both systems. This is remarkable in view of the fact that (1) the mixed complex containing AO and X^{-2} has low stability under the conditions of the rate measurements and (2) the final product is Ni(EDTA)$^{-2}$. Using organic dicarboxylic anions, a rough correlation exists between the accelerating effect and the thermodynamic stability of the mono- and di-nickel(II) complexes of the dicarboxylic acid. However, a chain length equal to or greater than six appears to decrease the rates compared to other similar ions. This latter change occurs only for the parent complex.

Isotopic ligand exchange rates are interesting in comparison with the rates of reaction with EDTA. These were carried out* using N-MeAO labeled with C^{14} in the N-methyl position. Preliminary results give $t_{1/2} = 485$ min, $R = 1.56 \times 10^{-5}$ $M/1$ min, $k = 1.63 \times 10^{-3}$ min^{-1} for [complex] $= 0.96 \times 10^{-2}$ $M/1$ [N-MeAO] $= 2.45 \times 10^{-2}$ $M/1$, pH $= 9.5$ and temp. $= 25.3\,^{\circ}$C. The addition of oxalate ion produces a large increase in the rate of isotopic ligand exchange: $t_{1/2} = 20$

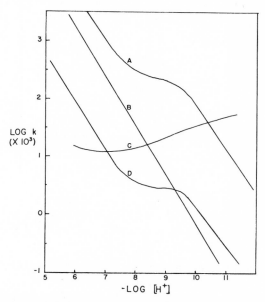

Fig. 2. Pseudo first-order rate constant (min^{-1}) vs pH (EDTA$_r$-0.10, 25.3°C). For bis-nickel(II) complexes of A, AO; B, i-prAO; C, tetraMeEn: and D, N-MeAO.

min, $R = 3.88 \times 10^{-4}$ $M/1$ min, $k = 3.92 \times 10^{-1}$ for [complex] $= 0.99 \times 10^{-2}$ $M/1$, [N-MeAO] $= 2.53 \times 10^{-2}$ $M/1$, [Oxalate ion] $= 0.01$ $M/1$, pH $= 9.5$, temp. $= 25.3\,^{\circ}$C. In this connection, it is interesting to note that neither the isotopic ligand exchange rate nor the rate of non-isotopic ligand substitution is dependent on AO concentration. In comparable situations the two rates are identically affected by the environment.

The activation energies for these reactions are about 16 kcal/mole with a PZ factor of about 2×10^{9}. No attempt has been made to explain changes in these values because of the lack of in-

---

*I am indebted to Mr. David L. Lewis for these measurements.

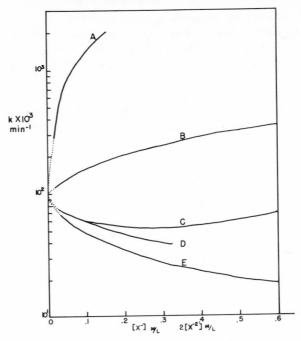

Fig. 3. Pseudo first-order rate constant vs negative ion concentration for [Ni(AC)$_2$-H]$^+$ (EDTA = 0.016, pH = 9.00, 25.3°C). A, glycine^{-1}; B, oxalate^{-2}; C, malonate^{-2}; D, OAc$^-$, NO$_3$; and E, adipate^{-2}.

formation about which molecule ions enter into the effective activated state.

Previous work on acid-dissociation of planar nickel complexes of substituted α-amineoximes has shown that an inverse relationship exists between the thermodynamic stability of the complex and its rate of reaction in acid. It has been postulated[2,5] that dissociation of the ligand plays a significant part in the mechanism of acid decomposition. It is immediately apparent that the reaction with EDTA in its various forms does not proceed by a simple dissociation and in fact a dissociation path can contribute only slightly to the overall reaction. Although the system is too complicated to be mechanistically understood in the light of available data, known facts seriously restrict the possibilities. Some of the observations which need to be taken into account in an explanation of the mode of reaction are:

1. The *N*-alkylAO complexes are slow compared to those of AO and there is little change with alkyl size. ENAO species are extremely stable to reaction with EDTA.

2. The slight changes in rate with increasing alkyl size and steric requirements are essentially a removal of the hump in the k vs. pH curve. This is completely removed when R = isopropyl.

3. The pH dependency of the [Ni(tetraMeEn)$_2$]$^{+2}$ reaction does resemble that of the AO complexes.

4. The order with respect to EDTA$_t$ varies with the complex. AO—first order term, N-alkyl AO—zero and first order terms, tetraMeEn—zero and first-order terms, ENAO—essentially zero order.

5. Large decreases in rate with increasing ionic strength.

6. The isotopic ligand exchange rate (corrected) for [Ni(N-MeAO)$_2$ – H]$^+$ is the same as the rate of reaction with EDTA when it is extrapolated to zero EDTA concentration.

7. The presence of divalent ions with chelating potential increases the rate in relation to their chelating ability. However,

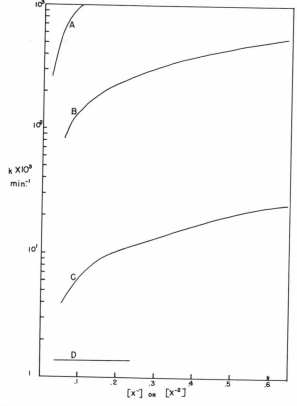

Fig. 4. Pseudo first-order rate constant vs negative ion concentration for [Ni(N-MeAO)$_2$-H]$^+$ (EDTA-0.016, pH-9.00 25.3°C). A, glycine$^-$; B, oxalate^{-2}; C, malonate^{-2}; and D, NO$_3^-$, OAc$^-$, adipate^{-2}.

with dicarboxylic acid anions whose chain length is long enough to span $trans$-octahedral positions, a rate lowering is observed for $[Ni(AO)_2 - H]^+$ but not for $[Ni(N-MeAO)_2 - H]^+$

These observations can be explained on the basis of three activated states leading to reaction: (1) normal one-ended dissociation of an AO ligand, (2) a weak coordination of a carboxylate oxygen of EDTA to the fifth nickel coordination position with presumably a water in the sixth position, and (3) chelation of the planar nickel molecule ion by two carboxylate oxygens of an EDTA molecule in $trans$-positions. Unaided one-ended dissociation (1), is quite slow with respect to ion-pair-aided dissociation (2), which is not nearly as effective as (3).

On this basis $[Ni(AO)_2 - H]^+$ exchanges its ligands by paths (1), (2), and (3) with path (3) predominating. Path (1) (EDTA independent) is too slow to be observed while (2) and (3) cannot be separated. $[Ni(N-MeAO)_2 - H]^+$ reactions proceed through the intermediates (1) and (2), thus showing EDTA-dependent and independent terms. Path (3) is sterically impossible with this complex. The slowness of $[Ni(N-MeAO)_2 - H]^+$ compared to $[Ni(AO)_2 - H]^+$, in spite of its thermodynamic instability, is attributed to the steric impossibility of chelating an EDTA molecule ion using $trans$-positions. $[Ni(tetraMeEn)_2]^{+2}$ reacts in a manner analogous to the parent AO complex (primarily paths (2) and (3) while $[Ni(EnAO)_2 - H]^+$ behaves and is sterically similar to $[Ni(N-MeAO)_2 - H]^+$.

The pH dependence of the rate may be explained equally well by several schemes. The rapid (almost inverse first order in H^+) drop in rate upon increasing the pH (pH 6 - 7.5) may indicate that the active form of the complex is $[Ni(AO)_2]^{+2}$. In this pH range, its concentration, being very small, would be directly related to $[H^+]$ to the first power. An alternative approach is to assume competition for $trans$-positions between OH^- and EDTA. The OH^- would have to be quite successful in replacing EDTA. Except for its unique position with respect to water, there is little reason to expect OH^- to be so much more effective than NO_3^-, AOc^-, etc.

The nearly level portion of the log k vs. pH curve (pH 8 - 9.5) probably results from the increased association between the planar nickel complex and EDTA due to the change-over from $EDTA^{-3}$ to $EDTA^{-4}$. This is counteracted by the previous inverse OH^- effect resulting in a leveling. At higher pH's (>9.0) a third factor becomes important. The planar complex begins to lose another H^+ and goes to $[Ni(AO)_2 - 2H]^\circ$ (waters omitted). This species is extremely stable to substitution but its formation results in lowering the concentration of $[Ni(AO)_2 - H]^+$ resulting in a slower rate.

Three factors need to be emphasized with respect to specific negative ion interaction. First the graph of k vs. $[X^-]$ or $2[X^{-2}]$ shows OAc^-, NO_3^-, SO_4^{-2} and malonate^{-2} ions to be nearly identically effective. Adipate ion lowers the rate considerably below this value for $[Ni(AO)_2 - H]^+$ but is identical with OAc^-, NO_3^-, SO_4^{-2} with $[Ni(N\text{-}MeAO)_2 - H]^+$. This is taken as evidence that adipate ion is able to span *trans*-positions and more successfully compete with EDTA. That this does not occur with the N-methyl derivative is in keeping with the postulate that path c, involving EDTA chelation is not important with this amine. The rapid increase in rate with oxalate^{-2}, glycinate$^-$, malonate^{-2} is an interesting "catalytic" effect but not directly related to the mechanism of the EDTA reaction. The evidence indicates a rapid replacement reaction by OX^{-2} or gly^{-1}.

$$[Ni(AO)_2 - H]^+ + OX^{-2} \rightleftharpoons [Ni(AO)(OX)]^{+n} + AO$$

Thermodynamically a species of the type $[Ni(AO)(OX)]^{+n}$ is not stable and so its concentration is small. Replacing a ligand lowers the combined C.F. stabilization energy of the ligands resulting in a destabilization of the planar state and very rapid reaction with EDTA. Two factors seem to be important in a ligands' ability to increase the rate: (1) its chelating ability, and (2) its crystal-field strength. These factors oppose each other in their effect on the rate.

Copper complexes of AO react in a similar fashion but at a much more rapid rate.

REFERENCES

1. F. Basolo and R. G. Pearson, *Mechanisms of Inorganic Reactions.* John Wiley & Sons, New York, P—172 (1958).
2. R. G. Wilkins, *J. Chem. Soc.,* 4521 (1957).
3. F. Basolo, Yung Ti Chen, and R. K. Murmann, *J. Am. Chem, Soc.,* **76**, 956 (1954).
4. R. K. Murmann, *ibid.,* **79**, 521 (1957).
5. R. K. Murmann, (to be published).

ENERGY LEVEL SPLITTINGS IN NON-CUBIC IONS, AND THE TWO-DIMENSIONAL SPECTROCHEMICAL SERIES

DONALD S. McCLURE*

RCA Laboratories
Princeton, New Jersey

The purpose of this note is to show that the spectrochemical series— the order in which ligands of a complex ion show decreasing d-orbital splitting—must be expanded into two dimensions in order to explain spectra of ions having less than cubic symmetry. In order to do this we first demonstrate a simple method of calculating crystal-field, or ligand-field splittings of d-orbitals in substituted octahedral transition metal complex ions. Instead of using a point charge model whose arbitrary field constants must be evaluated by experiment or a molecular orbital theory whose integrals would have to be computed, [1,2] we use another heueristic approach which is simpler and is physically close to the real system. The field constants are replaced by the antibonding energies experienced by the d-orbitals of the metal ion in the environment provided by the ligands. Each anion of the environment is supposed to exert its influence on the d-electrons through a σ-antibonding and a π-antibonding contribution. The major splitting into the two classes of cubic d-orbitals is brought about by the difference in the strength of σ- and π-antibonding orbitals. The e-class is σ-antibonding, and the t-class is π-antibonding. If the complex remains strictly octahedral, these two bonding types will remain unmixed, and we will suppose this to be so. Figure 1 shows the relation between the σ- and π-bonding and antibonding effects of the ligands on the d-orbitals.

When one of the ligands differs from the others, its σ- and π-antibonding contributions will differ in certain directions, and the spatial degeneracy of the three t- and of the two e-orbitals will be removed. This phenomenon leads to splitting of the absorption bands in the electronic spectrum of the complex. If the substituents are quite different in their electronic properties, the d-orbitals must become polarized to an extent which is not negligible, and then the t and e-orbitals

---

*The author wishes to thank Professor E. L. King for asking the questions which led to this work

498

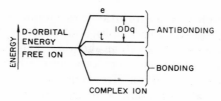

Fig. 1. Illustrating the effect of bonding and antibonding between a transition metal ion and an octahedral array of ligands. Both σ- and π-bonding effects are shown. The spectroscopic splitting factor, 10 Dq, is equal to the difference between the energy of the σ-antibonding and the π-antibonding orbital.

split a great deal and may in some symmetry classes, become mixed. In this paper we will confine ourselves to cases in which the perturbation represented by the substituent is so small that t and e-orbital mixing does not occur to any serious extent.

Orbital Splitting

With this reservation, the minor orbital splittings can be worked out simply by using the geometry of the orbitals. Figure 2 illustrates the

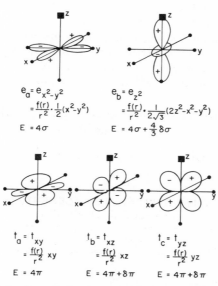

Fig. 2. Interaction of the five d-orbitals with the ligands. The example given here is that of a monosubstituted octahedral complex. It can be seen that, due to their orientation, the various orbitals are perturbed by the substitutent by different amounts. The formula for the distribution of the orbital in space and its energy in the array of ligands is given in each case.

ligand-fields to which t- and e-orbitals are subjected in a mono-substituted octahedral complex. The substituted position lies on the positive z-axis in the coordinate system chosen. The t-orbitals form π-bonds to the ligands, while the e-orbitals form σ-bonds. The relative importance of bonding in a given direction for one of these orbitals is determined by the relative amount of charge density in the bonding direction. The $e_{x^2-y^2}$ orbital evidently has equal σ-bonding power along four of the metal-ligand bonds in a coordinate plane ($x-y$ in this case). The other e-orbital makes the following contributions relative to the $e_{x^2-y^2}$ orbital:

$$\text{positive } z\text{-axis} \quad 4/3 \text{ times } e_{x^2-y^2} \text{ bond}$$
$$x, \text{ or } y \text{ axis} \quad 1/3 \text{ times } e_{x^2-y^2} \text{ bond} \tag{1}$$

The energy of the orbital $e_{x^2-y^2}$ can therefore be written as 4σ indicating four contributions from equivalent σ bonds. The energy of e_{z^2} is $4/3\,\sigma + 4/3\,\sigma' + 4\,(1/3\,\sigma) = 8/3\,\sigma + 4/3\,\sigma'$, the result of contributions from five normal σ bonds, and from the one different bond, whose contribution is denoted σ'.

It is important to have the $e_a = e_{x^2-y^2}$ and $e_b = e_{z^2}$ orbitals oriented as shown, since they are symmetry orbitals of the system in this case, while in another orientation they would not be symmetry orbitals, and there would be a cross term between them.

The t_{xy} orbital does not encounter the substituent, and therefore has four equal π-bonding contributions. Both t_{xz} and t_{yz} encounter the substituent in the same way, and for a symmetrical substituent they would have equal π-bonding effects. Their energy contributions are therefore $3\pi + \pi'$.

In order to simplify the numerical results, we define:

$$\sigma' = \sigma + \delta\sigma \text{ and } \pi' = \pi + \delta\pi \tag{2}$$

The band splitting will be given in terms of $\delta\sigma$ and $\delta\pi$, as shown in Table 1.

TABLE 1. RELATIVE ORBITAL DISPLACEMENTS IN SUBSTITUTED OCTAHEDRAL COMPLEXES

	$e_{x^2-y^2} = e_a$	$e_{z^2} = e_b$	$t_{xy} = t_a$	$t_{xz} = t_b$	$t_{yz} = t_c$
Mono	0	$4/3\,\delta\sigma$	0	$\delta\pi$	$\delta\pi$
di-*trans*	0	$8/3\,\delta\sigma$	0	$2\,\delta\pi$	$2\,\delta\pi$
di-*cis*	$2\,\delta\sigma$	$2/3\,\delta\sigma$	$2\,\delta\pi$	$\delta\pi$	$\delta\pi$
tri-*sym*	$2\,\delta\sigma$	$2\,\delta\sigma$	$2\,\delta\pi$	$2\,\delta\pi$	$2\,\delta\pi$
tri-*unsym**	$2\,\delta\sigma$	$2\,\delta\sigma$	$2\,\delta\pi$	$3\,\delta\pi$	$\delta\pi$

*The e_a and e_b orbitals are not eigen-orbitals separately. The cross term is

$$(e_a \,|\, V \,|\, e_b) = 2/\sqrt{3}\,\delta\sigma$$

For *trans* disubstituted complexes the system of quantization is the same as in Fig. 2, and the energies are given in Table 1.

For *cis* disubstituted complexes, the e orbitals of Fig. 2 are symmetry orbitals if the substituents are placed on the positive x and y axes. The orbital t_{xy} is also a symmetry orbital under these conditions. The linear combinations $\frac{1}{\sqrt{2}}(t_{xz} \pm t_{yz})$ are the other symmetry orbitals. The energy calculation turns out the same as by using t_{xz} and t_{yz} separately, however, as there is no cross term between them. The results are given in Table 1.

The calculation can be done without symmetry orbitals, but then the cross term between the e-orbitals must be considered. To illustrate this, the substituents are placed on the x and z axes with the orbitals in the positions of Fig. 2. The contributions of the e orbitals are:

$$e_b : 4\sigma + 5/3\ \delta\sigma$$
$$e_a : 4\sigma + \delta\sigma$$

The cross term arises because the orbitals overlap on the x and y axes, giving rise to an integral which is the product of the square roots of the density functions for the two orbitals. The contributions of the normal σ-bonds cancel out, because the phase of the overlap is opposite on the x and y axes. Thus the cross term is $\sqrt{1} \cdot 1/\sqrt{3} \cdot \delta\sigma$. The correct energies are then found by solving the following secular equation (with 4σ subtracted from the diagonal elements):

$$\begin{vmatrix} 5/3\ \delta\sigma - e & 1/\sqrt{3}\ \delta\sigma \\ 1/\sqrt{3}\ \delta\sigma & \delta\sigma - e \end{vmatrix} = 0$$

The roots of this equation are $2 \pm \dfrac{2}{3}\ \delta\sigma$, giving a splitting of $4/3\ \delta\sigma$ as was found before.

In the case of unsymmetrical trisubstitution, the two e-orbitals fall into the same symmetry class, A_1 of C_{2v}, regardless of how the substituents are placed relative to the orbitals. A secular equation must be solved in this case. With substituents on $+x$, $-x$, $+z$, the equation is:

$$\begin{vmatrix} 2 - e & 2/\sqrt{3} \\ 2/\sqrt{3} & 2 - e \end{vmatrix} = 0$$

where units of $\delta\sigma$ are understood. The roots are $e = 2 \pm 2/\sqrt{3}$ and the splitting is $4\delta\sigma/\sqrt{3}$. The t orbitals present no problem as they do not overlap. They have three different energies, and with substituents on $+x$, $-x$, $+z$, they are shown in Table 1.

Symmetrical trisubstitution gives no splitting in our approximation. If we put substituents on $+x$, $+y$, $+z$, each t orbital has an energy increment of $2\,\delta\pi$, and the two e-orbitals one of $2\,\delta\sigma$, with zero cross term. This result is experimentally confirmed to a good approximation, as trigonal splitting in crystals is found always to be rather small even for large asymmetry. The splittings which are found must be due to non-octahedral character, rather than to differences in bonding power between the ligands.

Many-Electron Systems

The most important applications of the foregoing orbital splitting results are to many-electron systems such as Cr^{+++} and Co^{+++} complexes. In trivalent complexes it is a good approximation to consider the states as being formed from a single configuration, while in the divalent ones, configuration mixing must be considered. A few types of configurations are of widespread importance. They are et (V^{+++}), et^2 (Cr^{+++}), t^5e (Co^{+++}), t^4e^3 (Co^{++}), t^5e^3 (Ni^{++}). Each of these configurations has two states, belonging to T_1 and T_2 representations of the cubic group, of the same multiplicity as the ground state. The wave functions of these states are all similar. Using the following simplified notation

$$e_{x^2y^2} = e_a, \qquad e_{z^2} = e_b$$

$$t_{xy} = t_a, \qquad t_{yz} = t_b, \quad t_{yz} = t_c$$

these states are:

$$
\begin{array}{llll}
et & {}^3T_2 & A & e_b t_a \\
& & E_1 & -\tfrac{1}{2}(\sqrt{3}\,e_a + e_b)\,t_b \\
& & E_2 & \tfrac{1}{2}(\sqrt{3}\,e_a - e_b)\,t_c \\[4pt]
& {}^3T_1 & A & e_a t_a \\
& & E_1 & \tfrac{1}{2}(\sqrt{3}\,e_b - e_a)\,t_b \\
& & E_2 & -\tfrac{1}{2}(\sqrt{3}\,e_b + e_a)\,t_c \\[4pt]
et^2 & {}^4T_2 & A & e_a t_b t_c \\
& & E_1 & -\tfrac{1}{2}(e_a - \sqrt{3}\,e_b)\,t_c t_a \\
& & E_2 & -\tfrac{1}{2}(e_a + \sqrt{3}\,e_b)\,t_a t_b \\[4pt]
& {}^4T_1 & A & e_b t_b t_c \\
& & E_1 & \tfrac{1}{2}(\sqrt{3}\,e_a - e_b)\,t_a t_b \\
& & E_2 & -\tfrac{1}{2}(\sqrt{3}\,e_a + e_b)\,t_c t_a.
\end{array}
$$

(4)

A product such as $e_a t_a$ means $\frac{1}{\sqrt{2}}[e_a(1) t_a(2) - e_a(2) t_a(1)]$ a triplet spin function, since the orbital part of a triplet state must be antisymmetric under electron interchange. Similarly $e_a t_b t_c$ is an antisymmetric determinental wave function. The antisymmetry property affects the transformation properties and selection rules for transitions, but does not affect the one-electron energies. The states with more than three electrons may be related to the ones given above as follows:

$$
\begin{aligned}
{}^3T_1 \ et \ &\longleftrightarrow \ (-) \, {}^3T_1 \ e^3 t^5 \\
{}^3T_2 \ et \ &\longleftrightarrow \ (-) \, {}^3T_2 \ e^3 t^5 \\
{}^4T_1 \ et^2 \ &\longleftrightarrow \ {}^1T_2 \ et^5, \ (-) \, {}^4T_1 \ e^3 t^4 \\
{}^4T_2 \ et^2 \ &\longleftrightarrow \ {}^1T_1 \ et^5, \ (-) \, {}^4T_2 \ e^3 t^4 .
\end{aligned}
\tag{5}
$$

The splittings of corresponding states are the same or inverted, as the minus signs indicate.

Having worked out the one-electron splitting, it is a straightforward matter to carry out the many-electron calculation. The matrix elements are those of a sum of one-electron operators, and therefore we obtain a sum of one-electron matrix elements. For example, the ${}^3T_2$ state of the et configuration is handled as follows, for the case of a *cis* disubstituted complex. We shall write the potential operator as $V(1) + V(2)$ for the two electrons, and we need consider only one term of the antisymmetrized wave functions. For the first partner of ${}^3T_1$ we have

$$
E(A) = (e_b t_a | V(1) + V(2) | e_b t_a) = (e_b | V(1) | e_b) + (t_a | V(2) | t_a).
$$

The values of the matrix elements may be written in from Table 1, and we have $\frac{2}{3}\delta\sigma + 2\,\delta\pi$. The other two partners give equal values:

$$
E(E_1) = E(E_2) = \frac{1}{4}(6\,\delta\sigma + \frac{2}{3}\delta\sigma) + \delta\pi.
$$

The splitting of the ${}^3T_2$ state is therefore

$$
E(A) - E(E) = -\delta\sigma + \delta\pi.
$$

The orbital A belongs to the symmetry class A_1, in C_{4v}, while orbitals E_1 and E_2 belong to class E. We will write such splittings as $E(A) - E(E)$, in order to have a convention to fix the sign of the splitting.

It is interesting to note that the ${}^3T_1$ state has the splitting

$$
E(A) - E(E) = \delta\sigma + \delta\pi.
$$

The σ and π contributions add in this case, so we expect ${}^3T_1$ to split more than ${}^3T_2$ does when $\delta\sigma$ and $\delta\pi$ have the same sign.

Another general result is that *trans* compounds have greater splittings than *cis*. The unsymmetrical trisubstituted compounds have a splitting as large as the *trans* compounds, but because there are three peaks equally spaced, the splitting may not be resolvable, but may only appear as broadening.

The results of the energy level and splitting calculations are given in Table 2.

TABLE 2: SPLITTING OF ABSORPTION BANDS FOR MANY-ELECTRON SYSTEMS

	$^3T_2(et)$	$^4T_2(et^3)$	$^3T_1$	$^4T_1$
	(+)	(−)	(−)	(+)
Mono	$\delta\sigma$ −	$\delta\pi$	$\delta\sigma$ +	$\delta\pi$
trans	$2(\delta\sigma$ −	$\delta\pi)$	$2(\delta\sigma$ +	$\delta\pi)$
cis	$-(\delta\sigma$ −	$\delta\pi)$	$\delta\sigma$ +	$\delta\pi$
symm. tri		0		0
unsymm. tri	$\pm(\delta\sigma$ +	$\delta\pi)$	$\pm(\delta\sigma$ −	$\delta\pi)$

A positive splitting is defined as $E(A) - E(E)$ where A and E are the nondegenerate and degenerate components.

Complexes of Cr^{+++} and Co^{+++} are so numerous that they deserve special mention here. The lower band of the principal excited configuration, et^2 for Cr^{+++} and et^5 for Co^{+++} is $^4T_2$ for Cr^{+++} and $^1T_1$ for Co^{+++}. In spite of the difference in symmetry designation the wave functions for these two states are essentially identical, and they split in the same way upon substitution. The same is true of the upper band of the configuration.

The change in Dq upon substitution may be written in terms of the quantities $\delta\sigma$ and $\delta\pi$. It is found that these changes depend only upon the number of substitutents and not on their positions. In fact, the change of Dq upon increasing the number of substiuents by one is $\frac{2}{3}(\delta\sigma - \delta\pi)$. Changes in Dq are difficult to differentiate from changes in other parameters, principally the electrostatic interaction parameters, and B and C.[1] Band shifts are made up of changes of both kinds. The change of Dq is therefore not so useful a parameter as the band splitting, which is nearly independent of changes in B and C.

Comparisons with Experiment

Splitting of Bands of $Co(NH_3)_5X$ and $Cr(NH_3)_5X$, where $X =$ halogen.[3] As shown in Fig. 3, the lower band splits while the upper one does not. In both Co and Cr complexes the splitting of the lower band is $-\delta\sigma + \delta\pi$, and that of the upper band is $+\delta\sigma + \delta\pi$. This result indicates that $\delta\sigma$ and $\delta\pi$ have opposite signs, since they reinforce each other in the lower band and cancel in the upper one. Chemical intuition would lead one to believe that $\delta\pi$ should be positive, be-

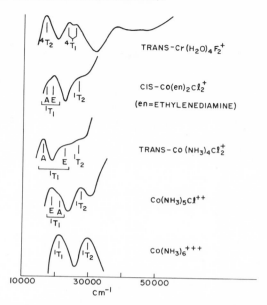

Fig. 3. Examples of spectra of substituted octahedral complex ions. Sources of data are: *trans*-Cr(H$_2$O)$_4$F$_2$ Ref. 7; others, Ref. 5.

cause NH$_3$ has no π-antibonding power, as its electrons are used in NH bonding, while the halogens have non-σ-bonding electrons which may be used for π-bonding. Similarly, one would expect the halogen to have a smaller σ-antibonding effect than NH$_3$, as the Dq values for halides are less than those for NH$_3$ complexes. Thus $\delta\sigma$ is expected to be negative. The splitting factor $-\delta\sigma + \delta\pi$ is therefore a large positive quantity for the lower band.

The test of this conclusion is that the lower band appears to split with a strong component lower than a weak one, which must mean that the doubly degenerate state, E, lies below the non-degenerate state, A. The theoretical formulas for the energy shifts for Cr^{+++}, $^4T_2$ are:

$$E(A) = 2\,\delta\pi$$
$$E(E) = \delta\sigma + \delta\pi.$$

The E state can only lie below the A state when $\delta\sigma < 0$, and $|\delta\sigma| > |\delta\pi|$. Thus there is qualitative agreement with our expectations. The polarization of the transitions as observed in crystals supports the assignments of the components which have been used here.[4]

The observed splitting values are about 2700 cm^{-1} for these Co and Cr complexes. Splittings of less than about half this value could not be detected by solution spectroscopy, considering the large bandwidths. An upper limit may thus be placed on the splitting of the upper band:

$$|\delta\sigma + \delta\pi| \leqslant 1500 \text{ cm}^{-1}$$

If $\delta\sigma + \delta\pi = -1500 \text{ cm}^{-1}$, then the reasonable values $\delta\sigma = -2150 \text{ cm}^{-1}$, $\delta\pi = 650 \text{ cm}^{-1}$ are obtained.

Dihalogenotetramminecobalt Complexes. There is a very large splitting of the first band in *trans* $Co(NH_3)_4Cl_2$ amounting to 5050 cm^{-1} (see Fig. 3).[5] The upper component of the first band is then about 6000 cm^{-1} from the second band, and there is some question about the neglect of the off-diagonal elements in our treatment. However, in strict tetragonal symmetry, D_{4h}, the upper component of band I belongs to the A_2 representation in this complex and cannot interact with either component of band II, A_1 and E.

The theoretical splitting is $2(-\delta\sigma + \delta\pi)$ so that $-\delta\sigma + \delta\pi = 2525$ cm^{-1}, whereas in the mono compound this quantity turned out to be 2630 cm^{-1}. The agreement is rather good, and shows that neglect of interaction between ligands is justified in this case.

The splitting of the first band is also observable for *cis*-$Co(NH_3)_4$-Cl_2, and amounts to 2200 cm^{-1}. The weak component lies below the strong component, as our theory says it should, when the parameters have the signs and magnitudes determined for the mono complex. The energy values for the two levels are:

$$E(A) = 2\,\delta\sigma + 2\,\delta\pi$$
$$E(E) = \delta\sigma + 3\,\delta\pi$$

The theoretical splitting factor, $\delta\sigma - \delta\pi$, is equal to -2200 cm^{-1}, which is somewhat smaller than the values obtained from the *trans* compound. The difference indicates the degree to which interaction between adjacent ligands may cause departures from our simple theory.

In the case of the *cis* difluoro complex, the splitting of the first peak is barely observable whereas the splitting is easily seen in the monofluoro complex. The smaller splitting caused by F^- as compared to Cl^- in the cobalt ammine complexes and the interaction between adjacent groups just mentioned, probably explain the absence of clearly discernable splitting in the *cis*-difluoro complex.

Fatty Acid Substituted Cobalt Ammines. The first band of the Co^{+++} complex is split by *trans* disubstitution of acetate for NH_3, but mono and *cis* compounds show no splitting.[6] The *trans* splitting is 3500 cm^{-1}, and the lower energy component is the more intense; hence $E < A$, and $-\delta\sigma + \delta\pi = 1750 \text{ cm}^{-1}$. Thus $\delta\sigma < 0$, $\delta\pi > 0$ as in the case of halogens, and for the same reasons. The smaller value of the splitting may be caused by a smaller value of $\delta\sigma$. Since the change from nitrogen to oxygen is less than the change from nitrogen to the halogens, a smaller value of $\delta\sigma$ is quite reasonable.

Aquo—F Complexes of Cr^{+++}. In $trans$-$[Cr(H_2O)_4F_2]^+$ the second band, $^4T_1$, is split into two peaks 2400 cm^{-1} apart while the first band is not split to an observable extent in solution spectra (see Fig. 3). Neither the cis nor the mono substituted compound shows any band splittings.[7]

The splitting factor for the $^4T_1$ band of the $trans$ complex is $2(\delta\sigma + \delta\pi)$. Thus in order to explain the splitting we must assume that $\delta\sigma$ and $\delta\pi$ have the same sign. They would tend to cancel in the $^4T_1$ band whose splitting factor is $2(-\delta\sigma + \delta\pi)$. We are not able to tell what the direction of the splitting is, so cannot say what the sign of the individual contributions must be. However, both $\delta\sigma$ and $\delta\pi$ are smaller in this case than when a halogen replaces NH_3, as would be expected: $|\delta\sigma + \delta\pi| = 1200$ cm^{-1}. The simplest explanation of the results is that $\delta\sigma$ is negative, as might be expected for a change from oxygen to halogen, and $\delta\pi$ is also negative. This is possible because H_2O has non-bonding electrons which may be strongly π-antibonding in a complex ion, and may in fact be more antibonding than those of F^-. The changes in π-antibonding would then parallel the changes in σ-antibonding in going from H_2O to F^-.

The absence of splitting in the mono and cis complexes is understandable since the maximum splitting of any band is $\delta\sigma + \delta\pi$, which is 1200 cm^{-1}, and is too small to be observed in solution spectra.

Splitting and the Spectrochemical Series

The spectrochemical series is an arrangement of ligands in order of the Dq which they produce when in a complex ion. According to the present theory the value of $10\,Dq$ increases by $2/3\,(\delta\sigma - \delta\pi)$ for each ligand added. The splitting depends on $\pm(\delta\sigma \pm \delta\pi)$; the large, easily observable splittings occur when $\delta\sigma$ and $\delta\pi$ work together. Thus the splitting parameters and the spectrochemical parameters are not necessarily the same, and the spectrochemical series does not necessarily indicate the order of increasing ability of a ligand to split absorption bands.

It is now necessary to form two series, one for σ and the other for π-antibonding power. When the two properties are plotted in two dimensions, we obtain an array of data such as that shown in Figure 4. This is the two-dimensional spectrochemical series. This figure is quite qualitative. It was constructed mainly to fit the cobalt ammines, but lacking accurate values of the separate parameters $\delta\sigma$ and $\delta\pi$,

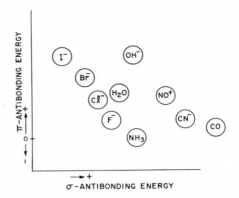

Fig. 4. The modified spectrochemical series showing both σ- and π-antibonding contributions of the ligands. The diagram is qualitative as it stands, but it could be made quantitative as explained in the text. There may be ligands which tend to accept the t-orbitals, in which case the negative region of the ordinate on the diagram would be occupied.

much of the diagram has had to be based on qualitative knowledge of chemical properties.

When more and better spectroscopic data become available, such a diagram can be constructed more accurately. Such data will have to come from spectra of crystals at low temperatures, where it is possible with the use of polarized light to separate the components of absorption bands even when the splitting is small. In this way the parameters $\delta\sigma$ and $\delta\pi$ can be obtained separately, and their chemical significance could be tested more stringently.

REFERENCES

1. D. S. McClure, *Solid State Physics*, **9**, 399 (1959).
2. K. Nakamoto, J. Fujita, M. Kobayashi, and R. Tsuchida, *J. Chem. Phys.*, **27**, 439 (1957),
3. M. Linhard and M. Weigel, *Z. anorg. allgem. Chem.*, **266**, 49 (1951).
4. C. J. Ballhausen and W. Moffitt, *J. Inorg. and Nuclear Chem.*, **3**, 178 (1956).
5. M. Linhard and M. Weigel, *Z. anorg. allgem. Chem.*, **271**, 101 (1952).
6. M. Linhard and M. Weigel, *Z. anorg. allgem. Chem.*, **264**, 321 (1951).
7. Y. T. Chia and E. L. King, private communication.

STEREOCHEMISTRY OF FLUORIDE COMPLEXES

E. L. MUETTERTIES*

E. I. du Pont de Nemours and Company
Wilmington, Delaware

The subject of this investigation is stereochemical relationships among inorganic fluorides and their complexes. Fluorides are of particular stereochemical interest in that the fluoride ion represents an extreme in electronegative ligand and because unusual coordination numbers, e.g., heptavalent, can be achieved with this compact ligand.

Tetrafluorides

Group IV tetrafluorides react exothermally with organic bases and most of the adducts conform to $MF_4 \cdot 2$ base stoichiometry. F^{19} spectra of solutions (0° or below) of the titanium and tin complexes consist of two triplets of equal intensity which unequivocally establish a preferred stereochemistry, a *cis* relationship of the donor molecules:

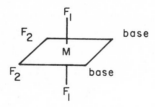

Cis structures are also favored in the solid state as Rao[2] has shown from an infrared study of some of the titanium complexes. Sterically, *cis* structures for trialkylamine complexes are not possible but *trans* forms are. Interestingly, *trans* 1:2 adducts do not form from SnF_4 or TiF_4 and trialkylamines; the products are polymeric 1:1 adducts in which the mode of association is probably through fluorine bridge bonds.

---

*The author is indebted to Dr. W. D. Phillips for many helpful discussions.

Neither the F^{19} spectra nor the solid-state compositions uniquely establish the number of base ligands bound to tungsten in the *solution* state of these complexes.

The F^{19} spectra of solutions of silicon and germanium complexes are single resonances down to $\sim -80°$. Since exchange collapse of multiplet structure is observed above $0°$ in the $SnF_4 \cdot 2$ base and $TiF_4 \cdot 2$ base solutions (ether or acetonitrile media) and since the silicon and germanium complexes are in general less stable thermodynamically than the titanium and tin complexes, the single line resonances *per se* cannot be considered as evidence for the *trans* structure. However, some of the silicon and germanium complexes may be *trans*. Infrared evidence in the dimethyl sulfoxide complexes supports a *trans* structure. No splitting of the S—O stretch is observed for $SiF_4 \cdot 2\ OS(CH_3)_2$ and $GeF_4 \cdot 2\ OS(CH_3)_2$, whereas a doublet is present in the spectra of the analogous *cis* tin and titanium complexes. It is noteworthy that X-ray studies establish a *trans* structure for $GeCl_4 \cdot 2NC_5H_5$[3].

Exclusive formation of *cis* structures in TiF_4 and SnF_4 complexes is inexplicable on purely steric and electrostatic grounds. Stabilization of the *cis* form must be due to secondary or π bonding. Overlap of p orbitals of the donor atoms of the base ligands with the metal d_{xy}, d_{xz} and d_{yz} orbitals may be more effective in the *cis*-MF_4X_2 structure than in *trans*. Such π bonding may not be significant in SiF_4 complexes because of the high energy level of the requisite metal d orbitals, and accordingly, the *trans* form should dominate. It is to be further expected that π bonding in the complexes should decrease in the series $MF_4 > MCl_4 > MBr_4 > MI_4$. This would appear to be the case. Rao[2] has reported that $TiCl_4 \cdot 2\ NC_5H_5$ and $TiBr_4 \cdot 2\ NC_5H_5$ are *trans* in the solid state. Rao also reported $TiI_4 \cdot 2\ NC_5H_5$ to be *cis*.

Complexes of Group VI fluorides, SF_4[1], TeF_4 and MoF_4[1], have been prepared. Those of SF_4 are not sufficiently stable for conventional structural analyses. The $TeF_4 \cdot P(C_6H_5)_3$ complex, prepared from TeF_6 and $(C_6H_5)_3P$ (Table 3), has in solution a single line F^{19} resonance. The same is true of the $MoF_4 \cdot$ base and $MoF_4 \cdot 2$ base adducts. The single line resonances here may be due to exchange collapse of multiplet structure or to a limiting condition of selection rules where $\delta_{F-F} < A_{F-F}$.

Trifluorides

Because of the preferred stereochemistry encountered in the metal tetrafluoride complexes, the acceptor behavior of the isoelectronic Group V trifluorides was examined. All of these function as simple acceptor molecules, with the exception of NF_3 and PF_3. Arsenic and antimony trifluorides react exothermally with most organic bases, but only in the case of antimony are crystalline complexes consistently obtained. Bismuth trifluoride reacts with organic bases, but requires forcing conditions, presumably because of its high lattice energy.

In only one case was a 1:2 complex obtained, $SbF_3 \cdot 2\ OS(CH_3)_2$. Solutions of this complex give a single F^{19} resonance which shifts significantly with temperature change. This indicates dissociation and accordingly precludes structural conclusions. The low stability of this complex is further demonstrated in its conversion to $3SbF_3 \cdot 2\ OS(CH_3)_2$ by "recrystallization" from hot chloroform. Stoichiometries of the other complexes include 1:1, 2:1 and 3:1. Salt structures could possibly account for this variation since complex fluoroantimonites have been described, e.g., $MSb_3F_{10}{}^4$. However, the complexes do not show the high SO_2 and CH_3CN solubility of the ionic tungsten complexes which are discussed in a later section of this paper. The tractability of the complexes decreases sharply in going from $SbF_3 \cdot 2\ OS(CH_3)_2$ to $SbF_3O(C_2H_4)_2O$ to $2SbF_3 \cdot N(CH_3)_3$, and it is suggested that this reflects association of SbF_3 octahedra through fluorine bridge bonds. For example, $3SbF_3 \cdot 2\ OS(CH_3)_2$ may be

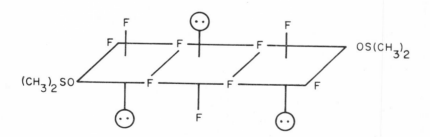

Accordingly, $2\ SbF_3 \cdot N(CH_3)_3$ may be considered $4\ SbF_3 \cdot 2\ N(CH_3)_3$. In any case, X-ray studies will be required to establish stereochemistry in these trifluoride complexes.

TABLE 1: SbF₃ AND AsF₃ COMPLEXES

Compound	m.p.	d_0^{25}	M Found	M Calcd.	F Found	F Calcd.	C (LECO) Found	C (LECO) Calcd.	N Found	N Calcd.
$SbF_3 \cdot 2(CH_3)_2SO$	55–57	1.948	36.82	36.34	16.69	17.01	13.96	14.34	18.83(S)	19.14
$SbF_3 \cdot$ (8-hydroxyquinoline)	200–202d	2.175	38.20	37.59	24.13	24.07	34.9	33.37	4.41	4.32
$3SbF_3 \cdot 2(CH_3)_2SO$	90–95d	2.9252	52.47	52.74	25.10	24.69	6.69	6.94	9.14(S)	9.26
$SbF_3 \cdot O(C_2H_4)_2O$	164–165d	2.332	45.33	45.63	21.78	21.36	16.90	18.00		
$SbF_3 \cdot (CH_3)_2NCHO$	76–77	2.374	48.21	48.37	23.43	22.64	10.93	11.31	5.64	5.56
$SbF_3 \cdot (CH_3)_2NC(CH_3)O$		2.422	45.14	45.80					4.90	5.27
$2SbF_3 \cdot [(CH_3)_2NCH_2^-]_2$	95–98d		50.93	51.41	24.13	24.07	13.84	15.21	5.39	5.91
$2SbF_3 \cdot C_5H_5N$	130–133d	2.872	56.39	55.77	26.67	26.10	13.52	13.75		
$2SbF_3 \cdot (CH_3)_3N$	133d	2.881	56.73	58.45	28.73	27.36	7.43	8.65	2.99	3.36
$AsF_3 \cdot$ (8-hydroxyquinoline)	124–127	1.777	21.99	27.04		20.57	40.4	38.98		
$AsF_3 \cdot O(C_2H_4)_2O$	60–70d	1.083			25.17	25.91	21.10	21.83		
$BiF_3 \cdot 2$ (8-hydroxyquinoline)	dec						36.24	39.51		

An interesting chemical property of the SbF_3 complexes is their facile and clean conversion to Cs_2SbF_5 by reaction with a concentrated aqueous CsF solution. (Anal.: calcd. for Cs_2SbF_5: Sb, 25.26; F, 19.67; found: Sb, 24.88; F, 19.36). In contrast, direct reaction of SbF_3 with aqueous CsF gives rise to variable compositions of the type $Cs_xSb_yF_{3y+x}$.

Pentafluorides

Phosphorus[5] and antimony pentafluorides* form crystalline 1:1 adducts with most organic bases. These are truly octahedral complexes. The F^{19} spectra of SbF_5 complexes consist of a doublet and quintuplet of relative intensities four and one, and the spectra of PF_5 complexes are analogous except there are two sets of doublet-quintuplet structure because of $P^{31}-F$ spin-spin coupling. Interestingly, the $F_1 - F_2$ coupling constants

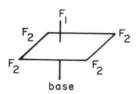

for the various PF_5 complexes are nearly identical, $A_{FF} = \sim 55$ cps, as are those for the SbF_5 derivatives, $A_{FF} = \sim 100$ cps. Thus, even with large variation in the steric and electronic properties of the base ligand, there is no significant change in $F_1 - F_2$ bond angles or in $M - F$ bond distances. The F^{19} spectrum of $AsF_5 \cdot C_5H_5N$ consists of four ($As^{75}-F^{19}$ coupling) doublets and four quintuplets of relative intensities four and one, respectively. The $F_1 - F_2$ coupling constant is 125 cps. This Group V series is one of several in which A_{FF} reaches a maximum with the third row element.

Of considerable interest is the geometry of the complexes of bromine and iodine pentafluorides. These pentafluorides have a non-bonding pair of electrons, and since in most fluorides, BrF_5 and IF_5 included, the nonbonding pair resides in a directed orbital, the complex should be isostructural with iodine heptafluoride.

---

*$SbF_5 \cdot HCON(CH_3)_2$, $SbF_5 \cdot OS(CH_3)_2$, $SbF_5 \cdot N(CH_3)_3$, $SbF_5 \cdot NC_5H_5$ and $SbF_5 \cdot OC[N(CH_3)_2]_2$. These were prepared by dissolving SbF_5 in CH_3CN, adding the base, and crystallizing the complex from the solution. Sample analysis: calcd. for $SbF_5 \cdot HCON(CH_3)_2$: Sb, 41.9; C, 12.4; found: Sb, 41.2; C, 12.2.

Potassium[6] and cesium hexafluoroiodates were prepared and recrystallized from IF_5 (calcd. for KIF_6: K, 13.9; F, 40.7; found: K, 13.2; F, 40.8; calcd. for $CsIF_6$: Cs, 35.6; F, 30.4; found: Cs, 36.2; F, 30.1). The F^{19} spectra of the molten fluorides and of their solutions in IF_5 consist of single-line resonances. Since tensimetric studies of the solid fluoriodates indicated dissociation below 100°,

$$MIF_6 \rightleftharpoons MF + IF_5$$

this dissociation unquestionably accounts for the exchange collapse of fine structure in spectra of melts and may also account for the rapid fluorine exchange between IF_6^- and IF_5 in the solutions. A *maximum* value for the fluorine atom lifetimes in a given environment in the solutions can be derived from the chemical shift between apical and basal positions in pure IF_5. The shift at 40 Mc is 1357 cps and the maximum lifetime must then be less than $\sim 10^{-4}$ sec.

Bromine pentafluoride was found to react exothermally with cesium fluoride to yield a white solid. This solid has an appreciable dissociation pressure of BrF_5 at 20° and the CsF/BrF_5 ratio is greater than unity. Confirmatory evidence for BrF_5—F^- interaction was found in the F^{19} spectra of BrF_5 solutions of CsF. As in the case of the analogous IF_5 solutions, the spectra are single-line resonances indicative of fast fluorine exchange ($k > 10^4$ sec^{-1}) among the various nonequivalent fluorine atom environments.

Scott and Bunnet[7] have reported that dioxane and IF_5 form a crystalline 1:1 compound. This reaction occurs with considerable evolution of heat. However, there are no differences in the F^{19} spectra of pure IF_5 and dioxane solutions of IF_5. The spin-spin coupling constant is identical (81 cps) for pure IF_5 and for IF_5 solutions in dioxane. Since the coupling constant is expected to be very sensitive to slight changes in bond angle or electronic structure, this result suggests that there is no significant perturbation of the IF_5 structure by dioxane in the liquid state. However, a dioxane-IF_5 complex could be present in the liquid state in concentrations approaching 5% and would not be detected in the n-m-r spectrum. Similar results to those obtained with dioxane were found for other weak donors such as ethyl acetate, acetonitrile and benzene. The stronger nitrogen bases, however, behave differently. Solutions of $IF_5NC_5H_5$ (calcd.: I = 42.2; C = 19.6; found: I = 41.3; C = 19.9) and $IF_5 \cdot HCON(CH_3)_2$ give single, relatively sharp fluorine resonances that are shifted slightly from the doublet of pure IF_5. This is consistent with structure A:

but structures like B and C cannot be ruled out since the single-line resonance may be the result of exchange collapse.

Exchange collapse of expected multiplet structure in the F^{19} spectrum of the SbF_5-IF_5 complex again precluded structural determination of an IF_5 derivative. The F^{19} spectrum of SbF_5-IF_5 in IF_5 at $70°$ is a single resonance; the chemical shift is nearly a linear function of the IF_5/SbF_5 mole ratio. Lifetimes of fluorine atoms bonded to iodine and to antimony are less than 10^{-4} sec.

Hexafluorides

It has been found that hexafluorides of tungsten, tellurium[8], uranium and molybdenum function as acceptor molecules toward organic bases, and a detailed study of these has been undertaken in the hope that the stereochemistry of seven- or eight-coordinate structures would be established.

Complexes of tungsten hexafluoride prepared in this work are listed in Table 2[9]. The F^{19} spectra of solutions of these complexes in liquid sulfur dioxide and in acetonitrile are identical. All consist

TABLE 2: COMPLEXES OF TUNGSTEN HEXAFLUORIDE

Compound	Spin-Spin Coupling Constant A_{FF}	M.P.
$WF_6 \cdot P(C_6H_5)_3$	54 cps	85° dec.
$WF_6 \cdot N(CH_3)_3$		150° dec.
$WF_6 \cdot (CH_3)_2NCH_2CH_2N(CH_3)_2$	52 cps	90–98° dec.
$WF_6 \cdot HCON(CH_3)_2$		
$2WF_6 \cdot 3NC_5H_5$	55 cps	115–120°
$2WF_6 \cdot 3N(CH_3)_3$	51 cps	
$3WF_6 \cdot 2(CH_3)_2NCH_2CH_2N(CH_3)_2$	53 cps	155° dec.

Sample Analysis: Calcd. for $3WF_6 \cdot 2(CH_3)_2NCH_2CH_2N(CH_3)_2$: W, 49.00; F, 30.36; C, 12.80; H, 2.86; N, 4.98. Found: W, 49.30; F, 30.53; C, 12.26; H, 3.19; N, 4.89.

of three peaks of relative intensities four, one and one. The peak of intensity four is a doublet and occurs at about − 95 ppm. (CF_3COOH reference), the second peak, a quintuplet, is at $\sim$ + 20 ppm. and the third, a singlet, is at $\sim$ + 50 ppm. It is difficult to devise a rational seven- or eight-coordinate structure that fits these data. In two possibilities

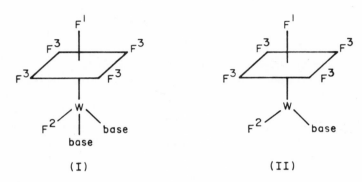

the four coplanar fluorine atoms, F^3, are not truly environmentally equivalent. Moreover, there should be significant coupling between F^1—F^3 and F^2—F^3 and to a lesser degree between F^1—F^2. The absence of splitting in one set suggests that one of the fluorine atoms is not bonded to tungsten. Possible ionic structures are

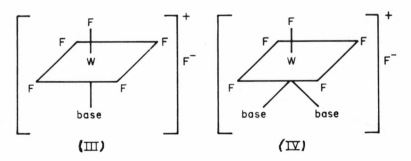

Both III and IV are wholly consistent with the F^{19} spectra. The varied stoichiometries (see Table 2) of the complexes do not permit an unequivocal choice between III and IV. However, since salts tend to form solvates, we tentatively suggest III as the correct structure. Those complexes isolated with "excess base" may be considered as as solvates, e.g., $2 WF_6 \cdot 3 NC_5H_5$ is $WF_5NC_5H_5{}^+F^- \cdot 0.5C_5H_5N$.

Further support for the ionic formulation is the fact that tungsten complexes do behave as electrolytes in liquid sulfur dioxide. The molar conductivities lie in the range 20–80 Ω^{-1}. Attempts are being made to effect metathetical reactions of these complexes in liquid SO_2 with various inorganic salts; demonstration of metathesis would unequivocally establish the proposed salt structure.

In the tungsten complexes the F–F coupling constants do not significantly vary as may be seen from Table 2. The results are consistent with the previously cited invariance of A_{FF} in octahedral complexes of PF_5 and of SbF_5 with change in donor ligand. The W^{183}—F^{19} coupling constant* in these complexes is ~ 72 cps which is considerably more than that in WF_6 itself, 48 cps [10]. This gross difference is unexpected and certainly reflects a significant difference in hybridization or in W—F bond distance between WF_6 and $[WF_5 \cdot Base]^+$.

Complexes of tellurium hexafluoride have been prepared and are listed in Table 3. It is notable that all are 1:2 (TeF_6 : ligand) complexes; the variation observed for tungsten complexes is not present in the tellurium system. The trimethylamine and ethylenediamine derivatives have significant solubilities in liquid sulfur dioxide and behave as very weak electrolytes. The F^{19} spectra of the solutions consist of single resonances. It is believed that this is a result of exchange collapse of multiplet structure since tellurium hexafluoride is a relatively weak acceptor molecule[†] These data unfortunately yield no definitive information about the structure of TeF_6 complexes, although the invariable stoichiometry suggests they may be eight-coordinate structures rather than salts.

The $Cs_2TeF_8^{11}$ and $K_2TeF_6(SCN)_2$ derivatives are ionic and have no solubility in inert solvents. The IR spectrum of $K_2TeF_6(SCN)_2$ is anomalous in that no absorption due to CN stretch is detectible.

Uranium hexafluoride is exothermally reduced by most organic compounds to give UF_4 and carbonaceous materials. However, 2-fluoropyridine reacts smoothly with UF_6 in the absence of solvent and in dichloromethane medium. Alone, the reactants produce a 1:2 adduct, and, in dichloromethane solution, a crystalline 1:1 adduct. Structural studies of these are in progress. Molybdenum hexafluoride forms a bright yellow complex with pyridine, $MoF_6 \cdot 2C_5H_5N$. The F^{19} spectrum consists of a strong doublet and a number of weak lines; no rational structural interpretation of this has been devised. Studies of other MoF_6 complexes are being made. Anal. Calcd. for $UF_6 \cdot 2NC_5H_4F$: U, 43.58; F, 27.83; C, 21.99; H, 1.48. Found: U, 42.75, F, 27.60; C, 22.03; H, 1.51. Calcd. for $UF_6 \cdot NC_5H_4F$: U, 53.18; C, 13.37; H, 0.90. Found: U, 54.19; C, 13.28; H, 1.49.

---

*These satellites are detected only for the doublet of intensity four.

[†]Unlike WF_6, tellurium hexafluoride does not form a stable complex with pyridine.

TABLE 3: TELLURIUM FLUORIDE COMPLEXES

Compound	Te		F		C		H			
	Calcd.	Found	Calcd.	Found	Calcd.	Found	Calcd.	Found	Calcd.	Found
$TeF_6[(CH_3)_2NCH_2]_2$	35.66	35.30	31.86	31.73	20.14	20.69	4.51	5.20		
$TeF_6 \cdot 2N(CH_3)_3$			31.72	30.03	20.03	19.71	5.04	5.31		
$TeF_4 \cdot P(C_6H_5)_3$*	27.39	26.96	16.31	16.18	46.41	45.52	3.25	3.49	6.65(P)	6.08
$K_2TeF_6(SCN)_2$	29.28	29.30	26.15	25.82	5.51	6.19			14.71(S)	14.65

* Prepared from TeF_6 and $(C_6H_5)_3P$.

REFERENCES

1. E. L. Muetterties, *J. Am. Chem. Soc.*, **82**, 1082 (1960).
2. G. S. Rao, *Naturwissenschaft.*, **46**, 556 (1959); *Z. Naturforsch.*, **14B**, 689 (1959); *Z. Anorg. allgem. Chem.*, **304**, 176,351 (1960).
3. R. Hulme, G. J. Leigh, and I. R. Beattie, *J. Chem. Soc.*, 366 (1960).
4. O. Ruff and W. Plato, *Ber.*, **37**, 673 (1904).
5. E. L. Muetterties, T. A. Bither, M. W. Farlow, and D. D. Coffman, *J. Inorg. Nucl. Chem.*, **16**, 52 (1960).
6. H. J. Emeleus and A. G. Sharpe, *J. Chem. Soc.*, 2206 (1949).
7. A. F. Scott and J. F. Bunnett, *J. Am. Chem. Soc.*, **62**, 3477 (1940).
8. E. L. Muetterties and W. D. Phillips, *ibid.*, **79**, 2975 (1957).
9. H. C. Clark and H. J. Emeleus have described $WF_6 \cdot 3NC_5H_5$. *J. Chem. Soc.*, 4778 (1957).
10. E. L. Muetterties and W. D. Phillips, *J. Am. Chem. Soc.*, **81**, 1084 (1959).
11. E. L. Muetterties, *ibid.*, **79**, 1004 (1957).

POLYMERIZATION OF PARAMAGNETIC IONS (FeIII) IN SOLUTIONS AS STUDIED BY SPECTROPHOTOMETRIC, MAGNETIC SUSCEPTIBILITY AND MAGNETIC RESONANCE METHODS

L. N. MULAY* and **MARY COPE NAYLOR**[†]

Department of Chemistry
University of Cincinnati
Cincinnati, Ohio

It may be stated at the outset that this study originated during attempts to obtain structural information on some hydrous oxides and hydroxides of transition metals, in general, and of iron, in particular. Many hydrous oxides and hydroxides [1,2] customarily called gels show unusual properties such as high surface areas. Amongst those containing paramagnetic ions, some show subnormal magnetic moments.[3] Very little is known about their structures; even the X-ray and electron diffraction techniques suggest only vague structural relationships due to difficulties in interpreting the rather diffuse patterns obtained for some gels such as the hydrous ferric oxide. Dehydration isotherms yield information about composition, while specific surface area studies prove that the particles are small, which is also inferred from the electron microscope studies. Our work dealing with the hydrous ferric oxide points to a polymeric structure. Evidence for this will be presented in some detail. Reference will be made to some aspects of polymerization of other paramagnetic ions. For the sake of clarity the nomenclature "ferric" for Fe(III) will be retained in referring to the hydrous oxides and hydroxides of iron.

Pascal[4] observed that the magnetic moment attributable to iron in colloidal ferric oxide is much lower than that found in typical Fe(III) salts such as $Fe_2(SO_4)_3$. Bose[5] observed that the magnetic moment of Fe^{3+} ion decreases with decreasing acidity in $FeCl_3$ solutions. A review[6] of the literature showed that for over sixty years a number

---

*The senior author wishes to thank the Research Corporation and the Monsanto Chemical Co. for supporting this work. He is also thankful to Professor P. W. Selwood for initiating this work and previous collaboration.

[†]Graduate student, Department of Chemistry. Part of this work is based on the M.S. thesis and doctoral work in progress.

of workers [7-14] investigated the magnetic and other physical properties of the (paramagnetic) hydrous ferric oxide in the solid and the colloidal state. (No reference will be made here to a large number of the ferromagnetic oxides of iron which are quite complex in nature.) All investigations showed that the magnetic moment per g-atom of iron in these paramagnetic systems was about 3.5 Bohr Magnetons, considerably lower than 5.92 Bohr Magnetons, expected for the $5d$ unpaired electrons in Fe^{3+}. This value is calculated on the basis of the "spin-only" formula $\mu = \sqrt{n(n+2)}$, where n = number of unpaired electrons, applicable to atoms or ions in the S-spectroscopic state. These investigations helped to confirm Pascal's original observations, but in general failed to explain the subnormal magnetic moment of iron in various systems.

It therefore appeared that unravelling the cause of this subnormal behavior might give a clue to understanding the structure of hydrous ferric oxide. Further, since the earlier studies on the solid and colloidal systems had failed to furnish any structural information, it seemed desirable to abandon studies on these systems and instead to study the nature of ionic species that are formed during the hydrolysis of Fe^{3+}, and which finally lead to the precipitation of hydrous ferric oxide. Therefore, a study of magnetic and optical properties of solutions of Iron(III) perchlorate at varying acidity was undertaken. The ClO_4^- anion was chosen in the belief that it will not complex with other ionic species in solution. Several reviews and papers [15-18] on the hydrolytic equilibria of metal ions have summarized work on the Fe(III) and other ions. Hence, no extensive bibliography is presented in this paper.

The magnetic and spectrophotometric studies on the hydrolysis of Fe^{3+} was carried out previously[6] on freshly prepared solutions containing 0.04 M $Fe(ClO_4)_3$ – 3 M $NaClO_4$ at different acidities over a range of temperature. The following equilibria proposed by Hedstrom [19] were considered:

$$Fe^{3+} + H_2O \xrightleftharpoons{K_{11}} [Fe(OH)]^{2+} + H^+ \tag{1}$$

$$2\,Fe^{3+} + 2\,H_2O \xrightleftharpoons{K_{12}} [Fe(OH)_2]^+ + 2\,H^+ \tag{2}$$

$$2\,Fe^{3+} + 2\,H_2O \xrightleftharpoons{K_{22}} [Fe(OH)_2Fe]^{4+} + 2\,H^+ \tag{3}$$

The magnetic data were explained on the basis that the hexaquo Fe(III) ion hydrolyses to form hydroxy species which are largely dimeric and that the dimeric ion is diamagnetic. It was also inferred that the absorption at 335 mμ is due exclusively to these species.

The absorption at 240 mμ was attributed to the hexaquo Fe^{3+} ions plus $[Fe(OH)]^{2+}$; the absorption due to the latter was shown to increase with increasing pH and to mask the concurrent decreasing absorption of the hexaquo Fe^{3+} ion.

The present study was undertaken with the following objectives:

1. To verify the earlier findings by extending the work to solutions (stored for about six months) containing (a) 0.015 M Iron(III) perchlorate in 3 M sodium perchlorate; and (b) 0.06 M Iron(III) perchlorate in 3 M sodium perchlorate.

2. To elucidate the structure of hydrous ferric oxide.

EXPERIMENTAL

Solutions and pH Measurements

Reagent grade iron(III) perchlorate and $NaClO_4$ (G. Frederick Smith and Co.) were used. A stock solution of iron(III) perchlorate was made which, on analysis by a standard method, was found to be 0.1524 M in the iron(III) ion. From this, solutions which were (1) 0.015 M in iron(III) and 3 M in $NaClO_4$ and (2) 0.06 M in iron(III) and 3 M in $NaClO_4$ were prepared by adequate dilution of the stock solution and the introduction of appropriate quantities of sodium perchlorate. The ionic strength in both cases was thus close to 3.

The pH of these solutions was found to be 0.3. From these a number of solutions of varying acidity were prepared by adding small quantities of sodium bicarbonate to aliquots, stirring and removing any dissolved carbon dioxide by applying suction and bubbling nitrogen gas prior to other measurements. A Beckman Model G S pH meter, designed to give measurements accurate to 0.02 pH unit was used in conjunction with a micro glass electrode and a specially constructed micro calomel electrode with a salt bridge of 0.1 N sodium chloride in place of the usual potassium chloride bridge, the use of which affected the pH measurements. This was caused by the formation of an insoluble precipitate of potassium perchlorate at the tip of the micro electrode due to the interaction between potassium ions from the salt bridge and the perchlorate ions from the solution. A satisfactory working of the 0.1 N sodium chloride salt bridge at room temperature was verified by checking against buffers of known pH.

All solutions were preserved for about six months in polyethylene bottles in a refrigerator ($\sim 20°C$) to prevent any precipitation which had been previously observed[6] in glass bottles at room temperature.

The pH of the solution pH$_S$ was calculated according to the following relation:

$$pH_s = pH_B + \frac{0.2\,(R_B - R_S)}{0.1984\,T}$$

where pH_S = pH of the solution being tested; and pH_B = pH of the buffer solution used to standardize the pH meter at the temperature of standarization.

R_B = Potentiometer reading obtained for the buffer solution
R_S = Potentiometer reading obtained for the solution being tested
T = The absolute temperature at which both readings of the dial, R_B and R_S were taken

Optical Density Measurements. A Beckman DU spectrophotometer was used. Measurements of optical density were made at 335 mμ at which the dimeric species are known to absorb.[6] A constant and narrow slit width was employed throughout. A matched pair of 1 cm silica rectangular cells and a pair of specially made silica inserts were used to provide a light path of 0.005 cm. This thin film-like path had to be used due to the high absorption by the solutions around 335 mμ. A 3 M NaClO$_4$ solution was used as a reference.

Magnetic Measurements. These were carried out with a Gouy magnetic balance; 25 ml of solution were used. Care was taken to remove dissolved oxygen and carbon dioxide by applying suction and bubbling nitrogen.

RESULTS AND THEIR DISCUSSION

Spectrophotometric Data

A few typical results obtained for the optical density at 335 mμ for the two solutions are summarized in Table 1.

TABLE 1: OPTICAL DENSITY (D) AS A FUNCTION OF ACIDITY FOR FERRIC PERCHLORATE—3 M SODIUM PERCHLORATE SOLUTIONS; OPTICAL PATH = 0.005 cm

	0.06 M Fe(ClO$_4$)$_3$ and 3.0 M NaClO$_4$			0.015 M Fe(ClO$_4$)$_3$ and 3.0 M NaClO$_4$	
Temp °C	pH	$D \times 10^2$	Temp °C	pH	$D \times 10^2$
21.0	0.27	4.7	22.5	0.94	3.6
23.0	0.33	5.9	21.0	0.95	3.4
21.5	0.39	7.0	23.0	1.09	5.4
22.0	0.48	10.4	23.0	1.41	12.8
22.0	0.93	35.3	22.5	1.44	10.1
20.0	1.05	45.6	23.0	1.56	12.2
22.0	1.38	68.0	23.0	1.60	14.6

We shall now consider the evaluation of the equilibrium constant K_{22} for the dimerization process. It is evident that the calculations of actual concentrations of the Fe^{3+} and the dimeric species $[Fe(OH)_2Fe]^{4+}$ required for this purpose need a priori knowledge of the corresponding molar absorbency indices (extinction coefficients). However, the molar absorbency indices and concentrations cannot be obtained for obvious reasons from one and the same set of data in the normal course. However, a derivation circumventing these difficulties was developed to evaluate K_{22}.

The equilibrium constant K_{22} for the dimerization,

$$2\,Fe^{3+} + 2\,H_2O \rightleftharpoons [Fe(OH)_2Fe]^{4+} + 2\,H^+$$

may be written as follows:

$$K_{22} = \frac{[\text{dimer}]\,[H^+]^2}{[C - 2\,[\text{dimer}]]^2}$$

where C is the total iron concentration and [dimer] is the concentration of $[Fe(OH)_2Fe]^{4+}$, both expressed in moles per liter. In the denominator (representing the concentration of Fe^{3+}), [dimer] is multiplied by 2 because each dimer contains two iron atoms. In this calculation the concentrations of $[Fe(OH)]^{2+}$ and $[Fe(OH)_2]^+$ are ignored as these were known[6,19] to be negligible in comparison with the concentrations of the two major species of iron considered in the above equilibrium. It is assumed that neither $[Fe(OH)]^{2+}$ nor $[Fe(OH)_2]^+$ shows any absorption in the 335 mμ region.

If d_D is the absorbence at 335 mμ with 1 cm optical path and a_M is the molar absorbency index of the dimer, then $[\text{dimer}] = d_D/a_M$. Substituting for dimer, we have

$$K_{22} = \frac{(d_D/a_M)\cdot[H^+]^2}{[C - 2\,(d_D/a_M)]^2}\,.$$

In the expansion of the denominator the term $4\cdot d_D^2/a_M^2$ may be neglected because a_M was estimated indirectly to be of the order of 10^4. For this, the concentrations of dimer obtained from the magnetic measurements and the corresponding optical densities for the solutions were employed.[6] Now,

$$K_{22} = \frac{d_D/a_M\,[H^+]^2}{[C^2 - 4\cdot C\cdot(d_D/a_M)]}$$

and

$$C^2 - 4\,(C\cdot d_D/a_M) = \frac{d_D\cdot[H^+]^2}{K_{22}\cdot a_M}$$

Dividing by $C^2 \cdot d_D$ and rearranging gives

$$\frac{1}{d_D} = \frac{[H^+]^2}{K_{22} \cdot a_M \cdot C^2} + \frac{4}{C \cdot a_M}$$

If, now, $1/d_D$ is plotted against $[H^+]^2$, we should obtain essentially straight line graphs provided the stoichiometry of the equilibrium and other assumptions are correct. The plots for the two solutions are shown in Figs. 1 and 2. The value of $[H^+]$ and $1/d_D$ used for this were interpolated from the corresponding smooth curves (not shown). This method was preferred to a direct plotting of the $[H^+]^2$ versus $1/d_D$ because any error in the determination of $[H^+]$ is magnified by squaring the value. Figures 1 and 2 show the expected linearity. It follows from these straight line graphs that

$$\text{Intercept on } y \text{ axis} = 4/C \cdot a_M$$

and

$$\text{Slope} = 1/C^2 \cdot a_M \cdot K_{22}$$

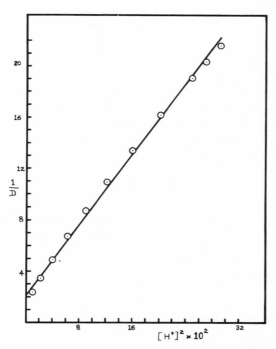

Fig. 1. Reciprocal of optical density D as a function of $[H^+]^2$ for a 0.060 M Fe(ClO$_4$)$_3$–3 M NaClO$_4$ solution; light path = 0.005 cm.

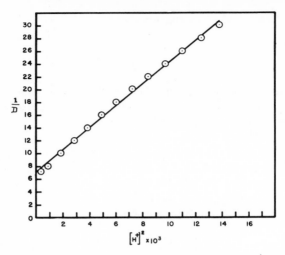

Fig. 2. Reciprocal of optical density D as a function of $[H^+]^2$ for a 0.015 M $Fe(ClO_4)_3$–3 M $NaClO_4$ solution; light path = 0.005 cm.

From these we write

$$K_{22} = \frac{\text{Intercept}}{4 \cdot C \cdot \text{slope}}$$

The values K_{22} calculated from figures 1 and 2 are 8.7×10^{-2} and 6.7×10^{-2}, respectively, giving an average of 7.7×10^{-2}.

It may be pointed out that although the reciprocal of optical density for a 1 cm light path needs to be plotted against $[H^+]^2$ in strict accordance with the derivation, in Figs. 1 and 2, the optical densities for the 0.005 cm path were used because this would have merely involved introducing a factor $1/0.005 = 200$ to convert all observed optical densities to a 1 cm path. Further, in the evaluation of K_{22} from $\frac{\text{Intercept}}{4\,C \cdot \text{slope}}$, any conversion factor introduced in the numerator and the denominator would cancel out. This brings out the advantage of the graphical method, that any error in the optical path employed will thus cancel out.

Magnetic Susceptibilities

Some typical results obtained at room temperature ($\sim 22\,°C$) are tabulated in Table 2, in which

C = Total iron concentration.

χ = Susceptibility per gram of the solution calculated from K, the volume susceptibility of the solution and its density.

χ_{Fe} = Susceptibility per gram atom of total iron in the solution, calculated from the molar susceptibility of total iron in solution and the susceptibility per gm-ion of $ClO_4^-(-34 \times 10^{-6})$. The susceptibility per gram of ferric perchlorate was calculated from χ and the weight fractions of the components. Wiedemann's additivity law and the following values for the susceptibility per gram of the constituents were assumed to apply: $H_2O = -0.720$ and $NaClO_4 = -0.355$ (all $\times 10^{-6}$).

f = fraction of total iron present as ferric ion, calculated from χ_{Fe} as explained below (therefore, $1 - f$ = fraction of total iron present as the dimer).

K_{22} = the equilibrium constant for dimerization =

$$\frac{(1 - f)[H^+]^2}{2 f^2 \cdot C}$$

The magnetic susceptibility per gram atom of total iron in solution is seen to decrease with increasing pH. In a more elaborate study [6] it was established that at a $pH \sim 2$ the magnetic moment per gram of the total iron decreases to half the original value (5.92 Bohr Magnetons), observed in a strongly acidic ($pH \sim 0$) solution. This indicates that any new species such as the dimer, produced in significant concentration during hydrolysis, may have a susceptibility considerably lower than that of the Fe^{3+} ion; ignoring the contributions from $[Fe(OH)]^{2+}$ and $[Fe(OH)_2]^+$ to the susceptibility per gram atom of total iron, one may write,

$$\chi_{Fe} = f \cdot \chi_{Fe^{3+}} + (1 - f)\chi_D$$

where $\chi_{Fe^{3+}}$ = susceptibility/g-atom of iron present in solution as Fe^{3+}; χ_D = susceptibility/g-atom of iron present as dimer; and f = wt fraction of total iron present as Fe^{3+}.

If the dimer is assumed to be diamagnetic, then whatever actual value χ_D may have is negligible in comparison with the paramagnetism

TABLE 2: TYPICAL RESULTS ON MAGNETIC SUSCEPTIBILITIES OF FERRIC PERCHLORATE SOLUTIONS CONTAINING 3 M NaClO$_4$ AT VARYING ACIDITIES (TEMP 22°C)

C	pH	$\chi \times 10^6$	$\chi_{Fe} \times 10^2$	f	$K_{22} \times 10^2$
0.06 M	0.39	0.0856	1.37	0.945	8.8
0.06 M	0.93	− 0.0743	1.04	0.718	6.2
0.015 M	0.95	−43.4	1.21	0.831	8.2
0.015 M	1.46	−49.2	0.73	0.501	7.8

of the Fe^{3+} ion. Hence,

$$f = \chi_{Fe}/\chi_{Fe^{3+}}$$

Using the value 1.45×10^{-2} observed for the susceptibility of Fe^{3+} in a strongly acidic solution ($pH \sim 0$), the values for K_{22} shown in the last column in Table 2 were obtained.

A comparison of the results obtained for the dimerization constant K_{22} by different workers is presented in Table 3. The agreement between the K_{22} values determined by the two independent techniques in this work verifies the earlier ideas that (1) the dimeric species are virtually diamagnetic, and (2) they show characteristic absorption at 335 mμ. The K_{22} values obtained in this study are about eight times greater than those reported by Mulay and Selwood[6]; however, this may be attributed to the prolonged storage of the solutions. If the dimerization is slow, it seems likely that long periods of time would increase the concentration of the dimer and decrease that of Fe^{3+} and thus give a large value for K_{22}. Considerable evidence[1] exists for the slow hydrolysis of Fe(III) salts. The dependence of K_{22} on time is being further investigated in detail.

The technique of measuring T_1 (spin lattice relaxation time in magnetic resonance experiments[20]) for protons was also employed by the author (L.N.M.) in earlier work carried out in collaboration with Broersma.[21] The dependence of T_1 for protons on magnetic moment μ is given by the following formula:

$$1/T_1 = 12\,\pi^2 \cdot \gamma^2 \cdot \eta \cdot N\,\mu^2/5\,KT^\circ$$

Where γ is the gyromagnetic ratio for protons, N is the number of paramagnetic ions per cubic centimeter of solution, K is the Boltzmann constant and T° is the temperature. The reciprocal dependence of T_1 on μ^2 was first verified extensively by Conger and Selwood[22] for ions in the S spectroscopic state and has since been investigated by several workers.[23] A study[21] of the variation in T_1 for protons in solutions of $Fe(CeO_4)_3$ did indicate a gradual decrease in the magnetic moment with increasing pH in conformity with the observations of Mulay and Selwood,[6] and substantiated the idea that the dimeric species are virtually diamagnetic. It was inferred that other species such as $[Fe(OH)]^{2+}$ and $[Fe(OH)_2]^+$ have the same magnetic moment as the Fe^{3+} ion.

Milburn and Vosburgh[24] studied spectrophotometrically the hydrolysis of Fe^{3+} ion in solutions ranging from 10^{-2} to 10^{-4} M in iron(III) perchlorate over a range of acidities and ionic strength. They obtained evidence for the importance of the dimeric species at a total iron concentration of 10^{-3} M or greater. They postulated the dimerization in the following manner:

TABLE 3: COMPARISON OF EQUILIBRIUM CONSTANT K_{22} FOR THE DIMERIZATION OF Fe(III) OBTAINED BY DIFFERENT WORKERS*

Workers	Technique	Molarity of Iron(III) Solution	Molarity of Sodium perchlorate	Temp °C	$K_{22} \times 10^2$
1 Mulay–Naylor (Present Study)	Spectrophotometric	0.060	3.0	20–23	~ 8.7
2 Mulay–Naylor (Present Study)	Spectrophotometric	0.015	3.0	20–23	~ 6.7
3 Mulay–Naylor (Present Study)	Magnetic Susceptibility	0.060	3.0	22	~ 7.5
4 Mulay–Naylor (Present Study)	Magnetic Susceptibility	0.015	3.0	22	~ 8.0
5 Mulay–Selwood[6]	Spectrophotometric	0.04	3.0	25	~ 1.1
6 Mulay–Selwood[6]	Magnetic Susceptibility	0.04	3.0	25	~ 0.7
7 Broersma[21] (Mulay)	T_1 for proton magnetic resonance	0.04	0.5 to 3	20	0.1 to 1.0
8 Hedstrom[19]	Electrometric titration	0.04	3.0	25	0.12
9 Milburn and Vosburgh[24]	Spectrophotometric	0.01 to 0.0001	0.1 to 3.0	25	2.6

*Results 1 to 4 are for solutions stored for about six months. Results 5 and 6 were obtained for freshly prepared solutions. Others are assumed to be for freshly prepared solutions. Result 9 is calculated from the author's 24 data, as discussed in the text.

$$2\,[\mathrm{Fe(OH)}]^{2+} \overset{K_d}{\rightleftharpoons} [\mathrm{Fe(OH)_2Fe}]^{4+}$$

and obtained values for K_d ranging from 170 to 1600 for ionic strengths varying between 0.1 to 3. It may be noted that K_{22} (equation 3) calculated from their data using the relation $K_{22} = K_{11}^2 \cdot K_d$ is still found to be in fair agreement with our value.

STRUCTURAL INTERPRETATIONS

The molar susceptibility 1.45×10^{-2} cgs units at $20°$ observed for the hexaquo iron(III) ion (observed in solutions at pH ~ 0) corresponds to a magnetic moment of 5.82 Bohr Magnetons, which approaches the theoretical moment calculated for 5 unpaired d^- electrons. The hexaquo iron(III) ion is regarded as an outer orbital complex having six sp^3d^2 bonds; the $3d$ shell is half filled and, therefore, the five electrons are unpaired. The $4s$, $4p$ and two of the $4d$ shells are filled with electron pairs donated by the oxygen atoms of water molecules to form coordinate covalent bonds.

Since a decrease in magnetic moment occurs when the dimeric ion is formed, a decrease in the number of unpaired electrons must occur. An inner orbital complex having d^2sp^3 hybrid bonds is postulated for each half of the dimer shown in Fig. 3. The distribution of electrons from four H_2O molecules and the hydroxyl groups in these orbitals leaves one unpaired electron on each iron atom. The dimeric ion is shown as a fusion of two octahedra sharing an edge which brings the

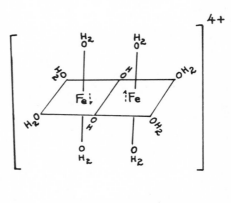

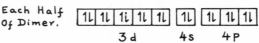

Each Half Of Dimer.

$3d$ $4s$ $4p$

Fig. 3. The dimeric ion. The bridging between the iron atoms may be through a diol or a dioxo bridge.

iron atoms rather close; it is postulated that this gives rise to exchange effects between the (antiparallel spins of) unpaired electrons
and thus makes the dimeric species virtually diamagnetic. The formation of polynuclear species through olation and oxolation has been
proposed[25,26] for a number of ions in solution. Whether the bridge between the iron atoms is an OL or an OXO bridge will not change the
general picture of the dimeric ion and its magnetic properties. The
inference that it is virtually diamagnetic is quite adequate at the
present time to explain our observations and to support the proposed
structure. Experimental work, currently in progress, is expected to
clarify finer aspects of its structure and to give exact magnitude for
the susceptibility for the dimeric (and other polymeric) species.

The concept that the dimeric ion is virtually diamagnetic ($\mu = 0$
Bohr Magnetons) or even an assumption that it is feebly paramagnetic
(with $\mu = 1$ to 2 Bohr Magnetons), which may be made for the sake of
argument, now helps us to understand the structure of hydrous ferric
oxide. It may be pointed out that prior to its precipitation, the dark
brown solution is quite rich in dimeric ions (more than 60% of total
iron is seen to exist in the form). The U.V. absorption spectra observed at this stage show[6] rather broad absorption bands which tend
to merge the absorptions at 240 mμ (for Fe^{3+} and $[Fe(OH)]^{2+}$) and at
335 mμ (for the dimeric ion). The magnitude of the Weiss constant is
found to deviate appreciably from zero with increasing hydrolysis. All
of this points towards a further polymerization of ions in solution.
Hence, for the hydrous ferric oxide we propose a polymeric structure
in which the dia- (or feebly para-) magnetic dimers are dispersed
amongst the distinctly paramagnetic aquo Fe^{3+} ions or their first and
second hydrolysis products. Such a combinations will naturally lead
to a lowering of the "overall" magnetic moment (that is, the average
moment per gram of iron atom) in the hydrous ferric oxide gel. Simple calculations show that one aquo Fe^{3+} ion ($\mu = 5.92$ Bohr Magnetons) must couple with a dimeric ion ($\mu \sim 0$) to bring down the average moment in the range 2–3 Bohr Magnetons. The polymeric structure
in Fig. 4 is shown to be linear for the sake of simplicity; however, a
three dimensional spreading of the polymeric chains with or without
"cross linking" through the OL and/or OXO is quite plausible.

POLYMERIZATION OF OTHER PARAMAGNETIC IONS

The evidence for dimerization or polymerization of ions is gradually
increasing. Sacconi and Cini[28] studied the magnetic susceptibility of
Mo(V) ions in solution and have proposed the formation of diamagnetic
dimers in solution. The diamagnetism of a binuclear complex,[29]
μ-oxychlororuthenate (IV), $K_4[Ru_2OCl_{10}]$ has been attributed[30] to the

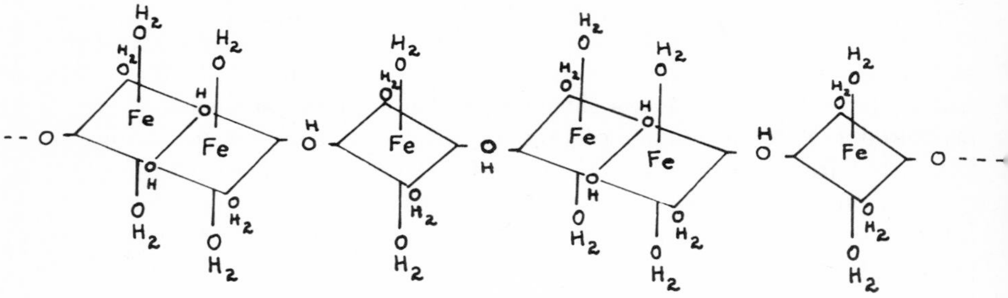

Fig. 4. Proposed structure for hydrous ferric oxide. The bridging may be depicted through OL and/or OXO groups. A three-dimensional spread of the chain is also possible.

formation of a double bond $Ru=O=Ru$, in which the oxygen atoms require two d-orbitals of ruthenium. Some workers[31] have proposed the following mechanism for Re(IV) complexes:

$$[Cl_5Re \cdot OH]^{2-} + [OH \cdot ReCl_5]^{2-} \rightleftharpoons [Cl_5Re\, OH : OH\, ReCl_5]^{4-}$$

The two paramagnetic ions $[ReOHCl_5]^{2-}$ with antiparallel spins are supposed to interact mutually. The dimer shown happens to be an intermediate in the formation of $[Cl_5\, Re{-}O{-}Re\, Cl_5]^{4-}$. However, the isolation of the dimer has helped to establish directly its practically diamagnetic behavior. Recent ion-exchange work by Ardon and Plane[32] indicates the formation of a binuclear complex $[(H_2O)_4Cr(OH)_2Cr(H_2O)_4]^{4+}$, similar to the iron(III) dimer and shows the possibility of formation of $-O-Cr(H_2O)_4-O-Cr(H_2O)_4-$ chains, which could either be joined to form a ring of three or more chromic nuclei or which could be terminated by a group like $[(H_2O)_5Cr-O-Cr(H_2O)_5]^{4+}$ or by the dimer itself.

Recently, using Ardon and Plane's ion exchange procedure,[32] we separated fractions containing the (a) a monomeric $Cr(H_2O)_6{}^{3+}$ and (b) a presumably binuclear complex $[(H_2O)_4Cr(OH)_2Cr(H_2O)_4]^{4+}$. Both contain Cr^{3+} with three unpaired d-electrons. Our preliminary magnetic measurements show that the values for the magnetic moment per gram atom of Cr in the two cases are (a) 3.87 and (b) 3.76 Bohr Magnetons, assuming that the Weiss constant is zero. These values are not significantly different and are quite close to the theoretical values 3.87 Bohr Magnetons, calculated by the "spin only" formula for three unpaired electrons. Further work on the temperature dependence and incomplete quenching of the orbital moment in these systems is in progress. The author (L.N.M.) is thankful to Mr. W. E. Querner for these measurements, and to Mr. G. Chaney for checking data on iron solutions.

REFERENCES

1. A. W. Thomas, *Colloid Chemistry*, McGraw Hill Book Co., Inc., New York, 1934.
2. H. B. Weiser, *Inorganic Colloid Chemistry*, Vol. II, "Hydrous Oxides and Hydroxides," John Wiley and Sons, Inc., New York, 1935.
3. P. W. Selwood, *Magnetochemistry*, Interscience Publishers, Inc., New York, 1956.
4. P. Pascal. *Ann.*, *Chim.* **16**, 571 (1909).
5. A. Bose, *Proc. Ind. Acad. Sci.*, *A* **1**, 754 (1934).
6. L. N. Mulay and P. W. Selwood, *J. Am. Chem. Soc.*, **77**, 2693 (1955). (This paper reviews briefly some aspects of magnetic, optical and electrochemical studies on Fe(III) system.)
7. L. Blanc, *Ann. Chim.*, **6**, 18 (1926).
8. C. Courty, Thesis, Faculty of Sciences, University of Paris, 1935.
9. A. Boutaric and P. Berthier, *J. Chim. Phys.*, **41**, 170 (1944).
10. B. Werbel, V. H. Dibeler, and W. C. Vosburgh, *J. Am. Chem. Soc.*, **65**, 2329 (1943).
11. R. J. Myers and D. E. Metzler, *ibid.*, **72**, 3772, 3776 (1950).
12. M. Aumeras and M. Mounic, *Bull. soc. chim.*, **4**, 523, 536 (1937).
13. R. Chevalier and S. Mathieu, *Compt. rend.*, **206**, 1955 (1938).
14. B. Tsai and J. Wucher, *J. Phys. Radium*, **13**, 485, 489 (1952).
15. G. Mattock, *Acta. Chem. Scand.*, **8**, 777 (1954).
16. L. Pokras, *J. Chem. Educ.*, **33**, 223 (1956).
17. L. G. Sillen, *Quart. Revs.*, **13**, 146 (1959).
18. G. H. Nancollas, *Quart. Revs.*, **14**, 402 (1960).
19. B. O. A. Hedstrom, *Ark. Kemi*, **6**, 1 (1953).
20. N. Bloembergen, E. M. Purcell, and R. V. Pound, *Phys. Rev.*, **73**, 679 (1948).
21. S. Broersma, *J. Chem. Phys.*, **26**, 1405 (1957).
22. R. L. Conger and P. W. Selwood, *J. Chem. Phys.*, **20**, 383 (1952).
23. J. A. Pople, W. G. Schneider, and H. J. Bernstein, *High Resolution Nuclear Magnetic Resonance*, McGraw Hill Book Co., Inc., New York, 1959. (This book reviews some work on the measurement of T_1 in solutions of paramagnetic ions—P207.)
24. R. M. Milburn and W. C. Vosburgh, *J. Am. Chem. Soc.*, **77**, 1352 (1955).
25. J. C. Bailar, Jr., *Chemistry of Coordination Compounds*, Reinhold Publishing Corp., New York (1957). (A chapter by C. L. Rollinson discusses olation and related processes.)
26. J. Jander and Jahr, *Kolloid Beihefte*, **43**, 305, 323 (1936).
27. L. Sacconi and R. Cini, *J. Am. Chem. Soc.*, **76**, 4239 (1954).
28. D. P. Mellor, *J. Roy. Soc. N.S. Wales*, **77**, 145 (1943).
29. A. M. Mathieson, D. P. Mellor, and N. C. Stephenson, *Acta Cryst.*, **5**, 185 (1952).
30. J. D. Dunitz and L. E. Orgel, *J. Chem. Soc.*, 2594 (1953).
31. B. Jezowska-Trzebiatowski and S. Wajda, *Bull. Acad. Pol. Sci.*, **2**, 249 (1954).
32. M. Ardon and R. A. Plane, *J. Am. Chem. Soc.*, **31**, 3197 (1959).

SYNTHESIS AND REACTIONS OF SOME NEW MOLYBDENUM TRICARBONYL COMPLEXES[1]

R. P. M. WERNER and **T. H. COFFIELD**

Ethyl Corporation
Research and Development Laboratories
Ferndale, Michigan

The displacement of metallo-carbonyl groups from molybdenum hexa-carbonyl by a number of ligands has been effected in the past. Most of the reported substituted molybdenum carbonyls contain a dative bond from a group V element to the metal or coordination of an un-saturate via π-bonding. These mixed carbonyls exhibit varying degrees of stability.

Molybdenum pentacarbonyl compounds containing ammonia,[2] quino-line[3] and triphenylphosphine[4] have recently been prepared. Tetra-carbonyl compounds with pyridine,[2] *o*-phenanthroline[5] and various other bidentate nitrogen compounds,[3] as well as with triphenylphos-phine[6] and *o*-phenylenebisdimethylarsine[7] have been isolated and characterized. The ligands found to form mononuclear molybdenum tricarbonyls include ammonia,[8] pyridine,[5] ethylenediamine,[5,8] *2,2′*di-aminodiethylamine,[8,9] and various *N*-alkyl hexahydrotriazines,[3] as well as triphenylphosphine,[8,9] -arsine[8,9] and -stibine.[9] Other such ligands are mixed phenyl phosphorus chlorides and phosphorus, arsenic and antimony trichlorides.[9] Finally, a stable bis(ditertiary arsine)molybdenum dicarbonyl[7] concludes the series of mixed molyb-denum carbonyls featuring a primarily dative group V ligand to metal bonding.

The reaction of the binuclear trihydrogen hexacarbonyl-μ-trioldi-molybdenum(0) with dimethyl sulfoxide[8] gave rise to tris(dimethyl) sulfoxide molybdenum tricarbonyl. This only moderately stable com-pound presumably contains an oxygen-metal bond.

The use of ethers for the preparation of Grignard reagents led to an early and extensive investigation of the etherates formed.[10] Very little attention has been given, however, to establishing the function of ethers in the numerous reactions of transition metal compounds where the presence of such solvents was found to be essential. The recent isolation of tritetrahydrofuranates of triphenylchromium,[11] chromium trichloride,[12] vanadium-trichloride,[13a] and titanium trichloride, [13b] indicates that more recognition is being paid to the use of ethers in preparative inorganic chemistry. In an effort to shed more light on this area, this paper describes the synthesis and reactions of a new type of organometallic complex derived from molybdenum hexacarbonyl and the tridentate diethyleneglycoldimethylether. The product represents the first example of an inner orbital etherate containing rare gas configurated, zero-valent metal. Substituted amide complexes of molybdenum hexacarbonyl are also described.

Discussion

The System Molybdenum Hexacarbonyl/Diethyleneglycoldimethylether/Benzene. It is known that the reaction of chromium hexacarbonyl with benzene yields benzenechromium tricarbonyl when carried out in an open system using diethyleneglycoldimethylether as a solvent. [14] When identical conditions were employed using molybdenum hexacarbonyl, however, an entirely different product was obtained. This material was a nonvolatile, water soluble, air-sensitive yellow solid. Subsequent recrystallization from hot diglyme furnished the pure thermally stable diamagnetic product. [15] Its analysis, infrared spectrum, and its reactive behaviour, which will be discussed in more detail, indicate its structure to be *2,5,8*-trioxanonane molybdenum tricarbonyl, henceforth referred to as diglyme-Mo(CO)$_3$. No benzene-molybdenum tricarbonyl [16] was isolated from this reaction and diglyme-Mo(CO)$_3$ was obtained in 74% yield. Molecular weight determinations showed the product to be monomeric.

The behavior of other metal carbonyls was investigated. When tungsten hexacarbonyl was heated in the presence of diglyme and benzene, no analogous product was isolated. In fact, no diglyme

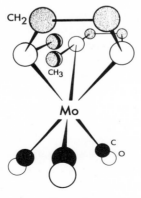

Figure 1

complexes of chromium and tungsten hexacarbonyls could be prepared.

The reaction of molybdenum hexacarbonyl in benzene and diethyleneglycoldibutylether-(diglybu) proceeded differently. Benzenemolybdenum tricarbonyl was isolated from the mixture. Heating of this product with diglybu produced the unstable diglybu-Mo(CO)$_3$ when conditions allowed removal of the aromatic hydrocarbon from the mixture. Thus, it appears that the equilibrium between the π-arenemolybdenum tricarbonyl and the molybdenum tricarbonyl diethyleneglycol dialkyletherate is decidedly influenced by the size and shape of the terminal alkyl groups. A qualitative comparison of the Fischer-Hirschfelder-Taylor molecular models supports this view, showing steric strain in the diglybu complex involving terminal butyl group overlap. Therefore, it is not surprising that the diglybu complex is the least stable of the two. The reaction scheme is pictured as follows:

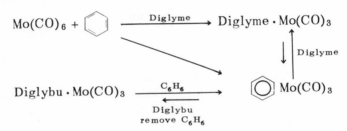

Treatment of benzene-molybdenum tricarbonyl with diglyme, as expected, gave diglyme-Mo(CO)$_3$. Also, it is interesting that heating diglyme-Mo(CO)$_3$ in diglyme at 150° gave the metal and Mo(CO)$_3$ with virtually no gas being evolved.

Repeated reprecipitation of diglyme-Mo(CO)$_3$ from tetrahydrofuran yielded what appeared to be the very deliquescent (THF)$_3$Mo(CO)$_3$ which was very air-sensitive. Complete analytical data could not be obtained on this material to support the proposed structure.

Molybdenum Hexacarbonyl and Dimethylformamide. The smooth reaction of DMF and Mo(CO)$_6$ produced tris(dimethylformamide)molybdenum tricarbonyl in over 65% yield. Benzene was not needed to promote this reaction and no benzenemolybdenum tricarbonyl could be detected when the reaction was carried out in its presence. The work-up procedure and properties of (DMF)$_3$Mo(CO)$_3$ are almost identical with those reported above for diglyme-Mo(CO)$_3$. The former shows slightly better stability towards air. Both show facile displacement of ligands by stronger ligands, suggesting a similar type of metal-ligand bonding. It appears reasonable that in the DMF complex, as well as in the diglyme complex, a dative oxygen to metal bond exists. This is consistent with the bis(dimethylformamide)-titanium tetrachloride complex in which the existence of oxygen to metal linkages has been proposed. [17]

Treatment of molybdenum hexacarbonyl with N,N-dimethylacetamide likewise gave tris(N,N-dimethylacetamide)molybdenum tricarbonyl, which was similar in properties and reactions to the DMF analogue.

Although the diglyme and DMF molybdenum tricarbonyl compounds obtained are similar in appearance and reactive behavior, it seems quite certain that the mechanism of formation is different for each. The monodentate dimethylformamide reacts with the carbonyl under relatively mild conditions without the presence of an aromatic hydrocarbon, thus permitting the assumption of stepwise CO displacement via $(DMF)_n Mo(CO)_{6-n}$, $n = 1, 2, 3$:

$$Mo(CO)_6 + 3\ HCON(CH_3)_2 \longrightarrow [HCON(CH_3)_2]_3 Mo(CO)_3 + 3\ CO$$

However, an entirely different mechanism seems to be responsible for the formation of diglyme $Mo(CO)_3$ since an aromatic is required for its formation. One concludes that benzenemolybdenum tricarbonyl is actually the intermediate compound formed, and is less stable than the diglyme complex under the chosen conditions. Thus, the mentioned equilibrium between benzenemolybdenum tricarbonyl and diglyme-$Mo(CO)_3$ is shifted in favor of the latter. The "backside approach" mechanism proposed for the formation of π-arene-metal tricarbonyl compounds [16] might offer a plausible explanation for the formation of diglyme-$Mo(CO)_3$. This would mean formation of the benzene complex with subsequent dislodgment of the π-bonded benzene by one of the neighboring diglyme molecules.

Reactions of Diglyme-Mo(CO)$_3$ and (DMF)$_3$Mo(CO)$_3$. Both diglyme-$Mo(CO)_3$ and $(DMF)_3 Mo(CO)_3$ react readily with ligands possessing more pronounced donor properties than the displaced ligands, diglyme and DMF. The solids as well as their aqueous or methanolic solutions have been utilized. In these solutions it appears reasonable to assume that a concentration-dependent equilibrium exists between the ether or amide ligand and the hydroxylic solvent.

A number of nitrogen compounds as well as other Group V ligands have been employed to produce, usually in smooth, immediate and practically quantitative reactions, the respective tricarbonyl compounds. These are generally water-insoluble, more stable than the parent compound, non-volatile and insoluble in non-polar solvents.

Triamminemolybdenum tricarbonyl [18] was obtained as a water-insoluble, faintly yellow, sparkling crystalline solid which was fairly stable to air.

Tris(dimethylamine)molybdenum tricarbonyl was soluble in water. The waxy dodecylamine and octadecylamine compounds showed some hydrocarbon solubility. The diethylenetriamine derivative is the nitrogen analogue of the diglyme compound and was more stable than the latter. It can also be obtained directly from $Mo(CO)_6$ and the amine.[18,19] Treatment of an aqueous diglyme-$Mo(CO)_3$ solution with triethylenetetramine produced no insoluble amine complex. This is presumed due to the presence of an uncomplexed amine group in the product formed. Insoluble pentamethyldiethylenetriaminemolybdenum tricarbonyl formed as yellow crystals and was perfectly air-stable.

Several nitriles were also found to react with diglyme-$Mo(CO)_3$ to yield tricarbonyl compounds which differed considerably in their properties. The tris-acetonitrile compound was only moderately air-stable while the analogous yellow benzonitrile derivative was completely stable to air.

Tri(vinylacetonitrile)molybdenum tricarbonyl and the analogous acrylonitrile compound were also prepared. Their properties differ considerably. The $(CH_2 =\!\!= CH - CH_2CN)_3Mo(CO)_3$, containing a non-conjugated system, was colorless, only slightly soluble in ether, fairly stable in air, and melted at 84–86° with decomposition. The $(CH_2 - CH \cdot CN)_3Mo(CO)_3$ containing a conjugated system was orange, soluble in ether, not stable in air, decomposed upon heating, and seemed to polymerize readily.

Addition of pyridine to an aqueous solution of diglyme-$Mo(CO)_3$ yielded quantitatively the deep yellow tripyridine compound.[5] On using 2,2'-dipyridylamine, not all three nitrogen atoms engage in dative bonding. The yellow, air-stable, beautifully crystalline solid obtained from its reaction with diglyme-$Mo(CO)_3$ was soluble in dilute mineral acid from which solutions it could be precipitated unchanged by adding base. Its stoichiometry indicated a di(2,2'-dipyridylamine)-molybdenum tricarbonyl structure.

The reaction of $(DMF)_3Mo(CO)_3$ in methanol with solutions of triphenylphosphine, triphenylarsine and triphenylstibine produced, respectively, the stable, pale yellow, crystalline tricarbonyl compounds tris(triphenylphosphine)molybdenum tricarbonyl, tris(triphenylarsine)molybdenum tricarbonyl and tris(triphenylstibine)molybdenum tricarbonyl.[18,19] Yields were over 80%. Of course, the π-character of the metal-ligand bond in these compounds results from the fact that the donor atoms P, As and Sb exhibit acceptor properties via available d orbitals which are not present in the aforementioned N-compounds. Thus, the compounds have enhanced stability, less polarity and correspondingly higher CO stretching frequencies.

The displacement of diglyme or DMF (or an oxygen-containing solvent ligand) by any one of the previously described ligands possessing stronger donor properties was in all cases accomplished in an instantaneous and practically quantitative reaction. This would suggest that these complexes might serve as interesting starting materials for obtaining new classes of unstable compounds under mild conditions.

The reaction with aromatic or olefinic systems was not investigated extensively. However, the heterogeneous system diglyme-$Mo(CO)_3$/mesitylene furnished mesitylenemolybdenum tricarbonyl after short heating. The undetermined yield was not high.

The diamagnetism of diglyme-$Mo(CO)_3$ demonstrates the chelating properties of the tridentate ether. This is unique since oxygen donors usually favor ionic-type bonds or chelating systems where resonance is possible, whereas sulfur or one of the group V elements in the ligand tends to favor covalence.[20]

The results of a comparative study of the reactive behavior of the group VI transition metal carbonyls towards cyclooctatriene have recently been published.[21] This study indicated a distinct correlation between the size of the central atom and the type and stability of the resulting mixed cyclooctatrienemetalcarbonyl π-complexes. Correspondingly, we can see no reason for not extending the same arguments to diglyme complexes. It is quite reasonable that the explanation for the preferential formation of diglyme-$Mo(CO)_3$ can be found here.

Synthesis and properties of other mixed metal carbonyl compounds are currently being studied at these Laboratories and the results will be given in forthcoming publications.

Experimental

All experiments were carried out in an atmosphere of dry nitrogen. Solvents used were carefully deaerated. Diethyleneglycoldimethylether and tetrahydrofuran were distilled over sodium benzophenone ketyl. Melting points given are uncorrected.

Reaction of Molybdenum Hexacarbonyl with Diethyleneglycoldimethylether: Formation of *2,5,8-Trioxanonanemolybdenum Tricarbonyl*. The mixture of 30.0 g (0.114 *M*) of $Mo(CO)_6$, 100 ml of diglyme and 30 ml (0.33 *M*) of benzene was refluxed for seven hours (124°), after which time 6 liters of gas (S.T.P.) had been evolved.

The hot solution was filtered, painstakingly excluding air, over a layer of dried Cellite filter aid. Some pyrophoric metal from partial decomposition was separated. Cooling of the clear, deep yellow-brown solution produced a crystalline precipitate, which was washed exhaustively with petroleum ether to remove $Mo(CO)_6$ and dried in vacuum. About 10 g $Mo(CO)_6$ were recovered. The yield of bright yellow, completely water soluble crystals was 17.5 g (74%, based on $Mo(CO)_6$ consumed).

The very air-sensitive solid was soluble in methanol and THF, insoluble in hydrocarbons. Its aqueous or methanolic solutions were stable under nitrogen, decomposed slowly in air and gave instantaneously typical precipitates with ammonia, pyridine and other compounds as described below. Addition of aqueous $NaB(C_6H_5)_4$ solution did not produce a precipitate. When heated in a sealed capillary under nitrogen, the compound decomposed, without melting, at 156 to 160°. After recrystallization from hot diglyme, it was found to be *diamagnetic*. Its infrared spectrum (KBr pellet) exhibited bands at 3.0 (*w*, wide), 3.5 (*m*), 4.9 (*w*), 5.05 (*sh*), 5.25 (*v.s.*, wide), 5.44 (*s*), 5.7–5.8 (*v.w.*), 6.9 (*m*), 7.45 (*m*), 8.05 (*w*), 8.15 (*w*), 8.35 (*m*), 8.9 (*sh*), 9.1 (*sh*), 9.25 (*s*), 9.8 (*w*), 10.1 (*w*), 11.6 (*sh*), and 11.7 (*m*) microns. *Anal*: Calcd. for $C_9H_{14}MoO_6$: C, 34.41; H, 4.49; Mo, 30.54. Found: C, 34.6; H, 4.7; Mo, 30.3.

In order to ascertain the role of benzene for the formation of this compound, a blank run was made. Heating of $Mo(CO)_6$ with diglyme did not give any gas evolution after one hour at 120°. When the temperature was raised to 150°, only decomposition with formation of metal was observed and no petroleum ether-insoluble product could be isolated from the filtered solution.

Preparation of Tris(dimethylformamide)Molybdenum Tricarbonyl. Gas evolution began at 90° when 13.2 g (0.05 *M*) of $Mo(CO)_6$ were heated with 40 ml of DMF. After 1 hour at 125–140° about 3000 ml of gas were collected. Cooling to room temperature caused precipitation of bright yellow crystals which were filtered, washed with ether and petroleum ether, dried and freed from traces of carbonyl by sublimation. Yield: 13.0 g (65%).

In an identical run adding 13.5 ml (0.15 *M*) of benzene produced (5-1/2 hours, 110°) 16.0 g (80%) of the same product. No benzene-molybdenum tricarbonyl could be isolated.

The compound was soluble in water, methanol and THF, slightly soluble in ether and insoluble in petroleum ether. It showed somewhat lower sensitivity towards oxidation than the analogous diglyme complex, but its appearance and reactions were the same. When heated in a nitrogen-filled capillary it decomposed, without melting, at 145–148°. Aqueous solutions of the DMF compound underwent the same reactions (with pyridine, ammonia, etc.) as did aqueous solutions of the diglyme complex.

The infrared spectrum showed bands at 2.9, 3.4, 5.1, 5.2, 5.4, 5.8, and 6.1 microns. *Anal*: Calcd. for $C_{12}H_{21}MoN_3O_6$: C, 36.1; H, 5.30; N, 10.53; Mo, 24.04. Found: C, 37.7; H, 5.51; N, 10.4; Mo, 24.1.

Trisdimethylacetamidetricarbonylmolybdenum(O) was prepared, as described above, by reacting $Mo(CO)_6$ and dimethylacetamide. *Anal*: Calcd. for $C_{15}H_{27}MoN_3O_6$: C, 40.82; H, 6.17; N, 9.52; Mo, 21.74. Found: C, 40.7; H, 6.22; N, 9.43; Mo, 21.7.

The Reaction of Molybdenum Hexacarbonyl with Diethyleneglycoldibutylether. Only decomposition of the carbonyl resulted from heating it with diethyleneglycoldibutylether. The presence of benzene, however, led to the formation of benzene-molybdenum tricarbonyl. Several runs were made, heating 13.2 g (0.05 mole) of $Mo(CO)_6$ with benzene (7.0 – 14.0 ml = 0.075 – 0.15 mole) and diglybu (25-50 ml) for 5 to 6 hours at 100–150°. In all cases, the gas evolution slowed down when about 1800 ml gas (S.T.P.) had been evolved. The crystalline greenish-yellow precipitate obtained after cooling the reaction mixture to room temperature was filtered. It consisted of excess $Mo(CO)_6$, which could be removed by sublimation (25°/0.1 mm), and of benzene-molybdenum tricarbonyl, which was identified by comparison with an authentic sample. [16]

The Reaction of Benzenemolybdenum Tricarbonyl with Diethyleneglycoldibutylether. Three grams of carbonyl-free crude benzene-molybdenum tricarbonyl were heated in an open, nitrogen-swept flask with 20 ml of diethyleneglycoldibutylether. After keeping the mixture for about 30 min. at 150°, filter-aid was added and filtered hot under nitrogen pressure. Cooling of the dark filtrate and slowly adding petroleum ether gave a somewhat gray-brown crystalline precipitate which was washed with petroleum ether and dried. The compound darkened and decomposed slowly even under nitrogen in the dark. On exposure to air it immediately deliquesced before igniting. For this reason, analytical data necessary to characterize this product completely could not be obtained (Calcd. for $C_{15}H_{26}MoO_6$: Mo, 24.1; found: Mo, 26 to 28.8%). However, the product, which was free of $C_6H_6Mo(CO)_3$ and $Mo(CO)_6$, reacted with acetonitrile to give a precipitate completely identical with that obtained from the diglyme complex.

Reaction of Diglyme-Tricarbonyl-Molybdenum with Dimethylamine. The described preparation of tris(dimethylamine)tricarbonyl-molybdenum is representative of numerous other reactions between diglyme-$Mo(CO)_3$ and various ligands which are summarized in Table 1. In the absence of solvent, an instantaneous reaction followed the addition of excess cold (−20°) dimethylamine to 4.9 g (0.016 M) of diglyme-$Mo(CO)_3$. The colorless, fine crystalline solid formed was only slightly soluble in the amine at its boiling point (+6°); it was

TABLE 1: TRICARBONYLMOLYBDENUM COMPOUNDS

Product	Reactant	Ligand	Solvent	Ref.		C	H	N	Mo	Remarks
$(NH_3)_3Mo(CO)_3$	Diglyme-Mo(CO)$_3$	Ammonia	Water	8	Calcd. / Found	15.60 / 16.2	3.93 / 4.12	18.8 / 17.3	41.52 / 40.4	Waxy solid, m.p. 92°, stable in air
$(C_{18}H_{37}NH_2)_3Mo(CO)_3$	(DMF)$_3$Mo(CO)$_3$	Octadecylamine	Methanol		Calcd. / Found	69.26 / 68.5	11.93 / 12.0	4.25 / 4.65		
$(C_4H_{13}N_3)Mo(CO)_3$	Diglyme-Mo(CO)$_3$	Diethylene-triamine	None or water	8,9	Calcd. / Found			14.84 / 14.8	33.89 / 32.7	Insol. ether, water, triethylenetetramine-derivative is water-soluble
$(C_9H_{23}N_3)Mo(CO)_3$	Diglyme-Mo(CO)$_3$	Pentamethyl-diethylenetri-amine	Methanol		Calcd. / Found	40.79 / 40.7	6.57 / 6.74	11.89 / 11.7	27.16 / 26.8	Recryst. acetone/ether, stable in air, yellow
$(CH_3CN)_3Mo(CO)_3$	Diglyme-Mo(CO)$_3$	Acetonitrile	Water		Calcd. / Found	35.66 / 35.7	3.00 / 3.05		31.65 / 31.3	Recryst. CH$_3$CN/ether, colorless, dec. in air
$(CH_2{=}CH\ CN)_3Mo(CO)_3$	Diglyme-Mo(CO)$_3$	Acrylonitrile	None		Calcd. / Found	42.5 / 40.7	2.67 / 3.0		28.3 / 32.0	Orange, highly unstable, no exact anal. obtained
$(CH_2{=}CH{-}CH_2{-}CN)_3Mo(CO)_3$	Diglyme-Mo(CO)$_3$	Allyl cyanide	None		Calcd. / Found	47.25 / 47.1	3.97 / 4.05	11.02 / 10.9	25.17 / 25.2	Colorless, fairly stable, m.p. 84–86° (dec.)
$(CH_6H_5CN)_3Mo(CO)_3$	Diglyme-Mo(CO)$_3$	Benzonitrile	None		Calcd. / Found	58.92 / 58.8	3.07 / 3.24	8.60 / 8.65	19.62 / 20.3	Yellow, stable in air
$(C_5H_5N)_3Mo(CO)_3$	Diglyme-Mo(CO)$_3$	Pyridine	None or water	5,9	Calcd. / Found	51.85 / 52.8	3.63 / 3.69			
$[(C_6H_5)_3P]_3Mo(CO)_3$	(DMF)$_3$Mo(CO)$_3$	Triphenyl-phosphine	Methanol	8,9	Calcd. / Found	70.8 / 70.7	4.7 / 5.04	P, 9.61 / P,10.2		M.P. 215–217°(dec.)
$[(C_6H_5)_3As]_3Mo(CO)_3$	(DMF)$_3$Mo(CO)$_3$	Triphenyl-arsine	Methanol	8,9	Calcd. / Found	62.31 / 61.7	4.13 / 4.38			M.P. 208–210°(dec.)
$[(C_6H_5)_3Sb]_3Mo(CO)_3$	(DMF)$_3$Mo(CO)$_3$	Triphenyl-stibine	Methanol	9	Calcd. / Found	55.24 / 54.9	3.66 / 3.87			M.P. 228–230°(dec.)
$(C_4H_8O)_3Mo(CO)_3$	Diglyme-Mo(CO)$_3$	Tetrahydro-furan	None		Calcd. / Found				24.22 / 25.8	Very unstable after repeated recryst. from THF

					C	H	N	Mo	
[HCON(CH₃)₂]₃Mo(CO)₃	Diglyme-Mo(CO)₃	Dimethyl-formamide	None	Calcd. Found	36.1 37.6	5.30 5.51	10.53 10.4	24.04 24.1	Identical with cpd. described above
$Mo(CO)_3$ (structure, 2,2'-dipyridylamine)	Mo(CO)₃ (DMF)Mo(CO)₃	2,2'-di-Pyridylamine	Methanol	Calcd. Found	52.88 53.0	3.48 3.74	16.09 15.15	18.37 18.5	Yellow., sol. dil. HCl, stable in air
$Mo(CO)_3$ (mesitylene structure)	Diglyme-Mo(CO)₃	Mesitylene	None	16					Identified by IR

filtered and washed with dimethylamine and petroleum ether and dried under vacuum. The yield was 4.4 g (90%) of product which was fairly stable to air, soluble in acetone, methanol and water. The infrared spectrum exhibited bands at 3.0, 3.4, 5.2, 5.3, 5.6, 5.7, 5.85 and 6.8 microns. *Anal:* Calcd. for $C_9H_{21}MoN_3O_3$: C, 34.29; H, 6.71; N, 13.33. Found: C, 34.0; H, 6.78; N, 13.0. The filtrate obtained after separation of the precipitate contained the displaced diglyme.

Reaction of Tris(dimethylformamide)tricarbonyl-Molybdenum with Dodecylamine. This reaction is representative of several others wherein $(DMF)_3Mo(CO)_3$ was treated with various ligands (see Table 1). A solution of 5.3 g (0.013 M) of $(DMF)_3Mo(CO)_3$ in 50 ml of methanol was added to a stirred solution of 9.27 g (0.05 M) of dodecylamine in 80 ml of methanol. The almost colorless voluminous precipitate obtained was washed with methanol, ether and then petroleum ether and dried. The waxy product melted at 92° (nitrogen-filled capillary). It was fairly stable to air, insoluble in water, slightly soluble in benzene, petroleum ether and CH_3OH, soluble in acetone, pyridine and carbon tetrachloride. The assigned structure for the compound, tris(dodecylamine)tricarbonylmolybdenum, is supported by its analysis. Calcd. for $C_{39}H_{81}MoN_3O_3$: C, 63.64; H, 11.09; N, 5.70. Found: C, 63.4; H, 11.3; N, 5.68. The infrared spectrum shows absorptions at 3.0, 3.5, 5.35, 5.7, 5.9, 6.3 and 6.8 microns.

REFERENCES

1. For a preliminary communication, see: R. P. M. Werner and T. H. Coffield, *Chem. and Ind.*, **936**, 1960.
2. W. Behrens and W. Haag, *Z. Naturforschg*, **14b**, 600 (1959).
3. A. Lüttringhaus and W. Kullick, *Tetrahedron Letters*, **10**, 13 (1959).
4. C. N. Matthews, T. A. Magee, and J. H. Wotiz, *J. Am. Chem. Soc.*, **81**, 2273 (1959).
5. W. Hieber and F. Mühlbauer, *Z. anorg. allg. Chem.*, **221**, 337 (1935).
6. W. Hieber and J. Peterhans, *Z. Naturforschg.*, **14b**, 462 (1959).
7. H. L. Nigam and R. S. Nyholm, *Proc. Chem. Soc.*, 321, 1957.
8. W. Hieber, K. Englert, and K. Rieger, *Z. anorg. allg. Chem.*, **300**, 295 (1959).
9. E. W. Abel, M. A. Bennett, and G. Wilkinson, *J. Chem. Soc.*, 2323, 1959.
10. See: E. Krause and A. von Grosse, *Die Chemie der Metallorganischen Verbindungen*, Borntraeger, Berlin, 1937.
11. W. Herwig and H. H. Zeiss, *J. Am. Chem. Soc.*, **79**, 6561 (1957); W. Herwig, W. Metlesics and H. H. Zeiss, *ibid.*, **81**, 6203 (1959).
12. W. Herwig and H. H. Zeiss, *J. Org. Chem.*, **23**, 1404 (1958).
13. (a) E. Kurras, *Z. Naturwiss.*, **46**, 171 (1959); (b) G. Natta, G. Pregaglia, and G. Mazzanti, *Gazz. Chim. Ital.*, **89**, 2065 (1959).

14. B. Nicholls and M. C. Whiting, *J. Chem. Soc.*, **1959**, 551.
15. We are indebted to Professor Stanley Kirschner at Wayne State University for carrying out the magnetic measurements.
16. E. O. Fischer *et al.*, *Ber.*, **91**, 2763 (1958). Angew. Chem., **73**, 358 (1961).
17. J. Archambault and R. Rivest, *Can. J. Chem.*, **36**, 1461 (1958).
18. See Ref. 8 for independent synthesis via base reaction of the hexacarbonyl.
19. See Ref. 9 for independent synthesis from π-cycloheptatriene molybdenum tricarbonyl.
20. A. E. Martell and M. Calvin, *Chemistry of the Metal Chelate Compounds*, Prentice-Hall, New York, 1952, p. 213.
21. E. O. Fischer, C. Palm, and H. P. Fritz, *Chem. Ber.*, **92**, 2645 (1959).

ON THE CALCULATION OF COMPLEXITY CONSTANTS BY THE METHOD OF LEAST SQUARES

JAN RYDBERG

University of Stockholm and
Research Institute of National Defense
Stockholm, Sweden

In complex chemistry one is commonly faced with the problem of fitting equations containing many parameters to a large number of experimental data. Since numerical methods, e.g., the method of least squares, lead to very extensive calculations, graphical methods have so far been mostly used. However, with the aid of high-speed digital computers it is possible to carry out least squares calculations on complexity equations in a matter of minutes. If it is assumed that all mistakes and systematic errors have been eliminated and that the accidental errors have a normal distribution according to the Theory of Errors,[2,3] it is possible to apply statistical considerations to the results obtained.

TYPES OF EQUATIONS ENCOUNTERED IN EQUILIBRIUM STUDIES

The ultimate nature of the problem is to determine the stability constant $\beta_{m,n,p}$ as defined by

$$\beta_{m,n,p} = \frac{[M_m A_n B_p]}{[M]^m [A]^n [B]^p} \tag{1}$$

for the complex $M_m A_n B_p$, where M is the central (metal) atom and A and B are two different kinds of ligands. Brackets may here indicate activities or concentrations; in the latter case it is assumed that the ratio of the activity coefficients of the various species involved in the equilibrium are constant. More complicated complexes may be defined,[4-6] but these are almost entirely of theoretical interest because of the practical difficulties in investigating such complexes.

The mathematical formulation of the equations as well as methods for calculating the stability constants for *complexes of type MA_n* have been thoroughly discussed by many authors, e.g., Bjerrum,[7] Sullivan and Hindman,[8] and Irving and Rossotti.[9] The general equation may be written

$$\sum_{0}^{N} (C_A - [A] - n \cdot C_M)\beta_n[A]^n = 0 \tag{2}$$

The equations for *mixed complexes of type* MA_nB_p can be formulated in many ways, as given, e.g., by Fronaeus [10] and Rydberg.[4] The primary equations all contain double sums; a representative example is given by

$$\overline{n}_A - \frac{C_A = [A]}{C_M} = \frac{\displaystyle\sum_{0}^{N} n\beta_{np}[A]^n[B]^p}{\displaystyle\sum_{0}^{N}\sum_{0}^{P} \beta_{np}[A]^n[B]^p} \tag{3}$$

where $\overline{n}_A$ is the average number of ligands A bound per metal atom.

Equations for the formation of *polynuclear complexes* have been elaborated by many authors, as for type M_2A_n, e.g., by Leden [11] and Fronaeus; [12] for type M_mA_n, e.g., by Brosset, [13] Ahrland, [14] Sillen [15] and Hedström; [16] for type $M_mH_jA_n$ (complexes between metals and acid ligands) e.g., by Schwarzenbach; [17] for type $H_jM_mA_n$ (poly-anions neutralized by jH^+) e.g., by Rossotti and Rossotti; [18] and for the core-and-link types by Graner [19] and Sillen. [19,20] The primary equations all contain double sums, as, for example, in

$$\overline{n}_A = \frac{C_A - [A]}{C_m} = \frac{\displaystyle\sum_{1}^{m}\sum_{1}^{n} n\beta_{mn}[M]^m[A]^n}{[M] + \displaystyle\sum_{1}^{m}\sum_{1}^{n} m\beta_{mn}[M]^m[A]^n} \tag{4}$$

THE METHOD OF LEAST SQUARES

The principle of least squares, which is founded on the normal probability equation (the "Gaussian curve"), says that the best or most probable value of a measured quantity is that value for which the sum of the weighted squares of the residuals (i.e., the difference between the computed and measured values of the dependent variable) is a minimum.[3] The application of this principle (i.e., the method of least squares) to curve fitting is extensively treated, e.g., by Deming.[21]

The method of least squares does not introduce any systematic computational errors. It gives the best set of constants obtainable from the data according to the Theory of Error, and it also permits the calculation of standard errors of these constants, which make it possible to subject the results to statistical tests (see, e.g., Fisher),[22] as will be demonstrated in the examples at the end of this paper.

The method is only applicable to equations which are linear or can be reduced to a linear form in the constants. In complex chemistry this is a rather serious limitation, because it is seen that none of the equations (3-4) fulfills this requirement. The linear and non-linear cases will be treated separately below.

Equations Linear in the Parameters

Equations for the investigation of the complex MA_n can often be reduced to[11,23]

$$y = \sum_{0}^{N} a_n[A]^n \tag{5}$$

The equation is linear in the parameter a_n, which is simply related to the constant β_n. The method of least squares is straight-forward in this case, and it has been applied by Irving and Rossotti[9] to a number of systems with $N = 2$, and by Kivalo and Rastas[24] and McMaster and Schaap[25] to polarographic studies with $N = 4$. While Irving and Rossotti, and Kivalo and Rastas made their calculations manually, McMaster and Schaap, as well as the investigators in the following references, used high-speed computer calculations. None of these authors used weighted data. Both Kivalo and Rastas, and McMaster and Schaap used an approximation technique in the calculations, and the latter authors did not calculate any standard deviations in their parameters.

Rydberg, Sullivan, and Miller[26-29] have applied equation (2) to potentiometric and equation (5) to solvent extraction studies, while Zielen[30] has applied equation (5) to cation exchange data. In all cases, weighted data were used, and the computers were programmed to calculate standard deviations in the parameters.

Equations Nonlinear in the Parameters

If the parameters do not enter the equation in a linear way, as is the case with equations (3-4), the Gauss method[31] may be used to reduce it to a linear form. The method requires estimated values of β_n, which usually can be obtained from graphical plots.

The principle has been used by Van Panthaleon van Eck[32] on data $\bar{n}([A])$, where all weights have been taken equal to unity. It has also been used with weighted data in kinetic studies of the reduction of Np(VI) by Zielen, Sullivan, Cohen and Hindman,[33] and on spectrophotometric investigations of the hydrolysis of Pu(IV) by Rabideau and Kline.[34]

Another use of estimated values is to study how the sum S of the squares of the residuals vary with the variation of one parameter at a time. When the minimum of S (S_{min}) is found for one parameter, this value is retained, and the next parameter is varied until S_{min} for that parameter is found. After S has been minimized for each parameter in turn, the procedure is started over again and continued in this manner until S is a minimum for all of the parameters. This trial-and-error technique will not guarantee that one will reach a true minimum for S. Also, there may be another set of parameters which gives an equally small value of S.[31] However, if the original estimate of the parameters is not too bad, it seems likely that this method will yield correct answers.

The use of this method for polynuclear complexes has recently been suggested by Dyrssen, Ingri and Sillen.[35] In this case, estimates of the parameters are obtained through graphical methods.

The Ni(II)—NH$_3$ System; a Potentiometric Investigation

The experimental data of Bjerrum[7] were directly introduced into equation (2), which was then solved for β_n by the method of least squares[27] using an IBM 704 computer. With the program used,[36] one run on the computer takes about one minute. All errors are assumed to belong to the experimental determination of $[A]$. Table 1 gives the results obtained, and also the results of the semi-graphical ligand-number method.[7] It is seen that the agreement is excellent.

The χ^2-test[22] may be applied to the data. Bjerrum estimates "the limit of experimental error" in the emf measurements to 0.2–0.5 m. which here is interpreted to a standard error of $\pm(0.1–0.25)$ m. A standard error of ±0.1 m. corresponds to a 0.54% error in $[A]$, i.e.,

TABLE 1: THE Ni(II) – NH$_3$ SYSTEM, 2 M NH$_4$NO$_3$ AT 30°C.

Gross Constant*	Bjerrum	Least Squares	Stepwise Constant*	Bjerrum	Least Squares
$\beta_1 \cdot 10^{-2}$	6.29	6.094 ± 0.048	$\log k_1$	2.795	2.785 ± 0.0034
$\beta_2 \cdot 10^{-5}$	1.084	1.111 ± 0.020	$\log k_2$	2.24	2.262 ± 0.0085
$\beta_3 \cdot 10^{-6}$	5.82	5.377 ± 0.173	$\log k_3$	1.73	1.686 ± 0.016
$\beta_4 \cdot 10^{-7}$	9.00	9.254 ± 0.414	$\log k_4$	1.19	1.249 ± 0.023
$\beta_5 \cdot 10^{-8}$	5.06	5.202 ± 0.262	$\log k_5$	0.75	0.737 ± 0.029
$\beta_6 \cdot 10^{-8}$	5.43	5.514 ± 0.396	$\log k_6$	0.03	0.026 ± 0.038

*$\beta_n = \pi k_n$

$\sigma[A] = \pm 0.0054\,[A]$. Using this error of internal consistency,[21] a χ^2-value is calculated (this calculation is incorporated in the computer program) to be 4.25. Since the number of degrees of freedom here is 5 (11 points minus 6 parameters), the χ^2-test shows a high degree of consistency between the experimental points and the curve calculated with the obtained constants. This consistency, found even for the smallest possible error assumed by Bjerrum, is very strong support for the basic hypothesis, i.e., that all stepwise complexes for Ni^{2+} to $Ni(NH_3)_6^{2+}$ exist.

The $VO^{2+} - F^-$ System; a Potentiometric Investigation

To this system[37] equation (2) is applicable in the same manner as described above. In Fig. 1, the original authors have plotted $\bar{n}([A])$. Since the points are obtained from 5 different sets of experiments, and the curve obtained with the three constants β_1, β_2 and β_3 seems

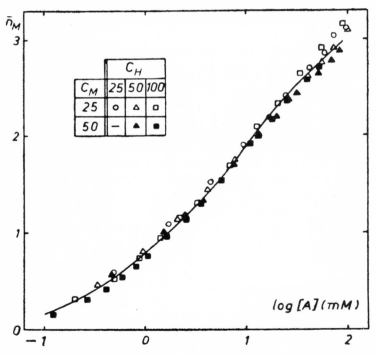

Fig. 1. The complex formation function of the vanadyl fluoride system. The points refer to titrations with different values of C_M and C_H, as indicated by the scheme given in the figure. The curve is calculated from the constants β_n finally found.

to fit well all the 5 sets of points, a statistical t-test[22] seems applicable.

A general look at Table 2 reveals 3 things: (1) of the 5 sets of experiments some rather high values of χ^2/G are obtained; (2) the β_n-values computed by the method of least squares for the various sets of experiments do not all agree within their errors; (3) Ahrland and Norén's β_n-values agree approximately well with the mean values calculated by the method of least squares. These points shall be discussed in turn.

If the error of external consistency is found by calculating what value forces $\chi^2/G = 1.0$, one finds that the error should be around 2% in $[A]$, with exception for set 4, where the error must be assumed to be about 5%. This agrees rather well with the ±0.2 m. error estimated for the emf measurements.

A t-test was carried out on the β_r-values ($r = 1,2,3,4$) to see if there were any significant deviations between them. The test was based on the assumption (1) that in each experimental set, the points have a normal statistical distribution, and (2) that all data were of the same relative weights. If these assumptions are not too incorrect, the t-test indicates significant differences between the β_r values. Thus, for $10^{-5}\beta_2 = 4.84 \pm 0.07$ (set 1) and 2.57 ± 0.11 (set 5), the test shows that the probability is $<1\%$ that the two β_2 values belong to the same normal population. After analyzing all β_r values, it must be concluded from a statistical point of view that the differences between these values must be caused by systematic differences among the five sets of experiments.

If all experimental points are taken together (i.e., are assumed to belong to the same normal population), the agreement between the mean values of the least squares calculations and the values obtained by Ahrland and Norén is quite reasonable. Figure 1 also shows how well the computed curve fits the experimental points. It is the author's opinion that graphical methods do not permit more information to be extracted from the data than have been obtained by the original authors.

The Ce(III)-SO$_4^{2-}$ System; a Cation Exchange Investigation

This is the only system[38] known to the author where the parameters are not linear in the equation and the trial-and-error least squares approach has been applied. In this particular case, the equation

$$\sum_0^N (Q_M - \lambda_n)\beta_n[A]^n = 0 \tag{6}$$

TABLE 2: THE $VO^{2+} - F^-$ SYSTEM. THE ERRORS GIVEN ARE MEAN SQUARE ERRORS AT THE 95% CONFIDENCE LIMIT (2 TIMES STANDARD DEVIATION).

Set	$[H^+] \times 10^2$	$C_M \cdot 10^3$	$\beta_1 \cdot 10^{-3}$	$\beta_2 \cdot 10^{-5}$	$\beta_3 \cdot 10^{-7}$	$\beta_4 \cdot 10^{-7}$	χ^2	G
1	25	25	2.29 ± 0.03	4.84 ± 0.07	1.75 ± 0.06	8.97 ± 0.64	0.64	4
2	50	25	2.16 ± 0.06	4.14 ± 0.16	1.31 ± 0.14	6.14 ± 1.31	5.30	5
3	50	50	2.13 ± 0.10	3.67 ± 0.28	1.15 ± 0.20	3.12 ± 1.73	41.4	6
4	100	25	1.97 ± 0.20	3.49 ± 0.60	1.53 ± 0.59	9.65 ± 9.23	198	7
5	100	50	1.53 ± 0.03	2.57 ± 0.11	0.93 ± 0.07	3.32 ± 0.90	20.6	10
Mean values of least squares calculations			2.02 ± 0.08	3.74 ± 0.24	1.34 ± 0.21	6.2 ± 2.8		
Values by Ahrland and Norén			2.0 ± 0.1	2.9 ± 0.3	1.4 ± 0.2	3.0		

is applicable, and the maximum number of parameters which have to be considered are λ_0, λ_1, β_1, β_3 and β_3. Of these constants λ_0 is known directly from the experiments (see below). In the following treatment we shall assume that we have no knowledge of the results of Fronaeus's calculations.

On the basis of the experiments, it can be assumed that all error can be attributed to the measured partition ratios Q and are of the size $\sigma_Q = \pm 0.03\ Q$. The experimental data $Q([A])$ comprises only 8 points. The curve through these points is anchored at $Q_0([A] = 0) = 0.787$, which is our λ_0 value.

We now make a number of runs on the computer with equations based on the following assumptions:

Run	Cerium Species in Solution	Cerium Species on the Resin
1	Ce^{3+}, CeA^+, CeA_2^-	Ce^{3+}
2–5	Ce^{3+}, CeA^+, CeA_2^-	Ce^{3+}, CeA^+
6	Ce^{3+}, CeA^+, CeA_2^-, CeA_3^{3-}	Ce^{3+}
7–10	Ce^{3+}, CeA^+, CeA_2^-, CeA_3^{3-}	Ce^{3+}, CeA^+

Here A^{2-} stands for SO_4^{2-}. Looking at runs 1–5 in Table 3, it follows from the χ^2/G values that the most probable λ_1 value is obtained for run 1 (χ^2/G value closest to 1.0). However, even though the χ^2/G value for run 1 is not improbable for a fit between the assumed equation and the experimental data, one of the computed points, $Q_7 = 0.0504$ seems somewhat too far off from the measured value 0.0483. We assume this is a significant difference, and therefore make a new set of runs, 6–10, where also CeA_3^{3-} is considered in the equation. Since χ^2/G has the same normal distribution as the sum S of the squares of the weighted residuals,[20] χ^2/G shall show a minimum for the most probable value of λ_1. No such minimum is achieved in runs 6–10, and no higher λ_1 value than 0.30 was tested because higher values seemed very improbable from a chemical point of view. As compared to runs 1–5, the χ^2/G values in runs 6–10 indicate that the functional form in the latter case is more probable. From this result it may be concluded that the experimental data can be best explained by considering the species Ce^{3+}, CeA^+, CeA_2^- and CeA_3^{3-} in the aqueous phase and the species Ce^{3+} and CeA^+ in the resin phase. This is the same conclusion as reached by Fronaeus.

Unfortunately, as the least squares calculations were made on the present data, the χ^2 test gives very little help in finding the best λ_1 value. We are therefore forced to make a subjective judgment.

TABLE 3: THE Ce(III) – SO_4^{2-} SYSTEM. G = 5 FOR RUNS 1–5, AND 4 FOR RUNS 6–10; $\lambda_0 = 0.752$

Run	λ_1	$10\beta_1$	$100\beta_2$	$1000\beta_3$	Q_1	Q_3	Q_7	χ^2/G
1	0.00	3.45 ± 0.14	1.65 ± 0.16	0	0.424	0.201	0.0504*	1.51
2	0.04	3.45 ± 0.20	2.90 ± 0.20	0	0.428	0.199	0.0514*	2.67
3	0.0787	3.46 ± 0.26	4.10 ± 0.23	0	0.430*	0.198	0.0521*	3.90
4	0.10	3.46 ± 0.29	4.76 ± 0.26	0	0.432*	0.197	0.0523*	4.58
5	0.30	3.48 ± 0.60	11.08 ± 1.09	0	0.444*	0.191*	0.0532*	9.94
6	0.00	3.47 ± 0.19	0.72 ± 0.51	0.48 ± 0.26	0.418	0.205	0.0479	0.994
7	0.04	4.01 ± 0.21	1.25 ± 0.55	0.95 ± 0.32	0.418	0.205	0.0481	0.946
8	0.0787	4.29 ± 0.24	1.86 ± 0.58	1.46 ± 0.40	0.418	0.206	0.0482	0.904
9	0.10	4.47 ± 0.26	2.25 ± 0.59	1.77 ± 0.44	0.417	0.206	0.0482	0.884
10	0.30	7.05 ± 0.60	8.38 ± 0.66	6.37 ± 1.21	0.417	0.206	0.0485	0.752
Fronaeus	0.0787	4.3 ± 0.3	2.2 ± 0.5	1.2 ± 0.3	0.414 ± 0.012	0.202 ± 0.006	0.0483 ± 0.014	...

*These values are outside the 3% standard error in the measured Q-values.

Since the λ_1 value is of greater importance for the higher complexes which dominate at the points of highest $[A]$ value (the $[A]$ value increases from point Q_0 to Q_7), we shall say that the best λ_1 is that which causes the smallest deviation between the computed and measured values (the measured values are given in the last line of Table 3) of point Q_7; this value turns out to be 0.0482 (runs 8 and 9). Since we here have two such values, we chose the one which causes the smallest deviation in the Q_3-value, which turns out to be for run 8, if the trend in Q_3 is considered. This corresponds to the same λ_1-values as Fronaeus has arrived at from somewhat different considerations. It should be observed that the approach used here can easily be stated mathematically, because what we have done is only to increase the weights of the points for the highest $[A]$ values. If this is stated in mathematical terms and introduced in our computations, we would probably find S_{min} in the same neighborhood we just arrived at. It may be added that the electronic computer can easily be ordered to try the various λ_n values automatically until the λ_n value, which gives the smallest S value is obtained.

If we compare the constants obtained by Fronaeus and by the method of least squares for $\lambda_1 = 0.0787$, we find an excellent agreement. This shows that complicated graphical treatments, when carried out with skill, yield results is in almost complete agreement with the method of least squares.

CONCLUSION

It is always necessary to check the computed results to see if they are reasonable from a chemical point of view. Of all tests which can be applied to the data, this is the most crucial. When a sufficient number of experimental points are at hand, it should also be checked that the points have a normal distribution around the computed curve. Under these circumstances, the method of least squares, in combination with high-speed digital computers, is both a powerful and time-saving tool for helping complex chemists in analyzing their experimental data.

REFERENCES

1. Also see J. Rydberg, *Acta Chem. Scand.*, in press.
2. H. Cramer, *Mathematical Methods of Statistics*, Princeton University Press, Princeton, 1946: *Sannolikhetskalkylen och några av dess användningar*, Almqvist och Wiksell, Uppsala, 1961.
3. J. B. Scarborough, *Numerical Mathematical Analysis* (4th ed.), The John Hopkins Press, Baltimore, 1958.
4. J. Rydberg, *Arkiv Kemi*, **8**, 101 (1955).

5. H. Irving, F. J. C. Rossotti, and R. J. P. Williams, *J. Chem. Soc.*, 1906 (1955).
6. L. G. Sillén, *Supplement to La Ricerca Scientifica*, **28** (1958).
7. J. Bjerrum, *Metal Amine Formation in Aqueous Solution*, P. Haase and Son, Copenhagen, 1941.
8. J. C. Sullivan and J. C. Hindman, *J. Am. Chem. Soc.*, **74**, 6091 (1952).
9. H. Irving and H. S. Rossotti, *J. Chem. Soc.*, 3397 (1953).
10. S. Fronaeus, *Acta Chem. Scand.*, **4**, 72 (1950).
11. I. Leden, "Potentiometriska undersökningar av några kadmiumsalters komplexitet," Thesis, Lund, 1943.
12. S. Fronaeus, "Komplexsystem hos koppar," Thesis, Lund, 1948.
13. C. Brosset, "Elektrokemisk och röntgenkristallografisk undersökning av komplexa aluminiumfluorider," Thesis, Stockholm, 1942.
14. S. Ahrland, *Acta Chem. Scand.*, **3**, 374 (1949).
15. L. G. Sillén, *Acta Chem. Scand.*, **8**, 299 (1954).
16. B. Hedström, *Acta Chem. Scand.*, **9**, 613 (1955).
17. G. Schwarzenbach, *Helv. Chim. Acta*, **33**, 947 (1950).
18. F. J. C. Rossotti and H. Rossotti, *Acta Chem. Scand.*, **10**, 957 (1956).
19. F. Granér and L. G. Sillén, *Acta Chem. Scand.*, **1**, 631 (1947).
20. L. G. Sillén, *Acta Chem. Scand.*, **8**, 318 (1954).
21. W. E. Deming, *Statistical Adjustment of Data*, J. Wiley and Son, New York, 1948.
22. R. A. Fisher, *Statistical Methods for Research Workers* (13th ed.), Hafnér Publ. Co., New York, 1958.
23. J. Rydberg, *Acta Chem. Scand.*, **4**, 1503 (1950).
24. P. Kivalo and J. Rastas, *Suomen Kemistilehti*, **30**, 128 (1957).
25. D. L. McMasters and W. B. Schaap, *Proc. Indiana Acad. Sci.*, **67**, 111 (1958).
26. J. Rydberg and J. C. Sullivan, *Acta Chem. Scand.*, **13**, 186 (1959).
27. J. C. Sullivan, J. Rydberg, and W. F. Miller, *Acta Chem. Scand.*, **13**, 2033 (1959).
28. J. Rydberg and J. C. Sullivan, *Acta Chem. Scand.*, **13**, 2057 (1959).
29. J. Rydberg, *Acta Chem. Scand.*, **14**, 157 (1960).
30. A. Zielen, *J. Am. Chem. Soc.*, **81**, 5022 (1959).
31. R. H. Moore and R. K. Zeigler, "The solution of the general least squares problem with special references to high-speed computers," LA-2367, Los Alamos Scientific Laboratory, New Mexico, 1960.
32. C. L. Van Panthaleon van Eck, Thesis, Amsterdam, 1958.
33. A. J. Zielen, J. C. Sullivan, D. Cohen, and J. C. Hindman, private communication.
34. S. W. Rabideau and R. J. Kline, *J. Phys. Chem.*, **64**, 680 (1960).
35. D. Dyrssen, N. Ingri, and L. G. Sillén, private communication (to be published).
36. Program 626/CHM 112. Applied Mathematics Division, Argonne National Laboratory, Argonne, Illinois.
37. S. Ahrland and B. Norén, *Acta Chem. Scand.*, **12**, 1595 (1958).
38. S. Fronaeus, *Svensk Kem. Tidskr.*, **64**, 317 (1952).

THE CRYSTAL STRUCTURE OF *TRANS*-DICHLORO-BIS-*l*-PROPYLENEDIAMINE COBALT(III) CHLORIDE HYDROCHLORIDE DIHYDRATE AND THE ABSOLUTE CONFIGURATION OF THE COMPLEX ION [Co *l*-pn₂Cl₂]⁺

YOSHIHIKO SAITO and **HITOSHI IWASAKI**

Institute for Solid State Physics
University of Tokyo
Tokyo, Japan

Stable five-membered chelate rings are often found in various co-ordination compounds. Ethylenediamine is the simplest and most important one of such chelating agents, and its compounds have played an important role in the development of coordination chemistry. Accordingly, ethylenediamine has been the subject of various investigations. For these several years the crystal structures of the following cobalt-ethylenediamine complexes have been determined by one of the present authors, (Y.S.), Kuroya *et al.*, and Becker *et al.*:

$$[Coen_2Cl_2]Cl \cdot HCl \cdot 2\ H_2O^1$$
$$[Coen_2Br_2]Br \cdot HBr \cdot 2\ H_2O^2$$
$$[Coen_3]Cl_3 \cdot 3\ H_2O^3$$
$$2D\text{-}[Coen_3]Cl_3 \cdot NaCl \cdot 6\ H_2O^4$$

and
$$[Coen_2Cl_2]Cl^5.$$

Structures of other metal-ethylenediamine complexes such as $[Cuen_2][Hg(SCN)_4]^6$, $[Nien_3](NO_3)_2^7$, $[Cuen_2](NO_3)_2^8$ and $[Cren_2Cl_2]Cl \cdot HCl \cdot 2\ H_2O^9$ have also been reported. A puckered form of the metal-ethylenediamine ring has thus been established.

In connection with this, the present investigation was initiated in order to determine the configuration of the cobalt-propylenediamine ring:

with special interest in the orientation of the substituted methyl group. Corey and Bailar[10] have recently discussed the geometry of various metal chelate rings. Their conclusion for the metal-propylenediamine ring agreed quite well with the results obtained.

The determination of the absolute configuration of the complex ion, $[Co\ l\text{-}pn_2Cl_2]^+$, is now in progress.

Experimental

Crystals of $[Co\ l\text{-}pn_2Cl_2]\,Cl\cdot HCl\cdot 2\,H_2O$ were prepared by the method of Werner and Fröhlich.[11]* They are well-developed dark green tablets, showing predominant (100) faces. In polarized light, they exhibit marked dichroism similar to that observed for $[Coen_2Cl_2]\text{-}Cl\cdot HCl\cdot 2\,H_2O$. This fact suggests that the structure is closely related to that of the ethylenediamine-analogue.

As the crystals of $[Co\ l\text{-}pn_2Cl_2]\,Cl\cdot HCl\cdot 2\,H_2O$ decompose gradually when exposed to air, special precautions had to be taken to preserve the crystals. It was found that adequate protection was afforded by a thin layer of grease. Specimens treated with grease were preserved intact for several weeks.

From measurements made by using X-ray diffractometer with Cu $K\,\alpha$ radiation ($\lambda = 1.5418$ Å) the unit cell is found to be monoclinic, with

$$a = 22.092 \pm 0.006\ \text{Å}$$
$$b = 8.406 \pm 0.003\ \text{Å}$$
$$c = 9.373 \pm 0.006\ \text{Å}$$
and $$\beta = 99°39' \pm 10'.$$

Space group is found to be $C2/m$, Cm, or $C2$ from Weissenberg photographs taken with Fe $K\,\alpha$ radiation. The cell contains four formula units of $[Co\ l\text{-}pn_2Cl_2]Cl\cdot HCl\cdot 2\,H_2O$ (density, calculated 1.494 g/cc; found, 1.495 g/cc at 26 °C). The former two-space group can be excluded since it is certain that the compound is optically active and cannot have a center or a plane of symmetry in the arrangement in the crystals.

The structure determination was based on analysis of the $(h0l)$ and $(hk0)$ reflections, which could be carried out in a quite straightforward fashion.

Intensity data for the $(h0l)$ and $(hk0)$ reflections were recorded on zero-level Weissenberg films about the b- and c-axes by the multiple-

---

*Optically active propylenediamine was kindly prepared by Prof. H. Kuroya of Osaka City University, to whom the authors' thanks are due.

film technique. Iron $K\alpha$ radiation was used ($\lambda = 1.937\,\text{Å}$). The intensities of the reflections were measured by visual comparison with an intensity scale. They were corrected for absorption, Lorentz and polarization factors. Observed structure amplitudes were brought to an absolute scale afterwards by scaling against the calculated values.

Patterson functions could be solved without difficulty by comparison with those of the ethylenediamine-analogues, yielding approximate positions not only for the heavy atoms but also for lighter atoms. Thus Fourier syntheses of the electron density projections along [001] and [010] could be computed.

Fourier refinements were repeated as usual. Final refinements are now going on. The best set of parameter values hitherto obtained is listed in Table 1. This gives the reliability index $R = \Sigma\|Fo\| -$

TABLE 1: ATOMIC PARAMETERS

	x	y	z
Co	0.250	0.000	0.250
Cl(1)	0.392	0.635	0.172
Cl(2)	0.108	0.319	0.328
Cl(3)	0.267	−0.022	0.017
Cl(4)	0.233	0.022	0.483
N (1)	0.268	0.232	0.251
N (2)	0.338	−0.036	0.320
N′(1)	0.231	−0.235	0.255
N′(2)	0.164	0.039	0.175
C (1)	0.334	0.250	0.261
C (2)	0.366	0.119	0.353
C (3)	0.434	0.117	0.343
C′(1)	0.169	−0.245	0.168
C′(2)	0.135	−0.109	0.212
C′(3)	0.067	−0.117	0.156
O (1)	0.442	0.510	0.472
O (2)	0.058	0.493	0.028

$\|Fc\|\,/\Sigma\,|Fo|$ of 0.16 and 0.19 for ($h0l$) and ($hk0$), respectively, excluding terms too weak to be observed. A projection of the structure along [010] is shown in Fig. 1.

Calculation of the structure factors as well as of the electron density projections was carried out with the PC-1 Parametron computer by the Faculty of Science of this University. In the calculation of the structure factors the atomic scattering factors were taken from the paper of Vand, Eiland and Pepinsky.[12] Over-all temperature factors with $B = 2.80\,\text{Å}^2$ and $3.30\,\text{Å}^2$ were applied for ($h0l$) and ($hk0$), respectively.

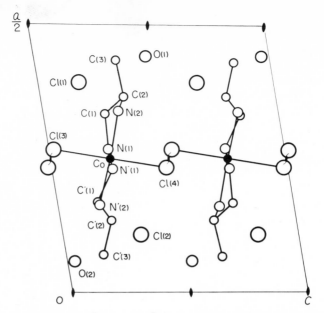

Fig. 1. Structure of $[Col\text{-}pn_2Cl_2]Cl \cdot HCl \cdot 2H_2O$ projected on (010).

Description of the Structure and Discussion

The determined structure seems most easily understood with the aid of the projection upon (010) shown in Fig. 1. The interatomic distances and bond angles are given in Table 2. The structure is essentially ionic and consists of the complexes $[Col\text{-}pn_2Cl_2]^+$, $[H_2O \cdot H \cdot H_2O]^+$ and Cl^- ion. In Fig. 2 is shown a perspective drawing of the $[Col\text{-}pn_2Cl_2]^+$ ion. The chlorine atoms are coordinated at a distance of 2.30 Å to a cobalt atom in *trans* positions. A line joining them is approximately perpendicular to the plane in which the four nitrogen atoms of the two propylenediamine molecules were found to lie. Within experimental errors these ligand atoms (4N and 2Cl) form

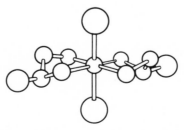

Fig. 2. A perspective drawing of the complex ion, $[Col\text{-}pn_2Cl_2]^+$.

TABLE 2: INTERATOMIC DISTANCES AND BOND ANGLES

Co	Cl(3)	2.29 Å	O(1)	O(1)	2.54 Å
	Cl(4)	2.29	O(2)	O(2)	2.54
	N(1)	1.99			
	N(2)	1.98	O(1)	Cl(1)	3.04
	N'(1)	2.02		Cl(2)	3.49
	N'(2)	1.95			
			O(2)	Cl(1)	3.82
N(1)	C(1)	1.45		Cl(2)	3.28
N(2)	C(2)	1.44			
C(1)	C(2)	1.50	C(3)	C(3)	3.77
C(2)	C(3)	1.53	C'(3)	C'(3)	3.76
N'(1)	C'(1)	1.47	<CoN(1)C(1)		108°
N'(2)	C'(2)	1.47	<N(1)C(1)C(2)		110°
C'(1)	C'(2)	1.49	<C(1)C(2)N(2)		113°
C'(2)	C'(3)	1.53	<C(2)N(2)Co		107°
			<C(1)C(2)C(3)		110°
N(2)	Cl(1)	3.29	<N(2)C(2)C(3)		110°
	Cl(2)	3.55			
N'(2)	Cl(1)	3.38	<CoN'(1)C'(1)		103°
	Cl(2)	3.01	<N'(1)C'(1)C'(2)		106°
			<C'(1)C'(2)N'(2)		108°
N(1)	Cl(3)	3.25	<C'(2)N'(2)Co		103°
N'(1)	Cl(4)	3.22	<C'(1)C'(2)C'(3)		113°
			<N'(2)C'(2)C'(3)		114°
C(3)	O(1)	3.51			
C'(3)	O(2)	3.48			

a distorted octahedron around a cobalt atom. The bond length found for Co—Cl agrees with those found in [Coen$_2$Cl$_2$]Cl·HCl·2 H$_2$O and [Co(NH$_3$)$_3$H$_2$O Cl$_2$]Cl. The chelating molecule assumes a *gauche* configuration with an azimuthal angle of 55° between the planes determined by C—C and C—N bonds. The azimuthal angles between the planes determined by the C—C and C—N bonds and that determined by Co—N and C—N bonds are, on the average, 38°. Consequently, the configuration of the five-membered cobalt propylenediamine ring can be assigned as *gauche-gauche-gauche* with respect to the N—C, C—C and C—N bonds.

The shape and size of this five-membered ring agree well with those of cobalt-ethylenediamine rings found in [Coen$_2$Cl$_2$]$^+$ and [Coen$_3$]$^{3+}$. The same type of puckered rings are also found in other metal-ethylenediamine complexes, such as [Cren$_2$Cl$_2$]$^+$, [Nien$_3$]$^{2+}$ and [Cuen$_2$]$^{2+}$.

The presence of a substituted methyl group on the carbon of the ethylenediamine molecule does not disturb the five-membered ring.

Within the experimental error the complex ion possesses two-fold symmetry around the Cl—Co—Cl bond. Therefore this complex ion assumes the *kk* form in Corey and Bailar's notation, that is, the two cobalt-propylenediamine rings take the same configuration. While the complex ions $[Coen_2Cl_2]^+$ and $[Codl\text{-}pn_2Cl_2]^{+}$ [13] are found to take the *kk'* configuration, two kinds of ligand molecules—the one being the mirror image of the other—are coordinated to the central atom in such a way that one is related by the operation of a center of symmetry to the other. According to Corey and Bailar the *kk* form is intrinsically more stable than the *kk'* form. The reason why the *kk'* form often occurs in crystals of various complex compounds may be that the *kk'* form is favored by specific intermolecular forces in the solid state.

Since the five-membered ring is puckered, there are two possibilities of the orientation of the C—Ch$_3$ group, namely, axial and equatorial types with respect to the Cl—Co—Cl bond. It was found that the bond is equatorial in the complex ion $[Col\text{-}pn_2Cl_2]^+$, in agreement with the conclusion of Corey and Bailar that the equatorial orientation is of lower energy than the axial orientation.

The position of hydrogen atoms cannot, in general, be determined by the method of X-rays in a structure containing heavy atoms; however, the fact that four molecules of water of crystallization form two pairs with O—O distances of 2.54 Å and the pairs possess exclusively Cl$^-$ ions as nearest neighbors, strongly suggests the existence of $[H_2O \cdot H \cdot H_2O]^+$ groups. A molecule of H$_2$O possesses two Cl$^-$ ions, Cl$^-$...O distances being shown in Table 2.

Thus every group $[H_2O \cdot H \cdot H_2O]^+$ is surrounded by four Cl$^-$ ions. The complexes $[H_2O \cdot H \cdot H_2O]^+$ form a chain of the composition:

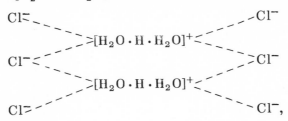

which runs parallel to the *c*-axis.

Such complexes have been found in crystals of Co—en analogues[1,2] and a Cr—en analogue[9] with an average distance of 2.60Å. The existence of the complex $[H_2O \cdot H \cdot H_2O]^+$ was suggested by Huggins [14] and this was indeed verified by our investigation of these coordination compounds.

As in the case of the en-analogues, the complex ions form a layer parallel to the plane (100). The Cl—Co—Cl bond is inclined to the plane (010) at an angle of 5 ° and the projection of this direction upon

(010) makes an angle of 9.5° with the c-axis. In the case of the en-analogues, these angles are 14.5° and 10° respectively. The closest distance of approach between the complex ions in the layer was found to be about 3.24Å: between a coordinated Cl atom of one complex ion and an N atom of the adjacent. Thus the complex ions are held together in layers by these Cl—N bonds. A complex ion has four nearest Cl^- ions. The closest approach of a complex ion and Cl^- ion is between N'(2) and Cl(2), the Cl...N distance being 3.01Å. Other Cl^-—N distances are 3.29 Å, 3.38 Å, and 3.55 Å. These values may be compared with those found in crystals of the en-analogues.

Between the layers of the complex ions, $[Col\text{-}pn_2Cl_2]^+$, are arranged the complexes $[H_2O \cdot H \cdot H_2O]^+$ and Cl^- ions. The O—O direction is perpendicular to the b-axis. The mode of successive arrangement of the layers of the complex ions is different from that of the en-analogues and this leads to a doubling of the a-spacing in the case of the pn-analogue.

Thin tabular crystals extended on (100) appear blue when the electric vector is parallel to the c-axis, while they appear yellowish green when the light is polarized along the b-axis. Such striking dichroism may be reasonable, since there is a large component of the Cl—Co—Cl bond along the c-axis. This dichroism is quite similar to that of the en-analogues. The dichroism of the latter crystals has been extensively measured by Yamada et al.[15]

The absolute configuration of the l-propylenediamine molecule will be discussed.

REFERENCES

1. A. Nakahara, Y. Saito, and H. Kuroya, *Bull. Chem. Soc., Japan,* **25,** 331 (1952).
2. S. Ooi, Y. Komiyama, Y. Saito, and H. Kuroya, *ibid.,* **32,** 263 (1959).
3. K. Nakatsu, Y. Saito, and H. Kuroya, *ibid.,* **29,** 428 (1956).
4. K. Nakatsu, M. Shiro, Y. Saito, and H. Kuroya, *ibid.,* **30,** 158 (1958).
5. K. A. Becker, G. Grosse, and K. Plieth, *Z. Krist.,* **112,** 375 (1959).
6. H. Scouloudi, C. H. Carlistle, *Acta Cryst.,* **6,** 651 (1953).
7. L. N. Swink and M. Atoji, *ibid.,* **13,** 639 (1960).
8. Private Communication from Dr. Y. Komiyama.
9. S. Ooi, Y. Komiyama, and H. Kuroya, *Bull. Chem. Soc., Japan,* **33,** 354 (1960).
10. E. J. Corey and J. C. Bailar, Jr., *J. Am. Chem. Soc.,* **81,** 2620 (1959).
11. A. Werner and A. Fröhlich, *Ber.,* **40,** 2228 (1907).
12. V. Vand, P. F. Eiland, and R. Pepinsky, *Acta Cryst.,* **10,** 303 (1957).
13. Y. Komiyama and Y. Saito (to be published).
14. M. L. Huggins, *J. Phys. Chem.,* **40,** 723 (1936).
15. S. Yamada, A. Nakahara, Y. Shimura, and R. Tsuchida, *Bull. Chem. Soc., Japan,* **28,** 222 (1955).

A SPECTROPHOTOMETRIC METHOD FOR THE DETERMINATION OF STABILITY CONSTANTS OF WEAK COMPLEXES: APPLICATION TO THE NEODYMIUM NITRATE SYSTEM

PAWEL KRUMHOLZ

Research Laboratory of Orquima S. A.
São Paule, Brazil

Spectrophotometric methods are frequently used to study step-wise complex formation between a metal ion and a ligand, in solution. Evaluation of stability constants requires that expressions derived from the mass action law be applied to experimental data from solutions of different composition. [1] Since variations of activity coefficients can rarely be taken into proper account, one attempts, in general, to restrain such variations by the use of a suitable salt background. [2]

In case of very weak complexes, however, the concentration of the reactants must be permitted to increase to large values, comparable to the concentration of the background electrolyte. Thus, the composition of the ionic medium will be subject to gross changes and activity coefficients may vary considerably, and in a quite unpredictable manner, even if the formal ionic strength of the solutions is maintained constant. Under such circumstances, unambiguous interpretation of experimental data from all but the simplest systems will be rather difficult. [3] If, in addition, the spectral properties of the complexed species are not very different from the properties of the uncomplexed metal ion, it may even become impossible to obtain a significant value of one single stability constant.

Due to such reasons, our attempts to study the formation of rare earth nitrate complexes by means of the usual spectrophotometric methods were rather unsuccessful. However, the spectral changes which accompany the formation of these complexes, are of a type which suggests, almost by itself, a new method for analysing such data. This method, which will be explained in the following, allows the direct determination of the complexed fraction of the total metal in a given solution, without making any use of the mass action law. Therefrom, the degree of formation of the lowest complex of a series and, finally, its stoichiometric stability constants, may be evaluated with reasonable precision.

The method now described rests upon simple considerations concerning the application of Beer's law to multicomponent systems composed of a metal ion M and of a number of its mononuclear complexes $ML_i (1 \leqslant i \leqslant n)$. We suppose that the $n + 1$ species ML_c $(0 \leqslant c \leqslant n)$ are present in solution at a total molarity C_M. Assuming that the species ML_c are the unique light absorbing components and that Beer's law is valid for all of them independently, we may express this law as

$$A/C_M = \bar{\varepsilon} = \sum_{c = 0}^{n} \alpha_c \varepsilon_c = \varepsilon_0 + \sum_{i = 1}^{n} \alpha_i (\varepsilon_i - \varepsilon_0) \qquad (1)$$

where A is the measured absorbance at 1 cm path length, $\bar{\varepsilon}$ the average molar absorptivity, α_x the fraction of C_M in form of the species ML_x and ε_x the molar absorptivity of that species. Usually, expressions like 1 are applied to experimental optical data obtained from solutions of different composition at one selected wavelength (and constant temperature). Correlation of such data obviously requires the use of the mass action law. We will, instead, regard the composition (and temperature) as constant and consider the ε's as function of the wavelength. $\bar{\varepsilon}(\lambda)$ then represents the experimental absorption curve of a given solution, resulting according to equation (1), from a superposition of the individual absorption curves of all species ML_c, in proportion to their respective "weight" factors α_c.

We now derive from equation (1) the expression

$$\varepsilon^x (\lambda) = S^{-1} (\bar{\varepsilon} - \varepsilon_0) + \varepsilon_0 = S^{-1} \sum_{i = 1}^{n} \alpha_i \varepsilon_i = \sum_{i = 1}^{n} g_i \varepsilon_i =$$

$$\varepsilon_1 + \sum_{k = 2}^{n} g_k (\varepsilon_k - \varepsilon_1) \qquad (2)$$

in which, $S = \sum_{i = 1}^{n} \alpha_i$ is the complexed fraction of C_M. This expression represents another composite absorption curve, now composed only of the absorption spectra of the complexed species ML_i. In view of the striking similarity of equations 1 and 2, $\varepsilon^x (\lambda)$ may be called the average molar absorptivity of the complexed species ML_i.

It will often be possible to obtain, from experimental observations, information on the shape of the absorption bands of the complexes ML_i and to infer therefrom the general form of the composite absorption curve $\varepsilon^x (\lambda)$ of a given solution. If, in addition, $|\bar{\varepsilon} - \varepsilon_0|$ is found to have, at a certain wavelength, a maximum which does not coincide with a maximum of $\varepsilon^x(\lambda)$, one may evaluate the complexed fraction of C_M, $\Sigma \alpha_i$, in the given solution, in the following way:

A number of composite absorption curves of the type of $\varepsilon^x(\lambda)$ are constructed from experimental values of $\bar{\varepsilon}$ and ε_0, by means of the expression

$$E(\lambda) = \xi(\bar{\varepsilon} - \varepsilon_0) + \varepsilon_0 \tag{3}$$

using values of ξ which are of the expected order of magnitude of S^{-1}. Depending on how much ξ differs from the true value of S^{-1}, the maximum of $|\bar{\varepsilon} - \varepsilon_0|$ will reflect on the composite absorption curves, $E(\lambda)$, to a larger or lesser degree. This can be easily inferred from the expression (derived from 2 and 3)

$$E(\lambda) = \varepsilon^x(\lambda) + (\xi - S^{-1})(\bar{\varepsilon} - \varepsilon_0) \tag{4}$$

Thus, unless the correct value of $\xi = S^{-1}$ is used, the form of the composite absorption curves, $E(\lambda)$, will be distorted in comparison with the true form of $\varepsilon^x(\lambda)$. The unknown value of $\Sigma \alpha_i$ in a given solution can thus be determined by finding that value of ξ, which allows reproduction of the known form of the composite absorption curve $\varepsilon^x(\lambda)$ with the least possible distortion.

The necessary information on the shape of the absorption bands of the species ML_i can often be obtained from spectral measurements on solutions of M containing varying amounts of the ligand L. A demonstration is provided by the spectra of neodymium perchlorate solutions, measured in the region of the 4272 Å band at different nitrate concentrations, and reproduced in Fig. 1.[4]

One notices that with increasing nitrate concentration the original 4272 Å peak decreases gradually in intensity, eventually disappearing completely; simultaneously a new peak emerges at longer wavelength. Such behaviour may be considered as direct evidence for complex formation; the absence of a true isosbestic point then suggests the existence of more than one complex in the system.

One may infer from that picture that nitrate complexing results in a shift of the whole 4272 Å band towards longer wavelength, accompanied by a broadening and loss of intensity. Except for the presence of a weak inflection on the bottom of the long wavelength wing, the 4272 Å band of uncomplexed neodymium ion displays a normal, Gaussian-type shape.[5] Experimental evidence, as well as consideration of the origin of that band,[6] both lead to the conclusion that the corresponding bands of the nitrate complexed species maintain the simple form of the original 4272 Å band. The extent of the spectral shift depends but little on the nitrate concentration (see Fig. 1). Apparently, the absorption peaks of the nitrate-complexed neodymium

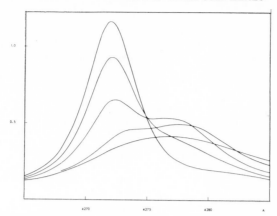

Fig. 1. Absorption spectra of 0.05 M solutions of neodymium perchlorate containing varying amounts of sodium nitrate and ammonium nitrate, respectively. Curves from the top to the bottom: (1) without nitrate; (2) 0.3 N NaNO$_3$; (3) 2 N NaNO$_3$; (4) 6 N NH$_4$NO$_3$; (5) 10 N NH$_4$NO$_3$. T = 25°C. Spectral band width, 0.9 Å.

species lie all close together. Thus, the composite absorption curve of these species, $\varepsilon^x(\lambda)$, will not greatly deviate from a Gaussian form.

One notices also from Fig. 1 that the values of $|\bar{\varepsilon} - \varepsilon_0|$ have pronounced maxima at, or close to, the position of the original 4272 Å peak. Thus, the spectral properties of the neodymium nitrate system in the 4272 Å region are particularly well suited for an analysis by the present method.

Figure 2 illustrates the procedure of determining $\Sigma\,\alpha_i$ by finding the least distorted composite absorption curve $E(\lambda)$. The three curves of Fig. 2 have been computed by means of equation (3), from experimental values of ε_0, and of $\bar{\varepsilon}$, measured in a 0.05 M solution of neodymium perchlorate, containing 0.3 moles/liter of sodium nitrate and using different values of ξ.

The upper and the lower curve of Fig. 2 deviate both from the normal Gaussian-type form expected for the composite absorption curve of the nitrate complexed neodymium species. The distortions which appear close to the position of the original 4272 Å peak in the form of an inflection or depression, prove that these two curves were computed with values of $\xi_- < S^{-1}$ and $\xi_+ > S^{-1}$, respectively. The middle curve is the least distorted, Gaussian-shaped band. The value of $\xi_0 = 3.7$, used to compute this curve, should be close to the true value of S^{-1}. Since ξ_0 differs by only about $\pm 10\%$ from the values of ξ_- and ξ_+, which both result in strongly distorted curves, we believe

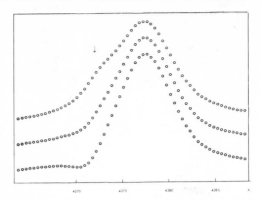

Fig. 2. Composite absorption curves E (λ), for a 0.05 M solution of neodymium perchlorate, 0.3 M in sodium nitrate. Curves, from the top to the bottom, computed with ξ = 3.3, 3.7, and 4.1, respectively. T = 25°C. Spectral band width, 0.9 Å. Curves are displaced vertically. The arrow indicates the position of the 4272 Å peak of uncomplexed neodymium ion.

that S^{-1} is thus determined with an accuracy of about ± 5%. One obtains for the complexed fraction of the total neodymium, in the forementioned solution, the value of $\Sigma \alpha_i = 0.27 \pm 0.015$. In the same manner, the values of $\Sigma \alpha_i$ in two other solutions, 0.05 M in neodymium perchlorate, 2 N and 4N in sodium nitrate, were determined and found to be 0.62 ± 0.03 and 0.76 ± 0.03, respectively.

The procedure just described becomes rather cumbersome if the complexed fraction of total metal is to be determined independently for a great number of solutions of different composition. Furthermore, results become inaccurate if the complexed fraction is low (< 0.2). It is therefore gratifying, that, with the help of the $\Sigma \alpha_i$ values, determined by the present method for the three forementioned solutions, the complexed fraction of total neodymium in any other solution, can be calculated directly from experimental $\bar{\varepsilon} - \varepsilon_0$ values.

If, at a certain wavelength, the molar absorptivities of the complexed species ML_i, ε_i, are all equal, equation (1) reads simply

$$\bar{\varepsilon} - \varepsilon_0 = \sum_{i=1}^{n} \alpha_i (\varepsilon_1 - \varepsilon_0) \qquad (1a)$$

It follows from equation (1a) that, at this particular wavelength, the ratio between the $\Sigma \alpha_i$ values of different solutions equals the ratio between the respective $\bar{\varepsilon} - \varepsilon_0$ values. If $\Sigma \alpha_i$ is known for at least two different solutions, one may attempt to find the wavelength at which the two ratios become equal and, thus, [equation (1a)] applicable.

We applied this procedure to the three afore-mentioned solutions for which $\Sigma \, \alpha_i$ values have been determined by the method illustrated in Fig. 2. It was found that the two ratios become equal, within the experimental accuracy, in certain spectral regions extending over 5–10 Å. The spectral regions around 5200 and 5235 Å, respectively, were finally selected as most suitable.

Relative values of $\Sigma \, \alpha_i$ computed, with the help of equation (1a), from experimental $\bar{\varepsilon} - \varepsilon_0$ values in these spectral regions should be accurate within a few percent. Absolute values of $\Sigma \, \alpha_i$ were computed using the value of $\Sigma \, \alpha_i$ from Fig. 2 as reference.

Values of $\Sigma \, \alpha_i$ for a number of solutions, 0.02 M in neodymium perchlorate and containing sodium nitrate at concentrations varying from 0.06 to 4 N, are listed in Table 1.

TABLE 1*

c_{NO_3}	$\Sigma \alpha_i$ $\times 10^2$	α_2 $\times 10^2$	α_1 $\times 10^2$	K_1
0.06	11.5 ± 0.6	0.3 ± 0.2	11.2 ± 0.8	2.2 ± 0.2
0.12	18.3 ± 1	1 ± 0.5	17.3 ± 1.5	1.8 ± 0.2
0.24	26.5 ± 1.5	2.5 ± 1	24 ± 2.5	1.4 ± 0.2
0.48	37 ± 2.5	4.5 ± 1.5	32.5 ± 4	1.1 ± 0.2
0.96	50 ± 3.5	8 ± 2.5	42 ± 6	0.9 ± 0.2
2.00	64 ± 4	16 ± 5	48 ± 9	0.7 ± 0.2
4.00	78 ± 4			

*The complexed fraction of total neodymium ($\Sigma \alpha_i$), degrees of formation of $Nd(NO_3)_2^+$ (α_2) and of $NdNO_3^{+2}$ (α_1), and stoichiometric stability constants of $NdNO_3^{+2}$ (K_1) in 0.02 M solutions of neodymium perchlorate containing varying concentrations of $NaNO_3$ (c_{NO_3}). $T = 25^{\circ}C$.

The values of $\Sigma \, \alpha_i$ for low nitrate concentrations, provide a first estimate of the degree of formation of the lowest complex, $NdNo_3^{+2}$, α_1. To obtain better values of α_1, it is necessary to evaluate, at least approximately, the amount of higher complexes present in the respective solutions.

If complexes higher than $Nd(NO_3)_2^+$ are neglected, and if $\varepsilon_1 = \varepsilon_0$, equation (1) reads

$$\bar{\varepsilon} - \varepsilon_0 = \alpha_2 \, (\varepsilon_2 - \varepsilon_0) \qquad (1b)$$

Determination of $\bar{\varepsilon} - \varepsilon_0$ at a wavelength where $\varepsilon_1 = \varepsilon_0$ provides, thus, a means for determining relative values of α_2. This wavelength may be localized by extrapolating the positions of the crossing points between the $\varepsilon_0 \, (\lambda)$ and the $\bar{\varepsilon}(\lambda)$ curves to zero nitrate concentration.

On the other hand, at least crude estimates of ε_2 may be obtained from an analysis of $\varepsilon^x \, (\lambda)$ curves at high nitrate concentrations, at which $Nd(NO_3)_2{}^+$ can be expected to exist as major component. With the help of the value of ε_2 at the wavelength, where $\varepsilon_1 = \varepsilon_0$, crude absolute values of α_2 may be computed.

These values are listed in Table 1 together with the values of α_1 obtained as difference between $\Sigma\, \alpha_i$ and α_2. The uncertainty of the α_2 values is rather great. However, in solutions of low nitrate concentration, α_2/α_1 is small, and even large errors of α_2 affect but little the final values of α_1. From the values of α_1, the corresponding stoichiometric stability constants, K_1, can be calculated; values of K_1 (at $25\,^\circ C$) are listed in Table 1.

Some attempts were made to determine the dependence of K_1 on the ionic strength in solutions 0.025 molar in neodymium perchlorate, 0.2 molar in sodium nitrate, and containing a varying amount of sodium perchlorate. At $25\,^\circ C$ and at ionic strengths of 0.35, 1, 2, and 4.15, the following values of K_1 were obtained: 1.5; 1.05; 0.9; 0.87 (with an uncertainty of about $\pm 10\%$). Further studies of the dependence of K_1 on the ionic strength and ionic composition are in progress. We hope to obtain from such studies information on the existence and the stability of weak rare earth ion pairs in solution.

REFERENCES

1. L. Newman and D. N. Hume, *J. Amer. Chem. Soc.*, **79**, 4571 (1957), and references cited there.
2. J. N. Brönsted and K. Pederson, *Z. phys. Chem.*, **103**, 307 (1923); J. Bjerrum, *Metal Ammine Formation in Aqueous Solution*, P. Haase and Son, Copenhagen (1941); G. Biedermann and L. G. Sillén, *Arkiv Kemi*, **5**, 425 (1953).
3. T. F. Young and A. C. Jones, in *Annual Rev. of Phys. Chem.*, **3**, 275 (1952).
4. For experimental details see P. Krumholz, *Spectroch. Acta*, **10**, 269 (1958); *J. Phys. Chem.*, **63**, 1313 (1959).
5. P. Krumholz, *Spectroch. Acta*, **10**, 274 (1958).
6. R. A. Satten, *J. Chem. Phys.*, **21**, 637 (1953).

ELECTRON EXCHANGE IN SOME COBALT(II)-COBALT(III) SYSTEMS

DONALD R. STRANKS

Department of Chemistry
University of Melbourne
Melbourne, Australia

Electron exchange between spin-paired Co(III) and spin-free Co(II) complexes is hindered by an energy barrier arising from the different molecular dimensions of these complexes. If electron transfer is to proceed *via* a tunnelling mechanism without significant orbital overlap, then the Co(II) and Co(III) complexes must first rearrange to some intermediate (transition) state in which their dimensions are virtually identical. In the case of the cobalt hexammines the Co^{III}—N distance is 2.05 ± 0.02 Å, whereas the Co^{II}—N distance is about 2.4 Å and the energy required to rearrange to the most probable Co—N distance of 2.18 Å has been estimated as 32 kcal./mole.[1] This large rearrangement energy should appear in an extraordinarily high activation energy for electron exchange in such systems. However an extensive investigation of a series of hydroxo-ammine complexes of Co(II) and Co(III)[2] (see Table 1 which contains data additional to those quoted in Ref. 2) reveals that the activation energy is relatively small and is constant within this series. The reactivity which arises from the progressive replacement of ammonia ligands by

TABLE 1: KINETIC PARAMETERS FOR ELECTRON EXCHANGE BETWEEN HYDROXO-AMMINES OF Co(II) AND Co(III)

Reactants	E_{act} (kcal/mole)	ΔS^* (cal/deg mole)
$Co(NH_3)_6^{3+} + Co(NH_3)_n^{2+}$	rate immeasurably slow	
$Co(NH_3)_6^{3+} \cdot OH^- + Co(NH_3)_n^{2+}$	12.9 ± 1.6	-35 ± 5
$Co(NH_3)_6^{3+} \cdot Cl^- + Co(NH_3)_n^{2+}$	13.6 ± 0.5	-37.5 ± 2.0
$Co(NH_3)_5OH^{2+} + Co(NH_3)_n^{2+}$	13.4 ± 0.4	-33.1 ± 1.4
$trans\text{-}Co(NH_3)_4(OH)_2^+ + Co(NH_3)_n^{2+}$	13.8 ± 0.9	-29.0 ± 2.0
$cis\text{-}Co(NH_3)_4(OH)_2^+ + Co(NH_3)_n^{2+}$	13.9 ± 0.6	-28.3 ± 2.0

$n = 4, 5$ or 6

hydroxo ligands resides in the entropies of activation which steadily become less negative. In fact, from the apparent variation in ΔS^* and constancy of E_{act}, the author[2] predicted that for the $Co_{aq}^{2+} + Co_{aq}^{3+}$ exchange system, one might observe that $E_{act} = 13.5$ kcal/mole and $\Delta S^* = -13$ cal/deg mole. Subsequently Hunt and Bonner[3] have reported that in this system, $E_{act} = 13.2$ kcal./mole and $\Delta S^* = -13$ cal./deg mole. Since it has been possible to demonstrate that electron transfer in the aquo-ammine series proceeds via a bridged transition state with transfer of the bridging ligand from oxidant to reductant, it is tempting to suggest that a hydrogen-bridged transition state is operative in the $Co_{aq}^{2+} + Co_{aq}^{3+}$ exchange. A similar study of a series of aquo-ethylenediamine complexes of Co(II) and Co(III) has been undertaken to test these conclusions further.

Electron exchange between the tris-ethylenediamine complexes of Co(II) and Co(III) has frequently been cited as a definite example of electron transfer by an "outer-sphere" transition state wherein interaction between the primary coordination spheres of the two complexes is insignificant. However the experimental evidence for this assertion is not unequivocal. The original study[4] was conducted at quite high ionic strengths and in chloride media where cation-anion association would be quite appreciable. In the one experiment used to demonstrate the absence of specific effects due to chloride ion, only some of the chloride was replaced by chlorate and then no variation in rate was observed. We have already demonstrated that in a closely related system, the $Co(NH_3)_6^{3+} \cdot Cl^-$ ion-pair can readily initiate electron exchange (see Table 1) and this possibility cannot be entirely dismissed in the ethylenediamine system. Similarly hydroxide catalysis was excluded on the basis of experiments conducted over a small pH range. Furthermore the activation energy measured for this system varied from 12.75 to 15.75 kcal/mole, depending on the ionic strength and the composition of the reaction mixture. For present purposes a much more accurate estimate of the activation energy is required.

General Experimental Procedures

The preparation of the cobalt complexes and other chemicals and the isotopic separation procedures were quite standard and require no further comment. All the exchanges are profoundly catalysed by oxygen and our experiments have therefore been conducted in an all-glass apparatus so designed that all operations are performed under an atmosphere of nitrogen containing less than 1 ppm of oxygen. Zero-time exchanges never exceeded 2%, which may be compared to 20% reported for the earlier work on the $Co(en)_3^{2+} - Co(en)_3^{3+}$ system.[4]   The exchanges are also photosensitive (a feature not recognised earlier) and must therefore be conducted in the dark.

All the exchange systems were conducted at ionic strengths not exceeding 0.2 M, with the concentration of the trivalent complex ion not exceeding 0.01 M and thus contributing less than 30% of the total ionic strength. At higher concentrations of the trivalent ion, the exchange rates become less than first-order in this concentration and inaccurate estimates of rate constants result. (Reaction orders as low as 0.58 have been previously reported for the tris-ethylenediamine system.) Less difficulty arises with the divalent complex ion, but again the concentration of this ion never exceeded 0.01 M. These precautions involve much slower reaction rates but do yield more reliable kinetic data. For all the anionic media investigated it has been established that the exchange rate is strictly first-order in the concentrations of both Co(II) and Co(III) complexes.

Exchange Between Co(II) and Co(III) Tris-ethylenediamine Complexes. Table 2 is a summary of all the kinetic data for this system.

TABLE 2: RATES OF ELECTRON EXCHANGE BETWEEN
$Co(en)_3^{3+}$ AND $Co(en)_n^{2+}$

Reactants	$10^3 \times k$ (1/mole-min;) 50°C, $\mu = 0.2$ M)	E_{act} (kcal/mole)	ΔS^* (cal/deg mole)
$Co(en)_3^{3+} + Co(en)_n^{2+}$	8.4 ± 0.5	13.8 ± 0.4	−31.0 ± 1.5
$Co(en)_3^{3+} \cdot OH^- + Co(en)_n^{2+}$	55 ± 8	13.9 ± 0.5	−27.1 ± 1.8
$Co(en)_3^{3+} \cdot Cl^- + Co(en)_n^{2+}$	30 ± 3	13.6 ± 0.5	−28.9 ± 2.1
$Co(en)_3^{3+} \cdot Br^- + Co(en)_n^{2+}$	18 ± 2	13.8 ± 0.7	−29.5 ± 2.3
$Co(en)_3^{3+} \cdot I^- + Co(en)_n^{2+}$	12 ± 3	13.9 ± 0.7	−30.0 ± 2.6
$Co(en)_3^{3+} \cdot SO_4^{2-} + Co(en)_n^{2+}$	7.8 ± 0.6	13.7 ± 0.4	−31.5 ± 1.6

$n = 1, 2$ or 3

The exchange was first studied in perchlorate media in which cation-anion association is presumably minimal, if not entirely absent. After allowing for the effects of different ionic strength and temperature, the rate constants measured in the present study were 30% higher than those previously reported since the latter work was performed under conditions where the exchange rate was less than first-order in $[Co(en)_3^{3+}]$. Systematic variation of the ethylenediamine concentration revealed that the exchange rate continued to increase beyond the stage where all the Co(II) was coordinated as $Co(en)_3^{2+}$. That this was due to hydroxide catalysis was verified by measuring the exchange rate in solutions up to 0.01 M in hydroxide, where it was found that the exchange rate was first-order in $[OH^-]$. The free ethylenediamine concentration may also be reduced to low concentrations $(10^{-3} - 10^{-4}$ $M)$ where the $Co(II)$ species are largely $Co(en)_2^{2+}$ and some $Co(en)^{2+}$, and at constant pH the exchange rate is almost unchanged. (Actually there may even be a very slight increase.) The activation energy is unchanged at 13.8 ± 0.4 kcal/mole. This suggests that the three species $Co(en)_3^{2+}$, $Co(en)_2^{2+}$ and $Co(en)^{2+}$ can exchange with $Co(en)_3^{3+}$ at equal rates. At low pH (7-8), where the contribution from the hydroxide-catalysed path is insignificant, the exchange rate is much slower but still measurable, and this presumably is a measure of the rate of exchange between unassociated $Co(en)_3^{3+}$ and $Co(en)_n^{2+}$.

The possibility of catalysis by other anions was investigated by conducting the exchanges in the pH range 7-8 and at an ionic strength of 0.2 M. Marked catalysis by chloride ion was found, but bromide or iodide ions had much smaller effects on the exchange rate. Sulphate ion, which associates very strongly with $Co(en)_3^{3+}$, had virtually no effect (perhaps even a slight retarding effect), as did nitrate ion, which associates very weakly.

Before definite rate constants can be ascribed to the exchange paths involving anions, a measure of the appropriate constants for ion-pair formation is required. A procedure has been described[5] by which reliable rate constants may be derived from association constants subject to considerable uncertainty. The increased rate due to anion catalysis $(R_{obs} - R_{uncat})$ is plotted as a function of the degree of association, α, yielding a linear plot of slope $(R_{ion-pair} - R_{uncat})$. When α is calculated from association constants one-hundred-fold different, the spread in the second-order rate constant derived by this method is only 28%. The values used for the association constants and heats of association for the various ion-pairs are listed in Table 3. Since the heats of association are quite low, large errors in the true activation energies (Table 2) do not arise

TABLE 3: ION-PAIR ASSOCIATION CONSTANTS AND HEATS OF ASSOCIATION

Ion Pair	K_a (mole/l., 50°C., $\mu = 0.2$ M)	ΔH (kcal/mole)
$Co(en)_3^{3+} \cdot OH^-$	12	3.8
$Co(en)_3^{3+} \cdot Cl^-$	4.5	2.8
$Co(en)_3^{3+} \cdot Br^-$	2.6	2.1
$Co(en)_3^{3+} \cdot I^-$	0.9	1.6
$Co(en)_3^{3+} \cdot SO_4^{2-}$	80	3.5

from this source. It is assumed that nitrate and perchlorate ions do not associate significantly with $Co(en)_3^{3+}$.

Strictly speaking, the experimental results yield only a rate law which is first-order in the concentrations of $Co(en)_3^{3+}$, $Co(en)_n^{2+}$ and the respective anion. However I have chosen to interpret this experimental law and ascribe the catalytic effects of various anions to their ion-pairs with $Co(en)_3^{3+}$, since, if an anion is to affect the electron transfer rate, it must be located within the second or third coordination spheres of the $Co(en)_3^{3+}$ ion. At this close distance of approach we customarily consider that a cation and an anion have established an ion-pair. In the case of the hydroxide-catalysed exchange path it might be argued that the reactive species is the amido ion $Co(en)_2NH_2CH_2CH_2NH^{2+}$. The ion-pair $Co(en)_3^{3+} \cdot OH^-$, which is a hydrated form of this imido species, is preferred since it is readily detected by its charge-transfer spectrum in the u.v., but a shift in the visible spectrum of $Co(en)_3^{3+}$ due to formation of the amido species is undetectable.

Exchange Between Co(II) and Co(III) Bis-ethylenediamine-Diaquo Complexes. Table 4 is a summary of the kinetic data obtained so far for this system.

In the pH range 6-11, the *cis* and *trans* isomers of the $Co(en)_2(H_2O)_2^{3+}$ ion (in hydroxo forms) exist in approximately equal proportions and the rates of interconversion are very rapid compared to the measured rates of electron exchange.[6,7] One therefore cannot study exchange rates for pure isomeric samples. The gross acidity constants for an equilibrium isomeric mixture are $pK_{1a} = 5.80$ and $pK_{2a} = 8.10$. The lowest accessible pH is 6.0 below which the ethylenediamine complexes of Co(II) are rapidly destroyed.

Most exchange rates have been measured in a free ethylenediamine concentration of 5×10^{-3} M wherein about 20% of Co(II) exists as $Co(en)_2^{2+}$ and 79% as $Co(en)_3^{2+}$. However the exchange rate and activation energy are unaffected by wide variations in the free

TABLE 4: RATES OF ELECTRON EXCHANGE BETWEEN $Co(en)_2(H_2O)_2^{3+}$ AND $Co(en)_n^{2+}$

Reactants	$10^2 \times k$ (1/mole-min;) 50°C, $\mu = 0.2$ M)	E_{act} (kcal/mole)	ΔS^* (cal/deg mole)
$Co(en)_2(H_2O)_2^{3+} + Co(en)_n^{2+}$	1.6 ± 0.3	13.9 ± 0.8	-29.6 ± 2.6
$Co(en)_2H_2O \cdot OH^{2+} + Co(en)_n^{2+}$	5.8 ± 0.4	13.6 ± 0.6	-27.8 ± 1.4
$Co(en)_2(OH)_2^+ + Co(en)_n^{2+}$	12.1 ± 0.6	13.7 ± 0.5	-26.1 ± 1.2
$n = 1, 2$ or 3			

ethylenediamine concentration (at constant pH), and this again suggests that all three Co(II)-en complexes exchange equally readily. Exchange rates in perchlorate media and $\mu = 0.2$ M, and at constant ethylenediamine concentration increase steadily with increasing pH. From this pH variation, the rate constants for exchange have been evaluated for the three Co(III) complexes: $Co(en)_2(H_2O)_2^{3+}$, $Co(en)_2H_2O \cdot OH^{2+}$, and $Co(en)_2(OH)_2^{+}$. In each case the activation energy is close to 13.7 kcal/mole. Above pH = 10.5, where only the $Co(en)_2(OH)_2^{+}$ ion exists, the exchange rate continues to increase and this may be attributed to a hydroxide-catalysed path probably via the ion-pair $Co(en)_2(OH)_2^{+} \cdot OH^{-}$. Similarly, at pH = 8, where approximately equal proportions of $Co(en)_2H_2O \cdot OH^{2+}$ and $Co(en)_2(OH)_2^{+}$ exist, the exchange rate is accelerated by a factor of about 1.4 by 0.1 M chloride. Insufficient data yet exist to quote reliable rate constants for the hydroxide- and chloride-catalysed paths, but the analogy to the tris-ethylenediamine system seems strong.

Discussion

The major conclusion from this study is that for all the exchange paths involving several ethylenediamine complexes, a common activation energy of 13.7 ± 0.5 kcal/mole is observed. This is virtually the same activation energy as already reported for the hydroxo-ammine cobalt complexes. Differences in rate reside solely in differences in the entropies of activation. It is suggested that in all cases electron transfer proceeds via a bridged transition state, thereby achieving significant overlap of Co(II) and Co(III) orbitals. Matching of the energies of these orbitals cannot be very close (i.e., the Co—N bond distances must still be quite dissimilar) since this should involve a large expenditure of energy, the magnitude of which would vary as the nature of the ligands alter in the present series. Presumably, then, a significant energy barrier to electron transfer must still exist in this bridged transition state and electron transfer must proceed by a tunnelling process whose probability is temperature-independent. This transition probability should increase the more closely the Co(II) and Co(III) orbitals are matched, i.e., the "stronger" the bridge formed between the two reactants. In turn this will be reflected in a less negative entropy of activation. It is interesting to note that Marcus[8] considers that in a transition state with large orbital overlap, electron transfer is quite probable even when the initial and final states differ in energy by 30 kcal/mole. This is probably the upper limit for the energy barriers envisaged for the present systems.

The enhanced exchange rate for $Co(en)_2(H_2O)_2^{3+}$, as compared to $Co(en)_3^{3+}$, would be explicable on this mechanism in terms of a lower energy barrier in the transition state for the former complex. The former complex may also participate more readily in a hydrogen-bridged transition state involving solvent water. The higher exchange rates for $Co(en)_2H_2O \cdot OH^{2+}$ and $(Co(en)_2(OH)_2^+$ would be attributed to the greater ease of formation of a hydrogen-bridged transition state as compared to the diaquo complex. These considerations also appear to apply in the hydroxo-ammine series of complexes studied earlier.

Significant anion catalysis should depend upon two factors: (1) a substantial degree of association with the cobalt(III) ion, and (2) the ability to form a strongly bonded hydrogen-bridged transition state. The rate constants quoted in Table 2 for catalysis by OH^-, Cl^-, Br^-, and I^- have already allowed for the relative extent of ion association and they reflect the relative efficiency of (2) for these anions. The high efficiency of OH^-, so often observed in electron exchange systems in water, is to be noted. The "unassociated" $Co(en)_3^{3+}$ undergoes electron exchange less rapidly than the anion-catalysed paths, but in all cases a common activation energy occurs. The evidence strongly suggests, but does not prove, that a similar mechanism operates, probably involving hydrogen bridging between amine ligands and solvent water. Although the sulphate ion associates quite strongly with $Co(en)_3^{3+}$, its catalytic effect is insignificant; this might be attributed to failure of condition (2), but the explanation is not wholly satisfying and the situation still remains unclear.

The common activation energy for ligands of different field strength suggests that the major atomic motion in the formation of the bridged transition state is that of hydrogen atoms in N—H and O—H linkages. Since these hydrogens readily exchange with the solvent, one would anticipate significant D_2O isotope effects in these exchange systems although the solvent is not necessarily involved. Secondary motions of nitrogen and oxygen atoms would occur (since all the Co-ligand bond distances vary in the two valence states) leading to N^{15} and O^{18} isotope effects.[9]

Electron exchange between Co(II) and Co(III) in a series of related ammine and amine complexes does seem to present a self-consistent kinetic picture and mechanisms of the type proposed may well operate in many other complexes, especially aquated cations.

REFERENCES

1. D. R. Stranks, *Discuss. Faraday Soc.*, **29**, 116 (1960).
2. *Ibid.*, p. 73.

3. J. P. Hunt and N. A. Bonner, *J. Am. Chem. Soc.*, **82,** 3826 (1960).
4. W. B. Lewis, C. D. Coryell, and J. W. Irvine, *J. Chem. Soc. (London),*
    S 386 (1949).
5. Ref. 1, p. 131.
6. J. Bjerrum and S. E. Rasmussen, *Acta. Chem. Scand.,* **6,** 1265 (1952).
7. J. Y. Tong and P. E. Yankwich, *J. Am. Chem. Soc.,* **80,** 2664 (1958).
8. R. A. Marcus, *J. Chem. Phys.,* **24,** 966 (1956).
9. R. K. Murmann, H. Taube, and F. A. Posey, *J. Am. Chem. Soc.,* **79,** 262
    (1957).

TRANS-DICHLORODIAMMINEPLATINUM(II). ACID HYDROLYSIS AND THE ISOTOPIC EXCHANGE OF THE CHLORIDE LIGANDS*

DON S. MARTIN, JR. and ROGER J. ADAMS

*Institute for Atomic Research
and Department of Chemistry
Iowa State University
Ames, Iowa*

Previous studies in this laboratory[1a-e] have utilized the potentiometric titration of the proton in the H_2O ligands to characterize the kinetics and equilibra for acid hydrolysis of $[PtCl_4]^=$, $[Pt(NH_3)Cl_3]^-$ and cis-$[Pt(NH_3)_2Cl_2]$ in aqueous solutions. For each of the previous systems, the isotopic exchange of chloride ligands with chloride ion has been shown to occur by either an acid hydrolysis (aquation) or by processes independent of chloride ion concentration, which could possibly be acid hydrolysis. These techniques have now served to characterize the exchange of chloride ligands of trans-$[Pt(NH_3)_2Cl_2]$ and its acid hydrolysis,

$$t\text{-}[Pt(NH_3)_2Cl_2] + H_2O \underset{R_1}{\overset{R_{-1}}{\rightleftharpoons}} [Pt(NH_3)_2Cl(H_2O)]^+ + Cl^-, K_1 \quad (1)$$

The usual preparation of t-$[Pt(NH_3)_2Cl_2]$ by heating $[Pt(NH_3)_4]Cl_2$ to 250°C was used.[2,3] It was purified by fractional crystallization from solutions in dilute HCl.

Solutions of the preparation, $ca.$ 4×10^{-4} M, were found to attain rather rapidly a molar conductivity of $ca.$ 35 l./ohm mole cm. Subsequently, fractional crystallizations of the compound were repeated as many as eight times without altering this behavior nor with any significant change in the ultraviolet absorption spectrum. Since divergent results have been reported for this compound and the absorption spectrum appears to provide the best criterion of purity, the ultraviolet absorption spectrum of a solution of our preparation is given in Fig. 1. The spectrum appears to agree closely with that published by Chatt, Gamlen, and Orgel.[4]

Because of low solubility and the need for sufficient concentra-

---

*Contribution No. 1005. Work was performed in the Ames Laboratory of the U.S. Atomic Energy Commission.

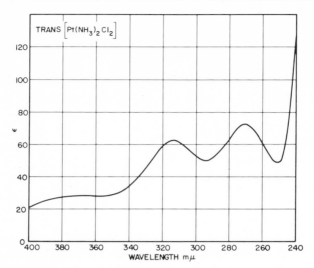

Fig. 1. Ultraviolet absorption spectrum of *trans*-$[Pt(NH_3)_2Cl_2]$. Extinction coefficient vs wave length. Spectrum obtained with a solution: 1.00×10^{-3} M *trans*-$[Pt(NH_3)_2Cl_2]$, 0.200 M KCl (to suppress hydrolysis) in a 10 cm cell in a Cary Recording Spectrophotometer, Model 12.

tions for titrations, the concentration range studied was severely limited. Also, crystals of t-$[Pt(NH_3)_2Cl_2]$ always dissolved slowly. For equilibrium titrations and the exchange studies a weighed quantity of the compound was shaken with the solution until the solid was completely dissolved and a steady state attained. However, for a kinetics evaluation in which a freshly prepared solution was needed, a sample was shaken with the solution for 10 min. The undissolved crystals were then filtered out. The concentration was evaluated either by a chloride analysis of the solution or from the equilibrium titre.

EXPERIMENTAL RESULTS AND DISCUSSION

Acid Hydrolysis Equilibrium

Titres for equilibrium solutions at 15°, 25° and 35°C are given in Table 1. For several experiments, but not for all, the indicated titres represented averages of two to four titrations. If the hydrolysis of a second chloride were negligible, the equilibrium titre, T_∞ (equiv. acid/l.) equals the concentration of $[Pt(NH_3)_2Cl(H_2O)]^+$. The equilibrium constant for reaction (1) is then given by

$$K_1 = \frac{[Pt(NH_3)_2Cl(H_2O)^+][Cl^-]\gamma_{\pm}^2}{[Pt(NH_3)_2Cl_2]\gamma_0} = \frac{T_\infty(b + T_\infty)\gamma_{\pm}^2}{(a - T_\infty)\gamma_0} \qquad (2)$$

a = Initial concn. t-[Pt(NH$_3$)$_2$Cl$_2$] (M) (before aging).

b = Initial concn. Cl$^-$ (M) (before aging).

(The γ's are the indicated activity coefficients.) For solutions in which the ionic strength was established at 0.318 M by added Na$_2$SO$_4$, the concentration quotient, K_1' defined by Eq. (3),

$$K_1' = K_1 \gamma_0/\gamma_{\pm}^2 \qquad (3)$$

was considered to be constant. This quotient was calculated for each of the high ionic strength solutions in Table 1. For solutions with no added salt, γ_0 was taken as 1, and $\gamma_\pm$ was taken equal to the activity coefficient of HCl in a solution of KCl[5] with an ionic strength equal to T_∞. From these activity coefficients and T_∞, K_1 was calculated from the data for low ionic strength in Table 1. The calculated equilibrium constants were substantially unchanged over the approximately 2.5-fold concentration range. Therefore the system appeared to be satisfactorily characterized by the equilibrium for Eq. (1). Accordingly, an upper limit of 2×10^{-5} M was set for a second hydrolysis equilibrium quotient. The acid, t-[Pt(NH$_3$)$_2$-Cl(H$_2$O)]$^+$, was indicated from the titration curves to have a pK of approximately 6.

The magnitude of the constant, K_1', from the present work is considerably below the estimate given by Grinberg and Shagisultanova[6] and is probably too small to be measured accurately by their method.

Kinetics for Acid Hydrolysis

If the following rate expressions apply:

$$R_1 = k_1[Pt(NH_3)_2Cl_2] \qquad (4)$$

$$R_{-1} = k_{-1}[Pt(NH_3)_2Cl(H_2O)^+][Cl^-] \qquad (5)$$

and if acid hydrolysis of [Pt(NH$_3$)$_2$Cl(H$_2$O)]$^+$ is negligible, the solution of the rate equation[1a] yields:

$$\ln(T_\infty - T)[T_0 - T_\infty + \sqrt{(K_1' + b)^2 + 4K_1'a}]/(T_\infty - T_0) \times$$
$$[T - T_\infty + \sqrt{(K_1' + b)^2 + 4K_1'a}] = -k_{-1}\sqrt{(K_1' + b)^2 + 4K_1'a}\ t \qquad (6)$$

It was found that titres of solutions of freshly dissolved t-[Pt-(NH$_3$)$_2$Cl$_2$] increased rapidly with time; indeed, this method could

TABLE 1: EQUILIBRIUM QUOTIENTS FOR THE ACID HYDROLYSIS OF
trans-[Pt(NH$_3$)$_2$Cl$_2$].

Ionic Strength μ (M)	Initial [Pt(NH$_3$)$_2$Cl$_2$] a (M × 10^4)	Equilibrium Titre T_∞ (M × 10^4)	Free Chloride Added* b (M × 10^4)	Equilibrium Quotient K' (M × 10^4)
		For 15.0°C.		
0.318	5.00	2.40	0.013	2.22
0.318	5.60	2.51	0.13	2.14
0.318	5.94	2.61	0.13	2.15
			Average	2.2
		For 25.0°C.		
0	4.08	1.48	0	0.84
0	8.16	2.23	0	0.81
0	8.44	2.27	0	0.80
			Average	0.82
0.318	7.82	3.73	0.013	3.42
0.318	7.53	3.51	0.013	3.07
0.318	4.33	2.44	0.013	3.16
0.318	8.26	3.75	0.013	3.13
0.318	3.73	2.17	0.013	3.03
0.318	5.86	3.05	0.013	3.31
			Average	3.2
		For 35.0°C.		
0	8.13	2.55	0	1.12
0	8.29	2.70	0	1.25
0	8.43	2.55	0	1.09
			Average	1.1
0.318	4.06	2.53	0.13	4.41
0.318	8.16	4.17	0.13	4.49
0.318	8.26	4.14	0.13	4.31
0.318	8.63	4.24	0.13	4.22
			Average	4.4

$\Delta H° = 5.5$ kcal.　$\Delta S° = 5$ e.u.
*The concentration of chloride was obtained from the analysis of the Na$_2$SO$_4$ added to adjust the ionic strength.

not have been used satisfactorily had the acid hydrolysis rate been much higher. Values for k_{-1} were obtained from the plots of the function expressed in Eq. (6), and k_1 was calculated from the expression

$$k_1 = K_1' \cdot k_{-1}. \tag{7}$$

The reactions could be followed satisfactorily for about two half-times. Results for experiments under various conditions are in Table 2. Rate constants could be duplicated generally to within about 15%. The exchange experiments described in the next section probably provided better values for the rate constants.

Since crystals of t-[Pt$(NH_3)_2Cl_2$] dissolve slowly, it is believed that in the experiments of Banerjea, *et al.*,[2] the rapid acid hydrolysis had attained equilibrium by the time they had complete solution. Thus, they observed no change in the small conductivity of the solutions, which they probably attributed to a low concentration of electrolytic impurity.

TABLE 2: RATE CONSTANTS FOR THE REVERSIBLE ACID HYDROLYSIS OF *trans*-[Pt$(NH_3)_2Cl_2$].

Temp. °C.	Initial [Pt$(NH_3)_2Cl_2$] a $M \times 10^4$	Initial Ionic Strength μ M	Equilibrium [Pt$(NH_3)_2Cl(H_2O)^+$] T_∞	Half-Time min.	k_1 ($\times 10^5$) sec^{-1}	k_{-1} sec^{-1}M^{-1}
15	2.68	0.318	1.56	147	3.2	0.145
25	3.00	0.318	1.89	60	8.9	0.28
25	5.23	0	1.70	22	10.0	1.2
35	9.03	0.318	4.44	13.2	28	0.65
35	6.27	0	2.14	8.8	27	2.5

Isotopic Exchange of Chloride Ligands

The rates of isotopic exchange were measured with Cl^{36} tracer only in solutions which were at chemical equilibrium. The solutions were contained in the dark, although in a few instances exposure to the laboratory lights did not change results. At various times, aliquots from a reaction solution were passed rapidly through anion exchange resins to replace Cl^- by NO_3^-. The columns had sufficient capacity to remove Cl^- completely, but a large excess of capacity was avoided. The effluent solutions were heated with excess NH_3 for 30 min. Acidification and the addition of $AgNO_3$ precipitated the chloride which had passed through the anion exchange in the neutral and positive complexes. The specific activity of the chloride in the precipitates was measured by methods which have been described in previous work.[1a,c,e]

For the description of isotopic exchange of chloride ligands the following terms are defined:

s = concn. of Cl^{36} in Cl^-, cts/min l

u = concn. of Cl^{36} in t-[Pt$(NH_3)_2Cl_2$], cts/min l

v = concn. of Cl^{36} in t-[Pt$(NH_3)_2Cl(H_2O)]^+$, cts/min l

$l = u + v + s =$ total conc. of Cl^{36}

$S = s/[Cl^-]$ (Specific activity of chloride ion)

$U = u/2[Pt(NH_3)_2Cl_2]$

$V = v/[Pt(NH_3)_2Cl(H_2O)]^+$

$Y = (u + v)/(2[Pt(NH_3)_2Cl_2] + [Pt(NH_3)_2Cl(H_2O)]^+)$

The experimental procedure yielded the quantity Y, and Y/Y_∞ was taken as F, the fraction of exchange. Normally, plots of $\log(1 - F)$ vs. t appeared linear over a period of at least twice the times of half-exchange. Conditions and results of the exchange experiments are collected in Table 3. Chloride ion suppresses the acid hydrolysis, Reaction (1), so in many of the experiments t-$[Pt(NH_3)_2Cl_2] \approx a \gg t$-$[Pt(NH_3)_2Cl(H_2O)^+]$. Under these conditions $Y \approx U$ and the exchange process can be treated as an exchange between the two components, t-$[Pt(NH_3)_2Cl_2]$ and Cl^-. The well-known expressions for the rate of the exchange, R_{ex}, in such systems apply and

$$R_{ex} = (\ln 2)\, 2ab/\tau_{1/2}(b + 2a). \tag{8}$$

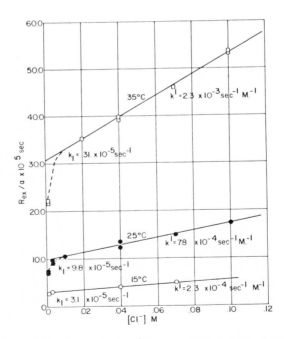

Fig. 2. Exchange experiments. Plots of R_{ex}/a vs chloride concentration for 15°C, 25°, 35°C. From the indicated rate constants $\Delta H^\ddagger$ $(k_1) = 19.6$ kcal, $\Delta S^\ddagger$ $(k_1) = -11$ e.u., $\Delta H^\ddagger$ $(k') = 19.6$ kcal, $\Delta S^\ddagger$ $(k') = -7$ e.u.

TABLE 3: EXCHANGE OF THE CHLORIDE LIGANDS OF trans-$[Pt(NH_3)_2Cl_2]$

Temp. (°C)	Initial $[Pt(NH_3)_2Cl_2]$ a (M × 10^4)	Initial Added $[Cl^-]$* b (M)	Equilibrium $[Pt(NH_3)_2(H_2O)Cl]^+$ T_∞ (M × 10^6)	Time of Half-exchange (min)	Rate of Exchange† R_{ex} (sec^{-1} M) × 10^8
15.0	5.95	0.001	100	390	1.6
	4.67	0.003	32	570	1.4
	4.98	0.040	2.7	560	2.0
	4.95	0.070	1.5	460	2.4
25.0	7.59	0.001	179	126	5.4
		0.003	81	160	7.3
		0.010	27	190	8.0
		0.040	6.9	160	10.6
		0.070	4.0	150	11.3
		0.100	2.8	130	13.2
	3.80	0.001	95	170	2.9
		0.003	41	190	3.7
		0.040	3.4	190	4.5
		0.100	1.4	130	6.6
35.0	7.59	0.001	194	42	16.5
		0.020	15	61	27.
		0.040	7.7	56	30.
		0.070	4.6	49	35.
		0.100	3.1	43	41.
	3.80	0.001	106	56	8.9
		0.040	3.8	58	14.9
		0.100	1.5	43	20.

*Ionic strength was adjusted to $\mu = 0.318$ by addition of Na_2SO_4.
†R_{ex} calculated with assumption that $R'' = 0$ and that $x \ll a$.

The quantity, R_{ex}/a, calculated from expression (8) for each of the experiments, has been plotted as a function of chloride ion concentration for 15°, 25° and 35°C in Fig. 2. For the experiments with $Cl^- > 0.003$ M, the points for each temperature fall rather closely along straight lines. The straight lines extrapolate to values of the ordinate which agree satisfactorily with values for k_1, so for $Cl^- > 0.003$ M the expression can be written

$$R_{ex} = R_1 + R' = k_1[Pt(NH_3)_2Cl_2] + k'[Pt(NH_3)_2Cl_2][Cl^-]. \quad (9)$$

The exchange rate contains a second-order (chloride-dependent) term, R', in addition to the expected acid hydrolysis term R_1. At $[Cl^-] = 0.1$ M, the two processes contribute about equally to the exchange.

At very low chloride concentrations the points in Fig. 2 deviate badly from the straight line function because the condition that $[Pt(NH_3)_2Cl(H_2O)]^+ \ll [Pt(NH_3)_2Cl_2]$ is no longer valid. The low chloride data provide information about the exchange of the [Pt-

$(NH_3)_2Cl(H_2O)]^+$ species. For example, in the solution at 25°C in which the initial $t\text{-}[Pt(NH_3)_2Cl_2]$ concentration, a, was 7.59×10^{-4} M and the KCl concentration, b, was 0.001 M, 13% of the complexed chloride was in the aquo-complex. The rate expressions for the introduction of Cl^{36} tracer into the complexes were taken as

$$du/dt = R_1 (S + V - 2U) + R' (S - U) \tag{10}$$

$$dv/dt = R_1 (U - V) + R'' (S - V). \tag{11}$$

R'' is considered to be the rate of exchange of chloride in $[Pt(NH_3)_2Cl(H_2O)]^+$ with Cl^-, and it contains any contribution from the acid hydrolysis of this complex. The solutions for these differential equations can be combined to yield the expression,

$$(1 - Y/Y_\infty) = C_1 e^{-\alpha_1 t} + C_2 e^{-\alpha_2 t}. \tag{12}$$

The parameters, C_1, C_2, α_1 and α_2, are determined by a, b, K_1, k_1, k' and R''/R_1. Calculated values of $(1 - Y/Y_\infty)$ were plotted for various values of R''/R_1 for the experiments with 0.001 M KCl added at 15°, 25° and 35°C. The calculations have been summarized in Table 4. The times of half-exchange for each of the experiments have been tabulated with the assumption that $R''/R_1 = 0$. Also, the value of R''/R_1 which will account for the observed time of half-exchange is given for each experiment. It is apparent that times of half-exchange with $R''/R_1 = 0$ did not differ greatly from the observed quantities so that R'' is not indicated accurately by these experiments. An upper limit of 0.5 k_1 can be set for a first-order rate constant k''. At the very least it is safe to conclude that the acid hydrolysis or other chloride exchange process of $[Pt(NH_3)_2Cl(H_2O)]^+$ can not be large compared to the acid hydrolysis of $[Pt(NH_3)_2Cl_2]$.

The rate constant, k_1, for the acid hydrolysis of $t\text{-}[Pt(NH_3)_2Cl_2]$ is 2.5 times larger than the value which Banerjea, et al.[2] reported for

TABLE 4: CHLORIDE EXCHANGE EXPERIMENTS FOR trans-[Pt(NH₃)₂Cl₂] AT LOW CHLORIDE CONCENTRATIONS

(added KCl = 0.001 M, μ = 0.318 M)

Temp. °C	Initial [Pt(NH₃)₂Cl₂] a $M \times 10^4$	Equilibrium [Pt(NH₃)₂Cl(H₂O)]⁺ T_∞ $M \times 10^4$	Time of Half-Exchange hr Obsd.	Cal. for $(R''/R_1) = 0$	Indicated R''/R_1
15.0	5.95	1.00	6.5	6.7	0.04
25.0	3.80	0.95	2.8	3.2	0.1
25.0	7.59	1.79	2.1	2.4	0.1
35.0	3.80	1.06	0.93	1.03	0.08
35.0	7.59	1.94	0.70	0.77	0.09

TABLE 5: EQUILIBRIUM AND RATE CONSTANTS FOR REACTIONS OF THE CHLORO-AMMINE COMPLEXES OF Pt^{II}

(Temp = 25 °C; μ = 0.318 M)

Complex	Equil. Consts. Acid Hydrolysis		Rate Consts. Acid Hydrolysis		Direct Exchange of Chloride Ligands Rate Const.
	First K_1' $\times 10^5$	Second K_2' $\times 10^5$	First k_1 sec^{-1} $\times 10^5$	Second k_2^* sec^{-1} $\times 10^5$	k_{Cl} sec^{-1} M^{-1} $\times 10^5$
$[PtCl_4]^=$	1500	50	3.9	3.3	< 3
$[Pt(NH_3)Cl_3]^-$	cis-1400	4	cis-3.6	3	< 3
	trans-< 200		trans-2.5	10	
cis-$[Pt(NH_3)_2Cl_2$	330	40	2.5	3.3	~ 3
t-$[Pt(NH_3)_2Cl_2]$	32	< 2	9.8	5	78
$[Pt(NH_3)_3Cl]^+$(9)	25		2		

*Based on the rate of a chloride-independent exchange of chloride ligand with Cl$^-$.

the isotopic exchange rate. However it is approximately equal to the first-order rate constants for a number of substitution reactions for t-$[Pt(NH_3)_2Cl_2]$ which they determined. One can now satisfactorily attribute the first-order dependence of these substitutions by glycine, analine, pyridine, and hydroxide to a rate-determining acid hydrolysis followed by a rapid replacement of H_2O by the substituting group or neutralization in the case of OH$^-$.

A summary of the acid hydrolysis equilibrium quotients and rate constants for platinum(II) complexes is given in Table 5, from which it can be seen that k_1 for t-$[Pt(NH_3)_2Cl_2]$ is larger than for any of the other chloro-ammine complexes. Only the rate constant for one of the chlorides of $[Pt(NH_3)(H_2O)Cl_2]$ is higher. Indeed, as Basolo and Pearson[7] have commented, the small range of variation in these constants is striking and argues against a simple dissociative mechanism with co-ordination number of 3. Also, the activation enthalpies, $\Delta H^\ddagger$ have all been within ±2 kcal of 19 kcal, which can hardly be evaluated more accurately. An ionic strength of 0.318 increases the equilibrium quotient K_1' to 4 times K_1. An increase would be expected because of the activity coefficient $\gamma_\pm^2$ in Eq. (3). However, the rate constant k_1 is substantially unchanged; all of the large ionic strength effect is reflected in k_{-1}. This feature strongly supports the hypothesis that the transition state for the hydrolysis has zero charge. A feasible scheme is shown in Fig. 3. It is proposed that the complex with its four square-planar ligands forms weaker bonds to solvent molecules along the normal to the plane which constitute labile ligands. The coordination figure is therefore a dis-

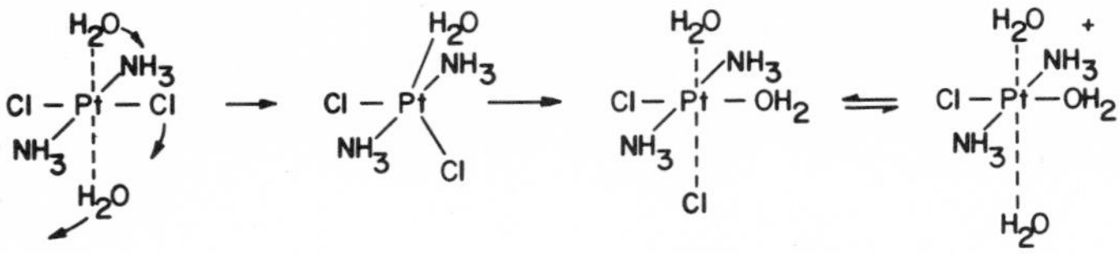

Fig. 3. Mechanism for the acid hydrolysis of trans-[Pt(NH₃)₂Cl₂].

torted octahedral arrangement. In the transition state, one of the H_2O groups moves in displacing the chloride to yield approximately a trigonal bipyramid arrangement. The similarity in rate constants results from the feature that the process is the identical intramolecular step in each case with little dependence upon ionic charge, and differences in rate must be due to rather subtle differences in structure.

The chloride-dependent exchange reaction with rate R' is the only such measurable process found with any of the chloroammine complexes of platinum(II) which have been studied. Instances in which chloride can compete with the solvent, which is present in such overwhelming excess, for displacing a chloride, are rather rare, although Rich and Taube[8] have found a chloride dependent contribution to the exchange of Cl^- with the square-planar $[AuCl_4]^-$. The rate constant k' for t-[Pt(NH₃)₂Cl₂] must be at least 25 times the rate constant for $[PtCl_4]^-$ or for cis-[Pt(NH₃)₂Cl₂], which were too small to be measured in the presence of the acid hydrolysis. This large factor is contrasted with the much smaller ratio of 2.3 in the acid hydrolysis rate constants.

The replacement of chloride ligands by Cl^- may be enhanced by changing the ionic charge on the complex in a positive sense. Thus the second-order reaction rate of the neutral complexes may be relatively more rapid than the acid hydrolyses of the anion species. There is evidence of such an effect in the k_{-1}'s for the various complexes, which are second-order rate constants for the replacement of H_2O ligands by chloride. However some of the variations in the k_{-1}'s as well as the difference in k_1 between cis- and t-[Pt(NH₃)₂Cl₂] must be attributed to rather obscure structural causes which are commonly disguised under the labeling of $trans$-$effect$.

REFERENCES

1. (a) L. F. Grantham, T. S. Elleman, and D. S. Martin, Jr., J. Am. Chem. Soc., 77, 2965 (1955); (b) T. S. Elleman, J. W. Reishus, and D. S. Martin, Jr., J. Am. Chem. Soc., 80, 536 (1958); (c) T. S. Elleman, J. W. Reishus, and D. S. Martin, Jr., J. Am. Chem. Soc., 81, 10 (1959); (d) C. I. Sanders and D. S. Martin, Jr., J. Am. Chem. Soc., 83, in press (1961); (e) J. W. Reishus and D. S. Martin, Jr., J. Am. Chem. Soc., in press (1961).

2. D. Banerjea, F. Basolo, and R. G. Pearson, *J. Am. Chem. Soc.*, **79,** 4055 (1957).
3. H. D. K. Drew, F. W. Pinkard, W. Wardlaw, and E. G. Cox, *J. Chem. Soc.*, 988 (1932).
4. J. Chatt, G. A. Gamlen, and L. E. Orgel, *J. Chem. Soc.*, 486 (1958).
5. H. S. Harned and B. B. Owen, *The Physical Chemistry of Electrolytic Solutions*, Reinhold Publishing Co., New York, 1943, p. 575.
6. A. A. Grinberg and G. A. Shagisultanova, *Zhur. Neorg. Khim.*, **5,** 280 (1960).
7. F. Basolo and R. G. Pearson, *Mechanisms of Inorganic Reactions*, John Wiley and Sons, Inc., New York, 1958, pp. 194–195.
8. R. L. Rich and H. Taube, *J. Phys. Chem.*, **58,** 1 (1954).
9. F. Aprile and D. S. Martin, Jr., (to be published).

MECHANISM OF ELECTROREDUCTION OF CO(III) COMPLEXES

A. A. VLČEK

Polarographic Institute
Czechoslovak Academy of Sciences
Prague, Czechoslovakia

There are two main types of redox reactions to be distinguished:

1. Reactions proceeding via charge or group transfer between particles in the same phase (e.g., reactions in solutions, in the gas phase, etc.).

2. Reactions in which a charge or a group transfer across a phase boundary takes place (e.g., reductions with metals, electrode reactions, etc.).

A special case of the latter type is represented by the reactions of particles in the solutions with polarized inert electrodes, i.e., reactions in the course of which only an electron transfer across the boundary solution-metal takes place and any dissolution of the electrode or any deposition of material at the electrode are excluded. This type of electrode reaction can be regarded as analogous to the homogeneous redox reactions, the polarized inert electrode representing one of the reactants, the ability of which to accept or supply electrons being a function of its potential only. The rate and the mechanism of a homogeneous redox reaction depend on the nature of both reactants; the rate and mechanism of an electrode reaction, on the other hand, are governed by the structure of the depolarizing particle only.

It has been pointed out by several authors that a parallelity between the electrode reactions considered and homogeneous redox reactions can be expected, but no deeper comparison of both types of reactions has been performed as yet, especially with regard to the paths of the reactions and the dependence of the rates on the structures of reacting particles. It has to be emphasized that direct comparison of the absolute values of the rate parameters of electrode reactions with that of homogeneous redox reactions is impossible. Only a symbolical relation of values obtained for larger series of compounds is to be expected. On the other hand, the mechanisms of both types of reactions can be compared directly.

The aim of the present paper is to describe our studies on the reductions of some Co(III)-pentammine and -tetrammine complexes on the dropping mercury electrode and to compare these results with those obtained for homogeneous reactions.

The homogeneous reduction of a series of Co(III)-ammonia complexes was studied very extensively (for a review, see [1-3]). The electroreduction of these complexes has been described by several authors,[4-8] but the results published to not make the complete determination of the reaction mechanism possible.

To determine the reduction mechanism of the complexes considered it was necessary to follow:

1. The nature of the primary reduction product.

2. The influence of the ion-pair formation in the solution on the rate of the process.

3. The influence of the hydrogen ion concentration on the rate and mechanism of the process.

4. The steric arrangement of the activated complex.

The rate and mechanism of the process depend strongly on the nature of the ligand so that all the influences mentioned above had to be followed in the dependence on the nature of the ligand.

The Composition of the Primary Reduction Product

All the ammine cobaltic complexes accept one electron, complexes of divalent cobalt being formed. These complexes are electro-inactive so that a direct electrochemical method cannot be used for the determination of their composition. The preparative electrochemical methods are also useless for they give information about the secondary product only.* Some evidence about the primary reduction products can be obtained by adding a strong oxidizing agent which is able to oxidize the primary product prior to the equilibration, and by following the complexes thus formed. Hydrogen peroxide, reacting rapidly with divalent cobalt complexes with the formation of cobaltic complexes, was used for this purpose.[9] As the increase of the reduction wave of the complex proper and the appearance of the wave of amine-aquocomplexes after the addition of hydrogen peroxide (Fig. 1) show, the *complexes studied are reduced with retention of their configuration*, and an equilibration takes place rather quickly after the electrode reaction. The scheme of the electrode process for the com-

---

*The primary product is a product formed directly by the electrode transfer proper. The secondary product is formed from the primary one by subsequent equilibration or other *chemical* reaction.

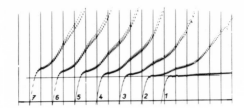

Fig. 1. Influence of H_2O_2 on the reduction of $Co(NH_3)_5 Cl^{2+}$. Solution: 3 M NH_3, $3 \cdot 10^{-2}$ M NH_4Cl; $[H_2O_2]$: (1) 0, (2) 6.5, (3) 12.4, (4) 25, (5) 36.5, (6) 49, (7) $63 \cdot 10^{-4}$ M. From OV (sat'd. calomel electrode); 208 mv./absc.; S = 1 : 100.

plex $Co(NH_3)_5Cl^{2+}$ is as follows:[†]

$$Co(NH_3)_5 Cl^{2+} \Longrightarrow Co(NH_3)_5 Cl^+$$
$$\downarrow$$
$$\sum_n Co(NH_3)_n (H_2O)_{6-n}^{2+} \tag{1}$$

$\sum Co(NH_3)_n(H_2O)_{6-n}^{2+}$ represents an equilibrium set of ammine-aquo

complexes, the portions of complexes with various n being a function of the concentration of free ammonia present in the solution.

This result represents a proof that *no substitution reaction or dissociation of the cobaltic complex takes place before the electron-transfer proper.* This statement holds only for solutions not containing free halide ions. In the presence of Cl^-, Br^- or I^- ions a substitution reaction prior to electron transfer takes place, this reaction being *catalysed by the adsorption of reactants* on the electrode surface.[10]

In this case the electrode process can be represented as follows (x being Cl^-, Br^- or I^- ion, L another ligand):

$$Co(NH_3)_5 L^{n+}$$
$$+X \downarrow \text{(surface)}$$
$$Co(NH_3)_5 X^{2+} \Longrightarrow Co(NH_3)_5 X^+ \tag{2}$$
$$\downarrow$$
$$\sum_n Co(NH_3)_n H_2O)_{6-n}^{2+}$$

[†]A double arrow $\Longrightarrow$ denotes an electron transfer, the arrow $\longrightarrow$ a chemical reaction.

Ion-Pair Formation

The formation of ion-pairs of cobaltic complexes with sulphate ions causes a decrease of the rate of the electroreduction which is manifested by the shift of the half-wave potential of the given complex ion towards negative potentials with increasing concentration of sulphate ions. In dilute solutions the following rate law is obeyed:

$$k_e = {}_ok_e \, (K \, [SO_4^{2-}] + 1)^{-1} \tag{3}$$

k_e is the rate constant of electroreduction at a given concentration of sulphate ions, ${}_ok_e$ the rate constant in solutions without sulphate and K is the association constant at the given ionic strength. The rate law (3) is obeyed for complex-ions with net charge $+3$ at ionic strength less than $0.05 \, M$ and with charge $+2$ up to the ionic strength $0.2 \, M$. At higher ionic strengths the influence of ion-pair formation is relatively small and is overwhelmed by other effects (*vide infra*, "Geometry"). Equation (3) can be rewritten

$$\frac{{}_ok_e}{k_e} = 10^{\frac{\Delta E_{1/2} \cdot \alpha}{0.059}} = K[SO_4^{2-}] + 1 \tag{3a}$$

where $\Delta E_{1/2}$ represents the shift of the half-wave potential of the complex caused by the addition of sulphate up to the concentration $[SO_4^{2-}]$ and α is the transfer-coefficient of the electrode process. Some of the experimental results are given in Figs. 2 and 3.

From equation (3) the constant K can be evaluated. For the ion $Co(NH_3)_6^{3+}$ at $\mu = 0.02$ a value 515 ± 50 has been obtained, in agreement with the value 470 given by Taube and Posey.[11] Values obtained for other complexes are summarized in Table 1.

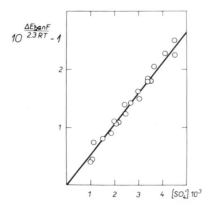

Fig. 2. Influence of ion-pair formation on the rate of reduction of $Co(NH_3)_6^{3+}$ in the system $ClO_4^- - SO_4^{2+}$; $\mu = 0.02 \, M$.

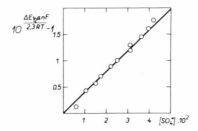

Fig. 3. Influence of ion-pair formation on the rate of reduction of $Co(NH_3)_5(NO_3)^{2+}$ in the system $ClO_4^- \!\!-\! SO_4^{2-};\ \mu = 0.2\ M.$

The fact that the rate law (3) is obeyed points to the conclusion[12] that the equilibrium between the ion-pairs and free complex ions is established very rapidly and that *the particle reacting with the electrode is the free complex and not the ion pair.*

TABLE 1: ION-PAIR ASSOCIATION CONSTANTS OF COBALTIC COMPLEXES WITH SULPHATE IONS DEDUCED FROM ELECTROCHEMICAL DATA;[12] $\mu = 0.1\ M$ (PERCHLORATE), 25 °C

Complex	K	Complex	K
$Co(NH_3)_6^{3+}$	$125 \pm 30^*$	$Co(NH_3)_5 Ac^{2+}$	45 ± 10
$Co(NH_3)_5 H_2O^{3+}$	~ 75	$Co(NH_3)_5 N_3^{2+}$	~ 15
$Co(NH_3)_5 NO_3^{2+}$	39 ± 10	$Co(NH_3)_5 F^{2+}$	< 70
$Co(NH_3)_5 NO_2^{2+}$	50 ± 10	$Co(NH_3)_5 SO_4^+$	~ 10

*Extrapolated value.

The Influence of Hydrogen Ion Concentration

The rate of electroreduction of most cobaltic complexes studied is not influenced by the hydrogen ion concentration in the region 10^{-2} $M - 1\ M$. For complexes with $L = F^-$, formate, acetate, butyrate and valerate, on the other hand, a great influence of hydrogen-ion-concentration on the reduction rate was observed. The rate law for pentammine complexes is represented by the equation:

$$k_e = {}_1k_e + {}_2k_e \cdot [H^+] \tag{4}$$

For complexes with $L = F^-$ or formate the terms ${}_1k_e$ and ${}_2k_e[H^+]$ are comparable up to $[H^+] = 0.15$, whereas, for other complexes, the first term is much smaller than the second in the range $0.05 - 1.5\ M$ H^+ and the rate of reduction increases linearly with increasing hydrogen ion concentration (see Fig. 4*). The experimental values of the activation energies, obtained from the temperature dependence of half-wave potentials,[17] are given in Table 2.

TABLE 2: ACTIVATION ENERGIES OF PROTONIZED ($_2Q^{\ddagger}$) AND UNPROTONIZED ($_1Q^{\ddagger}$) COMPLEXES; REFERENCE POTENTIAL, 0.1 N CALOMEL ELECTRODE; PERCHLORATE ADDED TO $\mu = 1.4$ M

Complex	$_1Q^{\ddagger}$	$_2Q^{\ddagger}$
$Co(NH_3)_5 F^{2+}$	11.2 kcal	6.8 kcal
$Co(NH_3)_5 Ac^{2+}$	12.5 kcal	8.5 kcal
$Co(NH_3)_5 Fo^{2+}$	12.8 kcal	8.5 kcal
$Co(NH_3)_5 Po^{2+}$	12.5 kcal	8.5 kcal

From these results it can be concluded that in solutions with a small concentration of hydrogen ions or at elevated temperatures the free complex is reduced, but at higher acidities or lower temperatures a protonization of the complexes takes place *before the electron transfer proper*, leading to a decrease of the activation energy of the electrode reaction. This decrease amounts to 4.5 kcal and is independent of the nature of the ligand.

A similar influence of hydrogen ion concentration could be expected for other complexes with ions of weak acids, like N_3^- or ONO^-, but no change of the rate of reduction was observed in the

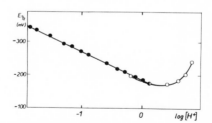

Fig. 4. Influence of the hydrogen ion concentration on the rate of reduction of $Co(NH_3)_5 Ac^{2+}$. $E_{1/2}$ measured against sat'd. calomel electrode; ● $\mu = 1.4$ M, ○ μ not constant.

---

*The half-wave potential of an irreversible one-electron reduction is correlated to the rate of the process by the equation (see, e.g.[13]):

$$E_{1/2} = \frac{2.3\,RT}{\alpha F} \log 0.87\, k_e\, t_1^{1/2}\, D^{-1/2} \tag{5}$$

where t_1 is the drop-time and D is the diffusion coefficient of the depolarizing particle.

given range of acidity. The pentammine complexes with anions of dibasic acids—oxalate (OxH^-), fumarate (FuH^-), maleate (MaH^-), etc., are, under the conditions studied, completely protonized to the first stage in the solution and *no further protonization was detected*, the rate of the reduction being almost constant in the range 0.05 *M* – 1*M* H^+. In the complexes *cis*- and *trans*-$Co(NH_3)_4Ac_2^+$ both acetate ligands are protonized before the electron transfer proper.

The described acid-catalysis of the reduction is analogous to that observed for the aquation of $Coen_2F_2^+$.[15] The protonization of the complex results in the inner redistribution of the charge in the complex particle which influences the geometry of the activated complex and thus the mechanism of the electron transfer (see below).

The rate of the electro-reduction of all cobaltic complexes studied, except $Co(NH_3)_5H_2O^{3+}$, decreases considerably when the concentration of hydrogen ions increases above 1.5 *M* (see Fig. 4 and 5).

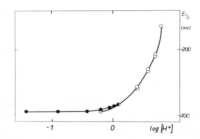

Fig. 5. Influence of the hydrogen ion concentration on the rate of reduction of $Co(NH_3)_5(NO_3)^{2+}$. $E_{1/2}$ measured against sat'd. calomel electrode; ● $\mu = $ 1.4 M, ○ μ not constant.

The reason for this decrease is as yet not clear, but it seems to be a general property of all pentammine cobaltic complexes.

Geometry of the Activated Complex

There is no direct method for the determination of the geometry of the activated complex of the electrode reduction, but some indirect evidence can be obtained from the dependence of the rate of the electrode process at a constant potential on the charge distribution in the electrode double layer. This charge distribution, i.e., the electric field in the nearest proximity of the electrode, can be altered by changing the ground electrolyte or by the addition of charged surface-active substances to the solution. To a first approximation it can be supposed that the change of the reduction rate caused by the change of electrode field is due to electrostatic effects only. It has been shown previously[16] that the electrostatic free energy of activation depends not only on the total charge of the reacting ion but also *on the distribution of the charge in the complex particle* and, thus, for particles with a non-homogeneous inner charge distribution, on their orientation with respect to the electrode field.

Table 3 summarizes the changes of the free energy of activation ($\Delta\Delta F^{\ddagger}$) caused by exchanging the perchlorate for sulphate. The addition of the sulphate ions (under conditions preventing ion-pair formation) causes a decrease of the reduction rate, this decrease depending on the charge of the complex ion and the distribution of this charge in the complex particle. It has been further shown[17] that the

TABLE 3: DIFFERENCE OF THE FREE ENERGY OF ACTIVATION IN THE PERCHLORATE AND SULPHATE SOLUTIONS ($\mu = 1.4$)

Complex	$\Delta\Delta F^{\ddagger}$
$Co(NH_3)_6^{3+}$	-3.0 kcal
$Co(NH_3)_5 H_2O^{3+}$	-1.7
trans-$Co(NH_3)_4(H_2O)_2^{3+}$	-0.5_5
$Co(NH_3)_5 NO_3^{2+}$	-0.9
$Co(NH_3)_5 NO_2^{2+}$	-1.0
$Co(NH_3)_5 Ac^{2+a}$	-1.1
$Co(NH_3)_5 Fo^{2+b}$	-0.6_5
$Co(NH_3)_5 F^{2+a}$	-1.0
$Co(NH_3)_5 F^{2+}$	-0.1
$Co(NH_3)_5 (ONO)^{2+}$	-0.6
$Co(NH_3)_5 SO_4^{+}$	-0.8
trans-$Co(NH_3)_4(NO_2)_2^{+}$	-0.1
trans-$Co(NH_3)_4 Ac_2^{+a}$	-0.6_5

[a]Protonized; [b]partly protonized.

increase of the negative charge in the electrode double layer results in a decrease of the reduction rate for pentammine complexes with $L = CxH^-$, FuH^-, and MaH^-, a very slight increase of the unprotonized fluoride complex and a considerable increase of the reduction rate for $L = NH_3$, H_2O, SO_4^{2-}, protonized acetate and fluoride. By increasing the positive charge in the double layer an opposite effect is caused.

By summing up all the electrostatic effects and comparing them with the probable charge distribution in various complexes, two main steric arrangements of the activated complex can be distinguished for pentammine complexes:

1. The hetero-ligand L is turned towards the positively charged electrode (holds for $L = OxH^-$, FuH^-, MaH^-, unprotonized F^- and anions of carboxylic acids).

2. The hetero-ligand L is on the "solution side" of the activated complex (holds for $L = H_2O$, NO_3^-, NO_2^-, SO_4^{2-}, protonized F^- and anions of carboxylic acids).

The complexes of these two groups differ not only with respect to the geometry of the activated complex but also with respect to the influence exerted by increasing ionic strength; with complexes of the first group a decrease of the reduction rate is observed, and the rate of reduction of complexes belonging to the second group increases with increasing ionic strength.

Influence of the Nature of the Ligand L

In previous chapters, differences in the mechanism arising from the ligand L have been described and it is now possible to follow the dependence of the rate of the reduction on the nature of the ligand L. Such a comparison can be made only for complexes having the same steric arrangement of the activated complex and for the same electrode field, i.e., the same potential of the electrode and composition of the solution. The kinetic parameters of the electroreduction are summarized in Table 4. The rate is expressed as the ratio $k_e/D^{1/2}$, for the diffusion coefficients are not known with sufficient accuracy for the given complexes. It can be supposed that the value of the diffusion coefficient is almost constant in the given series of complexes, so that the ratio given is a direct measure of the rate of the electrode reduction.

As has been pointed out,[18] a parallelity between the activation energy of the electrode process and the excitation energy of the given complex exists. The plots of $\Delta Q^\ddagger$ vs $\Delta \gamma$, where $\Delta \gamma$ is the difference of the wave numbers of the first absorption bonds of the given complex and of the symmetrical complex $Co(NH_3)_6^{3+}$, are represented in Fig. 6 and 7, and show that there exists a direct proportionality between the activation energy of the electrode reduction and excitation energy of the cobaltic complexes. Similar results have been obtained for some series of Cr(III) and Rh(III) complexes.[18]

In the plot $\Delta D^\ddagger - \Delta \nu$ of the pentammine series the values for complexes having different steric arrangements occupy two different lines, the difference between them being 4.5 kcal. This difference arises undoubtedly from the different effects exerted by the electrode field on the reacting particle. All cobaltic complexes followed have in their ground states (configuration d_ε^σ) a very small electron affinity

TABLE 4: KINETIC PARAMETERS OF THE REDUCTION OF SOME COBALTIC COMPLEXES AT THE DROPPING MERCURY ELECTRODE (SOLUTION: 0.14 M HCIO$_4$, 1.26 M NaClO$_4$; ALL VALUES RELATED TO THE 0.1 N CALOMEL ELECTRODE)

Complex	$k_e/D^{1/2}$*	$\Delta Q^{\ddagger}$ (kcal)	α
$Co(NH_3)_6^{3+}$	$2.1 \cdot 10^{-4}$	12.6	0.67
$Co(NH_3)_5 H_2O^{3+}$	$2.6 \cdot 10^{-2}$	9.5	0.56
$Co(NH_3)_5 NO_3^{2+}$	$1.7 \cdot 10^{-1}$	9.3	0.53
$Co(NH_3)_5 NO_2^{2+}$	$1 \cdot 10^{-3}$	15.2	0.59
$Co(NH_3)_5 F^{2+}$	$4.2 \cdot 10^{-4}$	11.2	0.51
$Co(NH_3)_5 F^{2+}$*	$1.3 \cdot 10^{-3}$	6.8	0.51
$Co(NH_3)_5 Fo^{2+}$	$4.8 \cdot 10^{-4}$	7.5	0.63
$Co(NH_3)_5 Ac^{2+}$	$9.5 \cdot 10^{-4}$	8.3	0.65
$Co(NH_3)_5 Po^{2+}$	$9.5 \cdot 10^{-4}$	8.5	0.64
$Co(NH_3)_5 N_3^{2+}$	$1.1 \cdot 10^{-1}$	10.5	0.55
$Co(NH_3)_5 (ONO)^{2+}$	$7 \cdot 10^{-4}$	15	0.5
$Co(NH_3)_5 (OxH)^{2+}$	$9.2 \cdot 10^{-4}$	12.7	0.59
$Co(NH_3)_5 (FuH)^{2+}$*	$6.7 \cdot 10^{-4}$	12.5	0.73
$Co(NH_3)_5 (MaH)^{2+}$*	$1.3 \cdot 10^{-3}$	12.5	0.76
$Co(NH_3)_5 (FuCH_3)^{2+}$*	$6.8 \cdot 10^{-4}$	12.0	0.71
$Co(NH_3)_5 SO_4^+$	$3.8 \cdot 10^{-3}$	9.3	0.49
cis-$Co(NH_3)_4(H_2O)_2^{3+}$	2.8	8.0	0.55
trans-$Co(NH_3)_4(H_2O)_2^{3+}$	$8.5 \cdot 10^{-1}$	7.5	0.52
cis-$Co(NH_3)_4(NO_2)_2^+$	$2.3 \cdot 10^{-2}$	14.2	0.54
trans-$Co(NH_3)_4(NO_2)_2^+$	$1.9 \cdot 10^{-4}$	15.5	0.6
cis-$Co(NH_3)_4 Ac_2^+$*	$2.5 \cdot 10^{-1}$	6.0	0.55
trans-$Co(NH_3)_4 Ac_2^+$*	$3.3 \cdot 10^{-1}$	4.8	0.52

*See Eq. 5.
[a]1.4 M HClO$_4$.

and, *without any change in the electronic configuration, reduction at considerably more negative potentials would be expected.* The reacting complex must be polarized by the electrode field to make the energy of the electron in both sites equal and, as follows from the experiments, *this polarization is much easier* for complexes with the hetero-ligand turned away from the electrode field. It has to be pointed out that all the reactions described proceed at a positively charged electrode, so that an electrostatically favoured arrangement is that with the hetero-ligand turned towards the electrode. In complexes which react in this way, the negative charge is concentrated on one or two atoms and a high electrostatic activation energy is needed to achieve the most favourable geometry of the activated complex, which could not be compensated for by a decrease of the energy

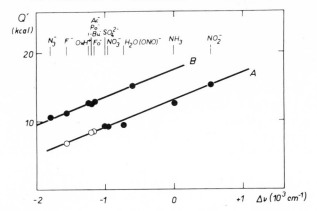

Fig. 6. Dependence $\Delta Q^{\ddagger} - \Delta \gamma$ for $Co(NH_3)_5 L^{n+}$. ● Nonprotonized complexes, ○ protonized complexes, $\mu = 1.4$ M perchlorate.

needed for polarization. The protonization of the complex, i.e., the decrease of the negative charge on the hetro-ligand, is accompanied by easier attainment of the favourable geometric arrangement and by a decrease in the activation energy.

Complexes reacting with the hetero-ligand turned away from the electrode field are either protonized on the hetero-ligand or contain large hetero-ligands with more atoms (as SO_4^{2-}, NO_3^- or NO_2^-) on which the negative charge can be distributed or partly shielded by the ionic atmosphere. This explanation is supported by the fact that the reduction rate of the complex $Co(NH_3)_5 SO_4^+$ *increases by addition of Th(IV) ions* to the solution, which are supposed to shield by way of *"local ion-pair formation"* the negative charge on the sulphate, thus decreasing the electrostatic activation energy needed for turning the negative ligand away from the positively charged electrode.

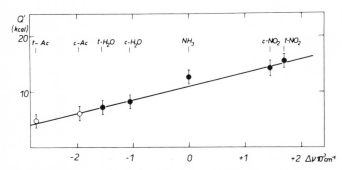

Fig. 7. Dependence $\Delta Q^{\ddagger} - \Delta \gamma$ for $Co(NH_3)_4 L_2^{n+}$. ● Nonprotonized complexes, ○ protonized complexes, $\mu = 1.4$ M perchlorate.

The electrostatic conceptions used to explain the observed results are necessarily oversimplified, but no deeper or quantitative treatment is at present possible due to our limited knowledge of the structure of the electrode double layers, ionic atmospheres, and charge distributions in the complexes.

There is another group of complexes which has to be discussed separately. It is represented by complexes with ligands having a large affinity for mercury ions, i.e., Cl^-, Br^-, I^-, CNS^- and $S_2O_3^{2-}$. The reduction of all these complexes at the mercury-dropping electrode proceeds at potentials more positive than the reduction of corresponding mercurous salts (Hg_2Cl_2, etc.), whereas at a platinum electrode, reduction at more negative potentials is observed.

This effect must be attributed to a catalysis by mercury. This catalysis probably does not result in a complete splitting off of the hetero-ligand, but may be due either to a specific adsorption of the complex on the surface of the electrode or to the formation of an adduct with mercury ions. A similar effect was observed for aquation reactions of halogenopentammine complexes.[19]

The last group to be discussed contains complexes with partly protonized anions of dibasic acids. The complex with oxalate is the only one which fits into the scheme of other complexes. The electroreduction of complexes with anions of unsaturated dibasic acids is characterized by such a high transfer coefficient that it is not possible to include these complexes into the plot on Fig. 6, in which they would occupy roughly the same place as the oxalate ion. We suppose that the reduction mechanism of these complexes is the same as that of oxalate ion, the higher transfer coefficient, i.e., the easier influence of the potential of the electrode, being connected with the unsaturated nature of the ligands.

For the series $Co(NH_3)_4L^{n+}$ the same linear plot Q- is observed as for the series $Co(NH_3)_5L^{n+}$, the values for *cis* and *trans* isomers being on the same line. To deduce the steric arrangement of the activated complex from the electrostatic data is impossible, but as higher frequency factors for *cis* isomers show, the probability of achievement of the most favourable configuration is higher for *cis* isomers than for *trans* isomers.

Discussion

The two geometric configurations of the activated complex correspond to two different mechanisms of the electroreduction. The path with the hetero-ligand turned away from the electrode field corresponds undoubtedly to the "outer-sphere activated complex mechanism."[1-3] A very weak interaction of the orbitals of the complex and of the electrode metal are supposed, and almost all the influence on the reacting particle is exerted by the electrode field. There are not sufficient data available for the homogeneous reactions to enable us to make a quantitative comparison for larger series of complexes. The only complexes which can be compared are $Co(NH_3)_6^{3+}$ and $Co(NH_3)_5H_2O^{3+}$, the ratio of the rate constants of which is almost the same as for the reduction with $Cr(dipy)_3^{2+}$ [20] and for the electro-reduction, 91 and 124, respectively.

The bridged activated complex, in the sense of Taube,[1-3] is almost impossible for an electroreduction. A greater interaction of the ligand and electrode-metal orbitals could not be assumed. But it cannot be excluded that some ligands, when turned toward the electrode, may function as "conductors" of electrons, the electron being transferred from the electrode to the metal orbitals across the electronic system of the ligand. Such a mechanism is more probable for large ligands, which hinder the approach of the complex to the electrode, especially if the ligands have a mobile electronic system. We believe such a mechanism operates for complexes with anions of unsaturated dibasic acids. The free acids are reduced at a more negative potential, but, due to complex formation and the influence of the electrode field, an activation of the π-electronic system may be assumed, which makes the transfer of electrons possible.

Generally, both types of reactions seem to be governed by the same factors, one being the change of the electronic configuration of the complex, the other the electrostatic effects which operate in the course of activated complex formation. As our experiments show, *it is not possible to regard the complex particles as conducting spheres*, but the internal charge distribution and the non-homogeneity of the ionic atomsphere have to be taken into account when calculating the electrostatic energy of activation. In this way chemical individuality is introduced into the calculations and many differences are observed which are not understandable from the point of view of simple electrostatic theories. The inner charge distribution also influences the energy levels of the complexes, and can thus be regarded as one of the fundamental parameters governing the reactivity of complexes.

REFERENCES

1. H. Taube, International Conference on Coordination Chemistry, *Special Publication of the Chemical Society*, No 13, London 1959, p. 57.
2. H. Taube, *Advances in Inorganic Chemistry and Radiochemistry*, Academic Press, New York, 1959, Vol. 1, p. 1.
3. H. Taube, *Canad. J. Chem.*, **37**, 129 (1959).
4. J. B. Willis, J. A. Friend, D. P. Mellor, *J. Am. Chem. Soc.*, **67**, 1680 (1945).

5. H. A. Laitinen, J. C. Bailar, Jr., H. F. Holtzclaw, Jr., and J. V. Quagliano, *ibid.*, **70**, 2999 (1948).
6. H. A. Laitinen and P. Kivalo, *ibid.*, **75**, 2198 (1953).
7. H. A. Laitinen, A. J. Frank, P. Kivalo, *ibid.*, **75**, 2865 (1953).
8. N. Maki, Y. Shimura, and R. Tsuchida, *Bull. Chem. Soc. Japan*, **32**, 23 (1959).
9. A. A. Vlček, *Coll. Czech. Chem. Comm.*, **25**, 2685 (1960).
10. A. A. Vlček and J. Kůta, *Nature*, **185**, 95 (1960).
11. H. Taube, and Posey, *J. Am. Chem. Soc.*, **75**, 1463 (1953).
12. A. A. Vlček, *Collection Czech. Chem. Comm.* in press.
13. R. Brdička, *ibid.*, **19**, 541 (1954).
14. A. A. Vlček, *ibid.*, **24**, 3538 (1959).
15. F. Basolo, W. R. Matoush, and R. G. Pearson, *J. Am. Chem. Soc.*, **78**, 4883 (1956).
16. A. A. Vlček, *Discussions Faraday Soc.*, **29**, 114 (1960).
17. J. Kůta, personal communication.
18. A. A. Vlček, *Discussions Faraday Soc.*, **26**, 164 (1958).
19. F. A. Posey and H. Taube, *J. Am. Chem. Soc.*, **79**, 255 (1957).
20. A. M. Zwickel and H. Taube, *Discussions Faraday Soc.*, **29**, 42 (1960).

ADVANCES IN THE CHEMISTRY OF HETEROPOLY ELEC-
TROLYTES AND THEIR PERTINENCE FOR COORDINATION
CHEMISTRY

LOUIS C. W. BAKER

Department of Chemistry
Boston University
Boston 15, Massachusetts

Introduction [1]

Heteropoly electrolytes constitute a large fundamental category of
compounds which has received relatively little study in modern terms.
They share numerous characteristics with conventional coordination
compounds, but there are certain basic differences. The work reported
below is part of a broad program aimed at elucidating the novel characteristics of heteropoly electrolytes and exploiting these novelties
to further the advance of theory.

A heteropoly electrolyte is the free acid or salt of a heteropoly anion. A heteropoly anion contains oxygen atoms and at
least two different kinds of atoms in positive oxidation states. For
purposes of definition, hydrogen atoms are not counted in to-
talling the number of atomic species of positive oxidation state
present. Examples are: $[P^{+5}Mo_{12}^{+6}O_{40}]^{-3}$, $[Ni^{+2}O_6W_6^{+6}O_{18}H_6]^{-4}$,
$[Co^{+2}O_6Co^{+3}O_4W_{12}O_{32+n}H_{2n}]^{-7}$, and $[As_2^{+5}Mo_{18}O_{62}]^{-6}$.

In a typical heteropoly anion there is a large atomic proportion of
one kind of positive-valent atom ("addenda atoms") and a much
smaller proportion of other kind(s) of atoms in positive oxidation
state(s) ("central atoms"). Mo, W, and V, in their highest oxidation
states, function as addenda atoms in a great many heteropoly anions.
A few additional elements can fulfill that role. Approximately 45
other elements, including most transition metals, can function as central atoms.

Since several heteropoly anions may exist for a given species of
central atom with a given addendum element (e.g., we have found at
least eight stable tungstocobaltates), the total number of possible
heteropoly anions is large. Complexes containing more than one element as addenda atoms also exist.

Heteropoly anions resemble discrete fragments of metal oxide structure of definite size and shape for a given species. The atoms in

positive oxidation state, other than H, are within polyhedra of oxygen atoms which share vertices and/or edges. In the compounds clarified thus far, every addendum polyhedron is sharing at least one oxygen atom directly with a central atom's polyhedron.

The anions differ from conventional coordination complexes in several important ways: (1) There are no discrete ligands coordinated to the central atom; but, instead, the structure coordinated to it is interconnected. The dissociation fragments do not coincide with any discrete ligands. (2) The size of heteropoly anions is quite large relative to most coordination complexes. Therefore, average charge density on the surface of polyanions is low. (3) The ionic weights are relatively large ($\sim 1000-4400$). (4) Solvation is apparently slight, for reasons developed below (Section IV). (5) It seems characteristic of these anions, in contrast to many conventional coordination complexes and linear inorganic polymers, that there is generally no evidence to suggest involvement of the anions in stepwise dissociation equilibria wherein sizeable proportions of intermediate heteropoly species exist. The structure of a known heteropoly complex usually represents an arrangement having marked relative stability; and intermediate heteropoly dissociation products, which must have short-lived existence during formation or dissociation of the stable species, seem not to exist in sizeable proportion at room temperature.

Other significant characteristics encountered in work with heteropoly electrolytes include: (1) unusual coordination numbers and geometries; (2) unusual high oxidation states for transition metal central atoms; (3) crystals frequently contain water of hydration in zeolytic channels; (4) geometrical isomerisms and optical isomerisms based on gross arrangements of addenda polyhedra within the anions; (5) solubility in water and frequent solubility in other oxygen-containing solvents; (6) the compounds commonly catalyze various organic reactions; (7) free acids are often obtainable as very soluble crystalline hydrates; (8) the several dissociation constants of a given acid often all differ by less than a factor of ten; (9) the acids are usually relatively strong (pK's about 2); and (10) all heteropoly anions are degraded by base, but the pH's where degradation becomes major vary widely for different complexes.

The Complete Independence of Diffusion or Dialysis Rates from Ionic Weight per se[2]

Recently as well as in the past, persons interested in heteropoly and isopoly electrolytes have expended a great deal of effort determining diffusion coefficients, dialysis coefficients, and coefficients of electrodialysis, for the purpose of estimating ionic weights of species in solution. Several of the most authoritative recent inorganic texts and reference works describe relationships between ionic weights and diffusion or dialysis coefficients; and, in the chapters on polyanions, detailed chemical interpretations are recorded which derive ultimately from "ionic weights" so determined.

On the other hand, it would be predicted on the basis of the most modern theories of diffusion in liquids[3,4,5] that molecular or ionic weights per se would play no role whatever in determining rates of diffusion. For a given solvent, only the size and shape of the diffusing species, plus the magnitudes of its interactions with adjacent particles, would be predicted to affect the diffusion coefficient.

An unambiguous test of the conflicting postulates was highly desirable. Heretofore all the ions studied have been so sufficiently dissimilar that discrepancies between observed diffusion rates and those predicted on the basis of ionic weight variation could be ascribed to a number of other factors.

Diffusion coefficients were measured, using the elegant open capillary method of Anderson and Saddington,[6] for two pairs of very stable isomorphous polyanions. $[SiO_4W_{12}O_{36}]^{-4}$ (ionic weight = 2875) and $[SiO_4Mo_{12}O_{36}]^{-4}$ (ionic weight $\approx$ 1820) anions are virtually identical in size, structure,[7] charge, and negligible degree of solvation.[8] Their diffusion coefficients at infinite dilution were found[2] to be identical, within the small experimental error, despite the large difference in ionic weights.

Diffusion coefficients were also measured, under identical conditions, for the isostructural,[9] probably unsolvated[10] anions, $[CrO_6Mo_6O_{15+n}H_{2n}]^{-3}$ and $[CoO_6Mo_6O_{15+n}H_{2n}]^{-3}$ (wherein n is probably 3).

The results show that "Riecke's Law" and its modifications are *wholly* invalid, there being no relationship between diffusion rate and ionic weight as such.

Since current literature about polyanions contains numerous interpretations based directly or indirectly, but often not obviously, on "ionic weights" deduced from such measurements, considerable care is indicated for readers.

The experiments also tested recent postulates[4] for relating diffusion rates of polyanions to the numbers of exterior oxygen atoms available for H-bonding to solvent. The results discourage hopes for that correlation. Section IV below provides reasons for the lack of correlation.

Exchanges of Radioactive Isotopes[11]

The first isotopic exchange studies involving heteropoly anions having transition metal central atoms are reported.

1. Exchanges of Mo^{99} between paramolybdate anion, $[Mo_7^{99}O_{24}]^{-6}$, and (a) 6-molybdochromate(III) anion, $[CrO_6Mo_6O_{15+n}H_{2n}]^{-3}$, and (b) its isomorph,[9, 10] 6-molybdoferrate(III) anion, $[FeO_6Mo_6O_{15+n}H_{2n}]^{-3}$, were studied over the pH range 2.5-4.5 at 29.5 °C. and at 0 °C.

One purpose was to ascertain the general lability of the molybdate functionality. While it might be predicted that this lability would be very high because $d°$ Mo—O bonds should be very labile, the overall result was by no means a foregone conclusion in view of (1) the interconnected nature of the coordinated molybdate, (2) the existence in solution of metastable heteropoly molybdate species[13] and resolved enantiomorphs, and (3) the relative thermal stabilities in solution[14] of the isomorphous 6-molybdates of Fe(III), Cr(III), Co(III), and Al(III).

The second major purpose was to examine the relative Mo exchange rates for a pair of very stable isomorphous complexes with a view to correlation with the electronic structures of their central atoms.

At 29.5 °C all the Mo exchanges were complete in less than 0.5 min. At 0 °C, $t_{1/2}$ was 35 min for Mo^{99} exchange with the d^3 Cr complex at pH 2.5, while the Mo^{99} exchange with the d^5 spin-free[14] ferric complex was 80% complete in less than 1 min at identical conditions. The Mo exchange rate increased with increasing pH.

A combination of these results with the structural limitations which apply if the anions have any of the probable heteropoly structures, indicates strongly[11] that the difference in exchange rates for the Cr and Fe complexes is *not* caused primarily by the relative ease of making and breaking Fe—O bonds as contrasted with Cr—O bonds. Instead, the difference is explainable primarily in terms of the inflexibility and compactness which crystal-field stabilization energy imparts to the CrO_6 central octahedron in contrast to the unstabilized flexible FeO_6 group. The greater flexibility very much increases the ease of attack by solvent oxygen atoms on many sites of the MoO_6 octahedra.

Because the heteropoly complexes have their Mo atoms coordinated, not directly to the central atoms, but merely to atoms which are in turn coordinated to the central atoms, it is possible to separate the factors of flexibility and compactness from that of ease of bond formation and breaking. This orients attention toward flexibility in considering substitution reactions of conventional complexes.

The exchange process is seen as most probably involving dissociation of MoO_x polyhedra away, probably as MoO_4^- groups, from both paramolybdate and the heteropoly species. In view of structural limitations, such a dissociation of the polyanion would almost certainly have to involve nearly simultaneous displacement attacks by at least two solvent oxygen atoms, on the MoO_6 octahedra of the complex.

2. The exchange of Cr^{51} between $[CrO_6Mo_6O_{15+n}H_{2n}]^{-3}$ and $[Cr^{51}(H_2O)_6]^{+3}$ was studied at $29.5\,^{\circ}C$, $\mu = 0.446$, and total $[H^+]$ between 0.1 and 0.01 (where hydrolysis products of chromic ion are negligible[15]). Half-times ranged between 4.3 and 45 min. Excellent separations were achieved. The exchange goes more rapidly as pH is *lowered*.

This appears to be the first Cr(III) complex (other than outer sphere complexes) which has been found to exchange its Cr rapidly.

Since $t_{1/2} \cong 40$ hours for O^{18} exchange between solvent and $[Cr(H_2O)_6]^{+3}$ under similar conditions,[16] it is proposed that CrO_6 is exchanging as a unit, with unbroken Cr—O bonds. This appears to be the first case where exchange of an intact MO_x polyhedral unit has been indicated.

The exchanges may also be looked upon as providing examples of rapidly exchanging polydentate groups.

The rate law: $R = k_1[A] + k_2[A][B]$, wherein $A = [CrO_6Mo_6-O_{15+n}H_{2n}]^{-3}$ and $B = [Cr(H_2O)_6]^{+3}$ is tentatively advanced, because the kinetic data collected at very nearly constant pH = 1.06 fit it fairly well when $k_1 = 1.4 \times 10^{-2}$ min^{-1} and $k_2 \cong 4 \times 10^{-1}$ liter mole^{-1} min^{-1}. Both $[A]$ and $[B]$ were varied between 0.005 and 0.05.

A preliminary study wherein $[H^+]$ underwent about 8-fold variation, gave a good fit to: $R = k_3[H^+][A] + k_2[A][B]$ wherein $k_3[H^+] = k_1$.

The Complete Structure of $[Co^{+3}O_4W_{12}O_{36}]^{-5}$; Properties of that Anion, its Co(II) Isomorph, and its Dicobalt Relatives[17-21]

In a cooperative program at Boston University, the X-ray group under Prof. Klaas Eriks and the inorganic chemists have determined the complete structure of the $[Co^{+3}O_4W_{12}O_{36}]^{-5}$ anion and elucidated its properties.[17]

Because this is the first discrete polyanion for which all of the oxygen atom positions have been determined directly by X-ray techniques, several results are especially noteworthy.

The oxygen atom positions are determined within 0.1 Å. and the W and Co positions within about 0.01 Å.[21] The salt used was $K_5[CoO_4W_{12}O_{36}] \cdot 20H_2O$.

This is the first complex containing any d^6 ion (Co^{+3}) in a tetrahedral site.[17] A weak Jahn-Teller contribution to distortion of the central CoO_4 tetrahedron is expected,[17] this being the first tetrahedral case wherein the degeneracy to be removed is in the e orbitals, for which only weak interactions are expected. In such a heteropoly anion the oxygen atoms of the central polyhedron are within the W framework and are subjected to counterbalancing pulls from the central atom and adjacent W atoms. Consequently, distortions initiated by weak Jahn-Teller forces might perhaps be considerably larger within heteropoly anions than in other situations.

The calculation yields Co-O distances which are all 1.88 Å., but the tetrahedron is elongated (2 short, 4 longer edges); and its opposite edges are slightly twisted so that they are no longer exactly mutually perpendicular. Two opposite O-O distances are 2.7 Å., two are 3.2 Å., and two are 3.3 Å. The whole heteropoly anion has tetrahedral symmetry, aside from a very slight distortion interpreted as a twist (through much less angle than the twist of the CoO_4); and there is no indication of elongation of the framework of the W atoms and other oxygen atoms. In the absence of a Jahn-Teller force, it seems probable that the heteropoly framework and the interior CoO_4 would be slightly twisted relative to each other, but that regularity of the central tetrahedron would be preserved. These possibilities will be discussed. Jahn-Teller distortion is not expected for the Co(II) isomorph. Refinement of its structure and refinement of three-dimensional data, now underway, should illuminate the foregoing.

The work confirms the gross structure proposed by Keggin[7] for 12-tungstophosphate anion. However, in the salt studied, the anions are arranged in spirals which surround relatively large columns of space. These accommodate potassium ions and zeolytic water molecules. The closest approach between centers of oxygen atoms of adjacent complexes is 3.7 Å.

Another feature of general interest is the extent to which the W atoms are off-center in their respective WO_6 octahedra. All W's are displaced toward the outside of the anion and the peripheral oxygen atoms are sucked somewhat inward. Within each octahedron the longest W-O distance, 2.49 Å., occurs between the W and an oxygen atom in the interior of the complex; but the W-O distances involving those peripheral oxygen atoms which are not shared by other W atoms are only 1.43 Å.[21]

The explanation for these distortions is seen primarily in the polarization of the peripheral, less-shared oxygen atoms in the direction of the interior of the complex, giving very high ion-induced dipole attractions toward the W(VI). Interior oxygen atoms have positive atoms near them on several sides, and therefore cannot be polarized so intensively in any one direction. X-ray methods determine centers of electron density of atoms. The exterior oxygen atoms, being heavily polarized inward, not only suck the W atoms outward but present backsides of very reduced nucleophilic character toward the outside of the complex. This would greatly inhibit tendencies of the exterior oxygen atoms to form H-bonds. This, together with the low overall charge density, is very consistent with measurements of diffusion rates[2] and viscosities[8, 10] which indicate very low solvation, the hydrodynamic radii not exceeding crystallographic radii. It is consistent with the strength of the acids.

The water solubilities of heteropoly acids and heteropoly salts of small simple cations may be explained in terms of low lattice energies and solvation of the cations.

The foregoing may also cast light on the nature of various metal oxide interfaces.

Time permitting, spectra, magnetic properties, structures, and redox behaviors may be discussed for the following:[20] $[Co^{+3}O_4W_{12}O_{36}]^{-5}$ $[Co^{+2}O_4W_{12}O_{36}]^{-6}$, $[Co^{+2}O_6Co^{+2}O_4W_{12}O_{32+n}H_{2n}]^{-8}$, $[Co^{+2}O_6Co^{+3}O_4-W_{12}O_{32+n}H_{2n}]^{-7}$, and related complexes.

$[NiO_6W_6O_{18}H_6]^{-4}$ and $[NiO_6Mo_6O_{18}H_6]^{-4}$ Isomorphs [22, 23, 11]

The formulas and structure of the above two nickelates(II) are established by analyses, potentiometric titrations, magnetic measurements, spectra (Dq's are 952 and 980 cm^{-1} for the Mo and W complexes respectively), fused hydrate cryoscopy, dehydration experiments, and single crystal x-ray work.

In the tungstate isomorph, for example, each Ni atom is at the center of an almost regular planar hexagon of W atoms. Each W atom is surrounded by an octahedron of O atoms, which shares an edge with each adjacent WO_6 and another edge with the NiO_6 octahedron. A strong argument can be made that the six H atoms are on the oxygen atoms surrounding the Ni.

The chief importance is that this is the first modern demonstration that heteropoly anions can contain non-ionizable H atoms (constitutional water). This opens many structural possibilities.

Chemical similarities and differences may be discussed.

The instability constant of $[NiO_6Mo_6O_{18}H_6]^{-4}$ is much greater than that of $[NiO_6W_6O_{18}H_6]^{-4}$. The instability constant of the Mo complex in saturated Na_2SO_4 solution at 32 °C was determined by fused salt cryoscopy to be about 10^{-31} on the basis of the equation:

$$[NiO_6Mo_6O_{18}H_6]^{-4} \rightleftharpoons Ni^{++} + 6MoO_4^{-} + 6H^{+}$$

Ionic Weights and Stabilities in Solution [9, 11]

Cryoscopy in fused Glauber's salt, using the sodium salts of these large anions, has proved to be highly accurate when proper precautions are taken. The numbers of empirical formulas per heteropoly anion, in saturated Na_2SO_4 solution at 32 °C., are revealed. The relative stabilities of isomorphs containing different central atoms or addenda species may be determined.[11]

The 6-molybdates of tervalent Fe, Cr, Co, and Al are monomeric in solution and have very high stability constants. They are monomeric in crystals.[24] 5-molybdocobaltate(III) is a stable dimer. Supplementary attack[11] establishes its formula as $[(CoO_6)_2Mo_{10}O_{24}]^{-6}$. A very plausible structure is suggested[11]. The 9-molybdates of P(V) and As(V) are isomorphous dimers of formula[11] $[(XO_4)_2Mo_{18}O_{54}]^{-6}$. The latter is of lower stability. Their tungsto isomorphs[25] have greater stability constants.

Surface Active Catalysts and Molybdocobaltates[11]

The first use of surface-active catalysts in reaction mixtures containing no complexes other than polyanions is reported. Different heteropoly products sometimes result, depending upon the presence or absence of such catalysts. Dimeric 5-molybdocobaltate(III) may be formed quantitatively by H_2O_2 oxidation in the presence of charcoal, among other novel effects.

To date, no anion from the system of interrelated molybdocobaltates corresponds in structure to any anion known in the system of interrelated tungstocobaltates. All the molybdocobaltates and some of the tungstocobaltates are based on CoO_6 octahedra.

Co-workers:

Active co-workers include: Prof. Klaas Eriks (X-ray Crystallography), Boston University; Drs. Umesh C. Agarwala, Michael T. Pope, Muraji Shibata, Violet E. Simmons, George A. Tsigdinos, Timothy J. R. Weakley, Nicholas F. Yannoni, and Mr. Murry L. Block.

REFERENCES

1. L. C. W. Baker, *Properties of the Heteropoly Molybdates*, Information Bulletin Cdb-12, Climax Molybdenum Co., New York, 1956.
2. L. C. W. Baker and M. T. Pope, *J. Am. Chem. Soc.*, **82**, 4176 (1960).
3. A. W. Adamson, *J. Phys. Chem.*, **58**, 514 (1954);
   A. W. Adamson, *Petroleum Trans. AIME*, **219**, 158 (1960).
4. B. Ottar, *Self-Diffusion and Fluidity in Liquids*, Oslo University Press, Oslo, Norway, 1958.
5. R. E. Powell, W. E. Roseveare and H. Eyring, *Ind. Eng. Chem.*, **33**, 431 (1941).
6. J. S. Anderson and K. Saddington, *J. Chem. Soc.*, **1949**, S381.
7. J. F. Keggin, *Proc. Roy. Soc. (London)*, **A144**, 75 (1934);
   J. W. Illingworth and J. F. Keggin, *J. Chem. Soc.*, **1935**, 575;
   R. Signer and H. Gross, *Helv. Chim. Acta*, **17**, 1076 (1934);
   W. Hückel, *Structural Chemistry of Inorganic Compounds*, Vol. I, Elsevier Publishing Co., Inc., Amsterdam, The Netherlands (1950), pp. 179-213.
8. T. Kurucsev, A. M. Sargeson and B. O. West, *J. Phys. Chem.*, **61**, 1569 (1957).

9. G. A. Tsigdinos, M. T. Pope and L. C. W. Baker, Abstracts of Papers Presented before Div. Inorganic Chem., Am. Chem. Soc. Natl, Mtg., Boston, April 1959.
10. M. T. Pope and L. C. W. Baker, *J. Phys. Chem.*, **63**, 2083 (1959).
11. G. A. Tsigdinos, Ph. D. Dissertation, Boston University, 1961.
12. C. W. Wolfe, M. L. Block and L. C. W. Baker, *J. Am. Chem. Soc.*, **77**, 2200 (1955).
13. H. Wu, *J. Biol. Chem.*, **43**, 189 (1920).
14. L. C. W. Baker *et al, J. Am. Chem. Soc.*, **77**, 2136 (1955).
15. C. Postmus and E. L. King, *J. Phys. Chem.*, **59**, 1208 (1955).
16. J. P. Hunt and H. Taube, *J. Chem. Phys.*, **19**, 602 (1951); R. A. Plane and H. Taube, *J. Phys. Chem.*, **56**, 33 (1952).
17. L. C. W. Baker and V. E. Simmons, *J. Am. Chem. Soc.*, **81**, 4744 (1959).
18. L. C. W. Baker and T. P. McCutcheon, *J. Am. Chem. Soc.*, **78**, 4503 (1956).
19. (a) V. E. Simmons, N. F. Yannoni, K. Eriks and L. C. W. Baker, Abstracts of Papers Presented before Div. of Inorganic Chem., Am. Chem. Soc. Natl. Mtg., Atlantic City, September 1959.
    (b) N. F. Yannoni, V. E. Simmons, K. Eriks and L. C. W. Baker, *ibid.*
    (c) K. Eriks, N. F. Yannoni, U. C. Agarwala, V. E. Simmons and L. C. W. Baker, Abstracts of Papers Presented before the Meeting of the International Union of Crystallography, Cambridge, England, August 1960; Acta Cryst., **13**, 1139 (1961).
20. V. E. Simmons, Ph. D. Dissertation, Boston University, 1961.
21. N. F. Yannoni, Ph. D. Dissertation, Boston University, 1961.
22. U. C. Agarwala, Ph. D. Dissertation, Boston University, 1960.
23. U. C. Agarwala and L. C. W. Baker, Abstracts of Papers Presented before Div. Inorganic Chem., Am. Chem. Soc. Natl. Mtg., Cleveland, April 1960.
24. H. T. Evans, Jr., Private Communication, 1960; for crystallographic data see: M. Shibata and L. C. W. Baker, Abstracts of Papers Presented before Div. Inorganic Chemistry, Am. Chem. Soc. Natl. Mtg., New York, September 1960.
25. B. Dawson, *Acta Cryst.*, **6**, 113 (1953).

ENERGY TRANSFER BETWEEN CATION-ANTIPYRINE AGGREGATES IN THEIR RARE EARTH HEXA-ANTIPYRENE SALTS.

L. G. VAN UITERT and **R. R. SODEN***

Bell Telephone Laboratories, Inc.
Murray Hill, New Jersey

Many of the fundamental properties of the rare earth ions are best determined by examining them under conditions in which they have minimal interaction with each other and find themselves in identical surroundings. Such conditions are found in the rare earth hexa-antipyrene tri-iodide and tri-perchlorate complexes.

Antipyrene is the common name for *1*-phenyl-*2, 3*-dimethyl-*5*-pyrazolone ($C_{11}H_{12}ON_2$). The structure of this material is such as to produce a strong electronegative potential at the oxygen atom. This allows it to form a strong dative bond with metal ions.

Terbium hexa-antipyrene tri-iodide and the comparable perchlorate show strong fluorescence from the terbium ions under ultraviolet excitation.[1] The samarium, europium and dysprosium complexes fluoresce weakly, and the other rare earth complexes do not fluoresce at all in the visible region. Previous work[2,3] has shown that energy gained through ultraviolet excitation can transfer between dissimilar rare earth hexa-antipyrene aggregates in the same crystal. The direction and relative ease of energy transfer between aggregates can be determined by comparing the effects of rare earth substitutions in the above compounds upon the fluorescence of terbium.

Preparation of Materials

Crystals having the compositions $Tb_x M_{1-x} (AP)_6 I_3$ and $Tb_x M_{1-x} (AP)_6 (ClO_4)_3$ where M = Y, La, Ce, Pr, Nd, Sm, Eu, Gd, Tb, Dy, Ho, Er, Tm and Yb; x = 1.0, 0.5, 0.25 and 0.10; and AP = antipyrene were prepared. Aqueous solutions containing 0.01 M of rare earth chloride and 0.06 M of antipyrene were combined. To these, solutions containing 0.03 M of KI or NH_4ClO_4 were added at room temperature. The total volume was about 100 ml in each case. These solutions rapidly produce small, well-defined crystals that are desirable for comparing emission intensities.

---

*The authors wish to acknowledge helpful discussions with A. D. Liehr and D. L. Wood of these Laboratories.

Measurements

Intensity measurements were made employing a Gaertner high dispersion spectrometer adapted with an AMINCO photomultiplier microphotometer using a 1P22 tube. Ten micron slit widths were employed. Emission was excited by illuminating a sample 1" long by 1/2" by 1/4" deep with either a 2537 Å Mineralight through a Corning 9863 filter or a Hanovia CH4 Spotlight through a Corning 5874 filter. The measurements were made at room temperature. The data represented in the figures are for the fluorescent emission intensity maxima of terbium found in the neighborhood of 5480 Å and are relative to 1000 for the straight terbium compositions measured under excitation from the 2537 Å Mineralight. They are relative to 100 for the same compositions when measured under 3660 Å excitation. The factor of 10 difference in reference points is employed to provide a clear separation of the data in accordance with excitation source in Fig. 1 and 2.

Structure

Details of the structure of $Tb(AP)_6I_3$ have been determined by Treuting and Romanow.[4] Its space group is $R\overline{3}$, C_{3i}^2. It has a rhombohedral unit cell with a 3-fold axis and a center of inversion. The rhombohedral cell dimensions are a = 13.26Å and a = 62.85°. The related hexagonal cell contains three molecules of $Tb(AP)_6I_3$ and has unit cell dimensions of a = 13.82Å and c = 31.77Å. The Tb^{3+} and I^- ions lie along the c-axis of the hexagonal unit cell. Referred to the hexagonal axes, Tb^{3+} is in the $3a$ positions at 0, 0, 0. The I^- ions are in the $3b$ positions at 0, 0, 1/2 and the $6c$ positions at 0, 0, ± 0.2167. The X-ray powder patterns of all of the materials under consideration show very close agreement in spacings and intensities and hence indicate that the complexes are isostructural.

Discussion

Fluorescence from rare earth ions can be markedly influenced by perturbations due to the environment in which they find themselves. The effects of these perturbations depend upon the geometry of the environment, the electron affinities of the surrounding ions, exchange coupling, and thermal conditions.[5] In salt-like crystals, such as the tungstates, lattice cohesive forces can be particularly important.[6] Variable influences from the above sources are largely eliminated in the rare earth hexa-antipyrene complexes. They are uniform in structure and have large separations between cations. Further, the antipyrene molecules have no residual charges but form strong dative bonds to the cations; hence, they are able to adjust their positions to meet the requirements of the rare earth ions.

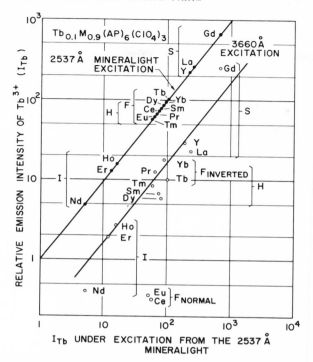

Fig. 1. Dependencies of I_{Tb} upon rare earth substitutions and excitation source in the iodide complexes.

Antipyrene shows an absorption edge at about 3000 Å in ethanol. In this medium, absorbance ($\log I_0/I$) is equal to about 5 at 2537 Å. This indicates that excitation from the 2537 Å Mineralight is largely absorbed by the antipyrene part of the rare earth-antipyrene aggregates. Figure 3 shows the dependencies of the relative emission intensity of Tb^{3+} upon its concentration in a number of rare earth substituted hexa-antipyrene tri-iodide complexes under this excitation. The several slopes show that the dissipation of the energy absorbed by the antipyrene molecules by processes other than those resulting in fluorescence from Tb^{3+} can vary markedly with the substituting rare earth ion.

In Fig. 1, the relative emission intensities of Tb^{3+} (I_{Tb}) for a representative group of hexa-antipyrene tri-iodide complexes are compared for excitation by the 2537 Å Mineralight and 3660 Å radiation. In these compounds, 10% of the rare earth ions are Tb^{3+}, and the remainder are the ions of the elements indicated. The horizontal coordinates are scaled to the logarithms of the intensities of emission observed under excitation from the 2537 Å Mineralight. The

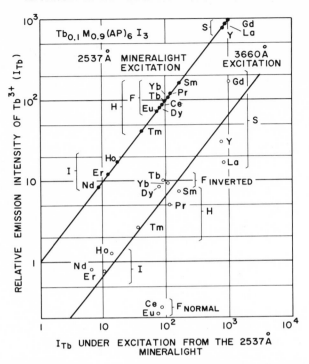

Fig. 2. Dependencies of I_{Tb} upon rare earth substitutions and excitation source in the perchlorate complexes.

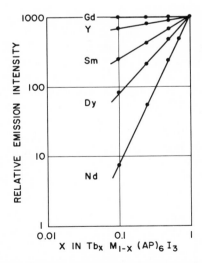

Fig. 3. The dependencies of relative emission intensity of Tb^{3+} upon its content in the presence of rare earth diluents under excitation from the 2537 Å Mineralight.

vertical coordinates represent the logarithms of the intensities observed under excitation from the 2537 Å Mineralight, based on Tb $(AP)_6I_3 = 1000$, and those observed under excitation from 3660 Å radiation, based on $Tb(AP)_6I_3 = 100$. The comparable values for Tb^{3+} substituting for itself are taken as $1/10$ of those for $Tb(AP)_6I_3$.

The data represented on the upper line show that there are correspondences between the intensity of emission from Tb^{+3} and the term designations of the ground states (S, F, H or I) of the other cations involved. The data indicate that the greater part of the energy captured by the antipyrene molecules attached to S state ions finds its way to the terbium aggregates.

The F state ions, which include Tb^{3+}, show approximately equal propensities to dissipate the absorbed energy. The H state ions behave similarly to the F state ions but show a greater spread. The presence of I state ions, however, strongly reduces the intensity of emission from Tb^{3+}. These relationships are consistent with the supposition that the ease of communication of energy between the antipyrene molecules and the rare earth ions increases with the total orbital angular momentum of the $4f$ subshell electrons of the latter. These are 0, 3, 5 and 6 for the S, F, H and I states, respectively.

The open circles in Fig. 1 represent the data obtained under 3660 Å excitation. In the 3660 Å region, energy is apparently absorbed by charge transfer processes occurring between the cations and the antipyrene molecules rather than by transitions within the antipyrene molecules themselves. This is indicated by the presence of details of the absorption edge of $Tb(AP)_6I_3$ close to 4000 Å, while the edge for antipyrene is near 3000 Å. With a few exceptions, the relationships observed under 3660 Å excitation are similar to those found under excitation from the 2537 Å Mineralight. The Gd^{3+} substituted material is brighter than $Tb(AP)_6I_3$ under 3660 Å excitation, and the Y^{3+} and La^{3+} substituted materials are relatively weaker than before. The greatest deviations from the data obtained under excitation from the 2537 Å Mineralight, however, occur among the F state ions.

Terbium and ytterbium lie close together in positions comparable to those taken by them on the upper curve. The intensity of emission of Tb^{3+} in the cerium and europium compositions, however, is decreased by a factor of approximately 35. This rather marked deviation indicates that when excitation takes place in the wavelength range of the charge transfer bands, energy can be readily transferred between aggregates with similar term designations. When, as in this case, ions with F ground states are involved, those with normal multiplets (Eu and Ce with ^7F_o and $^2F_{5/2}$ ground states respectively) dissipate energy preferentially to those with inverted multiplets (Tb and Yb with $^7F_6$ and $^2F_{7/2}$ ground states, respectively).

The relationships shown for the tri-iodide compositions in Fig. 1 are given for the tri-perchlorate compositions in Fig. 2. The same generalities apply to these data.

Manganese hexa-antipyrene di-iodide shows a bright band fluorescence in the red under ultraviolet excitation. This provides a possibility for a future study of the effects of divalent metal ions upon the fluorescence of manganese in these complexes.

REFERENCES

1. L. G. Van Uitert, R. R. Soden, and R. G. Treuting, *J. Appl. Phys.*, **30**, 2017 (1959).
2. L. G. Van Uitert and R. R. Soden, *J. Chem. Phys.*, **32**, 1161 (1960).
3. R. R. Soden, *J. Appl. Phys.* (1960).
4. R. G. Treuting and W. J. Romanow (to be submitted).
5. L. G. Van Uitert, *J. Elecrochem. Soc.* **107**, 803 (1960).
6. L. G. Van Uitert and R. R. Soden (to be submitted).

FLUOROCARBON DERIVATIVES OF METALS

R. B. KING, E. PITCHER, S. L. STAFFORD, P. M. TREICHEL,
AND F. G. A. STONE

Department of Chemistry
Harvard University
Cambridge, Massachusetts

A significant development in fluorine chemistry came a little over a decade ago when Eméleus and Haszeldine and their co-workers[1,2] discovered that perfluoroalkyl iodides* would react directly with certain non-metals and metalloids to afford hitherto unknown fluorocarbon derivatives, e. g.,

$$(CF_3)_3P \qquad (C_2F_5)_3As \qquad (CF_3)_3Sb \qquad (CF_3)_2S_x \qquad (CF_3)_2Se$$
$$CF_3PI_2 \qquad (CF_3)_2AsI \qquad\qquad (x = 2,3 \text{ or } 4)$$

It was also found that perfluoroalkylmercury compounds could be obtained from perfluoroalkyl iodides:

$$R_FI + Hg \xrightarrow[\text{or U.V.}]{\text{Heat}} R_FHgI \xrightarrow[\text{amalgam}]{\text{Cadmium}} (R_F)_2Hg$$

Unfortunately, bis(perfluoroalkyl)mercury compounds on treatment with metals or metal halides did not yield new perfluoroalkyl compounds of other metals, thereby differing from dialkylmercury compounds which readily transfer their alkyl groups to many metals.

In another approach to fluorocarbon derivatives of metals perfluoroalkyl Grignard reagents were formed from perfluoroalkyl iodides and magnesium in basic solvents such as tetrahydrofuran. However, the Grignard reagents readily decomposed. Therefore, it is not surprising that perfluoroalkyl Grignard reagents have not as yet played a major role in the synthesis of fluorocarbon derivatives of metals. Perfluoroalkyl compounds of lithium and zinc are also unstable and as synthetic reagents have proved to be no more useful than their mercury or magnesium analogs.

The failure of chemists to develop the potentially large field of fluorocarbon-metal derivatives left a significant gap in our knowl-

---

*The term *perfluoro-* designates an organo-group in which all hydrogen atoms are replaced by fluorine atoms, and perfluoroalkyl groups will be abbreviated R_F.

edge. The properties of the few known fluorocarbon-metal derivatives were in marked contrast to those of alkyl-metal compounds,* suggesting that a general study of fluorocarbon-metal derivatives would have an important impact on our knowledge of the metal-carbon bond. For this reason in 1958 we began to develop new methods of synthesis. Initially, perfluoroalkyl compounds of tin and lead were obtained via the following reactions:[3,4]

$$R_3Sn\text{---}SnR_3 + R_FI \xrightarrow[\text{U.V.}]{\text{Heat or}} R_3SnR_F + R_3SnI$$

$$R_{4-n}SnCl_n + R_FI \xrightarrow[\text{in tetrahydrofuran}]{\text{Magnesium}} R_{4-n}Sn(R_F)_n$$

$n = 1$ or 2

$$R_4Pb + R_FI \xrightarrow[\text{U.V.}]{\text{Heat or}} R_3PbR_F$$

Cleavage of tin-tin bonds of hexaorgano-Ditin compounds by perfluoroalkyl iodides was independently discovered by Clark *et al.*[5,6] The properties of the R_F—Sn and R_F—Pb linkages were found to differ significantly from those of their unfluorinated analogs. Thus, perfluoroalkyl groups are easily removed from tin or lead by aqueous sodium hydroxide but are not removed by protonic acids. It is well known that the latter cleave organo-groups from tetraorganolead and -tin compounds, while, under mild conditions, bases do not significantly affect the R—Sn and R—Pb linkages.[7] The properties of perfluoroalkyl-tin and -lead linkages, as well as those of the perfluoroalkyl-mercury bond, are understandable in terms of the relatively high electronegativity of perfluoroalkyl groups. For the CF_3 group the electronegativity has been estimated to be between that of fluorine and that of chlorine.[8]

The high electronegativity of perfluoroalkyl groups suggested that it should be possible to σ-bond fluorocarbon groups to transition metals, thereby making many new complex compounds, even though the least stable organo-derivatives of these metals are those in which an alkyl-group is σ-bonded to the metal. This idea was prompted by the following consideration. Since 1955 there have been major successes in the preparation of transition metal alkyls and aryls resulting from the realization of certain electronic conditions for stability.[9] The most important of these conditions from the standpoint of fluorocarbon-transition metal chemistry is the electronegativity factor which may play an important part in determining the stability of

---

*Thus bis(perfluoromethyl)mercury proved to be a white water-soluble solid more like a mercury(II) halide in behavior than like a diorganomercury derivative.

metal-carbon σ-bonds. The more electronegative the σ-bonded organo-group is, the less electron density will be associated with the metal. Thus the ionic resonance energy is increased, with a commensurate rise in stability of the M-C linkage.[10,11] In agreement with these ideas concerning the probable stability of fluorocarbon derivatives of transition metals, it has been found possible to prepare a variety of such compounds. The preparative routes used and the properties of the new compounds are summarized below.

Preparation

The discovery[11,13] that acylmanganese- and acylrhenium-pentacarbonyl compounds may be decarbonylated to give organomanganese and organorhenium pentacarbonyl compounds suggested that perfluoroalkyl derivatives of certain transition metals might be obtained from the alkali metal salts of the metal carbonyls and perfluoroacyl halides. This proved to be the case,[14-16] e.g.,

$$R_F COCl + M(CO)_5 Na \xrightarrow{\text{Tetrahydrofuran}} R_F COM(CO)_5 + NaCl$$

$$R_F COM(CO)_5 \xrightarrow[\substack{(b) > 120^\circ \text{ if } M = \text{Re}}]{\text{Heat at } (a)\ 80^\circ \text{ if } M = \text{Mn}} R_F M(CO)_5 + CO \uparrow$$

$$M = \text{Mn* or Re}$$

In some instances treatment of the sodium salt of a metal carbonyl in tetrahydrofuran with a perfluoroacyl chloride gives the perfluoroalkyl-metal compound directly, since the intermediate perfluoroacyl derivatives are unstable with respect to release of carbon monoxide,[15,16] e.g.,

$$Fe_3(CO)_{12} \xrightarrow[\text{Tetrahydrofuran}]{\text{Sodium dispersion}} Na_2 Fe(CO)_4 \xrightarrow{R_F COCl} (R_F)_2 Fe(CO)_4 +$$

$$CO \uparrow + NaCl$$

Certain perfluoroalkenyl halides react with the sodium salts of metal carbonyls to give fluorocarbon-metal compounds. In this type of reaction the rearrangement of a perfluoroallyl group to a perfluoro-propenyl group has been observed:[14,16]

$$CF_2 : CFCF_2 Cl + NaMn(CO)_5 \xrightarrow{\text{Tetrahydrofuran}} CF_3 CF : CFMn(CO)_5$$

$$CF_2 : CFCF_2 Cl + NaFe(CO)_2 C_5 H_5 \xrightarrow{\text{Tetrahydrofuran}}$$

$$CF_3 CF : CFFe(CO)_2 C_5 H_5$$

---

*During the early part of our work the existence of the two compounds $CF_3 COMn(CO)_5$ and $CF_3 Mn(CO)_5$ was reported by T. H. Coffield, J. Kozikowski and R. D. Closson, *Abstracts of the International Conference on Coordination Chemistry,* London, April 1959, p. 126.

The pseudo-halogen behavior of fluorocarbon groups in perfluoro-alkyl iodides was recognized soon after the discovery of these io-dides.[17] Thus the cleavage of tin-tin bonds by perfluoroalkyl iodides, mentioned above, is similar to the cleavage of hexaorgano-ditin com-pounds by iodine. This suggested that perfluoroalkyl iodides might react directly with those metal carbonyls known to afford metal car-bonyl iodides on treatment with iodine, an idea confirmed experimen-tally with iron pentacarbonyl and cyclopentadienylcobalt dicar-bonyl:[15,16,18,19]

$$Fe(CO)_5 + R_F I \xrightarrow{\sim 70^\circ} R_F Fe(CO)_4 I + [R_F Fe(CO)_3 I]_2$$

$$C_5 H_5 Co(CO)_2 + R_F I \xrightarrow[45^\circ]{Benzene} C_5 H_5 Co(Co(CO)(R_F)I$$

In the direct reaction between perfluoroalkyl iodides and iron pen-tacarbonyl, perfluoroalkyliron tetracarbonyl iodides are the main prod-ucts. The dimeric perfluoroalkyliron tricarbonyl iodides, formed in lesser amounts, are better obtained via the reaction:[16]

$$2R_F Fe(CO)_4 I \xrightarrow{50-70^\circ} [R_F Fe(CO)_3 I]_2 + 2CO$$

This reaction has its counterpart in manganese and rhenium chem-istry.[20,21]

$$2M(CO)_5 X \xrightarrow{Heat} [M(CO)_4 X]_2 + 2CO \ [M = Mn, Re]$$

suggesting an analogy between the chemistry of perfluoroalkyliron tetracarbonyl iodides and the pentacarbonyl-halides of manganese or rhenium.

An entirely different synthetic route was used to obtain the novel heterocyclic complexes I and II. These substances were obtained by heating together tetrafluoroethylene and the appropriate metal car-bonyl.[18,22] The tendency of tetrafluoroethylene to form perfluoro-cyclobutane is well known, so presumably I and II are produced as the tetrafluoroethylene polymerizes in the presence of the carbonyls.

(I)   (II)

As an example of methods we have developed for preparing fluoro-carbon derivatives of the transition metals, the hydrometallation of fluoroölefins is of special interest, because of the variety of compounds that have already been prepared in this way, implying the existence of several new types of transition metal complexes. It has been found that transition metal hydrides will add to many highly fluorinated olefins under mild conditions of temperature and pressure, e.g.,

$$C_5H_5Mo(CO)_3H + C_2F_4 \longrightarrow C_5H_5Mo(CO)_3C_2F_4H$$

As yet this type of addition reaction has been studied most thoroughly using manganese pentacarbonyl hydride, because this compound is one of the most thermally stable of the simple metal carbonyl hydrides, and side reactions, such as formation of the metal carbonyl, are minimized. Interestingly, in those reactions studied so far, the direction of hydromanganation places the most highly fluorinated carbon atom next to manganese, e.g.,

$$HMn(CO)_5 + CF_2 : CCl_2 \longrightarrow HCCl_2CF_2Mn(CO)_5$$

Properties

Some representative fluorocarbon derivatives of transition metals are listed in Table 1. The perfluoroacyl and perfluoroalkyl derivatives of manganese and rhenium are air stable, very volatile, white to pale yellow solids. The normal boiling point of $C_2F_5Mn(CO)_5$ is near $155°$.[14] The iron compounds are also volatile, bis(perfluoroethyl) iron tetracarbonyl subliming at $25°(0.1$ mm). The bis(perfluoroalkyl) iron tetracarbonyl complexes, very pale-yellow in color, are air stable and are unaffected by moisture. However, those perfluoroalkyliron compounds which contain iodine are decomposed by moist air, the iron-iodine bonds being attacked. The perfluoroalkyliron carbonyl iodides are orange in color, while the cobalt compounds of type $C_5H_5Co(R_F)(CO)I$ are black.

TABLE 1: SOME FLUOROCARBON DERIVATIVES OF TRANSITION METALS

Compound	M.p. °C	Compound	M.p. °C
$C_2F_5COMn(CO)_5$	49–50	$C_2F_5Mn(CO)_5$	15–17
$C_3F_7CORe(CO)_5$	54	$C_3F_7Re(CO)_5$	~ 27
$(C_3F_7)_2Fe(CO)_4$	88–90	$(CF_2)_4Fe(CO)_4$	76.5–77
$CF_3Fe(CO)_4I$	91–94	$[C_2F_5Fe(CO)_3I]_2$	110–112 decomp.
$C_3F_7Co(C_5H_5)(CO)I$	120–122	$C_5H_5Co(CF_2)_4CO$	106–107
$HCClFCF_2Mn(CO)_5$	43–44	$HCF_2CF_2Mn(CO)_5$	30.5–31.5
$CF_3CF : CFFe(CO)_2C_5H_5$	70	$CF_3CF : CFMn(CO)_5$	72

In general the fluorocarbon groups of fluoroalkyl derivatives of transition metals are fairly resistant to cleavage by acid or base. Whereas perfluoroalkyltin compounds release their perfluoroalkyl groups quantitatively on treatment with aqueous base well below $100°$, reaction between $(C_2F_5)_2Fe(CO)_4$ and aqueous sodium hydroxide at $60°$ gives only a trace of pentafluoroethane, and the latter is formed in only about 20 per cent yield from $C_2F_5Fe(CO)_4I$ and concentrated sodium hydroxide at $120°$.

The effect of bromine or iodine on the fluorocarbon-metal compounds varies. Carbon monoxide and the fluorocarbon group tend to be removed, although the extent of reaction depends on the particular compound and the reaction conditions. Thus a sample of $(CF_2)_4$-$Fe(CO)_4$ has been observed to be unaffected by bromine after 60 hr at $50°$, whereas the complex $HCF_2CF_2Mn(CO)_5$ reacts with bromine at $120°$ to form HCF_2CF_2Br and carbon monoxide quantitatively.

At elevated temperatures fluorocarbon derivatives of the transition metals decompose via a fluoride shift to afford fluoroölefins, e.g.,

$$(CF_2)_4Fe(CO)_4 \xrightarrow{160°} \overline{CF_2CF{=}CFCF_2}$$

$$CF_3Fe(CO)_4I + C_2F_4 \xrightarrow{100°} (CF_2)_3$$

Studies of the infrared and ^{19}F nuclear magnetic resonance spectra of the fluorocarbon-metal compounds have provided important information. Table 2 lists the infrared bands in the carbonyl region of some

TABLE 2: INFRARED SPECTRA IN THE CARBONYL REGION OF SOME PERFLUOROALKYLIRON COMPOUNDS*

Compound	Carbonyl Stretching Frequencies
$(C_2F_5)_2Fe(CO)_4$	2151 (w); 2101, 2095 (s,d); 2083, 2078, (m,d)
$(C_3F_7)_2Fe(CO)_4$	2150 (w); 2100, 2095 (s,d); 2081, 2078, (m,d)
$CF_3Fe(CO)_4I$	2147 (m); 2107 (vw); 2087 (vs); 2054 (m)
$C_2F_5Fe(CO)_4I$	2146, 2140 (m, d); 2112 (vw); 2087 (vs); 2056 (m)
$C_3F_7Fe(CO)_4I$	2145 (m); 2111 (vw); 2088 (vs); 2054 (m)
$[C_2F_5Fe(CO)_3I]_2$	2110 (m); 2075 (vs); 2053 (s)
$[C_3F_7Fe(CO)_3I]_2$	2110 (m); 2075 (vs); 2053 (s)

*Measured in tetrachloroethylene solution, using a calcium fluoride prism.

perfluoroalkyliron compounds. The perfluoroalkyliron tetracarbonyl iodides show four carbonyl stretching bands, the number predicted by simple group theory for the *cis*-isomer. The presence of three infrared active carbonyl stretches in the spectra of bis(perfluoroalkyl) iron tetracarbonyls again suggests the presence of the *cis*-isomer.

The fluorine n.m.r. spectra of the fluorocarbon-metal compounds have been examined at 40 and 56.4 Mcs. Some of the observed chemical shifts are summarized in Table 3 along with those for certain phosphorus compounds. A number of chemical shift relationships can be deduced from these tabulated results. Two of the most important correlations appear to be the following.

(1) The chemical shift of the resonance due to the fluorine atoms of the CF_3 groups is relatively constant in both the perfluoroethyl and the perfluoropropyl compounds. Furthermore, in the latter the absorption due to the β-CF_2 group does not greatly vary from one compound to another. On the other hand, chemical shifts due to fluorine atoms of the α-CF_2 groups vary considerably from compound to compound.

(2) A large shift to low field is found for a CF_2 group bonded directly to manganese, rhenium, iron or cobalt. In contrast to this behavior, when a carbonyl group is interposed between a transition metal and a CF_2 group, no unusual shift of the α-CF_2 group absorption to low field is observed. Moreover, this shift is also absent in perfluoroalkyltin and perfluoroalkylphosphorus compounds. These relationships are discussed more fully elsewhere.[23]

TABLE 3: FLUORINE CHEMICAL SHIFTS OF SOME FLUOROCARBON METAL COMPOUNDS *†

Compound	CF_3	β-CF_2	α-CF_2
$C_2F_5Mn(CO)_5$	84.0	. . .	68.8
$C_2F_5COMn(CO)_5$	80.3	. . .	114.5
$(C_2F_5)_2Fe(CO)_4$[a]	83.7	. . .	74.0
$(C_2F_5)_2Sn(CH_3)_2$	83.7	. . .	118.9
$C_2F_5Fe(CO)_4I$	84.2	. . .	59.0
$C_3F_7Re(CO)_5$	78.5	115.1	72.7
$C_3F_7CORe(CO)_5$[a]	81.0	126.7	113.7
$(CF_2)_4Co(CO)C_5H_5$[a]	. . .	135.0	67.5
$(CF_2)_4Fe(CO)_4$	. . .	136.9	70.6
$C_3F_7Sn(C_4H_9)_3$	80.3	122.7	118.2
$HCF_2CF_2Mn(CO)_5$	. . .	121.5	59.8
$(C_3F_7)_2PCl$	81.2	122.7	120.1

*Chemical shifts are in *ppm* increasing to high field relative to CCl_3F.
†Unless otherwise stated, CCl_3F was the solvent and solution concentrations were 15 per cent or less.
[a]Tetrahydrofuran solution.

Examination of the [19]F n.m.r. spectra of the fluorocarbon derivatives of the metal carbonyls has also aided structure determinations. Thus in the hydrometallation of fluoroölefins the direction of addition of the metal-hydrogen bond to the double bond of the olefin has frequently been established by the n.m.r. spectra of the product. Furthermore, the ^{19}F n.m.r. spectra of the heterocyclic compounds I and II are in accord with the structures proposed. The spectrum of I consists of two triplets of equal intensity centered at 70.6 and 136.9 ppm, with separations indicating a spin coupling constant of 2.4 cps between fluorine atoms at the α- and β-positions. Because a CF_2 group not adjacent to a hetero-atom in cyclic perfluoro-compounds shows a resonance near 135 ppm, while the data in Table 3 show that the ^{19}F resonance of a CF_2 group adjacent to a transition metal may occur between 55–75 ppm, the triplets at 70.6 and 136.9 ppm in the spectrum of I are assigned to the α-CF_2 and β-CF_2 groups, respectively. The spectrum of II consists of two distinct multiplets at 67.5 and 135 ppm.[22] The 67.5 ppm multiplet, attributable to the α-fluorine atoms, is basically an AB pattern, indicating that the asymmetrical arrangement of ligands around the cobalt atom produces non-equivalence between the fluorine atoms on opposite sides of the ring. From the observed line separations in the 56.4 Mcs spectrum, assuming α,β-interaction to be first order, the chemical shift between the two α-fluorine atoms is calculated to be 354 cps (6.27 ppm), and the coupling constant 218 cps. The corresponding values calculated from the 40 Mcs spectrum are $\delta = 250$ cps (6.25 ppm) and $J = 218$ cps, in agreement with the interpretation proposed.

REFERENCES

1. H. J. Emeléus, *Chemistry and Industry*, 1235 (1952); *J. Chem. Soc.*, 2979 (1954).
2. R. N. Haszeldine, *Ann. Reports Chem. Soc.*, **51**, 279 (1954); *Angew. Chem.*, **66**, 693 (1954).
3. H. D. Kaesz, J. R. Phillips, and F. G. A. Stone, *Chemistry and Industry*, 1409 (1959); *J. Am. Chem. Soc.*, **82**, 6228 (1960).
4. F. G. A. Stone and P. M. Treichel, *Chemistry and Industry*, 837 (1960).
5. R. D. Chambers, H. C. Clark, and C. J. Willis, *ibid.*, 76 (1960).
6. H. C. Clark and C. J. Willis, *J. Am. Chem. Soc.*, **82**, 1888 (1960).
7. G. E. Coates, *Organo-Metallic Compounds*, (2nd ed.) London, Methuen.
8. J. J. Lagowski, *Quart. Revs.*, **13**, 265 (1959).
9. G. E. Coates and F. Glockling, Chapter 9, Am. Chem. Soc. Monograph 147, *Organometallic Chemistry*, Ed. H. Zeiss, New York, Reinhold, 1960.
10. H. H. Jaffé and G. O. Doak, *J. Chem. Phys.*, **21**, 1118 (1953); *ibid.*, **22**, 1462 (1954).
11. R. D. Closson, J. Kozikowski, and T. H. Coffield, *J. Org. Chem.*, **22**, 598 (1957).
12. W. Hieber and G. Wagner, *Ann.*, **618**, 24 (1958).
13. W. Hieber, G. Braun, and W. Beck, *Ber.*, **93**, 901 (1960).
14. H. D. Kaesz, R. B. King, and F. G. A. Stone, *Z. Naturforschg.*, **15b**, 763 (1960).

15. R. B. King, P. M. Treichel, and F. G. A. Stone, *Proc. Chem. Soc.*, 69 (1961).
16. R. B. King, S. L. Stafford, P. M. Treichel, and F. G. A. Stone, *J. Am. Chem. Soc.*, in press.
17. H. J. Emeléus, *Proc. Chem. Soc.*, 234 (1960); and references cited therein.
18. T. A. Manuel, S. L. Stafford, and F. G. A. Stone, *J. Am. Chem. Soc.*, **83**, 249 (1961).
19. R. B. King, P. M. Treichel, and F. G. A. Stone, *ibid.*, in press.
20. E. W. Abel, G. B. Hargreaves, and G. Wilkinson, *J. Chem. Soc.*, 3149 (1958).
21. E. W. Abel and G. Wilkinson, *ibid.*, 1501 (1959).
22. T. D. Coyle, R. B. King, E. Pitcher, S. L. Stafford, P. M. Treichel, and F. G. A. Stone, *J. Inorg. Nucl. Chem.*, in press.
23. E. Pitcher, A. D. Buckingham, and F. G. A. Stone, *J. Chem. Phys.*, in press.

CHROMIUM AMMINES: STABILITY AND CATALYTIC PHENOMENA

CLAUS ERIK SCHÄFFER*

Department of Inorganic Chemistry
University of Copenhagen
Copenhagen, Denmark

For many years we have been working with chromium compounds, with the main purpose of preparing samples for spectroscopic investigation. During this time we have made qualitative observations which could make the basis for interesting quantitative studies.

The object of this paper is to communicate some knowledge about the formation of chromic ammines from oxidation of chromous-ammonia solutions.

S.M. Jørgensen's[1] original procedure for the preparation of chromium(III) hexammine (luteo) is based on this oxidation which takes place spontaneously under release of hydrogen. We have tried to repeat Jorgensen's experiment, but in our case the evolution of hydrogen always takes some ten times longer than stated by Jørgensen and the formation of luteo almost completely fails. A closer inspection of Jørgensen's recipe shows its indication of the necessity of applying ammonium chloride in three times the amount that can be dissolved under the given conditions. There is not much doubt that his ammonium chloride has embedded in it one or more impurities, which have acted catalytically on the spontaneous hydrogen evolution. Mori,[2] in his improvement of Jørgensen's recipe, adds ferrous ammonium sulphate to the reaction mixture and we are here going to report other catalytic phenomena in connection with the reaction with which we are concerned.

In most of the experiments referred to here the Cr(II) has been obtained by reduction of green chromic chloride with Zn or Zn-amalgam in a solution acidified with hydrochloric acid. After having transferred the reduced solution to ammonia, the total concentrations in the deep blue solutions are Cr(II) 0.3 M, Zn 0.2 - 1 M, NH_4^+ 4 - 6 M

*Peter Andersen is thanked for his excellent experimental assistance and Professor Jannik Bjerrum for originally allotting the problem of the hexammine formation to the author as a student.

and NH_3 8 M. Sometimes the solutions contained sulphate[†], but, generally, the only anion present was chloride.

Heterogeneous Catalysts

The Pt-metals were added in 10–50 mg lots per 300 ml of chromous solution. The metals were freshly reduced by dissolving their hexa- or tetra-chloride complexes in 1–5 ml water and adding 0.5 ml 80% formic acid before boiling until reduction had taken place.[*] The addition generally had a tremendous effect.[†] A violent hydrogen formation took place, and with Pt (50 mg), which perhaps acted the best, the reaction was essentially finished after 10 min at 20°C. The rate of hydrogen evolution decreased only slightly with time throughout the reaction. In an approximate way the reaction could be said to proceed to a little more than zeroth order. If hexammine was required, cooling was preferable. At 50°C, little hexammine was formed. The solution then contained hydroxo-pentammine and dihydroxotetrammine. When metals were added as their chloro salts, they did not seem to work.[‡] They were not reduced to metals. Perhaps hydrides were formed,[3] perhaps only ammines. If auric chloride was added, a precipitate (probably the metal) formed and the violent catalytic influence gave a result similar to that mentioned for Pt. Raney Ni worked similarly to Pt, though perhaps less strongly.

A quite different kind of heterogeneous catalysis was experienced with charcoal. This substance also catalyzed the hydrogen evolution, only it worked more than an order of magnitude slower than Pt. At 30° C, the reaction proceeded as zeroth order until almost half completion, then the order increased. At 20°C, the zero order characteristics were not pronounced. However, the most conspicuous difference between the effect of charcoal and that of the other heterogenous catalysts was the final chromium(III) solution which now had an average number of bound ammonia molecules per chromium of about three. It will be shown below that we were concerned here with the equilibrium mixture.

[†]Mori[2] in his recipe for luteo formation recommends the addition of ammonium sulphate, which increases the ammonium ion concentration and results in the formation of luteo chloride sulphate which is less soluble than the chloride.

[*]Osmium was used as OsO_4 and in this case Pt(IV) and Ru(IV) sodium formate had to be added in order to bring about the reduction to metal.

[†]This was not true for Os and Ir. These metals promoted the reaction too little (see below) for hexammine to be formed. The sequence of decreasing catalytic effect upon hydrogen formation seemed to be Pt > Pd ~ Rh >> Ru >> Os $\gtrless$ Ir.

[‡]Only Pt(II), Pt(IV) and Rh(III) were tried.

Homogenous Catalysis

The divalent metal ions of the first transition series were tried as possible catalysts since Mori[2] could use the ferrous salt. Twenty-five mole per cent (relative to Cr(II)) of V^{++}, Fe^{++}, Co^{++} and Ni^{++} were added as Tutton salts. The first two metal ions had little effect, whereas the metal ions of the iron-group gave pronounced catalysis, Co^{++} acting an order of magnitude more effectively than Fe^{++} and Ni^{++}. The latter two produced a good yield of luteo salt overnight at $0°C$; the former did the same after less than two hours.

With Co^{++} the reaction has an autocatalytic development. The rate increases to a maximum and proceeds at almost zeroth order for about 75% of the entire amount of hydrogen, and falls off again near the end of the reaction. A solution to which Co had been added as $CoCl_2$ behaved similarly after filtration. This is one reason why we believe that the catalysis is homogenous. When carbonatotetraminecobalt(III) chloride was used as the cobalt source, the autocatalytic increase in reaction rate was delayed (or masked) until 25% of the reaction had taken place. This is probably due to a slow reduction of cobalt(III). With Co(II) catalysis, an increase in ammonia concentration causes a decrease in the rate of hydrogen evolution, whereas the opposite is true when no catalyst is present.[9]

Spontaneous Reaction without an Added Catalyst

The hydrogen evolution takes place even when *pro analysi* chemicals are used. Here the experiments are difficult to reproduce having a half-life of about a week at $20°C$. Common to all of them, however, is an autocatalytic development,[9] such as when cobalt(II) is added. A paraffined vessel gave some reduction in reaction rate, though it may not be significant. A very small amount of a heterogeneous catalyst would be able to assert itself, but the resemblance to the cobalt(II) catalyzed reaction, on the other hand, suggests it to be homogenous in character. This has been found recently by Taube[4] for a similar reaction with some polyamines, in which case the reaction proceeds much faster. The final mixture, as compared with the equilibrium solution, had here only a slightly higher average number of ammonia molecules bound per chromium, but distinguished itself by its wider spectrum of different ammines.

Other Methods of Oxidation

It is a rule that the faster the oxidation at a given temperature, the higher will be the number of coordinated ammonia molecules per chromium(III) ion. This seems to mean that the higher chromium(II) ammines which (according to Pecsok and Bjerrum[5]) always exist in low concentration, react much faster than the lower ammines. With air as the oxidant rhodo ions are formed as studied recently by Joyner and Wilmarth.[6] If, however, charcoal is added before the air oxidation, no rhodo is formed at all. If the oxidation is rapid and at low temperature, hydroxo-pentammine is formed because the charcoal will not have time to establish the equilibrium. Hydrogen peroxide,[6] even without charcoal, will yield an ammine mixture from which luteo and roseo can be isolated.[1]*

The Equilibrium Solution

If hexamminechromium(III) chloride is added to a chromium(II) ammine solution and then charcoal, the luteo will break down, and, after shaking for 10 minutes at 20°C, no luteo can be detected any more. The fact that the highly robust hexamminechromium(III) ion reacts so smoothly indicates strongly that the charcoal treatments lead to an equilibrium in the chromium(III) ammine system, provided Cr(II) is present. This is supported by the fact that slow air-oxidation at room temperature with charcoal present leads to the same ammine solution (proved spectroscopically) as that obtained from the spontaneous reaction with charcoal. Bjerrum[7] found an enhancing effect of Co(II) on the catalytic influence of charcoal on the cobalt(III)-ammine system. The mechanism is a redox one and a measurable amount of Co(III) gets reduced by the charcoal.[10] The reason charcoal cannot effectively catalyze the Cr(III) system when alone becomes understandable, in view of the low oxidation potential of the chromous-chromic souple. Another noteworthy difference between Co(III) and Cr(III) is that in the ammine equilibrium solution of the latter metal, no hexammine, no pentammine and perhaps no tetrammine is present. The mixture consists of bridged structures (as evidenced below) and the mononuclear units are probably mostly of triammine type.

Measurement of Oxidation Potential

We have tried to measure the redox potential in a solution brought to equilibrium with charcoal. A titration curve can be determined using the hydrogen evolved as a measure of the extent of reaction, and a mercury electrode to measure the redox potential. The potential for stoichiometrically half reaction is approximately 1060 mv below that of the normal hydrogen electrode. We have only preliminary re-

---

*By this oxidation and also by air oxidation in dilute solution (where rhode is not formed) a transient yellowish brown substance can be observed.

sults as yet, but we hope from the titration curve to be able to determine the degree of polymerization (nuclearity) of the Cr(III) ammine(s) at equilibrium. The potential mentioned has no simple meaning as in the similar cobalt ammine system,[7] but when the potential corresponding to half oxidation of the chromous-chromic aquo system (about 400 mv) is subtracted, the result indicates that the chromium-(III) hexaquo equilibrium concentration is reduced some 10^{11} times more than is the chromium(II) aquo ion. This is due partly to ammine, partly to hydroxide complex and partly to bridge formation.

Analysis of Solutions

In order to get an impression of which ammines were present in the solutions obtained, the following procedure was used. The spectra of the ammoniacal solutions were determined. Then the ammonium chloride was partially frozen out and removed, the ammonia removed by evacuation, and the resulting solution titrated with perchloric acid to an excess, giving approximately 1 M free perchloric acid. At this stage any hexammine and monomeric pentammine present had been precipitated together with ammonium perchlorate and could be identified by their spectra. Some bridged complexes could stand this treatment as exemplified by the equilibrium solution which showed a blue shift of the first absorption peak of only 5 mμ on going from the ammoniacal to the acid solutions. This figure serves as a proof of the complexes being bridged and is to be compared with the shift of 30 mμ on going from hydroxo-pentammine to aquo pentammine.*

After cleavage with hydrogen chloride, the mononuclear constituents of the bridged complexes were identified partly by precipitation reactions and partly by their spectra. A second method, and this is a very convenient one for Co(III) complexes also, was to remove the chloride with mercuric nitrate or perchlorate. This can be done in a few minutes and thus gives another check by the measurement of the spectra of the aquo ions formed (e.g., we mention the important equilibrium solution). After having demonstrated the lack of hexammine and pentammine with perchloric acid (1, 2, 6) trichlorotriamminechromium(III) alone was obtained with hydrogen chloride. The substance appeared as grayish-blue crystals of much the same color as those of chromium(III) hexaquo chloride, and gave with Hg^{++} a solution whose spectrum could be certainly identified as due to (1, 2, 3)-triaquotriamminechromium(III) ions. This result suggests that the

---

*A blue shift so small as that observed for the equilibrium solution can also be explained by a splitting off of ammonia by the influence of the acid. This is, however, not probable in view of the robustness known for the mononuclear species.

dinuclear μ-triol-di(triammine)dichromium(III) ion is the main constituent of the equilibrium solution. This conclusion is furthermore supported by the fact that the spectrum of the equilibrium solution is very similar to that of the rhodoso ion which has the same average environment[8] around the chromium nuclei.

Discussion

The method of measuring the redox potential in a Cr(II)/Cr(III) system unfortunately has limited applicability because of the limited overvoltage of the mercury electrode towards hydrogen.[7] However, stability in a chromium(III) system can, in principle, be studied by analytical procedures if equilibrium can be established with a catalyst and the catalyst can then be removed. Charcoal may work here and may also turn out to be useful for preparative purposes.

The preparative procedures that were developed in connection with this work will be published in *Inorganic Syntheses*.

REFERENCES

1. S.M. Jørgensen, *J. prakt.Chem.*, **2**, 30 1 (1884).
2. M. Mori, *J. Inst.Polytechnics Osaka*, **3**, 41 (1952).
3. L. Vaska, *J.Am.Chem.Soc.*, **83**, 756 (1961).
4. K.D. Kopple, G.F. Svatos, and H. Taube, *Nature*, **189**, 393 (1961).
5. R.L. Pecsok, and J. Bjerrum, *Acta Chem. Scand.*, **11**, 1419 (1957).
6. T.B. Joyner and W.K. Wilmarth, *J. Am. Chem. Soc.*, **83**, 516 (1961).
7. J. Bjerrum, *Metal Ammine Formation in Aqueous Solution*, Haase & Son, Copenhagen, 1941 and 1957.
8. C. Klixbüll Jörgensen, *Acta Chem. Scand.*, **10**, 887 (1956).
9. A. Asmanow, *Z. anorg. Chem.*, **160**, 209 (1927).
10. F. P. Dwyer and A. M. Sargeson, *Nature*, **187**, 1022 (1960).

PHOSPHITE COMPLEXES OF TRANSITION METALS

JOHN G. VERKADE* and T. S. PIPER†

Department of Chemistry
William Albert Noyes Laboratory of Chemistry
University of Illinois
Urbana, Illinois

One of the authors recently reported the synthesis and properties of the previously unknown phosphite ester 1-methyl-4-phospha-3,5,8-trioxabicyclo[2.2.2]octane (Phos).[1] In this article we will report on some of the unusual coordination compounds formed by this compound with transition metal ions.

This phosphite ester is derived from the triol 2-hydroxymethyl-2-methyl-1,3-propanediol and has the structure:

$$P\underset{OCH_2}{\overset{OCH_2}{\underset{\diagdown}{\overbrace{}}}}CCH_3.$$

Additional support for the postulated[1] bicyclic structure stems from the proton nmr spectrum which exhibits a methyl singlet at $+6.6$ ppm and a methylene doublet at $+3.4$ ppm with respect to chloroform. Structures of lower symmetry would reveal more proton splittings. This was shown in the spectrum of liquid triethyl phosphite which revealed a methylene pentuplet ($J_{PH} = 8$ cps) at $+3.8$ ppm and a methyl triplet ($J_{HH} = 8$ cps) at $+6.4$ ppm with respect to chloroform in a capillary. That the methylene splitting in Phos is due to proton interaction through the carbon-oxygen bond with the phosphorus nucleus ($J_{PH} = 1$ cps) is confirmed by the fact that spectrum of the 4-arsa analogue of Phos exhibits a methylene singlet at the same frequency.

Comparison of the chemical shift of phosphorus in triethyl phosphite[2] (-139 ppm) and Phos (-93 ppm) with respect to phosphoric

*Present address: Iowa State University, Ames, Iowa

†The authors are grateful to the National Science Foundation and Research Corporation for financial assistance. Mr. Joseph Nemeth and his staff of the University Microanalytical Laboratory are also to be thanked for their analytical data. The authors also wish to thank Mrs. J. Verkade of the University Infrared Laboratory for the infrared spectra.

acid yields no secure information concerning the relative electron densities around the phosphorus atom since orbitals higher than *s* are involved. It is apparent, however, from the chemical shift and the coupling constants for the phosphorus-hydrogen interaction that a change in hybridization has taken place on constraining the molecule into a bicyclic structure.

The bicyclic structure of Phos is essentially strainless. It is highly symmetric, possessing a three-fold axis of symmetry. It has an unusually high dipole moment (4.15 Debye)[3] compared to triethyl phosphite (1.82 Debye).

Previous attempts to prepare complexes with trialkyl phosphites have met with only limited success. Trialkyl phosphites form complexes with heavy transition metals such as platinum(II)[4] and a few of the post-transition metals such as mercury(II). However, first-series transition metals such as cobalt(II) and nickel(II) invariably yield only intractable oils although some reaction is indicated by color changes [5] It is interesting to note, however, that cobalt and nickel salts form a variety of stable complexes with Phos. [6]

A variety of polymeric complexes of copper (I) and silver(I) have been isolated as well as monomeric gold(I) complexes with various trialkyl phosphites [4,5]

Our experiments indicate that Phos is an excellent donor for many of the transition elements. The greater donor power of Phos is largely due to the reduction of ligand-ligand steric repulsion and elimination of steric hindrance to coordination by constraint of the alkoxy moiety.

DISCUSSION

The compounds synthesized in this work are given in Table 1 together with conductance values and probable configurations. The structures are in full accord with the conductivity data and the well-known bonding tendencies of the individual metal atom. For comparison of molar conductance (λ) values with expected values of the complexes, reference compounds have been interspersed at appropriate places.

The most remarkable aspect of this series of complexes is that for the perchlorates and nitrates, the maximum coordination number is achieved with only Phos molecules in the coordination sphere. This is the strongest experimental evidence for the low steric hindrance of this ligand.

Recently Cotton and Goodgame[8] have reported the isolation of complexes of triphenyl phosphine with various silver(I) and copper(I)

TABLE 1: CONDUCTIVITY DATA AND PROBABLE CONFIGURATIONS OF PHOS COMPLEXES

	λ	Config.
$[Cu(Phos)_4]ClO_4$ *		tetrahedral
$[Cu(Phos)_4]NO_3$	147^a	tetrahedral
$[Ag(Phos)_4]NO_3$	162^a	tetrahedral
$(n{-}C_4H_9)_4NNO_3$	158^a	
$[Ag(Phos)_4]ClO_4$	29^b	tetrahedral
$(n{-}C_4H_9)_4NClO_4$	31^b	
$[Au(Phos)_2Cl]_2^*$	5.6^a, 3.6^c	tetrahedral
$[Pd(Phos)_2Cl_2]$	2.6^a	sq. planar
$[Pt(Phos)_2Cl_2]$	5.9^a	sq. planar
$(n{-}C_2H_9)_4NBr^\dagger$	150^a, 123^c	
$[Rh(Phos)_4Cl_2]Cl \cdot 2H_2O$	153^d	octahedral
uni-univalent complex‡	$118{-}131^d$	

*Not sufficiently soluble.

†The difference in ionic conductance between the bromide and chloride (3%) is sufficiently small to justify use of the more moisture-stable bromide as a reference for the gold, platinum and palladium complexes.

‡Typical range for uni-univalent coordination compounds.

^{a}Acetonitrile; ^{b}nitrobenzene; ^{c}acetone; ^{d}water.

salts. In the case of the perchlorates, four triphenyl phosphine molecules were found in the coordination sphere. It is interesting that when nitrate is the anion, only two triphenyl phosphine molecules enter the copper(I) coordination sphere. It is probable that nitrate ion is in some way coordinated to the copper ion in the triphenyl phosphine complex.[8] Since four Phos molecules are found in the copper(I) nitrate complex, it is evident that Phos is a stronger ligand in this case.

Although two- and three-covalent gold(I) ammine complexes are known,[9] only monomeric two-covalent complexes are found with phosphorus[4,5,10] and arsenic.[10] Furthermore, these complexes possess only one phosphorus- or arsenic-containing ligand while the other coordination position is occupied by a halogen. It is significant, therefore, that the gold(I) complex of Phos is a dimeric 4-covalent system with two Phos molecules and two chlorides in the coordination sphere. Although the stoichiometry and molecular weight of the compound have been established, the structure has not. It is very probable, however, that the chlorine atoms function as bridges in the tetrahedral structure. That the gold(III) ion has indeed been reduced to the monovalent state is supported by the isolation of an unstable chloro derivative of Phos. Barnes and Hoffman[11] find that reaction of Phos with bromine yields a compound having the formulation $O{=}P(Br)(OCH_2)_2C(CH_3)CH_2Br$. The intermediate in this reaction is postulated to have the structure

and can undergo hydrolysis to the 4-oxide of Phos. [11] Since water
(from the chlorauric acid trihydrate) is present in the gold(III) reduction with Phos, a similar reaction might be expected to take place.
However, no 4-oxide of Phos could be isolated from the reaction mixture. It is probable, therefore, that cleavage by chlorine occurs before hydrolysis to the 4-oxide can take place. It is significant to
observe, however, that the oxidation product in the formation of the
copper(I) complex from the copper(II) ion is the stable 4-oxide of
Phos.

It has not as yet been determined whether the configurations of the
palladium and platinum complexes are *cis* or *trans*. The insolubility
of the compounds precluded efforts to obtain dipole moment data. It
is evident from the solubility and conductance data, however, that
these complexes are not appreciably ionized and hence are not
double salts (i.e., $[M(Phos)_4][MCl_4]$).

It is not clear at present what configuration the rhodium complex
possesses. The conductivity data in water indicates a relatively
slow aquation of both chlorides in the coordination sphere. Extrapolation of the molar conductance to zero time reveals a molar conductance corresponding to a uni-univalent electrolyte.

The C–H, C–CH$_3$ and P–O–C infrared absorptions of Phos are within
the range generally assigned to alkyl phosphites. [12] A comparison of
these readily assignable infrared absorptions in Phos and the complexes formed with this ligand reveals no significant change in any
of the frequencies.

The data obtained from the ultraviolet-visible spectra of the complexes of Phos appear in Table 2. Band maxima (λ max), extinction
coefficients (ε) and wave numbers (Δ) for the $d \longrightarrow d$ transition for
two platinum(II) complexes studied by Chatt, Gamlen and Orgel [15]
have been included for the purpose of comparison. The spectrum of
the silver complex with Phos exhibited no absorption. The rho-
dium(III) complex was insoluble in ethanol. Undoubtedly the absorption at 230 mμ in the platinum(II) complex with Phos can be assigned
to charge transfer because of its high extinction coefficient. It is
probable, however, that the absorption at 250 mμ is due to the first
spin-allowed transition in the square coplanar complex ($d_{xy} \longrightarrow$

TABLE 2: ULTRAVIOLET-VISIBLE SOLUTION SPECTRA*

	$\lambda_{max}(m\mu)$	ε	$\Delta(cm^{-2})$
$[Pt(Phos)_2Cl_2]$	230	3396	
	250	1165	40,000
trans-$[Pt(piperidine)(P(OMe)_3)Cl_2]$[13]	299	319	33,400
trans-$[Pt(piperidine)_2Cl_2]$[13]	315	78	31,750
$[Au(Phos)_2Cl]_2$	230	4000	
$[Cu(Phos)_4]ClO_4$	213 (shoulder)	9800	
$[Pd(Phos)_2Cl_2]$	230	3400	

*Ethanolic solutions of the order of 0.001 M were employed in all cases.

$d_{x^2-y^2}$). Chatt and co-workers [13] observed that substituting one trimethyl phosphite molecule for a piperidine molecule in the complex trans-dichloro-bis-piperidine-platinum(II) resulted in an increase in extinction coefficient and a decrease in wave length for the $d \rightarrow d$ spin allowed transition (see Table 2). It is not unexpected,* therefore, that two Phos molecules cause a further increase in extinction coefficient ($\varepsilon = 1165$). If it is assumed that the absorption at 250 mμ is due to the $d \rightarrow d$ spin-allowed transition, it is apparent from the energies of separation that the ligand-field of Phos in platinum(II) is greater than that of trimethyl phosphite.

It has been postulated that trimethyl phosphite is capable of accepting electron density from the π-orbitals of the platinum atom as well as donating electron density through the σ-bond. [13] Results of the hydrolysis experiments of Barnes and Hoffman indicate that Phos is a poorer electron donor than trimethyl phosphite. It may well be that a relatively large amount of π-bonding, in addition to low ligand-ligand repulsion, accounts for the high energy of separation in the $d \rightarrow d$ transition of the platinum(II) complex of Phos.

Under the conditions employed in this research complexes of Phos with chromium(II), manganese(II), iron(II), zinc(II), cadmium(II), mercury(I) and mercury(II) were not observed. It has been proposed [14] that the weakening of phosphine complexes on passing from silver to cadmium is an indication that the strength of the dative π-bonding from the metal atom to the ligand declines sharply at the end of a transition series. It is possible that the same reasoning holds for the isolation of stable complexes of Phos with copper, silver and

---

*Although the configuration of the platinum(II) complex with Phos is unknown, the configuration is irrelevant for the crystal-field splitting in the approximation of pure d-orbitals.

gold and the apparent lack of such complexes with zinc, cadmium and mercury. The stability of the d^5 configuration in manganese(II) may preclude coordination by Phos. It is possible that more vigorous reaction conditions are necessary to cause coordination of Phos with the other metal ions.

REFERENCES

1. J. G. Verkade and L. T. Reynolds, *J. Org. Chem.*, **25**, 663 (1960).
2. J. Van Wazer, C. Callis, J. Shoolery, and R. Jones, *J. Am. Chem. Soc.*, **78**, 5715.
3. To be published elsewhere.
4. A. E. Arbuzov and V. Zoroastrova (Kazan State Univ.), *Izvest. Akad. Nauk SSSR Otdel, Khim. Nauk*, 1952; 809–17; *Chem. Abstracts,* **47**, 9898h (1953).
5. A. E. Arbuzov and V. Zoroastrova (Kazan State Univ.), *Doklady Akad. Nauk SSSR* **84**, 503–6 (1952); *Chem. Abstracts*, **46**, 10038f (1952).
6. To be published.
7. M. Sneed and J. Maynard, *General Inorganic Chemistry*, D. Van Nostrand Company, New York, 1942, p. 813.
8. F. A. Cotton and D. M. L. Goodgame, *J. Chem. Soc.*, 5267 (1961).
9. N. V. Sidgwick, *The Chemical Elements and Their Compounds,* Clarendon Press, Oxford, 1950, Vol. 1, p. 137.
10. *Ibid.*, p. 140.
11. R. A. Barnes and J. A. Hoffman, in press.
12. L. Bellamy, *The Infrared Spectra of Complex Molecules,* John Wiley & Sons, Inc., New York, (2nd ed.), 1958.
13. J. Chatt, G. A. Gamlen, and L. E. Orgel, *J. Chem. Soc.*, 1047 (1959).
14. S. Ahrland, J. Chatt, N. R. Davies, and A. A. Williams, *J. Chem. Soc.*, 1403 (1958).

STUDIES OF SOME CARBON COMPOUNDS OF THE TRANSITION METALS. PART III. THE CRYSTAL STRUCTURE OF TRI-CYCLOPENTADIENYLTRINICKEL DICARBONYL*

A. A. HOCK and **O. S. MILLS***

Department of Chemistry
University of Manchester
Manchester, England

It has been known for some years that carbon, when linked to oxygen, nitrogen or, recently, ring systems, can act as a bridge between two metal atoms. More recently it has been proposed that carbon can bridge three such atoms. Thus in the cation[1,2] $[(C_6H_6)_3Co_3(CO)_2]^+$ and the neutral paramagnetic $[(C_5H_5)_3Ni_3(CO)_2]$, of the two structural models considered,[3] the one preferred contains CO groups linked symmetrically to three metal atoms (see Fig. 1). Recently[4] it has been proposed that the structures of compounds of the type $[Co_3(CO)_9-(RC_2H)H]$, (e.g., R = H, CH_3, phenyl)[4,5] also contain a carbon atom likewise attached to three cobalt atoms, but in these compounds the carbon atoms concerned presumably form four single bonds. The object of this investigation was to verify the over-all molecular geometry and to obtain, if possible, accurate values of the $C\!=\!C$ and $C\!=\!O$ bond lengths, though it was realised at the outset that in structures of this kind which involve a high proportion of the scattering electrons in heavy atoms, it is precisely these values which are subject to least precision. A sample of $[(C_5H_5)_3Ni_3(CO)_2]$ was kindly supplied to us by Professor E. O. Fischer.

Crystal Data

Tricyclopentadienyltrinickel dicarbonyl, $[(C_5H_5)_3Ni_3(CO)_2]$. Hexagonal, $a = 9.26 \pm 0.05$, $c = 10.70 \pm 0.06$ Å. Volume of unit cell 794 ± 14 Å.[3]

---

*We thank the Department of Scientific and Industrial Research for a grant towards X-ray apparatus, and Esso Research Ltd. for a grant towards the expenses of this work. We are indebted to the staff of the Computing Machine Laboratory, University of Manchester for permission to use the MERCURY computer, to Dr. J. S. Rollett, whose S.F.L.S. programme[12] was used extensively, and to Dr. R. A. Sparks for his molecular geometry and distance-angles programmes.[12]

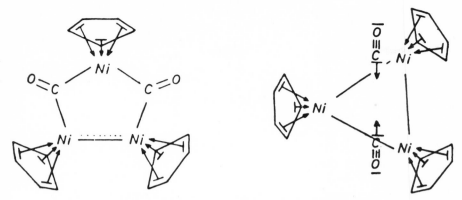

Fig. 1. Possible structures considered by Fischer and Palm.

Density (measured) 1.81 ± 0.02 g-cm^{-3}.
Density (calculated) 1.79 ± 0.04 g-cm^{-3}.
Two formula units per unit cell.
Systematic absences: 001 when l odd (observed up to l = 11).
Probable space groups: $P6_3$ or $P6_3/m$.
Absorption coefficient for Co K_α radiation = 66.8 cm^{-1}.

Experimental

Three-dimensional Weissenberg diffraction data were collected by the multiple film method (Co K_α radiation) from a single crystal whose maximum dimension did not exceed 0.2 mm. This yielded 329 unique reflections of which 37 were too weak to be estimated. Intensities were measured visually. No corrections for absorption were applied.

Solution of the Structure

The structure has been determined without recourse to chemical assumptions, though we have been guided by the chemical formula. The systematic absences in the diffraction data can arise from either of the space groups $P6_3$ or $P6_3/m$; amongst other symmetry elements the former space group contains a pair of three-fold axes, whereas the latter, in addition, contains two mirror planes perpendicular to these axes (i.e., inverse hexads) at $z = \frac{1}{4}, \frac{3}{4}$. The six nickel atoms per unit cell can be accommodated therein, subject to the space group requirements, in three ways:

1. Linear symmetric: Three nickel atoms per molecule are located on each three-fold axis. In space group $P6_3/m$ the central atom lies in the mirror plane.

2. Linear unsymmetric: The atoms are located on the three-fold axes as in (1). This arrangement is incompatible with space group $P6_3/m$.

3. Equilateral triangular: The three-fold axes pass through the centres of the triangles. The z coordinates of all the nickel atoms can become $\frac{1}{4}$, $\frac{3}{4}$.
The alternatives (1) and (3) are shown in Fig. 2.

The space group requirements can only be satisfied if the carbonyl groups lie on the three-fold axes. The cyclopentadiene groups must occupy general positions in spacegroup $P6_3$ so that their orientation is unrestricted by symmetry, but in the space group $P6_3/m$ they must either lie in, or be perpendicular to, the mirror planes. These two arrangements correspond to σ- and possible π-bonding alternatives. All of these groups have been located without further assumption.

Electron density along 3-fold axis.
at x=2/3, y=1/3.

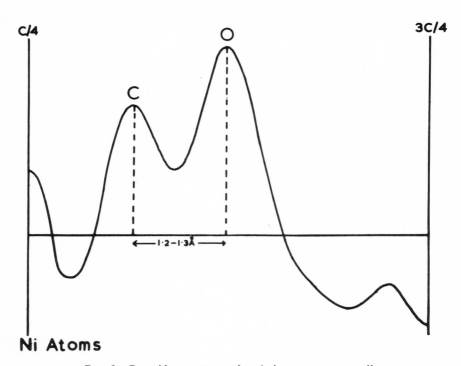

Fig. 2. Possible positions of nickel atoms in unit cell.

The nickel atoms were located from the three-dimensional Patterson synthesis $P(UVW)$, and in particular from the Harker sections $P(UVO)$ and $P(UV\frac{1}{2})$. The two model systems (i.e., linear and triangular) give rise to distinctive interatomic vector peaks perpendicular to the c axis. These are shown in Fig. 3 together with the experimentally determined sections. It is clear that the triangular arrangement holds, and from it we deduce that the Ni=Ni separation is $ca.$ 2.4 Å.

The second structural feature, the three-point attachment of the carbonyl group, was confirmed by evaluation of the electron density along the three-fold axis. The phases assigned to the observed structure amplitudes were derived from the Ni positions deduced above. As the phases are based on these atoms alone, at this stage, the resulting electron density calculation shows mirror symmetry about the plane containing the nickel atoms irrespective of which space group is assumed. Hence the CO groups should appear symmetrically above and below the nickel ring. This electron density calculation is shown in Fig. 4. Only two pairs of peaks occured and the first, and smaller, peak was at a reasonable distance from the nickel atoms ($ca.$ 2 Å.). There was no evidence, e.g., the presence of "ghost" peaks on the axis, to suggest any other less symmetrical arrangement of the CO groups.

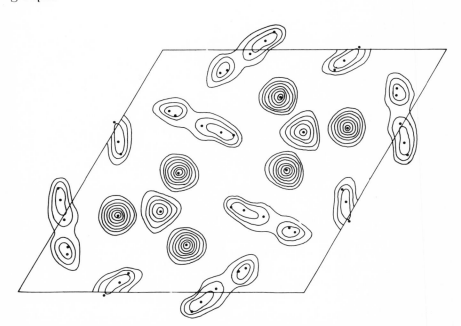

Fig. 3. Comparison of Harker sections with linear and triangular models.

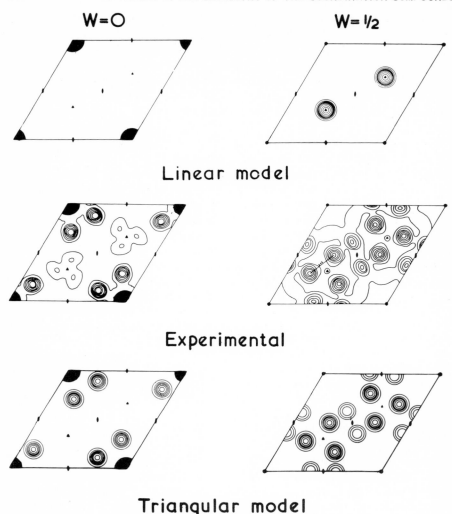

Fig. 4 Electron density along 3-fold axis.

The final structural feature was determined by calculation of the electron density projected down the c axis. The phases assigned were based on the positions of the Ni atoms and CO groups and one typical such projection is shown in Fig. 5, which clearly shows the cyclopentadiene rings parallel to the projection and perpendicular to the lines joining the Ni atoms to the centre of the triangles. The structure thus fully confirms the prediction of Fischer and Palm.

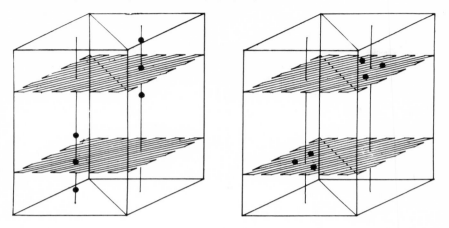

Fig. 5. Fourier projection down c axis.

Refinement of the Structure

The less symmetrical arrangement given by space group $P6_3$ does not constrain the five-membered ring to be perpendicular to the plane of the nickel atoms, nor restrict one of the carbons to lie in that plane, nor need the CO groups lie symmetrically above and below the plane. In an attempt to determine these more detailed features of the molecule we refined the atomic positions and thermal parameters, by the method of least-squares, consistent with the requirements of space group $P6_3$.

The nickel atoms alone result in relative phases of 0 and π and such deviations as occur from these values are due only to the movements of the light atoms away from the symmetrical positions. We found that the refinement of the atomic positions of the five-membered ring was slow and erratic. When the maximum shift had eventually been reduced to less than 0.01 Å, a set of bond lengths were calculated. It was quite clear that the model which we were using was not an adequate representation of the detailed structure in the crystal, although the agreement index $R = \Sigma\,||Fo| - |Fc||\,/\Sigma\,|Fo|$ had been reduced to less than 10%, for the C—C distances within the rings were highly improbable, e.g., variations between 1.30 and 1.60 Å. In spite of this disagreeable feature, it was also clear that the over-all picture was correct independent of the low value of R. For, although these carbon atoms showed C—C variations of up to 0.3 Å, nevertheless they were fairly accurately coplanar (the maximum deviation from the best least-squares plane through these atoms was less than 0.02 Å). Further, the normal to this least-squares plane was parallel with the line from the centre of the nickel triangle through the nickel atom within an angle of 0.5° which is well within experimental error. Thirdly, the Ni—C distances were much more consistent (2.13 – 2.17 Å) than the C—C distances involving the same carbon atoms. This implies that the carbon atoms lay on the circumference of a circle whose origin lay on the extended line from the centre of the nickel ring through the nickel atom and whose plane was normal to this line. The radius of this circle was found to be 1.21 Å and this corresponds to a regular pentagon of side 1.43 Å. We hence conclude that the model is insufficient to describe the lateral distribution of electron density within the ring, and this is probably because the cyclopentadienyl rings are disordered in the solid. We have sought to represent the features of the molecule in this region by a "smeared" cyclopentadiene ring involving two regular pentagons superimposed but with angular separation of 36°. This disordered model gives an adequate representation of the electron distribution in this position as shown by a difference synthesis calculation in the plane of the smeared rings. The introduction of this disorder implies a symmetry consistent with that of the space group $P6_3/m$ when taken together with the position of the rings. We have, therefore, completed the refinement in this space group. During the latter stages the atomic positions of the smeared carbons were not permitted to shift. The refinement was based on 291 non-zero reflections, reflection 002 being omitted on the grounds that it probably suffered from extinction. All of the 37 unobserved reflections have structure factors which calculate less than the minimum observed.

Discussion

The over-all geometry clearly confirms the structure first suggested by Fischer and Palm. Due to the rotational disorder present in the crystal, we are unable to determine accurate Ni—C(ring) or C—C distances within the cyclopentadiene ring. However, the results are consistent with the reported Ni—C and C—C distances in $(C_5H_5)_2Ni$. A list of distances, together with their estimated standard deviations, is given in Table 1, and a list of atomic coordinates in Table 2. A list of calculated and observed structure factors can be obtained from the authors. The final value of the agreement index, R, is 9.4% for the 291 reflections.

The nickel atoms form an exactly equilateral triangle by crystal symmetry and the CO groups are, for the same reason, exactly equidistant from each nickel atom. Few values of Ni—Ni bond lengths have been reported. In the metal the distance is 2.49 Å. There appears to be evidence for a gradual reduction in metal-metal separa-

TABLE 1: INTERATOMIC DISTANCES.

	$\overset{\circ}{A}$.	$\sigma(\overset{\circ}{A})$.
Ni—Ni	2.39	0.00_7
Ni—C (carbonyl)	1.93	0.01_5
C—O	1.19	0.02_5
Ni—C (ring)	2.12	
C—C (ring, implied)	1.41	
Ni—C—O	$134°$	
Ni—C(carbonyl)-Ni	$77°$	

tions for the series Fe—Co—Ni as shown below:

	Distance $\overset{\circ}{A}$	3σ	Ref.
Fe, Fe	2.46 Å	...	6
	2.49	0.02	7
	2.49	0.01	8
Co, Co	2.47	...	9
	2.46	0.02	10
	2.43	0.01	11
Ni, Ni	2.39		

The Ni—C (carbonyl) distance must be close to that expected for a single bond. It is difficult to decide what radius should be ascribed to the carbon atom in this arrangement, but a value between 0.74 and 0.77 would lead to expected Ni—C distances of 1.94-1.97 Å. The experimental value is in accord with these.

The C—O distance is 1.19 Å. It is hard to predict, even in retrospect, what might have been expected for this length, and although infrared absorption occurs at low wavenumbers (e.g., 1625 cm^{-1} in $[(C_6H_6)_3Co_3(CO)_2]^+$),[2] it has been established that CO absorption frequencies may be modified without change of bond type. The distances between molecules corresponds to van der Waals separations.

TABLE 2: ATOMIC COORDINATES

	x/a	y/b	z/c
Ni	0.5091	0.3146	1/4
C (carbonyl)	2/3	1/3	0.3757
O (carbonyl)	2/3	1/3	0.4871
Carbon atoms of the smeared rings	0.2489	0.1421	1/4
	0.2605	0.1705	0.3159
	0.2906	0.2448	0.3567
	0.3278	0.3368	0.3567
	0.3579	0.4111	0.3159
	0.3695	0.4395	1/4

REFERENCES

1. E. O. Fischer and O. Beckert, *Angew. Chem.*, **70**, 744 (1958).
2. P. Chini and R. Ercoli, *Gazz. Chim. Ital.*, **88**, 1171 (1959).
3. E. O. Fischer and C. Palm, *Chem. Ber.*, **91**, 1725 (1958).
4. U. Krüerke and W. Hübel, *Chem and Ind.*, 1264 (1960).
5. R. Markby, I. Wender, R. A. Friedel, F. A. Cotton, and H. W. Sternberg, *J. Am. Chem. Soc.*, **80**, 6529 (1958).
6. H. M. Powell and R. V. G. Ewens, *J. Chem. Soc.*, 286 (1939).
7. O.S. Mills, *Acta Cryst.*, **11**, 620 (1958).
8. A. A. Hock and O. S. Mills, *Acta Cryst.*, **14**, 139 (1961).
9. W. G. Sly, *J. Am. Chem. Soc.*, **81**, 18 (1959).
10. O. S. Mills and G. Robinson, unpublished results on the triclinic form of $Co_2(CO)_9HCCH$.
11. O. S. Mills and G. Robinson, unpublished results on the orthorhombic form of $Co_2(CO)_9HCCH$.
12. O. S. Mills and J. S. Rollett, *Glasgow Conference on Computing Methods and the Phase Problem in X-ray Crystal Analysis*, 1960, Pergamon Press, New York, 1961.

RELATIVE RATES OF ALKALINE HYDROLYSIS OF SOME *CIS* AND *TRANS* COMPLEX IONS OF THE TYPE [Coen $_2$(OCOR) $_2$] $^+$

FERRUCCIO APRILE, VINCENZO CAGLIOTI, VINCENZO CARUNCHIO, and GABRIELLO ILLUMINATI

Instituti di Chimica Generale delle Universita di Roma e di Trieste, Italy, and Centro di Chimica Generale del C. N. R., Rome, Italy

Reactivity problems in coordination chemistry can be approached in a number of different ways, among which are studies of the structural effects on reaction rates of the transition metal, the inert ligands and the displaced ligand.[1] For a given transition metal and a given reaction, an extensive knowledge of these effects can provide useful information about susceptibilities to polar changes, mechanism of electronic transmission, steric requirements and possible correlations with reaction paths.

The conjugated bases of carboxylic acids are ligands which are very suitable for extensive investigation of the effect of the displaced ligand in the hydrolysis reaction. The first application of this approach was reported by Basolo, Bergmann and Pearson[2] in the case of the ions $[Co(NH_3)_5OCOR]^{++}$, containing aliphatic carboxylato groups. A system which deserves special attention is the bis(ethylenediamine) complex ion $[Coen_2(OCOR)_2]^+$ as it allows the study of *cis-trans* pairs and is accessible to aliphatic as well as aromatic carboxylato ligands.

We have reported the rate data for the alkaline hydrolysis of the complexes of the aromatic series elsewhere.[3] In this paper we wish to present, in a preliminary form, similar data from current investigations with the complexes of the aliphatic series and to compare these with all available data concerning the displaced ligand of the general type RCO_2^-. Such data are collected in Table 1. The rate behavior, as displayed by these data, differs markedly from that shown by either $[Co(NH_3)_5OCOCR_3]^{++}$ or $[Coen_2(OCOC_6H_4X)_2]^+$ ions. There are two convenient bases of comparison with the data at hand: the correlation with the acid strengths of the carboxylic acids from which the displaced ligands are derived, and the effect of the *cis-trans* configuration.

TABLE 1: RELATIVE RATES OF ALKALINE HYDROLYSIS OF THE FIRST FUNCTIONAL GROUP IN SOME CIS AND TRANS $[COEN_2(OCOR)_2]CIO_4$ COMPLEXES IN WATER AT 25° (*).

R	Cis complexes	Trans complexes	Trans/cis Rate Ratio	$[Co(NH_3)_5OCOR]^{++}$ (Ref. 2)†
H	2.5	10.6	4.2	—
CH_2Cl	—	7.7	—	5.9
$CH_2C_6H_5$	0.25	0.62	2.4	—
CH_3	0.46	1	2.2	1
CH_2CH_3	0.19	0.35	1.8	0.64
$CH(CH_3)_2$	0.11	0.22	2.1	0.79
$C(CH_3)_3$	0.017	0.028	1.6	0.43

* Rates relative to trans-$[Coen_2(OCOCH_3)_2]^+ (= 1)$.
‡ Rates relative to $[Co(NH_3)_5OCOCH_3]^{++} (= 1)$.

Correlation with the Acid Strength of Carboxylic Acids

Several plots of the log k's for the alkaline hydrolysis of the complexes vs the log K_a's for the dissociation of the carboxylic acids are shown in Fig. 1. As already pointed out by Basolo et al.,[2] there is a fair correlation for the pentammine complexes (aliphatic series) with no significant steric effect of the increasing size of the alkyl group from methyl to t-butyl or of the varying size of the groups of the type CH_mX_n $(m + n = 3)$ (Plot 2).

A fair correlation is also found in our recent work[3] with the trans-bis(ethylenediamine) complexes of the aromatic series even though it involves a more limited range of pK_a's (Plot 3, empty circles). Also the susceptibilities to the change in polarity of the ligands in these two cases are not too different as indicated by the slopes of the solid lines. In contrast to this, bis(ethylenediamine) complexes of the aliphatic series show no general correlation with acid strengths and the behavior is essentially similar in the cis and trans series (Plot 1, empty and solid circles). The comparison is particularly significant with the pentammine complexes. A reasonably narrow band parallel to line 2 embraces the trans data for all $R = CH_2X$ groups $(X = H, CH_3, Cl, C_6H_5)$ and leaves the data for $R = H$ (having distinctly less steric requirements) above the line and the data for $R = CH(CH_3)_2$ and $C(CH_3)_3$ (in the order of increasing steric requirements) below the line. From Table 1 it can be seen that the ratio k_{CH_2Cl}/k_{CH_3} for $[Coen_2(OCOR)_2]^+$ is 5.7, very close to the value (5.9) for the corresponding ratio for $[Co(NH_3)_5OCOR]^{++}$. Also the ratio k_{Alk}/k_{CH_3} decreases quite rapidly from methyl to t-butyl in the former complexes but only slightly in the latter.

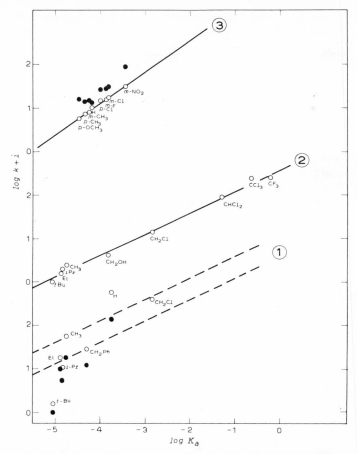

Fig. 1. Correlation of rate data for the alkaline hydrolysis of Co(III) complexes containing organic acido ligands with the dissociation constants of carboxylic acids in water at 25°. Plot 1: $[Coen_2(OCOR)_2]^+$, cis (solid circles) and trans (empty circles) series (this work), Plot 2: $[Co(NH_3)_5-OCOR]^{++}$ (ref. 2). Plot 3: $[Coen_2(OCOC_6H_4X)_2]^+$, cis (solid circles) and trans (empty circles) series (ref. 3). The dotted band for this plot is referred to the *trans* data; a similar bond can be drawn for the *cis* data. The log k's are reported on an arbitrary scale, *i* being an integer number.

Effect of *Cis-Trans* Configuration

The main differences in the effects of configuration of the complexes $[Coen_2(OCOR)_2]ClO_4$, with regard to dependence on the nature of the displaced ligand, can be stated as follows: (1) in the aliphatic series the *trans* isomers have been found in all cases to be more reactive than the *cis* isomers (Table 1) while the reverse is true in the aromatic series; (2) in the aromatic series the *cis* isomers show poor linear correlation with the dissociation constants of the acids in contrast to the *trans* isomers (Plot 3, solid circles). The deviations are in the direction of "increased" reactivity, as clearly shown by the effect of a *para* methoxygroup which is abnormally activating (Plot 3, solid circles). In the aliphatic series neither *cis* nor *trans* isomers show linear correlation with acid strengths.

Conclusions

The reactions of $[Co(NH_3)_5OCOR]^{++}$ ions and of $[Coen_2(OCOR)_2]^+$ ions have similar susceptibilities to the polar effects of the displaced ligands. However, in contrast to the pentammine complexes containing aliphatic ligands, the aliphatic series of the bis(ethylenediamine) complexes is much more susceptible to steric effects due to the size of the alkyl group in the RCO_2^- ligand. Such steric effects are retarding and depend on the *cis-trans* configuration, but to a minor extent. They are equally consistent with either an S_N2 or an S_N1CB mechanism, and in the latter case require that the pre-equilibrium stage rather than the subsequent dissociation stage be involved. Also, in agreement with a previous assumption,[3] the abnormal behavior of the *cis* aromatic series is of different origin and probably is a rate-accelerating field and/or solvation effect consistent with the dissociative stage of an S_N1CB mechanism. Whereas there are indications for the hydrolysis in the aromatic series $[Coen_2(OCOAr)_2]^+$ to involve cobalt-oxygen bond cleavage (3), nothing can be said at present for the hydrolysis in the aliphatic series $[Coen_2(OCOR)_2]^+$. This point should (and will) be further investigated. The present results have also stimulated extension of the work to other carboxylic acids and, even, to other classes of organic acids for use as displaced ligands in alkaline hydrolysis.

Experimental

The preparation of the bis(ethylenediamine) complexes of the aliphatic series have been reported previously[4] except for the pivalate and the phenylacetate terms. The alkaline hydrolysis was followed kinetically by a potentiometric titration procedure as described elsewhere.[3] The configuration of the complexes was determined by spectral measurements in the visible region.[3]

REFERENCES

1. For extensive surveys on the subject, see F. Basolo and R. G. Pearson, *Mechanism of Inorganic Reactions*, J. Wiley and Sons, Inc., New York, 1958; and D. R. Stranks in J. Lewis and R. G. Wilkins' *Modern Coordination Chemistry*, Interscience Publishers, New York, 1960.

2. F. Basolo, J. G. Bergmann and R. G. Pearson, *J. Phys. Chem.*, **56**, 22 (1952).
3. F. Aprile, V. Caglioti and G. Illuminati, *J. Inorg. Nucl. Chem.*, in press.
4. V. M. Linhard and G. Stirn, *Z. anorg. allg. Chem.*, **268**, 105 (1952).

CHELATE CATALYSED AUTOXYDATION
OF IRON(II) COMPLEXES

THOMAS KADEN AND SILVIO FALLAB

Anstalt für Anorganische Chemie
der Universität Basel
Basel, Switzerland

Vor einiger Zeit studierten wir die Reaktion des Bis-(1-hydrazino-phtalazin)-Eisen(II)-Komplexes (Fig. 1a) mit O_2.[1] Verschiedene Beobachtungen führten uns zum Schluss, dass die Hydrazinogruppe zur Hydrazyl-Radikalstufe oxydiert wird und anschliessend innerhalb des Koordinationsverbands eine Dimerisierung zweier solcher Radikalliganden zu einem Tetrazan stattfindet, das als 3-zähniger Ligand an das zentrale Fe^{II} gebunden bleibt (Fig. 1b).

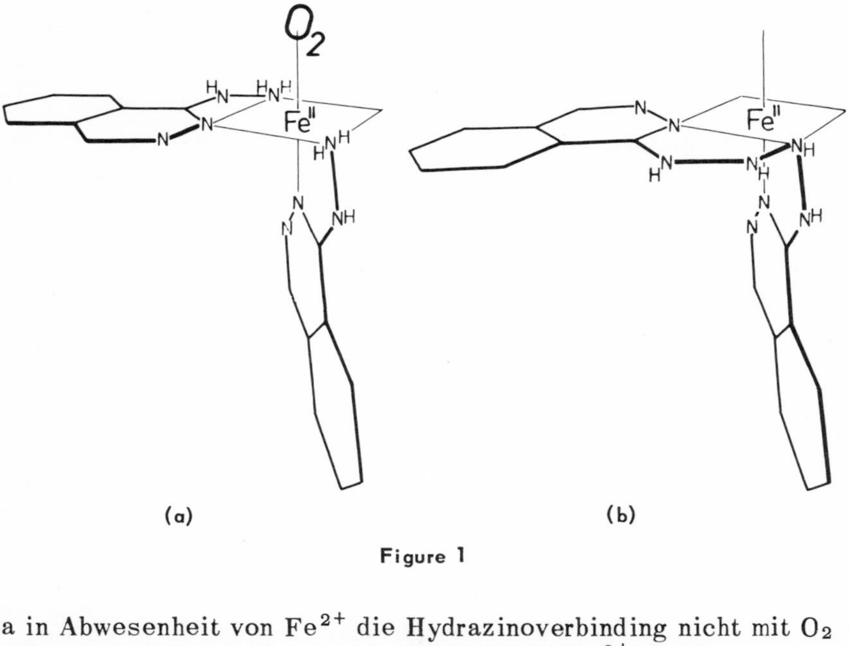

(a)   (b)

Figure 1

Da in Abwesenheit von Fe^{2+} die Hydrazinoverbinding nicht mit O_2 reagiert, handelt es sich um eine spezifische Fe^{2+}-Katalyse. Auf Grund kinetischer Messungen konnten wir zeigen, dass die Oxydation

durch Anlagerung eines O_2-Moleküls an einer freien Koordinations-
stelle des Fe^{II}-Hydrazinophthalazinkomplexes eingeleitet wird (Fig.
1*a*).

Ueber den Mechanismus des geschwindigkeitsbestimmenden Oxyda-
tionsschrittes konnte nichts Sicheres ausgesagt werden. Die folgenden drei Möglichkeiten müssen diskutiert werden:

1. Elektronenübergang von der Base auf O_2.

$$[Fe^{II}(-NH_2)(O_2)] \longrightarrow [Fe^{II}(-NH_2^{+})(O_2^{-})] \tag{1}$$

2. H-Transfer von der Hydrazinogruppe auf O_2.

$$[Fe^{II}(-NH_2)(O_2)] \longrightarrow [Fe^{II}(-NH \cdot)(HO_2)] \tag{2}$$

3. Oxydation zum entsprechenden Fe^{III}-Komplex durch O_2 (3*a*) und
anschliessend Oxydation der Hydrazinogruppe durch Fe^{III} (3*b*).

$$[Fe^{II}(-NH_2)(O_2)] \longrightarrow [Fe^{III}(-NH_2) + O_2^{-}] \tag{3a}$$

$$[Fe^{III}(-NH_2)] \longrightarrow [Fe^{II}(-NH \cdot)] + H^{+} \tag{3b}$$

Dieses Problem gab uns den Anstoss zum Studium von Reaktionen
vom Typus (3*a*) auf breiterer Basis. Wir versuchten, Anhaltspunkte
über die Tendenz zur Realisierung des Elektronenübergangs (4) in

$$Fe^{II}X + O_2 \longrightarrow Fe^{III}X + O_2^{-} \tag{4}$$

Abhängigkeit von der Natur des Liganden X zu gewinnen, der selbst
gegen Oxydation mit O_2 stabil sein soll.*

Ueber die Wirkung von organischen Komplexbildnern X auf die Geschwindigkeit von (4) ist bisher, abgesehen von Beobachtungen
qualitativer Art (siehe z.B. A.Szent-Györgyi *et al.*),[8] wenig Sicheres
bekannt geworden. In einer Review jüngeren Datums von R. J. P.
Williams[9] wird das Problem in Zusammenhang mit der Autoxydierbar-
keit biologischer Fe^{II}-Systeme, der Porphyrine, diskutiert.

Die Resultate unserer bisher durchgeführten, zum Teil bereits
publizierten Reaktionsstudien[10, 11] lassen sich ganz kurz in einer
Regel zusammenfassen: Komplexbildner X, die über N-Atome an das
zentrale Fe^{II} gebunden sind, haben keinen oder nur geringen Einfluss auf die Geschwindigkeit von (4), währenddem Komplexbildner
mit O-Ligandatomen den Elektronenübergang (4) stark begünstigen.

Es liegt nahe, diese bemerkenswerten Reaktivitätsunterschiede auf
Verschiedenheiten in der Elektronenstruktur von $Fe^{II}X$ zurückzu-

---

*Reaktion (4) war in den vergangenen Jahren Gegenstand verschiedener
kinetischer Untersuchüngen. Insbesondere ist die katalytische Wirkung
anorganischer Liganden X in saurer Lösung studiert worden: Cl^{-},[2] F^{-},[3]
ClO_4^{-},[4] SO_4^{2-},[5] $H_2PO_4^{-}$,[6] $H_2P_2O_7^{2-}$.[7]

führen. Der im folgenden skizzierte Versuch, die katalytische Wirkung von RO^--Liganden auf die Autoxydation von Fe^{II}-Partikeln durch einzelne Bindungseffekte zu erklären, soll vorerst im Sinne einer Arbeitshypothese aufgefasst werden, die durch das vorliegende Untersuchungsmaterial noch nicht als bewiesen angesehen werden darf.

Es kann angenommen werden, dass bei der Reaktion von $Fe^{II}X$ mit O_2 ein kurzlebiger Stosskomplex $[Fe^{II}(X)(O_2)]$ entsteht.† Ueberlappung eines π^*2p Antibindungsorbital des O_2-Moleküls mit einem d_ε-orbital des Fe^{II} dürfte einen wesentlichen Bindungsanteil liefern. Der Elektronenübergang (4) kann daher sinnvoll mit (5) wiedergegeben werden (Koordinaten entsprechend der schematischen Darstellung in Fig. 2).

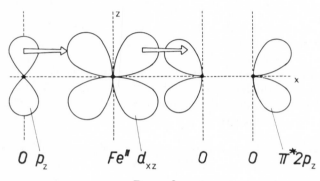

Figure 2

$$[Fe^{II}(d_{xz})^2]\,[O_2(\pi^*2p_z)] \longrightarrow [Fe^{III}(d_{xz})]\,[O_2(\pi^*2p_z)^2] \qquad (5)$$

Eine solche Formulierung stellt natürlich nur ein grob vereinfachtes Schema des sich in Wirklichkeit abspielenden Vorgangs dar. Sie lässt aber verstehen, wie die Art der Bindung in $Fe^{II}X$ den Elektronenübergang (4) be-einflussen kann. Wenn $X = RO^-$, besteht infolge $p_\pi d_\pi$-Ueberlappung die Möglichkeit einer π-Donorbindung (Fig. 2), die die Elektronendichte in der d_ε Untergruppe erhöht und somit den Elektronenübergang auf O_2 begünstigt.* Die Bindung Fe^{II}-N ist in

---

†Diese Vermutung wird unter anderem gestützt durch die Tatsache, dass die Aktivierungsenergien von Reaktion (4) relativ gering sind. So wurde z.B. für X = Sulfosalicylsäure $E_A \leqslant 5700$ cal/mol gefunden.[10] Zum gleichen Schluss gelangen P. George und J. S. Griffith[12] bei ihrer Diskussion der möglichen Reaktionsmechanismen für (4).

*Ein ähnliches Argument gebrauchen R. G. Pearson und F. Basolo[13] zur Deutung ihrer kinetischen Resultate bei Hydrolysenversuchen mit Pt^{II}- und Co^{III}-Komplexen.

erster Linie eine σ-Donorbindung, die die Elektronen in d_ε nur wenig beinflusst. Der π-Elektronenpush durch RO^--Liganden wird verstärkt, wenn R selbst π-Donor-Eigenschaften hat, wie z.B. beim Phenolat-Anion. Diese Erwartung konnte bestätigt werden durch Versuche mit den Fe^{II}-Komplexen von Sulfosalicylsäure,[10] Brenzcatechin-*3,5*-disulfonsäure und *1,8*-Dihydroxynaphthalin-*3,6*-disulfonsäure,[11] in welchen Fe^{11} im Vergleich zu $FeOH^+$ eine stark erhöhte Autoxydationstendenz zeight.

Um unsere Hypothese weiter zu untermauern, untersuchten wir in der vorliegenden Arbeit den Einfluss von bestimmten Donorgruppen auf die Geschwindigkeit von (4) an einer Serie von räumlich ähnlich gebauten Liganden X. Wir wählten hierfür mehrzähnige Aminocarbonsäuren mit verschiedener Anzahl von Amino- bzw. Carboxylgruppen: Iminodiessigsäure (I), Aethylendiamin-N,N-diessigsäure (II), Nitrilotriessigsäure (III), Aethylendiamintetraessigsäure (IV), *2*-(*2*-Aminoäthyl)-pyridin-N,N-diessigsäure (V).

Die einfachste Methode zur Verfolgung von $- d[Fe^{II}]/dt$ besteht in der spektrophotometrischen Bestimmung der $[Fe^{II}]$ nach Ueberführung in den Tris-(*2,2'*-Bipyridyl)-Eisen(II)-Komplex. $(NH_4)_2\ Fe^{II}(SO_4)_2$. $12\ H_2O$ wurde in bestimmter Anfangskonzentration $([Fe^{II}]_0 = 10^{-4}M)$ zu einer den Liganden X in grossem Ueberschuss enthaltenden Lösung von bestimmtem pH und bestimmter Ionenstärke gegeben. Die $[O_2]$ betrug in solchen Lösungen immer $2,5 \cdot 10^{-4}$ und war vom pH, von der Ionenstärke und von Temperaturschwankungen ziemlich unabhängig. In bestimmten Zeitabständen wurden 5 ml einer solchen Reaktionslösung herauspipettiert, mit 1 ml einer $10^{-2}M$ *2,2'*-Bipyridyl-Lösung versetzt und die Extinktion des roten Fe^{II}-Tris-bipyridylkomplexes bei 5350 Å gemessen. Die Funktion $E_{5350} = f(t)$ gibt so direkt die zur Zeit vorhandene Konzentration an $[Fe^{11}]_{tot}$ und $[Fe^{III}]_{tot}$, und aus der Steigung der Tangente an $E = f(t)$ lässt sich direkt $v_R = - d[Fe^{II}]_{tot}/dt$ erhalten.

Bei den oben erwähnten Versuchen mit aromatischen Hydroxyverbindungen[10,11] fanden wir, dass (4) geschwindigkeitsbestimmend für die Gesamtreaktion ist, und dass die Geschwindigkeit der uns interessierenden Teilreaktion (4a) mit $v_+ = v_R/4$ angegeben werden kann. Im allgemeinen dürften aber mehrere Teilreaktionen für die experimentell ermittelte Geschwindigkeit v_R auschlaggebend sein, und die Berechnung von v_+ ist dann problematisch. Wir setzten den folgenden, im wesentlichen auf den Arbeiten von F. Haber und J. Weiss[14] basierenden Mechanismus voraus:

$$Fe^{II}X + O_2 \underset{v_-}{\overset{v_+}{\rightleftharpoons}} Fe^{III}X + O_2^- \qquad (4a,4b)$$

$$O_2^- + H^+ \rightleftharpoons HO_2 \tag{6}$$

$$Fe^{II}X + HO_2 \underset{v_{2-}}{\overset{v_{2+}}{\rightleftharpoons}} Fe^{III}X + HO_2^- \tag{7a,7b}$$

$$HO_2^- + H^+ \rightleftharpoons H_2O_2 \tag{8}$$

$$Fe^{II}X + H_2O_2 \xrightarrow{v_3} Fe^{III}X + OH + OH^- \tag{9}$$

$$Fe^{II}X + OH \xrightarrow{v_4} Fe^{III}X + OH^- \tag{10}$$

Eine Berechnung der uns interessierenden Geschwindigkeit v_+ aus
der gemessenen resultierenden Geschwindigkeit v_R dürfte ziemlich
verwickelt sein, wenn alle diese Teilreaktionen berücksichtigt
werden sollen. Eine erste grobe Abschätzung von v_+ kann jedoch
leicht erhalten werden unter den Annahmen, dass (1) die Gleichge-
wichte (6) und (8) sich momentan einstellen, (2) (9) und (10) sehr
rasch sind im Vergleich zu den übrigen Teilreaktionen und (3) $v_{2-} \ll$
v_{2+}.

Unter Anwendung der Methode der "steady state approximation"
findet man alsdann:

$$d[O_2^-]/dt = v_+ - v_- - v_{2+} = 0 \tag{11}$$

$$v_R = v_+ - v_- + 3v_{2+} \tag{12}$$

$$v_R/4 = v_+ - v_- = k_+[O_2][Fe^{II}X] - k_-[O_2^-][Fe^{III}X] \tag{13}$$

$$v_R/4 = k_+'[Fe^{II}]_{tot} - k_-'[Fe^{III}]_{tot} \tag{13a}$$

$$v_R = \frac{4 k_{2+} k_+[Fe^{II}X]^2[O_2]}{k_-[Fe^{III}X] + k_{2+}[Fe^{II}X]} \tag{14}$$

Bei Elimination von $[O_2^-]$ erhält man die Beziehung (14), aus der
ersichtlich wird, dass die Anfangsgeschwindigkeit v_R bei konstanter
$[Fe^{3+}]$ unter Umständen mit dem Quadrat der Konzentration der reak-
tiven Fe^{II}-Partikel ansteigen kann.[4] Aus (13a) kann die uns interes-
sierende Geschwindigkeitskonstante k_+ mit Hilfe eines graphischen
Verfahrens bestimmt werden. (13a) stellt die Gleichung einer Geraden dar, wenn die drei Messgrössen v_R, $[Fe^{II}]_{tot}$ und $[Fe^{III}]_{tot}$
eingesetzt und k_+' und k_-' als Variable genommen werden. Solche
Geraden verschiedener Messpunkte müssen sich in einem Punkt
schneiden, wenn k_+' und k_-' tatsächlich Konstanten sind und der der
Gleichung zugrunde gelegte Mechanismus zutrifft. Aus den Koordinaten dieses gemeinsamen Schnittpunktes erhält man direkt k_+' und
k_-'. Die scheinbaren Geschwindigkeitskonstanten k_+' und k_-' für
Hin- und Rückreaktion sind ungefähr gleich gross für die Autoxyda-

tion des Fe^{II}-Komplexes von Iminodiessigsäure. Bei den Komplexbildnern II–V ist $k_-' \ll k_+'$. Die Rückreaktion macht sich daher hier
erst nach einiger Zeit bemerkbar und k_-' kann nur grössenordnungs-
mässig bestimmt werden. Aus demselben Grund gilt in erster Nähe-
rung für die Anfangsgeschwindigkeiten $v_+ = v_R/4$.

In einer Reihe von Versuchen haben wir Fe^{III} in verschiedener
Konzentration zur Reaktionslösung zugesetzt. Die auf Grund von
(13) und (14) zu erwartende Aenderung von v_R deckte sich mit der
beobachteten Hemmwirkung. Die ausgezeichnete Uebereinstimmung
der aus solchen Versuchen berechneten Geschwindigkeitskonstanten
ist ein guter Beweiss für den mit (4) bis (10) wiedergegebenen
Reaktionsmechanismus.

Die Autoxydation in Gegenwart von Nitrilotriessigsäure (NTA) und
Aethylendiamin-tetraessigsäure (EDTA) verläuft so rasch, dass mit
Vorteil eine polarographische Methode zur Bestimmung der Geschwindigkeit v_R angewendet wurde.* Die Halbwellenpotentiale von Fe^{2+},
Fe^{3+} und O_2 liegen in schwach saurem Milieu so günstig, dass
$-d[Fe^{II}]/dt$ bei konstanter Spannung amperometrisch verfolgt werden
kann. Die Methode bietet zudem die Möglichkeit, die $[O_2]$ zu vari-
ieren. In einer grossen Vorratsflasche wurde Luft im gewünschten
Verhältnis mit N_2 gemischt und dann der ganze Versuch mit diesem
Gasgemisch durchgeführt. Auf diese Weise konnten wit zeigen, dass
v_+ streng proportional $[O_2]$ ist.

Für die Berechnung der Geschwindigkeitskonstanten k_+ (13) benö-
tigten wir die jeweiligen Stabilitätskonstanten von $Fe^{II}X$, die wir,
soweit vorhanden, der Literatur entnahmen [14] oder nach der von G.
Schwarzenbach [15] ausführlich beschriebenen pH-metrischen Methode
bestimmten.

Unter Umständen tragen verschiedene Partikel $Fe^{II}X$ zur Autoxydation bei (15). In diesen Fällen konnten die einzelnen Konstanten k_{+i}
durch Untersuchung der pH-Abhängigkeit von v_+ ermittelt werden.

$$v_+ = [O_2] \, \Sigma k_{+i} \, [Fe^{II}X]_i \qquad (15)$$

Bei der Diskussion der die Geschwindigkeitskonstante k_+† be-
stimmenden Faktoren wird zunächst die Annahme gemacht, dass die
thermodynamische Stabilität des Stosskomplexes $[Fe^{II}(X)(O_2)]$ nur in

---

*Die Anwendung des oben beschriebenen Verfahrens zur Bestimmung von
k_+' und k_-' versagt hier. k_+ wird scheinbar kleiner im Verlaufe der Reaktion. Das bedeutet, dass auch die Rückreaktion v_{2-} in erheblichem Masse
eintritt. v_+ wurde daher bei allen Versuchen mit NTA und EDTA durch
graphische Bestimmung der Anfangsgeschwindigkeit v_R ermittelt.

†Die im folgenden diskutierten k_+-Werte sind in $mol^{-1} \, lt \, min^{-1}$ angegeben.

geringem Masse von X abhängig ist. Für eine Reihe von struktur-
ähnlichen X scheint es gerechtfertigt, die Unterschiede in der Reaktivität von $Fe^{II}X$ gegenüber O_2 auf die Strukturfaktoren von $Fe^{II}X$:
(1) räumliche Anordnung der Donorgruppen und (2) Elektronenvertei-
lung in den einzelnen Eisen-Donorbindungen, zurückzuführen.

Ueber den räumlichen Bau der Fe^{II}-Komplexe der Verbindungen
I–V in wässriger Lösung ist nichts Sicheres bekannt.[16] Der Einfach-
heit halber ist im folgenden für die perspektivischen Darstellungen
der Koordinationsverbände immer die oktaedrische Konfiguration ge-
wählt worden. Es dürften aber, wie z.B. für EDTA-Komplexe von L.
A. K. Staveley und T. Randall[17] wahrscheinlich gemacht worden ist,
erhebliche Abweichungen vom regelmässigen Oktaeder vorkommen.
Ia und IIa reagieren mit O_2, wie auf Grund der Strukturähnlichkeit zu
erwarten ist, ungefähr gleich rasch.

Ia $k_+ = 1.8 \cdot 10^2$ *IIa* $k_+ = 1.6 \cdot 10^2$ *IIb* $k_+ = 2.8 \cdot 10^2$

Die erhöhte Reaktivität—gemessen an der Reaktionsgeschwindigkeit
von $Fe^{II}(H_2O)_6$ mit O_2[4]—kann, entsprechend der eingangs formulier-
ten Hopothese, auf die π-Donorwirkung der beiden Carboxylatgruppen
auf das zentrale Fe^{II} zurückgeführt werden. Die Bindung einer wei-
teren Aminogruppe (IIb) führt nur zu einer insignifikanten Erhöhung
von k_+.

Ein Ersatz des *2*-Aminoäthylrestes durch einen Acetatrest (IIIa)
führt jedoch zu einer wesentlichen Erhöhung von k_+. Noch stärker
wirkt die Einführung einer dritten π-Donorgruppe in IIb. k_+ ist in IVa

IIIa $k_+ = 1.5 \cdot 10^3$ *IVa* $k_+ = 2.3 \cdot 10^4$ *IIb* $k_+ = 2.8 \cdot 10^2$ *Va* $k_+ = 0.6 \cdot 10^2$

gegenüber IIb um *ca.* einen Faktor 80 erhöht. Die Unterschiede der Reaktivitäten von III*a* und IV*a* dürften auf die verschiedene räumliche Anordnung der π-Donorgruppen zurückzuführen sein. Interessant ist noch der Vergleich von II*b* und V*a*. Substitution der 2-Aminoäthyl-durch eine 2-Pyridylmethyl-Gruppe hat ein Absinken des k_+-Wertes um *ca.* einen Faktor 5 zur Folge. Der Pyridinstickstoff scheint demnach eine deutliche π-Akzeptorwirkung auf das zentrale Fe^{II} auszuüben.*

Bei der Autoxydation der Fe^{II}-Komplexe von NTA (III) und EDTA (IV) haben wir die pH-Abhängigkeit der Geschwindigkeit von (4) etwas genauer studiert. Bei NTA steigt $\log v_0$ linear mit dem pH-Wert an bis *ca.* pH 4 (Fig. 3).

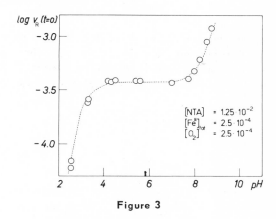

Figure 3

Von pH 4 an ist die Komplexbildung des im Unterschuss vorhandenen Fe^{II} vollständig und v_0 wird daher pH-unabhängig. Von pH 7,5 steigt $\log v_0$ erneut linear mit dem pH. Dieser Anstieg ist auf die Bildung eines Hydroxykomplexes III*b* zurückzuführen. Die zusätzliche Hydroxylgruppe führt zu einer wesentlichen Erhöhung der Reaktivität gegenüber O_2. Bei den Versuchen mit EDTA ergab sich eine wesentlich andere pH-Abhängigkeit (Fig. 4). Die Reaktivität gegenüber O_2

---

*Es muss hier auch die Möglichkeit in Betracht gezogen werden, dass die Komplexe II*b* und V*a* in Lösung einen tetraedrischen Bau aufweisen. Eine Reaktion mit O_2 kann unter diesen Umständen nur nach vorausgegangener Dissoziation einer Ligandengruppe erfolgen. Bei kinetisch stabilen Komplexen wäre dann die Autoxydationsgeschwindigkeit durch die Geschwindigkeit dieser Dissoziation begrenzt. A. K. S. Ahmed und R. G. Wilkins[18] haben gezeigt, dass in 2-Aminomethylpyridin-Ni-Chelaten die Bindung an den Pyridinstickstoff kinetisch stabiler ist als die Bindung an den Aminostickstoff. Es wäre demnach denkbar, dass die Reaktivitätsunterschiede von II*b* und V*a* auf einen derartigen kinetischen Effekt zurückzuführen wären.

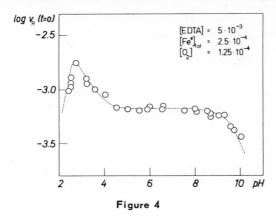

Figure 4

erreicht ein Maximum bei pH 2,75. Hier beginnt die Deprotonierung der vierten Essigsäuregruppe. Es ist jedoch unsicher, ob alle vier Acetatgruppen an das zentrale Fe^{II} gebunden sind [16,17] (IVb). Der gegenüber IVa erniedrigte k_+-Wert lässt ein Gleichgewicht IV$b \rightleftharpoons$

IIIb $k_+ = 1.8 \cdot 10^5$ IVb $k_+ = 5.4 \cdot 10^3$ IVc

IVc vermuten. Bei pH 7 beginnt die Bildung eines Hydroxykomplexes IVd. v_+ bleibt aber bis $ca.$ pH 9 konstant, d.h. unabhängig vom pH, und fällt erst ab, wenn sich ein Dihydroxykomplex IVf zu bilden

IVd $k_+ = 4.6 \cdot 10^3$ IVe IVf

beginnt. Der k_+-Wert von IVf lässt sich aus unseren Messungen nicht berechnen. Die Autoxydationsgeschwindigkeit ist aber über pH 10 sehr gering. Das ist verständlich, da die totale Besetzung der 6 Koordinationsstellen des Fe^{II} eine Annäherung von O$_2$ sehr erschwert. Merkwürdig ist die relativ hohe Reaktivität von IVd, da in IVd ebenfalls eine vollständige Besetzung der 6 Koordinationsstellen zu erwarten ist. Diese Erscheinung könnte erklärt werden durch die Annahme eines Gleichgewichts IV$d \rightleftharpoons$ IVe analog IV$b \rightleftharpoons$ IVc. Unsere Versuchsresultate führen demnach zu dem Ergebnis, dass zwei der Carboxylatgruppen im Fe^{II}EDTA-Komplex nur sehr lose an das zentrale Fe^{II} gebunden sind.

ANMERKUNGEN

(References)

1. D. Walz and S. Fallab, *Helv. Chim. Acta*, **44**, 13–9 (1961).
2. A. M. Posner, *Trans. Faraday Soc.*, **49**, 382–8 (1953).
3. J. Weiss, *Experientia*, **9**, 61–2 (1953).
4. P. George, *J. Chem. Soc.*, **1954**, 4349–59.
5. A. Lamb and L. W. Elder, *J. Am. Chem. Soc.*, **53**, 137–63 (1931); R. E. Huffman and N. Davidson, *ibid.*, **78**, 4836–42 (1956).
6. M. Cher and N. Davidson, *ibid.*, **77**, 793–8 (1955).
7. J. King and N. Davidson, *ibid.*, **80**, 1542–5 (1958).
8. *Z. physiol. Chem.*, **254**, 172 (1938).
9. *The Enzymes*, Vol. 1, p. 391–441, Academic Press, Inc., New York, 1959
10. Th. Kaden, D. Walz, and S. Fallab, *Helv. Chim. Acta*, **43**, 1639–45 (1960).
11. Th. Kaden and S. Fallab, *ibid.*, **44**, (1961), im Druck.
12. *The Enzymes*, Vol. 1, p. 386, Academic Press Inc., New York, 1959.
13. *J. Am. Chem. Soc.*, **78**, 4878–83 (1956).
14. S. Chaberek and A. E. Martell, *Organic Sequestering Agents*, John Wiley & Sons, New York, 1959.
15. *Helv. Chim. Acta*, **33**, 947–62 (1950).
16. G. Schwarzenbach, *ibid.*, **34**, 576–91 (1951).
17. *Discus. Faraday Soc.*, No. **26**, 157–63 (1958).
18. *J. Chem. Soc.*, **1960**, 2895–900.

COMPLEXES OF PYRIDINE-2-ALDOXIME

CHUI FAN LIU

University of Michigan
Ann Arbor, Michigan

and

C. H. LIU

Polytechnic Institute of Brooklyn
Brooklyn, New York

Pyridine-*2*-aldoxime (*a*) is an unsymmetrical chelating agent. When the four coordinated nitrogens are arranged in a square-planar fash-

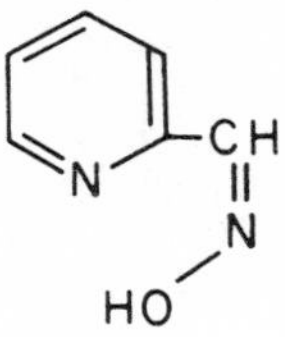

A

ion, two-to-one complexes with metals should be able to assume either the *cis* (*b*) or the *trans* (*c*) configurations. From these com-

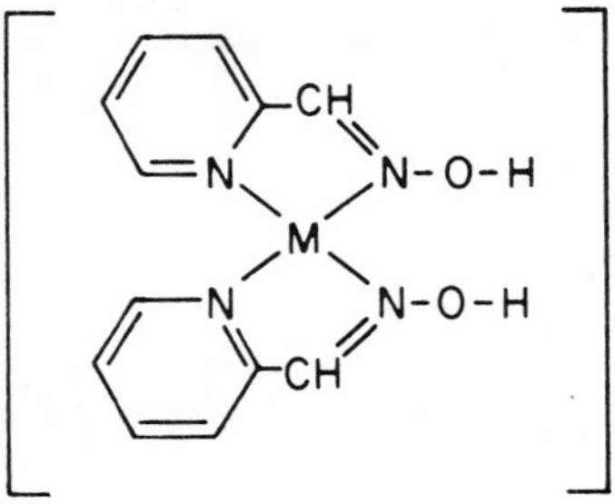

B

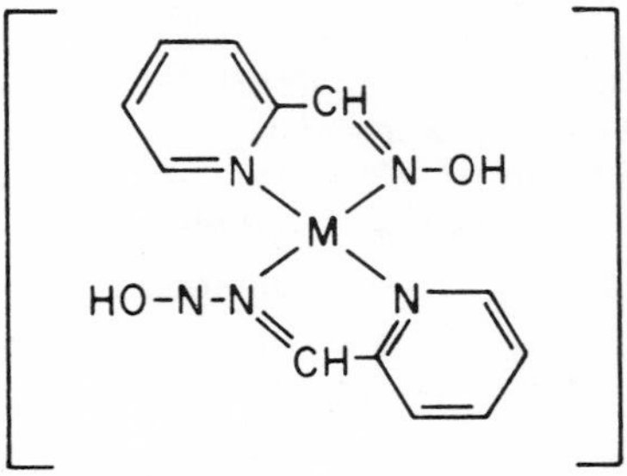

C

plexes it may be expected that the oxime protons are acidic and may be neutralized with strong bases. In the *cis* configuration the oxime groups are arranged much as they are in the dimethylglyoxime complexes. It seems that in this case intramolecular hydrogen bonding may occur to form a pseudo six-membered ring and further stabilize the complex (*d*). In the present paper pyridine-*2*-aldoxime comlexes of copper(II), platinum(II) and palladium(II) are discussed.

D

Copper(II) Complexes

*p*H titrations show the K_a for the oxime hydrogen of the uncoordinated pyridine-*2*-aldoxime to be 9.1×10^{-11}, and the K_b for the heterocyclic nitrogen to be 3.8×10^{-11}. Titration of solutions containing pyridine-*2*-aldoxime and copper(II) ion in the molar ratio of two-to-one show that the complex in solution behave is as a dibasic acid with two distinct equal steps of neutralization. The successive dissociation constants for the two acid hydrogens are determined to be 1.7×10^{-3} and 2.0×10^{-7}. Some constants are observed when the isolated dihydrogen-bis-(pyridine-*2*-aldoxime) copper(II) sulfate, and mono-hydrogen-bis-(pyridine-*2*-aldoxime) copper(II) nitrate and chloride are titrated. These results suggest that in solution the complex exists in only one form and not as a mixture of the *cis* and *trans* isomers. The large ratio of the first to the second ionization constants, K_1/K_2, further suggests that the complex exists in solution in the *cis* configuration with internal hydrogen bonding.

The internal hydrogen bonding is also observed in the isolated, purified, solid compounds. The infrared spectrum of dihydrogen bis-pyridine-*2*-aldoxime copper(II) sulfate shows a weak band at 1710 cm^{-1}. This band is quite similar to those observed by Rundle and Parasol[1,2] and Fujita, Nakahara and Tsuchida[3] while studying dimethyl glyoxime complexes. They are attributed to O—H stretching in the symmetrical, intramolecular by hydrogen-bonded oxime groups. Upon deuteration of the dihydrogen compound the band disappears, while the rest of the spectrum stays identical with those of the original undeuterated compounds. Therefore, both in solution and in the solid state the copper(II) compounds have the structure indicated in (*d*).

Polarographic studies show the inner complex of copper(II) and pyridine-*2*-aldoxime is reduced in two one-electron steps,

$$[Cu(PyA)_2]^{\circ} + e^- \longrightarrow [Cu(PyA)_2]^-$$

$$[Cu(PyA)_2]^- + e^- + Hg \longrightarrow Cu(Hg) + 2\ PyA,$$

where PyA is the pyridine-*2*-aldoximate ion. The dissociation constants for bis-pyridine-*2*-aldoxime copper(II) and bis-pyridine-*2*-aldoxime copper(I) are 2.1×10^{-19} and 3.3×10^{-15}, respectively.

Platinum(II) and Palladium(II) Complexes

Monohydrogen bis-(pyridine-*2*-aldoxime) platinum(II) ion is quite easily prepared by the reaction between potassium tetrachloroplatinate(II) with pyridine-*2*-aldoxime in a water-alcohol mixture. The ion has been isolated as the chloride, bromide, iodide, perchlorate, nitrate, and tetrachloroplatinate(II). Neutralization of this ion with sodium hydroxide yields the *cis*-bis-(pyridine-*2*-aldoxime)platinum(II) inner complex as the dihydrate. Reaction between pyridine-*2*-aldoxime and tetraammineplatinum(II) in concentrated aqueous ammonia yields directly the *trans*-bis-(pyridine-*2*-aldoxime)platinum(II) inner complex, also as the dihydrate. The *cis* inner complex is very easily isomerized to the *trans* configuration by heating for a few minutes at $140\,^{\circ}C$. The isomerization of the *trans* inner complex to the *cis* isomer is much more difficult, and must involve the monohydrogen-bis-(pyridine-*2*-aldoxime) platinum(II) ion as intermediate. It is accomplished by dissolving the trans-inner complex in 0.1 N HCl on the steam bath then neutralizing the solution with sodium hydroxide. The dissolution requires a long period of time; heating on the steam bath for two weeks may be necessary. The *cis* inner complex can also be converted into the *trans* isomer by a different method. It is first dissolved in 1 N HCl and heated on the steam bath, then, on neutralization of the solution, the *trans* isomer is obtained. The isomerization may be presented in the following scheme:

$$Cis\text{-}[Pt(C_6H_5N_2O)_2]\cdot 2\ H_2O \xrightarrow[140^{\circ}\ C]{\Delta} trans\text{-}[Pt(C_6H_5N_2O)_2]\cdot 2\ H_2O$$

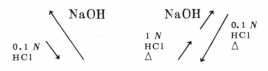

$$[Pt(C_6H_5N_2O)_2H]^+$$

The palladium(II) complexes are quite analogous to the platinum(II) compounds. Again, the monohydrogen bis-(pyridine-2-aldoxime) palladium(II) ion is formed simply by heating potassium tetrachloropalladate(II) with stoichiometric quantity of pyridine-2-aldoxime in a water-alcohol mixture. This ion has been isolated as the chloride, the bromide, the iodide, the nitrate, the perchlorate, and the tetrachloropalladate(II). The monohydrogen bis-(puridine-2-aldoxime) palladium(II) ion seems more acidic than the corresponding platinum ion. When the chloride is dissolved in water and the solution left standing, the *trans*-bis-(pyridine-2-aldoxime)palladium inner complex gradually crystallizes out as the dihydrate. This complex very easily dissolves in 0.1 N hydrochloric acid to yield the monohydrogen compound. Unlike the platinum inner complexes, the *cis* palladium inner complex has not been prepared. Neutralization with sodium hydroxide solution gives exclusively the *trans* compound. Even when the neutralization is carried out at 0°C, no appreciable amount of *cis*-inner complex is formed.

Hetero- and Homo-polynuclear Chelates

As indicated by (D), the mono-hydrogen compounds of the metals exhibit intramolecular hydrogen bonding, and a six-membered ring is formed with the proton as one of the ring members. When this proton is neutralized, and, if the inner complex stays in the *cis* configuration, it can be seen that the oxygens on the oximate groups are in an excellent position for chelation of other metal ions. Investigations show that homo- and hetero-polynuclear chelates indeed can be formed in solution and can also be isolated. Interaction between silver(I) ion and bis-(pyridine-2-aldoxime)copper(II) has been studied using a potentiometric method. Silver(I) ion forms a one-to-one complex with bis-(pyridine-2-aldoxime)copper(II). The dissociation constant of this complex is 2×10^{-3}. This complex ion can also be isolated as the perchlorate. From the infrared spectrum it seems that the silver complex has the same structure as the monohydrogen bis-(pyridine-2-aldoxime) copper(II) ion.

Silver(I) ion also forms one-to-one complexes with bis-(pyridine-*2*-aldoxime)palladium(II) and *cis*-bis-(pyridine-*2*-aldoxime)platinum(II). The nitrate and perchlorate of these complex ions have been isolated. Copper(II) ion also interacts with these complexes. The following hetero- and homo-polynuclear chelates have been isolated.

or

or

REFERENCES

1. Nakamoto, Margoshes, and Rundle, *J. Am. Chem. Soc.*, **77,** 6480 (1955).
2. Rundle and Parasol, *J. Chem. Phys.*, **20,** 1487 (1952).
3. Fujita, Nakahara, and Tsuchida, *J. Chem. Phys.*, **23,** 1541 (1955).

DISTORTED OCTAHEDRON CONFIGURATIONS IN SOLID AND LIQUID SUBSTANCES CAUSED BY sp HYBRIDISATION

H. KREBS*

*Laboratorium für anorganische und analytische Chemie
der Technischen Hochschule
Stuttgart, Germany*

In April 1950, for the celebrations at Bonn University of Paul Pfeiffer's 75th birthday, we had a coin minted depicting on one side Paul Pfeiffer himself, and on the other a model of the lattice structure of NaCl with an octahedron in the centre. This was to commemorate an important paper of Pfeiffer's [1] in which he pointed out a connection between the octahedron configuration in the NaCl lattice and the coordination theory of A. Werner.

This paper of Pfeiffer's is not much remembered, since crystallographers under the influence of Goldschmidt and Pauling with great success have made use of the ionic model in interpreting the crystalline structure of salt-like substances. To what extent is this model actually valid?

In search of an answer to this question let us first consider the electron density on the shortest line connecting a Li and a F atom in the LiF crystal.

The heavily drawn-out curve shows the experimental values of Krug, Witte and Wölfel. [2] This curve can be easily explained as a superposition of the electron densities of the Li^+ and F^- ions (Fig. 1, dotted line). If, on the other hand, we add the electron densities of the neutral Li and F atoms we get nearly the same curve (Fig. 1, dashed lines). This result at first sight is astonishing, but is easily understood if one considers the large extent of the valency electron of the Li atom.

Figure 2 shows the valency electron density for free F and Li atoms in their ground states; in each case the total electron density/

*I am greatly indebted to my co-workers Messrs. P. Drodten, D. Kallen, H. Weyand, and L. Winkler. Our investigations were made possible by financial help from the Ministerium für Atomkernenergie und Wasserwirtschaft der Bundesrepublik Deutschland, from the Kultusministerium des Landes Nordrhein-Westfalen and from the Deutsche Forschungsgemeinschaft.

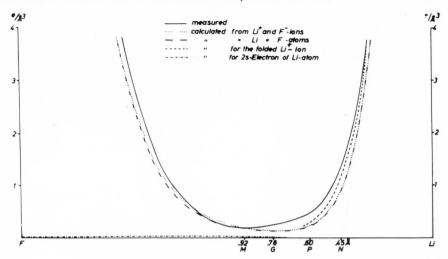

Fig. 1 Electron density in LiF.

Ångström on a sphere of radius r is plotted against r. The origins of the r-coordinate are in the centres of the Li and F atoms respectively. The 2s-electron of Li has its nodal sphere at 0.45 Å. Its position probability only assumes noticeable values outside a sphere corresponding to the ionic radius of Goldschmidt or Pauling. It penetrates into the influence sphere of the F nucleus to a great extent; 35% of the total position probability of the Li valency electron in its ground state lies outside a sphere of radius corresponding to the mutual distance of the Li and F atoms in the crystal.

The ionic model, i.e., the assumption of Li^+ and F^- ions, is therefore a good approximation of the bond system. A more exact consideration, however, will have to take into account the fact that all the 8 valency electrons—7 coming from the F and 1 from the Li atom—are attracted by both nuclei. The s- and p-eignefunctions of both atoms are occupied by these valency electrons. The nuclear forces of Li are extremely weak as compared with those of F, so that the influence of the Li eigenfunctions is relatively small and can often be neglected when, instead of applying quantum mechanics, one makes use of classical electro-dynamics, i.e., the ionic model. Lack of space does not permit me to give a detailed account of why formulations which speak of a mixture of ionic and homopolar bond forces. I have also used these in previous papers and they are valuable in the treatment of bond problems, but, on the other hand, they give only a distorted picture of the actual behaviour of the electrons. One should rather speak of covalent bond forces between atoms of con-

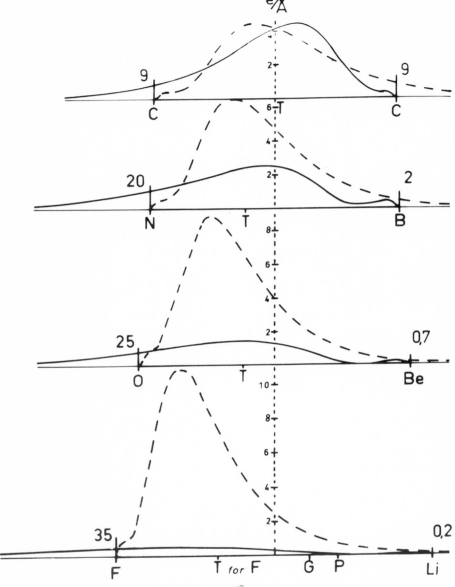

Fig. 2 Valency electron density $4\pi r^2$ in e/ Å (integrated over a sphere) for the atoms in the ground state in the order LiF, BeO, BN, and CC. The atomic distance in the figure corresponds to that in the crystal.
  − − − valency electron density for the atom on the left.
  ——— valency electron density for the atom on the right.

siderably different effective nuclear charge, i.e., occupation of the eigenfunctions of both atoms by the valency electrons. The word *co-valent* means that both atoms together have a certain value in forming a bond; with the word homopolar on the other hand, we would normally associate the idea that the position of the electron is halfway between the nuclei. This, of course, is impossible for salts— for instance LiF.

Figure 2 also shows the transition to the typical homopolar bond of the aliphatic carbon in the isoelectronic sequence LiF, BeO, BN and CC. Due to the change of nuclear charge, the valency electron cloud of the one atom contracts, and that of the other expands.

Chemists have long been accustomed to regard the bond in BeO and BN in analogy to the aliphatic bond, because of their diamond-like structure. We speak of a covalent bond in which the ψ function (or better ψ^2), i.e., the position probability of the binding electron pair, is shifted in the direction of the non-metallic atom.

The above approach is in this case natural to the chemist as the tetrahedrally arranged sp^3 hybrid states are characteristic for the bond in the three cases.

The same considerations should also lead one to speak of a co-valent bond even if the binding function is not well known to the chemist, as for instance, in the case of bonds which are not found in organic compounds. The valency electron distribution in the chalcogenides of the divalent elements of the carbon group is very similar to that of BeO and BN as we see in the example of GeS (Fig. 3).

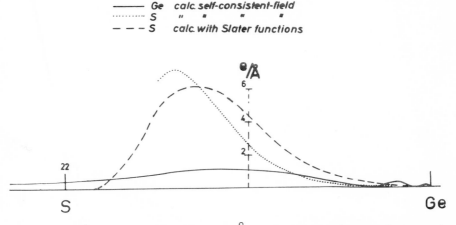

Fig. 3 Valency electron density $4\pi r^2$ in e/ Å for the atoms in the ground state and the shortest distance in the GeS-lattice.

In this case the ionic picture is certainly no longer adequate as the atomic eigenfunctions of both atoms give noticeable contributions. Let us consider PbS. This crystallizes in the NaCl lattice, each atom lying in the centre of a regular octahedron. The p-eigenfunctions possess the geometry of the lattice; in crystal-field theory we speak of a non-splitting of the p-states. Four p-electrons of the S and two of the Pb together form a $p\delta$-bond system as shown in Fig. 4. In the graph the space diagonal of the cell is shown vertically. The drawn-out and dashed arrows represent the positive and negative branches of the p-eigenfunctions. We notice mesomeric bond sys-

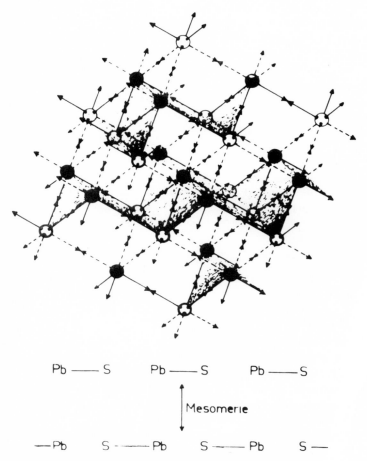

Fig. 4 Simplified representation of the bond system in cubic PbS and its homologes. The arrows (⟵ --→) show the bond directions of the p-valency electrons. Mesomeric bond systems run along the lattice lines [100].

tems represented by the two types of arrows—running through the
lattice parallel to the lattice lines [100]. From the chemistry
of organic compounds we know that mesormeism results in the absorption of light in the low-energy regions—for instance, giving the
black colour and metallic electriacl conductivity of graphite. Similarly, PbS is black and a semiconductor.

Let us now consider the elements As, Sb and Bi which are isoelectronic with PbS. If the valency electrons could be described by
pure *p*-eigenfunctions, the elements would also have to crystallize
in the same NaCl-type of lattice. Their structures are, however, only
similar to that of NaCl (Fig. 5). In those regions of the lattice in

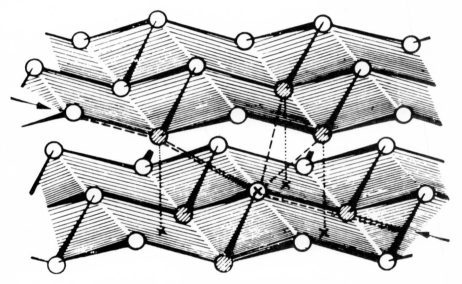

Fig. 5 The layer-structure of rhombohedral As.

which in PbS the heavily drawn-out arrows point towards one another,
we observe shorter atomic distances; greater atomic distances are
found in the regions indicated in PbS by the dashed arrows. Layer
lattices are built. For As, the atomic distance between adjacent
double layers is 24% greater than the distance between adjacent
atoms of the same double layer; for Bi, only 10%. This implies that
with rising atomic mass in the sequence As, Sb, Bi, the lattice becomes increasingly similar to that of NaCl. We also find that the
bond angles (in the graph, between the heavily drawn-out lines),
which go from 96°27′ for As over 95°50′ for Sb to 93°52′ for Bi, come
increasingly near to the value of 90° which is expected if *p*-electrons

form the bond. The cause of this lattice deformation, i.e., the formation of double layers, is found in the hybridisation of the p-with the
s-quantum states.

Figure 6 gives a picture of the possibilities of hybridisation. On
the left, the four quantum states of an sp^3 hybrid are symbolized by
arrows. The dashed arrows are a measure of the extension of the
eigenfunctions in the backward direction. On the right, three
p-eigenfunctions are represented by double-arrows and the s-eigen-
function by a circle as it is spherically symmetric. Transition states
are depicted in the centre of the graph. The positive branches of the
p-eigenfunctions are enlarged by a weak hybridisation with the s-function,
and their three axes spread out. The rear parts of the hybrid-functions
(dashed arrows) have smaller values. Due to the admixture of the

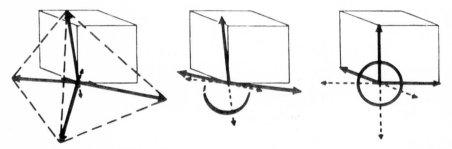

Fig. 6 Representation of the transition of four sp^3-hybrid eigen functions in one s-
and three p-eigenfunctions. The axes of the eigenfunctions (bond directions)
are shown by arrows: (⟶) positive branches of the eigenfunctions (direc-)
tions of strong bonds) and (---→) negative branches of the eigenfunctions (directions of weak bonds).

p-eigenfunctions, the s-function contracts in the form of a calotte.
The deformed NaCl-like structures of As, Sb and Bi can evidently be
explained by such binding functions. The free electron pair occupies
that state which has the form of a calotte, and the three valency
electrons occupy those states in which the p-part predominates.

How can we prove these ideas?

1. The conception of mesomerism—i.e., the two possibilities of
forming a bond either by the positive or by the negative branches of
the eigenfunctions—is confirmed by the metallic lustre and the
metallic electrical conductivity.

2. The atomic distance must decrease in the positive direction
with increasing hybridisation as the concentration of valency electrons in the positive direction reduces the repulsion between the
positively charged nuclei. This also results in a spreading of the

bond angles. The values given in the literature did not show this behaviour. We have therefore made new measurements to determine the position of the atoms of half-metals in the solid state. Table 1 gives an extract from our results.

TABLE 1: ATOMIC DISTANCES IN LATTICES OF METALLOIDS

	r_1*	r_2†	r_2/r_1	ϕ
β as glassy	2.48	3.82	1.54	—
γ as glassy	2.48	3.82	1.54	—
α as metal	2.515	3.115	1.238	$96°27'$
Sb explosive	2.88	3.75	1.30	—
Sb metallic	2.896	3.357	1.159	$95°50'$
α se red	2.34	3.80	1.63	$105°$
β se red	2.34	3.80	1.63	$105°$
Se glassy	2.36	3.71	1.57	
Se hexagonal	2.374	3.426	1.443	$102°50'$

*r_1 shortest atomic distance in Å
†r_2 atomic distance in backward direction
ϕ bond-angle

In the glassy modifications of As and Sb the double layers are further away from each other than they are in the rhomboedrical metallic forms. The shortest distance between atoms of one double layer is therefore smaller for the glassy forms.

These rules are more evident in the case of the element Se as here we can also compare with the red modifications whose structures have been determined.[3,4] In these red modifications a large distance is found between the Se_8 rings which is due to van der Waals forces. The atomic distance of 2.34 Å in one ring is relatively small; it increases successively when going from the red over the glassy to the hexagonal modifications of Se. The latter has a structure which is similar to that of NaCl, as Von Hippel[5] has discussed. The backward bond length with a value of 3.426 Å is now almost 0.4 Å shorter than in the red modifications of Se.

The atomic distances we have found are not in accordance with the rule of bond order derived by Pauling.[6] Goldschmidt has shown that the atomic distance in salts and metals increases with increasing coordination number. The same law also applies to the substances mentioned above which show distorted octahedral configuration. This behaviour is not explained by the ionic model but by the covalent picture given above.

3. The relationship between the bond systems of the metals As and Sb, on the one side, and the semiconducting chalcogenides, on the other, were proved by the easy formation of mixed crystals over a wide range. Table 2 shows their limits on the metallic side. On the left-hand side of Fig. 7 the variation of lattice constants in the system Sb/SnTe is shown. This is linear but does not coincide with the line of Vegard which is given dashed in Fig. 7. On the right we have the system As/GeTe. Here the range of formation of mixed crystals extends to 37 mol% of GeTe.

This formation of mixed crystals is the best proof for the relationship in the bond system. This shows that there is only a gradual difference, but not one in principle between the bond system in the metals As, Sb and Bi, on the one side, and the semi-conducting chalcogenides, on the other.

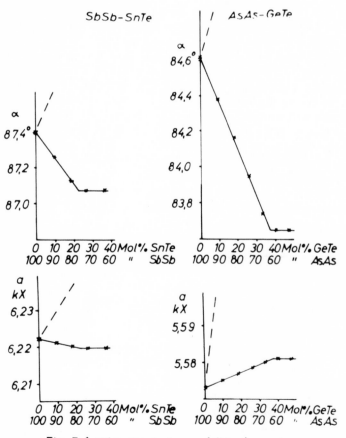

Fig. 7 Lattice constants a and α in the systems.

TABLE 2: LIMITS OF THE FORMATION OF MIXED CRYSTALS, IN MOL %

AsAs — GeSe	70 : 30		SbSb — GeTe	63 : 37
AsAs — GeTe	63 : 37		SbSb — SnTe	78 : 22

GeTe is an especially interesting substance. Schubert and Fricke[7] have shown that in analogy to the alloys it has a certain phase width and crystallizes at temperatures of over 400°C in a NaCl-structure. Below 400 °C we observe a distortion of the lattice which increases with falling temperature; as in the metallic As, doubly-layer develop. At low temperatures this distortion is certainly caused by the inclination of Ge to *sp*-hybridisation. Figure 8 shows how this hybridisation is cancelled by temperature motion. The Ge-atom lies in the potential field of the adjacent Te-atoms of its own double layer (shown on the left of Fig. 8), and also in the potential field of the more distant Te atoms of the next double-layer. The resulting potential curve is drawn in dots and dashes. The bottom of the potential well has only a slight inclination. The oscillation amplitude of the Ge atom increases with rising temperature, especially towards the right; it comes increasingly near the Te atoms of the next double-layer. The hybridisation being not quantized, it can adapt itself to the instantaneous state of motion of the atoms. When, with rising temperature, the differences of the atomic distances are averaged out, the

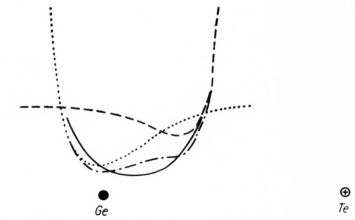

Te   Ge   Te

Fig. 8 Schematic representation of the potential curve for the bond of a Ge-atom along a mesomeric chain in the lattice of GeTe:
..... potential curve for the strong bond inside the double layers.
- - - potential curve for the weak bond between two double layers.
..... resultant for the two potential curves
_____ resultant potential curve for the bond of *p*-electrons in cubic GeTe.

valency electrons finally become p-states. The crystal now has the symmetry of the NaCl lattice.

This picture of the adaptability of the hybridisation to the state of motion of the atoms also explains the behaviour of some metalloids and compounds of metalloids in the melting process. The layer structure of Sb[8] and Bi is lost in the molten state and a short-range order arises, similar to that of NaCl.

Ge and InSb crystallize in a diamond-like lattice with a tetrahedral orientation of the atoms. In sp^3 hybrids the valency electrons are localized in the space between two atoms. These substances belong to the high polymers which cannot melt without cracking processes or changes in structure taking place. Ge and InSb in the molten state have a short-range order which is similar to that of NaCl. A mesomeric bond system between the p-electrons explains the metallic conductivity of the melt, and also the mobility of the atoms. For as we have seen in the case of GeTe, the bond system can follow the temperature motion of the atoms. By hybridisation with s-states the binding power can be concentrated on that side of the atom on which it keeps its coordination partners.

Our calculation of the atomic distribution curves of the elements Bi, Ge and Sn in the super-cooled and the strongly heated fluid states is not quite finished. The curves were, however, shown at the Conference.

REFERENCES

1. P. Pfeiffer, *Z. anorg. allg. Chemie,* **92**, 376 (1915).
2. J. Krug, H. Witte, and E. Wölfel, *Z. phys. Chemie, Neue Folge,* **4**, 36 (1955).
3. R. D. Burbank, *Acta Cryst.,* **4**, 140 (1951).
4. R. E. Marsh, L. Pauling and McCullough, *ibid.* **6**, 71 (1953).
5. A. R. von Hippel, *J. Chem. Physics,* **16**, 372 (1948).
6. L. Pauling, *The Nature of the Chemical Bond,* Cornell University Press, Ithaca, N.Y., 1960.
7. K. Schubert and H. Fricke, *Z. Naturforsch.,* **11a**, 78 (1956).
8. H. K. F. Muller, and H. Hendus, *Z. Naturforsch.,* **12a**, 102 (1957).

INDEX OF CONTRIBUTORS

LEARNING IN ADULTHOOD

JB JOSSEY-BASS

LEARNING IN ADULTHOOD

A Comprehensive Guide

Third Edition

Sharan B. Merriam

Rosemary S. Caffarella

Lisa M. Baumgartner

1807

WILEY

2007

John Wiley & Sons, Inc.

Published by Jossey-Bass
A Wiley Imprint
989 Market Street, San Francisco, CA 94103-1741   www.josseybass.com

Jossey-Bass books and products are available through most bookstores. To contact Jossey-Bass directly
call our Customer Care Department within the U.S. at 800-956-7739, outside the U.S. at 317-572-3986,
or fax 317-572-4002.

Jossey-Bass also publishes its books in a variety of electronic formats. Some content that appears in
print may not be available in electronic books.

Library of Congress Cataloging-in-Publication Data

Merriam, Sharan B.
  Learning in adulthood : a comprehensive guide / Sharan B. Merriam, Rosemary S. Caffarella,
Lisa M. Baumgartner. — 3rd ed.
     p. cm. — (Jossey-bass higher and adult education series)
  Includes bibliographical references and index.
  ISBN-13: 978-0-7879-7588-3 (cloth)
  ISBN-10: 0-7879-7588-5 (cloth)
  1. Adult learning. I. Caffarella, Rosemary S. (Rosemary Shelly), 1946- II. Baumgartner, Lisa, 1964-
III. Title.
  LC5225.L42M47 2006
  374—dc22
                        2006019145

Printed in the United States of America
THIRD EDITION
HB Printing 10 9 8 7

CONTENTS

The Jossey-Bass Higher
and Adult Education Series

PREFACE

Learning in adulthood is an intensely personal activity. Yet at the same time, a multibillion-dollar enterprise has arisen in response to adult learning interests—an enterprise that spends more dollars than elementary schools, high schools, and postsecondary schools combined. Indeed, the field of adult and continuing education is characterized by a bewildering array of programs, agencies, and personnel working to assist adults in their learning. It is precisely the focus on adults as learners, however, that unites an otherwise extraordinarily diverse field. It is also the life context of adults and some of the distinguishing characteristics of the adult learning process that differentiate adult education from other kinds of education. To facilitate the process of learning, it is especially important to know who the adult learner is, how the social context shapes the learning that adults are engaged in, why adults are involved in learning activities, how adults learn, and how aging affects learning ability. *Learning in Adulthood* addresses these topics, among others.

There is a voluminous literature on adult learning, ranging from technical articles on various aspects of adult learning to handbooks, guides, and pamphlets summarizing material for the new instructor of adult students. If one goes to a database such as the Educational Resources Information Center (ERIC), which catalogues journal articles, monographs, conference proceedings, papers, and so on, or does some random exploring on the World Wide Web, one encounters thousands of citations under the topic "adult learning." Further, there are dozens of books with either a central or secondary focus on adult learning.

For this third edition of *Learning in Adulthood* we have paid particular attention to work published since the last edition of the book. This third edition of *Learning in Adulthood* builds on material in the 1999 edition, bringing together the important contributions of the past decade to our understanding of adult learning. While we have preserved important foundational material (such as a discussion of andragogy), we have also brought to bear the most recent thinking and research. We have strived to put together a comprehensive overview and synthesis of what we know about adult learning: the context in which it takes place, who the participants are, what they learn and why, the nature of the learning process itself, new approaches to adult learning, the development of theory in adult learning, and other issues relevant to understanding adult learning.

The book also takes into account recent work in sociology, philosophy, critical social theory, and psychology. In most writing on adult learning, the sociocultural perspective has been widely neglected in favor of the predominant orientation to the individual learner and how to facilitate her or his learning. In addition to the focus on the learner, we attend to the context in which learning takes place and to learners' interactive relationship with that context and with the learning activity itself. We look at how the social structure influences what is offered and who participates, how the sociocultural context creates particular developmental needs and interests, and how social factors such as race, class, and gender shape learning.

This book is intended primarily for educators of adults. We have organized the material so that it will make sense to readers who are new to adult education and at the same time will challenge those who are already familiar with the knowledge base of the field. The organization and presentation of this material reflect our efforts over the years to find the best way to organize courses, workshops, and seminars in adult learning and development for audiences with varying levels of expertise. We have endeavored to put together a book that is at once readable, thorough, and up-to-date in its coverage. In particular, the book is designed for use in courses in adult learning. In addition to those associated with the field of adult education itself, however, those in counseling, health, social work, human resource development, administration, and instructional technology and in such institutions as libraries, churches, business and industry, and higher education often deal on a daily basis with adult learners. We also intend this book to be a resource for practitioners in these fields who would like to know more about adult learners and the learning process.

OVERVIEW OF THE CONTENTS

This third edition of *Learning in Adulthood* is substantially reorganized from the previous edition. We realized that in most courses using this text, the chapters specific to adult learning theory and models were read before chapters on traditional learning theory, cognition, and psychosocial developmental frameworks. We have organized accordingly. This edition is divided into four parts. Part One describes the context of adult learning. Part Two focuses on theories and models of adult learning. The chapters in Part Three address newer approaches to adult learning, and those in Part Four present material on topics that intersect with adult learning, such as memory and cognition, adult development, and so on.

The chapters in Part One, "Adult Learning in Contemporary Society," focus on the context of adult learning. Chapter One sets the sociocultural context for adult learning in North America. In it, we discuss three forces—demographics, globalization, and technology—that have shaped adult learning today. It is important to understand how the interaction of those three factors has led to changes in both what adults want to learn and the learning opportunities provided for them. Directly related to the sociocultural context of adult learning are the environments where learning takes place, the subject of Chapter Two. These range from educational and noneducational institutions, such as hospitals and government agencies, to nonformal and community-based agencies, to incidental and informal learning that is more self-directed than structured by others. New in this edition is the online environment, which interfaces with formal, nonformal, and informal modes of learning. Also in this chapter we explore the concepts of organizational learning and the learning organization, and lifelong learning and the learning society. Chapter Three summarizes the literature on who participates in primarily formal adult learning activities, why people participate, and what they choose to learn. We also take a critical look at key questions of access and opportunity, and examine the gaps between the rhetoric and the reality in the provision of formal and nonformal learning activities in our society.

Part Two, "Adult Learning Theory and Models," builds on foundational material in adult learning, material that is at the heart of our field of adult education. The topics covered in these chapters represent the field's efforts in distinguishing itself from the education of children. We begin Chapter Four with a description and critique of the best known of these theories: Knowles's (1980) concept of andragogy. Based on five characteristics of adult learners, andragogy focuses on the adult learner as distinguished from preadult learners. In this chapter we also cover three other models of learning, two of which are fairly recent additions to our literature. McClusky's (1970) theory of margin, which has great intuitive appeal to adult learners introduced to it, is explained first. This is followed by Illeris's (2004a) three dimensions of learning model, and the most recent iteration of Jarvis's (2006) learning model. In Chapter Five we explore the rich array of work that has been completed on self-directed learning. Addressed are the goals and processes of self-directed learning, the concept of self-directedness as a personal attribute of the learner, recent approaches to self-directed learning, and some suggestions for building research and theory in this area. Currently, transformational learning has taken center stage in research and writing. Chapter Six summarizes the development of transformational learning, reviews the recent research in this area, and examines unresolved issues inherent in this approach to adult learning. In Chapter Seven, the last chapter of Part Two, we look closely at the role of experience in learning: both how adult learning builds on prior experience and how experience shapes learning. The concepts of experiential learning, reflective practice, and situated cognition are also examined in this chapter.

Part Three, "Newer Approaches to Adult Learning," contains two totally new chapters. We felt that the burgeoning interest in embodied or somatic learning, spirituality and learning, and narrative approaches to learning warranted a chapter (Chapter Eight) in this edition of *Learning in Adulthood*. We uncovered so much recent material in these areas that, had space allowed, we could have devoted more than one chapter to these topics. Chapter Nine on non-Western approaches to adult learning is also new. Although the great majority of the knowledge base represented in *Learning in Adulthood* is from a Western perspective, representing cultural values of privileging the individual learner and cognitive processes over more holistic approaches, we wanted to introduce readers to other epistemologies, other ways of thinking about learning and knowing. We hope we have done that through brief introductions to five non-Western perspectives. The final chapter in Part Three is an update of critical theory, postmodernism, and feminist pedagogy. These three perspectives draw from literature outside the field of adult education. Scholars have applied these perspectives to our field, enlarging our understanding by inviting us to question how the structural inequities based on race, gender, class, sexual orientation, able-bodiedness, and so on affect learning.

Part Four, which we have titled "Learning and Development," brings together material from philosophy, psychology, sociology, biology, and so on, that has a bearing on adult learning. In Chapter Eleven, on traditional learning theory, we review five traditional theories about learning—behaviorism, humanism, cognitivism, social learning theory, and constructivism—along with their implications for adult learning. Where one aligns oneself with these theories manifests itself in the view of the adult learner, the role of instructor-facilitator, and the goals of the learning transaction itself. Chapter Twelve focuses on adults' developmental characteristics. Beginning with biological and psychological perspectives on adult development, we move to sociocultural and integrated perspectives. The work on adult development in recent years places less emphasis on age and stage models and more on the effect of such factors as race, gender, class, and ethnicity. Much has been written lately about cognitive development in adulthood, and so this is treated separately in Chapter Thirteen. Here we review several theoretical models of cognitive development as well as present the concept of dialectical thinking. Chapter Fourteen reviews the work on intelligence, especially as it has been studied from a developmental or aging perspective. Drawing on several disciplines and summarizing recent work on memory and aging, expertise, cognitive and learning styles, and brain-based research, Chapter Fifteen is one of the few compilations of its kind in an adult learning textbook.

Finally, in the last chapter we step back from the accumulated knowledge base to summarize and integrate the material on adult learning presented in earlier chapters. Chapter Sixteen also reflects how we ourselves have come to think about learning in adulthood.

ACKNOWLEDGMENTS

This third edition of *Learning in Adulthood* is a direct response to the field's burgeoning literature base on research and theory in adult learning and the need for a single, comprehensive, up-to-date textbook to use in our adult learning classes. In a very real sense, it has been the students in our programs and the participants in our workshops and seminars who have challenged us to revise and update the previous edition of the book. We were pleased that Lisa Baumgartner agreed to join our team for this edition. Her fresh perspective has undoubtedly made this edition of *Learning in Adulthood* the best yet! Others, of course, have been of invaluable assistance at various stages of the project. David Brightman, our editor at Jossey-Bass, was enormously supportive in assisting us through the process. Colleagues Ralph Brockett, Carolyn Clark, Bradley Courtenay, Ed Taylor, and Libby Tisdell unselfishly provided us with updated materials and took time out from their own work to read and critique draft chapters. Their comments, insights, and suggestions considerably strengthened this book. A special thanks goes to Young Sek Kim, Ph.D. student and graduate research assistant at the University of Georgia, for tracking down references, assisting in editing, and seeing to the technical matter of getting the book ready for the publisher. To all of you we offer our heartfelt thanks. Finally, we thank our family members and friends for their support and patience over the last year.

Athens, Georgia
Ithaca, New York
DeKalb, Illinois
June 2006

SHARAN B. MERRIAM
ROSEMARY S. CAFFARELLA
LISA M. BAUMGARTNER

THE AUTHORS

Sharan B. Merriam is professor of adult education at the University of Georgia. Merriam's research and writing activities have focused on the foundations of adult education, adult development, adult learning, and qualitative research methods. She has published more than twenty books and dozens of chapters and articles and held major editorship roles over the past twenty-five years. For five years she was coeditor of *Adult Education Quarterly,* the major research and theory journal in adult education. Currently she is coeditor for the book series Professional Practices in Adult Education and Lifelong Learning. She has won the Cyril O. Houle World Award for Literature in Adult Education for three different books. Various of her books have been translated into Chinese, Korean, Japanese, and French. Based on her widespread contributions to the field of adult education, Merriam has been inducted into the International Adult and Continuing Education Hall of Fame and was the first to receive the American Association of Adult and Continuing Education's Career Achievement award. She has served on steering committees for the annual North American Adult Education Research Conference, the Qualitative Research in Education Conference held annually at the University of Georgia, and the Commission of Professors of Adult Education. She has conducted workshops and seminars on adult learning and qualitative research throughout North America and overseas, including countries in southern Africa, Southeast Asia, the Middle East, and Europe. In 1998 she was a senior Fulbright scholar to Malaysia, and in 2006 a visiting scholar to South Korea.

Rosemary S. Caffarella is professor and chair of the Department of Education in the College of Agriculture and Life Sciences at Cornell University. Her research and writing activities have focused on adult learning, program planning, and designing culturally appropriate programs for adults. Caffarella has authored or coauthored seven books—two of which have been translated into Chinese and one into Japanese—and numerous book chapters and articles. She received the prestigious Cyril O. Houle World Award for Literature in Adult Education for *Learning in Adulthood: A Comprehensive Guide* (2nd ed., 1999), coauthored with Sharan Merriam. Her most recent book, *Planning Programs for Adult Learners* (2nd ed., 2002), is a detailed guide for adult educators and trainers working in a variety of settings. In addition, in 2003 she was awarded an honorary degree of Doctor of Humane Letters from the College of Lifelong Learning in the University of New Hampshire system. She has conducted workshops and presented papers and lectures throughout the United States, Canada, Malaysia, Taiwan, and Australia. Her current project, in partnership with the Universiti Putra Malaysia and a number of other Malaysian organizations and individuals, is educating Malaysian women, their families, and health care professionals about breast cancer treatment and prevention. The project highlights working in a culturally and linguistically sensitive manner in a multicultural nation.

Lisa M. Baumgartner is an associate professor of adult education at Northern Illinois University, DeKalb. Her research and writing focus on adult learning and development and women's contributions to the field of adult education. A recipient of the W. K. Kellogg Foundation Cyril O. Houle Scholars Research Grant for Emerging Scholars in Adult Education, she completed a study on civil rights activist Septima P. Clark's lifelong contributions to social justice adult education. In addition, she coedited *Adult Learning and Development: Multicultural Stories* with Sharan Merriam (1999). She has served on the steering committee for the annual North American Adult Education Research Conference. She is a consulting editor for the *International Journal of Qualitative Studies in Education* and the *Qualitative Report*. In 2004, she received the Commission of Professors of Adult Education Early Career Award, which honors individuals in the early stages of their academic career who have made significant contributions in scholarship and service to the field.

LEARNING IN ADULTHOOD

PART ONE

ADULT LEARNING IN CONTEMPORARY SOCIETY

It is very much the perspective of this book that learning is a personal process—but a process that is shaped by the context of adult life and the society in which one lives. Compare how industrialization of the early years of the twentieth century affected what an adult needed and wanted to learn with the knowledge economy of the early twenty-first century. This learning in turn affects the social context. For example, as we become more technologically savvy, businesses respond by developing more sophisticated systems and gadgets that then require us to keep learning. It is indeed an interactive process between the learner and the social context. The three chapters in Part One explore the sociocultural context of the United States, the range of learning opportunities available to adults in this context, and who takes advantage of these opportunities and why.

Chapter One describes three factors characteristic of American society today that affect what adults want to learn. First, dramatic changes are occurring in the demographic base of our society. Adults outnumber those under eighteen years old for the first time ever. Moreover, the percentage of the population over age sixty-five continues to grow, commanding the attention of policymakers, businesspeople, and educators alike. Our population as a whole is also better educated than ever before, and there is more cultural and ethnic diversity. Therefore, there are simply more adults seeking learning opportunities, as well as more groups of adults with particular learning needs.

The second and third factors shaping the learning enterprise are globalization and technology. These are very much interrelated, of course; technology has had an enormous impact on the economy. Robotics and automation displace production workers but create other jobs; technology has fostered whole new work structures, such as job-sharing and telecommuting. The effect of the global economy and technological advances on the nature of adult learning is staggering. Adults find that they must continue their learning past formal schooling in order to function at work, at home, and in their communities. The need for new knowledge, for updating old information, for retraining, has resulted in a multibillion-dollar educational enterprise.

Some of this learning takes place in formal settings sponsored by myriad institutions and agencies. As might be expected, business and industry and educational institutions offer a large number of adult learning opportunities, but so do the military, cooperative extensions, churches, hospitals, and other institutions. Chapter Two explores how the context of formal institutional settings influences the learner and the learning process. Also reviewed are learning opportunities that are nonformal, such as those offered by community-based agencies, and informal, incidental, and self-directed opportunities, as might happen in the course of the workday or by watching a television program. In addition, we discuss online learning, a fourth environment for learning that overlays formal, nonformal, and informal modes of learning. In the second half of this chapter, we explore the interrelated concepts, first, of organizational learning and the learning organization, and second, of lifelong learning and the learning society.

Chapter Three profiles who participates in adult learning, why adults participate, and what an adult chooses to learn. Most of this information on participation and motivation is in reference to formal learning, such as that provided by educational institutions and employers. Estimates of the percentage of the adult population that participates in learning have steadily risen over the past forty years, with the most current study suggesting that approximately 46 percent of all adult Americans participate. Studies of self-directed learning and other nonformal types of education put the percentage even higher. Clearly, adult learning is an important activity for today's adults. What motivates adults to participate and what deters participation is important information, especially for program developers. This chapter also reviews motivational studies.

The final section of Chapter Three "problematizes" the concept of participation. By examining the assumptions that underlie participation we squarely confront the issues of access and opportunity in adult education. The gap between the better educated who seek out continuing education and those who do not continues to widen. Adult learning seems to have become a vehicle for solidifying a socioeconomic structure that limits access and opportunity, contrary to the stated goal of equal access to education in our society. We examine the rhetoric, which espouses one set of values, and the reality, which demonstrates another, in the provision of adult learning opportunities.

CHAPTER ONE

THE SOCIAL CONTEXT OF ADULT LEARNING

Learning, even self-directed learning, rarely occurs "in splendid isolation from the world in which the learner lives; . . . it is intimately related to that world and affected by it" (Jarvis, 1987, p. 11). What one wants to learn, what is offered, and the ways in which one learns are determined to a large extent by the nature of the society at any particular time. Contrast the young male apprentice of colonial times learning to be a blacksmith with today's middle-aged woman learning a new software program, or the preparation needed to become a medical doctor at the turn of the twentieth century—less than a high school diploma—with today's long and specialized training.

It can also be argued that the nature of society at any particular point in time determines the relative emphasis placed on adult learning. In preindustrial societies, the rate of change was such that what a person needed to know to function as an adult could be learned in childhood. In societies hurrying to catch up, however, and in our own society with its accelerated rate of change, the urgency of dealing with social realities is felt by adults. Society no longer has the luxury of waiting for its youth. As Belanger (1996) notes, "The question is no longer whether adult learning is needed, and how important it is. The issue today is how to respond to this increasing and diversified demand, how to manage this explosion" (p. 21). Youth, in fact, "who are sent out into life with a dwindling sackful of values, . . . face a situation in which they have to keep filling up their sack. This leads adult education to take 'lifelong learning' as its motto." Further, "the hole in the ozone layer

5

provides the stimulus for courses to which people turn for advice, mad cow disease pushes up the numbers attending vegetarian cooking courses, and backache creates a need for posture classes" (Geissler, 1996, pp. 35–36).

While adult education is responsive to the context in which it takes place, it also in turn affects that same context. Take, for example, enormous changes in our society brought on by computer technology. Auto mechanics must now be trained to diagnose engine problems using computers; you can save time at the local grocery by doing your own scanning, bagging, and checkout all by computer; airline boarding passes can be accessed at home; and so on. Adult education has responded to this computerization of our world by offering courses—courses where we can learn this technology so that we can better function in our digital environment. But the fact that millions of adults have become computer literate interacts with our environment in that we now *expect* to use our skills in an ever-widening range of applications—forcing institutions and agencies to adopt and expand these technologies.

Although the preceding are particularly contemporary examples, historically there has always been an interlocking of adult learning needs with the social context in which they occur. The skills needed in colonial America reflected the agrarian context; further, since early settlers were fleeing religious persecution in Europe, there was a moral and religious imperative in learning to read so that one could study the Bible. After the revolutionary war, the newly independent nation needed leaders and informed citizens to build the democratic society. Eclipsing religious education, civic education, which included learning about philosophy, science, and politics, became paramount in the education of adults.

With the Industrial Revolution of the late nineteenth and early twentieth centuries, industry-based skills training became a necessity. Also, because of the massive influx of immigrants to the United States at this time, "Americanization" and citizenship programs became a prominent form of adult education. It was felt that these immigrants needed to learn the ways of their adopted country so that they would "melt" into society. Interestingly, immigrants themselves organized their own schools to maintain their culture, but these were largely invisible to society at large.

Although a major thrust of adult education at any particular time reflects the sociohistorical context, varied purposes and learning interests coexist. We might argue that technology is a major thrust of learning today, but there is still job-training, literacy, civic education, liberal (such as Great Books clubs) and leisure learning, along with community-based social-action initiatives. As Stubblefield and Keane (1994, p. 312) observed from their survey of adult education from colonial times until the present, regardless of the historical era, "Americans learned because there was knowledge to master, technology to adapt, and life's uncertainties to be resolved."

Thus, to a large extent, the learning that goes on in adulthood can be understood through an examination of the social context in which it occurs. How is learning in adulthood shaped by the society in which it takes place? How does the sociocultural context determine what is learned and by whom?

This chapter explores three conditions characteristic of the current sociocultural context that are shaping the learning needs of adults in today's world: changing demographics, the global economy, and information and technology. Although we present each of these separately at first, these three factors are very much interrelated, and thus their convergence and subsequent impact on learning in adulthood are discussed in the final section of this chapter.

CHANGING DEMOGRAPHICS

Changing demographics is a social reality shaping the provision of learning in contemporary American society. Demographics is about people, groups of people, and their respective characteristics. For the first time in our society, adults outnumber youth, there are more older adults, the population is better educated than ever before, and there is more cultural and ethnic diversity. For various reasons, individuals and groups of people seek out learning experiences; for other reasons, society targets learning activities for certain segments of the population. Thus, certain learning activities are learner-initiated and others are society-initiated in response to the changing demographics. The field is concerned with the growth and development of adult learners, while at the same time, there are emerging groups of learners with special needs.

To begin, there are simply more adults in our society than ever before, and the population will continue to age. In comparison to colonial times when half the population was under age 16, in 1990, fewer than one in four Americans were under age 16 and half were age 33 or older. The median age of the American population of 36.0 years in 2004 is expected to increase to 39.1 in 2035 (U.S. Bureau of the Census, 2004b). The so-called baby boomers—the seventy million people born between 1946 and 1964—are a contributing factor to this change in the population. Bills (2004, p. 122) notes that "the baby boom has influenced all American social institutions—health care, housing, consumerism, retirement, even death and the projected 'tomb boom'—but none more than education and work." Although we might hear more about youth, they have less of an impact on the economy than the boomers. "In America, they [over-50s] control four-fifths of the money invested in savings-and-loan associations and own two-thirds of all the shares on the stock market" ("Over 60 and Overlooked," 2002).

The shift from a youth-oriented to an adult-oriented society is solidified by the increasing numbers of older adults in the population. In 1987, for the first time ever, Americans over the age of sixty-five outnumbered those under twenty-five. Furthermore, the oldest old, those over eighty-five-years old, are the fastest-growing segment of the older population. As of July 1, 2004, there were more than four million eight hundred thousand adults over eighty-five-years old, an increase of 13.4 percent from the 2000 census (U.S. Bureau of the Census, 2005). The number of adults over age eighty-five is expected to increase to about seven million in 2020 and to twenty million in 2050 (U.S. Bureau of the Census, 2004b).

Today's older adults are also increasingly better educated, in better health, and economically better off than previous cohorts. Society is already heeding their learning needs with policies like tuition waivers for higher and continuing education programs and specially designed programs, such as the popular Elderhostel program and learning-in-retirement institutes. There has also been a subtle change in the philosophical rationale—at least among those working in the fields of gerontology and educational gerontology—underlying the provision of education for this group. Along with an economic rationale (the better educated need fewer social services) and a social stability rationale (millions of healthy retired people need something to do) is an awareness that older adults as well as younger ones have an unending potential for development. Williamson (1997, p. 175) suggests that our culturally endorsed notion about what represents "appropriate" learning over the course of the life span tends to "reinforce prevailing myths about retirement and aging as processes of withdrawal and decline." This mindset ignores the exciting possibilities for personal growth and societal contributions among older members of the population. As Thomas (2004, p. 31) observes, "There is great power hidden with old age, but we will remain ignorant of the depth and breadth of that power as long as we insist on simply comparing youth to age."

Thus, more adults and an increase in the number of older adults are two demographic factors influencing the provision of learning activities in our society. So, too, is the rising level of education characteristic of our population. This is dramatically illustrated by the fact that 83 percent of today's twenty-five- to thirty-four-year-olds have completed high school compared with 65 percent of adults age sixty-five and over (U.S. Bureau of the Census, 2000). Since previous education is the single best predictor of participation in adult education, the rising educational level of the adult population is a contextual factor of considerable import. Participation data from the Center for Education Statistics show, for example, that 22 percent of adults with fewer than four years of high school participate in organized adult education, while 34 percent of high school graduates and 66 percent of college graduates do (Kim, Collins Hagedorn, Williamson, & Chapman, 2004).

Nevertheless, even as the educational attainment level of the population as a whole continues to rise, an alarming number of high school students drop out before graduating. And "as a high school education becomes the minimum educational standard, those who drop out are more likely to become members of an educational underclass, from which adult education (especially in the form of adult basic and secondary education) may be the only hope of escape" (Rachal, 1989, pp. 10–11). Unfortunately, as mentioned earlier, adults with less than a high school diploma are least likely to participate in adult education activities overall, with only 6 percent in work-related courses, 7 percent in basic skills education, and 1 percent in vocational or technical diploma programs (Kim et al., 2004).

Another demographic characteristic of the social context is the growing cultural and ethnic diversity of America's population. In contrast to the influx of European immigrants at the end of the nineteenth century (which continued into the middle decades of the twentieth), today's immigrants are more likely to come from

Asia and Latin America. In 2002, for example, 52 percent of U.S. immigrants were from Latin America, 25 percent from Asia, and only 14 percent from Europe (Alfred, 2004).

If current trends in immigration and birthrates persist, it is projected that between the years 2000 and 2010, the Hispanic population will account for 34.1 percent of the total population growth, Asians about 33.3 percent, and African Americans 12.9 percent (U.S. Bureau of the Census, 2004b). In 2001, Hispanics became the largest minority group in America, with African Americans the second largest (U.S. Bureau of the Census, 2005).

Furthermore, the average age of minority populations is decreasing, while the majority population is growing older. For example, in 2004 the median age of Hispanics was 26.9 years whereas that of the White population was 40.0 years (U.S. Bureau of the Census, 2005).

Not only is the composition of the minority population changing, so too are the overall numbers. In 2000, minorities made up 31 percent of the population; by 2050, minorities will account for nearly 50 percent of the overall population (U.S. Bureau of the Census, 2004b).

The socioeconomic and cultural diversity of today's immigrant population presents special challenges to adult educators. As Alfred (2004, p. 14) observes:

Today's immigrant population reflects a pattern of demographics that reveals deep polarization between the most educated and wealthiest and the least educated and poorest. This emergent pattern of immigrant adaptation seems to follow a new hourglass segmentation found in the U.S. economy and society (Sparks, 2003; Suarez-Orozco & Suarez-Orozco, 2000). Noticeably, there are those immigrants who are quickly achieving upward mobility, primarily through education and high-tech jobs, while on the opposite end of the hourglass, large numbers of low-skilled workers find themselves locked in low-wage service jobs. Those in between approximate norms of the majority culture and disappear into U.S. cultural institutions without much notice (Sparks, 2003). This polarization in the composition of the immigrant population suggests that planners of adult and higher education programs face a challenging task as they attempt to meet the variety of needs and expectations that immigrants bring to the new country.

The growing ethnic and cultural diversity of our population was identified over fifteen years ago by Naisbitt and Aburdene (1990) as one of the megatrends of the twenty-first century. They observed that "even as our lifestyles grow more similar, there are unmistakable signs of a powerful countertrend: a backlash against uniformity, a desire to assert the uniqueness of one's culture and language. . . . Outbreaks of cultural nationalism are happening in every corner of the globe" (p. 119). Adult educators are slowly becoming aware of the instructional implications of the fact that "as our outer worlds grow more similar, we will increasingly treasure the traditions that spring from within" (Naisbitt & Aburdene, 1990, p. 120).

In summary, the composition of society is an important factor in the provision of learning opportunities for citizens of all ages. In the United States, there are more adults than youth, the number of older adults is growing, the population as a whole is better educated than ever before, and the population is more diverse—racially, ethnically, and culturally—than ever before.

GLOBALIZATION

Globalization is an overarching concept encompassing changes taking place worldwide. But globalization is not a new concept because it can be argued that the world has always sought to connect through travel, trade, and cultural exchange. "Although it builds on a history of international relations between nation-states, it is new in the sense of the growing extensiveness of social networks involved, the intensity and speed of flows and interconnections within these networks, and the reach of its impact" (Glastra, Hake, & Schedler, 2004, p. 292). Since the 1980s, the term has been used to reflect the increasing integration of economies around the world, particularly through trade and the flow of finances. In addition to finances, this "flow" also includes the movement of people and information. One definition of globalization is "a movement of economic integration, of cultural homogenization, and of technological uniformization" (Finger, 2005b, p. 269). An incredibly complex and controversial phenomenon, we can only try to convey some of its essential characteristics and some of the issues and speculate as to how it is shaping adult learning in our context.

Images most associated with globalization are economic, having to do with the loss of low-wage manufacturing jobs to less developed corners of the world, with transnational companies operating in a space outside national boundaries and control, with consumerism and commercialism supplanting all other interests. As one writer observed, globalization is resulting in the world becoming "one big shopping mall" (Cowen, 2003, p. 17). Although the market economy is clearly a driving force in globalization, so too is information technology. Changes in information technology "almost make state boundaries redundant in respect to the flow of information across the globe" (Jarvis, 2004, p. 3).

But globalization is not only about economics. Brysk (2003, p. 22) contends that it is combination of four elements:

- *Connection* means greater traffic in bodies, goods, services, and information across borders.
- *Cosmopolitanism* describes the growth of multiple centers of power and influence above, below, and across national governments: international organizations, grassroots groups, and transnational bodies from Microsoft to Greenpeace.
- *Communication* is an increase in technological capacity that strengthens transnational networks of all kinds (from multinational corporations to nongovernmental organizations [NGOs] to terrorists) and diffuses ideas and values more quickly and broadly.
- *Commodification* is the expansion of world markets, and the extension of market-like behavior across more states and social realms. Increases in global capital flows, privatization of formerly state-owned enterprises, and increasing employment of children are all examples of commodification.

Brysk goes on to show how these elements of globalization are both a plus and a minus for human rights issues: "Connection brings human rights monitors to Chiapas, but it also brings sex tourists to Thailand. Cosmopolitanism creates a U.N. Human Rights Commission and countless NGOs to condemn China's abuse of political dissidents and religious minorities; yet commodification makes China the United States's second-leading trade partner" (p. 22).

Part of the controversy surrounding globalization has to do with economics. Those countries that can be competitive are already better off and become even richer through globalization, while others "like Zambia are virtually excluded from the market. Similarly, those people who are employable can—if they wish—play an active part (to greater or lesser extent) in being citizens, but those who have no job are socially excluded" (Jarvis, 2004, p. 5). That globalization is exacerbating the differences between rich and poor is creating ethnic hatred and global instability, argues Chua (2003). The United States, for example, is home to only 4 percent of the world's population but is "seen everywhere as the principal engine and principal beneficiary of global capitalism. We are also seen as 'almighty,' 'exploitative,' and 'able to control the world,' whether through our military power or through the IMF-implemented austerity measures we have heartlessly forced on developing populations" (p. 16). Is it no wonder, she asks, that we are the object of mass resentment?

Finger (2005b) echoes this same sentiment in his observations of cultural globalization underlying global consumption. With the movement of goods, people, ideas, and cultural artifacts across borders, the global culture is characterized not by diversity but "by the spread of individualism, Western values, and homogenization in general. Yet, simultaneously, cultural globalization is triggering numerous cultural reactions against this very process, leading, among others, to fundamentalism" (p. 270). September 11, 2001, and other terrorist attacks are the deadly consequences of ignoring this resentment.

What does all this mean for adult learning? For one thing, "it does a worker very little good to train specifically for a job with a company that outsources the position, downsizes, or sells to a foreign owner who reorganizes or 'reengineers' the company, selling off pieces, leaving the worker trained and unemployed" (Tomlin, 1997, p. 20). Global economics has led to changing work practices, which require different kinds of preparation and training. This has resulted in the control of education shifting to business. The emphasis now is on improved product and service quality, greater worker responsibility, and teamwork approaches. Adult education and human resource development, in particular, have responded with broad-based workplace literacy programs and training and development packages designed to address a wide range of economy-driven needs. Globalization's effect on adult education has even reached "the professional and executive training area, by either helping individuals and firms take advantage of commercialization and industrial development, or by supporting individuals in coping with the negative consequences of the same commercial developments" (Finger, 2005b, p. 272). Indeed, human resource development (HRD) and corollary concepts such as organizational learning have become a parallel adult education system, one lodged in the workplace where responsiveness to globalization is paramount.

The global economy is having an impact on learning in broader ways too. We have become, in the words of Usher, Bryant, and Johnston (1997, p. 4), "a culture of consumption. . . . The factory, the assembly line, large-scale manufacturing—are being increasingly displaced by centres of consumption—financial services, small-scale specialised enterprises, shopping malls and superstores, entertainment complexes, heritage and theme parks." This shift is evidenced in a changing relationship between educator and learner to one of a "market relationship between producer and consumer. Knowledge is exchanged on the basis of the performative value it has for the consumer" (p. 14). Educational institutions themselves "become part of the market, selling knowledge as a commodity and increasingly reconstructing themselves as enterprises dedicated to marketing their commodities and to competing in the knowledge 'business'" (p. 14). As Hadfield (2003, p. 19) observes, "*Customer* is exactly how adult learners think of themselves, and they hold our institutions of higher education accountable for providing paid-for results and educational experiences that make a difference in their lives. They pay for these experiences with precious resources, not the least of which is their time. They are savvy, demanding customers who know how to shop. When they do not find what they want at one school, they transfer to another."

This shift to the marketplace as the primary site of adult learning has divided adult educators into deciding "whether to locate their practice in civil society or the economic sector" (Cunningham, 2000, p. 577). Others are concerned that adult education has lost its social action perspective; rather, "adult education practice in the age of globalization increasingly becomes a toolkit for quick fixes by means of tailor-made and individualized short-term, yet lucrative, trainings" (Finger, 2005b, p. 272). Schied, Mulenga, and Baptiste (2005) suggest educators should confront "the totalizing gaze of the ideology of globalization as an inevitable force of nature because it negates the centrality of human agency" (p. 397). Adult educators need to become involved in "building capacities for local groups to engage and confront globalization and its effects" at all levels—local, national, and international (p. 397).

Intertwined in globalization is a shift from a society employed in producing goods to one employed in providing services. The decline in industrial labor stems from automation and competition from other countries with low labor costs. Dislocated workers from both the industrial and agricultural sectors, with few if any transferable skills, find themselves in low-skill, low-paying service jobs. Ironically, the availability of displaced workers with limited employable skills leads to equally low wages in the service sector, thus promoting the general growth of the service sector. Referring to a report by Hecker (2001), Bills (2004) observes that the fast growth of the service sector is paralleled by fast growth in professional and related occupations. "The important thing about these projections is that these two occupations are at the opposite ends of the education and earnings distribution. That is, professional occupations require extensive educational preparation and are generally well-rewarded. Service jobs require lower educational credentials, with corresponding lower job rewards" (p. 97).

Concurrent with the shift to a service economy is the shift to what has been called the information society—a shift that has had a major impact on workers as economic units. "In an industrial age, workers are expendable cogs in the machine; in an information age (and to a lesser extent, in a service age), human capital is the most valuable capital an organization has" (Bills, 2004, p. 20). The implications for learning—and in particular for work-related training—are enormous. Already the amount spent annually by business, industry, and government agencies on job-related training is in the billions of dollars and exceeds that spent on public higher education. Furthermore, because skills learned in preparation for a job or career cannot keep pace with the demands of the world of work, the ability to learn becomes a valuable skill in and of itself. This factor is underscored by the fact that 50 percent of all employee skills become outdated in three to five years (Shank & Sitze, 2004); in high-tech areas workers may need to learn to operate a new machine, or a new software program, or a new hardware configuration every eighteen months or less (Desimone, Werner, & Harris, 2002).

Developing simultaneously with the emphasis on learning to learn is the notion of the learning organization (see Chapter Two). To survive in the global economy, an "organization needs to evolve into 'a learning organization' whereby new and expansive patterns are permitted, allowing employees to learn individually and collectively (continually learning how to learn)" (Gardner, 1996, p. 43). The growing body of literature on the learning organization positions learning, information processing, and problem-solving skills as central to the survival of both the individual worker and the organization. Ulrich (1998) underscores how globalization necessitates the creation of learning organizations. Globalization requires companies "to move people, ideas, products, and information around the world to meet local needs. They [companies] must add new and important ingredients to the mix when making strategy: volatile political situations, contentious global trade issues, fluctuating exchange rates, and unfamiliar cultures. They must be more literate in the ways of international customers, commerce, and competition than ever before. In short, globalization requires that organizations increase their ability to learn and collaborate and to manage diversity, complexity, and ambiguity" (p. 126).

Closely related to shifts to a service and information economy are changes in America's labor force. The largest job-growth categories are jobs in health and service (such as foodservice) followed by jobs in education, training, and sales and related occupations (Hecker, 2004).

Not surprisingly, women, minorities, and the elderly are overrepresented in the lower-paying service jobs. Since the middle of this century, however, the labor force has changed from one dominated by blue-collar occupations to one where the majority of jobs are considered white collar. Significant changes in the composition of the workforce are also occurring along racial and ethnic lines. Although White non-Hispanic workers account for the great majority of workers (81 percent in 2005; U.S. Bureau of Labor Statistics, 2005), their rate of growth is much lower than the rate of growth for the Black, Asian, and Hispanic groups. According to the U.S. Bureau of Labor Statistics (2005), in 2005 Hispanics were the second-largest ethnic worker group (13 percent) and African Americans the third group at 11 percent.

Perhaps the greatest change of all has been the steady increase of women in the workforce. In 1960, 37.7 percent of women in the population were members of the workforce, compared with 59.2 percent in 2004. Currently, women represent 46 percent of the total United States labor force (U.S. Department of Labor, n.d.). Economic necessity and the freeing of occupations traditionally assigned to men have contributed to this change.

In summary, economic factors are shaping the nature of our society, and by extension, the nature of learning that adults are most likely to undertake. A global economy, the shift to a service and information society, and consequent changes in the configuration of the labor force are determining to a large extent where learning takes place, what is offered, and who participates.

TECHNOLOGY

There is no more apt metaphor for reflecting the rate of technological change than the computer. Itself a major component of our highly technological age, computer language has invaded the ways in which we talk of adult learning. We process students and information; we plan learning activities with an eye to inputs, flow, and outputs; we provide feedback to individual learners and to programs. Indeed, we program learning experiences and ourselves. Technology has had an enormous impact on society and adult learning. It has been instrumental in bringing about the information society, which has created new jobs and eliminated others. And as we have seen, globalization is technology driven.

The move to an information society has been a function of technological developments associated with an information explosion. Within a short span of time, electronic, communication, and information technologies have changed society as a whole and affected how people go about their daily lives. From ordering pizza by computer, to instant communication via the cell phone, to faxing a request to the local radio station, everyday life has been irrevocably influenced by technology.

Concurrent with these technological advances has been an information explosion. Lyman and Varian (n.d.) estimated that in 2002 about five exabytes (one exabyte equals over one billion gigabytes) of new information were produced: "Five exabytes of information [are] equivalent in size to the information contained in 37,000 new libraries the size of the Library of Congress book collections" (¶ 2). They also estimated that "the amount of new information stored on paper, film, magnetic, and optical media has about doubled in the last three years" (¶ 3). Others have speculated that half of what most professionals know when they finish their formal training will be outdated in less than five years, perhaps even in months for those in technology-related careers. Thus, the need for continuing education has dramatically escalated with the increase in knowledge production. There is not only considerably more information than ever before, but its storage, transmission, and access have been made more feasible than ever before through links with technology.

Laser technology, in particular, is revolutionizing the dissemination of information, as well as its storage and retrieval. A compact disk using laser technology makes it possible to store huge amounts of information in a very small space, and the Internet and World Wide Web have become repositories for more information than any one person could access in a lifetime. Also promoting the explosion of information is the decreasing price of magnetic media. According to Lyman and Varian (n.d.), in 2002, magnetic media, primarily hard disks, stored 92 percent of new information. Film stored 7 percent of the total new information, paper 0.01 percent, and optical media 0.002 percent. Huge amounts of information and the development of technology that finds and easily retrieves this information have had a significant impact on teaching and learning from public school through graduate and adult education.

A major societal shift, such as moving from an industrial to an information society, results in profound changes in the society's structure. In an industrial society, machine technology extended physical ability; in an information society, computer technology extends mental ability. Material wealth has great value in an industrial society; knowledge and information are key assets in an information society. The social structure changes from hierarchies and bureaucracies to multicentered and horizontal networks. These changes in society's underlying structure can be seen most dramatically in changes in the workforce. As noted earlier, the shift is eliminating certain classifications of work while creating others not previously dreamed of.

In addition to the creation and elimination of jobs, technological changes are affecting workers in other ways, such as where work is done. As Gardner (1996, p. 48) observes, "Computer technology frees labor from a particular location. . . . Knowledge workers can work anywhere; they simply have to have access to a computer connection. Even within the team framework, workers can stay engaged in their mutual tasks even if not in close proximity to each other. Delocalizing work has been touted as one of the more appealing aspects of technological advances in the workplace." Telecommuting, or *home work,* some assert, has increased because of the new technologies, and it is considered desirable because it fits in with alternative family patterns (such as more single-parent families), worker concerns for control of time and work site, and organizational efforts to cut costs and remain flexible by contracting out for services rather than hiring more workers. Estimates of the number of people who currently telecommute vary because of different interpretations of this new work structure. However, estimates from a 2001 national survey found that nearly twenty-nine million, or one in five U.S. workers, participated in some form of telecommuting, and this number was expected to increase to more than forty million by 2010 (Potter, 2003).

Yet others have cautioned against the unquestioning adoption of technology in the workplace, for information technologies have created something of a paradox. Designed to get more work done more efficiently by fewer employees, information technologies have instead offered more ways to communicate, increased the demand for information, and raised the level of expectations with regard to the print and graphic presentation of material. Think of the volume of mail one now handles through e-mail; this technology seems to have increased our workload and expectations of timely responses.

Clearly, technology and the information age that it spawned are changing the nature of adult learning. Professionals whose knowledge becomes outdated in a few years, auto mechanics who must now master sophisticated electronic diagnostic systems, adults who must learn new ways to bank or shop from home computers: all must be able to function in a fast-changing society, and this necessitates continued learning. Technology is not only making learning mandatory, it is providing many of the mechanisms for it to occur. Computer-assisted instruction, teleconferencing, interactive videodisk, the Internet, and the World Wide Web are expanding the possibilities of meeting the growing learning needs of adults.

Simultaneous with the development of technologically sophisticated delivery systems is the development of new roles for educators and trainers. Having access to unlimited information is not the same as being able to search efficiently for the most significant information, or even to know what is most significant. Heclo (1994, p. B2) states that "in the long run, excesses of technology mean that the comparative advantage shifts from those with information glut to those with ordered knowledge, from those who can process vast amounts of blab to those who can explain what is worth knowing and why." Ratinoff (1995, p. 163) points out that the information explosion has had both positive and negative effects: "On the positive side, the myths and riddles of power are more exposed to public scrutiny. To fool all people is very difficult under the present circumstances." On the downside, "information has been growing faster than the individual and institutional capacities required to make sense of the new diversity of signals and messages" (p. 164).

Whitson and Amstutz (1997) suggest a number of strategies for dealing with the information and technology overload. First, adult educators should "build more and better connections with those who directly teach information access skills," especially librarians, but also computer specialists (p. 133). Educators can also focus on developing students' "higher-level thinking skills" so that judgments can be made about the credibility and usefulness of information (p. 137). Since much information is available electronically through the Internet and the World Wide Web, the authors underscore the need for educators themselves to become comfortable in this environment, to the point that they can help learners take advantage of technology. Finally, "we have an obligation to consider the ethical implications of our information access processes. . . . The rights of poor people to have access to information and the ways in which information should be made accessible to them are important concerns. We need to resist the growing tendency for business, industry, and government to control access to information" (p. 141).

The more affluent and better-educated adults with home computers have access to information and instructional packages that make them even more informed. On a global level, the "have" nations can communicate and exchange information in ways that will never be a reality for the majority of the world's people. Even job training necessitated by technological change tends to favor the haves.

Nevertheless, technology's potential for increasing access to learning for people of all ages and possibly all economic levels is unlimited. In more and more communities, computers can be found in libraries, restaurants, Laundromats, and other public places. Naisbitt and Aburdene (1990) argue that technology is "empowering." In their opinion, "there are fewer dictators on the planet today because they can no longer control information. . . . Computers, cellular phones, and fax machines empower individuals, rather than oppress them, as previously feared" (pp. 303–304). Finally, "the proliferation of information technologies and exponential increases in the production of information have created greater opportunities for informal learning . . . for people in all walks of life" (Livingstone, 2001, p. 20).

THE CONVERGENCE OF DEMOGRAPHICS, GLOBALIZATION, AND TECHNOLOGY

Demographics, globalization, and technology are closely entwined with each other. Advances in technology, for example, are interrelated with changes in the economic structure. Automation and robotics displace production workers but create other jobs. Technology creates alternative work structures. The need to be competitive in the world market leads to further technological sophistication. Demographics and economics are clearly related. The baby boom cohort that is now in the labor force, for example, is saturating middle- and upper-management career levels, forcing younger people to consider career alternatives. In another example, the growing number of older adults in our society is having several effects on the economy. Some older adults are being asked to retire early to make room for younger workers; with increased longevity and good health, others are pursuing second or third careers; and some employers, especially those in the service sector, are recognizing the human resource potential of this group and are actively recruiting older workers.

Embedded in this convergence of demographics, economics, and technology is a value system based on the political and economic structure of capitalism. Nearly two decades ago, Beder (1987, p. 107) explained how these three forces are linked in the value system: "The beliefs undergirding the capitalist system emphasize material values. The health of the system is gauged in terms of national wealth as embodied in the gross national product, and social equality is assessed in terms of economic opportunity—the potential of members of the underclasses to amass more income. Hence, the political and social systems become directed toward . . . economic productivity, and economic productivity under the rationale of human capital theory becomes the predominant rationale for all publicly funded social interventions including adult education." This value system directly shapes adult education in the United States in several ways. First, economic productivity becomes "the dominant rationale for all public subsidy of adult education" (p. 109). Second, social justice becomes equated with economic opportunity in that "the just society is a society that provides opportunity for members of the underclasses to amass more income and material goods" and adult education "helps learners acquire the skills and knowledge" to do so (p. 109). The emphasis is on productivity and efficiency, both of which benefit from advances in technology. Thus technology, in the service of economic productivity, converges with changing demographics in shaping the adult learning enterprise.

Nowhere is this more visible than in higher education. Before globalization and the market economy, higher education was a local enterprise serving a predominately local or national constituency. Academic foci shaped the nature of the student body and concerns of the institution. With the shift to a consumer approach to higher education, the institution worries about its "brand" appeal, its profitability, its "share" of the market. Globalization in conjunction with communication technology is reshaping higher education in terms of:

- International communications-based telecommunications, information, and media technologies, which facilitate transnational circulation of text, images, and artifacts,
- International movement of students to study in other countries as well as a demand for online courses without a residency requirement in another country,
- Increasing multicultural learning environment whether online or on campus,
- Increasing global circulation of ideas and particularly Western pedagogical systems and values,
- Rise of international and virtual organizations offering Web-based education and training. [Mason, 2003, p. 744]

There are problems with the globalization of higher education, however, not the least of which is its lag behind economic deregulation; that is, credit transfer is a serious barrier even inside a country, let alone across borders. Further, those countries without the technological infrastructure will be "disenfranchised." And assuming there are those who have access, how ready "are the potential students of global education . . . to be self-directed, self-motivated, and resourceful e-learners?" (Mason, 2003, pp. 744–745).

As already pointed out, a number of writers would like to see the values and purposes of adult education reexamined in the wake of the wide-scale social and economic changes taking place. In a postmodern world characterized by large-scale changes in global activity resulting in economic, social, and political uncertainty, adult education tends to be an entrepreneurial instrument of the so-called new world order. Adult education is particularly sensitive to a restructured workplace, reliance on technology to produce knowledge, and a market demand for multiskilled workers. Petrella (1997) emphasizes the decreased importance placed on individuals in the new market economy in observing that humans as "resources" take precedence over humans as human beings. As well, knowledge has become an important business commodity that is readily marketed, due, in part, to the explosion of the Internet and other information technologies. Finger (2005b) and others (Cunningham, 2000; Schied, Mulenga, & Baptiste, 2005) believe that adult education is in danger of losing its social action orientation as it focuses on helping individuals cope with the overwhelming economic and other challenges that threaten their identities and survival. Learning in a global community can be empowering but it "can also serve as a mechanism for exclusion and control. The move to a knowledge-based economy means that those who have the lowest level of skills and the weakest capacity for constant updating are less likely to find sustainable employment" (Schied, Mulenga, & Baptiste, 2005, p. 396).

While globalization has extended economic and cultural boundaries, it has also served to fragment society in many ways. For example, although minorities and other ethnic groups may be perceived as valuable contributors in a society, conflict results when scarce educational and other resources are allocated. Minority groups may become more isolated from mainstream society. In other ways, too, individuals in a society may experience fragmentation as they struggle to make sense of their disordered and sometimes disrupted lives. In a time when nations, companies, and families are splintering, there is little sense of security. Job security in particular no longer exists: "A new bargain replaces the old social contract between employers and workers that ensures security of employment in return for good and loyal work effort. Some employers now agree to maintain the future employability of workers through education and training in return for good performance" (Maehl, 2000, p. 20).

If the postmodern world is characterized by fragmentation and diversity, it is also characterized by new alliances and interactions. Demographics, the global economy, and technology have come together in adult education in the blurring of the field's content and delivery mechanisms. For example, adult education has been variously divided into formal, nonformal, and informal learning activities (see Chapter Two). Formal learning takes place in educational institutions and often leads to degrees or some sort of credit. Nonformal learning refers to organized activities outside educational institutions, such as those found in community organizations, cultural institutions such as museums and libraries, and voluntary associations. Informal learning refers to the experiences of everyday living from which we learn something. Today, many formal providers offer learning experiences that are noncredit, leisure oriented, and short-term. Similarly, nonformal learning and informal life experiences can be turned into formal, credit-earning activities.

Another blurring can be noted in higher education. Once composed of learners eighteen to twenty-two-years old, the student body has grayed along with the population. In fact, students twenty-five years of age and older now make up close to 50 percent of all college enrollments in the United States (Kasworm, Sandmann, & Sissel, 2000). Similar subjects may be taught at the local community college for credit and at the public adult school for noncredit. The part-time adult student taking a course during the day at a college is an adult learner as much as the sixteen-year-old studying for a high school diploma in a local evening class. There is also a blurring between higher education and business and industry. Many postsecondary institutions have business institutes that provide training and development services to business. Conversely, a growing number of private companies, such as McDonald's Hamburger University and the Rand Graduate Institute, are offering accredited degrees (Eurich, 1990).

Finally, a blurring of content and delivery is found in such popular slogans as "workplace literacy," "learning to learn," "critical thinking," and "media literacy." Educators, employers, and society at large are focusing attention on developing the skills needed to be productive and informed members of a fast-changing and highly technical society. With the erosion of boundaries in the content and provision of adult learning, we may be witnessing the emergence of what has been called the *learning society*. Taking human beings rather than educational institutions as its beginning point, the learning society is a response to the social context.

SUMMARY

Adult learning does not occur in a vacuum. What one needs or wants to learn, what opportunities are available, the manner in which one learns—all are to a large extent determined by the society in which one lives. This chapter has discussed several characteristics of American society today that are shaping the nature of learning in adulthood.

Demographics, globalization, and technology are three forces affecting all of society's endeavors, including adult learning. With regard to the American population, adults outnumber youth, there are more older adults, adults are better educated, and there is more cultural and ethnic diversity among the population than ever before.

Globalization is linking the world through economics and consumerism, but there is also a cultural dimension to globalization. Unfortunately, even the cultural aspects of globalization are Western dominated (Finger, 2005b), a factor leading to resentment and terrorist activity.

Technology is integral to the global economy and has contributed to, if not caused, the shift to an information society, which is creating dramatic changes in the workforce. Although we have treated them separately, these three forces are interactive and firmly embedded in the American capitalist value system. Adult education both reflects and responds to the forces prevalent in the sociocultural context. Among the implications discussed in the chapter are the field's responsiveness to special groups of people, the economic productivity rationale behind much of adult education, the potential of technology for enhancing or impeding learning, and the blurring of content and delivery in current adult education.

CHAPTER TWO

LEARNING ENVIRONMENTS AND LEARNING CONCEPTS

Whenever we ask adults about their learning, they most often mention education and training programs sponsored by the workplace, colleges and universities, public schools, and other formal organizations. They first picture classrooms with "students" learning and "teachers" teaching in a highly structured format. Yet when we ask these same adults about what they have learned informally over the last year, they typically respond with descriptions of learning activities outside these formal settings. They discuss, for example, remodeling a house, which has involved everything from reading and talking with friends to conversations with carpenters, plumbers, and electricians. Or they may focus on an important change in their life, such as an illness, parenthood, or divorce, which has precipitated numerous learning events, sometimes over an extended period of time. In considering the spectrum of learning opportunities available to adults, it is important to acknowledge all of these arenas of learning, from the highly structured to the more informal ways adults go about learning.

Why is it important that educators of adults recognize that learning happens in so many and varied places in the lives of adults? First, appreciating and taking into consideration the prior knowledge and experience of learners has become a basic assumption of our practice as educators of adults, wherever this knowledge was learned. In working with welfare recipients, for example, instructors might recognize that parents on welfare have had to learn how to take care of their children on very constrained budgets, keep their families safe and healthy under difficult living conditions, and in general make do with very little. Rather than asking questions about how they have learned to do this successfully, what is focused on most often is their lack of formal education and skills training. Formal schooling and skills training are important, but so are the ways they have informally learned about life skills that have kept them and their families fed and clothed. Likewise, workshop leaders putting on staff development programs in schools might learn as much as possible about the background and experience of the teachers in that school and what their knowledge base is with respect to the content of the workshop. There is nothing that turns off teachers more in these programs than being treated as if they know very little about the subject matter, especially if they have been dealing with it on a daily basis.

Second, if educators helped learners recognize the many places and ways they have gone about learning in adulthood, more adults might see themselves as active learners. As a result, they might be less cautious about learning new things and even be more willing to enter formal programs of learning. One of our favorite stories is about a duck carver who was interviewed as part of a study on self-directed learning (Berger, 1990). This man, who considered himself both a nonreader and "definitely not a very good student," taught himself how to carve ducks. He started this process by carving some ducks by himself and then taking them to duck carving shows, where he could talk with other artists about his initial attempts. In addition, he read every book he could get his hands on related to duck carving (and remember, he thought of himself as a nonreader). He now raises ducks so he can have live models, in itself another learning project. As a result of the interview process, this man saw himself as much more of a learner than he had before. Our hope is that as more individuals view themselves as active and competent learners, at least in some areas, they might be better able to address the many life challenges that come in adulthood, through both formal and informal learning modes.

In exploring the spectrum of learning opportunities in adulthood, we first discuss each of the primary arenas in which adult learning occurs: those sponsored by formal institutions, nonformal community-based learning activities, and learning that is more informal or self-directed in nature. We then explore online learning as a fourth site for learning, one that overlays formal, nonformal, and informal modes of learning. While there are other terms in use, we have chosen to use the term *online learning* because it is the most common term used to refer to learning through the use of computers anchored to communication networks. A second section of the chapter presents two related concepts—organizational learning and the learning organization. Finally, we end the chapter with a discussion of lifelong learning and the learning society.

WHERE LEARNING OCCURS

In this section we first present a framework for three types of settings in which learning occurs for adults: formal institutional settings, nonformal settings, and informal contexts. This framework is an adaptation of one proposed by Coombs (1985, 1989; Coombs, Prosser, & Ahmed, 1973), in which he classified lifelong learning according to these three broad categories. The biggest difference between their conceptualization and our framework is that we have added the concepts of self-directed learning (which is synonymous with Coombs's definition of informal learning) and indigenous forms of learning. Although we are aware of the problems of trying to divide the landscape of learning opportunities into three separate categories, we are assuming that all three categories are of equal importance in the adult learning enterprise. There will always be overlaps among the three, something that educators of adults can capitalize on when designing educational activities. Online learning is a fourth site of learning, one that spans formal, nonformal, and informal learning.

FORMAL AND NONFORMAL SETTINGS

For most people, learning in adulthood brings to mind classroom settings and this is indeed what Coombs (1985) and Coombs, Prosser, and Ahmed (1973) had in mind with their classification of *formal education*. Formal education is highly institutionalized, bureaucratic, curriculum driven, and formally recognized with grades, diplomas, or certificates. It is "the institutional ladder that goes from preschool to graduate studies" (Schugurensky, 2000, ¶ 2) and thus can include "adult basic education programs that follow the prescribed curriculum and employ certified teachers" (Schugurensky, 2000, ¶ 3).

Historically, formal education, whether it be in public schools or postsecondary institutions, has had as its primary mission to serve youth. In more recent years the populations of some of these institutions—such as many community colleges, vocational-technical institutes, and colleges and universities—have changed so dramatically that they are now reaching more adult learners than traditional-age students. In fact, nearly half of the students in postsecondary institutions are over the age of twenty-four (Kasworm, Sandmann, & Sissel, 2000). For formal settings, we envision adults sitting in a classroom, with an instructor, learning in a variety of ways, from formal lectures to small-group interactions. When we ask participants what they remember as positive about learning in formal settings, they often cite well-organized, knowledgeable, and caring instructors; participatory instructional methods and well-crafted lectures; relevant and useful materials; and respect for them as adults and learners. And, conversely, when we ask participants to recall some of their worst experiences, they talk about arrogant instructors who have no sense of them as people or learners, poorly delivered content whatever the method used, and poorly organized and irrelevant materials.

The term *nonformal education* has been used most often to describe organized learning opportunities *outside* the formal educational system. These offerings tend to be short-term, voluntary, and have few if any prerequisites. However, they typically have a curriculum and often a facilitator. Nonformal educational opportunities are usually local and community-based, such as those programs offered by museums, libraries, service clubs, religious and civic organizations; mass media is also classified as a nonformal delivery system. Some insights into these nonformal settings are revealed in Taylor's studies of educators working in the nonformal settings of state and local parks (Taylor & Caldarelli, 2004) and home improvement stores (Taylor, 2005b). Instructors in both settings emphasized the informality, compressed time, and hands-on, interactive nature of the learning in which the needs and interests of the participants are paramount in the encounter.

While nonformal adult education is outside the formal schooling or education system, three subtypes can be discerned, all of which are "reactions to the limitations or failures of formal education" (Brennan, 1997, p. 187). The first subtype proposed by

Brennan (1997) is nonformal education as a *complement* to the formal system. Targeted are those who have dropped out of the formal system, or who, for whatever reason, failed to obtain basic skills such as literacy while in the system. Adult literacy classes offered by the local public library or community college would be an example of this type of nonformal education.

A second type of nonformal education Brennan terms *alternative* to the formal system. This includes traditional and indigenous education, which we discuss in more detail in the following section. Nonformal education can also be seen as a *supplement* to formal education. Supplemental nonformal education he sees as related to a response to national and global imperatives: "This type of NFE is required as a quick reaction to educational, social and economic needs because formal education is too slow in its response (if it does in fact decide to respond) to these needs" (p. 187). An example of nonformal education as supplemental might be National Issues Forums sponsored by the Kettering Foundation. These forums are held in local communities and focus on civic issues such as the health care crisis, immigration, terrorism, and so on (see www.nifi.org).

Nonformal education is also associated with international development programs designed to improve the living conditions of people in developing countries through community projects and training programs. These programs are typically sponsored by nongovernmental agencies (NGOs) and private voluntary agencies. Nonformal educational programs in developing countries (as well as some nonformal programs in the United States) are "expressly concerned with social inequities and often seek to raise the consciousness of participants towards social action" (Merriam & Brockett, 1997, p. 170).

Despite efforts to distinguish between formal and nonformal education, some adult learning opportunities that could be placed in this nonformal category often more closely resemble programs in formal educational institutions. Coombs (1989) himself identifies "homegrown hybrids" of formal and nonformal, such as programs for out-of-school youth, community learning centers, and so on. And in the United States, for example, how does one classify a corporate training center or a proprietary school? So does using this term *nonformal* have utility today? We believe that it does, both in terms of recognizing the many educational programs in developing nations as well as focusing on the community-based programs of adult learning in all environments that fit the parameters of less structure, more flexibility, and concern with social inequalities. In addition, another type of learning usually associated with nonformal education—indigenous learning—is again being recognized as an important form of learning. Therefore, in describing nonformal educational learning opportunities, we highlight two types of these opportunities: community-based adult learning programs and indigenous learning.

Community-Based Learning

Varied pictures come to mind when we talk about community-based learning opportunities. We see people gathered in churches, the community center, or the local library organizing to overcome a specific problem or issue they believe to be important in improving life in their community. These problems have ranged from addressing racial hatred and inequality to ensuring adequate housing and sanitary living conditions. Other images of community-based learning programs include men and women learning to read and write while at the same time gaining marketable job skills, adults learning CPR at the local Red Cross, farmers being introduced to new methods and crops as a way to build economic control over their lives, and spouses who batter being taught non-violent ways of handling their anger and frustration.

One common goal of many of these programs is their focus on social action and change for the betterment of some part of the community. Educators who work in these programs believe that education and training can be a powerful tool in assisting learners to take control over their own lives. Sometimes these programs are not welcomed by the mainstream community, especially if one of their main purposes is to challenge the existing way of life, including the current social and economic structures of that community. Vivid examples include the worldwide human rights movement, the continuing struggle to eliminate poverty and hunger, community-based actions exposing hazardous waste dumps, and local attempts to end discriminatory practices based on race, class, gender, sexual orientation, and so on.

Working with adults in community-based learning settings has both its blessings and its curses. Flexibility in administration and programming is often recognized as its greatest benefit. Because these types of organizations "start small and are typically organized as freestanding organizations with fairly simple structures . . . , they can often move relatively quickly to identify problems and develop programmatic solutions" (Hemphill, 1996, p. 21). This can translate into quicker response times, in terms of both developing funding proposals and getting resources to where they are needed. "New people can be brought in (or unfortunately let go more quickly) as needed. Curricula can be rapidly developed or revised. Teaching assignments can be quickly modified" (p. 22). Being able to move more quickly does mean that checks and balances must be in place to ensure both a focused program direction based on community needs and quality learning opportunities that are useful. In addition, people attracted to work in community-based adult learning programs, whether paid or volunteer staff, often come with a passion for a cause that gives them the drive to stay with this work, even under the most trying conditions. On the downside, the very nature of many community-based organizations often puts them on the path to an unending search for resources. This continuing search for and worry about resources, in combination with long and often difficult working conditions, can lead to staff burnout very quickly, even for the most committed individuals.

Indigenous Learning

Indigenous learning is learning linked with a culture. It refers to processes and structures people in particular societies have used to learn about their culture throughout their history (Graveline, 2005). Conscious use of indigenous forms of learning, which are often steeped in oral traditions and art forms, can enhance nonformal and perhaps even formal educational programs. Storytelling, for example, is often used by African-American women to teach about the joys and sorrows of life. When teaching these women, instructors could incorporate storytelling as an important method of learning about the topic at hand, from surviving in modern-day organizations to basic literacy skills. In another example, Hicks and Rowel (2004) studied the nonformal indigenous learning of six public housing community leaders who were inspirational in helping others in their community. These women were effective in helping others by modeling exemplary leadership, practicing what they preached, and communicating with diverse groups.

Descriptions of indigenous forms of learning can be found in both scholarly and more popular literature (see Chapter Nine). Cajete (1994) eloquently describes the tribal foundations of American Indian education, which he sees as "shared by Indigenous cultures of the world" (p. 33). In tracing these foundations, Cajete observes:

> We are tracking the earliest sources of human teaching and learning. These foundations teach us that learning is a subjective experience tied to a place environmentally, socially, and spiritually. Tribal teaching and learning were intertwined with the daily lives of both teacher and learner. Tribal education was a natural outcome of living in close communion with each other and the natural environment. The living place, the learner's extended family, the clan and tribe provided the context and source for teaching. . . . Informality characterized the greater part of American Indian teaching and learning. . . . However, formal learning was usually required in the transfer of sacred knowledge.
>
> Hahoh is a Tewa word sometimes used to connote the process of learning. Its closest English translation is to "breathe in." Hahoh is a sacred metaphor describing the perception of traditional Tribal teaching—a process of breathing in—that was creatively and ingeniously applied by all tribes. . . . Through these methods [such as storytelling, dreaming, tutoring, and artistic creation], the integration of inner and outer realities of learners and teachers were fully honored, and the complementary educational processes of both realities were fully engaged. [Cajete, 1994, pp. 33–34]

Cajete beautifully expresses what teaching and learning mean to him: "A parable that often flashes through my memory during times of quiet, deep relaxation, or just before I fall asleep: 'It is an essential, life-sharing act of each generation of a People to nurture that which has given them Life and to preserve for future generations the guiding stories of their collective journey to find life'" (1994, p. 187).

Brennan (1997, p. 191) has observed that "the lack of attention to the indigenous learning structure may have been initially the work of missionaries who viewed indigenous culture as inferior and non-Christian and therefore to be ignored or if necessary repressed." He goes on to suggest a four-stage process for recognizing indigenous learning as an essential part of the nonformal system of learning for adults. In Stage 1, approaches or techniques that may be relevant to educational or developmental activities are identified—for example, the role of traditional dance and music and the use of legends, myths, tales, and proverbs. Stage 2 involves classifying these approaches and techniques into a system that educators in more formal settings can understand and integrate into their own ways of thinking. "The third stage," he writes, "is associated with advocacy for the exploration of a broader indigenous learning 'system' . . . [and] the fourth stage is represented by the development of more detailed and comprehensive learning 'systems' for a particular cultural group" (pp. 192–193). Indigenous forms of learning could also be seen as informal or self-directed learning, as was described by Cajete and is examined in the next section.

INFORMAL LEARNING

Informal learning is the third form of learning in Coombs's typology. Defined by him as "the spontaneous, unstructured learning that goes on daily in the home and neighborhood, behind the school and on the playing field, in the workplace, marketplace, library and museum, and through the various mass media" informal learning is by far the most prevalent form of adult learning (Coombs, 1985, p. 92). Illeris (2004a) calls this type of learning "everyday learning" because it "takes place in all the private and non-organised contexts of everyday life" (p. 151). It is, as Livingstone (2001) points out, learning that takes place without the externally imposed curriculum of either formal or nonformal educative programs.

The very nature of informal learning is what makes it so difficult for adults to recognize. Embedded as it is in our everyday activities, whether we are at work, at home, or in the community, and lacking institutional sponsorship, adults rarely label these activities as learning. However, studies of informal learning, especially those asking about adults' self-directed learning projects, reveal that upwards of 90 percent of adults are engaged in hundreds of hours of informal learning (see Chapter Five). It has also been estimated that the great majority (upwards of 70 percent) of learning in the workplace is informal (Kim, Collins Hagedorn, Williamson, & Chapman, 2004), although billions of dollars each year are spent by business and industry on formal training programs.

Informal learning, Schugurensky (2000) suggests, has its own internal forms that are important to distinguish in studying the phenomenon. He proposes three forms: self-directed learning, incidental learning, and socialization, or tacit learning. These differ among themselves in terms of intentionality and awareness at the time of the learning experience. Self-directed learning, for example, is intentional and conscious; incidental learning, which Marsick and Watkins (1990) describe as an accidental by-product of doing something else, is unintentional but "after the experience she or he becomes aware that some learning has taken place" (p. 4); and finally, socialization or tacit learning is neither intentional nor conscious (although we can become aware of this learning later through "retrospective recognition") (Marsick & Watkins, 1990, p. 6).

Of the three forms of informal learning, self-directed learning is the most visible and the most studied (see Chapter Five). The following two scenarios illustrate the informal nature of self-directed learning:

Scenario 1: Charlie has a passion for model railroading. He spends hours in his basement planning his layout, tinkering with his equipment, and laying track. He subscribes to every railroad magazine published and talks shop with acquaintances who also have model trains. Every once in a while, he attends a model railroad show, but for the most part, this is a hobby he enjoys pursuing on his own. Over the years he has learned a great deal about model railroading and is proud of his layout, though as he says, "I'll never be totally satisfied. There are always new things coming out which I like to fiddle with."

Scenario 2: Trudy has just learned that she has breast cancer. Once over the initial shock, she decides to take an active role in planning her treatment. So that she can speak intelligently with the myriad medical personnel she knows she must face, she gathers as much information as she can about the disease from a number of sources, including the American Cancer Society, her local Reach for Recovery Program, the Internet, and an oncology nurse who is a friend of a friend. Moreover, she learns of a local support group for cancer patients and decides to join for both information and emotional solace, thereby choosing a nonformal learning opportunity as part of her own self-directed efforts. Her husband and best friend have joined her in her fight, and both are reaching out to a number of different sources for advice and counsel.

These scenarios, representing the independent pursuit of learning in natural settings, with or without the support of institutional resources, are very common in adult life. Yet even with the many verification studies that have been completed, self-directed learning in this form is not recognized by many adults, or even by some educators of adults, as "real learning." There are a lot of Charlies out there, learning all kinds of things on their own, from model railroading to making quilts and crafting clay pots. Some find friends or independent mentors to assist them in their learning, and some deliberately choose institutional resources that might be helpful to them as part of their self-directed activities. There are also numerous Trudys whose self-directed learning activities "arise from and seek to resolve a problem or situation" (Candy, 1991, p. 199). These learners often combine resources in their natural environments with those supplied by institutions, from educational materials to people who can assist them with their learning. What becomes evident is that this type of informal learning does not necessarily mean learning alone, a major myth about self-directed learning (Brockett, 1994). Rather, adults often use other people, and even groups, whether they are institutionally based or not, in their self-directed learning pursuits.

Schugurensky (2000) makes just this point in summarizing the three forms of informal learning—that is, informal learning can occur individually or in groups and "learners can use a variety of sources for their learning, including books, newspapers, TV, the Internet, museums, schools, universities, friends, relatives, their own experience, etc." (¶ 20). He also notes that informal learning can complement and reinforce or *contradict* learning acquired in formal and nonformal settings:

> For instance, one can learn in school curriculum that the capitalist system is a great contribution to humanity, and learn through informal ways that such a system is detrimental to humanity. Likewise,

one can be socialized by the surrounding community into a bigot, and learn virtues of tolerance in the public school. Moreover, one can go to a school and be aware that through the formal curriculum she or he is learning A (e.g. math), without being aware that through the hidden curriculum she or he is learning B (e.g. homophobia). [¶ 23]

Schugurensky also makes the point that informal learning can be additive, in the sense of acquiring more knowledge or skills, and it can be transformative (see Chapter Six).

In summary, we have presented a framework that encompasses three types of settings or contexts in which learning in adulthood occurs. The first two settings, formal and nonformal, involve some form of organizational or community sponsorship. The third opportunity, informal learning, is more of a hybrid. Although the majority of learning opportunities in this last category are planned and initiated primarily by learners in natural settings (such as the home, on the job, or through recreational pursuits), the learning processes and methods used in self-directed and informal learning have been incorporated by some formal and nonformal settings in the way they carry through their instructional programs.

ONLINE LEARNING

In more recent years, as the use of technology has increased in the delivery of learning programs, our picture of learning in formal settings has expanded dramatically. We now see learners doing individualized or group learning in computer labs, participating in interactive teleconferences, and interacting from their homes with fellow participants and instructors via the Internet.

And while most of the research and theorizing about online learning is occurring in the formal education sector, online learning is also going on in nonformal settings. Many businesses have their own intranet, where employees have access to company policies, events, and activities as well as learning that can be shared through chat rooms and e-mail. Local communities often use the Internet to stimulate citizen participation, and nonformal educational institutions such as museums facilitate learning through online activities. After getting a traffic ticket, one can even take a traffic school course online, endorsed by traffic court, to avoid getting "points" on one's driving record! And in a fascinating study of online social action, Hollenbeck (2005) explored how three online communities organized and educated their members worldwide in the art of social protest. She studied anti-McDonald's, anti–Wal-Mart, and anti-Starbucks communities, which she labeled *antibrand* communities. All three had formed for the purpose of educating others "by providing resources for getting involved and taking action" against capitalist corporate giants (p. 207). These antibrand online groups organized e-mail campaigns protesting corporate policies, publicized and supported local protests, and offered a space for employees who were overworked and underpaid to "vent" (a number of people in these online communities were disgruntled employees of the organization in question).

Informal learning has also been affected by this technology. How many of us have been curious about something and done a Web search to learn more about it? Even older adults are accessing the Web for up-to-date information on many aspects of their lives—from travel, to the "best places to live," to their health condition (Valente, 2005). Hayes (2005) has also demonstrated how sophisticated one's learning can become through participating in the virtual world of video and role-playing games. She observed, for example, that since some of these virtual worlds are "not solely text-based, these worlds offer opportunities for learning through a wider range of modalities, including visual, auditory, and even kinesthetic modes, and rely less on verbal (i.e., reading and writing) skills for participation. These varied modalities may encourage or require different forms of identity construction, meaning-making, and social interaction" (p. 194).

As we noted earlier, it is from the formal education sector that we have learned the most about online learning, and it is to developments in this arena that we now turn. Online learning is a form of distance education, which has a long history of serving adults who otherwise would not have access to continuing and higher education. The defining characteristic of all forms and generations of distance education is the separation of student and teacher in time or space. What in the literature is often termed *first-generation distance education* consisted of print-based correspondence courses, a form still in existence. How many generations follow differs by author, but the simplest model has the second generation being broadcast and television technologies, followed by the third generation of information technologies of which Web-based courses are a part (Moore & Kearsley, 1996). This generation is distinguished by "an increased degree of learner control and flexibility, interactive communication and group-oriented processes" (Conrad, 2005, p. 445).

The phenomenal growth of online learning is reflected in some statistics that will be outdated before this book is published. Internet World Stats (2005) has estimated that there are more than 223 million Internet users in North America, or 68 percent of the population. Furthermore, 81 percent of higher education institutions in the United States offered at least one fully online or blended course in 2002–03, and over 1.9 million students were studying online in fall 2003 (Allen & Seaman, 2004). According to Moore (2001), those who are enrolled in online courses tend to be women, older rather than young adults, and people employed outside the home.

As online learning has become almost commonplace in higher education, research has shifted from its technical aspects and its staying power to more pedagogical concerns encompassing "all aspects of the learning transaction, including its very important social dimension and its sub-parts, community and social presence; culture and facilitation styles; and theory-building" (Conrad, 2005, p. 445). At the same time, there are overarching concerns about this forum for learning. One big concern is with access, what some are characterizing as the *digital divide*. Distance education began in the nineteenth century to serve those who had little or no access to the traditional education system. While online learning is also designed to open up access, and does so for thousands of adults who need the flexibility of time and space for their learning, it may also be widening the gap between the haves and the have-nots:

> To access the new forms of distance education, obviously you have to have access to the new technology, and richer people have that and poorer people do not have that. In the United States, high-income households are twenty times more likely to have access to the Internet than low-income families. In the United States, two-thirds of college-educated people have access to the Internet and only 6% of those with primary or elementary education. [Moore, 2001, ¶ 25]

From a global perspective, it is estimated that of the world's 6.4 billion people, only 14.6 percent are Internet users (Internet World Stats, 2005). But the digital divide is not a matter of access alone. In a study of rural learners who had access to computers in community settings, Page (2005) found that other sociocultural and psychological factors impeded their use. Factors such as "uncertainty about change, fear of technology, need for guidance, inexperience, relevance, the social context of the persistently impoverished county, and the perceived need" revealed the complexity of the digital divide (p. 334).

There are other issues of concern to adult educators when considering the growth of online learning. Moore (2001) and others talk about the commercialization of Internet education. A number of private, for-profit institutions have sprung up promising learning anytime, anywhere, for anyone. But the promise of convenience and ease (for a price) may fool some students in terms of the commitment involved and the independent learning skills needed. Or, these institutions may have poor quality courses if instructors at the institution do not live up to its advertising. Private, for-profit Phoenix University, which is a largely online university, now has two hundred thousand students and expects to serve five hundred thousand by 2010 (Selingo, 2005), yet little is known about student success or lack of success in such a fast-growing institution.

In an analysis of the rhetoric of online learning, Kelland (2005) critiques three themes that characterize the promotion of online learning. The first theme, which she calls a myth, is that online learning is inclusive and democratic. In promoting online learning to disadvantaged groups (who, as we saw earlier, do not have the cultural capital to take advantage of it), governments and institutions "continue to ignore barriers that discourage, and even prevent, disadvantaged learners from participating in on-campus programs" (p. 254). The second theme, that online learning is accessible and flexible, is countered by the digital divide that characterizes even Western countries such as the United States. The third theme, that online learning is cost-effective, does not necessarily mean that lower institutional costs are passed on to students; further, students in industrial countries have trouble getting financial aid for their distance learning.

In summary, online learning presents both opportunities and challenges to adult educators. As we have seen, online learning occurs in formal, nonformal, and informal settings. What we as adult educators need to think about is how the Internet is facilitating adult learning in all three settings and how we can maximize its potential. At the same time, online learning presents challenges particularly with regard to access, even in the information-rich, technologically advanced United States. Access issues, which are discussed more fully in the next chapter on participation, have haunted the field of adult education since its inception. It appears that online learning is yet another manifestation of this worrisome social issue at the heart of our adult education practice.

ORGANIZATIONAL LEARNING AND THE LEARNING ORGANIZATION

The concepts of organizational learning and the learning organization are so interrelated that it is difficult to speak of one without reference to the other. Illeris (2004a, p. 88) concurs, stating that "there is no clear distinction" between the two "except for the discussion on what exactly it means that an organization learns." Indeed, sections on the learning organization and organizational learning in the recent *International Encyclopedia of Adult Education* (English, 2005b) position each term with reference to the other. Recognizing the embeddedness of one concept in the other, we begin with a discussion of organizational learning, a concept that preceded that of the learning organization.

Learning has always gone on in organizations. At least since the industrial revolution, employees have had to be trained in the technical skills needed for their jobs. This learning, or more precisely, training, was "removed from the immediate work environment on which it [was] expected to have an impact" through the "'transfer' of skills and understanding back to the milieu" (Laiken, 2001, p. 6). As much of this training failed to transfer, and as organizations entered a more competitive environment, broader thinking about learning in organizations emerged. Argyris and Schön's 1978 book, *Organizational Learning: A Theory of Action Perspective,* defined the concept of organizational learning. As described by them, "Organizational learning occurs when members of the organization act as learning agents of the organization, responding to changes in the internal and external environments of the organization by detecting and correcting errors in organizational theory-in-use, and embedding the results of their enquiry in private images and shared maps of organization" (p. 16). A number of key points about organizational learning are present in this definition. First, it is individuals who do the learning, but in service to the organization, so that the organization can adapt and develop in response to the environment. Second, theories-in-use versus "espoused theories" (what people do versus what they say they do) form the basis for practice. Finally, this learning must become "embedded in the images of organization held in its members' minds and/or in the . . . artifacts (the maps, memories, and programs) embedded in the organizational environment" (Argyris & Schön, 1996, p. 16).

As it has evolved, organizational learning is a flexible concept spanning a number of disciplines and perspectives so that it is now "impossible to capture with a single definition" (Fenwick, 2005b, p. 446). Further, the field of organizational development (OD) and the idea of knowledge management (KM) intersect with organizational learning in terms of how to incorporate learning into changing an organization's practices and culture, and how to employ the knowledge generated through individual and group learning. Today, all organizations are grappling with issues that include "generating innovation, integrating new technologies, improving existing processes, predicting and adapting to turbulent conditions, restructuring staff, improving performance, ensuring equitable opportunity, and fostering quality of work" (Fenwick, 2005b, p. 448).

Although learning has always gone on in organizations, it was not until the publication in 1990 of Peter Senge's book *The Fifth Discipline: The Art and Practice of the Learning Organization* that the notion of the learning organization became a popular concept capturing the imagination of organizations worldwide. Senge defined it as "a place where people continually expand their capacity to create the results they truly desire, where new and expansive patterns of thinking are nurtured, where collective aspiration is set free, and where people are continually learning how to act together" (p. 3). Implicit in this definition is the recognition that the learning organization is a vibrant, *social* entity;

further, individuals learning in conjunction with each other has a synergistic effect—the overall learning is greater than a single individual's.

It is Senge's contention that "organizations learn only through individuals who learn" (p. 140). This is a necessary but not sufficient condition for creating a learning organization. There are also five core disciplines, or "component technologies," that individuals must adopt for the learning organization to become a reality. Senge views *systems thinking* as the cornerstone of the learning organization. He believes that it is critical for people to shift their thinking from "seeing parts to seeing wholes, from seeing people as helpless reactors to seeing them as active participants in their reality, from reacting to the present to creating the future" (p. 69). Without this shift in thinking, he views the other four disciplines (developing personal mastery, changing mental models, building shared vision, and participating in team learning) as useless.

Watkins and Marsick's (1993) view of the learning organization is a bit broader. They see the learning not just with individuals but also taking place in "teams, the organization, and even in the communities with which the organizations interact. Learning is a continuous, strategically used process—integrated with, and running parallel to [the] work [of the organization]" (p. 8). Watkins and Marsick have outlined six *action imperatives* needed to create and sustain learning organizations. The first imperative is to create continuous learning opportunities at all levels of the organization. These opportunities range from on-the-job learning experiences to hosting global dialogue teams, with the goal that learning becomes an integral part of the everyday work life. To promote this continuous learning, two other action imperatives are brought into play: inquiry and dialogue, and collaboration and team learning. These learning strategies seem to form the heart of most organizational learning efforts, with the emphasis on the collective and interdependent nature of these processes. The fourth imperative, establishing systems to capture and share learning, involves "building organizational capacity for new thinking that is then embedded and shared with others" (Watkins & Marsick, 1993, p. 15). This fourth imperative, along with the fifth—empowering people toward a collective vision—mirrors Senge's disciplines of changing one's mental models and building shared vision. The final imperative, connecting the organization to its environment, acknowledges the connections between the organization and its external constituents, including its customers and the various local, national, and international communities that affect the work of the organization. These connections are symbiotic. It is not only the external constituents that affect the organization; the organization also affects these external groups.

This learning capability improves an organization's capacity to respond quickly and in novel ways, thus increasing its ability to foster innovation and change. Organizations with this ability to make rapid changes may have a competitive advantage in the marketplace, although there is little research that actually confirms this claim. In one of the few research studies to test this assumption, Ellinger, Ellinger, Yang, and Howton (2002) correlated results of a learning organizational questionnaire with objective measures of 208 U.S. manufacturing firms' financial performance. While they caution that this study was exploratory, they did find positive associations between the learning organization concept and firm performance.

Today the learning organization goes by a number of names including *adaptive, resilient,* and *innovative* organizations (Marsick & Watkins, 2005). However it is conceptualized, there are some consistent features of a "healthy" learning organization. These include: "(a) openness across boundaries, including an emphasis on environmental scanning, collaboration, and competitor benchmarking; (b) resilience or the adaptability of people and systems to respond to change; (c) knowledge/expertise creation and sharing; and (d) a culture, systems and structures that capture learning and reward innovation" (p. 357).

In thinking about the process of building and sustaining learning organizations, Dixon (1997) offers the metaphor of the hallway as a useful analogy. She defines hallways as "places where collective meaning is made—in other words, meaning is not just exchanged, it is constructed in the dialogue between organizational members" (p. 25). Although the dissemination of complete and accurate information is needed to enable this process to work, it is not sufficient to promote shared meanings among people. Dixon contrasts this accessible meaning of the hallways to that of private meaning, which is knowledge known only to individuals and not accessible to others. Collective meanings of organizational members are held in what she terms the organization's storeroom. This collective meaning, which includes norms, strategies, and assumptions about how the organization functions, is the glue that holds the organization together. She acknowledges that this collective meaning, if not allowed to be questioned, can have a negative impact on organizations' being able to learn and change.

Finally, Dixon outlines seven critical elements that characterize hallway learning: (1) reliance on discussion, not speeches; (2) egalitarian participation; (3) encouragement of multiple perspectives; (4) nonexpert-based dialogue; (5) use of a participant-generated database; (6) the creating of shared experiences; and (7) the creation of unpredictable outcomes. We find the last element especially intriguing; it asks those of us who choose to create learning organizations to move away from the predictable aspects of learning and into the realm of reframing problems in unexpected ways and finding possibilities never thought of before.

There are, of course, numerous barriers or inhibitors to creating learning organizations. Among the most critical are the inability of organizational members to recognize and change their existing mental models, the lingering power of individualism in organizations versus the spirit of collaboration and team learning, the lack of skills and developmental readiness by people to undertake "systemwide learning," and "truncated learning or the ghosts of learning efforts that took root because they were interrupted or only partially implemented" (Watkins & Marsick, 1993, p. 240). Another major barrier to creating learning organizations is that power is often in the hands of a few who may or may not buy into these ways of working and thinking (Cervero & Wilson, 2005).

As we have just seen, it is not possible to talk of the learning organization without reference to organizational learning. We believe that the concepts of organizational learning and the learning organization offer a way of working and thinking for educators in both formal and nonformal settings. It allows us to move beyond planning just for individuals and groups of learners in terms of affecting both learning processes and outcomes. Creating learning organizations, whether we are associated with educational, quasi-educational, or noneducational institutions, provides a way to foster learning communities that are open to change and innovative practices.

LIFELONG LEARNING AND THE LEARNING SOCIETY

In recent years nearly all people, and especially those of us in education, have heard the terms *lifelong learning* and *learning society*. But what do we mean by these terms and what do they mean for the field of adult education and adult learners in particular? Are they a convenient slogan to promote our field? Will their use result in more adults having access to learning opportunities? There are, of course, no simple answers to these questions. What we can do in this section is explore these concepts and in particular the issues they raise with regard to practice.

Before lifelong learning there was lifelong education, promoted chiefly by UNESCO in the 1960s and 1970s. The now-famous UNESCO report, *Learning to Be* (Faure et al., 1972), was seen as a blueprint for reforming the entire educational system. Both idealistic in its goals and humanistic in its concern with individual growth through learning, lifelong education, it was hoped, "would result in the creation of a learning society where access to and learning in education would be taken for granted—an inalienable human right like clean water or a roof over one's head" (Boshier, 2005, p. 373).

However, as societies became more conscious of the need to develop a skilled workforce to be competitive in the marketplace, the humanistic focus of lifelong education gave way to more of an economic framing of lifelong learning. By the early 1990s the term *learning* had supplanted *education*. This shift was also marked by a significant publication, this time from the Organization for Economic Cooperation and Development (OECD) in 1996, titled *Learning for All*. It is significant that the OECD represents the economic interests of mostly affluent countries, for this report established "the political-economic *ideology* of lifelong learning (Illeris, 2004a, p. 29). Secondary to the economic focus, this report also acknowledged the importance of lifelong learning for personal development and social unity: "We are all convinced of the crucial importance of learning throughout life for enriching personal lives, fostering economic growth and maintaining social cohesion" (OECD, 1996, p. 21).

Most recently the OECD conceptualization of lifelong learning has been augmented by reports from the European Union and the World Bank. The 2000 report of the Commission of the European Communities acknowledges that learning need not be so highly institutionalized, highlighting the importance of nonformal and informal learning contexts. The report maintains the economic aim of lifelong learning, but also says an "equally important aim" is promoting active citizenship. The World Bank's report on lifelong learning, while including Third World and transitional economies, states the aim of lifelong learning to be the creation of a workforce "able to compete in the global economy" (World Bank, 2003, p. xviii).

Although in the United States use of the concept of lifelong learning has lagged behind other countries, we have our own report urging the nation to make adoption of a system of lifelong learning a national priority (Commission for a Nation of Lifelong Learners, 1997). The five recommendations of this report are to "acknowledge the link between lifelong learning and global economic success, establish equity of access, incorporate new technologies in lifelong learning, rethink and reorganize educational delivery, and make resource commitments commensurate with lifelong learning's importance" (Maehl, 2000, p. 7)

Lifelong learning, at least in the United States today, is more a "principle or organizing concept than a functioning system" (Maehl, 2000, p. 4). This is partly because of the decentralization of our educational system and the myriad institutions, agencies, and programs that offer learning opportunities. There is no public policy on lifelong learning and certainly no unified funding source. The result is that the concept is shaped by whatever entities take it up. Postsecondary education, for example, seems to be in the forefront in shaping lifelong learning as access to higher education for adults of any age and stage in life. The Department of Labor, in contrast, sees lifelong learning as access to training to develop skills needed in the workforce.

The proliferation of interpretations of lifelong learning has led to some vigorous debate and discussion about its merits and limitations. The most vociferous critique of lifelong learning is that it is a tool for restricting its application to "labor market expectations that enable governments and corporations to exploit the idea of human capital" (Dale, Glowacki-Dudka, & Hyslop-Margison, 2005, p. 113). Or, because lifelong learning is so pervasive throughout society, knowledge becomes a commodity that is produced, packaged, and sold to the consumer. Crass commercialization begins to define lifelong learning. Yet, the notion of lifelong learning has also opened up our thinking of learning as broader than what goes on in school. Nonformal, informal, and self-directed learning are much more visible as legitimate sites for learning.

The most vexing issue, one raised earlier with regard to online learning, is the question of access. As Boshier (2005, p. 376) points out, "[L]ifelong learning is used as a rationale for inflicting (often oppressive and authoritarian) forms of mandatory continuing education on citizens already marginalized and experiencing social difficulties." Illeris (2004a) notes that while all the international reports "are quite explicit about the necessity of giving priority to those who are poorest in economic, social, and educational terms," he wonders if in reality this is happening "in a way that is relevant seen from the life situation and perspectives of these participants" (p. 34). Finally, Holford and Jarvis (2000) raise the fundamental question of who benefits in the learning society, pointing out that the rhetoric and the reality do not match. For example, lifelong learning with regard to the workplace "will emphasize types of learning and knowledge that make sense in concrete contexts and will be widely available. Unfortunately—whatever the potential benefits to all of privileging practical knowledge—access to learning opportunities at work remains highly unequal" (p. 655).

Despite the issues involved in a society such as ours promoting the notion of lifelong learning, the concept does seem to have some usefulness in conveying the wide variety of learning activities and sites where it can occur. It also reflects what some see as the "postmodern" condition, full of change and opportunity. As Edwards and Usher (2000) write, "[C]hange and uncertainty require lifelong learning and 'lifelong learning' is itself a signifier of the uncertainty and change of the contemporary" (p. 99).

This notion of change and uncertainty also underlies the concept of the learning society. Just as the learning organization is designed to respond to environmental and economic developments, the learning society acts in response to social change: "The more prevalent or profound the changes that occur in a society, the greater the likelihood that it will be regarded as a learning society" (Jarvis, 2004, p. 15). China is a prime example. Undergoing enormous change, the Sixteenth Congress of the Chinese Communist Party in 2002 declared China's intention to promote lifelong learning and create a learning society. To bring about this learning society, the government has set up and is supporting sixty-one experimental learning communities throughout the nation. Using the present administrative infrastructure, which links provinces, municipalities, districts, streets, and neighborhoods, these communities are engaging people of all ages in nonformal and informal learning activities designed to bring learning to the fore as a priority in their lives and in their communities. Local governments in the experiment areas have integrated the work of building the learning community into their administrative responsibilities; learning streets and learning families in these local learning communities attest to the scope of these efforts (Bo Chang, personal communication, September 7, 2005).

The magnitude of China's efforts to create a learning society makes the concept difficult to grasp. It is perhaps easier to think in terms of learning "regions" or learning communities, cities, towns, or villages. Learning regions, according to Walters (2005), refer to a geographic area of any size that has made a commitment to linking "lifelong learning with economic development to compete globally" (p. 360). The important characteristics of learning regions such as a city, state, or province is that all forms of learning—informal, nonformal, and formal—are promoted for all ages. As Boshier (2005) explains:

> In a learning city (town or village) there are attempts to foster all forms of learning for citizens old and young in many contexts. . . . Learning cities are committed to learning as a core aspect of development. As well as catching dogs and servicing sewers, the city fosters learning. They seek to sustain economic activity by building social capital. . . . A learning city (town or village) is: a form of community development in which local people from every community sector act together to enhance the social, economic, cultural and environmental conditions of their community. [pp. 376–377]

Boshier also includes learning festivals as part of the learning society. Such learning festivals are part learning, part cultural expression, and part entertainment. What is key to learning regions, cities, or festivals is not technology, which "helps but is not essential. What matters most are local places and spaces" (Boshier, 2005, p. 376).

The learning society then can be considered as an expression of lifelong learning, one that is place-bound. What it means to be a learning society (or learning city, community, or region) will differ according to the particular society. What does the learning society look like, for example, in "middle-income countries like Brazil, India and South Africa' or "in contexts of widespread poverty and social polarization" (Walters, 2005, p. 360)? Certainly, this concept of the learning society, along with the concept of lifelong learning, will undergo change as societies grapple with implementing learning for all across all segments of society.

SUMMARY

Learning opportunities for adults are found in a variety of settings, from formal institutions to one's home or place of employment. The importance of understanding this vast array of learning opportunities for adults is twofold. First, acknowledging prior knowledge and experiences of learners, wherever gained, is important to the practice of adult educators. Second, if more than just formal types of adult education are made visible, individual learners, even those without formal schooling, may be better able to recognize their abilities and skills as lifelong learners.

There are three primary types of opportunities or sites in which learning occurs for adults: formal settings, nonformal settings, and informal or self-directed contexts. A fourth site explored in this chapter is online learning, which spans formal, nonformal, and informal settings. Although the categorization of these learning opportunities and the language used within these categories helps us think about learning, what is more crucial is the recognition that learning opportunities come in many sizes, shapes, forms, and places. The most critical actions that educators of adults can take is to recognize the equal importance of the various types of adult learning and advocate that people use them in whatever situation or setting they find themselves.

A second section of this chapter explored the concept of organizational learning and its manifestation in the learning organization. In learning organizations, learning—whether done by individuals, groups, or the organization as a whole—is a central, valued, and integral part of organizational life. The heart of the learning organization is the willingness of organizations to allow their employees and other stakeholders related to the organization to suspend and question the assumptions by which they operate, then create and examine new ways of solving organizational problems and means of operating. This process requires that people at all levels of the organization be willing to think in a systems framework, with the emphasis on collective inquiry, dialogue, and action. Creating learning organizations could allow educators of adults, whether they are associated with formal or nonformal settings, to develop learning communities in which change is accepted as the norm and innovative practices are embraced.

Finally, we reviewed the evolution of the concept of lifelong learning, which has replaced lifelong education. Lifelong learning is a broader term than lifelong education because it incorporates all forms of learning, not just the formal educational system. Lifelong learning recognizes the prevalence and value of nonformal and informal learning along with the traditional formal system. This broader perspective can be seen in practice in some societies' efforts to implement lifelong learning in their societies, communities, and learning cities and regions. The term *learning society* is an attempt to capture these efforts.

CHAPTER THREE

ADULT LEARNERS: WHO PARTICIPATES AND WHY

Adult education is a large and amorphous field of practice, with no neat boundaries such as age, as in the case of elementary and secondary education, or mission, as in higher education. Adult education with its myriad content areas, delivery systems, goals, and learners defies simple categorization. In the previous chapter, we looked at the spectrum of settings where adult learning takes place, ranging from formal institutional settings, to nonformal community-based sites, to one's home, and more recently, to a computer. One way to grasp something of the field is to find out who is involved in the activity itself—hence, studies of participation.

Knowing who participates in adult education activities and why adults are participating (or not) is necessary information for both providers and policymakers. Since participation in adult education is largely a voluntary activity, knowing who is participating, reasons for participating, and what conditions are likely to promote greater participation can help providers better serve adult learners. An understanding of participation patterns can also raise important questions about assumptions underlying what is offered, who is benefiting from participating, and whose needs are *not* being met.

Knowledge about participation is useful to policymakers, particularly in terms of funding. At the federal level, for example, funding for literacy and other programs is a function of who is now participating, in conjunction with the perceived needs of nonparticipants. Along with current numbers and rates of participation of various segments of the adult population, other sociopolitical and economic factors play important parts in federal policy formation, not the least of which is the desire to maintain a stable, democratic society and a globally competitive workforce. For those who plan learning activities and instruct adults, it is certainly helpful to know as much as possible about the clientele being served.

This chapter first offers a descriptive profile of who participates in adult learning activities, and the reasons why adults engage in learning. The second half of the chapter problematizes the concept of participation, asking who really has access to learning and who benefits from participating.

WHO PARTICIPATES?

Almost all studies of participants in adult education focus on formal, institutionally based programs. This, of course, is due to the ease of gathering this information from learners and institutions that sponsor programs. It is much more difficult to assess participation in nonformal, community-based activities or in informal self-directed learning. We first review participation of adults in formal adult education—that is, institutionally sponsored courses or classes. What little we do know about who participates in nonformal and informal learning will be reviewed at the end of this section.

JOHNSTONE AND RIVERA'S LANDMARK STUDY

In 1962 an "inquiry into the nature of adult education in America" was funded by the Carnegie Corporation and carried out by researchers Johnstone and Rivera (1965) at the National Opinion Research Center (NORC) in Chicago. The study sought to describe participation in formal and informal educational activities, assess attitudes and opinions held by adults concerning education, describe the organizations delivering adult education in a typical urban community, and focus on the educational and work experiences of young adults ages seventeen to twenty-four. The findings of this first national study have provided a baseline against which the findings of subsequent studies have been compared.

Since comparisons are made, it is important to know how *adult education* and *adult* are defined in this study. Realizing the import of this function, Johnstone and Rivera (1965, p. 26) struggled to come up with a definition of an adult educational activity that was broad enough to capture systematic efforts at learning but not so broad as to include "a host of activities . . . which would fall beyond the range of any reasonable or workable definition of adult education." They decided that an adult education activity would have as its main purpose the desire to acquire some type of knowledge, information, or skill and that it would include some form of instruction (including self-instruction). They thus measured involvement as a full-time adult student, as a part-time participant in adult education activities, and as a participant in independent self-education. An adult was defined as anyone either age twenty-one or over, married, or the head of a household. Interviews with a random national sample of nearly twelve thousand households formed the data set.

Using the preceding definitions, Johnstone and Rivera (1965) estimated that 22 percent of American adults participated in "one or more forms of learning" between June 1961 and June 1962 (p. 1). They also discovered that what adults were learning was largely practical and skill oriented rather than academic: "Subject matter directly useful in the performance of everyday tasks and obligations accounted for the most significant block of the total activities recorded. Together, the vocational and home and family life categories alone represented 44 percent of all formal courses studied and 47 percent of the subjects people studied on their own" (p. 3).

This landmark study also identified the major demographic and socioeconomic characteristics of participants. Age and formal schooling were delineated as the primary correlates of participation in adult education. Johnstone and Rivera's often-quoted profile of the typical adult learner has held up, with minor deviations, in all subsequent national studies of participation. Their profile is as follows: "The adult education participant is just as often a woman as a man, is typically under forty, has completed high school or more, enjoys an above-average income, works full-time and most often in a white-collar occupation, is married and has children, lives in an urbanized area but more likely in a suburb than large city, and is found in all parts of the country, but more frequently in the West than in other regions" (p. 8).

One of the strengths of Johnstone and Rivera's study is that they included "independent self-education" along with participation in formal courses and community-based activities. Unfortunately, with one exception, subsequent national studies have limited participation to organized instruction offered by educational institutions, business or industry, and community organizations.

National Studies of Formal Participation

Beginning in 1969, the National Center for Education Statistics (NCES) in the U.S. Department of Education undertook a set of triennial surveys of participation of adults in education. The results of the first six surveys (1969, 1972, 1975, 1978, 1981, and 1984) and three studies in 1991, 1995, and 1999 can be loosely compared with each other to reveal participation trends. In these surveys, adult education is equated with organized instruction: "Adult education is defined as any course or educational activity taken part-time and reported as adult education by respondents seventeen years old and over" (U.S. Department of Education, 1986). These courses or activities are considered "formal" because they are sponsored by educational institutions or employers. Changes in methodology and sample design over the years warrant caution in making comparisons (Collins, Brick, & Kim, 1997). Nevertheless, certain trends emerge.

One clear trend is that the number of adults participating part-time in organized instruction has increased from a low of 10 percent in the 1969 survey to 14 percent in 1984, 38 percent in 1991, 40 percent in 1995, and 46 percent in 1999 (Kim & Creighton, 2000). In a comparison of the 1991 and 1999 NCES studies, Creighton and Hudson (2002) note an overall increase in participation "among virtually every group of adults" surveyed (p. ix).

The most recent NCES survey of adult education participation was conducted in 2001. As in previous studies, NCES employed a random, national digit dial (RDD) telephone survey of civilian, noninstitutionalized persons ages sixteen and older not enrolled in secondary school at the time of the interview. In this survey, "formal" coursework or training was defined as those activities having an instructor. For the first time, informal educational activities (those that do not involve an instructor) were also surveyed. The results of this study with regard to formal participation are quite congruent with previous national studies (Kim, Collins Hagedorn, Williamson, & Chapman, 2004). As can be seen in Table 3.1, the overall rate of participation in formal educational activities was

TABLE 3.1. NUMBER OF ADULTS AND RATES OF PARTICIPATION IN SELECTED ADULT EDUCATION ACTIVITIES, BY SELECTED DEMOGRAPHIC, EDUCATIONAL, AND OCCUPATIONAL CHARACTERISTICS, 2000–01.

Characteristics	Total Adults (in Thousands)	Overall Participation	
		Percentage	Standard Error
Total	198,803	46	0.5
Age			
16–30	46,905	53	1.5
31–40	41,778	53	1.4
41–50	41,255	55	1.5
51–65	39,523	41	1.2
66	29,342	22	1.1
Sex			
Male	94,955	43	0.8
Female	103,848	49	0.8
Race/ethnicity			
White, non-Hispanic	144,147	47	0.6
Black, non-Hispanic	22,186	43	1.5
Hispanic	21,537	42	2.3
Other	10,932	49	2.5
Educational attainment			
Less than high school	31,343	22	1.5
High school diploma or its equivalent	64,606	34	0.9
Some college	52,559	58	1.1
Bachelor's degree or higher	50,295	66	1.1
Marital status			
Married	121,455	47	0.7
Living with a partner, unmarried	14,009	43	2.5
Separated/divorced/ widowed	30,503	38	1.3
Never married	32,836	52	1.5

TABLE 3.1. NUMBER OF ADULTS AND RATES OF PARTICIPATION IN SELECTED ADULT
EDUCATION ACTIVITIES, BY SELECTED DEMOGRAPHIC, EDUCATIONAL, AND
OCCUPATIONAL CHARACTERISTICS, 2000–01, CONTINUED.

Characteristics	Total Adults (in Thousands)	Overall Participation	
		Percentage	Standard Error
Employment/occupation			
Employed in the past 12 months	145,249	54	0.7
Professional and managerial	42,230	71	1.1
Service, sales, or support	65,298	55	1.0
Trades	37,722	34	1.3
Not employed in the past 12 months	53,553	25	0.9
Continuing education requirements			
Yes	50,549	64	1.1
No	148,253	40	0.6
Household income			
$20,000 or less	40,246	28	1.3
$20,001–$35,000	38,876	39	1.2
$35,001–$50,000	33,035	48	1.5
$50,001–$75,000	40,725	56	1.5
$75,001 or more	45,922	59	1.3
Children under 10 years old in household			
Yes	55,333	52	1.3
No	143,469	44	0.6

Source: Kim, Collins Hagedorn, Williamson, & Chapman, 2004, pp. 9–10.

46 percent. Prior educational attainment, professional or managerial employment status, and household income were all positively related to participation. While in the 1990s surveys there was no significant difference in men and women's participation rates (Valentine, 1997), in this most recent survey, women had a slightly higher participation rate than men (49 versus 43 percent). For overall participation, there were no significant differences among White, Black, or Hispanic learners.

Johnstone and Rivera's profile of the typical adult learner remains apt forty years later. Compared to those who do not participate, participants in adult education are better educated, younger, and employed full-time and have higher incomes. But as Creighton and Hudson (2002, p. ix) point out, "[A] closer look at participation in specific activities reveals some troubling signs of groups being left behind—especially Hispanics, those with lower levels of education, those with lower status jobs, and those who are employed part-time. . . . Thus, although the widespread increase in participation in adult education has been accompanied by an elimination of some inequities, in many cases the highly educated and high status groups that have been the traditional beneficiaries of adult education remain the main beneficiaries today."

NONFORMAL AND INFORMAL PARTICIPATION

As noted earlier, studies of participation most often focus on formal educational institutions or employer-sponsored programs. Partly because of definitional problems, it has been more difficult to assess participation in nonformal or informal learning activities.

Hamil-Luker and Uhlenberg (2002) studied participation in what they termed nonformal adult education activities—those sponsored by community organizations (libraries, neighborhood centers, community groups, religious organizations). Using the NCES databases from 1991 and 1999, they compared participation rates in three categories of provider—credential program (meaning educational institutions), business or industry, and community organizations. With one minor exception, participation increased for all age groups across the three providers. However, "by far the largest increase in adult education occurred in programs provided by community organizations, where participation rates more than doubled. Increases in these nonformal educational programs were fairly uniform across the age categories" (p. S327).

The first statistics that we have on informal learning are again from the Johnstone and Rivera (1965) study in which they included "self-taught" or independent learning activities. Included almost as an afterthought, the authors admit that the "most surprising" estimate in their study is the "close to nine million persons who were active in independent studies." Further, "the incidence of self-education throughout the adult population is much greater than we had anticipated" (p. 37).

The 2001 NCES study of participation has been the first NCES study to include informal learning in the workplace as one form of participation. "Work-related informal learning activities included supervised training or mentoring, self-paced study using books or videotapes, self-paced study using computers, attending 'brown-bag' or informal presentations, attending conferences or conventions, and reading professional journals or magazines" (Kim et al., 2004, p. vi). An astounding 63 percent of adults reported participating in informal workplace learning. However, as with the overall participation profile, "those adults with some college or more education, those in professional or managerial occupations, and those with higher household incomes were generally more likely to participate in work-related informal learning activities" (p. xii). But unlike participation in formal education, males participated more than females (67 versus 59 percent) and Whites more than Hispanics (no significant differences were observed when comparing Black adults with White or Hispanic adults).

Although most adult educators suspect that the majority of adult learning is informal—that is, embedded in everyday life—it is particularly difficult to measure because most adults themselves have trouble identifying these episodes. One mechanism for assessing participation in informal learning has been through studies of self-directed learning. For example, Penland (1979) was interested in corroborating Tough's (1971) findings that more than 90 percent of adults are engaged in independent learning projects (see Chapter Five). Briefly, Tough felt that adults were engaged in learning as part of their everyday lives—learning that was not necessarily institutionally based and not easily recognized by the learners themselves because of the association of learning with formal instruction. Consequently, Tough and Penland asked adults to think about major learning activities that were clearly focused efforts to gain and retain knowledge or skill. A learning project had to have occurred over at least a two-day period, totaling at least seven hours of learning. Respondents in both studies were given a list of things people learn about—a foreign language, gardening, raising children, and so on. Penland's 1,501 respondents were selected from the U.S. population by means of a modified probability sample. He found that "almost 80 percent (78.9) of the population of eighteen years and over perceive themselves as continuing learners whether in self-planned or formal courses" and "over three-quarters (76.1 percent) of the U.S. population had planned one or more learning projects on their own" (p. 173). Furthermore, of the nine areas of study, personal development and home and family ranked highest in popularity, followed by hobbies and recreation, general education, job, religion, voluntary activity, public affairs, and agriculture or technology.

In summary, the answer to the question of who participates in adult learning activities depends on whether we are talking about formal, nonformal, or informal settings. For formal adult education, participation rates have steadily increased to a high of 46 percent recorded in the recent NHES study of 2001. Further, the profile of the typical adult learner in formal, instructor-led educational or training activities has remained remarkably consistent across studies. We have much less data on participation in nonformal and informal adult education; however, what we do have suggests very high rates of participation. Next we discuss why adults do or do not choose to participate in learning activities.

WHY ADULTS DO OR DO NOT PARTICIPATE

Adults are busy people. Most spend at least eight hours a day working and often as many hours attending to family, household, and community concerns. Why do literally millions of these adults enroll in adult education classes, seek private instruction, or engage in independent learning projects? Teachers, counselors, administrators, and policymakers all have a keen interest in understanding why people do or do not participate in learning activities.

One approach to answering this question is to ask people their reasons for participating, and this has been done as part of the national survey studies already cited. Another approach is to try to determine the underlying motivational orientations or barriers to participation of certain groups of learners. These approaches are discussed in the following paragraphs.

Survey Studies

Hundreds of local, state, and national studies have asked adults their reasons for engaging in educational pursuits. In most of these studies, respondents are presented with a list of reasons why people might participate in organized learning activities and asked to indicate which ones apply to them. Most respondents report multiple reasons. If asked to indicate the *main* reason (as they were in the NCES surveys), however, they most commonly cite job-related motives.

The strength of employment-related motives was first uncovered by Johnstone and Rivera (1965). Thirty-six percent of respondents indicated that they were "preparing for a new job or occupation" (p. 144), and 32 percent said they participated in education "for the job I held at that time." The authors concluded that "vocational goals most frequently direct adults into continuing education" (p. 144). The nine surveys of participation conducted by the NCES have consistently revealed job-related reasons as the most frequently cited.

In a study conducted by the United Nations Educational, Scientific, and Cultural Organization (UNESCO; Valentine, 1997), fully 90.6 percent of those surveyed in the United States cited career- or job-related reasons for participation and 9.4 percent cited "personal interest." When asked about the goal of the learning activity, the largest percentage (58 percent) said it was professional or career upgrading, 18.3 percent "other," 17.6 percent to earn a college or university degree, 3.8 percent to earn a vocational or apprenticeship certificate, and 2.3 percent to complete secondary school (Valentine, 1997). Clearly, there is a strong linkage between one's work life and participation in adult education.

Approaching people's reasons for participating in adult education from a somewhat different angle, Aslanian and Brickell (1980) sought to test the hypothesis that life transitions motivate adults to seek out learning experiences. Of the 1,519 adults over age twenty-five randomly sampled, 744, or 49 percent, reported having learned something formally or informally in the year prior to the study. They found that 83 percent of the learners in their sample could describe some past, present, or future change in their lives as reasons for learning. The other 17 percent were engaged in learning for its own sake—that is, to stay mentally alert—or for the social aspects or because learning is a satisfying activity. Those going through transitions, such as marriage, retirement, job changes, birth of children, and so on, were able to identify specific events, such as getting fired or promoted, that triggered their transition. The authors noted seven kinds of transitions. Those relating to career and family accounted for 56 percent and 16 percent of the transitions, respectively. The other transitions, in descending importance, concerned leisure (13 percent), art (5 percent), health (5 percent), religion (4 percent), and citizenship (1 percent). "To know an adult's life schedule," the authors conclude, "is to know an adult's learning schedule" (pp. 60–61).

In a similarly designed study, Aslanian (2001) also found that participation in higher and continuing education is largely due to a life transition. Of seven possible transitions, 85 percent named a career transition as their reason for wanting to learn, and hence participate, in higher and continuing education courses.

The survey studies have been helpful in identifying the reasons adults give for participating in learning activities. Since the majority of adult learners are employed (only 25 percent of adults surveyed in the 2001 NCES study had not been employed in the twelve months prior to the survey) and derive much of their identity from their work, it is not surprising to find that at least half of them are involved in education for job-related reasons. Other investigations have sought to go beyond these self-reported data in trying to understand the why of participation.

MOTIVATIONAL ORIENTATIONS OF LEARNERS

Interest in categorizing the various reasons given for participating in adult learning has spurred a line of inquiry in addition to the survey studies. This area of investigation was initiated with the publication by Houle of *The Inquiring Mind* in 1961. Choosing a small, select sample of twenty-two adults "conspicuously engaged in various forms of continuing learning" (1961/1988, p. 13), Houle conducted in-depth interviews that explored his subjects' history of learning, factors that led them to be continuing learners, and their views of themselves as learners. An analysis of the interview data revealed three separate learning orientations held by the adults. The now-famous typology consists of goal-oriented learners, who use education as a means of achieving some other goal; activity-oriented learners, who participate for the sake of the activity itself and the social interaction; and learning-oriented participants, who seek knowledge for its own sake.

Houle's research stimulated a number of studies attempting to affirm or refine the original typology. By far the most extensive work has been done with Boshier's forty-eight item Education Participation Scale (EPS), later refined to forty-two items (Boshier, 1991). Factor analysis of the forty-two items suggests the following seven factors, each containing six items: communication improvement of verbal and written skills; social contact, meaning meeting people and making friends; educational preparation, the remediation of past educational deficiencies; professional advancement, concerned with improving job status or moving to a better one; family togetherness, concerned with bridging generation gaps and improving relationships in families; social stimulation, meaning escaping boredom; and cognitive interest, seeking knowledge for its own sake (Boshier, 1991).

Boshier himself conducted an extensive test of Houle's typology using his EPS scale (Boshier & Collins, 1985). Using cluster analysis instead of factor analysis, because the technique is more congruent with Houle's original conceptualization of three separate but overlapping orientations, he analyzed the responses of 13,442 learners from Africa, Asia, New Zealand, Canada, and the United States. Boshier and Collins were able to effect a three-cluster solution "loosely isomorphic with Houle's topology" (p. 125). They found that "Cluster I consisted of the Cognitive Interest items and was congruent with his [Houle's] learning orientation." Cluster II, the activity orientation, "was multifaceted and composed of items normally labeled Social Stimulation, Social Contact, External Expectations, and Community Service" (p. 125). Cluster III consisted of the Professional Advancement items and thus resembled Houle's goal orientation. The authors note that although their three-cluster solution is "loosely isomorphic," the grouping of items to make up the activity cluster that matches Houle's typology is "overly generous." They conclude that "Houle's intuition has been partly collaborated; two of the six clusters were as he described them" (p. 127).

Using Boshier's EPS, Fujita-Starck (1996) analyzed responses from 1,142 students in programs at a large state university. Results confirmed the seven-factor typology proposed by Boshier in 1991 (communication improvement, social contact, educational preparation, professional advancement, family togetherness, social stimulation, and cognitive interest). The author also found the scale to be reliable "in differentiating among a diverse group of students with varying reasons for participating in continuing education" (p. 38).

Despite the limitations of this line of research (Courtney, 1992), it has become evident that learners' motivations for participating in adult education are many, complex, and subject to change. The search for an underlying motivational structure related to participation is likely to continue, however, for such knowledge "can assist educators and administrators in identifying and meeting the needs of a wide spectrum of learners relative to program content, as well as the time, duration, and location of related activities" (Fujita-Starck, 1996, p. 39).

BARRIERS TO PARTICIPATION

Knowing why adults participate in formal adult education does not tell us why many do not. That is, we cannot assume that those who are not participating are happily employed and satisfied with their family, community, and leisure activities. In fact, one of the field's biggest mysteries is why more adults, especially those who might benefit the most, are not involved in adult education. This question has prompted research into why adults do not participate in adult education.

The two most often cited reasons for nonparticipation are lack of time and lack of money. These are socially acceptable reasons for not doing something, of course, and probably very legitimate reasons for adults who are busy people trying to become or stay economically solvent and take care of their families and themselves.

Johnstone and Rivera (1965) in their national study of participation found that 43 percent cited cost as a reason for not attending adult education courses and 39 percent said they were too busy. These were also the two main reasons for nonparticipation cited in the UNESCO study (Valentine, 1997). Forty-five percent of respondents said lack of time was a barrier for job-related education; this figure climbs to 60.1 percent for non-job-related education. Interestingly, 33.4 percent gave cost as a barrier for job-related education, but 25.4 percent reported cost as a barrier for non-job-related education (Valentine, 1997). For both types of education, "family responsibilities" was cited as the next most salient barrier.

Reasons why adults do not participate have been clustered by several researchers into types of barriers. Johnstone and Rivera (1965) clustered ten potential barriers into two categories: external, or situational, and internal, or dispositional, barriers. External barriers are "influences more or less external to the individual or at least beyond the individual's control" (p. 214), such as cost of the program. Internal barriers reflect personal attitudes, such as thinking one is too old to learn. Older adults, for example, cited more dispositional barriers, and younger people and women were more constrained by situational barriers. In contrast, Valentine's (1997) analysis of the UNESCO data revealed that situational barriers affected both men and women: "Women were more likely than men to report that family responsibilities interfered with both job-related and non-job-related education. Men were more likely than women to report that work demands interfered with non-job-related education" (p. 107).

Darkenwald and colleagues have gone beyond the three-part or four-part barrier typologies in developing a scale of deterrents to participation that can be factor-analyzed to reveal the structure of reasons underlying nonparticipation (in much the same way the EPS does for participation). A form of the Deterrents to Participation Scale (DPS) used with the general adult public revealed six factors of nonparticipation: lack of confidence, lack of course relevance, time constraints, low personal priority, cost, and personal problems (such as child care, family problems, and personal health; Darkenwald & Valentine, 1985). In a later analysis of the same data, Valentine and Darkenwald (1990) derived a typology of adult nonparticipants. According to their analysis, the adult nonparticipants in the general public cluster into five distinct groups. People are deterred from participating by personal problems, lack of confidence, educational costs, lack of interest in organized education generally, or lack of interest in available courses.

ADDING A SOCIOLOGICAL LENS TO EXPLANATIONS OF PARTICIPATION

Viewing participation from the perspective of barriers lends another dimension to the field's attempt to understand why some adults participate in adult education and others do not. But this perspective tells only part of the story. The bulk of research in North America on nonparticipation has been from the perspective of the individual's motivation, attitudes, beliefs, behaviors, position in the life cycle, and so on. This has not always been the case, however, as Courtney (1992) points out in his historical analysis of participation research. Prior to the 1960s, a popular topic among researchers was social participation. General social participation refers to the extent to which a person is an active participant in family and community life; participating in adult education activities was considered just one component of social participation. Benn (1997) has revisited this notion of social participation in a survey study of 259 adults in a range of educational programs. She concludes that the extent of one's general social activity affects learning activity, a finding that has implications for marketing and recruitment: "Rather than blanket publicity, a more effective approach might be to advertise through social groups and organizations. Adult education does not choose its students, they choose (or do not choose) adult education" (p. 34).

For some, a combination of psychological and social factors act as a barrier to participation. Rubenson (1998, p. 259) points out that "only when we include structural factors and analyze the interaction between them and the individual conceptual apparatus does an interpretation become possible. Adults' readiness to learn and barriers preventing it . . . can be understood in terms of societal processes and structure, institutional processes and structure and individual consciousness and activity." Hall and Donaldson's (1997) study of why women without a high school diploma chose not to participate provides examples of how the social and the psychological interact. Preadult factors such as parents' education, early pregnancies, and economic status formed part of the picture. Lack of a support system was a second factor. Conventional barriers such as lack of time, information, and child care were also operative. The fourth dynamic Hall and Donaldson termed *lack of voice:* "At the heart of nonparticipation lies a 'deterrent' so deeply embedded in some women that no theory can fully capture its meaning. The way a woman feels about herself, her self-esteem and self-confidence, and the way she can express herself are significant elements in her decision about whether to participate in adult education" (p. 98).

Since the early 1990s the field of adult education has become much more conscious of the impact of sociocultural factors on shaping participation in adult education. Rubenson (1998, p. 261) characterizes this approach to participation as consisting of two dimensions—"the long arm of the family as reflected in the relationship between social background, educational attainment and participation . . . and the long arm of the job: the increased importance of adult education and training as investment." Using data collected in the International Adult Literacy Survey (IALS) from ten countries, Boudard and Rubenson (2003) predicted that literacy skills would determine participation in adult education and training. Instead, they found educational attainment to be "the most important single factor predicting participation in adult education and training" (p. 279). Further analyses revealed that "readiness to learn is formed early in life and further developed through educational and work experiences . . . the long arm of the family and the long arm of the job" (p. 279).

An even more recent analysis of participation in the United Kingdom (Gorard & Selwyn, 2005) found that participation could be predicted from variables "we could have known when each person was born"; in particular, "the influence of parental background is key" (p. 79). The authors point out that "where individuals create, for themselves and through their early experiences, a 'learner identity' inimical to further study, then the prospect of learning can become a burden rather than an investment for them" (p. 71).

Race, class, gender, ethnic group, and so on can also act as barriers to participation. Sissel's (1997) study of parent involvement in Head Start programs found that "power relations were expressed in the withholding or allocation of programmatic resources, and functioned to either impede or promote participation" (p. 123).

She recommends that more research be conducted on "specific structural factors" (such as race and gender) that "enhance or impede participation" (p. 135). Davis-Harrison (1996) also found race and class to be important variables in investigating the non-participation of blue-collar male workers.

Working from this same critical perspective, Jarvis (1985) makes the case for a class analysis in that the middle-class bias found in all studies of participation can be explained by the idea that adult education is organized by the middle class, and the presentation of knowledge is middle class in both language and content. Furthermore, previous school experiences select out "those who were labeled as successful in education" (p. 204), and those who will be labeled successful is pretty much predetermined by one's class, age, sex, and educational background. Jarvis would concur with McClenaghan (2000) that one's "social capital"—how one is positioned in society in terms of "the totality of actual and potential resources individuals can mobilise through membership in organisations and social networks" (p. 568)—can help explain differing levels of participation in both formal and informal adult education.

Finally, two studies examined how the social structure determines participation. Nordhaug (1990) examined participation in Norwegian adult education not from the individual participant's perspective but from macrolevel variables over which individuals have no control, such as material resources and population density related to the structure of municipalities. He found that the amount of educational resources (as measured by the community's level of educational attainment) was "the most efficient predictor of adult education activity . . . on a regional level" (p. 205). In a U.S. study, Jung and Cervero (2002) used national data sets on postsecondary education to determine which contextual variables in each of the fifty U.S. states would best predict the rate of participation of adults in higher education. Out of eleven variables, the two best predictors of adult participation in a state's higher education system were availability of undergraduate education (number of seats available, public and private) and educational attainment of the state's adult population (percentage of adults with high school or higher).

In summary, looking at social structure rather than individual needs and interests reveals some very different explanations as to why adults do or do not participate in adult learning activities.

These competing perspectives imply different strategies for increasing participation. If individual interests and motivation account for participation, then recruitment efforts would center on responding to an adult's perceived learning needs and stimulating motivation. If, in contrast, participation or nonparticipation is seen as a function of the social structure, then one would work toward changing aspects of this structure in ways that would facilitate participation. The most robust explanation of participation is likely to be found in considering both the psychological and sociological perspectives.

PROBLEMATIZING THE CONCEPT OF PARTICIPATION

Most of what we have presented thus far on participation reflects what we know about who participates and the reasons for participating (or not) in mostly formal adult education. In this section of the chapter we stand back and question some of the assumptions that underlie the dominant discourse of participation. As Crowther (2000) points out, this discourse has been narrowly conceived around four assumptions: (1) participation is a good thing; (2) participation equals formal learning; (3) learners are abstract, not socialized, individuals; and (4) there are barriers to participation, not resistance. We take each one of these assumptions in turn to critique the concept of participation.

PARTICIPATION IS A GOOD THING

Studies of participation assume that everyone should want to engage in adult education because it is a good thing to do. Underlying many of the stated purposes of adult education in America is the assumption that the ideal of a democratic society must be maintained, and that education is one way to do this. Individualism, independence, and a Protestant-capitalist work ethic frame the actual provision of adult education in America. Further, because this is a democratic society, all individuals have access and the opportunity to benefit through education. As Lindeman (1926/1989) proposed early in the founding of the field, adult education had a dual purpose of improving both society and the individual. In practice, however, a case can be made that education

statistics of active participants seem to confirm this

is "an apparatus for social control" (Cunningham, 1988, p. 133) rather than empowerment, and that adult education in the United States is elitist and exclusionary. As evidence of adult education's elite bias, Cunningham points to middle-class participation patterns, the homogeneous, technically oriented training of adult educators, the "psychology of individual deficit" that serves as a basis for explaining social inequities, and the erosion of the voluntary nature of adult education.

Discuss this

Most societies in fact use education to preserve the status quo rather than to bring about change or address inequities. In reviewing the common functions of adult education, Jarvis (1985) points out how they can be used in the service of maintaining the status quo. Adult education maintains the social system and existing social relations because "the education of adults transmits the dominant culture and in the process it reproduces the cultural system which, in itself, is a force for the retention of the status quo rather than social change" (p. 139). Individual advancement and selection, while appearing to develop individuals, is actually a selective process carefully monitored by the system itself. Another function—offering a second chance and legitimization—also promotes the dominant culture since "second chance education actually produces an appearance of greater equality of opportunity and, hence, reinforces the existing social structures" (p. 143). Even leisure-time pursuits have as a latent function "the retention of stability in the social system at a time when many people do not have work to occupy their time and their minds" (p. 147). Finally, development and liberation can be goals of adult education, although one should be aware that such development and liberation may actually be designed to enable people to fit more easily into the existing social system.

The problems to which adult educators respond tend to be identified by those who have a value perspective not necessarily shared by the target population. As Cunningham (1988, p. 141) has noted, much program planning is based on an individual deficit model rather than an examination of "the oppressive structures in which people live." Programs are thus designed around learner deficiencies that may or may not be of concern to the learner. What is necessary, Cunningham and others assert, is for socially responsible adult educators to become aware of the "social as well as personal dimensions of learning and the capacity of education to respond" (Cunningham, 2000, p. 574). Cunningham goes on to point out that "if one conceptualized any nation as composed of the state (governmental sector), civil society (voluntary sector), and the market (economic sector), then how these sectors are related and how education serves these sectors become critical questions in understanding the relationships between adult education and society" (p. 574).

Nevertheless, "adult education is given public support when the public can see the connection between education and the solution to a threatening situation" (Griffith & Fujita-Starck, 1989, p. 172). Most "threatening" are challenges to economic stability and social order. The emphasis may shift with changes in society's social, cultural, and economic structures. Literacy education in colonial America was invested in for a greater religious purpose; this gave way to a citizenship orientation in the wake of independence during the mid-eighteenth century, which in turn was eclipsed by vocational training and immigrant education at the turn of the twentieth century.

In light of the social forces documented in Chapter One—demographics, economics, and technology—the purposes of adult education today for which there is public support cluster around the United States sustaining a competitive edge in a global economy. This translates into preparing and then maintaining an informed and efficient workforce. Along with this economic imperative is the assumption that social stability is both a product and a goal of adult education and training. Thousands of restless, illiterate, unemployed, or underemployed adults pose a threat to the stability of the social order, not to mention a drain on social resources. So although the rhetoric of adult education suggests some rather lofty ideals for the purpose of the endeavor, the reality suggests a more conservative purpose: maintenance of the status quo, which today means a capitalist economic system that values individuality, independence, and entrepreneurialism. Thus we see a growing emphasis on human resource development and training, continued provision for basic skill acquisition, and ever-expanding postsecondary opportunities for adults.

PARTICIPATION EQUALS FORMAL LEARNING

In writing this chapter on participation we would have liked to present as comprehensive a picture as possible. However, as we stated earlier, nearly all of the studies are of participation in formal institutionally sponsored programs. Yet we know that adults engage in learning activities sponsored by community-based nonformal groups. Further, adults learn informally on their own. Even in business and industry it has been estimated that upwards of 70 percent of learning in the workplace is informal (Bruce, Aring, & Brand, 1998).

What accounts for this bias in participation studies? It has to do in part with the ease of collecting information from educational institutions; in part it is due to adult learners themselves not recognizing the informal learning embedded in their everyday lives. And certainly the bias in part has to do with policy and funding. While the field is proud of its service orientation and the voluntary nature of participation, in reality what is offered cannot be uncoupled from the question of who finances the various adult learning opportunities. And the answer to this question of who finances adult education is easier to find in reference to formal adult education.

In North America, there are many providers of formal learning opportunities, including government at all levels, employers, educational institutions, and community institutions such as libraries. Because much of the expenditure for this form of learning is hidden under a variety of budgetary labels—at one time more than 270 federal programs alone had some adult learning component (Griffith & Fujita-Starck, 1989)—it is difficult to measure the relative financial power of various providers.

To complicate the matter, what is offered at any particular time "will almost inevitably relate to the pressures generated in the social system. Social pressures act in such a manner as to create an imbalance in the system to which institutions, other than that generating pressure, respond by seeking to restore the system to some form of equilibrium" (Jarvis, 1986, p. 57). Institutions are currently being pressured to respond to the issues of an increasingly diverse workforce, technological obsolescence, and health threats such as AIDS. This notion of mobilizing institutions in the service of maintaining social equilibrium is but one explanation for the shifts in curriculum emphasis.

Crowther (2000) points out that it could be argued that the monopoly of formal adult education is being challenged "by developments in experiential learning, the growth of new educational technologies, distance learning and procedures such as the accreditation of prior learning" (p. 485). He goes on to ask, "Are these not examples of a more democratic, pluralistic, learning process which both facilitates access and disperses control over the curriculum?" (p. 485). However, these mechanisms of dealing with and recognizing informal experiential learning can also be seen as "reaffirming, rather than undermining, the dominant assumptions about control over definitions of educationally relevant knowledge" (p. 485). In other words, when the recognition of informal learning is tied to the formal system as in accreditation of prior learning, control still rests with the system that has predetermined what counts as learning. That the formal system will serve its own interests is underscored by an interesting article in *Training & Development* about "free agent learners" (Caudron, 1999). Acknowledging the rise of employees learning on their own, Caudron warns that "companies have to be willing to accept the new ideas such employees are bringing to work" and that "free agent learners threaten corporate governance because the more that people learn, the more competent and confident they become" (p. 30).

Participation equals formal learning because of ease of measurement but also because the formal system controls what gets "counted" as adult education. In a pluralistic society such as ours, there is no single answer to the question of who decides what learning opportunities to offer. In reality, for formal learning programs at least, decisions are made by those who pay—whether that means the learners themselves, government, employers, or educational institutions. And those who pay are in positions of power to determine which social pressures will be addressed and how those responses will be structured. Those not in positions of power rarely decide what learning opportunities are offered. Their role is limited to deciding whether to participate.

LEARNERS ARE ABSTRACT, NOT SOCIALIZED, INDIVIDUALS

As we have already noted in this chapter, the predominate view of adult learner participation is through the lens of individual learners who have chosen to participate in a learning activity. Much of the discourse on participation explains nonparticipation from an individual deficit stance—that is, there is something wrong with or deficient about nonparticipants or they would be clamoring to be in our adult education programs. Further, these nonparticipants are probably most in need of what adult education has to offer.

This discourse fails to take into account the sociocultural context of adult learners and the structural characteristics of the adult education enterprise itself. Although we have addressed some of these factors in the preceding section, "Adding a Sociological Lens to Explanations of Participation," there is more that can be said about this major misconception about participation.

The democratic ideals of equal opportunity and open access make the current reality of uneven and unequal participation in formal adult learning particularly worrisome to some policymakers, educators, and researchers. Most explanations focus on a person's stated reasons for nonparticipation, such as cost, time, transportation, and lack of confidence. When viewed from a social perspective, other explanations emerge. Rubenson (1989, p. 64) argues, for example, that "through socialization within the family, the school, and, later on, in working life, a positive disposition towards adult education becomes a part of some group's habitus but not of others."

Those adults who have been socialized into valuing and acquiring the attitudes and skills of the middle class will be the ones to take advantage of learning opportunities. Since most providers of such opportunities are themselves middle-class, little effort is expended trying to understand and provide for other populations. The modus operandi of most providers is to offer a set of activities that they assume learners will want. A response, however, is predicated on the assumptions that learners know about the program, can attend at the time it is offered, and can afford it; that the subculture of the institution is conducive to their own; and that what is offered corresponds with what they need (Jarvis, 1985). Rubenson (1989, p. 65) argues that "a system of adult education that implicitly takes for granted that the adult is a conscious, self-directed individual in possession of the instruments vital to making use of the available possibilities for adult education—a system that relies on self-selection to recruit the participants—will by necessity widen, not narrow, the educational and cultural gaps in society."

There are other reasons why certain adults have more access to learning opportunities than other adults. Where one happens to live, what one's primary language is, what color, age, or sex one happens to be, what one does for a living all contribute to the participation pattern in adult education. Cropley (1989, p. 146) calls these factors "framework conditions," which "are largely a function of the circumstances in which people live, especially of factors such as the values, attitudes, habits, priorities and the like of the social groups to which they belong, the economic structure of their society, even features of the education system itself." The result is that "some individuals are more equal than others in the choices available to them" (p. 146).

By way of illustrating how these framework conditions can determine who is more likely to benefit from adult learning opportunities, where and how one lives make a difference. It is common knowledge that there is less accessibility in rural areas than in urban or suburban centers. The picture is a bit more complicated than just a rural-urban split, however. Those in small-town rural areas are better off than those living in isolated areas, and some urban centers are as impoverished as the most rural areas. Worldwide, access to learning opportunities in rural areas is a problem at all levels of education. Further, there are those who lack a geographical place altogether—migrant, transient, homeless, and refugee populations. Migrants, for example, "are the most undereducated major subgroup in the United States, with a high school dropout rate larger than that of any other group. Their mobility, their language differences, and the cultural differences experienced as they move from one community to another combine with health and nutritional problems to negatively affect school achievement. Migrant lifestyles revolve around working, moving on to find other work, and working again" (Velazquez, 1996, p. 28). For any of these geographically mobile groups, there is little more than sporadic access to education or social services.

Age is another condition that often determines who benefits from learning opportunities. Older adults not only have the lowest levels of participation in adult education generally (Creighton & Hudson, 2002) but also receive far less training in the workplace than younger workers. In some settings and in other parts of the world, age in combination with gender makes for another condition affecting access. For example, in the United States, since managerial and professional workers and all nonmanual workers receive more training than manual workers—and women are underrepresented in these positions—women, and older women in particular, are much less likely to receive employer-sponsored training than are men (Stacy & To, 1994).

THERE ARE BARRIERS, NOT RESISTANCE

Readers will recall that there is a section of this chapter on barriers to participation. In that section we reviewed the studies that identify personal barriers such as lack of interest, personal problems, thinking one is too old to learn, and so on as well as situational barriers such as lack of time and money. We also pointed out that the individual's motivation, beliefs, and behaviors and life situation explain only part of the picture. Social structural factors such as family of origin, class, race, and so on shape one's level of participation in formal adult education.

What Crowther (2000) is proposing from a critical theory perspective is that nonparticipation can be construed as an act of resistance. Rather than being prevented from participating because of some insurmountable barrier, the learner chooses not to participate—that is, resistance is a matter of deliberate choice. While resistance has been studied more frequently with secondary school populations, several adult educators have written about this phenomenon, especially in reference to literacy education (Belzer, 2004; Quigley, 1990; Sandlin, 2000).

In summarizing this notion of nonparticipation as resistance rather than barriers, Crowther (2000, pp. 489–490) writes:

> It seems reasonable to surmise that many people find adult education unattractive and irrelevant to their daily lives. Despite many well intentioned efforts to attract people the sense of frustration felt by their failure to respond to what is offered is often evident. It is easy thereafter to assume people are "apathetic" and have limited horizons. Redefining non-participation as a form of resistance may, however, open up the possibility of rethinking what adult education is for and where it occurs. . . . If we started to think about participation in these terms then the problem of participation could be faced the right way round—that is, that adult education is part of the problem rather than simply the solution.

Summary

Participation is one of the more thoroughly studied areas in adult education. We have a sense of who participates, what is studied, and what motivates some adults and not others to enroll in a course or undertake an independent learning project.

Although there were numerous small-scale studies of participation in the forty years between the inauguration of the field of adult education and the 1960s, it was not until 1965 that the first national study of participation was published. Johnstone and Rivera's study, with its care in defining participation and selecting methods of data collection and analysis, remains a benchmark contribution to this literature. Subsequent surveys by the National Center for Education Statistics (NCES) and UNESCO (Valentine, 1997) have contributed to this database. Regardless of the study, the profile of the typical adult learner in formal educational activities remains remarkably consistent: white, middle-class, employed, younger, and better educated than the nonparticipant. Further, employment-related reasons account for the majority of participant interest in continuing education.

Why adults do or do not participate in adult education is an important question, having implications for both theory and practice. Surveys have uncovered both reasons for, and barriers to, participation. The work on determining an underlying structure of motivational orientations begun by Houle (1961/1988) has been carried on most notably by Boshier's research using the Educational Participation Scale (EPS). Further, explanations of participation have been advanced from a sociological rather than a psychological perspective. In these analyses, people's decisions to participate have less to do with their needs and motives than with their position in society and the social experiences that have shaped their lives.

Finally, we "problematized" the current understanding of participation by questioning and critiquing four assumptions about participation presented by Crowther (2000). These four assumptions are that participation is a good thing, that participation equals formal learning, that learners are abstract, not socialized individuals, and that there are barriers, not resistance, to participating in formal adult learning activities.

PART TWO

ADULT LEARNING THEORY AND MODELS

The accumulation of information and experiences grounded in practice often leads to thinking about how the parts of what we know might fit together to form some sort of explanatory framework. In Part Two of *Learning in Adulthood,* we review a number of efforts to explain adult learning. Some of these efforts, as in the work on self-directed learning, are in fact tentative frameworks for ordering research—frameworks suggesting future directions for theory. Other efforts can properly be labeled models, if we define model as a visual representation. A theory, which may have a model accompanying it, is a set of interrelated concepts that explain some aspect of the field in a parsimonious manner.

We begin Chapter Four with a discussion of Knowles's (1980) concept of andragogy, which he originally termed a theory of adult learning. Probably the best-known set of principles or assumptions to guide adult learning practice, andragogy actually tells us more about the characteristics of adult learners than about the nature of learning itself. The first half of the chapter is devoted to a thorough review and critique of andragogy. The second half of Chapter Four reviews three other models of adult learning: McClusky's (1970) theory of margin, Illeris's (2002, 2004b) three dimensions of learning model, and Jarvis's (2006) model of the learning process.

Since Tough's work on adult learning projects was published in 1971, self-directed learning and individual learning projects have captured the imagination of researchers and writers both inside and outside the field of adult education. Although learning on one's own is the way most adults go about acquiring new ideas, skills, and attitudes, this context has often been regarded as less important than learning that takes place in more formal settings. Chapter Five discusses three types of models—linear, interactive, and instructional—developed to describe the process of learning when that learning is primarily managed by the learners themselves. Most adults use more of an interactive model in that they do not necessarily plan what, how, or when they want to learn. Scholars have also focused on studying self-direction as a personal attribute of the learner. Two ideas that have received the greatest attention in this approach are the notion of readiness for self-directed learning and the concept of autonomy. The chapter concludes with a review of the major issues researchers need to address in building future research agendas in self-directed learning.

Changes in cognition and consciousness constitute the focus of transformational learning reviewed in Chapter Six. Mezirow's (1991) perspective transformation and Freire's (1970) conscientization contend that changes in perspective or consciousness are the defining characteristic of learning in adulthood. Mezirow's theory in particular has stimulated considerable debate and research during the past ten years. Using Taylor's (2005b) "lenses" for organizing the literature on transformational learning, the first half of the chapter reviews the various theoretical bases for transformational learning. Also examined are three concepts key to understanding transformative learning: the centrality of life experience, the nature of critical reflection, and the connection between transformative learning and adult development. We then discuss the extent to which transformative learning theory takes context into account, whether the theory relies too heavily on rationality, the role of relationships, the place of social action, and the educator's role in facilitating transformative learning.

In the last chapter of Part Two we explore the role of experience and learning, which has a long legacy in the writings on adult learning. Discussed first in the chapter are representative theories that offer varying conceptual views of the process of learning from experience, including the seminal work of Dewey (1938) and Kolb (1984), and the contemporary work of such scholars as Jarvis (2001), Boud and Walker (1991), Fenwick (2003), and Usher, Bryant, and Johnston (1997). Although the focus of this work has been on individual learners, in recent years there has been a shift to understanding how the context affects learning and how it is an integral component of the learning process. We then describe reflective practice, one of the primary ways in which educators have structured learning from experience. We conclude the chapter with an overview of situated cognition and descriptions of two instructional approaches—cognitive apprenticeship and anchored instruction—that are based in situated cognition, stressing how "authentic experiences" grounded in real-life situations are viewed as key components in operationalizing this concept.

CHAPTER FOUR

KNOWLES'S ANDRAGOGY, AND MODELS OF ADULT LEARNING BY MCCLUSKY, ILLERIS, AND JARVIS

Do adults learn differently than children do? What distinguishes adult learning and adult education from other areas of education? What particular characteristics about the learning transaction with adults can be identified to maximize their learning? Prior to the 1970s, adult educators relied primarily on psychological understandings of learning in general to inform their practice (see the chapters in Part Four). With the publication of Houle's *The Design of Education* (1972), Kidd's *How Adults Learn* (1973), and Knowles's *The Adult Learner: A Neglected Species* (1973) and *The Modern Practice of Adult Education* (1970), attention turned to research and theory-building efforts in adult learning. Attempts at codifying differences between adults and children as a set of principles, a model, or even a theory of adult learning have been, and continue to be, pursued by adult educators. However, just as there is no single theory that explains all of human learning, there is no single theory of adult learning. Instead, we have a number of frameworks, or models, each of which contributes something to our understanding of adults as learners. The best known of these efforts is *andragogy,* a concept Knowles introduced from Europe in a 1968 article. Andragogy focuses on the adult learner and his or her life situation, as do a number of other models presented in this chapter.

The first part of the chapter is devoted to describing and critiquing andragogy. In the second half of the chapter we review three other models of the adult learning transaction: McClusky's theory of margin, Illeris's three dimensions of learning model, and Jarvis's learning process.

ANDRAGOGY

Nearly forty years ago Malcolm Knowles (1968, p. 351) proposed "a new label and a new technology" of adult learning to distinguish it from preadult schooling. The European concept of andragogy, meaning "the art and science of helping adults learn," was contrasted with pedagogy, the art and science of helping children learn (Knowles, 1980, p. 43). Andragogy is based on a number of assumptions about the adult learner. Knowles originally advanced the following four assumptions:

1. As a person matures, his or her self-concept moves from that of a dependent personality toward one of a self-directing human being.
2. An adult accumulates a growing reservoir of experience, which is a rich resource for learning.
3. The readiness of an adult to learn is closely related to the developmental tasks of his or her social role.
4. There is a change in time perspective as people mature—from future application of knowledge to immediacy of application. Thus, an adult is more problem centered than subject centered in learning. [Knowles, 1980, pp. 44–45]

In later publications, Knowles also referred to a fifth and a sixth assumption:

5. The most potent motivations are internal rather than external (Knowles & Associates, 1984, p. 12).
6. Adults need to know why they need to learn something (Knowles, 1984). (For a review of which of Knowles's writings contain which assumptions, see Holton, Swanson, & Naquin, 2001.)

Knowles clearly saw these assumptions as foundational to designing programs for adults. From each of these assumptions, Knowles drew numerous implications for the design, implementation, and evaluation of learning activities with adults. For example, with regard to the first assumption that as adults mature they become more independent and self-directing, Knowles suggested that the classroom climate should be one of "adultness," both physically and psychologically. The climate should cause "adults to feel accepted, respected, and supported"; further, there should exist "a spirit of mutuality between teachers and students as joint inquirers" (1980, p. 47). Being self-directing also means that adult students can participate in the diagnosis of their learning needs, the planning and implementation of the learning experiences, and the evaluation of those experiences.

This theory, "model of assumptions" (Knowles, 1980, p. 43), or "system of concepts" (Knowles, 1984, p. 8), as Knowles has also called it, has given adult educators "a badge of identity" that distinguishes the field from other areas of education, especially childhood schooling (Brookfield, 1986, p. 90). Andragogy became a rallying point for those trying to define the field of adult education as separate from other areas of education. However, it also stimulated controversy, philosophical debate, and critical analysis matched only, perhaps, by the recent discussions on transformational learning (see Chapter Six).

At first the main point of contention was whether andragogy could be considered a "theory" of adult learning (Elias, 1979). Davenport and Davenport (1985, p. 157) chronicled the debate, noting that andragogy has been classified "as a theory of adult education, theory of adult learning, theory of technology of adult learning, method of adult education, technique of adult education, and a set of assumptions." They are a bit more optimistic than other critics for andragogy's chances of possessing "the explanatory and predictive functions generally associated with a fully developed theory" (p. 158). For them, the issue can be resolved through empirical studies that test the underlying assumptions.

Hartree (1984) observed that it was not clear whether Knowles had presented a theory of learning or a theory of teaching, whether adult learning was different from child learning, and

Discussion about what makes a Theory

whether there was a theory at all—perhaps these were just principles of good practice. The assumptions, she noted, "can be read as descriptions of the adult learner . . . or as prescriptive statements about what the adult learner should be like" (p. 205). Because the assumptions are "unclear and shaky" on several counts, Hartree concludes that while "many adult educators might accept that the principles of adult teaching and conditions of learning which he [Knowles] evolves have much to offer, and are in a sense descriptive of what is already recognized as good practice by those in the field, conceptually Knowles has not presented a good case for the validity of such practice. . . . Although he appears to approach his model of teaching from the point of view of a theory of adult learning, he does not establish a unified theory of learning in a systematic way" (pp. 206–207).

Brookfield (1986, p. 98), who also raises the question of whether andragogy is a "proven theory," assesses to what extent a "set of well-grounded principles of good practice" can be derived from andragogy. He argues that three of the assumptions are problematic when drawing inferences for practice. The first assumption about self-direction is more a desired outcome than a given condition. The third and fourth assumptions relating learning to particular social roles and focusing on immediate application can lead to a narrow, reductionist view of learning. These two assumptions "could lead practitioners to equate the sum total of adult learning with instrumental learning; that is, learning how to perform at an improved level of competence in some predefined skill domain," in essence ignoring the complexity of learning (p. 99). Brookfield finds only the experience assumption to be well-grounded. However, we feel that even this assumption can be questioned. The fact that adults have lived longer than children and thus have a quantity of experience greater than children does not necessarily translate into quality experience that can become a resource for learning; indeed, certain life experiences can function as barriers to learning (Merriam, Mott, & Lee, 1996). Further, children in certain situations may have a range of experiences qualitatively richer than some adults (Hanson, 1996).

As for the fifth assumption on motivation, although adults may be more internally than externally motivated to learn, in much of workplace learning and continuing professional education, not to mention governmental or socially mandated learning (as in the case of driving school, job preparation, welfare programs, and prison education, for example), participation is required. The sixth assumption, which appears in only a couple of Knowles's publications, that adults need to know why they need to learn something, may be true much of the time, but some studies also suggest that adults may learn for the sheer enjoyment of learning (see Chapters Three and Five of this volume).

On the issue of whether andragogy can be considered a theory of adult learning, perhaps Knowles himself put the issue to rest. In his autobiographical work, *The Making of an Adult Educator* (1989, p. 112), he wrote that he "prefers to think of [andragogy] as a model of assumptions about learning or a conceptual framework that serves as a basis for an emergent theory."

A second point of criticism was Knowles's original inference that andragogy, with all its technological implications for instruction, characterized adult learning, while pedagogy, with another set of implications, characterized childhood learning. Close scrutiny of the assumptions and their implications for practice by educators in and out of adult education led Knowles to back off his original stance that andragogy characterized only adult learning. The clearest indication of this rethinking was the change in the subtitles of the 1970 and 1980 editions of *The Modern Practice of Adult Education*. The 1970 subtitle is *Andragogy Versus Pedagogy,* whereas the 1980 subtitle is *From Pedagogy to Andragogy*. Knowles's later position, as reflected in the 1980 subtitle, is that pedagogy-andragogy represents a continuum ranging from teacher-directed to student-directed learning and that both approaches are appropriate with children and adults, depending on the situation. For example, an adult who knows little or nothing about a topic will be more dependent on the teacher for direction; at the other extreme, children who are naturally curious and who are "very self-directing in their learning outside of school . . . could also be more self-directed in school" (Knowles, 1984, p. 13). Andragogy now appears to be situation-specific and not unique to adults.

RECENT CRITIQUES OF ANDRAGOGY

More recent critiques of andragogy have pointed out that in its slavish focus on the individual learner, the sociohistorical context in which learning takes place is virtually ignored (Grace, 1996b; Pearson & Podeschi, 1997; Pratt, 1993). Knowles's reliance on humanistic psychology results in a picture of the individual learner as one who is autonomous, free, and growth oriented. There is little or no awareness that the person is socially situated, and to some extent, the product of the sociohistorical and cultural context of the times; nor is there any awareness that social institutions and structures may be defining the learning transaction irrespective of the individual participant.

Grace (1996b) points out how Knowles himself and his theory of andragogy were logical products of the 1960s, "a period of rapid change; action-oriented curricula that valued individual experience were advocated. The individual had to keep up and self-improvement was in *vogue*. The andragogical model in the face of pedagogy was welcomed by many adult educators as revolutionary" (p. 383). But although its influence on adult learning has been substantial ever since it was originally proposed, "Knowles never proceeded to an in-depth consideration of the organizational and social impediments to adult learning; he never painted the 'big picture.' He chose the mechanistic over the meaningful" (Grace, 1996b, p. 386).

Lack of attention to the context in which learning takes place is a critique emanating from a sociological perspective (Jarvis, 1987) and more recently, from critical perspectives. Sandlin (2005) applied critical, feminist, and Africentric theoretical orientations to andragogy and identified five issues that cut across the three different perspectives. First, andragogy is criticized for assuming education is value-neutral and apolitical. Second, andragogy assumes adult learners all look and learn the same—and this universal image is of a White middle-class individual learner. Third, other ways of learning are ignored, thus resulting in silencing other voices. Fourth, the relationship between self and society is ignored, and—"consequently, andragogy does not take into account structural systems of privilege and oppression, based on race, gender, and class, that influence learning and does not consider how culture impacts a person's development and ways of learning" (Sandlin, 2005, p. 28). The fifth issue to cut across critical, feminist, and Africentric perspectives is that andragogy thus reproduces society's inequalities and supports the status quo.

While Sandlin summarizes the critical perspectives on andragogy, Lee (2003) and Alfred (2000) examine andragogy from specific cultural lenses. Lee considers andragogy's application to foreign-born learners. In citing several studies with different immigrant groups ranging from Hmong refugees to Caribbean immigrant women, Lee concludes: "These studies . . . illustrated that andragogical assumptions do not characterize the experiences of some adult immigrants. Moreover, . . . by overgeneralizing the characteristics of a particular group of learners as those of all adult learners, Knowles effectively silenced and marginalized various social groups, including the adult immigrant learners whose values, experiences, and realities do not likely resemble the discourse of the dominant population" (p. 15).

Using four tenets from an Africentric feminist perspective, Alfred (2000) assessed how applicable andragogy is to African-American learners. First, personal experience is necessary to establish meaning and credibility. While andragogy certainly acknowledges personal experience, it does not acknowledge "the facilitator's experience as a valuable part of the pedagogical process" (p. 20). Further, "African American experience is centered in a culture of race, class, and gender oppression, which is often managed through wisdom or intuitive knowledge," while andragogy values objective ways of knowing (p. 20). Second, from an Africentric perspective, "for knowledge to be validated, it must be made public, and that is done in relationships with individuals or within a community," while andragogy stresses individual learning (p. 21). Third, an ethic of care characterizes this perspective; while care and a trusting environment are emphasized in andragogy, the political dimensions of this environment are not considered. Finally, the Africentric tradition evaluates "not only the knowledge that is articulated, but also the person who is making the claim" (p. 21). Andragogy does not consider the credibility of the learner and his or her claims of knowledge.

In reference to the workplace in particular, Kessels and Poell (2004) argue that andragogy in conjunction with social capital theory can transform the workplace into a conducive learning environment. Social capital theory stresses social networks, mutual trust, communities of practice, and relational forms of capital. Andragogy and social capital theory together offer HRD "assumptions on the facilitation of learning in the workplace, the strong motivational aspects of self-directedness and autonomy in competence development, and the network of meaningful relationships that helps learning integrate in the social contexts of the day-to-day work environment" (p. 154). Finally, St. Clair (2002, p. 2) states that adult education and human resource development are moving closer together: "Although adult education programs have become more instrumental and employment focused, training and development in the business world have increasingly emphasized the holistic development of workers. . . . This convergence is further underlined by the way HRD practitioners have worked to address the shortcomings of the andragogical model by remodeling it to recognize contextual factors more fully" (Holton & Swanson, 1999).

RESEARCH ON ANDRAGOGY

Considering that andragogy has been the primary model of adult learning for over forty years, relatively little empirical work has been done to test the validity of its assumptions or its usefulness in predicting adult learning behavior. A few studies have focused on the relationship between andragogical assumptions and instruction. Beder and Darkenwald (1982) asked teachers who taught both adults and preadults if their teaching behavior differed according to the age of the students. Teachers reported viewing adult students differently and using more andragogical techniques. Gorham (1985), however, actually observed teachers who taught both adults and preadults. She found no differences in how a particular teacher instructed adults or preadults, although teachers claimed that they did treat the two age groups differently.

With regard to involving learners in planning their own learning, Rosenblum and Darkenwald (1983) compared achievement and satisfaction measures between groups who had planned their course and those who had it planned for them. No differences were found in either achievement or satisfaction. Courtenay, Arnold, and Kim (1994) reviewed all previous literature and research and conducted their own quasi-experimental study of learner involvement in planning. They found previous research results to be inconclusive (indeed, "capricious"); from their own study, which attempted to address some of the shortcomings of previous studies, they found that "participation in planning does not appear to affect learning gain or satisfaction, even when the amount of participant input in planning is increased; the relationship between classroom environment and achievement or satisfaction is inconsequential; and classroom environment . . . may simply be a function of the satisfaction of the learner" (p. 297). They recommended that more thought be given to both the independent variable (that is, just what constitutes learner participation in planning) and the dependent variables (for example, perhaps unintended learning is as important as achievement).

Most recently, Rachal (2002) reviewed eighteen studies on andragogy conducted between 1984 and 2001, all of which attempted to assess the efficacy of an andragogical versus pedagogical instructional design. Based on measures of achievement, attendance, and/or satisfaction, studies revealed mixed results due to the varied "customizations" of the studies. For example, some studies did not segment adult undergraduates from traditional-age students, several studies had predetermined objectives, some used paperpencil tests of content acquisition, two studies involved mandated participation, and so on. To bring more rigor and comparability to empirical studies of andragogy, Rachal proposed seven standards or criteria for designing future studies. Briefly, these seven are that participation should be voluntary, participants should be clearly adults (and not students of traditional college age), objectives should be collaboratively determined, assessment should be performance-based, or where achievement is not the primary objective, satisfaction with the learning experience should be measured, an adult learning environment should be in place, and research methodological issues should be attended to (like random assignment to treatment groups where possible).

The studies reviewed by Rachal were mostly dissertations and all were experimental or quasi-experimental in design. While certainly this is one approach to assessing the validity of andragogy, it reinforces the psychologically driven, individually focused aspect of andragogy. Social context was not considered, for example, nor were any qualitative designs included.

Perhaps the nature of andragogy, with its assumptions for adult learner–focused practice, makes it particularly difficult to validate directly. As Rachal (2002, p. 224) himself comments, "It may well be that researchers examining the effectiveness of andragogy will perpetually be stymied by its fluidity, even its amoeba-like form-lessness. In that view, its art will forever be paramount, and its science forever elusive."

Although assessing the validity of andragogy directly may prove difficult to do, one could consider the extent to which a broader range of research in adult learning may or may not support the assumptions underlying andragogy. For example, the research on self-directed learning that finds upwards of 90 percent of adults are engaged in self-directed learning projects and that 70 percent of projects are planned by the learner (see Chapter Five) would tend to support the assumption that adults are self-directed and can plan their own learning. Further, studies on participation (see Chapter Three) indicate that participation is clearly linked to adult roles of worker, family member, and so on, lending support to the assumption that the readiness of an adult to learn is closely linked to the developmental tasks of his or her social roles. That the developmental issues of adulthood lead to learning was also underscored in Aslanian and Brickell's (1980) findings that 83 percent of adult learners were engaged in learning activities because of some transition in their lives. Nevertheless, the growing prevalence of mandated continuing education and training could be cited to argue against the assumption that adults are internally motivated.

Despite some writers' grim predictions of andragogy's demise, practitioners who work with adult learners continue to find Knowles's andragogy, with its characteristics of adult learners, to be a helpful rubric for better understanding adults as learners. As St. Clair (2002, p. 2) suggests, "[A]s a guide to teaching adults, andragogy has a great deal more to offer when it is approached, as Knowles originally suggested, as a set of assumptions." Further, the implications for practice that Knowles draws for each of the assumptions are also considered to be good instructional practice for all ages, especially adults. Thus, we see andragogy as an enduring model for understanding certain aspects of adult learning, and as maintaining "its role as a necessary component of the field's shared knowledge" (St. Clair, 2002, p. 2). It does not give us the total picture, nor is it a panacea for fixing adult learning practices. Rather, it constitutes one piece of the rich mosaic of adult learning.

OTHER MODELS OF ADULT LEARNING

Although andragogy remains the best-known model of adult learning, there are a number of other models that offer us some insights into adult learning. Three have been selected for review here. First, we have chosen to present McClusky's theory of margin (which actually predates andragogy) because it continues to captivate learners who find they can readily relate their life situation and their learning to this model. Second, we present a recent model, Illeris's three dimensions of learning, because it captures major components of the learning process in an easy-to-grasp visual of an inverted triangle. The third model is Jarvis's learning process. Originating in research with over two hundred adult learners more than twenty years ago, this model has undergone several revisions as Jarvis comes closer to understanding the learning process—"a mirage," he says, "since the closer you get the further away the goal appears" (personal communication, August 15, 2005). His model draws from a wide philosophical base as well as psychology and sociology.

McClusky's Theory of Margin

McClusky first presented his theory of margin in a 1963 publication, followed by discussions of application in 1970 and 1971. His theory is grounded in the notion that adulthood is a time of growth, change, and integration in which one constantly seeks balance between the amount of energy needed and the amount available. This balance is conceptualized as a ratio between the "load" (L) of life, which dissipates energy, and the "power" (P) of life, which allows one to deal with the load. "Margin in life" is the ratio of load to power. More power means a greater margin to participate in learning.

Both load and power consist of external and internal factors. Hiemstra (1993, p. 42) explains: "The external load consists of tasks involved in normal life requirements (such as family, work, and community responsibilities). Internal load consists of life expectancies developed by people (such as aspirations, desires, and future expectations). Power consists of a combination of such external resources . . . as family support, social abilities, and

how does this margin systematically vary for different groups & how do this relate to learning?

economic abilities. It also includes various internally acquired or accumulated skills and experiences contributing to effective performance, such as resilience, coping skills, and personality."

Taking both power and load into consideration, McClusky (1970, p. 83) explains how the theory works:

> Margin may be increased by reducing Load or increasing Power, or it may be decreased by increasing Load and/or reducing Power. We can control both by modifying either Power or Load. When Load continually matches or exceeds Power and if both are fixed and/or out of control, or irreversible, the situation becomes highly vulnerable and susceptible to breakdown. If, however, Load and Power can be controlled, and, better yet, if a person is able to lay hold of a reserve (Margin) of Power, he [sic] is better equipped to meet unforeseen emergencies, is better positioned to take risks, can engage in exploratory, creative activities, is more likely to learn, etc.

To engage in learning, then, an adult must have some margin of power "available for application to the processes which the learning situation requires" (McClusky, 1970, p. 84). Adult students in particular have to be adept at juggling multiple responsibilities and demands on their time. Take the hypothetical case of Caroline, a single parent who wants to upgrade her skills. She enrolls in the local community college, where she can learn to be a physician's assistant, a job she would like and that pays more than her current job on the housekeeping staff of a local hospital. On top of juggling her shift work at the hospital and her class schedule, Caroline has to find child care for her youngest and transport her older child back and forth to school. If one of the children or Caroline herself gets sick, she will have to miss class or work or both. Caroline has very little margin to deal with her present situation, let alone respond to any other demands on her time and energy. In contrast, Michele is a high-salaried vice president of a marketing company. She is married and has a nanny who comes to her home to care for her two children while she is at work. Michele has always wanted to be a master gardener and considers taking a course at the local botanical garden. Michele's skills, education, income, and support network are sources of power that she can adjust to deal with her load, affording her a comfortable margin wherein she can take the class.

Maintaining some margin of power in order to engage in learning is a concept adults readily relate to. As Hiemstra (1993, p. 42) observes, adult students' first encounter with McClusky's theory is often "an epiphany in terms of their own life circumstances."

McClusky (1970) also saw his theory as helpful in explaining the developmental changes characteristic of adult life (see Chapter Thirteen). Changes adults undergo as they age could be translated into adjustments of load and power. These adjustments are made "as a person accumulates and later relinquishes adult responsibilities and modifies the varying roles which the successive stages of the life cycle require" (p. 84). Since learning in adulthood is often a function of changing roles and responsibilities and physical and mental development, McClusky's theory can be used in understanding this link between changing social roles and learning.

Several studies have in fact investigated this link. Baum (1980) used the theory as a framework for exploring the power and load of one hundred randomly selected widows. Self-identified problems encountered in widowhood were viewed as load factors, and services and resources available to widows were categorized as power factors. She found that negative attitudes toward widowhood predicted more problems (load), but that it also led to finding more resources (power). As load increased, power increased, resulting in a fairly stable margin in life.

Using an instrument developed to measure margin in life, Stevenson (1980) compared the load, power, and margin patterns of independent older adults, nursing home residents, and young and middle-aged adults. She found that the two groups of older adults perceived themselves as having slightly more power (and less load) than the young and middle-aged adults.

A number of studies have used McClusky's theory to study adult student needs, performance, and participation in continuing and higher education (Demko, 1982; Garrison, 1986; Hansen, 1988; James, 1986; Mikolaj, 1983; Root, 2000; Schawo, 1997; Walker, 1996; Weiman, 1987). Findings across these studies are mixed, so no clear-cut generalizations can be drawn about the validity of McClusky's theory for predicting aspects of participation in continuing and higher education. His theory has also been used in a study of employees' readiness to change in the workplace

(Hanpachern, Morgan, & Griego, 1998). Based on 131 employees of a manufacturing company, "overall MIL and five work subscales had significant positive relationships with readiness for change" (p. 339). Londoner (1993) developed a load-power matrix exercise for assessing work and personal loads and the powers available to address the load. He suggests that this matrix can be used as a tool by HRD counselors and others in helping professions. The matrix is a device "to help adults manage stress and crises more effectively by developing and implementing specific change strategies that create favorable margin in their lives" (p. 126).

McClusky's theory has appeal in that it speaks to the everyday events and life transitions that all adults encounter. It is perhaps a better counseling tool than it is an explanation of adult learning, however. In fact, there is a striking similarity between McClusky's power, load, and margin concepts and the components of Schlossberg's model for counseling adults in transition. In her model, one determines the ability to work through a transition by assessing the relative strength of four factors: the situation, the self (internal strengths), external supports, and strategies one has developed to handle stress (Schlossberg, 1984, 1987). Indeed, McClusky's theory has been operationalized as an assessment tool to counsel applicants about their readiness for continuing pastoral education (Association for Clinical Pastoral Education, n.d.).

Although life events and transitions certainly precipitate many (and some would say the most potent) learning experiences, McClusky's model does not directly address learning itself but rather when it is most likely to occur. One might also question whether a reserve of energy or margin of power is necessary for learning to arise. Learning can happen under conditions of stress, or in McClusky's terms, when load is greater than power. Wolfin's (1999) study, for example, found that "overloaded" adults were as likely to learn as those with a surplus of power: "A surplus of power over load is not a 'necessary condition' or 'crucial element' for adults to be more likely to learn. . . . Overloaded Adults will do all they can, regardless of their inhibiting activities if those Over-loaded Adults perceive the subject matter as essential, meaningful, or worthwhile and perceive the learning method as convenient" (p. 281). In addition, the fact that learning itself has the potential to increase one's power is not addressed by McClusky.

ILLERIS'S THREE DIMENSIONS OF LEARNING MODEL

While McClusky's theory of margin focuses on how learning intersects with an adult's life situation, Illeris (2002) is most interested in the learning process itself. In his model there are three dimensions involved in learning—cognition, emotion, and society. As can be seen in Figure 4.1, he pictures these dimensions as an inverted triangle, with cognition and emotion at the top and environment at the bottom of the inverted apex; all three aspects of learning occur within society, represented by the circle around the triangle. Although one dimension might be emphasized over the other two, all three are always present in a learning activity. The cognitive dimension involves knowledge and skills while the emotional dimension consists of feelings and motivation. Cognition and emotion are internal processes that interact simultaneously in the acquisition of knowledge or skills. Cognition is what psychologists have concentrated on when studying learning and refers to "both knowledge and motor learning, both of which are controlled by the central nervous system" (2002, p. 18). Emotions, in contrast, involve "psychological energy, transmitted by feelings, emotions, attitudes and motivations which both mobilize and, at the same time, are conditions that may be influenced and developed through learning" (p. 18).

The dimension he labels "environment" or "sociality" in the triangle "is the dimension of external interaction, such as participation, communication, and cooperation. It serves as the personal integration in communities and society and thereby also builds up the sociality of the learner" (Illeris, 2004b, p. 83). This dimension is about interacting with other people as we learn, or it can refer to contributions of others to our learning (Illeris, 2002). Society wherein all three aspects of learning are encompassed is the context for our learning. That is, our learning is always within the society or social context in which we live and this context interacts with and shapes our learning.

How the process of learning begins is with one of five stimuli, what he calls the "raw material" of the process: (1) perception is "where the surrounding world comes to the individual as a totally unmediated sense impression" (Illeris, 2002, p. 120); (2) transmission, wherein someone else passes on information or transmits

FIGURE 4.1. LEARNING PROCESSES AND DIMENSIONS.

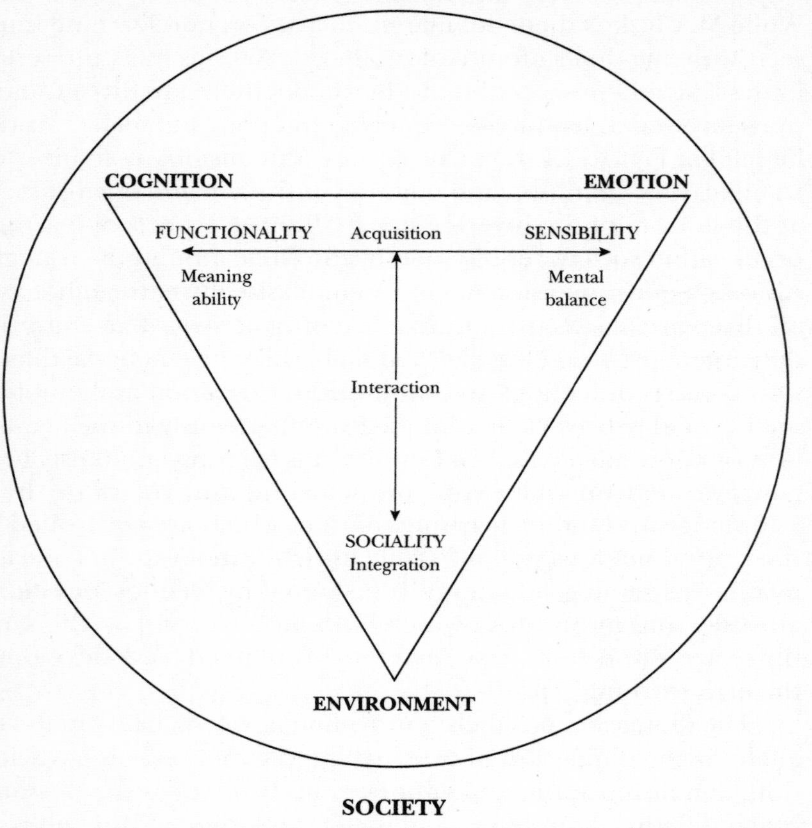

Source: Illeris, 2004b, p. 82. Reprinted by permission.

"specific sense impressions or messages" (p. 120); (3) experience, which while it can include both perception and transmission, we could also "limit the use of the word so that experience presupposes a particular activity, i.e., that the learner is not simply receiving, but also acts in order to benefit from the interaction" (p. 120); (4) imitation occurs when the learner attempts to imitate or model another's actions; and (5) activity or participation in which the learner is engaged in a goal-directed activity sometimes participating with others as in a community of practice. Illeris cautions that these five "input[s] of the learning process . . . should not be regarded as separate, but rather as characteristics which can be combined in a single learning event, each of them being more or less present or prominent in a pattern unique to the specific situation" (p. 227).

Illeris gives an example of how the three dimensions of cognition, emotion, and society might play out in a learning process. His example is a chemistry lesson that has as its focus the cognitive content of learning a particular chemical process. But each student experiences this lesson in a specific way, which involves emotions, motivations, and psychological energy. The result of the learning "will be closely connected with how the emotional dimension has been functioning" (p. 20). For example, depending on the cognitive-emotional and social interaction it is possible the learning could be "distorted, or perhaps no learning at all will take place, or something quite different will be learned: maybe a negative impression of the teacher, of some other students, of the subject, or of the school situation in general" (p. 21). Finally, external societal conditions will influence the process, such as whether the learning is to be examined, or whether the learning is needed to function in society.

This model, of course, can be applied in the same way to any type of adult learning activity. An adult learning to read, for example, engages both the cognitive and emotional dimensions, and this learning activity will be influenced by social interaction with instructor and fellow students. Further, society's expectations, internalized by the learner, that being literate is both desirable and necessary to function in today's world, interacts with the other two components of the process.

The strength of Illeris's model lies in its comprehensiveness but also its simplicity. We can all relate to how a learning activity reflects cognitive, emotional, and social dimensions. Much of adult learning research and theory building emphasizes the cognitive, so Illeris's inclusion of emotional and social dimensions is a real strength. Further, his model can be used to understand resistance to or rejection of learning as well as something as powerful as transformational learning: "Very special and demanding situations, often with a crisis-like character, can lead to deep and comprehensive transformative learning processes that include simultaneous changes in all the three learning dimensions and have to do with the very identity of the learner" (2002, p. 229). And while he does not claim it to be a model of *adult* learning per se, its application to preadults seems limited due to their level of cognitive and emotional development and their awareness of the societal context.

JARVIS'S LEARNING PROCESS

Jarvis's model begins with an adult's life situation, or more correctly, an adult's experience: "Even miseducative experiences may be regarded as learning experiences. . . . *All* learning begins with experience" (1987, p. 16; italics in original). Some experiences, however, are repeated with such frequency that they are taken for granted and do not lead to learning, such as driving a car or household routines. At the start of the learning process is a disjuncture between biography (all that a person is at a particular point in time) and experience—an incident that a person is unprepared to handle. "Disjuncture occurs when our biographical repertoire is no longer sufficient to cope automatically with our situation so that our unthinking harmony with our world is disturbed to some degree or other" (Jarvis, 2006, p. 9). "No longer can previous learning cope with the present situation, people are consciously aware that they do not know how to act. We have to think, to plan or to learn something new. Learning then always begins with experiencing" (Jarvis, 2004, p. 93). This "inability to cope with the situation unthinkingly, instinctively, is at the heart of all learning" (1987, p. 35).

Jarvis theorizes that all learning begins with the five human sensations of sound, sight, smell, taste, and touch. He believes that "our learning is ultimately dependent on our body and biology is a significant factor in the learning process—not because of our genes, but because of the way that our senses function" (2006, p. 13). In our everyday lives we meet unfamiliar situations; for instance, we hear a new sound or we read a word whose meaning we do not know. Through asking others or by chance or by design we acquire the meaning of the unfamiliar sensation. This meaning is memorized and practiced (for example, we may try to use a word whose meaning we have just learned) until it becomes a part of us and we once again take the world for granted. "The significant thing is that the original sensations have been transformed into knowledge, skills, attitudes, values, emotions, and so on" (p. 14).

For Jarvis, all experience occurs within the learner's world (that individual's world, not *the* world), which is ever changing—"[I]t changes over time in relation to the changes that occur both in the wider world, in which it exists, and to the individual's involvement in it, and so we cannot depict a simple relationship with it in respect of learning. . . . [T]he person exists in a 'flow of time' within the lifeworld" (Jarvis, 2006, p. 7).

The learner is more than a cognitive machine. The learner is a whole person made up of the mind and the body and comes to a learning situation with a history, a biography that interacts in individual ways with the experience that generates the nature of the learning. As can be seen in Figure 4.2, Jarvis's model of the learning process begins with the whole person who encounters an experience in her social context, one that cannot be automatically accommodated or assimilated. This creates the disjuncture

FIGURE 4.2. THE TRANSFORMATION OF THE PERSON THROUGH EXPERIENCE.

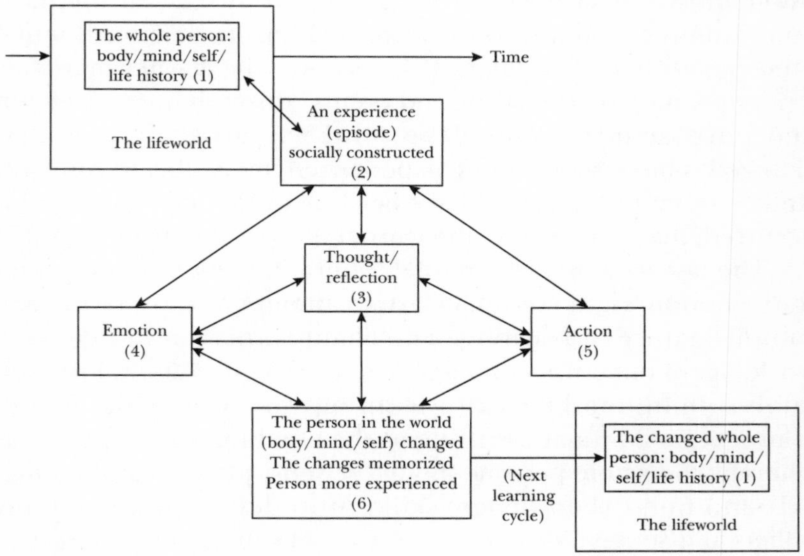

Source: Jarvis, 2006, p. 16. Reprinted by permission.

between one's biography and the experience, a state of unease that can trigger learning. If, in contrast, the individual chooses to ignore or dismiss this unease, no learning occurs (as evidenced by the two-way arrow between Boxes 1 and 2).

The next level of the model portrays three ways of learning, thinking, doing, and feeling (experiencing emotion). Each of these can occur in any combination with the others, as the arrows among the three boxes indicate. Jarvis explains that different combinations can produce different types of learning, "critical thinking, problem-solving learning, reflective learning, action learning, and so on." He speculates that "it is perhaps through the emotions that thought can be transformed into action. However, either of these two can dominate in the process of learning and a number of different types of learning can occur: contemplation, rational thinking, desiring, planning, action learning, and so on. In addition, the emotions can have a considerable effect on the way that we think, on motivation and on beliefs, attitudes and values" (2006, p. 11).

The result of this learning, as seen in Box 6, is a person affected in some way by the learning. There are three possible ways a person is changed. One is "the person's self is changed both by the acquisition of all the things we have discussed mentally, emotionally . . . but also in terms of identity, self-confidence, esteem, and so on" (2006, p. 17). Second, "the learner may place a new meaning on the world and events" through both incidental and purposeful learning. The third way a person may have changed is he or she "is more experienced, more able to cope with similar situations and problems because of the learning that has occurred, that is to say that the learner is more intelligent" (p. 17).

The last section of the model, where the first box is repeated in the bottom right corner, is Jarvis's attempt to capture the continuous nature of learning. The changed person in her social world again encounters an experience that stimulates learning. Jarvis's definition of human learning summarizes the model: "I now regard human learning as the combination of processes whereby the whole person—body (genetic, physical and biological) and mind (knowledge, skills, attitudes, values, emotions, beliefs and senses)—experiences a social situation the perceived content of which is then transformed cognitively, emotively or practically (or through any combination) and integrated into the person's individual biography resulting in a changed (or more experienced) person" (p. 7).

Jarvis's model is perhaps the most comprehensive of models reviewed in this chapter. Furthermore, his model situates learning in a social context; learning is an interactive phenomenon, not an isolated internal process. In his most recent book (2006) he presents each component in detail. Not just the learning process, but also concepts of the whole person, the social context, types of learning, and the nature of experience itself are dealt with in depth, drawing from a wide body of literature. Although his early work on this model was constructed from research with adult learners, it is clear that his interest is understanding and explaining *human* learning, not just adult learning. He does, however, imply that his model is perhaps easier to apply when speaking of adults, because young children do not have the cognitive skills, emotional range, or action alternatives available to adults. Further, the child and the adult's life situation or context are quite different, leading to different kinds of experiences shaping the learning. His model has been unfolding over the past twenty years, so that the most recent iteration looks quite different from the original 1987 version. However, the processing of experience remains fundamental to his thinking.

SUMMARY

Although there was sporadic attention given to adult learning in the early decades of the twentieth century, it was not until the 1970s that adult educators themselves began to focus systematically on some of the distinguishing characteristics of adult learning as separate from the body of information from psychologists' and educational psychologists' investigations of learning in general. This shift in focus was part of the field's efforts to differentiate itself from other areas of education. It also led to the search for a single theory of adult learning, one that would differentiate adults from children, include all types of learning, and was at once elegant and simple. But just as there is no single theory that explains human learning in general, no single theory of adult learning has emerged to unify the field. Rather, there are a number of theories, models, and frameworks, each of which attempts to capture some aspect of adult learning.

The best-known theory of adult learning is Knowles's andragogy. Nevertheless, it is less a theory and more a set of assumptions about adult learners that learners and educators alike can use to strengthen the learning transaction. The assumptions regarding an adult's self-concept, experience, readiness to learn, problem-centered focus, and internal motivation all have some intuitive validity, making andragogy popular with practitioners in many fields. These assumptions were critiqued in this chapter, as was Knowles's isolation of the individual learner from the learning context.

The chapter then turned to reviewing other, less well-known models of adult learning. Like andragogy, McClusky's theory of margin is more about the personal life situation of adults than learning per se. McClusky's theory of margin emphasizes both personal characteristics (internal load and power factors) and situational characteristics (external load and power factors). His model has more to say about adult development and the timing of learning, though, than about the actual learning transaction.

Two other models do focus on the learning process itself, although neither claims to be about adult learning only. Illeris's three dimensions of learning model positions learning as the continuous interaction among cognition, emotions, and social context. Jarvis's model of the learning process links the whole person (body, mind, self, life history) with an experience encountered in the person's social context. The disjuncture between the person's biography and the experience leads to learning that involves emotion, thought, and action. The result is some change in the person.

Each model discussed in this chapter contributes in its own way to advancing our understanding of adult learners. However, there has been little research testing the power of the models to explain or predict adult learning behavior. The process of model and theory building does, however, stimulate inquiry and reflection, all of which may eventually provide some of the answers to our questions about adult learning.

CHAPTER FIVE

SELF-DIRECTED LEARNING

Since Tough's work on adult learning projects was published in 1971, self-directed learning has captured the imagination of researchers and writers both inside and outside the field of adult education. Many public schools and colleges and universities have used this concept to describe one of the primary goals of their institutions: to enable their students to be lifelong, self-directed learners. While certainly adults have always learned on their own, serious study of this phenomenon is relatively recent in comparison to other aspects of learning, such as memory, cognition, and intelligence (see the chapters in Part Four). This lag is due in part to much of self-directed learning occurring outside of formal institutional settings, and therefore being so embedded in people's everyday lives as to be invisible. Tied in with this perspective is the role of educators of adults. Should we be working with learners outside the formal institutional environment? And might we be cutting into our own "business" as educators if we acknowledge that many adults can learn very effectively without our assistance? Despite these concerns, the study of self-directed learning has emerged as one the major thrusts of adult education research. There is, in fact, a voluminous literature base to draw from, an annual conference on the topic, and a recently inaugurated Web site (www. sdlglobal.com), which houses, along with other resources, an online journal devoted to self-directed learning.

Tough (1967, 1971), building on the work of Houle (1961/1988) and others, provided the first comprehensive description of self-directed learning as a form of study that he termed *self-planned learning*. Drawing on a study of the learning projects of sixty-six people from Ontario, Canada, he found that "highly deliberate efforts to learn take place all around you. The members of your family, your neighbors, colleagues, and acquaintances probably initiate and complete several learning efforts, though you may not be aware of it" (Tough, 1971, p. 3). Writing about the same time as Tough, Knowles proposed that one of the hallmark assumptions of adult learning is that learners become increasingly self-directed as they mature (Knowles, 1970, 1980). Knowles's thinking about self-directed learning is grounded in his concept of andragogy, discussed in Chapter Four. Although there have been challenges to his assumption that adult learners strive toward greater self-direction, there are many who treat it as fact and structure their practice accordingly.

Building on the pioneering work of Houle (1961/1988), Tough (1978, 1979), and Knowles (1970), the earlier research in this arena was primarily descriptive in nature (Brockett, 1985; Caffarella & O'Donnell, 1987). The emphasis in this early work was on verifying that adults do deliberately learn on their own and on discovering how they go about doing this. Following these descriptive studies, researchers began providing more in-depth conceptual models (for example, Brockett & Hiemstra, 1991; Candy, 1991; Garrison, 1997). Scholars also initiated a debate about what the goals of self-directed learning should be (Brockett & Hiemstra, 1991; Brookfield, 1986; Collins, 1988; Mezirow, 1985) and started exploring the personal characteristics and attributes of those who are self-directed in their learning (Candy, 1991; Chene, 1983; Oddi, 1986). In addition, a number of writers sought to bring greater clarity and precision to the term and the many related terms that have been used to describe this phenomenon.

In reviewing this rich array of work on self-directed learning (SDL), we have grouped the literature into three broad categories, each outlining a major facet of self-directed learning. We report first on literature that explores the goals of self-directed learning. We then examine research that describes self-directed learning as a process or form of study. Third, we review self-directedness as a personal attribute of the learner. We conclude the chapter with a discussion of recent applications of SDL and the important challenges to be considered in building future research and theory in self-directed learning.

GOALS OF SELF-DIRECTED LEARNING

Often defined by the underlying philosophical position of the writer, the three main goals of self-directed learning can be grouped as follows: (1) to enhance the ability of adult learners to be self-directed in their learning, (2) to foster transformational learning as central to self-directed learning, and (3) to promote emancipatory learning and social action as an integral part of self-directed learning.

The first goal, to enhance the ability of adults to be self-directed in their learning, has stemmed primarily from the work of Knowles (1980) and Tough (1979). This ability to be self-directed in one's learning is conceived as both a set of personal attributes and specific skills (Caffarella, 2000; Brockett & Hiemstra, 1991; Caffarella & O'Donnell, 1989). Within this goal, the assumption is that part of the job of educators of adults is to help learners, whether they are learning on their own or in formal learning programs, to be able to plan, carry out, and evaluate their own learning. For example, in the independent pursuit of learning, educators might provide assistance to individuals or groups of learners in locating resources or mastering alternative learning strategies. The learners themselves would seek out this assistance, perhaps in community learning centers or through learning technologies. Of course, as some writers point out, we cannot wait until adulthood to begin developing self-directed lifelong learners. This goal is something that needs to be attended to at all levels of schooling from primary education through university and professional training (Schrader-Naef, 2000; Williams, 2001). This first goal has spawned the majority of research in self-directed learning.

Goal One is grounded primarily in humanistic philosophy, which posits personal growth as the goal of adult learning. Brockett and Hiemstra (1991, pp. 26–27), for example, have stated that their model of self-directed learning, the Personal Responsibility Orientation (PRO) model, is based on three fundamental ideas espoused by this philosophy: "[T]hat human nature is basically good, . . . that individuals possess virtually unlimited potential for growth . . . [and] that only by accepting responsibility for one's own learning is it possible to take a proactive approach to the learning process." Accepting responsibility and being proactive take into account two other tenets of humanistic philosophy: personal autonomy and free will to make individual choices.

Goal Two, to foster transformational learning as central to self-directed learning, is found primarily in the work of Mezirow (1985) and Brookfield (1985, 1986). Mezirow (1985, p. 27) suggests that "there is probably no such thing as a self-directed learner, except in the sense that there is a learner who can participate fully and freely in the dialogue through which we test our interests and perspectives against those of others and accordingly modify them and our learning goals." In essence, adults need to reflect critically and have an understanding of the historical, cultural, and biographical reasons for their needs, wants, and interests. "Such self-knowledge is a prerequisite for autonomy in self-directed learning" (p. 27). For Mezirow, the "key" to self-directedness is "becoming critically aware of what has been taken for granted about one's own learning" (p. 17). Brookfield (1985, 1986) echoes Mezirow's ideas by calling on adult educators to distinguish clearly between the techniques of self-directed learning and the internal change in consciousness. More specifically, Brookfield (1986, p. 38) asserted that "the most complete form of self-directed learning occurs when process and reflection are married in the adult's pursuit of meaning." The critical reflection component of the second goal is foundational to the third goal of self-directed learning: promoting emancipatory learning and social action.

Writers advancing Goal Three have been some of the strongest critics of the first goal of self-directed learning: enhancing the ability of individual learners to be more self-directed in their learning. The heart of their criticism is that this first goal is too narrow, with the focus of that goal being primarily instrumental learning and assisting individual learners. In contrast, authors who support the goal of promoting emancipatory learning and social action want included not only the examination by learners of the sociopolitical assumptions under which they learn and function but also the incorporation of collective action as an outcome. Unless the definition of self-directed learning is broadened to include these components, these proponents view self-directed learning as merely a technique "to condition the individual into taken-for-granted acceptance of what is offered" (Collins, 1996, p. 115). Collins has been the most persistent and eloquent in echoing these concerns about how self-directed learning has been conceptualized and practiced. Collins emphasizes the importance of having an "unequivocal focus of emancipation as a core concern" in the study of self-directed learning and adult learning in general (p. 119). By this Collins means that participatory research methods should be used to foster democratic and open dialogue about self-directed learning, and ethical and political concerns about self-directed learning should be a part of this dialogue. To foster the study of this critical practice of self-directed learning, Collins suggests that researchers use critical theory and interpretive and participatory research approaches. An example of this orientation is a study by Andruske (2000) wherein she investigated the self-directed learning projects of women on welfare. She found that the women became "political change agents as they attempt[ed] to control and to initiate change in their everyday worlds in response to oppressive external structures" (p. 11).

In this same vein, Brookfield (1993, p. 227) asserts that "any authentic exercise of self-directedness requires that certain political conditions be in place." More specifically, Brookfield argues first that having learners exercise control over all educational decisions needs to be a consistent element of self-directed learning. As such, educators of adults in formal and nonformal settings need to shift to learners as much control as possible in the learning process. Brookfield views this shift as difficult to accomplish in settings where the culture itself is highly controlling, such as some higher education institutions or corporate environments. Therefore, he asserts that educators "might decide to work collectively at changing the political culture of institutions. . . . Control from this perspective would be seen in our coming to understand the origins, functioning and contradictions of the system and in our working to change or replace it with one that honors our daily activities as educators" (1993, p. 235). Second, Brookfield calls for more easily accessible and adequate resources so that learners can more readily exercise control over their learning, especially learners who have been denied access to resources because of cost or preferential treatment for privileged groups.

Most of the process models reviewed in the next section reflect Goal One, enhancing the ability of adult learners to be self-directed in their learning, and to a lesser extent, Goal Two, fostering transformational learning.

SELF-DIRECTED LEARNING AS A PROCESS

Self-directed learning as a process of learning, in which people take the primary initiative for planning, carrying out, and evaluating their own learning experiences, has received a great deal of attention in the literature. We contend, as described in Chapter Two, that this form of learning can take place both inside and outside institutionally based learning programs. For the most part, however, being self-directed in one's learning is a natural part of adult life. Within this category of self-directed learning as a process, three types of models—linear, interactive, and instructional—have been extensively discussed in the literature. In the next three subsections we set out descriptions and critiques of the most prominent and the most promising models of self-directed learning. These models represent a mixture of conceptual, empirical, and experientially derived views of the process of self-directed learning.

LINEAR MODELS

The early models of self-directed learning, those proposed by Tough (1971) and Knowles (1975), were linear in nature. Learners moved through a series of steps to reach their learning goals in a self-directed manner. The resulting frameworks of the learning process for these models included many elements of the traditional teaching process.

Tough (1967, 1971, 1979) proposed the first comprehensive description of self-directed learning, which he termed self-planned learning. Drawing on a study of the learning projects of sixty-six people from Ontario, Canada, he found that 70 percent of all learning projects were planned by the learners themselves. He defined a learning project as "a highly deliberate effort to gain and retain certain definite knowledge and skill, or to change in some other way. To be included, a series of related learning sessions (episodes in which the person's primary intention was to learn) must add up to at least seven hours" (Tough, 1978, p. 250). Tough found that learners used thirteen steps in self-planned learning projects, representing key decision-making points about choosing what, where, and when to learn along with deciding on resources for learning, detecting possible barriers to learning, and so on.

Tough's research on self-directed learning became the basis for numerous dissertations and research studies around the world. In the 1970s and early 1980s a range of specific populations were studied using Tough's original or modified interview schedule. These studies confirmed the prevalence of self-directed learning in adults' lives. Although there is some variance across these studies in the amount and type of self-directed learning that goes on in the general population, we can say without reservation that the existence of the independent pursuit of learning in adulthood has been established (Brookfield, 1984; Caffarella & O'Donnell, 1987; Owen, 2002).

Knowles's (1975) description of self-directed learning consists of six major steps: (1) climate setting, (2) diagnosing learning needs, (3) formulating learning goals, (4) identifying human and material resources for learning, (5) choosing and implementing appropriate learning strategies, and (6) evaluating learning outcomes. His steps are somewhat similar to those proposed by Tough (1979). Knowles includes numerous resources for both learners and teachers for completing each of these tasks. Among the materials he describes, we have found the ones on learning contracts and evaluation to be the most useful. Although the work of Tough and Knowles "has provided the language, the concepts, and more importantly the descriptive terms for key elements and processes of self-planned learning" (Kasworm, 1992, p. 56), other scholars have conceptualized different processes.

INTERACTIVE MODELS

A second portrait of self-directed learning is that this learning process is not so well planned or linear in nature. Rather, there is an emphasis on two or more factors, such as opportunities people find in their own environments, the personality characteristics of learners, cognitive processes, and the context of learning, which collectively interact to form episodes of self-directed learning.

Three such models are discussed as illustrative of the work in this arena: the models of Spear (1988), Brockett and Hiemstra (1991), and Garrison (1997).

Spear's Model

Spear (1988), building on his earlier work with Mocker (Spear & Mocker, 1984), has presented a model that rests on three elements: the opportunities people find in their own environments, past or new knowledge, and chance occurrences. Spear proposed that each self-directed learning project is composed of sets or clusters of those elements. For example, a move from an apartment to a single-family residence affords an opportunity to pursue gardening. This fortuitous action in conjunction with some prior knowledge of gardening, perhaps in combination with a chance encounter with an old friend who is an accomplished gardener, results in a self-directed learning project.

Spear also concluded from his study that self-directed learning projects do not generally occur in a linear fashion—that is, one cluster does not necessarily bear any relation to the next cluster. Rather, information gathered through one set of activities (one cluster) is stored until it fits in with other ideas and resources on the same topic gleaned from one or more additional clusters of activities. A successful self-directed learning project is one in which a person can engage in a sufficient number of relevant clusters of learning activities and then assemble these clusters into a coherent whole. Spear (1988, p. 217) concludes, "The learner is perhaps in greatest control when the assembling of the clusters begins and decisions are made regarding what knowledge is of most and least importance."

Although only a few studies have been conducted using all or parts of Spear's framework (for example, Berger, 1990; Padberg, 1994), other researchers have come to similar conclusions in their work. Danis and Tremblay (1987, 1988), for example, who studied ten long-term adult learners, found that their respondents were able to specify learning goals only when they had mastered certain knowledge or skills, and that in general these learners went about learning on their own using multiple approaches as opposed to only one approach. In addition, they noted that the impact of random events stood out in that these learners took advantage of any opportunities offered to them. Berger (1990), in her study of twenty white males with no formal degrees beyond high school, found little evidence that her subjects did any preplanning in their self-directed learning activities. Her subjects "constantly redefined their projects, changed course, and followed new paths of interest as they proceeded" (p. 176). In essence, the majority of her respondents adopted a trial-and-error approach, with an emphasis on hands-on experience and practice, guiding themselves by both their successes and their mistakes as they moved on to new levels of learning.

Brockett and Hiemstra's Model

In their Personal Responsibility Orientation (PRO) model, Brockett and Hiemstra (1991, p. 26) provide a new framework for what they term *self-direction in learning*, which comprises "both instructional method processes (self-directed learning) and personality characteristics of the individual learner (learner self-direction)." In the instructional processes dimension, learners assume primary responsibility for planning, implementing, and evaluating their learning experiences. The authors note that "an educational agent or resource often plays a facilitating role in this process" (p. 24). In this facilitation role, instructors must possess skills in helping learners do needs assessments, locate learning resources, and choose instructional methods and evaluation strategies. Many of these skills have been discussed in previous literature on self-directed learning (for example, Knowles, 1975, and Tough, 1979) and are stressed in their model, with an emphasis on the interactive nature of the teaching and learning process.

Their second dimension, related to the personality characteristics of individual learners, "centers on a learner's desire or preference for assuming responsibility for learning" (Brockett & Hiemstra, 1991, p. 24). The notion of personal responsibility, which they define as "individuals assuming ownership for their own thoughts and actions" (p. 26), is the point of departure for understanding their concept of self-direction in adult learning. Their concept of personal responsibility is grounded in the concepts of humanism and human potential. Although they agree that individual learners are central to the idea of self-direction, they also regard the context, or social milieu, in which that learning activity transpires as important. In acknowledging these contextual factors, they recognize the importance of situational factors in the self-directed learning process, which mirrors others' descriptions of the process of self-directed learning.

Hiemstra (1992) and Hiemstra and Brockett (1994) have further described various aspects of using self-directed learning as an instructional method. Further, two recent dissertations were based on the PRO model. Stockdale (2003) developed an instrument to assess the two components (teaching-learning and learner characteristics) of the model. Her thirty-five-item Personal Responsibility Orientation to Self-Direction in Learning Scale (PRO-SDLS) was found to be highly reliable with the sample of graduate and undergraduate education students. Fogerson's (2005) study correlated Stockdale's PRO-SDLS instrument with selected satisfaction variables in an online higher education course. While the reliability of the PRO-SDLS was confirmed, no significant correlations were revealed between the scale and satisfaction. Fogerson speculates that this finding might be due to the student population, who were older and had experience with online courses; they also reported being "satisfied" or "very satisfied" with the course.

Garrison's Model

Garrison (1997) is the most recent scholar to propose a multidimensional and interactive model of self-directed learning. His model (see Figure 5.1), grounded in a "collaborative constructivist" perspective, "integrates self-management (contextual control), self-monitoring (cognitive responsibility) and motivational (entering and task) dimensions to reflect a meaningful and worthwhile approach to self-directed learning" (p. 18).

The first dimension, self-management, acknowledges the social milieu in which learners are interacting, whether they are in formal or informal settings. It involves learners' taking control of and shaping the contextual conditions so that they can reach their stated goals and objectives. "Control," says Garrison, "does not translate into social independence or freedom from influence. Educational self-management concerns the use of learning materials within a context where there is opportunity for sustained communication. Self-management of learning in an educational

FIGURE 5.1. DIMENSIONS OF SELF-DIRECTED LEARNING.

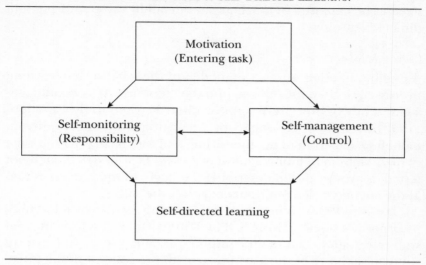

Source: Garrison, 1997, p. 22. Reprinted by permission.

context must consider the opportunity to test and confirm understanding collaboratively" (1997, p. 23), which translates into
increased responsibilities for the learner.

"The next two dimensions of the model—self-monitoring and
motivation—represent the cognitive dimensions of self-directed
learning" (1997, p. 24), which Garrison believes have been given
little attention in the literature on self-directed learning. Self-
monitoring describes the ability of learners to be able to monitor
both their cognitive and metacognitive processes, which includes
their being able to use a repertoire of learning strategies and the
ability to think about their thinking. "Self-monitoring is synonymous with responsibility to construct meaning . . . [and] is very
much associated with the ability to be reflective and think critically"
(pp. 24–25). The motivational dimension involves what influences
people to participate or enter into a self-directed learning activity
and what keeps them participating in the activity or task: "Motivation and responsibility are reciprocally related and both are facilitated by collaborative control of the educational transaction"

(p. 29). Garrison observes that self-monitoring and motivation need to be explored in much greater detail by those studying self-directed learning.

Other Models

A number of other interactive models of the self-directed learning process have been introduced into the literature. After conducting a case study of how the Wright brothers learned to fly, Cavaliere (1992) identified five stages of a learning project—inquiring, modeling, experimenting, theorizing, and actualizing. Within each of these steps were four cognitive processes. Her model, though not tested, is provocative in describing the stages of the process as well as the cognitive elements that cut across the stages.

Danis's (1992) "framework" for studying self-directed learning incorporates research from SDL, self-instruction, and learning and study strategies. The main components thus consist of learning strategies, phases of the learning activity, the content of the learning, learner or collective learner characteristics, and the external context of the learning activity. Unlike the other models reviewed, Danis explicitly takes into account the context as well as the potential of self-taught groups of learners. A recent study (Rager, 2003) of the self-directed learning of women with breast cancer, underscores the importance of context and seems to fit well with Danis's framework. Rager's study uncovered the emotional context as critical in shaping participants' SDL: "As reported by the participants, emotions interfered with their ability to begin learning and their ability to make use of some resources, influenced their reactions to some of the information they did find, and impaired their ability to stay focused" (2003, p. 290).

Other models of the self-directed learning process can be found in studies of specific populations or topics. For example, Valente (2005) studied the self-directed learning process of older adults who managed their own health care. Her model begins with a "health event." Once a health event is diagnosed, the cycle of self-directed learning begins. Health care professionals are consulted, which stimulates the older adult to acquire and assess information, followed by choosing a treatment option. The treatment is monitored and reflected upon and adjustments in lifestyle or treatment or both are made. The cycle then repeats itself as the learner acquires and assesses more information, often in consultation with health care professionals.

Roberson and Merriam (2005) also uncovered a process of self-directed learning in their study of rural older adults. The process begins with an incentive, often related to late life changes, to learn; if the person has an interest in the topic or activity, he or she will pursue it. Next, resources are accessed and systematic attention and time are given to the project. Adjustments are made as the project progresses. An interesting component of the process is that the motivation and intensity to learn are often enhanced by a catalyst, such as another person stimulating interest, or a late-life change in family or health.

INSTRUCTIONAL MODELS   *How to: developmental model of learners*

The third category of self-directed learning models represents frameworks that instructors in formal settings could use to integrate self-directed methods of learning into their programs and activities. Two models are highlighted that were designed with formal settings in mind: those of Grow (1991) and of Hammond and Collins (1991).

Grow's (1991, 1994) Staged Self-Directed Learning (SSDL) model outlines how teachers can help students become more self-directed in their learning. Grow, who grounded his model in the situational leadership model of Hersey and Blanchard (1988), describes four distinct stages of learners:

Stage 1: Dependent learner: Learners of low self-direction who need an authority figure (a teacher) to tell them what to do

Stage 2: Interested learner: Learners of moderate self-direction who are motivated and confident but largely ignorant of the subject matter to be learned

Stage 3: Involved learner: Learners of intermediate self-direction who have both the skill and the basic knowledge and view themselves as being both ready and able to explore a specific subject area with a good guide

Stage 4: Self-directed learner: Learners of high self-direction who are both willing and able to plan, execute, and evaluate their own learning with or without the help of an expert

At each of these stages, Grow outlines possible roles for the teacher or facilitator. Figure 5.2 shows how the four types of learners, four roles of the facilitator, and appropriate instructional methods are interrelated. Grow also explores the problems that may arise when there is a mismatch between the role or style of the teacher and the learning stage of the participants. Grow emphasizes that good teachers individualize their teaching strategies to match the learners' stage of self-direction and allow the students to become more self-directed in their learning. Therefore, integrating self-directed learning as a way to organize learning experiences is situational in nature.

FIGURE 5.2. APPLYING THE STAGED SELF-DIRECTION MODEL TO A COURSE.

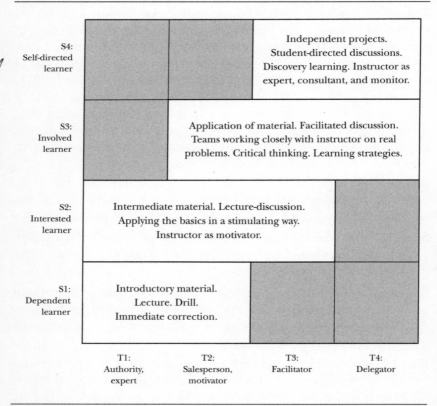

	T1: Authority, expert	T2: Salesperson, motivator	T3: Facilitator	T4: Delegator
S4: Self-directed learner			Independent projects. Student-directed discussions. Discovery learning. Instructor as expert, consultant, and monitor.	
S3: Involved learner		Application of material. Facilitated discussion. Teams working closely with instructor on real problems. Critical thinking. Learning strategies.		
S2: Interested learner	Intermediate material. Lecture-discussion. Applying the basics in a stimulating way. Instructor as motivator.			
S1: Dependent learner	Introductory material. Lecture. Drill. Immediate correction.			

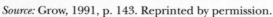

Source: Grow, 1991, p. 143. Reprinted by permission.

The instructional model proposed by Hammond and Collins (1991) is the only model that explicitly addresses the goal of promoting emancipatory learning and social action as a central tenet of self-directed learning. Grounding their work in studies of critical pedagogy, popular education, and participatory research, these authors have outlined a seven-component framework for assisting learners in formal settings to engage in the critical practice of adult education. In their model, learners take the initiative for:

1. Building a cooperative learning climate
2. Analyzing and critically reflecting on themselves and the social, economic, and political contexts in which they are situated
3. Generating competency profiles for themselves
4. Diagnosing their learning needs within the framework of both the personal and social context
5. Formulating socially and personally relevant learning goals that result in learning agreements
6. Implementing and managing their learning
7. Reflecting on and evaluating their learning

What makes their model different from Knowles's and other process models is the purposeful inclusion of the critical perspective through the examination of the social, political, and environmental contexts that affect their learning, and the stress on developing both personal and social learning goals.

Although greater control of the learning process is what Hammond and Collins see as the immediate goal for learners using their model of critical self-directed learning, their "ultimate goal is to empower learners to use their learning to improve the conditions under which they and those around them live and work" (1991, p. 14). As with other models of SDL, such as Garrison's (1997) and Cavaliere's (1992), we found no studies where the researchers used Hammond and Collins's model as their conceptual framework.

SELF-DIRECTION AS A PERSONAL ATTRIBUTE OF LEARNERS

An important focus in the research literature on self-directed learning has been self-directedness as a personal attribute or characteristic of the learner. The assumption underlying much of this work is that learning in adulthood means becoming more self-directed and autonomous. Recall that one of Knowles's (1980, p. 43) four major tenets of andragogy is that mature "adults have a deep psychological need to be generally self-directing." Brockett and Hiemstra (1991) echo Knowles's assumption in that they see a link between learner self-direction, which they define as characteristics of learners that predispose them toward taking primary responsibility for their own learning, and a positive self-concept. Tennant and Pogson (1995) have asserted that "the idea of autonomous or self-directed learning is firmly entrenched in contemporary thinking about adult education and there has been a great deal of scholarly interest in the subject" (p. 121).

Research into the nature of the self-directed learner asks the who and what questions: Are these learners introverts or extroverts? What is their learning style? What level of education have they achieved, and does this affect their ability to be self-directed? Are they more autonomous than other learners? How do we know if learners are ready for self-directed ways of learning? Basically, researchers are trying to gain an understanding of the typical self-directed learner's characteristics or attributes. More specifically, researchers have tried to link a number of different variables, such as learning style, level of education, or life satisfaction, with being self-directed in one's learning. Findings from these studies have been, for the most part, inconclusive. The focus on SDL as a personal attribute has also been studied with the use of instruments assessing the presence of self-direction as a trait, and of the readiness to be self-directed; further discussions center on the concept of autonomy and its relationship to self-direction.

ASSESSING SELF-DIRECTEDNESS

Two instruments, the OCLI and the SDLRS, have been widely used to assess aspects of self-directedness as a personality trait. The Oddi Continuing Learning Inventory (OCLI) is a twenty-four-item Likert scale that measures one's self-directedness as a personality trait (Oddi, 1986; Oddi, Ellis, & Roberson, 1990). More than twenty-five variables have been positively correlated with self-directedness as measured by the OCLI; some of these variables are self-efficacy, self-concept, personal responsibility, on-the-job learning, grade point average, and left brain hemisphericity (Owen, 2002). It might be mentioned that the OCLI was developed by a nurse educator particularly interested in participation in continuing professional education (CPE); hence, a number of studies with the OCLI are in areas of CPE.

Readiness, which implies an internal state of psychological readiness to undertake self-directed learning, has received the most attention in the study of self-directed learning in terms of data-based studies (Guglielmino, 1997). Guglielmino (1977) has provided the most-used operational definition for self-directed learning. She states that it consists of a complex of attitudes, values, and abilities that create the likelihood that an individual is capable of self-directed learning. She identifies the psychological qualities involved in readiness for self-directed learning as initiative, independence, and persistence in learning; acceptance of responsibility for one's own learning; self-discipline; a high degree of curiosity; a strong ability to learn independently; enjoyment of learning; a tendency to be goal oriented; and a tendency to view problems as challenges rather than obstacles. These qualities undergird her Self-Directed Learning Readiness Scale (SDLRS), of which there are two versions, one of them a self-scoring version (the Learning Preference Assessment).

The SDLRS is the most frequently used quantitative measure in studies of self-directed learning. Examined in studies using the SDLRS are a wide range of issues from relating readiness for self-directed learning with job satisfaction, course grades, occupation, self-concept, life satisfaction, job performance, and so on (Owen, 2002). Many of these studies are correlational, examining the relationship of SDLRS scores with scores on other instruments. For example, in a report of three dissertations using the SDLRS, one correlated the SDLRS with a scale measuring cross-cultural adaptability, another correlated the SDLRS with a learning style instrument, and the third used a scale measuring creativity (Beswick, Chuprina, Canipe, & Cox, 2002). All three studies found positive relationships between self-directed learning readiness scores and scores on the instruments measuring cross-cultural adaptability, learning styles, and creativity.

Examples of the most far-reaching implications, based on studies using readiness as a major variable, are that "individual readiness for self-directed learning could be an important factor in matching certain types of jobs with applicants seeking those jobs" (Guglielmino & Roberts, 1992, p. 271) and that "employees who score lower in readiness for self-directed learning should be given opportunities to become effective self-directed learners" (Durr, Guglielmino, & Guglielmino, 1996, p. 355).

Over the years claims and counterclaims have been made about the basic reliability and validity of the SDLRS. Without getting into the intricacies of these claims, we concur with Brockett and Hiemstra's (1991, pp. 74–75) assessment:

> We believe that despite several apparent substantive and methodological concerns, the SDLRS has made a most important contribution to the present understanding of the self-directed learning phenomenon by generating considerable research, controversy and dialogue. We think that this contribution ultimately outweighs the limitations that seem to be inherent within the instrument. At the same time, we believe that the criticisms raised cannot be overlooked. There remains too many questions, particularly relative to the validity of the scale. We are unwilling to dismiss the scale [like Field and Straka]. However, we do recommend that the SDLRS be used with the same discretion as any other standardized instrument.

AUTONOMY AND SELF-DIRECTEDNESS: INNATE OR SITUATIONAL?

The relationship of autonomy and self-directedness in learning has been discussed primarily at the conceptual level. Chene (1983), for example, defines three elements that describe an autonomous learner: independence, the ability to make choices and critical judgments, and the capacity to articulate the norms and limits of a learning society. Candy (1991) adds to Chene's notion of the autonomous learner by characterizing autonomous people as those with a strong sense of personal values and beliefs. These values and beliefs give them a solid foundation for conceiving goals and plans, exercising free choice, using rational reflection, having the willpower to follow through, and exercising self-restraint and self-discipline. The same overarching concepts of independent thinking, self-responsibility, and control over actions of learning are also highlighted by Brockett and Hiemstra (1991), Garrison (1992), and Tennant and Pogson (1995).

Autonomy, however, is not necessarily context-free; there is a relationship between the personal and situational variables that must come into play for a person to be autonomous in certain learning situations. Knowles (1975, 1980) was the first to express the importance of context in his descriptions of andragogy. He qualified his assertion that adults are naturally self-directing when he observed that people move toward self-directedness at differing rates and not necessarily in all dimensions of life, and that in some situations adults may need to be at least "temporarily dependent" in learning situations. For example, when coping with a crisis, such as a flood or an earthquake, people may need or want to rely on the information and direction of others, both during the event itself and at least for a time in the aftermath of the event. This same sentiment, that even those adults who can and want to be self-directed in their learning may choose not to exhibit or pursue this characteristic at certain times, has been expressed by a number of authors (Brockett & Hiemstra, 1991; Candy, 1987, 1991; Pratt, 1988; Tenant & Pogson, 1995).

A recent study has confirmed the situational characteristic of autonomy in SDL (Poulton, Derrick, & Carr, 2005). Using a path-analytic model relating resourcefulness and persistence in SDL of 492 adults, the authors found that although adults might intend to persist in valued learning activities, they often do not choose to engage in such activities. They attribute this to the nature of adulthood: "Although an adult may anticipate the future rewards of present learning and even prioritize such learning over nonlearning activities in terms of value attribution, the lawn may need mowing, the kids may need to be taken to soccer practice, or perhaps a friend may need consoling now. . . . The exhibition of autonomy is presently argued as domain specific. That is, one can be an autonomous lawn mower or an autonomous learner" (p. 124).

Four major variables appear to have the most influence on whether individual adult learners exhibit autonomous behavior in learning situations: their technical skills related to the learning process, their familiarity with the subject matter, their sense of personal competence as learners, and their commitment to learning at this point in time. "Since this combination will vary from situation to situation, a learner's autonomy is also likely to vary from one context to another, and educators must avoid the automatic assumption that simply because a person has successfully learned something in the past either in an instructional setting or outside it, he or she will be able to succeed in a new area: Orientation, support and guidance may all be required in the first stages of a learning project" (Candy, 1991, p. 309). In addition, moving from an individual to more of a collective context, Candy (1991) and Tennant and Pogson (1995) posit that the socially constructed nature of the self and knowledge may also limit adults' capacity for autonomy or self-directedness in learning. Adults, in part, are their historical and cultural selves and often find themselves in learning situations where others around them determine what is worth knowing and how that knowledge should be used.

In a similar vein, Boucouvalas (1988) has challenged the exclusive emphasis on the autonomous self as only a partial explanation of what selfhood is all about. Although autonomy reflects independence and uniqueness, homonomy is "the experience of being part of meaningful wholes and in harmony with superindividual units such as family, social group, culture, and cosmic order" (p. 58). The prime motivations for the autonomous self are achievement and conquest, whereas participation in something beyond the individual self is the motivation for the homonomous (connected) self. Other writers in self-directed learning agree with Boucouvalas's observation and call for further exploration of the social and cultural aspects of self-directedness and the concept of interdependence in the learning process (Ahteenmaki-Pelkonen, 1994; Brown, 2000; Nah, 2000; Rowland & Volet, 1996). Nah (2000), for example, points out that for Koreans to cultivate self-directedness and independence "without being interdependent passes for immaturity or self-centeredness" (p. 18). Giving wider recognition to this connected or interdependent part of the self may allow for a fuller explanation of the collaborative aspects of self-directed learning referred to by Tough (1978, 1979), Knowles (1975), and Caffarella (1993) in activities such as teamwork, shared resources, and peer networks.

RECENT APPLICATIONS OF SDL AND BUILDING RESEARCH AND THEORY

Recent research and writing in SDL demonstrates an interest in the concept's applicability to lifelong learning, human resource development, and online learning. Schrader-Naef (2000) makes the case that to implement lifelong learning in society, "schools of all levels have to set the foundations for self-directed lifelong learning and adult education has to build on those foundations" (p. 143). No longer can educational systems "hand on knowledge to the next generations"; rather, schools from primary through university must "develop the conditions, foundations and motivation" for people to see learning as "their own responsibility and motivation" (p. 144).

The professions in particular are recognizing the importance of developing practitioners to be lifelong learners. Nowadays, formal training is only a beginning; knowledge is accumulating at such a fast rate that one must continue to learn to be effective (Williams, 2001). Indeed, most professions mandate that their members continue learning in order to maintain their license to practice. Self-directed learning activities, such as journal reading, are growing in acceptance as one form of CPE (Cole & Glass, 2004). Research to better understand the nature of SDL in professional lives is another form. Sipe (1995) studied experimentally "open" teachers and found that they valued SDL, collaboration, reflection, and challenge; risk taking in their learning was seen as an opportunity, not a threat. Dunlap and Grabinger (2003) make the case that in order to prepare students in higher education to be lifelong learners, we must develop their capacity for self-direction, metacognitive awareness, and a disposition toward learning. They propose three teaching strategies to facilitate these ends: problem-based learning (PBL), intentional learning environments, and cognitive apprenticeships. Similar to Dunlap and Grabinger's work is Bolhuis's (2003) process-oriented teaching for self-directed lifelong learning. He argues that since learning is a social phenomenon, even in SDL we need to consider how the social context, prior knowledge, and emotional aspects of learning foster self-directed lifelong learning.

The role of SDL in human resource development (HRD) practice is also drawing attention. Some propose how SDL can be harnessed to address the needs of the organization. For example, Piskurich (1993, p. 330) defined SDL as "a training design in which trainees master packages of predetermined material, at their own pace, without the aid of an instructor," noting that there is little choice in learning objectives on the trainees' part, particularly in technical and skills training. Smith (2002) also advances this utilitarian notion of SDL by pointing out that "there is considerable commercial value in encouraging employees" to be self-directed learners because they can then "contribute to competitiveness without the need for all learning to occur when there is direct training by an instructor" (p. 111). Guglielmino and Guglielmino (2005) have in fact explored the relationship between self-directed learning readiness, dimensions of culture, and economic indicators for seven countries. They found strong positive relationships between self-directed learning readiness and gross domestic product per capita and per-capita income.

Other writers consider how the self-directed part of SDL can enhance the workplace. Brown (2000) examined the interaction between social influences at work and the individual's commitment to being self-directed. Clardy's (2000) study of job-related self-directed learning projects of fifty-six employees from five organizations found three types of projects—induced, voluntary, and synergistic. Induced SDL projects are undertaken by an employee because of some perceived imbalance between current and needed skills, voluntary projects are those an employee undertakes because of a personal desire to learn, and synergistic projects "arise in situations where there are new enabling organizational conditions that ignite a latent employee readiness to act and learn" (p. 121). Interestingly, among the five organizations studied, the one where the most synergistic and voluntary projects were found was an organization that "used a system of organizational practices that formed a culture of learning" (p. 118).

That SDL and the learning organization are interrelated is explored by Cho (2002). Cho points out that although "the primary purpose of SDL has been recognized as personal growth, interaction and collaboration with others can play very important roles in the process. . . . Such interdependent and collective aspects of SDL appear to be fully consistent with some essential characteristics of the learning organization" (2002, pp. 468–469).

One of the most thoughtful examinations of the linkages between SDL and HRD is by Ellinger (2004). She reviews the literature on SDL with special attention to how instructional models, organizational characteristics, and assessment tools can all be incorporated into promoting SDL in an HRD context. The article concludes with a number of suggestions for research and theory building in this area, such as assessing the prevalence of SDL in the workplace, how it is linked with organizational learning, the cultural and ethical issues involved, and so on.

One of Ellinger's suggestions for research is to examine the impact of technology on SDL. This is definitely an area of growing interest with the prevalence of the Internet and Web-based instructional strategies. Recent studies of SDL have uncovered the fact that the Internet is an important learning resource (Roberson, 2003; Valente, 2005). But the Internet is not only a resource in SDL; many studies of online learning at least acknowledge if not foster the need for self-direction on the part of learners in this environment. Freed (2003), for example, examined how graduate students in an online discussion used reflection, dialogue, and self-direction to construct knowledge. Another study attempted to correlate self-directed learning readiness with student success as measured by grades in Web-based courses (Pachnowski & Jurczyk, 2000). Self-directedness turned out not to be a good indicator of success, but this may have been due to the very low participation rate and the difficulties of collecting data from distance education students. Finally, it is an interesting speculation that younger generations of students and workers "for whom the Web is becoming a natural habitat," may already be "adapting to change by developing a self-directed learning orientation" (Kerka, 1999, p. 2).

Research on self-directed learning continues to engage both academics and practitioners, as noted earlier in this chapter. There is also an active research group at the University of Tennessee exploring the literature on SDL. This group has reviewed dissertations produced between 1980 and 2002 (Canipe & Fogerson, 2004) and analyzed ERIC documents that appeared between 1993 and 2003 (Canipe, Fogerson, & Duffley-Renow, 2005). Analyses of both databases suggest a steady interest in and research on SDL.

There is a sense, however, that research and theory building in self-directed learning is in need of fresh questions. Brockett (2000) attributes the decline in the number of *published* articles (in contrast to the dissertations and ERIC documents already mentioned) on SDL since the mid-1980s with the shift away from "the individual adult learner toward looking at the sociopolitical context of adult education" (p. 543). This sociopolitical context is, of course, one of the very questions that could be explored with regard to SDL. Brockett (2000) also suggests that the field consider developing "new ways to measure self-directedness" and "raise questions about the limits of self-direction, and how self-direction interfaces with issues of power and conflict in various practice settings" (pp. 543–544). From Brockett's (2000), Ellinger's (2004), and our own thinking, we suggest the following areas for investigation, all of which could expand our understanding of adult learning through SDL:

- How do issues of power and control interact with the use of SDL in formal settings?
- Does being self-directed as a learner have an impact on one's own instructional and planning activities?
- Are there public policy issues at the national, state, or local level related to SDL? If so, what roles could adult educators play in advocating and developing such policies?
- Should policy and procedures be formulated related to SDL in formal settings, such as the workplace, so that SDL is recognized as an integral part of education and training programs?
- What constitutes the critical practice of self-directed learning? How can critical SDL practice be incorporated in our work as educators?
- To what extent is SDL situational or cultural?
- How do cultural and contextual factors shape SDL?
- How is technology relating to and affecting SDL?

Summary

Self-directed learning is one of the most researched topics in adult learning. Although learning on one's own has been the principal model of learning throughout the ages, serious studies of this subject did not become prevalent until the 1970s and 1980s. In reviewing this research, what became clear is that self-directed learning is a multifaceted concept. Therefore, we grouped the work that we reviewed into three broad categories: the goals of self-directed learning, processes and applications of self-directed learning, and self-direction as a personal attribute of learners.

In discussing the goals of self-directed learning, three major ones were identified. The first goal, that of enhancing the ability of adults to be self-directed in their learning, has generated the most research in self-directed learning. The fostering of transformational learning as central to self-directed learning, the second goal, is foundational to the third goal, that of promoting emancipatory learning and social action. Our assumption is that each of these goals is of equal importance in capturing the essence of self-directed learning.

Within the broad category of self-directed learning as a process, three types of models have been extensively discussed in the literature: linear, interactive, and instructional. The linear models often reflect more traditional ways of thinking about teaching, although they could be applied to learners' informal learning as well as to formal and nonformal settings. The interactive models more closely resemble how learners go about learning primarily on their own, and the instructional models are specifically designed to be used as ways to organize instruction in formal and nonformal settings. Although a rich array of models is now available, little data-based research has been conducted using these models as frameworks, except for studies using Tough's (1979) work.

Assessing self-directedness and the concept of autonomy have received the greatest attention from scholars who are studying self-direction as a personal attribute of learners. Two popular scales, the OCLI and the SDLRS, were reviewed. Readiness, which implies an internal state of psychological readiness to undertake self-directed learning, has generated the majority of the data-based studies. The relationship of autonomy and self-directedness in learning has been discussed primarily at the conceptual level. An important question regarding autonomy and self-directedness is the extent to which the context of the learning situation affects learner autonomy.

The chapter concluded with a review of recent applications of SDL to lifelong learning, human resource development, and online settings. Finally, suggestions for building future research agendas in self-directed learning were discussed.

CHAPTER SIX

TRANSFORMATIONAL LEARNING

Geri, a mother of two, was a successful lawyer and master gardener. She expected to be named a partner at the law firm within the next year. At age thirty-seven, she was diagnosed with bone cancer. She researched treatment options and joined a support group. Before the diagnosis, Geri's priorities included buying a larger house in an upscale neighborhood, purchasing her "dream car," and spending time with her family on a vacation in Europe. After her diagnosis, Geri reflected on her priorities and she recognized that her relationships with family and friends were more important than material possessions.

Geri's story exemplifies transformative learning. *Transformative* or *transformational* (terms used interchangeably in the literature) learning is about change—dramatic, fundamental change in the way we see ourselves and the world in which we live. Unlike informational learning, which refers to "extend[ing] already established cognitive capacities into new terrain" (Kegan, 2000, p. 48), transformational learning refers to "chang[ing] . . . *what* we know" (p. 49; italics in original). The mental construction of experience, inner meaning, and reflection are common components of this approach.

This chapter examines transformational learning theory through seven lenses (Taylor, 2005a); we review three individualistic conceptualizations and four sociocultural perspectives on transformative learning. Next, three important concepts in transformational learning are discussed: experience, critical reflection, and development. Last, we highlight several unresolved issues in transformational learning theory in addition to discussing recent trends in the transformative learning literature.

THE LENSES OF TRANSFORMATIONAL LEARNING

Lenses simultaneously allow us to see things and limit our view. It is the same with the lenses through which we see transformative learning. While not exhaustive, these lenses provide a reasonably holistic view of transformative learning. Taylor (2005a) provides seven lenses through which to view transformative learning. He divides them into two groups based on their "locus of learning" (Taylor, 2005a, p. 459). The first group comprises those perspectives whose locus of learning concerns the *individual*—namely, the psychocritical, psychodevelopmental, and psychoanalytic perspectives. The second group is composed of approaches where the focus of learning is *sociocultural*, including the social-emancipatory, cultural-spiritual, race-centric, and planetary approaches.

The lenses that focus on the individual are represented by the works of Jack Mezirow, Laurent Daloz, and Robert Boyd. Mezirow's psychocritical perspective is a fully developed theory of adult learning that has generated a plethora of articles, books, and dissertations. Less well known are Daloz's psychodevelopmental approach and Boyd's psychoanalytic perspective. Daloz focuses on the intuitive nature of transformative learning, which champions the importance of stories in the process. Boyd's psychoanalytic approach explains the importance of symbols and the unconscious in the transformative learning process.

The best-known sociocultural approach is Freire's social-emancipatory view of transformative learning. Freire's orientation emerges from a context of poverty and oppression and focuses on radical social change. The three other sociocultural perspectives represent relatively recent developments in the transformative learning literature. Tisdell delineates the cultural-spiritual view of transformative learning. This approach emphasizes the connection between individuals' various socially constructed positionalities (race, class, gender) and their knowledge construction through storytelling. This perspective emphasizes fostering cultural and spiritual awareness (Taylor, 2005a). The race-centric view concentrates on the experiences of individuals of African descent within the "socio-cultural, political, and historical context" in which they find themselves (Sheared, 1994, p. 36). Transformative learning is seen as a daily, conscious strategy in this view (Johnson-Bailey & Alfred, 2006). Last, the planetary view, detailed by O'Sullivan, examines the "interconnectedness between the universe, planet, natural environment, human community, and the personal world" (Taylor, 2005a, p. 462).

MEZIROW'S PSYCHOCRITICAL APPROACH

Based on interviews with women who returned to college after an extended hiatus, Mezirow's theory, introduced in 1978, has invited philosophical critique and a burgeoning of empirical research since the 1990s. The first national conference on transformative learning was held at Teachers College, Columbia University, in April 1998 (Wiessner & Mezirow, 2000). It continues to be a biannual, much anticipated event where transformative learning in general and Mezirow's theory in particular are discussed. In 2005, approximately eighty-five papers were presented at the conference.

Mezirow's theory concerns how adults make sense of their life experience. Mezirow defines learning as "the process of using a prior interpretation to construe a new or a revised interpretation of the meaning of one's experience in order to guide future action" (2000, p. 5). He differentiates between *types* of meaning structures, including frame of reference, habits of mind, and points of view. Mezirow indicates that a "*frame of reference* is a 'meaning perspective,' the structure of assumptions and expectations through which we filter sense impressions. It involves cognitive, affective, and conative dimensions. . . . It provides the context for making meaning within which we choose what and how a sensory experience is to be constructed and/or appropriated" (p. 16; italics in original).

There are two dimensions to our frame of reference: a habit of mind, and a point of view (Mezirow, 2000). A habit of mind is "a set of assumptions—broad, generalized, orienting predispositions that act as a filter for interpreting the meaning of experience" (p. 17). There are several varieties of habit of mind, including moral/ethical, philosophical, psychological, and aesthetic generalized predispositions. For example, a habit of mind may be ethnocentrism—the belief that one's group is superior to others (Mezirow, 1997a).

A point of view is made up of *meaning schemes,* which are "sets of immediate, specific beliefs, feelings, attitudes, and value judgments" (Mezirow, 2000, p. 18). A resulting point of view of ethnocentrism may be the specific beliefs one has regarding particular groups of people outside one's own group (Mezirow, 1997a). Points of view change more easily than habits of mind because we receive feedback on points of view and are more aware of them than we are of habits of mind (Mezirow, 1997a).

Transformative learning occurs when there is a transformation in one of our beliefs or attitudes (a meaning scheme), or a transformation of our entire perspective (habit of mind) (Mezirow, 2000). Transformative learning, says Mezirow, is "the process by which we transform our taken-for-granted frames of reference (meaning schemes, habits of mind, mindsets) to make them more inclusive, discriminating, open, emotionally capable of change, and reflective so that they may generate beliefs and opinions that will prove more true or justified to guide action" (2000, p. 8). Through transformative learning we are freed from uncritical acceptance of others' purposes, values, and beliefs. Transformations in our habits of mind may be sudden and dramatic (epochal) or they may be slower, incremental changes in our points of view (meaning schemes), which eventually lead to a change in our habits of mind (meaning perspective) (Mezirow, 2000). For example, two of Andy's friends have revealed that they are gay over the past several years. As a result, Andy begins to question his homophobic reaction to gays and lesbians. Over time, Andy changes his point of view (meaning scheme) about gays and lesbians and is no longer homophobic (change in meaning perspective).

Mezirow recognizes that not all learning is transformative. He states, "We can learn simply by adding knowledge to our meaning schemes or learning new meaning schemes . . . and it can be a crucially important experience for the learner" (1991, p. 223). For example, in a study that examined the stability of the perspective transformation in HIV-positive adults over time, the authors noted that the perspective transformation (new worldview) had not only held over time but people continued to make new meaning schemes, such as the "adoption of a future-oriented perspective" (Courtenay, Merriam, Reeves, & Baumgartner, 2000, p. 110). A subsequent study with the same participants almost two years later noted additional changes in meaning schemes, including a more tolerant, forgiving attitude toward others (Baumgartner, 2002).

Mezirow's transformative learning theory is made up of ten steps or phases. However, there are four main components of the transformative learning process: experience, critical reflection, reflective discourse, and action. (A more in-depth discussion of experience and critical reflection appears later in the chapter.) The process begins with the learners' experiences. However, just *having* the experience is not enough. The learner must critically self-examine the assumptions and beliefs that have structured how the experience has been interpreted. This sets in motion a revision of "specific assumptions about oneself and others until the very structure of assumptions becomes transformed" (Mezirow, 1981, p. 8).

The new meaning created by a perspective transformation is highly subjective and changeable. To test whether our new meanings are true or authentic (Mezirow, 1995), and to arrive at the best possible judgment, we seek out a variety of opinions, including ones that challenge the status quo, and we engage in the Habermasian concept of "discourse" (Mezirow, 2000, p. 10). Discourse is "dialogue devoted to searching for a common understanding and assessment of the justification of an interpretation or belief" (Mezirow, 2000, pp. 10–11). People weigh evidence for and against the argument and critically assess assumptions. Clearer understanding is achieved through talking with others.

Drawing from Habermas, there are "ideal" conditions for discourse: having complete information, being free from self-deception, being able to evaluate arguments objectively, having empathy, having an "equal opportunity to participate in the various roles of discourse," and so on (Mezirow, 2000, p. 13). Mezirow is aware that these are *ideal* conditions; nevertheless, fostering this discourse is "a long established priority of adult educators" (p. 14).

Mezirow clearly states: "Discourse is not a war or a debate; it is a conscientious effort to find agreement, to build a new understanding" (1996, p. 170). Adult educators must be aware that helping adults learn how to move from an argumentative mindset to an empathic understanding of others' views is a priority (Mezirow, 2000).

Discourse can occur in one-to-one relationships, in groups, and in formal educational settings. Several publications have focused on applications, experiences, and suggestions for educators interested in facilitating this type of learning in educational settings

reframe of arguing -

(Cranton, 1996, 2002; Lee & Greene, 2003; Sawyer, 2004; Yorks & Sharoff, 2001).

Action is the final component of the transformative learning process. The person may take "immediate action, delayed action or reasoned reaffirmation of an existing pattern of action" (Mezirow, 2000, p. 24). Action can range from making a decision about something to engaging in radical political protest. For critics, who see the goal of adult education as social action, Mezirow's theory, with its emphasis on individual transformation, is too egocentric (Taylor, 1997a). However, Mezirow speaks to social action in certain circumstances: "When the disorienting dilemma is the result of oppressive action, the person needs to take individual or collective action against the oppressor" (Mezirow, 1997b, p. 60). Mezirow continues, "Personal transformation leads to alliances with others of like mind to work toward effecting necessary changes in relationships, organizations, and systems, each of which requires a different mode of praxis" (1992, p. 252). A three-step process for social action begins with becoming aware of a need to change (Mezirow, 1993). This need arises through critically reflecting on assumptions and biases. Next, "a feeling of solidarity with others committed to change" (p. 189) needs to be established. And finally, one has to learn what actions are appropriate in particular situations to implement change.

To illustrate this three-step process, let us take the case of Karen, who returns to college as an adult. She has always had trouble in math courses and had assumed she was not academically inclined. Nevertheless, she decides to try again to get her college degree. Once again, she encounters problems and she considers withdrawing. However, she has done exceptionally well in other courses, and one of her instructors suggests she be tested for a learning disability. This suggestion causes her to question assumptions about her academic ability, and when a learning disability is confirmed, Karen seeks accommodations that allow her to stay in school. In the process, her image of herself changes. She locates others with learning disabilities, and they form a support and advocacy group. The group works toward raising awareness and changing attitudes on campus regarding learning disabilities.

According to Mezirow, the process is most often set in motion by a disorienting dilemma, that is, a particular life event or life experience such as the death of a loved one or an illness that a person experiences as a crisis. This crisis cannot be resolved through the application of previous problem-solving strategies. In the preceding example, Karen's diagnosis of a learning disability may be her "disorienting dilemma." The disorienting dilemma is the first step in the ten-phase or ten-step process. (See Mezirow, 1991, for a delineation of all ten steps.) Next, the learner engages in self-examination, which is often accompanied by "feelings of fear, anger, guilt or shame" (Mezirow, 2000, p. 22). Initially, Karen may feel shame or anger at being learning-disabled. Self-examination is included in the third step of a critical assessment of assumptions. After the initial shock of the diagnosis, Karen starts to recognize that the diagnosis of a learning disability means she can begin to think more positively about her academic abilities. After all, she is not "dumb" or "incompetent"; she just has a weakness in one area. This assessment leads to the fourth phase of recognizing that others have gone through a similar process. When Karen seeks accommodations for her disability and joins a support group, she recognizes that she is not alone. Step 5 consists of exploring options for forming new roles, relationships, or actions, which leads to formulating a plan of action. This plan has four steps: acquiring knowledge and skills, trying out new roles, renegotiating relationships, and building competence and self-confidence in the new roles and relationships. In our example, Karen may try being an advocate for people with disabilities. She gains skills and builds confidence as a spokesperson for people with disabilities in her effort to raise awareness and change people's attitudes toward people with disabilities. The final step or phase of the process is a reintegration back into one's life based on the new, transformed perspective (Mezirow, 2000). Mezirow (1995, p. 50) comments that although "a perspective transformation appears to follow" the process of creating meaning, it is not necessarily "in this exact sequence."

Empirical studies of transformative learning reviewed by Taylor, although generally supportive of this process, have added depth to the recursive and evolving nature of the transformative learning process (for example, Taylor, 1994; Saavedra, 1995, as cited in Taylor, 2000a). Several studies also revealed a number of other factors inherent in the transformative learning process. For example, Erickson (2002) reasoned that individuals' *level* of meaning-making may influence how they experience the transformative learning process. Erickson used Lahey, Souvaine, Kegan, Goodman, and Felix's (1988) subject-object interview to determine participants' current level or order of meaning-making (as cited in Erickson, 2002). Next, Erickson analyzed the interview for Mezirow's ten-phase process of perspective transformation. Participants' meaning-making capacity influenced their experience of the perspective transformation. For example, those at more advanced orders of meaning-making "seemed more purposeful and less accidental" in their exploration of new roles, relationships, and actions (Mezirow's Phase 5) than participants at a lower order (Erickson, 2002, p. 105). Likewise, Merriam (2004) argued that "mature cognitive development is foundational to engaging in critical reflection and rational discourse necessary for transformational learning" (p. 65). Yet, she noted that two studies confirmed that people "had transformed their perspective without being aware of the change process" (p. 66). Merriam concluded that Mezirow should "expand the theory of transformational learning to include more . . . affective and intuitive dimensions on an equal footing with cognitive and rational components" (pp. 66–67).

In sum, Mezirow's psychocritical approach to transformative learning has produced a plethora of scholarship and research. His recursive ten-step, or ten-phase, model contains four main components: experience, critical reflection, reflective discourse, and action. In short, the learner must critically reflect on his or her experience, talk with others about his or her new worldview in order to gain the best judgment, and *act* on the new perspective. Recent research adds depth to a theory long criticized for its overreliance on rationality. Studies indicate that one's cognitive development may influence his or her ability to experience a perspective transformation (Merriam, 2004) or experience of the perspective transformation process (Erickson, 2002).

DALOZ'S PSYCHODEVELOPMENTAL PERSPECTIVE AND BOYD'S PSYCHOANALYTIC APPROACH

Perhaps less well known, but equally important, Daloz's psycho-developmental perspective and Boyd's psychoanalytic approach to transformative learning augment Mezirow's ideas. While Mezirow sees transformation as a more rational endeavor and emphasizes critical reflection, Daloz and Boyd view transformative learning as more holistic and intuitive (Dirkx, 1998).

A teacher and administrator, Daloz focuses on adults who are returning to higher education. In his view, the goal of transformative learning is lifelong personal development, with the teacher serving as a mentor in the transformative learning process (Taylor, 2005a). Like Mezirow, Daloz recognizes that people need to make meaning of their experiences and that individuals are often in a developmental transition when they seek higher education to "help them make sense of lives whose fabric of meaning has gone frayed" (Daloz, 1999, p. 4). Education is a "transformational journey" (Daloz, 1986, p. 16) that should "promote development." (Further discussion of adult development as it relates to transformative learning appears later in the chapter.)

The mentor serves as guide, cheerleader, challenger, and supporter during the learning process. The teacher/mentor challenges students to examine their conceptions of self and the world and to formulate new, more developed perspectives. Like Mezirow, for Daloz dialogue/discourse is integral to the process of transformation. However, unlike Mezirow, Daloz concentrates on the importance of stories on the journey toward an expanded worldview. He notes, "The first business of a guide is to listen to the dreams of the pilgrim. How are our students moving? What do they want for themselves? How do they tell their own stories?" (Daloz, 1986, p. 21). Next, the mentor can *tell* the student stories in an effort to promote development. It is through this mutual storying of lives that development can occur. Stories also assist mentors in doing three things for students: providing support, challenging students, and providing a vision (Daloz, 1999).

Daloz (1999, p. 43) offers three "maps" of adult development but he does not prescribe an end point to this transformational journey. The first map consists of phase theories of adult development such as presented by Daniel Levinson in *Seasons of a Man's Life* (Levinson, Darrow, Klein, Levinson, & McKee, 1978) and *Seasons of a Woman's Life* (Levinson & Levinson, 1996). This family of theories examines "common tasks that people confront as they face the problems associated with aging" (Daloz, 1986, p. 47). These tasks can be culturally determined and may vary depending on a variety of sociocultural factors including gender, class, and ethnicity. Stage theories, the second map, such as Kegan's *The Evolving Self* (1982), examines cognitive growth and the ability to think outside of one's cultural reference. The third map, Perry's model of intellectual and ethical development (1970, 1999) helps us look at how we and our students make "the journey from naïve and simplistic thinking to complex and relativistic reasoning" over time (Daloz, 1986, p. 48).

To summarize, Daloz takes a storied approach to development and transformative learning. Through storytelling, Daloz and his students journey toward a more holistic and transformed worldview. Like Mezirow and Freire, Daloz recognizes the importance of cognitive growth. He acknowledges the importance of the whole person in that growth.

Boyd's psychoanalytic approach to transformative learning (Boyd, 1989, 1991; Boyd & Myers, 1988) predates the recent flurry of attention given to spirituality in adult education (Fenwick & English, 2004; Kovan & Dirkx, 2003; Tisdell, 2003). His work, grounded in depth psychology, sees transformation as an inner journey of individuation from parts of the psyche such as the ego and the collective unconscious (Boyd, 1991). He defines transformation as "a fundamental change in one's personality involving conjointly the resolution of a personal dilemma and the expansion of consciousness resulting in greater personality integration" (1991, p. 459). By coming to terms with one's inner psychic conflicts, one can achieve self-actualization. To integrate the emotional and spiritual parts of learning into ourselves, we must make sense of the symbols and images in our psyche. Only then can we understand how the unconscious influences our daily lives (Dirkx, 1998).

Like Mezirow and Daloz, Boyd indicates that dialogue is important to the transformative learning process. Dirkx states (1998), "The goal of transformative learning is to identify these images . . . and to establish an intrapersonal dialogue with them" (p. 7). The dialogue occurs between the ego and other "unconscious structures that populate the psyche, such as the Shadow, Anima, and Animus" (p. 7). Through dialogue we can individuate and become less subject to "compulsions, obsessions, and complexes," which may be the more unconscious manifestation of the individuation process (p. 7).

Freire's Social-Emancipatory Philosophy

Brazilian educator Paulo Freire's philosophy of transformative learning is the best-known sociocultural approach to transformative learning. His perspective emerged from his literacy work with rural Brazilian farmers in the mid-twentieth century (McLaren, 2000). Unlike Mezirow's theory, which is based on the experiences of White, middle-class women and concentrates primarily on personal transformation, Freire's theory emerges from the context of poverty, illiteracy, and oppression and is set in a larger framework of radical social change. In Freire's approach, personal empowerment and social transformation are inseparable processes. His conceptions of conscientization and empowerment have contributed significantly to the underlying theoretical framework of transformational learning.

Freire differentiates between two kinds of education: banking and problem posing. *Banking education* is teacher-centered as the "all-knowing" teacher deposits knowledge into the passive students who serve as receptacles for this knowledge (Freire, 2000). The teacher decides the content of the course and is the authority in the classroom. Banking education resists dialogue. Students are oppressed and live in a "culture of silence" because their respective worlds are defined by the teacher (oppressor) (Freire, 1985, p. 72). Banking education serves the oppressors because it domesticates the oppressed. In contrast, the purpose of *problem-posing education* is liberation. Central to the learning is a changed relationship between teacher and student. They are coinvestigators into their common reality, the sociocultural situation in which they live (Freire, 2000). Further, dialogue is considered "indispensable to the act of cognition which unveils reality" (p. 64).

The process of conscientization, which is an ongoing process where the learner becomes increasingly aware of the various oppressive forces in his or her life and eventually becomes part of the process of social change (Heany, 2005), begins with dialogue. Through dialogue, generative themes or concerns are posed by the learners themselves and become the content of a learning situation. For example, in asking learners for some words that capture their everyday experience, the word for "slum" or "land" or "taxes" or "illness" or "government" might come up. These words are then broken down into syllables and used in various contexts in learning how to read. At the same time, participants engage in discussions about these concepts. These discussions raise their awareness about their life situations (Freire, 2000).

Conscientization occurs at several levels. At the least-aware levels is a magical, fatalistic consciousness in which nothing about one's world is questioned; external forces are in charge, and there is nothing that can be done to change things as they are. Midway between being totally unaware and critical consciousness, people begin to sense that they may have some control over their lives and turn to questioning things as they are. The most sophisticated stage of consciousness is critical consciousness. Here one achieves an in-depth understanding of the forces that shape one's life space, and becomes an active agent in constructing a different, more just reality.

The ultimate goal of education is liberation, or praxis, "the action and reflection of men and women upon their world in order to transform it" (Freire, 2000, p. 60). Note that a key component of Freire's philosophy, like Mezirow's, is critical reflection. Critical reflection occurs through problem posing and dialogue with other learners.

Freire has operationalized his theory of education with techniques that have demonstrated success in combating illiteracy in numerous countries, including Chile, Switzerland, Tanzania, Australia, and Italy (McLaren, 2000). Its application in North America has been limited, owing perhaps to the necessary corollary of social change. Although conscientization is always a political act in Freire's theory, it can be seen as similar to perspective transformation in its characterization of adult learning as the process of becoming aware of one's assumptions, beliefs, and values and then transforming those assumptions into a new perspective or level of consciousness (Mezirow, 1995).

EMERGING SOCIOCULTURAL PERSPECTIVES: THE CULTURAL-SPIRITUAL, RACE-CENTRIC, AND PLANETARY APPROACHES

Tisdell (2003) discusses the main concepts of the cultural-spiritual approach. Tisdell posits that "spirituality . . . is fundamentally about how we make meaning in our lives" through conscious and unconscious processes such as dreams and symbols (p. 31). In this way, Tisdell's perspective seems similar to Boyd's (1989) conceptualization. However, Tisdell also includes the role of culture in the transformative learning experience. This approach examines how learners, in various cultural contexts and with different positionalities (for example, race, class, gender, sexual orientation), "construct knowledge as a part of the transformative learning experience" (Taylor, 2005a, p. 461). Whole-person learning, including personal, political, historical, and sacred learning, is emphasized. In this view, the teacher serves as a collaborator and helps the learners share and revise their narratives as new meaning is made.

Tisdell (2003) names several factors that foster spiritual-cultural transformative learning. First, cross-cultural relationships allow us to be exposed to different ways of thinking and being in the world. Second, educators need to be spiritually and culturally grounded in order to promote authenticity in students. When we are authentic and open to experiences, transformation can occur. Third, transformative learning may occur more easily in community-based, culturally relevant settings because community-based educators feel "freer to use different modalities to provide a different kind of experience for people or simply to go with how communities draw on the spirituality that is part of their lifeblood" (p. 195). Last, the environment needs to allow for explorations on the cognitive, affective, relational, and symbolic levels.

The race-centric approach to transformative learning is a "culturally bounded, oppositional, and non-individualistic conception of transformative learning" that puts people of African descent at the center (Taylor, 2005a, p. 461). It is culturally bounded in that it emerges from the experiences of people of African descent. Johnson-Bailey and Alfred (2006) explain that this perspective is "grounded in oppositional spirit" because Blacks (and other minority cultures) live in opposition to the cultural norm. The race-centric perspective focuses on the transformative learning of the group in an effort to raise race consciousness.

Central to this view is Sheared's (1994) conception of polyrhythmic realities or attention to African descendents' "lived experience within a sociocultural, political, and historical context" (p. 36). Johnson-Bailey (Johnson-Bailey & Alfred, 2006) recalls an experience where these polyrhythmic realities intersected. At age five, in the segregated southern United States of the 1950s, Johnson-Bailey was told she could no longer play with her best friend—a White girl named Dianne. Johnson-Bailey writes, "This lesson on race, on difference, on power, would become more sophisticated and theoretical over my life span. . . . [I]t was the first . . . that would transform my way of thinking . . . my way of existing" (p. 50). Johnson-Bailey notes that because of racism and sexism, Black women's conceptions of themselves and the world in which they live are transformed. She continues, "Most of my Black women colleagues see transformational learning as the only medium in which we exist, learn, and teach. Since it is the air we breathe, maybe [we] just take it for granted and don't attend to or claim it sufficiently" (p. 51).

In order to foster transformative learning, this perspective promotes inclusion of voices traditionally silenced and a sense of belonging as a member of the group (Johnson-Bailey & Alfred, 2006). The race-centric approach understands the importance of intra- and intercultural negotiation in the transformative learning process. Finally, similar to other transformative learning approaches, people deconstruct their assumptions through dialogue with others.

Last, the planetary view of transformative learning "recognizes the interconnectedness between the universe, planet, natural environment, human community and the personal world" (Taylor, 2005a, p. 462). The goal of this perspective is planetary consciousness. It emphasizes "quality of life issues, fostering a community's sense of place, diversity within and between communities, and an appreciation of spirituality" (p. 462). Its uniqueness amongst the perspectives is in its attention to how people relate to the physical world.

For O'Sullivan (2002), visionary transformative education includes several elements. First, people must move beyond the limited vision of a global market economy and locate their lives "in a larger cosmological context much more breathtaking than the market vision of our world" (p. 7). Second, we must adopt a definition of development that "links the creative evolutionary processes of the universe, the planet, the earth community, the human community, and the personal world" (p. 8). Third, we need to understand how our quality of life goes beyond our standard of living to include our need for community and the necessity of diversity within and between communities. Last, transformative education must address spirituality.

In sum, all perspectives possess commonalities. All theorists are constructivists. That is, they view knowledge as constructed by the learner rather than "out there" to be discovered (Dirkx, 1998). Second, dialogue is necessary for transformative learning to occur. Dialogue with others, or intrapsychically in Boyd's case, assists the learner in expanding her views. Third, critical reflection on the origin and nature of our submerged assumptions, biases, beliefs, and values, and in Boyd's case, symbols, is also necessary for change and growth to occur. Fourth, most theorists mention social change as a result of transformative learning (Daloz, 2000; Freire, 2000; Mezirow, 2000; O'Sullivan, 1999).

KEY CONCEPTS IN TRANSFORMATIONAL LEARNING

Three key concepts of transformative learning emerge: life experience, the nature of critical reflection, and the connection between transformative learning and development. We draw from several sources to discuss these three areas.

EXPERIENCE

Experience is integral to learning. One of the assumptions of andragogy is that adults bring with them a depth and breadth of experience that can be used as a resource for their and others' learning (Knowles, 1980). These experiences come in different *dimensions*. For example, a "direct embodied experience" is "an immediate encounter in the here-and-now, planned or unplanned, involving us physically, emotionally, sensually, mentally, and perhaps spiritually" (Fenwick, 2003, p. 13). Other dimensions of experience include vicarious experiences, simulated experiences, collaborative experiences, and introspective experiences such as meditation.

However experience is construed, the ways in which it can be used in learning differs according to one's theoretical orientation. Tennant (1991) delineates several uses: "First, . . . teachers can link their explanations and illustrations to the prior experiences of learners. . . . Second, teachers can attempt to link learning activities to learners' current experiences at work, home, or in the community" (pp. 196–197). Third, teachers can create activities such as simulations, games, and role-plays. These activities can lead to learners' critical reflection of assumptions.

Clearly, Tennant's third level is most congruent with the use of experience in transformative learning. Equally obvious is that not all experiences trigger learning—whether the learning is a simple addition to our prior knowledge or a fundamental change in our perspective. Further, the identical experience—a job change or a divorce, for example—can trigger learning for some people but not others. Adults may be unable to respond to a new experience. It is "at this point of disjuncture" that "individuals are forced to ask why this has occurred to them or what it means. These questions are located at the start and at the core of human learning" (Jarvis, 1992, p. 15).

CRITICAL REFLECTION

With an experience that one cannot accommodate into the prior life structure, the transformative learning process can begin. Necessary to the process is critical reflection, the second key concept. As Criticos (1993, p. 162) points out, "Effective learning does not follow from a positive experience but from effective reflection." Reflection is a cognitive process. We can think about our experience—muse, review, and so on—but to reflect critically, we must also examine the underlying beliefs and assumptions that affect how we make sense of the experience.

Mezirow (2000) differentiates among three types of reflection, only one of which can lead to transformative learning. *Content reflection,* the first type, is thinking about the actual experience itself. *Process reflection* is thinking about ways to deal with the experience—that is, problem-solving strategies. *Premise reflection* involves examining long-held, socially constructed assumptions, beliefs, and values about the experience or problem.

Much has been written about critical reflection, especially under the more common topic of critical thinking and reflective practice (see Chapter Seven). There are a number of adult educators in addition to Mezirow who have focused on critical thinking, especially as it relates to transformative learning. For example, Cranton's (2002)

scholarship concerns fostering transformative learning in the class-room. In order to engage learners in self-reflection, Cranton suggests using reflective journals in which students reflect on various incidents in their lives to foster the critical reflection that promotes transformative learning.

The most prominent adult educator writing about critical thinking is Brookfield (1987, 1994). He presents a rationale as to why critical thinking is important and how adults can become critical thinkers in their family, work, and personal lives and in relation to mass media. Especially relevant to the link between critical thinking or critical reflection and transformative learning is his model of critical thinking.

The model consists of five phases very similar to Mezirow's conceptualization. First is what he calls a trigger event, "some unexpected happening [that] prompts a sense of inner discomfort and perplexity" (Brookfield, 1987, p. 25). The next stage, appraisal, captures several of the steps in Mezirow's process, including a self-examination of the situation, "brooding" about our discomfort, and finding others who are experiencing a similar problem. In the third phase of exploration, we examine new and different ways of explaining or accommodating the experience that has led to our discomfort. The fourth phase is one of developing alternative perspectives. Basically, we try on a new role, a new way of behaving, a new way of thinking about the problem or experience, and simultaneously gain confidence in the new perspective. Finally, we are able to integrate these new ways of thinking or living "into the fabric of our lives" (p. 27).

In subsequent writing (1996, 2000, 2005a), Brookfield has clarified and expanded his notion of critical thinking. He now believes that critical thinking helps us scrutinize (2000, p. 136) "how we view power relationships in our lives" and helps us analyze "hegemonic assumptions" (Brookfield, 2000, p. 138). Hegemonic, or taken-for-granted assumptions about the world, serve the status quo and keep others disenfranchised. An example of a hegemonic assumption is the idea that "adult education is a vocation requiring self-abasement of practitioners on behalf of learners" (Brookfield, 2000, p. 138). If adult educators believe this assumption, administrators can "guilt" them into taking on more work and reducing costs. In this view, critical reflection is employed to examine social inequities. Brookfield acknowledges that his definition of critical reflection is a stricter and more radically political definition than Mezirow's because Mezirow "allows for the possibility of implicit critical reflection 'as when we mindlessly choose between good and evil because of our assimilated values'" (Mezirow, 1998, p. 186, as cited in Brookfield, 2000, p. 131).

DEVELOPMENT

In addition to the centrality of experience and critical reflection, there is in transformational learning theory the notion of individual development. Individual development is both inherent in and an outcome of the process. The ability to think critically, which is mandatory to effecting a transformation, is itself developmental; that is, we can become better, more critical thinkers. Elias (1997, pp. 3–4) explains how individual and cognitive development are intertwined:

> What are transformed through the processes of transformative learning are several capacities of mind or consciousness. First is the development of a "conscious I" capable of exercising critical reflection. Second is a transformed capacity for thinking, transformed to be more dialectical or systemic, thinking (for example) that perceives polarities as mutually creative resources rather than as exclusive and competitive options and that perceives archetypes as partners for inner dialogue. Third is the capacity to be a conscious creative force in the world, as expressed, for example, as the capacity to intervene in and transform the quality of discourse in a group or learning community.

Mezirow (1995) acknowledges that other scholars make important contributions to understanding adult critical reflection. King and Kitchener's (1994, 2002) model, which draws on the earlier work of Perry (1970), consists of seven stages, of which only the last two are characteristic of critical reflection (see Chapter Thirteen for a further explanation of this model).

Development is also the outcome of transformative learning. Mezirow (1991, p. 155) states clearly that the process of perspective transformation is "the central process of adult development."

And "meaning perspectives that permit us to deal with a broader range of experience, to be more discriminating, to be more open to other perspectives, and to better integrate our experiences are superior perspectives" (1990b, p. 14).

K. Taylor (2000) discusses changing *how* one knows in developmental terms. She explores movement along five dimensions. First, learners move "toward knowing as a dialogical process" (p. 160). They learn how they construct knowledge and they reconstruct knowledge in light of new experiences and reflections. Second, learners move "toward a dialogical relationship with oneself" by learning who they are and that they can choose to be another way (p. 163). Third, individuals move "toward being continuous learners" (p. 163). They become aware that learning is up to them. Next, they move "toward self-agency and authorship," where they "increasingly recognize their responsibility for their actions, choices, and values and for the decisions they may make based on those values" (p. 163). Finally, they move "toward connections with others," where they learn in community but retain their individuality (p. 163).

That the outcome of transformational learning is development is congruent with the growth orientation of much of adult learning literature generally. Underpinning this orientation is humanist psychology. Rogers (1961, p. 115) contended that "significant learning" results in a more mature self who is open to experience, to "new people, new situations, new problems." Knowles's (1980) model of andragogy is written quite explicitly from this humanistic perspective, defining adult learning as "a process that is used by adults for their self-development" (p. 25) and "to mature" (p. 28). Similarly, Kegan (1994, p. 287) wrote that higher and adult education's "mission" is to "assist adults in creating the order of consciousness the modern world demands."

This fact raises yet another dimension to the link between transformation and development. Tennant (2000) argues that what constitutes psychological development is itself a social construction; that is, in any society at any particular point in time, there are normative expectations about "what it means to be enlightened or developmentally more mature" (Tennant, 1993, p. 41). He warns that changes that are part of the expected life course (instances of normative development) should not be confused with actual changes in perspective.

Although there are certainly other factors important to transformational learning, we have discussed three that are central to the process. First, transformative learning posits experience as its starting point and as its content for reflection. Engaging the life experience in a critically reflective manner is a necessary condition for transformation. Finally, the entire process is about change—change that is growth-enhancing and developmental.

UNRESOLVED ISSUES IN TRANSFORMATIONAL LEARNING THEORY

The growing prominence of transformative learning theory has generated closer scrutiny of several aspects of the theory. Mezirow's psychocritical perspective has been critiqued for its inattention to context and its overreliance on rationality in the meaning-making process. In addition, scholars have examined the role of relationships in transformative learning, the place of social action, and the educator's role in fostering transformative learning.

CONTEXT

Clark and Wilson (1991) were the first to point out that Mezirow's theory appeared to be acontextual. Derived as it was from research on women returning to school, they note that the women's experiences "were studied as if they stood apart from their historical and sociocultural context, thereby limiting our understanding of the full meaning of those experiences" (p. 78). Further, they contended, Mezirow's own orientation toward autonomy uncritically reflects the values of the dominant culture in our society—masculine, White, and middle-class. In addition, Taylor's (2000a) review of the empirical research on Mezirow's theory revealed a number of studies that found that aspects of the individual's biographical history and sociocultural factors shaped the nature of the transformative learning. Taylor points out that more attention to such factors can help explain, for example, why a disorienting dilemma might lead to a perspective transformation for one person but not another. Indeed, studies accounting for individual biography and context are beginning to give a richer picture of transformative learning. Recent studies have explored transformative learning in the urban context (Kappel & Daley, 2004), in an experiential Hawaiian ecological course that emphasized indigenous knowledge (Feinstein, 2004), and in corporate America (Henderson, 2002). All have indicated that the context affects the transformative learning process.

Power, an interrelated aspect of context, has not been adequately addressed in Mezirow's theory. McDonald, Cervero, and Courtenay (1999) examined the role of power in ethical vegans' transformative learning process. The authors acknowledged that while vegans experienced a perspective transformation when they journeyed from being meat eaters to vegans, "the sustained power of the normative ideology . . . brought subtle changes in the vegans' praxis over time" (p. 19). They remained vegans but were worn down by "social-cultural and interpersonal challenges to veganism," and "their praxis became less outspoken" (p. 19). Likewise, in a longitudinal study of international service program participants in Nicaragua, participants indicated that upon returning to the United States, respondents had a "chameleon complex" where they held unpopular views on global issues but felt "compelled to conform and blend in with mainstream views on local and global issues even though they disagree[d]" (Kiely, 2003, p. 221).

Mezirow (1996, 2000) has attempted to explain better how context fits into his theory. He acknowledges, "The justification for much of what we know and believe, our values and our feelings, depends on the context—biographical, historical, cultural—in which they are embedded" (Mezirow, 2000, p. 3). He maintains that certain sociocultural factors such as racism, sexism, and classism may impede or encourage critical reflection and reflective discourse. "Transformation Theory," Mezirow (1996, p. 169) writes, "does not suggest a disengaged image of the individual learner, but of a learning process characterized by dialogical voices. The social dimension is central, but so are the historical and cultural dimensions of the process."

RATIONALITY AND AFFECT

The second major issue with Mezirow's view of transformational learning theory is what appears to be an overreliance on rationality as the means of effecting a perspective transformation; other forms of knowing are secondary at best. Rational thinking is a particularly Western concept, a product of the Enlightenment and

Descartes' mind-body split. The idea that emotions and cognition are separate and that emotions are "less evolved" continues to this day despite evidence to the contrary (Taylor, 2001). Even in the West, rationality, and in particular its separation from experience, is also gender-specific, privileging men, those of the middle and upper classes, and Whites. Mezirow (1998, pp. 187–188) has responded to these charges, noting that rationality is not in itself an ideology; rather, "the justification for embracing an ideology depends upon advancing and supporting reasons for doing so. . . . Arguments against the universality of rationality and critical reflection themselves demonstrate the necessity of assessing reasons and becoming critical of assumptions. Once these critics enter into rational discourse, they have no choice but to agree to observe universal principles of rationality."

Although Mezirow's (2000) work briefly acknowledges other ways of making meaning, including intuition, imagination, and dreams, and acknowledges the role of feelings in the transformative learning process, Taylor (2000a) notes of Mezirow's theory that "critical reflection is granted too much importance and does not give enough attention to the significance of affective learning—the role of emotions and feelings in the process of transformation" (p. 303). Further, Taylor (2000a) cites several studies indicating that people's emotions must be worked through before they can engage in critical reflection. The interdependence of affect and critical reflection cannot be overlooked. For example, Mulvihill (2003) discusses the importance emotion plays in the transformative learning experiences of survivors of clergy abuse. Mulvihill writes, "When individuals and groups can be encouraged to uncover the emotional impact of perspectives and meanings, and to blend this information with other ways of knowing, a more holistic transformative paradigm might be embraced" (2003, p. 325). In addition, the exploration of feelings leads to greater self-awareness (Taylor, 2001).

As previously noted, other transformative learning scholars delve more deeply into the importance of learning through other ways of knowing, including emotion and intuition (Blacksher, 2001; Johnson, 2001), "soul learning" (Dirkx, 1998), and levels of consciousness (Boucouvalas, 1993), and through stories (Rossiter, 2002), the physical body (Amann, 2003), and the subconscious (Scott, 1997). For example, using Boyd's extrarational approach to transformative learning as a framework for their study, Kovan and Dirkx (2003) sought to understand the "role of learning in sustaining commitment to nonprofit work" of environmentalists (p. 100). They discovered that the participants' transformative learning was "a struggle for consciousness in a largely unconscious world, a process that Jung referred to as individuation" (p. 107). For these participants, transformation was an ongoing process, which involves the whole person including the "head, heart and spirit" (p. 114).

Last, in an effort to explain how participants in several studies experienced a perspective transformation *without* critical reflection, Taylor (2001) explored the literature on neurobiology. He found that "nonconscious memory . . . has a tremendous influence on how we think and act" (p. 228). He continues, "Implicit memory of experience can be received, stored and recovered without conscious awareness of the individual" (p. 226). Examples of implicit memory include learning category-level knowledge such as grammar. People know the rules of grammar but are unable to say exactly what guides their speaking. A second form of implicit memory is learning a conditioned response (Taylor, 2001). For example, people may be conditioned into accepting the norms of a new culture. Taylor (1994) found that people in cultures different from their own developed new habits and uncritically accepted many of the routines and norms of the culture. They "absorbed" cultural norms without trying to make meaning of them. Yet, despite this uncritical acceptance of the culture, participants reported experiencing a perspective transformation.

In sum, the charge that Mezirow's (2000) theory relies too heavily on rationality has sparked discussions about the role of feelings and the unconscious in the transformative learning process. In addition, researchers have explored how people experience a perspective transformation in the absence of critical reflection.

ROLE OF RELATIONSHIPS IN THE TRANSFORMATIVE LEARNING PROCESS

Closely tied to the role of feelings in the transformational learning process is the role of relationships. Taylor (2000a) indicates the importance of "relational ways of knowing" (p. 306) in the transformative learning process. In particular, he indicates that elements such as "trust, friendship, and support" are necessary for effective reflective or rational discourse to occur (p. 306). Receiving support, connecting with family, and developing trust were all ways in which relationships were evident in the transformative learning process.

Recent studies support the assertion that relationships are an important part of the transformative learning process. Harvie (2004) found that the transformative learning process for undergraduates was a highly social process, with interpersonal support being an important component of the process. Likewise, Hwang (2004) analyzed the transformative learning of Korean Presbyterian disciples in training. Hwang indicates, "The transformative learning experiences did not appear to rely upon rational discourse for critical reflection of assumptions. . . . Instead, participants experienced transformative learning through relationship dialogue based on the relationships among group members and the relationship with God" (abstract).

Both the importance and the *nature* of the relationships in the transformative learning process have received attention (Taylor, 2003). For example, Carter (2000) uncovered four types of developmental relationships in the lives of midcareer women: utilitarian, memory, imaginative relationships with self, and love relationships. The author discovered: "Psychosocial support functions that predominate in love, memory and imaginative relationships generated proportionally more instances of transformative learning than did mostly career-enhancing functions of utilitarian relationships" (p. xiii).

SOCIAL ACTION

The place of social action in transformational learning theory remains controversial. Mezirow in particular has been criticized for focusing too much on individual transformation at the expense of social change. Mezirow (1990a, p. 363) indeed states that "we must begin with individual perspective transformations before social transformations can succeed." As previously mentioned, for Mezirow "action can mean making a decision, being critically reflective or transforming a meaning structure as well as a change in behavior" (1995, pp. 58–59). Perspective transformation may also result in social action. For Mezirow, though, the role of adult education is to promote and facilitate individual critical reflection in which "the only anticipated learning outcome . . . is a more rational and objective assessment of assumptions" (1995, p. 59). To assume that the outcome is social action is to require "the learner to share the convictions of the educator's own view of social reality [which] would be tantamount to indoctrination" (p. 59).

Both Freire and Mezirow have been criticized for romanticizing the social change process. Both educators "start with the oppressed or the person trapped within a culturally induced dependency role, and both require these victims to liberate themselves, albeit with the help of the dialogic or transformative educator" (Newman, 1994, p. 241). Newman believes this offers little help to those who are oppressed. Newman believes that adult teaching and learning should focus on identifying strategies to deal with oppression at the same time that we help learners "build up their skills, increase or regenerate their knowledge, and rework their meaning perspectives in order to be better able to carry out those strategies" (p. 241). Mezirow (1997b, p. 62) has responded to Newman's critique, arguing that "often learners are unaware of being oppressed; they internalize the values of the oppressors." In these situations, it may be necessary to engage in the "'deconstruction' of reified frames of reference" before action can be taken "on one's own behalf" (p. 62).

THE EDUCATOR'S PLACE IN FOSTERING TRANSFORMATIVE LEARNING

There is yet another dimension to this issue of the place of social action in transformational learning theory. The ethical issues involved have been little addressed. For example, what right do adult educators have to tamper with the worldview (mental set, perspective, paradigm, or state of consciousness) of the learner? How invasive is it to study adults in the process of transformation (Courtenay et al., 2000)? How is the goal of educational intervention, whether it is social or personal change or something else, to be determined? What is the educator's responsibility for the action component of praxis?

The educator who supports personal and social transformation as the goal of adult education is confronted by a more practical issue: how exactly to facilitate such learning. Brookfield (1987, 1996) offers some help through his critical questioning techniques and through a critical incident activity. Daloz (1986) suggests that mentors use the strategies of challenging, supporting, and visioning to facilitate the learner's personal journey of transformation. Freire (1970) and Hart (1990) discuss techniques for consciousness-raising in groups. Vella (1994) presents twelve principles of adult learning with specific case examples of their implementation in popular education sites around the world.

The most extensive discussions of techniques for fostering transformative learning can be found in Cranton's work (1996, 2002). Recognizing individual differences and learning preferences, Cranton suggests drawing from a repertoire of strategies, including critical questioning and experiential techniques such as role-plays and simulations, journal writing, and life histories. In addition, Lamb (2003) investigated best practices for fostering transformative learning in the workplace. She studied three corporate workplace programs that indicated transformative learning was an outcome. Lamb uncovered eight conditions that fostered transformative learning, including "putting participants in unfamiliar and new situations, . . . maximizing the diversity mix of participants, . . . and repeated team opportunities balancing action and reflection" (pp. 266–267).

Mezirow (1995) lays out the "ideal conditions" of discourse for fostering transformative learning, which have found some support in recent studies. Taylor (2000b) reviewed twenty-three empirical studies that explored the practice of fostering transformative learning in the classroom. He found that the studies supported Mezirow's ideal conditions for fostering transformative learning, including providing a trusting environment for learning, promoting autonomy and collaboration, and utilizing activities that "encourage exploration of alternative personal perspectives and critical reflection" (p. 9). Other themes that arose from the literature included "fostering group ownership and individual agency, . . . promoting value-laden course content, . . . recognizing the interrelationship of critical reflection and affective learning and the need for time" (p. 10).

To summarize this section on some of the unresolved issues surrounding transformative learning, it is clear that questions of context, rationality and affect, the role of relationships in the transformative learning process, social action, and implementation are not as discrete as presented. To understand the biographical and sociocultural context of the individual learner is to consider other equally if not more powerful ways of knowing than pure rationality. It also means to consider what the appropriate action might be as a result of personal transformation; clearly such action may reside with the person or may be mobilized for some form of collective, social action. Ethical and professional considerations pervade the process, a process that most adult educators are little prepared to handle.

TRENDS IN THE TRANSFORMATIONAL LEARNING LITERATURE

Recently, scholars have looked more closely at the emotional and spiritual aspects of transformative learning (Amann, 2003; Davis, 2003; Lennox, 2005; Ludwig, 2005; Sawyer, 2003). For example, through in-depth interviews with twelve participants, Davis (2003) explored "the human experience of spirit and its relationship to the transformative learning process" (p. 130). Participants reported spiritual experiences, that is, "intrapersonal conversations with spirit" that were transformational (p. 132). This "dialogue with the soul" is unique to this form of transformative learning (p. 134). Sawyer (2003) detailed the role of cognition, emotion, and spirituality in cellular biologist Bruce Lipton's transformation from holding a "materialist-reductionist-determinist worldview . . . to a quantum physics–based understanding of the universe, founded on energetics, holism and uncertainty" (p. 372). Sawyer concludes that Lipton's experiences help us see the relationship between the "cognitive, emotional, spiritual, physical, and behavioral dimensions of experience and pave the way for more integrative perspectives on how human beings learn, adapt, and grow" (p. 373).

A second area of inquiry includes transformative learning and technology (Cranton & Dirkx, 2005; Cranton & Lin, 2005; Dirkx & Smith, 2005; Lewis, Adams, & Southern, 2005). For example, Cranton and Dirkx (2005) explore how their online dialogue with each other led them toward a more inclusive perspective on transformative learning. Dirkx and Smith (2005) examined how people "worked through the problem of the relationship of the individual to the group, and the transformative processes and dynamics associated with this learning and development" (p. 114). Findings suggested that while individuals valued collaborative online learning, they also wanted to be evaluated individually. Participants noted that the online format did not lend itself as well to social connections as a face-to-face course would have; they did not feel as connected to each other as they would have in a face-to-face course. The authors concluded that the facilitating process in the online environment needs more development in order to facilitate transformative learning.

A third area of interest involves transformative learning in the workplace. Transformative learning in groups and organizations is a topic of interest (Baumgartner, 2001). For example, Yorks and Marsick (2000) utilized action learning in an organization. Action learning involves people working in teams toward a solution to a problem. Through dialogue and reflection, the teams solved the problem, and the organizational culture was transformed. Bierema (2005) examined the need for critical human resource development education. She maintained that much of the HRD literature is performance-based. Bierema encouraged HRD educators to teach critical HRD by "building awareness of the many dimensions and contradictions inherent in HRD" (p. 36) and by helping learners critique and analyze HRD readings and the language used in the text. These techniques will help transform the field and practice of human resource development.

SUMMARY

This chapter has presented a discussion of transformational learning theory. Probably more than any other approach, this theory has captured the attention of adult educators over the past fifteen years. Whether transformational learning will remain a centerpiece of adult learning theory is, of course, not predictable. It would seem, however, that the theoretical foundations presented by Taylor (2005a) are sufficiently robust to foster continued debate, discussion, and research.

In addition to reviewing seven "lenses" through which transformative learning can be seen, this chapter also offered a detailed discussion of three of its key components: the centrality of experience, the process of critical reflection, and transformative learning's link to adult development. In the final section of the chapter, we explored unresolved issues surrounding transformational learning: the extent to which context has been neglected, the overreliance on rational forms of knowing at the expense of honoring feelings and other ways of knowing, the role of relationships in the transformative learning process, the nature of the relationship between individuals and social change, and questions regarding preparation for and implementation of this type of learning. In addition, we examined new trends in the transformative learning literature.

CHAPTER SEVEN

EXPERIENCE AND LEARNING

Aaron, a psychotherapist with twenty years of experience, attends a workshop concerning new treatments for depression. Aaron has treated many clients with this disorder and wants to remain abreast of new treatment modalities. The workshop instructor, Dr. K., asks participants to introduce themselves, explain their reasons for being at the workshop, and tell what they want to learn. Dr. K. indicates that he wants to know participants' experiences treating people with depression and provides activities and opportunities for workshop attendees to interact and learn from each other. Dr. K. tailors the workshop to the needs of the participants. On the workshop evaluation, Aaron writes, "The interaction with peers was the most beneficial part of the workshop. Dr. K.'s willingness to value our experiences made this a successful workshop." Aaron's colleague Gloria attends a different workshop on the same subject. Participants listen to lectures and briefly interact with the presenter in a question-and-answer session at the end of the workshop. Gloria's experiences are never solicited. Her workshop evaluation reads, "I could have read this information in a book. The workshop was a waste of time." The difference between the two workshops was Dr. K.'s recognition that learners have a vast array of experiences that can be used for learning.

 We learn from experience in a variety of ways. As in the vignette, Aaron learned as the result of a direct embodied experience that engaged him mentally, physically, and emotionally in the moment. Other dimensions of experience include learning from a simulated experience or reliving a past experience. In addition, people may make sense of their experience through collaboration with others in a community (sometimes referred to as a community of practice) or through introspective experiences such as meditation or dreaming (Fenwick, 2003).

In addition to there being different dimensions to experiential learning, there are different theoretical conceptualizations of this type of learning. Fenwick (2003) proposes five perspectives that "raise important questions about the nature of experience" (p. 38): (1) reflecting on concrete experience (constructivist theory of learning); (2) participating in a community of practice (situative theory of learning); (3) getting in touch with unconscious desires and fears (psychoanalytic theory of learning); (4) resisting dominant social norms of experience (critical cultural theories); and (5) exploring ecological relationships between cognition and environment (complexity theories applied to learning). The constructivist approach focuses on "reflection on experience" (Fenwick, 2003, p. 22). People have concrete experiences; they reflect on them and construct new knowledge as a result of these reflections. In this view, the focus is on the learners' meaning-making processes as the result of an experience.

Unlike the constructivist paradigm, which emphasizes reflection on experience, the situative theory posits that knowing is intertwined with doing. Fenwick (2003) states, "Learning is rooted in the situation in which the person participates, not in the head of that person as intellectual concepts produced by reflection" (p. 25). Participation in a community of practice is the goal of this perspective. Fenwick continues, "The outcome of experiential learning as participation is that the *community* refines its practices, develops new ones, or discards and changes practices that are harmful or dysfunctional" (p. 27; italics in original).

The psychoanalytic perspective sees our unconscious as interfering with our conscious experiences. As a result, we must work through psychic conflicts to learn (Fenwick, 2003). This approach recognizes the complex role of desire in our learning. We may have conflicting desires in a learning situation that affect our learning experience (Fenwick, 2001). The fourth lens through which experiential learning is viewed, the critical cultural perspective, "seeks to transform existing social orders, by critically questioning and resisting dominant norms of experience" (Fenwick, 2003, p. 38). Last, the complexity theory says learning is produced through interaction "among consciousness, identity, action and interaction, objects and structural dynamics of complex systems" (p. 37). In this view, the focus is not on the experience itself but on the "*relationships* binding them [the dynamics] together in complex systems" (Fenwick, 2003, p. 37; italics in original).

Numerous adult educators have underscored the fundamental role that experience plays in learning in adulthood. For example, Lindeman (1961, p. 6) states that "the resource of highest value in adult education is the learner's experience." Experience then becomes "the adult learner's living textbook . . . already there waiting to be appropriated" (p. 7). Similarly, one of the primary assumptions underlying Knowles's (1989, p. 58) work on andragogy is that "[a]dults come into an educational activity with both a greater volume and a different quality of experience from youths." As adults live longer they accumulate both a greater volume and range of experiences. Knowles also observes that adults tend to define themselves by their experiences, describing themselves as parents, spouses, workers, volunteers, community activists, and so on. Kolb (1984) states, "Learning is a continuous process grounded in experience. Knowledge is continuously derived and tested out in the experiences of the learner" (p. 27). Kolb notes that these experiences can be personal (for example, the experience of happiness) or objective/environmental (for example, years of experience at a place of employment).

Although adult educators have accepted the connection between experience and learning, we are still learning about this connection and how to use it most effectively in both formal and nonformal learning situations. A number of questions puzzle us: What leads to learning from experience? Is the context in which the experience happens important? Are there ways we can design learning episodes to capture this experiential component best? In this chapter we explore responses to these and other important questions related to experience and learning. First, we briefly discuss John Dewey's view of experience and learning. Next, we delineate several models of experiential learning. Third, we explore educators' purposes, roles, and learning designs for experiential learning and delve into four methods associated with experiential learning: reflective practice, situated cognition, cognitive apprenticeships, and anchored instruction. Last, we detail criticisms and pedagogical debates in the experiential learning literature.

LEARNING FROM LIFE EXPERIENCES

John Dewey (1938), in his classic volume *Experience and Education*, made some of the most thoughtful observations about the connections between life experiences and learning. More specifically, Dewey postulated that "all genuine education comes about through experience" (p. 13). However, this "does not mean that all experiences are genuinely or equally educative" (p. 13). In fact, some experiences "mis-educate," in that they actually "distort growth . . . narrow the field of further experiences . . . [and place people] in a groove or rut" (p. 13). Judging whether experiences actually produce learning can be difficult because "every experience is a moving force. Its value can be judged only on the ground of what it moves toward and into" (p. 31). For example, being diagnosed as HIV-positive may make some people so bitter and angry that any positive or growth-enhancing learning from that life change is almost impossible. In contrast, others become highly active inquirers and participants in maintaining their health as well as become involved in caring for those with full-blown AIDS.

For learning to happen through experience, Dewey (1938, p. 27) argued that the experience must exhibit the two major principles of continuity and interaction: "The principle of the continuity of experience means that every experience both takes up something from those which have gone before and modifies in some way the quality of those which come after." In other words, experiences that provide learning are never just isolated events in time. Rather, learners must connect what they have learned from current experiences to those in the past as well as see possible future implications. For example, we can assume that people who are enjoying their retirement have been able to connect their past experiences to those of the present. Glennie, a retired salesperson, who may have always traveled vicariously through the Sunday paper's travel section, has bought a small travel trailer and now spends six months of the year exploring new places.

The second principle, that of interaction, posits that "an experience is always what it is because of a transaction taking place between an individual and what, at the time, constitutes his environment" (Dewey, 1938, p. 41). Going back to the example of Glennie, she is learning about new places firsthand because she now has the time and means to visit them. Through her travels, she has developed an interest in Native American culture and so seeks out new tribal groups to explore. As illustrated through Glennie's interest in Native American culture, the two principles of continuity and interaction are always interconnected and work together to provide the basis for experiential learning. What Glennie has learned in visiting one reservation "becomes an instrument of understanding" for attending the next tribal celebration with a different group of Native Americans. In translating Dewey's ideas into educational practice, what is key is how important the situation becomes in promoting learning. Developing a welcoming and comfortable atmosphere, providing the right materials, and linking these materials to learners' past and future experiences are critical in assisting adults to learn from their experiences.

While Dewey (1938) explored how people learned from life experiences, Kolb and Kolb (2005) went one step further. They examined the works of John Dewey, Jean Piaget, Carl Jung, and Carl Rogers, among others, and they compiled six general propositions of experiential learning theory. First, "learning is best conceived as a process, not in terms of outcomes" (p. 194). Second, "learning is relearning" (p. 194). Students' ideas must be drawn out, discussed, and refined. Next, learning requires a resolution of "dialectically opposed modes of adaptation to the world"; that is, learners must move between "opposing modes of reflection and action and feeling and thinking" (p. 194). Fourth, learning is holistic. Fifth, learning involves interactions between the learner and the environment. Last, learning is constructivist in nature. These propositions are evident in some of the models of experiential learning that are discussed in the next section.

MODELS OF EXPERIENTIAL LEARNING

Clearly, people learn from experience. However, scholars' perceptions of *how* people learn differ depending upon their theoretical orientation. Kolb's (1984) and Jarvis's (1987) models arise from the constructivist paradigm, while Boud and Walker (1991) and Usher, Bryant, and Johnson's (1997) models are situative in nature. Although the psychoanalytic, critical, and complexity approaches to experiential learning proposed by Fenwick (2003) do not have models per se, their theoretical underpinnings show us how people learn.

Kolb (1984), building primarily on the work of Dewey, Piaget, and Lewin, conceptualized that learning from experience requires four different kinds of abilities: (1) an openness and willingness to involve oneself in new experiences (concrete experience); (2) observational and reflective skills so these new experiences can be viewed from a variety of perspectives (reflective observation); (3) analytical abilities so integrative ideas and concepts can be created from their observations (abstract conceptualization); and (4) decision-making and problem-solving skills so these new ideas and concepts can be used in actual practice (active experimentation). Kolb pictured these capabilities as interrelated phases within a cyclical process, starting with the concrete experience and then moving through reflective observation and abstract conceptualization to active experimentation. Whatever action is taken in the final phase becomes another set of concrete experiences, which in turn can begin the experiential learning cycle again. (See Miettinen, 2000, for a critique of Kolb's conceptualization of Dewey's work.) For Kolb, the ultimate goal of this experiential learning process is to obtain "a fully integrated personality" (Malinen, 2000, p. 89).

A critique of Kolb's model is that the learner's context is not taken into consideration (Fenwick, 2003). Experience and reflection seem to exist in a vacuum. Kolb does not account for issues of power in his model. Jarvis's (1987, 2001) model addresses some of Kolb's (1984) shortcomings. Jarvis's model shows that the person brings his or her biography into the situation. Our construction of our experiences is affected by our "psychological history" (Jarvis, 2001, p. 52). There are two main types of learning from experiences. We may engage in *nonreflective learning*, which includes remembering an experience and repeating it or just doing what we are told to do. In contrast, we may engage in *reflective learning* when we "plan, monitor, and reflect upon our experiences" (p. 52). Jarvis includes both experimental learning (the result of a person experimenting on the environment) and reflective practice (thinking about and monitoring one's practice as it is happening) with what he conceives as the highest forms of learning. Jarvis notes that, ironically, often the more experiences we have, the less likely we are to learn from them. Instead, we tend to choose what is familiar and deny ourselves new learning (Jarvis, 2001; see also Chapter Four for Jarvis's model, 2006. For a critique of Jarvis's model, see Le Cornu, 2005. Le Cornu critiques three dimensions of Jarvis's model including "its time-centered base, its weak process of internalization, and the notion of non-learning" (p. 166). She suggests several modifications of the model.)

Boud and Walker (1991) take a situated approach to experiential learning. These scholars augmented Kolb's model in two ways. First, they recognized that "specific contexts shape an individual's experience in different ways" (Fenwick, 2001, p. 11). Second, they were "interested in how differences among individuals—particularly past histories, learning strategies, and emotion influence the sort of learning developed through reflection on experience" (p. 11). Boud, Keogh, and Walker's (1985, 1996) original model consisted of three stages: (1) returning to and replaying the experience, (2) attending to the feelings that the experience provoked, and (3) reevaluating the experience. The authors state that people need to work through any negative feelings that have arisen and eventually set those aside while retaining and enhancing the positive feelings. If the negative feelings are not addressed, what commonly happens is that learning becomes blocked. In the reevaluation stage, our aim is to use this experience as a way of getting us ready for new experiences, and thus new learning. Four processes may contribute to this reevaluation stage: "association, that is, relating of new data to that which is already known; integration, which is seeking relationships among the data; validation to determine the authenticity of the ideas and feelings which have resulted; and appropriation, that is, making knowledge one's own" (Boud, Keogh, & Walker, 1996, pp. 45–46).

In addition to Boud, Keogh, and Walker (1996), other authors also recognize the importance of emotion in experiential learning (Beard & Wilson, 2002; Dirkx, 2001a, 2001b). Beard and Wilson (2002) note, "The affective domain can be seen to provide the underlying foundation for all learning" (p. 119). In order for people to interpret experiences positively and to learn effectively they need to have confidence in their abilities, good self-esteem, support from others, and trust in others. In contrast, distorted learning can occur if a person is told he or she is not talented, or distressed learning can occur when we are forced to learn something (Beard & Wilson, 2002).

Beard and Wilson (2002) discuss several methods for working with emotions in the classroom. They suggest that fear can block learning and can manifest itself through perfectionism, anger, and aggression. By reflecting and mapping our fears via journaling or writing down "inner rules" and reflecting on them, we can address our fears (p. 119). The authors suggest writing down the rule, then writing down what this rule *really* means, and then revising the rule. For example, perhaps a person's inner rule is: "I must never cry in public." This rule may really mean that the person would be embarrassed if he or she cried in public. The revised rule may read: "I would rather not cry in public, but if I do, it wouldn't be the worst thing in the world. I could handle it." This new rule takes some of the fear away from crying in public. Techniques for creating positive emotion in the classroom include using various aromas to help the learning process. For example, they suggest that the scent of lemon increases mental clarity and they have specific instructions for dealing with anger, promoting calm, disputing the internal critic in all of us, and being assertive.

Usher, Bryant, and Johnston (1997) approach the situated or contextual nature of experience in a very different way from most other scholars who discuss experience as foundational to learning. Although they acknowledge that Jarvis (1987) and Boud and Walker (1991), among others, use a contextual or sociological frame for learning from experience, they still view the work of these authors as centered on an individualized self who uses experiences as the material to be acted upon by the mind through observations and reflection. Grounded in the assumption that "the self is a culturally and historically variable category," Usher, Bryant, and Johnston (1997, p. 102) view experience instead as a text to be used in learning—as "something to be 'read' or interpreted, possibly with great effort, and certainly with no final, definitive meaning" (p. 104). These authors assert that "the meaning of experience is never permanently fixed; thus, the text of experience is always open to reinterpretation" (p. 105). Usher, Bryant, and Johnston have proposed a "map" of experiential learning within the framework of postmodern thought. With this model, "learning does not simplistically derive from experience; rather, experience and learning are mutually positioned in an interactive dynamic" (p. 107). In posing this model, these authors view the use of experience as part of the learning process as "inherently neither emancipatory nor oppressive, neither domesticating nor transformative.

Rather . . . it is perhaps most usefully seen as having a potential for emancipation and oppression, domestication and transformation, where at any one time and according to context both tendencies can be present and in conflict with one another" (p. 105).

Usher, Bryant, and Johnston's model, shown in Figure 7.1, is structured around two intersecting continua—autonomy-adaptation (empowerment of individuals to act independently to being able to adapt one's actions in relation to the context) and expression-application (being able to apply what one knows in real-world contexts)—and four quadrants, referred to as lifestyle, vocational, confessional, and critical. Learning from experience happens both between and within the quadrants, which represent different types of learning venues.

Lifestyle practices center on the achievement of autonomy through individuality and self-expression, particularly in taste and style (for example, ways of speaking, clothes, leisure pursuits, vacations). Experience is used as a means of defining a lifestyle that is actively sought by people but also influenced by socially and culturally defined norms.

FIGURE 7.1. MAP OF EXPERIENTIAL LEARNING IN THE SOCIAL PRACTICES OF MODERNITY.

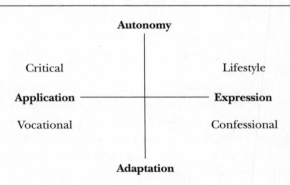

Source: Usher, Bryant, & Johnston, 1997, p. 106.

Vocational practices are conveyed through the market. Learners need to be highly motivated in the direction of a personal change linked to the needs of the socioeconomic environment. Vocationalism then is designed to produce flexible competencies and a predisposition to change. As a result of learning adaptive skills through experiential means, learners become more empowered to respond to their changing vocational environments.

In *confessional practices* our private, self-regulating capacities become public. In other words, realizing oneself, finding out the truth about oneself, and accepting responsibility for oneself become both personally desirable and economically functional. The emphasis in this process is on self-improvement, self-development, and regulation. Experience is used as enabling access to knowledge and the innermost truths about self, which in turn creates productive and empowered people in a number of roles (for example, as active citizen, ardent consumer, enthusiastic employee).

Finally, in Usher, Bryant, and Johnston's (1997) fourth quadrant, *critical practices,* there is a recognition that experience is never a basic given. The focus is on changing particular contexts rather than adapting to them, and therefore working with learners becomes a political practice. Experiential learning becomes a strategy designed to find and exercise one's voice in the service of self and social empowerment and transformation and is not regarded as something that leads to knowledge, but rather as knowledge itself.

Although no particular model exists to represent the psychoanalytic perspective that focuses on the issue of desire and the unconscious in experiential learning, Jacques Lacan's work exemplifies this approach. Lacan's idea that a person's "identity is split between conscious and unconscious desires" may help explain why people are conflicted in some experiential learning situations (Fenwick, 2001, p. 30).

Experiential learning from the critical cultural perspective looks at "power as a core issue in experience" (Fenwick, 2001, p. 39). Emancipatory learning exemplifies this perspective on experiential learning. People critically examine how power works in society, and they rise from their oppression and take action that makes a difference in their lives and others' lives. This perspective concentrates on the community, not the individual. The community recognizes that it needs to act, takes collective action, and understands that learning arises from conflict. For example, a group of HIV-positive individuals realize that many HIV-positive individuals could die without access to affordable medication. They unite to lobby the state for free or low-cost medications for HIV/AIDS. They learn how to lobby their legislature and as a result the state passes a bill that helps supply low-cost HIV/AIDS medications to state residents.

Clearly the role of experience in learning is highly complex. Perhaps equally complex are the roles of the adult educator in the experiential learning process. In the next section we explore educators' roles and purposes in the classroom.

EDUCATORS' ROLES AND PURPOSES

As we have seen, experiential learning models focus on different aspects of the process, depending on their theoretical orientation. Likewise, educators' purposes, roles, and learning designs for experiential learning differ depending on the lens through which they view experiential learning.

Those who see experiential learning through a constructivist lens want to foster critical reflection on experience and challenge learners' assumptions while validating personally constructed knowledge (Fenwick, 2003). Educators serve as facilitators of reflection and encourage learners to discuss and reflect on concrete experiences in a trusting, open environment. For example, they challenge students' assumptions by having them reflect on specific work situations. A second role the teacher plays is that of catalyst. Instructors involve students in role-plays or problem-based learning exercises where learners must solve a dilemma. This activity reveals learners' assumptions and creates ample opportunities for reflection. Third, the adult educator may become the student's coach or mentor. Coaching is generally associated with "specific skill learning" while mentors serve as life guides (Fenwick, 2003, p. 117). Last, the teacher becomes the assessor of the learners' prior experiential learning. Typical assessment tools that emphasize reflection are portfolios, learners' analyses of their life or work experience, and interviews in which learners explain their "learning outcomes of their past experience" (p. 118).

The educator's role from the situative framework is to get learners involved in a community of practice (Fenwick, 2003). The educator arranges real situations in which the learners participate. Fenwick states, "The educator's role . . . is in providing just-in-time assistance to enable confident action in situations where confident competence is lacking" (p. 121). Fenwick adds that the instructor may also help those who become stuck or immobilized in situations to move ahead. The situative orientation can be found in service-learning activities. These experiences "are often community-based volunteer work with different non-profit organizations . . . and are typically organized for a short-term period of a few weeks" (p. 149). Cognitive apprenticeships (discussed later in the chapter) exemplify the type of experiential learning promoted by this theoretical orientation.

Facilitators who view experiential learning through the psychoanalytic lens want to facilitate analysis of learners' psychic conflicts that may impede learning (Fenwick, 2003). Educators can do this by encouraging students to pay attention to their dreams, behavior, and odd images that may arise in their minds. Activities that may facilitate these goals include finding materials such as images, film clips, or texts that elicit emotion. These emotions may lead us to uncover aspects of our unconscious that block our learning (Dirkx, 2001a, 2001b). Students are encouraged to respond as educators listen and compassionately help them examine resistance and bring to light unconscious feelings associated with the material. Another technique used to help learners analyze their desires and anxieties in their workplace is to ask employees a series of questions about their most pleasant, frustrating, or anxious moments at work. In addition, Dirkx (2001a) suggests having learners "name an emotion or feeling they experienced during an assignment or classroom meeting" (p. 16). Next, they should describe the emotion in their journal and also write anything they associate with the emotion. They may also want to draw or paint any images that come to mind.

For those educators looking at experiential learning through the critical cultural lens, the educator's purpose includes helping learners see the influence of power relationships on their lives. Teachers support and encourage resistance against oppression and help learners see beyond the immediate struggle to solutions (Fenwick, 2003). Educators engage in what Freire (1970) called *problem-posing*. The issues of concern come from the people, and educators help "identify general causes and outcomes of these issues" (Fenwick, 2003, p. 162). Instructors encourage people to critically analyze their situations and work toward a solution. For example, workers in a factory may be concerned about the working conditions and wages. The teachers ask questions to allow the workers to see they are oppressed and help workers find an empowering solution to their problems. The learners then may, for example, engage in social action through forming a union or fighting as a group for better working conditions.

Individuals who view experiential learning through the complexity theory lens do not instigate change through organization but "seek to open spaces for the system to experiment with change itself" (Fenwick, 2003, p. 132). The emphasis is on seeking change within complex systems. One of the teacher's roles in this environment is to be an interpreter in order to help students understand the changes in the complex systems in which they find themselves. In addition, instructors "attune the learner and the learning community to the disturbances: drawing attention to the new possibilities created, while helping to divert patterns that may start to create unsafe spaces or power inequities" (p. 134). The teacher helps learners explore changes by having them dialogue about issues in order to develop insights. Unlike the educators from the critical cultural perspective, these teachers are not expected to help the community "link its experiences to larger forces perpetuating exploitation and inequity" (p. 169).

In sum, educators' roles and purposes differ according to their theoretical orientation. Constructivists foster critical reflection on students' assumptions and assess learners' prior experiential learning. Teachers from the situative framework engage students in a community of practice through service activities and cognitive apprenticeships. Those from the psychoanalytic framework want to help learners bring to light unconscious conflicts that may impede learning; they can assist learners by providing activities that elicit emotion and listening to learners. Instructors who take a critical cultural approach help learners see the influence of power in their lives; they encourage resistance against oppression and help learners find solutions. Last, those utilizing the complexity theory help students understand change within complex systems and work toward solutions.

METHODS ASSOCIATED WITH REFLECTIVE AND SITUATIVE PARADIGMS

In the previous section, we explored how educators' purposes, roles, and learning designs for experiential learning differ depending on their theoretical orientation. Since much of the experiential learning literature focuses on procedures used by practitioners from the constructivist and situative paradigms, we choose to investigate four methods in detail. Namely, we will discuss reflective practice, situated cognition, cognitive apprenticeships, and anchored instruction.

REFLECTIVE PRACTICE

Reflective practice allows one to make judgments in complex and murky situations—judgments based on experience and prior knowledge. Although reflective practice is most often associated with professional practice, this process can be applied to other types of learning situations, both formal and informal. Practice knowledge, the cornerstone of reflective practice, consists of much more than abstract theoretical or technical knowledge (Cervero, 1988; Schön, 1983). The knowledge we gain through experience and the way we practice our craft are just as important. The initiation of reflective practice involves using data in some form, which almost always includes our past and current experiences. Our tacit knowledge about practice—that is, knowledge that we use every day, almost without thinking about it—is an important part of these data.

Researchers define reflective practice in a number of ways. Perhaps one of the most inclusive, useful definitions comes from scholars interested in using reflective practice to improve schools. They write: "Reflective practice is a deliberate pause to assume an open perspective, to allow for higher-level thinking processes. Practitioners use these processes for examining beliefs, goals, and practices, to gain new or deeper understandings that lead to actions that improve learning for students. Actions may involve changes in behavior, skills, attitudes, or perspectives within an individual, partner, small group, or school" (York-Barr, Sommers, Ghere, & Montie, 2001, p. 6.).

The authors focus on several elements of reflective practice. First, reflective practice requires a deliberate slowing down to consider multiple perspectives. Second, maintaining an open perspective is also necessary. The purpose of reflective practice in a group is not in needing to be right or in winning but in openness to a variety of perspectives, for it is only in openness that new understandings can occur (York-Barr et al., 2001). Third, reflective practice requires "active and conscious *processing of thoughts*," which may include analysis, synthesis, and metacognition (thinking about thinking) in order to achieve a "broader context for understanding" (p. 7; italics in original). Fourth, beliefs, goals, and practices must be examined. Beliefs are formed from experiences and influence behavior, while goals include "desired aims, outcomes, or intentions," which may be general or specific (p. 7). Practices include one's "dispositions, behaviors, and skills in specific areas of performance, such as designing instruction and assessment strategies, interacting with students, developing relationships with families" (pp. 7–8). The outcome of reflection is to gain deeper insights that lead to action.

Although reflective practice theoretically should result in the most thoughtful and useful solutions to practice problems, this may not be the case depending on the beliefs educators have about this practice. Wellington and Austin (1996) have argued that depending on their beliefs and values, practitioners have very different orientations toward reflective practice. These differing orientations influence how reflective practice is used, and therefore the possible outcomes of this practice. For example, do those involved believe that education should be a liberating or "domesticating" form of practice? And what is more important to them: system or human concerns? Wellington and Austin have depicted a way of thinking about reflective practice that acknowledges how it could be filtered through the belief and value systems of practitioners, which in their view results in five orientations toward reflective practice: the immediate, the technical, the deliberative, the dialectic, and the transpersonal.

Practitioners who use the immediate orientation, focusing basically on survival, rarely use any form of reflective practice. Those who view practice as more of a domesticating activity—that is, who see societal needs as taking precedence over individual needs— lean toward the technical and deliberative orientations. The technical mode "uses reflection as an instrument to direct practice"

(Wellington & Austin, 1996, p. 308), usually within predetermined guidelines and standards. The deliberative orientation "places emphasis on the discovery, assignment and assessment of personal meaning within an educational setting" (p. 310). Those operating from this orientation are typically humanistic, stress communication, and believe that the attitudes and values of learners are important. Although people whose orientation is deliberative sometimes are uncomfortable with the organization in which they work, they nevertheless tend to work within that system. And finally, those who view educational practice as liberating primarily have the dialectic and transpersonal orientations. Practitioners whose orientation toward reflective practice is dialectical "reject the limitations of authorized organizational structures and parameters and are uncomfortable working within them. . . . They tend to . . . focus on political and social issues . . . [and] advocate political awareness and activism" (p. 310). In contrast, the transpersonal orientation "centers on universal personal liberation. . . . They question educational ends, content and means from a personal, inner perspective" (p. 311). This orientation, applied to groups, is the basis for what is called *organized reflection*. This is a type of reflection that occurs "within and as a collaborative entity," where groups critically question the status quo (Welsh & Dehler, 2004, p. 20). It examines power relationships in groups and emancipation is its aim.

Wellington and Austin (1996) cast these orientations not as competing views of what reflective practice should encompass but as different ways of going about reflective practice. They believe that practitioners need to recognize their own predominant modes, as well as respect the preferred orientations of others. "When practitioners become aware of their own preferences and prejudices across models, they can begin to reflect upon a wider range of questions and develop a wider range of responses" (p. 314). No matter what orientation people have, two basic processes have been identified as central to reflective practice: reflection-on-action and reflection-in-action.

Reflection-on-Action
Reflection-on-action involves thinking through a situation after it has happened. This mode of reflection is presented by most authors as primarily an analytical exercise, which results in new perspectives

on experiences, changes in behavior, and commitments to action. In reflection-on-action, we consciously return to the experiences we have had, reevaluate these experiences, decide what we could do differently, and then try out whatever we decided to do differently. Different authors have offered various models of carrying out this reflective cycle. Kolb's (1984) model, or adaptations of his model, is the one most often used in practice. The cyclical nature of the model allows for a process of continued change and growth. Boud, Keogh, and Walker (1985, 1996) have added to Kolb's work on reflection-on-action by stressing that we must attend to the feelings created by our experiences in order for the reflective process to be truly effective. In addition, they have added more in-depth descriptions of four cognitive processes (association, integration, validation, and appropriation) that can contribute to the reflective process.

Osterman and Kottkamp (2004), borrowing from the work of Argyris and Schön (1978), set reflective practice within the framework of espoused theories (beliefs) and theories-in-use (actions). Within this framework, they view the reflective practice cycle as helping practitioners become aware of, and act on, the discrepancies between their beliefs (their espoused theories) and what they actually do. In contrasting espoused theories with action, people may ask themselves, "Was our action consistent with our intent? Did we act as we wanted to act, in a way consistent with our values?" (Osterman & Kottcamp, 2004, p. 34). For example, a teacher may espouse the theory that she is responsible for helping students who are disruptive in class. She knows that their anger is a cry for help. However, instead of directly addressing the disruptive students, she glares at them. Osterman and Kottcamp (2004, p. 35) state, "[The teacher] consciously knows that student misbehavior is frequently a cry for help (espoused theory) but her gut reaction is an angry one. The response may reflect a deeper assumption (theory-in-use)"—for example, that angry students are intentionally disrespectful students.

Critical examination of discrepancies between espoused theories and theories-in-use often begin with a feeling that something could be improved upon in one's practice (Osterman & Kottcamp, 2004). In the process of improving their practice, people think about their espoused beliefs, examine what they actually do and the results of their actions, and contrast their espoused beliefs with their practice to unearth their theories-in-use.

Descriptions are plentiful on how to put reflection-on-action into practice (for example, Osterman & Kottkamp, 2004; York-Barr et al., 2001). Some of the most popular methods used in education and other fields are portfolio development, journal writing, mapping (a form of journal writing that can be more fluid and visual than a journal), and critical reflection. Key to all of these methods is the framing of critical observations and questions as part of the reflection-on-action process. For example, York-Barr et al. (2001, p. 47), delineate a four-step process that can guide reflection. First, individuals must pick an event and ask themselves what happened. Second, they need to analyze and interpret the event by asking themselves questions such as, "Why did things happen this way? Why did I act the way I did? How did the context affect the experience? Did past experiences affect the way I reacted?" Third, people have to make sense of the event by asking themselves, "What have I learned from this event? How can I improve? How might this change my future thinking, behaving, interactions?" Last, people must think about implications for action by querying, "What am I going to remember to think about the next time this situation comes up? How could I set up conditions to increase the likelihood of productive interactions and learning?"

Reflection-in-Action

In contrast, reflection-in-action reshapes "what we are doing while we are doing it" (Schön, 1987, p. 26). "Thinking on your feet" and "keeping your wits about you" are commonly used phases that describe reflection-in-action. Schön (1983, 1987, 1991, 1996) is perhaps the best-known author who has challenged professionals to incorporate this form of reflective process as an integral part of professional development. In Schön's view, reflection-in-action is triggered by surprise. What we have been thinking and doing all along as professionals no longer works. "We think critically about the thinking that got us into this fix or this opportunity; and we may, in the process, restructure strategies of action, understanding of phenomena, or ways of framing problems. . . . Reflection gives rise to on-the-spot experiment" (Schön, 1987, p. 28).

For example, in running an institute for professionals, the institute staff sense that the sessions on a particular day have not gone well. Over coffee, they ask for feedback from participants, and the

general observation is that they are finding the material too eso-
teric and are tired of being "talked at." The next presenter, who is
listening to these conversations, has also planned to lecture.
Although Ron knows he is an excellent lecturer, he decides that
unless he changes the way he presents the material, he will totally
lose the audience. Knowing that many of the people in the audience have experience related to his content area, he asks for volunteers to join him in a panel discussion on the topic, explaining
that he is changing his format to respond to their needs as learners. While Ron works with the panel members on their roles, he
asks the rest of the participants to generate questions they would
like to ask panel members. Although he has never used this format
in quite this way before, he believes it might work and is willing to
take a chance to recapture the interest of the participants. In this
way, Ron is using his expertise as an instructor to change on the
spot what he is doing as a presenter as he goes along. Schön goes
on to observe that competent and experienced professionals use
reflection-in-action as a regular part of their practice, although
they may not verbalize they are doing this. This form of reflective
practice allows professionals to go beyond the routine application
of rules, facts, and procedures and gives them the freedom to practice their craft more as professional artistry where they create new
ways of thinking and acting about problems of practice.

There have been both validation of and criticisms to Schön's
model of reflection-in-action. Ferry and Ross-Gordon (1998), for
example, in exploring the links between experience and practice,
support Schön's theory that "reflection-in-action goes beyond
'stable rules' by devising new methods of reasoning" (p. 107) and
fostering new ways of framing and responding to problems. Educators who were reflective in their practice used both reflection-
on-action and reflection-in-action to build their expertise. They
did not find, however, that the amount of experience a person pos-
sessed necessarily had anything to do with that person using reflective practice.

In contrast, Usher, Bryant, and Johnston (1997) assert that
although Schön adequately describes the reflection-in-action
process, in his own work he did not use "his own practice as a producer of text . . . [and they view that as] a problem of the absence
of reflexivity in his own work" (p. 143). By this, Usher, Bryant, and

Johnston meant that Schön did not question how the context of his work, being academic in nature, could get in the way of the message. Overall, Usher, Bryant, and Johnston believe that despite Schön's clear message that reflection-in-action should be implemented in a critical manner, the way in which he conveyed that message makes it easy for practitioners to co-opt the process into a technical and rationalistic dialogue.

SITUATED COGNITION

Although reflective practice and situated cognition both involve learning from real-world experiences, how these experiences are interpreted is often vastly different. In most models of reflective practice, learning from experience is still viewed as something that goes on in someone's head. Individuals, whether by themselves or in groups, think through problems presented to them and then act on those problems by changing their practice on the spot or as they encounter similar situations at a later date. Experience provides the catalyst for learning in reflective practice, but most often it is seen as separate from the learning process itself.

In situated cognition, one cannot separate the learning process from the situation in which the learning is presented. Knowledge is not received and later transferred to another situation "but part of the very process of *participation* in the immediate situation" (Fenwick, 2003, p. 25; italics in the original). The proponents of the situated view of learning argue that learning for everyday living (which includes our practice as professionals) happens only when people interact with the community (including its history and cultural values and assumptions), "the tools at hand" (such as technology, language, and images), and the activity at hand (Fenwick, 2003, p. 25). In other words, the physical and social experiences and situations in which learners find themselves and the tools they use in that experience are integral to the entire learning process.

Machles (2004), through his study of the situated learning of occupational safety by biotechnical employees, provides us with an example of how situated cognition translates into practice. In his study, participants interacted with each other in the workplace to learn occupational safety on the job. Steve, a study participant, stated, "I think most everything I have learned, especially about safety . . . has been learned from other people. . . . It was learned from my co-workers and stuff. There was never a class" (p. 145). The tools for learning can be physical tools or concepts learned at the workplace. Machles (2004) observed that workers' tools included physical equipment, such as the eye wash and shower used to treat chemical accidents, as well as concepts such as "don't hesitate, respond quickly" (p. 154). A study respondent, James, spoke about how he used both the physical tools of the eye wash and shower and the concept of "respond quickly" to save a colleague's sight after a chemical accident. James stated, "Another guy got something in his eye. . . . I got him in the safety shower. I kept him there 20 minutes. . . . It's kind of an automatic reflex. Grab and go" (p. 113).

In viewing learning from a situated perspective, two other ideas are key. The first is that the emphasis in the learning process changes from being concerned about memory and how we process information internally to perception and the settings in which those perceptions are made (Hansman, 2001). In essence, according to Clancey (1997), "[E]very human thought and action is adapted to the environment, that is, situated, because what people perceive, and how they conceive of their activity, and what they physically do develop together" (pp. 1–2). According to proponents of the situative perspective, this situated nature of cognition makes the transfer process from using learning gained from one situation to the next more problematic, which has led some theorists to question whether knowledge, especially practical knowledge, can really transfer across situations (Anderson, Reder, & Simon, 1996). However, constructivists maintain that the transfer of learning from one situation to another is possible (Fenwick, 2003). Scholars who study organizational learning indicate that knowledge transfer of tacit knowledge (knowledge evident in our actions but that may not be explicitly articulated), occurs through socialization with others (Fenwick, 2003). They also recognize that explicit knowledge can be transferred.

Second, making the assumption that learning and knowing are primarily cultural phenomena moves the study of cognition (and therefore, learning from experience) into the social and political realm and raises the issue of knowledge and power as a legitimate part of the study of cognition (Fenwick, 2003; Kirshner & Whitson, 1997). Although this issue of power and knowledge is fundamental to the theory of situated cognition, it has often been downplayed or overlooked in favor of how to apply the concept practically (Fenwick, 2003). In acknowledging cognition and learning from experience as a cultural phenomenon, the perspectives of critical, feminist, and postmodern thinkers become crucial. Among the major results of thinking about cognition from a cultural frame are the critiques that have been fostered about traditional educational theory and practice (Brown, Collins, & Duguid, 1989; Lave, 1988). Foremost among these critiques is a challenge to the fundamental notion that learning is something that occurs within the individual. Rather, learning encompasses the interaction of learners and the social environments in which they function.

In using experience in the framework of situated cognition, the emphasis is on "providing enabling experiences in authentic versus decontextualized contexts" (Choi & Hannafin, 1995, p. 53). As Greeno (1997) has thoughtfully observed, "When we recognize that all learning involves socially organized activity, the question is not whether to give instruction in a 'complex, social environment' but what kinds of complex, social activities to arrange, for which aspects of participation, and in what sequence to use them" (p. 10). From this perspective education and training by just abstraction is of little use. Rather, "to meet the test of 'authenticity,' situations must at least have some of the important attributes of real-life problem solving, including ill-structured complex goals, an opportunity for the detection of relevant versus irrelevant information, active/generative engagement in finding and defining problems as well as in solving them, involvement in the student's beliefs and values, and an opportunity to engage in collaborative interpersonal activities" (Young, 1993, p. 45). Cognitive apprenticeships and anchored instruction are two ways in which the concept of authentic experiences has been put into practice by educators.

COGNITIVE APPRENTICESHIPS

Cognitive apprenticeships have received much attention in the literature. "Cognitive apprenticeship methods try to enculturate [learners] into authentic practices through activity and social interaction in a way similar to that evident—and evidently successful—in craft apprenticeship" (Brown, Collins, & Duguid, 1989, p. 37). The cognitive nature of the apprenticeship places emphasis on teaching learners different ways of thinking about whatever they are learning, as well as any skills associated with the apprenticeship. Fenwick (2003) adds, "Cognitive apprenticeship moves away from the purely situative view of learning, treating learners as independent reflective constructors of knowledge" (p. 152).

Based on a study of different forms of cognitive apprenticeship used in several professions, such as engineering, medicine, and educational administration, Brandt, Farmer, and Buckmaster (1993) have created a five-phase model (see Table 7.1). The first phase, modeling, is where the model demonstrates the activity as he or she verbally describes the activity. Phase 2, approximating, consists of the learner doing the activity with the teacher providing support (scaffolding) and coaching the learner. In Phase 3, the coaching and scaffolding are gradually removed and the learner works in less defined situations individually and in groups. The student is self-directed in Phase 4 and assistance from the instructor is only provided when requested. In Phase 5, generalizing, the generalizability of the skill is discussed and students are encouraged to try the skill in new situations.

Several studies indicate that the cognitive apprenticeship model produces better results in the classroom than traditional instruction (Hockly, 2000; Mayer, Moutone, & Prothero, 2002; Snyder, 2000; Walker, 2003). Meyer, Mautone, and Prothero required college students to solve geology problems using a computer game. Those who were given instructional support and scaffolding outperformed those who received basic instruction. Cope, Cuthbertson, and Stoddart (2000) surveyed nurses who had completed their practice placements in nursing. Results demonstrated the benefits of scaffolding and mentoring for nurses in a practicum setting.

ANCHORED INSTRUCTION

The purpose of anchored instruction is to create situations in which learners, through sustained experiences, can grapple with the problems and opportunities that experts encounter (Cognition and Technology Group at Vanderbilt, 1990, 2000). To do this, the instructional

TABLE 7.1. COGNITIVE APPRENTICESHIP PHASES.

	Role of Model	Role of Learner	Key Concepts
Phase 1: Modeling	Model real-life activity that learner wants to perform satisfactorily. Model states aloud the essence of the activity. He or she can include tricks of the trade.	Observe performance of total activity, not merely the individual steps. Develop a mental model of what the real thing looks like.	Articulation, domain-specific heuristics
Phase 2: Approximating	Provide coaching to the learner. Provide support when needed.	Approximate doing the real thing and articulate its essence. Reflect on the model's performance. Use self-monitoring and self-correction.	Scaffolding, coaching
Phase 3: Fading	Decrease coaching and scaffolding.	Continue to approximate the real thing. Operate in increasingly complex, risky, or ill-defined situations. Work individually or in groups.	Fading
Phase 4: Self-directed learning	Provide assistance only when requested.	Practice doing the real thing alone. Do so within specified limits acceptable to profession and society.	Self-directed learning
Phase 5: Generalizing	Discuss the generalizability of what has been learned.	Discuss the generalizability of what has been learned.	Generalizability

Source: Brandt, Farmer, & Buckmaster, 1993, p. 71.

process is anchored in what the Cognition and Technology Group calls *macrocontexts,* which are complex problems explored over extended periods of time and through multiple lenses (Cognition and Technology Group at Vanderbilt, 2000). These macrocontexts, which in essence become the tools of learning, can take many forms. For example, instructors might provide videodisks containing the problems to be explored or they might ask learners to prepare problem-based case studies. The goal of anchored instruction is to have learners "experience what it is like to grow from novices who have only rudimentary knowledge . . . to relatively sophisticated experts who have explored an environment from multiple points of view" (Cognition and Technology Group at Vanderbilt, 1990, p. 9).

An Appraisal of Experiential Learning

Differing philosophical viewpoints provide several critiques of experiential learning. First, scholars debate whether people consist of one unified self or if they are a collection of multiple selves (Fenwick, 2003). The constructivist approach maintains that "[t]he learner is assumed to be a stable fixed identity, with transparent access to experience through rational reflection" (p. 77). However, the psychoanalytic perspective on experiential learning counters that the self is split between "conscious and unconscious desires" (Fenwick, 2003, p. 77). The conflict between these desires can affect our learning and reflection processes.

Those professing the psychoanalytic viewpoint also take issue with the prominence of cognitive reflection in experiential learning. They maintain that the focus on cognitive reflection in the experiential learning literature is limited (Fenwick, 2003). In the constructivist view of learning, the impact of desire and resistance is not taken into account in the learning process.

A third critique of experiential learning involves the separation of the learner from the context of the experience. The learner's context includes "the social relations and political cultural dimensions of the community, . . . the nature of the task, . . . the vocabulary and cultural beliefs through which the individual makes meaning of the whole situation, and the historical, temporal, and spatial location of the situation" (Fenwick, 2003, p. 79). Kolb's (1984) model, in particular, is criticized for its inattention to context, and although Boud and Walker (1991) mention context, it is presented as a "static space" (p. 79) that the learner experiences. However, notes Fenwick (2003, p. 80), "Social relations of power exercised through language or cultural practices are not theorized as part of knowledge construction" in Boud and Walker's (1991) model.

Last, say critics, experiential learning needs to be bounded (Fenwick, 2003). Experiential learning can occur in a variety of contexts. How does experiential learning differ from experiences in classrooms such as class discussions and reflection? If all of life's activities are considered experiential learning, what does this mean for the educator?

In addition to critiques of experiential learning, there are debates about the content, design, and role of the educator in experiential learning. For example, critics maintain that educators' management of learners' experiential learning interferes with the basic tenet that experiential learning should liberate and not oppress learners. Scholars argue that management of experiential learning in the workplace may worsen social problems. In the workplace, "workers' experiential learning becomes human capital with great potential economic benefits for the organization" with no attention given to the workers' dignity and freedom (Fenwick, 2003, p. 90).

A second, related criticism is that the assessment of learning by organizations "becomes a tool to control lives" (Fenwick, 2003, p. 91). In North America, institutions of higher learning assess learners' experiences to "help adults gain credits in postsecondary education" (p. 91). However, the interests and biases of the institution color what *counts* as experience worthy of credit. Fenwick states, "People's knowing is colonized by being squeezed into . . . categories and identities" (p. 92).

Some critics counter that although interference in adult learners' experiential learning can be oppressive, it is necessary so that bad practices do not continue. Fenwick (2003) states, "Unsupervised people may make do, finding ways to participate that actually reinforce negative practices that a community is trying to eliminate" (p. 93). Educators can intervene and help create positive practices and reaffirm the adult learner.

SUMMARY

The experiences of adults have always been viewed as a critical component of learning in adulthood. Various theoretical perspectives emphasize different aspects of experiential learning. The constructivist perspective highlights reflecting on the concrete experience and making meaning of it. The situative approach focuses on getting learners involved in a community of practice because in this view learning is intertwined with doing. The psychoanalytic lens emphasizes the learner's need to get in touch with his or her unconscious desires and fears. The critical approach focuses on the need to resist dominant social norms. Last, the complexity theory of experiential learning emphasizes the relationships among experiences.

Although exploring the role of experience in learning has a long history, we continue to discover more about the connections between learning and experience and how to assist adults in formal and nonformal settings to capture the richness of learning from experience. Discussed in this chapter were the theories of Dewey (1938), Kolb (1984), Jarvis (1987), Boud and Walker (1991), and Usher, Bryant, and Johnston (1997), which offer varying conceptual views of the process of learning from experience. Central to all of these writers is the notion that learning from experience involves adults' connecting what they have learned from current experiences to those in the past as well to possible future situations.

We investigated common methods employed in experiential learning, including reflective practice, situated cognition, cognitive apprenticeships, and anchored instruction. Reflective practice, one of the main ways in which educators have structured learning from experience, focuses on helping learners make judgments based on experience related to primarily complex and murky problems. Situated cognition acknowledges the importance of the social and cultural context of learning. In other words, the physical and social experiences and situations in which learners find themselves and the tools they use are integral to the learning process. The importance of the authenticity of the experience in which adults learn is stressed in the situated framework. Two ways educators have put this concept of authentic experiences into formal practice are cognitive apprenticeships and anchored instruction.

Last, there are several criticisms of experiential learning. For example, some critics assert that the focus on cognitive reflection in the experiential learning literature is a limited perspective and that the learner is separated from the context of the experience in experiential learning (Fenwick, 2003). Finally, current debates in the experiential learning literature center on the role of the educator in the process. Critics assert that the educator's control over the experiential learning situation may be viewed as oppressive.

PART THREE

NEWER APPROACHES TO ADULT LEARNING

In the more than seven years between the last edition of *Learning in Adulthood* and this third edition, there has been a burgeoning of interest both in other ways of knowing and learning, and in applying the tools of critique and postmodernism to our more traditional understandings of adult learning. Thus in this Part Three we have added two totally new chapters. The first attempts to capture the noncognitive dimensions of learning, learning that is embodied, spiritual, and narrative or "storied." The second new chapter takes us to other cultures and systems of knowing and learning, for insights with which we can augment our Western orientation to learning. Although certainly noncognitive and non-Western understandings of learning are not at all "new" in the world, their emergence in our adult learning literature and practice is relatively new. The third chapter in Part Three updates critical, feminist, and postmodern perspectives on adult learning.

Most of our knowledge of adult learning is centered on the mind—that is, cognitive processes related to acquiring, storing, and making meaning of new information. But the whole person is always involved in learning, even when we think it is just our brain. First discussed in Chapter Eight is learning through the body, or what is called *somatic* or *embodied* learning. This type of learning is learning *in* an experience as it occurs, rather than from reflecting *on* the experience after it occurs. The body actually has receptors throughout that take in sensory information. At times we attend to this information better than at others, as when we have a physical, emotional, or "gut" reaction to what is transpiring around us. In this chapter we also explore the notion of spirituality, by its nature difficult to define and grasp. Nevertheless, the notion of spirituality and its place in our lives and our learning has captured the attention of not only the popular press but also adult educators. What is being acknowledged is that our spiritual selves help define who we are, whether we are at work, at home, or in a classroom. Finally, whether our learning is through our mind, our body, our spirit, or some combination of these, we often make sense of this learning through narrative, through putting it into a story format. We learn from "storying" our experience.

Chapter Nine explores non-Western approaches to learning. Immersed as we are in our own Western orientation to learning and knowing, an orientation that privileges cognition, individuality, autonomy, and independence of thought, we know little about other cultures and systems of knowing and learning. In this chapter we discuss the value of learning from others and some key concepts for understanding this approach. Then we provide a sampling of five non-Western perspectives on learning: Confucian, Hindu, Maori, Islamic, and African indigenous knowledge. We conclude the chapter by identifying some themes common to non-Western and indigenous perspectives. Emphasized are the notions that learning is interdependent, communal, holistic, and informal.

The last chapter in Part Three is titled "Critical Theory, Postmodern, and Feminist Perspectives." While some of the work from these perspectives has been available for decades, it has only been since the early 1990s that adult educators have thought about how these ideas might apply to adult learning and the practice of adult education today. Underlying all three of these approaches is questioning the way things are. Each approach, to varying degrees, has directed attention to how race, class, and gender shape the learning transaction, how power and oppression are inherent in the process, and how knowledge and truth are construed depending on the theoretical framework. In addition to these general concepts, which cut across several perspectives, we look specifically at the contributions made by each of the three schools of thought: critical theory, postmodernism, and feminist pedagogy.

CHAPTER EIGHT

EMBODIED, SPIRITUAL, AND NARRATIVE LEARNING

The whole person is made up of mind, body, and spirit. Rarely, however, are the body and spirit taken into account when we talk about learning. Our Western heritage has defined learning as a mental process that takes place in the mind—never mind that we cannot locate the "mind." The brain, which we can locate, becomes the place of learning, severed from something as concrete as the body and as ephemeral as the spirit. This focus on the mind is partly due to Western science's investigation of learning as a mechanistic process—one designed to produce responses to stimuli, or to process information, or more recently, to construct knowledge largely through reflection on experience (see Chapter Eleven for a review of these traditional learning theories).

This emphasis on the mind goes back even before twentieth-century learning theory to Descartes, a seventeenth-century French philosopher who declared that "I [that is, my mind, by which I am what I am] is entirely and truly distinct from my body" and that "body, figure, extension, motion, and place are merely fictions of my mind" (Descartes, 1637/1960, pp. 165, 118, cited in Michelson, 1998, p. 218). This separation of the mind and body was reinforced by eighteenth-century Enlightenment philosophers who believed that knowledge could be obtained through reason alone; other sources of knowledge at that time, such as faith, tradition, and authority, were rejected by many.

As a result of Cartesian and Enlightenment thinking, learning has come to be equated with mental processes, with knowing through thinking or cognition. Not until the last few decades of the twentieth century has the role of the body and the spirit in adult learning theory been considered. Feminist theorists and multicultural theorists in particular have significantly shaped this discussion, along with a number of adult educators.

This chapter will first discuss the nature of what is being labeled *somatic* or *embodied* learning—that is, learning through the body. An even larger set of writing and some research is on spirituality and its role in learning. This will be reviewed in the second section of the chapter. Finally, whether our learning is located in the mind, the body, or the spirit, or some combination of these, we often make sense of this learning through storytelling. How we learn through narrative is explored in the last section of the chapter.

EMBODIED OR SOMATIC LEARNING

Everyone can name times when the body communicates to us, whether it be a panic attack brought on by stress, a "gut" reaction to a racist comment, an upset stomach as we contemplate complaining to a teacher or boss, or being drained and exhausted from an intense encounter. So why have we tended to ignore the body as a site for learning? The main reason seems to be the Western privileging of mind over body. The focus of learning and education is "a change in a mental state, from one of ignorance, to one of knowledge. . . . In Western education, the highest status is reserved for the most abstract and immaterial learning, irrespective of its utility, and the lowest status is accorded to concrete, material learning, much of which we learn in daily embodied action" (Beckett & Morris, 2001, p. 36). Michelson (1996) observes how absurd this separation can be when an institution of higher education engages in awarding credit for prior experiential learning: "To be accredited, knowledge must be detached from the site of its production. . . . Knowledge is credited only to the degree that experience has been transcended, so that both the site of its production and the particularities of the self have been excised" (p. 190).

REJECTION OF THE BODY

But the rejection of the body may be even more basic than privileging cognitive knowledge. Goldenberg, Pyszczynski, Greenberg, and Solomon (2000) advance an interesting hypothesis that the body is problematic because it is a perpetual reminder of the inevitability of death. The dilemma is that, on the one hand, "we are animals with a deeply rooted instinct for self-preservation; on the other, we are intelligent beings with sophisticated cognitive abilities that are immensely adaptive but also render us aware of the inevitability of our own death" (p. 201). To deal with this dilemma, we engage in cognitive distancing, "strip[ping] the body of its creatureliness" and replacing it with cultural symbols and standards of beauty, sex, and so on. They conclude that "our flight from our physical nature causes us to lose a bit of what it means to be human" (p. 215).

Fleeing from the "creatureliness" of the body extends to ignoring, covering up, or satirizing our physical characteristics, bodily functions, and sexuality. But we live in our bodies, and we learn about ourselves, about who we are, through what our bodies can and cannot do and how we experience sexuality and other bodily functions. Chapman (2002) for example, analyzes the interrelationship of power and her identity through examination of bodily functions. In attending an English boarding school, eating constructed her identity: "We ate at school, every day, the food of Empire . . . seated in the dining room under the gaze of John Smith, our famous 'old boy,' sternly subduing the female colonial body of waif-like Pocahontas. We learned/ate to be future wives of the Empire. In food and eating, we position bodies in relation to others in terms of class and ethnicity, as well as morally, as in good food and bad food" (pp. 75–76).

Popular culture reflects a growing interest in reconnecting the mind and body. Both *Time* (January 17, 2005) and *Newsweek* (September 27, 2004) devoted entire issues to this topic. As the lead story in the *Newsweek* issue titled "The New Science of Mind & Body" states:

> So why is *Newsweek* devoting this Health for Life report to the mind-body connection? Because the relationship between emotion and health is turning out to be more interesting, and more important, than most of us could have imagined. Viewed through the lens of 21st-century science, anxiety, alienation and hopelessness are not just feelings. Neither are love, serenity and optimism. All are physiological states that affect our health just as clearly as obesity or physical fitness. And the brain, as the source of such states, offers a potential gateway to countless other tissues and organs—from the heart and blood vessels to the gut and the immune system. The challenge is to map the pathways linking mental states to medical ones, and learn how to travel them at will. [Benson, Corliss, & Cowley, 2004, p. 46]

The mind-body connection is not only made in terms of health and medicine. Take, for example, the Academy Award–winning movie *Ray*, depicting the life and music of Ray Charles. Clearly, this blind musician navigated the world through his body just as the genius of his music flowed through his body.

But while we can find that attention is being paid to uniting the mind and the body in popular culture, and we can even come up with personal examples of times when we have learned through our bodies, embodied or somatic knowing and learning are only now being sporadically researched and theorized about in education and other social sciences (Kerka, 2002). We now turn to definitions, examples, and theorizing related to embodied learning.

RECLAIMING THE BODY IN LEARNING

Embodied learning is most often linked to experiential learning in the sense that we learn *in* an experience. Somatic knowing, as is also true of spiritual and narrative knowing, is connected to adult learning through meaning-making. Attending to these noncognitive dimensions of knowing can bring greater understanding to our lives; they enable us to make meaning of our everyday experiences.

Learning *in* the experience is immediate, physical, emotional. It is, as Siegesmund (2004, p. 80) writes, "a felt reaction of rightness within an experience." This is not to deny that the body has a social and material location; as Michelson (1998) points out, "[L]earning is an active, world-creating process inscribed on the body and at the same time subject to particular material and discursive conditions that constrain the body within culture and in history" (p. 225). For example, a woman who physically registers a sexist comment may in the moment understand something about sexism or patriarchy. At the same time, however, this learning would be "a function of a gendered subjectivity, or a social existence lived within a woman's body in which the traces of past angers and hurt feelings, of personal and collective memories reside" (p. 226). The body, in fact, has long been a central point of analysis in feminist research and theory (Somerville, 2004).

Other examples of embodied learning are offered by Matthews (1998) and Crowdes (2000). Matthews recalls his early schooling days where by and large he had to sit still and endure, rather than be actively engaged in learning. One exception was a fifth-grade teacher who understood "the power of embodied action even at the level of ritual, [when] she provided white lab coats for us to wear, which we kept in the cloak room. She explained that when we put on these coats we would *become* scientists" (p. 238).

Crowdes (2000) noticed the irony of critical social analysis courses taught at her university in which students became quite sophisticated in analyzing issues of power and social inequity but were "detached from their bodies and agency in matters of conflict resolution and change" (p. 25). She redesigned the course and called it "Power, Conflict, and Change in Social Interaction: What's a Body to Do?" Incorporated into the course are embodied exercises to convey what is really meant by these terms and how the body can be employed, along with the intellect, to negotiate change. In one exercise called *bowing,* partners in dyads are assigned roles, with one being superior and all-powerful to whom the other must bow. The roles are reversed in the second step. After each phase students are asked to reflect on how they *felt* in either role. The third step was for each partner to bow to the other in a mutually loving and respectful way. The three phases of the exercise allow students to experience the multifaceted nature of power and power relations. It is in the experience that power relations become *meaningful.*

It is, of course, easier to see how embodied learning takes place in a physical activity such basketball or dance. But even in the realm of dance, "dance educators often seem embarrassed to speak too much about the body, thinking that to note the physical labor of dance demeans it in the eyes of intellectuals, and to call attention to the sensory, bodily pleasure of dancing makes us seem mere hedonists" (Stinson, 1995, p. 46). Stinson goes on to say that for her to really know something involves "thought as something that occurs throughout my body, not just above my neck" (p. 46). Dance choreography is that effort to convey lived experience through artistic form.

In the same way, conducting research is an embodied process beginning with a *passionate* connection to the topic one is going to research. Data gathering, Stinson (1995) points out, is very embodied, whether interviewing or observing. Sorting through the data gathered is also an embodied activity "in [an] effort to find the form and content of the work" being constructed (p. 49). So too, insights with regard to important theoretical considerations and the final form of the project "could not have arisen without attention to embodied knowledge. . . . We can think only with what we know 'in our bones,' and . . . attending to the sensory, followed by reflection, is essential in research" (p. 52).

In yet another example of embodied knowing, Yoshida (2005) describes how writing Japanese calligraphy, at first cognitive, became an embodied experience. He recounts writing the Japanese character for river *(Kawa),* which requires three strokes:

> When I finished the third stroke, I recognized a strong feeling that remained in my body. I stopped and put the brush down, and went into that feeling. It was similar to a feeling in my palm which I remembered from canoeing in the wildness. . . . The beautiful scene came back. I closed my eyes with this image. And again I wrote *Kawa* with a brush as if I was paddling with the flow of the river. In the left sidestroke the water flows with a paddle (brush). In the middle stroke, I hold the water and stop the brush. For the third, I sink the paddle deep down, holding the heavy water for the longest stroke. I push it all the way down.
>
> I felt the *Kawa* character written in this way came alive, as if flowing in front of me. I encountered the vital life of the *Kawa* character in this way. . . . The character is no longer an object outside myself, it is something living within. [p. 133]

Although the aforementioned examples of embodied learning involve the body in learning, there are also subtle differences. Amann (2003) teases out these differences in her four-part model of somatic knowing. She feels there are four dimensions to this type of knowing—kinesthetic, sensory, affective, and spiritual. Athletes, artists, dancers are all concerned with the movement of the body, or *kinesthetic learning*. This "movement and action . . . often yields lessons about discipline, diligence, dealing with stress, or solving problems" (p. 28). *Sensory learning,* she maintains, is "inherently somatic" because by definition it is how we access information through our senses; we then "relate that information to our experience and extrapolate meanings significant to our lives" (p. 28).

Embodied learning has a strong emotional or feeling dimension, which Amman labels *affective learning.* Dirkx (2001b), for example, speaks to the power of emotions wherein "meaningful learning is fundamentally grounded in and is derived from the adult's emotional, imaginative connection with the self and with the broader social world" (p. 64). Actually, science has known for some time that nerve endings extend throughout the body through which we receive impulses from outside the body (see Chapter Fifteen). Further, "emotions are enmeshed in neural networks involving reason. . . . Emotions increase the strength of memories and help to recall the context of an experience, rendering it meaningful" (Hill, 2001, p. 76). Mulvihill (2003, p. 322) is even more explicit about the neurological dimension of learning:

> There is no such thing as a behaviour or thought, which is not impacted in some way by emotions. There are no neurotransmitters for "objectivity"; rather even the simplest responses to information signals are linked with possibly several "emotional neurotransmitters" (Haberlandt, 1998). Because the neurotransmitters, which carry messages of emotion, are integrally linked with the information, during both the initial processing and the linking with information from the different senses, it becomes clear that there is no thought, memory, or knowledge which is "objective," or "detached" from the personal experience of knowing.

In making the case for including dance and the arts in education, Ross (2000) underscores the interconnectedness of emotions with somatic knowing: "The arts are firmly rooted in these exchanges between the psyche (mind) and soma (body), and the senses and emotions are the conduits of these experiences" (p. 31). Emotions are embodied and thus are an integral component of this type of learning.

The fourth component of Amann's somatic learning model is *spiritual*. The spiritual aspect of somatic learning is meaning-making through music, art, imagery, symbols, and rituals and overlaps or intersects with the other three dimensions (see Chapter Nine). Interestingly, Yoshida presents his example of somatic knowing in writing the Japanese word for river as relating to his "spiritual" roots: "As soon as the characters unfold their life, they unfold the soul, not only in me, but also in all the souls of the people who lived and wrote this character throughout Japanese history" (2005, p. 133). Götz (2001) links the embodied with the spiritual in a number of ways, citing, for example, numerous athletes who through intense physical activity have experienced spiritual moments.

Other writers have conceptualized embodied or somatic learning as *embodied cognition* (Cheville, 2005), as *ontological performance* (Beckett & Morris, 2001), or as a *somatic epistemology for education* (Brockman, 2001). Cheville proposes "a theoretical frame that locates the human body at the intersection of culture and cognition"; that is, "the human body is at once an object of culture and a subject of cognition" (p. 86). To illustrate how the body is at the intersection of culture and cognition, Cheville conducted an ethnographic study of the athletic and academic learning of a women's basketball team. Cultural expectations manifested themselves in the players having to assert their femininity off the court to counter their physicality (associated with males) on the court. Further, the African-American players fought against being seen solely as athletes, which, along with entertainers, were among the common culturally prescribed roles for Blacks. Court learning was a matter of negotiating one's body both spatially and temporally; this learning was overlaid with asymmetrical power relations between coach and players and more experienced and less experienced players. Cheville summarizes: "Only by 'being there' together in body did players enter into reflexive consciousness. For Jenny [one of the players] and her teammates, the orchestration of bodily activity was the means to a collective mindset. Learning was necessarily a political process, demanding that coaches and players negotiate their understanding through social and bodily engagement" (p. 98).

The relationship between identity, learning, and the body is explored in Beckett and Morris's (2001) article. To illustrate their thesis that identity is constructed through embodied actions in context, they studied two work settings, one an aged-care facility (ACF) and the other an English as a Second Language (ESL) classroom. In the ACF, most of the staff were female with little formal training or education. However, their physical experience in the facility, reading each situation as it occurred and finding "what works," created a community of practice where their identities as health practitioners were secure. The authors characterize this workplace as a "site of powerful adult learning for the staff," a place where "practical logic, aimed at what will work by drawing laterally on embodied experiences, prevails" (p. 41).

Beckett and Morris (2001) go on to cite two examples from the ESL classroom of what they call ontological performance. The first had to do with a Muslim woman who at first wore the headscarf but later in the course came covered in a full veil and gloves. The teacher could not understand the change, which was explained by student as, "Well, I'm closer now to my religion. I'm more . . . I'm a better person now because I do this" (p. 42). The authors point out that while the teacher saw the body as a cultural representation, "the learner presents a very different version of culture, one that is lived, where knowledge, beliefs, and experiences are located in the body, where the body is the medium for having a world" (p. 42). In the second example from the ESL classroom, learners were preparing for a two-week work experience placement. The teacher's version of the "good worker" was one who stays in his or her place, acts politely, and does not challenge the boss. The students, several of whom had many years of work experience in their home countries, continually questioned and resisted the teacher's construction of them as docile workers. These learners were "'active bodies' constructing and reconstructing their sense of self and occasionally resisting others' construction of them" (p. 43).

Brockman's (2001) somatic epistemology for education is the final conception of somatic knowing. In today's world of diversity, postmodernism, and multicultural education, he asks the important question of how we are to assess and deal with cultural "evils." All cultures perpetuate certain beliefs, values, customs, practices, and ideologies that are oppressive and even physically abusive (sanctioned violence against women, for example). Yet cultural relativism mitigates against our making a moral judgment of these behaviors. As an example, he asks what a U.S. schoolteacher should do if the teacher observes a Turkish boy beating his sister who has flirted with boys at school. "In Turkish culture, a strong value is placed on a girl's honor, so her brother is merely putting into effect the norms of their culture" (p. 328). Relying on cultural-linguistic knowledge does not provide a satisfactory basis for dealing with this moral dilemma.

What is needed, Brockman (2001) maintains, is an epistemology based on somatic knowing. Knowing through the body is more fundamental than what we know through culture. "In short, neither culture nor language are the *source* of somatic knowledge. Somatic knowledge is received from with*in* the human being; cultural knowledge is received from with*out* the human being" (p. 331). With regard to the Turkish schoolgirl, while she may cognitively know that her brother's actions are culturally appropriate, she "knows somatically the abusive and harmful nature of her brother's behavior; it is a cultural evil" (p. 331). The teacher should "stop the beating, in the name of the body—her body" (p. 333). For those who worry that an outside standard of moral behavior is being placed on a particular cultural context, Brockman responds, "The body is a criterion of knowing inclusive within every cultural context, though not independent of context. Therefore, somatic knowing offers great promise in answering the problem of relativism, because it recognizes dimensions of knowing (and reality) common within all cultural contexts" (p. 332). A somatic epistemology also holds greater promise for "a broader theory of learning than would a strictly multicultural theory" (p. 332).

In summary, reclaiming the body in learning contributes to a broader theory of learning, one that recognizes the body as a source of knowledge. This recognition alone challenges the dominant culture's claims to knowledge based predominately on reason. Legitimizing somatic knowing can also lead to developing empathy, as Crowdes (2000) attempted to do with her course on critical social theory. It is also, as Matthews (1998, p. 237) points out, "a political argument for greater educational equity." Finally, embodied knowing is linked to adult learning through its power to contribute to making sense of, or making meaning of, our lives.

SPIRITUALITY AND LEARNING

One of us (Merriam) offers this insight:

> As is true of most decade birthdays I was not looking forward to turning sixty. I basically ignored it and managed to schedule some workshops in South Korea at that time. On the exact date of my birth I and a Korean colleague were high in the mountains in the southeast part of the country engaging in an overnight Buddhist temple stay. We attended prayers, ate in silence with the monks, and spent an evening in seminar with a monk who explained the life of the monastery and basic Buddhist beliefs. During the visit I felt a sense of peace and of being "present" that I had not experienced before; the fact that I had just turned sixty seemed not to matter and my angst about it evaporated.

For the author, this was a spiritual learning experience in that the "flow" or "life force" that she felt in that mountain retreat enabled her to make meaning of her own aging. Like somatic-embodied knowing, spiritual knowing or learning is also about meaning-making, though perhaps more difficult to accommodate than embodied learning, which does have a tie to physical sensations. While most would acknowledge that human beings are spiritual beings as well as corporal and thinking beings, our image of the adult learner has been bereft of anything remotely "spiritual." Rather, the learner is "merely an animal to be socialized, a computer to be programmed, a unit of production to be harnessed and utilized, a consumer to be won" (Sloan, 2005, p. 27). Further, the sense of wonder and awe characteristic of a spiritual stance has been "trivialized" in "the contemporary market-driven world" to the point that "we have ended up attempting to reinvent it in Disneyland or through virtual reality (Mander, 1991)" (O'Sullivan, 2005, p. 70).

These gloomy images of learners in a virtual world are being countered by an outburst of writing and discussion on the place of spirituality in our lives generally, and in adult and higher education and human resource development specifically. Popular culture vehicles of movies, books, television shows, and magazine articles are reflecting this interest, perhaps, as some writers have speculated, because of the aging baby boom generation. Developmental psychologists dating back to Carl Jung have asserted that as adults move into midlife and beyond, there is an inward turning to contemplate the meaning of life and spiritual aspects of oneself. Indeed, in a longitudinal study of spiritual development in adulthood, "all participants, irrespective of gender and cohort, increased significantly in spirituality between late middle (mid-50s/early 60s) and older adulthood" (Wink & Dillon, 2002, p. 79).

Interest in the topic is manifest in bookstore titles, continuing education courses, and solidly conservative agencies such as the National Institutes of Health and the American Medical Association, both of which are investigating how spiritual practices such as meditation, yoga, and prayer can affect physical health. Spirituality has become a popular topic in even as unlikely a site as America's profit-driven corporate world. Dozens of articles and books such as Mitroff and Denton's *A Spiritual Audit of Corporate America* (1999), Bolman and Deal's *Leading with Soul: An Uncommon Journey of Spirit* (1995), and Briskin's *The Stirring of Soul in the Workplace* (1996) are calling for management to integrate spirituality into workplace practices and allow for its expression in the workplace. Coming from another perspective, and perhaps influenced by Goleman's (1995) popular book on emotional intelligence (EQ), Zohar and Marshall (2000) are proposing a spiritual intelligence (SQ) to go along with EQ and IQ. This kind of intelligence helps us "solve problems of meaning and value" (p. 4).

It is a similar picture in higher and adult education. Books, conference presentations, journal articles, and student theses and dissertations are grappling with the topic and making visible what has long been ignored—that there is a spiritual side to our learning despite the domination of rationality in the classroom. Perhaps because of the nature of this topic, with only a few exceptions, the great majority of the writing has been philosophical in nature. Drawing from these many sources, we first grapple with defining spirituality and its place in adult and higher education. Next, we have distilled from the literature a number of practices and strategies that can cultivate the spiritual dimension of our learning.

DEFINING SPIRITUALITY

There are as many definitions of spirituality as there are people writing about it. Some use other words, such as grace, heart, flow, life force, and soul, perhaps partly to avoid the inevitable confusion of spirituality with religion. While for some people spirituality and religion might be related, writers on the topic of spirituality are emphatic about the difference between the two. As Tisdell (2003, p. 29) writes, "Religion is an organized community of faith that has written doctrine and codes of regulatory behavior. Spirituality, however, is more personal belief and experience of a divine spirit or higher purpose, about how we construct meaning, and what we individually and communally experience and attend to and honor as the sacred in our lives."

Tisdell's (2003) definition of spirituality is derived from a study of thirty-one higher and adult educators specifically engaged in anti-oppression pedagogy. She presents seven assumptions about the nature of spirituality, especially as they relate to an educational setting. These assumptions are helpful in grasping what this dimension in learning is all about:

1. Spirituality and religion are not the same. . . .
2. Spirituality is about an awareness and honoring of wholeness and the interconnectedness of all things. . . .
3. Spirituality is fundamentally about meaning-making.
4. Spirituality is always present (though often unacknowledged) in the learning environment.
5. Spiritual development constitutes moving toward greater authenticity or to a more authentic self.
6. Spirituality is about how people construct knowledge through largely unconscious and symbolic processes, often made more concrete in art forms such as music, art, image, symbol, and ritual which are manifested culturally.
7. Spiritual experiences most often happen by surprise. [pp. 28–29]

Unlike most who write about spirituality from the individual's perspective, Tisdell embeds spirituality and learning in a cultural context. That is, one's spirituality is informed by and manifested in culturally defined experiences, symbols, myths, and rituals. While significant spiritual experiences are found in all cultures, "the meaning of those experiences is not only valued differently by different cultural communities, it is also manifested and given further expression symbolically differently in different cultures—in art, music, or ritual" (p. 86).

Tisdell's participants were also selected for their social justice orientation to practice. English (2005a) identifies this form of spirituality as "secular" or "public" in nature versus spirituality as purely private and individual in nature. English makes the case that this public form of spirituality goes hand in hand with adult education's social change agenda and that "accepting a strong twofold purpose—spirituality and social change—will move adult educators closer to reconciling the personal and collective divide in our field" (p. 1187).

In one of the few other empirical studies of spirituality, Courtenay and Milton's (2004) sample of adult educators and learners identified three components of spirituality: a sense of connectedness, a search for meaning, and an awareness of a transcendent force or energy beyond the self. And in an interesting angle on spirituality, McDonald (2002) looked at the role of spirituality in the life and work of committed environmentalists. Ten of the eighteen participants expressed a pantheist view in which everything is an expression of the "vital force" (p. 270). All eighteen were engaged in "the making of spirit"—that is, "the actions and experiences that bring spirit into being" (p. 269).

Although they are not empirically based, there are some helpful discussions in the literature about the nature of spirituality. Lemkow (2005, p. 24) cites David Bohm, a physicist-philosopher: "What is spirit? The word is derived from a Latin word meaning 'breath' or 'wind'—like respiration or inspiration. It is suggested by the trees moving with the invisible force of the wind. We may thus think of spirit as an invisible force—a life-giving essence that moves us deeply, or as a source that moves everything from within."

A number of writers capture this notion of wind, energy, or movement as characteristic of spirituality. Foehr (1997) speaks of "*spiritually empowering forces* or *energies* . . . having to do with creativity, imagination, inspiration, intuition, kinesthetic knowledge, felt sense, passion for knowing, the aha experience, archetypal energy, and the collective unconscious" (pp. 46–47; italics in original).

Using the word *grace* instead of spirituality, and speaking of its place in pedagogy, Graves (1997) notes its transcendent nature as well as its more common understanding as "harmony of movement, coordination, poise under pressure" (p. 15). Graves's notion of grace is not tied to a religious perspective; rather, grace, he writes, "moves to its own rhythm, follows its own agenda, and it is always beyond our power to control or manipulate" (p. 16). Grace happens "in the ordinary experiences of daily life . . . in everyday routines and habits . . . in the small joys and disappointments of life. Moreover, it shows up in the most unlikely places. Grace lurks among the vegetables in the supermarket. Grace sits on a bar stool and smokes a cigarette. Grace roams the corridors of a big city hospital. Grace is always there, everywhere; we don't see it, but it changes our lives when we experience it" (p. 16).

He recounts several stories of how grace can transform human consciousness, such as one story of a teacher, widowed with small children, feeling depressed. Upon looking outside her classroom window she sees a rabbit on the lawn below: "Somehow I realized that if that rabbit, who seemed so full of peace and so much a part of nature, would be all right then I would be too" (p. 17). Graves goes on to say that we do not find grace; rather, "*to be found by grace*—we must live not only in the immediate moment but let go of ego involvement in that moment, for grace comes in by the back door. . . . While the attention is elsewhere, grace is at work in the unconscious" (p. 16).

This notion of grace as serendipitous is echoed in Dirkx's (2001b) understanding of the soul being accessed through images. "Emotionally charged images," he writes, "are not under the willful control of the ego." Rather, they tend to appear spontaneously during the learning process. "They arrive as they so choose, as acts of grace" (p. 69). Drawing from Jungian psychology, these images reflect archetypes from the collective unconscious. "From an archetypal perspective, to teach in adult or higher education settings is to participate in a timeless story or myth" (Dirkx, Pratt, & Taylor, 2002, p. 95). Such conscious participation "can help us connect in a more profound manner with the animating forces of our lives" (p. 95).

In relating grace to pedagogy, Graves (1997) delineates several characteristics of grace. First, it is *transforming,* as in the preceding story of the teacher. Second, it is *healing;* stress and anger, grief, the most impoverished, can find healing in moments of grace. Third, grace *transcends the ego.* "Grace provides the perspective to see ourselves in the larger context, not just as students and teachers but as individuals connected with each other and with the world beyond ourselves" (p. 18). *Opening the possible* is the fourth characteristic. "Grace cuts through the boundaries of culture, language, race, social class, economic level, age, handicaps, intelligence level, geography, and birth. Grace interrupts the expected and creates its own channel" (p. 19). *Pointing toward what is right* is the fifth characteristic. The moral and ethical tone of grace echoes others' writings. English, Fenwick, and Parsons (2003, p. 3) for example, write that "the most straightforward way to promote a spiritual dimension in teaching and learning is to make a deliberate attempt to think and act ethically," simply because "ethical choices implicitly include a basic recognition of the person as spiritual" (p. 4). Grace is also about *enhancing creativity,* Graves's sixth characteristic. Finally, grace is *surprising,* it—"shows up in unexpected places, in coincidences that prove to be extraordinary, and in synchronistic events" (p. 19). It might be recalled that surprise is one of Tisdell's (2003) seven assumptions.

Given the nature of spirituality as delineated by these and other writers and researchers, it is not surprising that strategies for enhancing or fostering spirituality, soul, or grace during the teaching-learning transaction are about <u>making space for it to happen.</u>

FOSTERING SPIRITUALITY IN ADULT LEARNING

To the extent that spirituality is about meaning-making, it can be argued that it has a place in adult learning. Unfortunately, formal programs of adult education, like any other institutionalized form of learning, suffer from "order, hierarchies, grades, tests, a gloried past, control, deprivation, remoteness of various kinds, and weighty seriousness" (Moore, 2005, p. 13). For spirituality or moments of grace to happen, "weighty seriousness" must be replaced with playfulness, openness, creativity, and imagination. If, as hooks (1994) writes, "we believe that our work is not merely to share information but to share in the intellectual and spiritual growth of our students," then we must "teach in a manner that respects and cares for the souls of our students . . . [and] provide the necessary conditions where learning can most deeply and intimately begin" (p. 13).

One of the "necessary conditions" identified by several writers is that the instructor must examine her or his own biography, acknowledging and "perhaps reconcil[ing] the influence of our religious upbringing on our current spiritual preferences and resistances" (Fenwick, English, & Parsons, 2001, p. 6). That our own spiritual or religious biography has an impact is underscored in Tisdell's study of thirty-one educators. She found that while only six practiced in their childhood religious traditions, all "continually spiraled back and reclaimed images, symbols, music that still had important meaning for them from their childhood religious traditions" and that these "often connected to their cultural backgrounds" (2005c, ¶ 12).

For moments of spiritual learning to occur there must be space in the learning environment. Such a space is safe, supportive, open, "sacred." Vella (2000) outlines three aspects of a sacred space—dialogue, respect, and accountability. A sacred space allows for dialogue where one listens to others' experiences without judgment. The <u>teacher is accountable</u> for designing a learning experi-<u>ence that both supports</u> and challenges the learners. We are accountable "to make the best plans possible," but at the same time we must "be ready to abandon them" (Graves, 1997, p. 20). As Graves observes, "If grace ever comes into pedagogy, it will be there not because it was planned but because the conditions were right and because some sensitive soul had the wisdom not to thwart it" (p. 20). The spontaneous and fluid nature of spirituality requires space where it can happen. An overly programmed, information dissemination–driven classroom leaves no space for significant, indeed, spiritual, learning to occur.

A number of writers underscore the importance of allowing for dialogue. English (2000) defines dialogue as "the interpersonal connections and interchanges among people that encourage and promote their spiritual development. . . . Dialogue . . . recognize[s] the other as an extension of one's self" (p. 34). It is also through dialogue that a sense of community can be effected. It might be recalled that "connection" is one of the components of spirituality. A community of learning is people-centered, and through dialogue, discussion, and sharing, learners have the opportunity to connect with others, with their inner, spiritual selves, and perhaps with a force or energy beyond the self. This is not to ignore the difficulties in creating community in the classroom, especially in one that is culturally diverse (Hart & Holton, 1993; Tisdell, 2003).

Mentoring is an activity that can promote spiritual development. Daloz's (1999) concept of the mentor as a guide to the holistic development of the mentee speaks of the process as a journey. The relationship is also reciprocal and nurturing of both the mentor and mentee. English, Fenwick, and Parsons (2003) position mentoring and coaching in adult education and human resource development settings. They are careful to point out that this activity "is not about increasing the bottom line. It is about relationship, support, and increasing the human spirit" (p. 93). That is not to say that the power dynamics of such a relationship be ignored; rather, it is a stance or reverence in which "the spirituality of the relationship is the reciprocity that constitutes the relationship" (p. 95).

In addition to examining one's own stance, creating space, and mentoring, one can foster spirituality through the use of creative and imaginative activities such as visualization, storytelling, and the use of literature, poetry, art, and music. These activities can assist us in looking for "connections in unlikely places, between apparently unconnected and disparate ideas and experiences" (MacKeracher, 1996, p. 179). Dirkx (2001b) speaks of these techniques as the *imaginal method:*

> Journal writing, literature, poetry, art, movies, story-telling, dance, and ritual are specific methods that can be used to help foster the life of the image in our relationships with adult learners. By approaching emotionally charged experiences imaginatively rather than merely conceptually, learners locate and construct, through enduring mythological motifs, themes, and images, deep meaning, value, and quality in the relationship between the text and their own life experiences. [p. 70]

Imagination, and more specifically cultural imagination, is the focus of Tisdell's (2005c) work in linking spirituality with diversity and multicultural issues in today's higher education classroom. Imagination is a meaning-making activity in that we put together insights, images, symbols, and ideas in new ways so that new meaning is revealed. Tisdell maintains that this imaginative activity cannot be separated from the person's cultural context and history. When imagination, which "helps people to see from multiple perspectives, to visualize new possibilities, and potentially to create something new" involves "cultural stories, histories, and issues, it engages cultural imagination" (¶ 50). Using teaching strategies that cross cultural borders such as "service learning opportunities, engaged dialogue about current issues, and problem-posing techniques" along with the cultural imagination (such as sharing personal cultural symbols with others) can bring about transformation. "Image, symbol, music, ritual, art, poetry, often touch off memory in conscious and unconscious ways, which sometimes connects to spirituality. . . . One can combine these ways of knowing that are part of cultural imagination, with the intellectual and critical analysis aspects of higher education to facilitate greater student learning and greater equity in society" (abstract).

Any summary of the role of spirituality in learning would be only a partial view given the array of understandings, definitions, and conceptualizations of the phenomenon. Spirituality is, by its very nature, difficult to capture in the rational prose of academia. However, given that this dimension of our experience deals with meaning-making, it is an appropriate topic to consider because most significant adult learning is about meaning-making. Whatever label one prefers, spirituality and the creative and imaginative techniques for eliciting its presence have a role to play in a more complete understanding of adult learning. However, what exactly that role is is open to question. While we have definitions of spirituality and conditions that might elicit it in an instructional setting, what we do not yet have is an understanding of or theoretical models of *spiritual learning* as we do, for example, with self-directed learning or transformational learning. Courtenay (personal communication, June 13, 2005) speculates that if we assume spiritual learning is about meaning-making, then:

> What does that mean? Am I able to make meaning better because I use spirituality in some way? Yes, OK, then in what way? Notice I didn't ask "use spiritual learning" in some way, because I don't know what spiritual learning means, nor have I seen an acceptable definition in the literature. Staying with meaning-making further, would it be easier to explain the link between spirituality and meaning-making if we provided the opportunity for instructors and learners to ask and discuss the fundamental questions that all of us have about the meaning of life? Why are we here? What are we to do while we are here? Is this all there is and what are the implications of my answer to this question? What do I value and why? What is non-negotiable in my life and why? . . . Further issues—when meaning making is facilitated by spirituality, how is it manifested? How might it occur in an adult education classroom?

These and other questions will, we hope, shape future research and theory building in this area.

NARRATIVE LEARNING

At the close of 2004, while people were vacationing in Thailand, fishing in a coastal village of India, or just relaxing in that lull between Christmas and New Year's, an earthquake-caused tidal wave of death and destruction engulfed southeast Asia. What was impossible to grasp was made human through the *stories* of individuals—stories of how they faced then ran from the tsunami, of a village leveled, of family members being separated, some never found, of filming the wall of water from a hotel rooftop. Only through these stories could we make some sense of what had happened.

Narratives are stories, "the oldest and most natural form of sense making" (Jonassen & Hernandez-Serrano, 2002, p. 66), and they have a place in adult learning because stories enable us to make meaning of our lives. The vignette presented earlier in this chapter on turning sixty during a stay at a Buddhist temple was a *story* used to illustrate spiritual learning. And like embodied and spiritual learning, narrative learning is firmly lodged in what may be called the nonscientific. Drawing from Bruner (1986), Rossiter (2005) sums up the difference between scientific and narrative knowing: "Narrative knowing . . . is concerned more with human meaning than with discrete facts, more with coherence than with logic, more with sequences than with categories, and more with understanding than with predictability and control" (p. 419).

We not only view our own lives as narratives but are surrounded by and embedded in narratives. We watch news stories on television, tell stories of our day at school or work, perhaps write the story of our day in our diary. Rossiter and Clark (in press) organize these surrounding narratives into four types—*cultural, familial, individual* (Keen & Valley-Fox, 1989), and *organizational* (Neuhauser, 1993).

Cultural narratives or myths are those that define the sociocultural milieu in which we live; they form the taken-for-granted assumptions on which we live our lives in the way that we do. The cultural narrative "is difficult to recognize—to notice and reflect upon—because we're immersed in it. It is as invisible to us as the air we breathe" (Rossiter & Clark, in press, p. 24 of ms.). In the United States, the individual being responsible for his or her own success, the right to material wealth, the United States as superpower, and so on, are parts of our cultural narrative but so embedded that we rarely recognize them as such. Sometimes it takes a catastrophic event to expose these narratives. For example, the authorities' lack of preparedness and Hurricane Katrina's devastation of the city of New Orleans challenged the cultural narrative of the United States being all-powerful and in control. Family narratives embrace certain values and beliefs, customs, roles, and rituals. "Who are the heroes of the family, whose stories are told with pride across the years? And who are the villains, the black sheep, whose crimes . . . [are] only suggested or whispered?" (p. 26 of ms.). Individual narratives are how we story our own lives.

Finally, "just as cultures, families and individuals have narratives, so do organizations, and organizational narratives express and create the lore of the organization as in cultures and families" (Rossiter & Clark, in press, p. 30 of ms.). In adult education, these narratives can be examined, reflected upon, challenged, and even revised. Interestingly, the field of adult education itself is involved in constructing a narrative of its identity: "Are we heroes engaged in the emancipation of the oppressed? . . . Are we tour guides in the business of actualizing the human potential of people who have leisure time? Are we entrepreneurs who sell job training in a competitive marketplace? Are we all of those characters?" (p. 33 of ms.).

LEARNING THROUGH NARRATIVE

The use of narratives is common in numerous disciplines, such as psychology and literature, and fields of practice, like medicine, law, social work, and more recently, education (Hopkins, 1994). Although it has only been since the 1990s that narrative learning has received some attention in adult education, the field's historical recognition of the importance of experience in learning, as well as learning as a meaning-making activity, have made for the ready acceptance of narrative as learning. Speaking of journals, a form of narrative, Kerka (2002, p. 1) writes that "a journal is a crucible for processing the raw material of experience in order to integrate it with existing knowledge and create new meaning."

Narratives can take a number of forms, each useful as a vehicle for learning. Rossiter (2005) and Rossiter and Clark (in press) identify three ways in which stories appear in practice: "storying" the curriculum, storytelling, and autobiography. In the first, the curriculum or the text of a course is treated as a story and students interact with these texts to come to some understanding or interpretation of the subject matter. For example, in a graduate research seminar on the development of the knowledge base of adult education, Merriam made use of research journals dating back to the 1930s, periodic reviews of research, and historical literature on the founding of professional associations and graduate programs in adult education. These materials were read and examined with the goal of telling a story (not necessarily *the* story) about how the knowledge base of adult education has come to be constructed as it has. Each student was asked to interpret these materials and to write a paper (a story) about the development of the knowledge base.

This storying of the curriculum is in itself a learning process. Clark (personal communication, July 30, 2005) explains this learning: "When we are learning something new, we're trying to make sense of it, to figure out its internal logic and how it's related to what we already know. We do this by narrating it, or trying to—that is, we work to story it, to make this new idea coherent to ourselves. . . . The construction of that narrative is how we see our understanding come together and make sense. . . . The narrativizing of our understanding is how we make our learning visible to ourselves, if only in our heads."

A second form of narrative, storytelling, in various forms—such as fiction (Baumgartner & Merriam, 1999), case studies, exemplars from practice, role-playing, or critical incidents—is a common means of engaging students in understanding concepts, principles, or theories. Jonassen and Hernandez-Serrano (2002) argue that stories in the form of cases are a good instructional technique to teach problem solving. They cite a number of studies with practitioners who understood their practice not from a technical or rational perspective but rather through stories and examples from experience. These stories of past experience were what guided future action. If practitioners in real-life situations solve ill-structured problems through narratives, stories, or cases, then "stories can function as a substitute for direct experience, which novice problem solvers do not possess. Supporting learning with stories can help students to gain experience vicariously" (p. 69).

Using stories to engage students in ideas that are part of course content may be the only way to allow understanding to occur. It is also a powerful means of making connections not only with ideas but with other learners, perhaps ultimately creating a learning community. Whether these stories are generated by students themselves, are case studies, or are fictional accounts, they draw us in, they allow us to see from another's perspective. In today's multicultural classrooms we cannot assume the rest of the world sees things the way we do. "The authenticity and immediacy of a story of lived experience takes us into the experience of another. In that way it deepens and expands our capacity for taking the perspective of another. In short, life story sharing reduces resistance to new or different points of view and serves to broaden the perspectives of all participants" (Rossiter & Clark, in press, p. 107 of ms.).

The third form of narrative, autobiographies, are by the self and about the self and can include journaling, dream logs, therapy, blogs, and what Dominice (2000) calls "educational biography." Human beings have kept records of their lives for centuries. Some of these self-authored stories have become famous, such as St. Augustine's *Confessions,* or *The Diary of Anne Frank.* Others, though not by famous people, have proved enormously helpful to historians who want to tell the story of some past time or event. Slave narratives, immigrant journals, and memoirs of prisoners in Nazi concentration camps are examples of such historical narratives. Blogs are the most recent form. A blog is a Web site where "you write stuff on an ongoing basis." A blog takes any number of forms; it can be "a personal diary. A daily pulpit. A collaborative space. A political soapbox. A breaking-news outlet. A collection of links. Your own private thoughts" (http://www.blogger.com/start).

An early approach to one form of autobiographical methods— journaling—began in the well-known intensive workshops of the 1970s by Progoff (1975). In these workshops, which are still held today, journaling is used to foster the participant's potential for growth and development. Indeed, research suggests there are a number of benefits in writing to the self and about the self. Brady and Sky (2003) studied fifteen older learners who kept a journal currently and had done so for at least three years. Interestingly, participants kept journals not as a lifelong activity but rather as a sporadic activity, which would be reignited by some critical life event, such as illness, death, family problems, and so on. These participants spoke of three benefits to journal writing. First, they described it as a means of coping with their day-to-day lives, including with decisions, with relationship issues, and "as an antidote to failing memory" (p. 159). A second benefit the researchers termed "the joy of discovery," meaning that journals were "a sort of milestone for measuring one's own progress in the journey of human development" (p. 159). Finally, journaling allowed for the nurturing of one's voice and spirit; that is, journaling confirmed that they had "something meaningful to say" (p. 160), and it allowed for contemplation and sometimes the realization of a new level of spiritual consciousness.

Although the benefits of journaling for Brady and Sky's older adult learners might be partially explained by their life stage, their findings have similarities with those of other studies. Wiener and Rosenwald (1993) interviewed twelve people between eighteen and fifty years of age to identify the subjective utility of keeping a diary, a more structured form of journaling. One benefit was in establishing and maintaining boundaries among different senses of the self, and different emotions and experiences. Like Brady and Sky, the researchers in this study were surprised to learn that most participants kept multiple diaries. Participants kept separate journals for family matters, emotional writing, travel, daily events, and so on. While one benefit was maintaining boundaries of the self, another seemingly opposite benefit was dissolving boundaries. Participants reported using diaries "to allow repressed material to surface" (p. 42) and to bring to the fore varying aspects of the self.

Three other benefits uncovered by Wiener and Rosenwald (1993) are that diaries help manage emotions, manage time (a diarist can preserve the past, or condense past and present), and function as "the self in a mirror" (p. 43). By this last the authors mean that a diary can be like looking into a mirror—"defining the self by objectivating and then observing it" (p. 45).

Journal writing, whether it is about the self or about one's learning, has been advocated as a tool for adult learning, especially if the learner is asked to *reflect* on the day's (or class's) events and activities. Kerka (2000, p. 1) offers a set of assumptions about how this learning occurs:

- Articulating connections between new and existing knowledge improves learning.
- Writing about learning is a way of demonstrating what has been learned.
- Journal writing accentuates favorable learning conditions—it demands time and space for reflection, encourages independent thought and ownership, enables expression of feelings, and provides a place to work with ill-structured problems.
- Reflection encourages deep rather than surface learning.

Connections and reflection are two aspects of learning that are also present in the construction of autobiographical stories and educational biographies. Autobiographical writing requires a bit more distance from the self than does journal writing. "Because autobiography involves not only recounting memories and expressions but also finding their larger meaning, and to the extent that the activity expands the individual's knowledge of self and the world, it constitutes learning" (Karpiak, 2000, p. 34). It is in autobiography that we can identify "patterns and meaning in our life, perhaps even building a theory of our life, or of life in general. Having stepped back and reflected, we know something now that we did not know before" (p. 34). Karpiak (2000) maintains that autobiographies are a particularly potent instructional activity, especially for courses in adult learning and adult development. As one student she interviewed said, "Autobiography helps an individual find how the course material fits into their life, as opposed to having the instructor do it for you" (p. 41). Another student said that in writing her autobiography, the concept of lifelong learning, which had previously been just a "buzz word," now had meaning. She could "see that in one's life each moment is a learning experience. . . . That actual living was learning" (p. 42).

Focusing on one's educational history or how one has come to know what one knows is what Dominice (2000) calls *educational biography*. He has developed this technique into a two-semester student experience of oral and written narratives involving individual and collaborative learning. Through these biographies students see how family, schooling, and the sociocultural environment have helped them construct their identities as adult learners. "Looking at the past, checking roots, and giving names to experiential learning help adults clarify the future they want to build" (Dominice, 2000, p. 143).

NARRATIVE LEARNING, ADULT DEVELOPMENT, AND TRANSFORMATIONAL LEARNING

As is evident in the techniques already reviewed, narrative learning has very strong links to both adult development and transformational learning. As a means of understanding adult development, a narrative framework sees the life course as an unfolding story, one constructed and interpreted by the individual. While the sociocultural-historical context interacts with and to some extent shapes the life course, the meaning of our life experiences constitutes our particular developmental trajectory.

In contrast to stage and phase theories of adult development, most of which have an end state (such as Erikson's [1963] final stage of ego integrity versus despair, for example), life narratives are retrospective, always in process, unfolding. And as Rossiter and Clark (in press) point out, development from a narrative perspective can be "empowering. While we do not have control over many of the events or circumstances of our lives, we do have some choice as to how we interpret them. If something unpleasant happens it is not imperative that we will see it as the end of all happiness forever and ever. This realization of choice in meaning-making is one of the most valuable aspects of the narrative orientation" (pp. 38–39 of ms.)

Adult development and transformational learning are closely intertwined (see Chapter Six). The chief architect of transformational learning theory, Jack Mezirow, unequivocally states that the process of perspective transformation is "the central process of adult development" (1991, p. 155). The process that he delineates, however, is quite cognitive and depends on the critical examination of assumptions, reflection, and rational discourse. Randall (1996) makes a convincing case for how narrative can be seen as transformational learning. Both methods are primarily cognitive dealing with the learner's lived experience through interpretation, through creating new meaning. While Mezirow's process most often begins with a "disorienting dilemma" that causes us to examine our underlying assumptions and values, Randall suggests that when we encounter a life experience that cannot be accommodated by our old story of ourselves and the world, we seek to *restory* our lives: "We seek restorying when our current lifestory (inside, at least) no longer coheres within itself, when it becomes incoherent, when the many are at war with the one. We seek it when our central self-story has either too little conflict and so fails to go anywhere, or too much and so threatens to fly apart. . . . We might seek restorying, for example, when a particular episode fails to fit with the dominant story we tell ourselves about who we are, where we have come from, and where we are going" (p. 238).

In Mezirow's framework, transformational learning results in a "more inclusive, discriminating, permeable, and integrative perspective," one that better accommodates the meaning one makes of one's experience (1990b, p. 14). Restorying one's life is quite similar: "Specifically, it is the question as to how I can compose a story *big* enough, with a horizon *broad* enough, to account for as much as possible of my actual life and render it available to me as a coherent, re-membered whole" (Glover, cited in Randall, 1996, p. 240).

But adult development and transformational learning also involve embodied and spiritual learning. How we story our lives includes not just cognitive but emotional, bodily, and spiritual dimensions. In a study of a culturally diverse sample of midlife men and their transformative spiritual development, Davis (2004) found that the men "cited their experiences of spirit as a time of challenge and opportunity to express emotion, connect with people, relinquish control, and move beyond the rational" (p. 122).

Life transitions and crises that trigger development, whether social, psychological, or spiritual, are often highly charged, physical, and sometimes spiritual (see Chapter Twelve). The birth of a child, a major health problem, the loss of a job, and so on are experiences that are holistic in nature. In a discussion of the role of somatic learning in transformational learning, Amann (2003) explores how kinesthetic, sensory, affective, and spiritual aspects "centraliz[e] the body so that it is integral to the learning experience. Combined with opportunities for reflection, somatic learning contributes a new perspective to the scope of transformative learning" (p. 31). Brooks and Clark (2001) point out that narratives of transformative learning are compelling *because of* their affective, somatic, and spiritual dimensions.

To summarize this section on narrative learning, it is clear that adult educators have a means of facilitating learning that all adults can relate to—stories that surround us, that define us, that we can construct, analyze, reflect upon, and learn from. Stories can be used to understand content, ourselves, and the world in which we live. Narratives are also windows into development and transformational learning. They enable us to make sense of our experience, which is what adult learning is all about.

SUMMARY

Embodied, spiritual, and narrative learning all have in common meaning-making that is embodied, constructed, and interpreted. These are not modes of learning that adhere to a way of thinking that elevates reason, logic, and theory over the body, the spirit, or the "story" of our experience.

Embodied or somatic knowing is knowing through the body. It is directly related to our physical being, our senses, and the experiences of the body. Examples of embodied learning were presented and discussed; these examples reflect Amann's (2003) model of somatic knowing, which consists of the four overlapping dimensions of kinesthetic, sensory, affective, and spiritual. This section of the chapter concluded with a review of three conceptualizations of embodied learning: embodied cognition, ontological performance, and a somatic epistemology for education.

In the second section of the chapter on spirituality and learning, we first grappled with defining spirituality as something different from but perhaps related to religion. Most of the authors we reviewed link spirituality to meaning-making in our lives, and on that basis it is an appropriate topic for exploration in adult learning. A number of instructional techniques were reviewed that foster spirituality in adult learning, including self-examination by the instructor of her or his views and assumptions, creating a safe space for this kind of learning to occur, mentoring learners, and engaging in creative and imaginative instructional activities.

The final section of the chapter dealt with narrative learning. Narrative learning is the use of stories in the construction of meaning, whether the meaning-making has to do with the self, with the content of instruction, or with the world around us. Using Rossiter and Clark's (in press) model, three uses of narrative in practice were reviewed: narrative as storying the curriculum, narrative as storytelling, and narrative as autobiography. A final section focused on a narrative perspective of adult development and transformational learning.

CHAPTER NINE

LEARNING AND KNOWING: NON-WESTERN PERSPECTIVES

The newborn infant only hours old is handed to the father who whispers into the newborn's ear, "God is Great. I bear witness there is no God but the one true God." So begins the Muslim's life journey. It is a journey of lifelong learning and discovery, a journey during which every Muslim discovers the greatness of God through the beauties and wonders of His creation.
—MAZALAN KAMIS

For those of the Islamic faith, learning is indeed lifelong. It is also considered a sacred obligation to learn not for personal benefit, but for sharing with the whole community. Unfortunately, we know little about this perspective and other epistemological systems as we are immersed in our own Western orientation to learning and knowing. Indeed, this edition of *Learning in Adulthood* is primarily lodged in Western values and culture.

Beginning with the 1928 publication of Thorndike et al.'s landmark study of adult learning (Thorndike, Bregman, Tilton, & Woodyard, 1928), the knowledge base that has developed around learning and adult learning has been shaped by what counts as knowledge in a Western paradigm. Research and theory in adult learning to a large extent assumes that the mind and body are split, thus leading to an emphasis on cognition, information processing, intelligence measures, cognitive development, and so on. Embedded in this focus are the cultural values of privileging the *individual* learner over the collective, and promoting *autonomy and independence* of thought and action over community and interdependence. Andragogy, self-directed learning, and much of the literature on transformational learning position self-direction, independence, rational discourse, and reflective thought as pinnacles of adult learning theory.

That Western notions of adult learning dominate is evidenced by the use of Western textbooks, journals, and conference proceedings in academic adult education programs not only in North America but in Asia and Africa. In addition, the curriculum that international students study in graduate programs in North America is, of course, primarily Western. While there is some recent work by Western scholars on spirituality, embodied or somatic knowing, emotions, aesthetics, and the "nonrational," these perspectives are still very much on the margins of the field (see Chapter Eight).

However, we need only look more closely inside our own borders, to Native Americans, for example, and beyond the borders of North America and Western Europe, to find major systems of thought and beliefs embedded in entirely different cultural values and epistemological systems that can be drawn upon to enlarge *our* understanding of adult learning. Some of these systems predate Thorndike by thousands of years and encompass the greater part of the world's peoples. For example, in a study of self-directed learning in the Korean context, most of the Western values were rejected (Nah, 2000). Rather, "a person becoming independent of his or her parents, teachers or other people, tends to be considered threatening [to] the stability of a community he or she belongs to. . . . Becoming independent without being interdependent passes for immaturity or self-centeredness" (p. 18). Moreover, in a country that has faced numerous enemies, "collectivism and collaboration are taught from one's childhood as one of the most important survival skills and moral virtues" (p. 18).

In yet another example, the notion of transformational learning from a Buddhist thought system involves "increased insight into the nature of reality result[ing] in an understanding of the interconnection of all living beings and a decrease in human suffering" (Brooks, 2000, p. 166). Brooks goes on to point out that "although Buddhism is a part of mainstream institutional culture in many

Asian nations, it stands as an alternative to the mainstream in the West" (p. 166).

This chapter has a number of purposes. First, we introduce readers to the value of learning about other perspectives. Second, we discuss some key concepts involved in this endeavor, concepts such as the Western/non-Western dichotomy itself, ethnocentrism, culture, and indigenous knowledge. At the center of the chapter are short introductions to five different perspectives on learning and knowing; these five perspectives were first presented as a symposium at the 2005 Adult Education Research Conference and are but examples of how much we have to learn from other systems of learning. Finally, we will close with some commonalities or themes found across non-Western perspectives that stand in contrast to our Western orientation to learning.

WHY STUDY OTHER WAYS OF LEARNING AND KNOWING?

Some readers of this book might argue that since a Western perspective dominates what is considered the legitimate knowledge of adult learning, we need not bother ourselves with considering yet other systems of learning. This view is quite ethnocentric; that is, "the tendency to view one's own cultural group as superior to others" (Reagan, 2005, p. 4), and being ethnocentric, reinforces the marginalization and oppression of other systems of knowing. The purpose of examining other systems is not to replace the Western tradition but rather to *expand* our understanding of learning and knowing.

Such exposure can affect our practice as adult educators in a number of ways. First, we might rethink our purposes as educators from largely transmitters of "validated Western information" to "a more compelling form of analysis . . . engaging students in the interpretation of various knowledges and modes of knowledge production" (Semali & Kincheloe, 1999, p. 34). Closely aligned with this purpose is that considering other ways of knowing leads us to examine how knowledge is produced, whose interests are being served by this knowledge, and how knowledge comes to be validated or "official" (see Chapter Ten). "Such an awareness is too often absent in Western education. In mainstream pedagogies we are taught to believe that the knowledge we consider official and valid has been produced in a neutral, noble, and altruistic manner. Such a view dismisses the cultural and power-related dimensions of knowledge production" (Semali & Kincheloe, 1999, p. 34).

Yet another purpose in becoming familiar with other knowledge systems is the benefit this knowledge will have in affecting our practice with learners having other than Western worldviews. Antone and Gamlin (2004) for example, argue that to be effective, literacy programs with Aboriginal people (a term they use to refer to First Nations, Inuit, and Métis persons and collectivities) must be more than "reading, numeracy and writing which is typically directed towards gaining access to mainstream employment" (p. 26). Rather, Aboriginal literacy

> is about sustaining a particular worldview and about the survival of a distinct and vital culture. Being literate is about resymbolizing and reinterpreting past experience, while at the same time honouring traditional values. Being literate is about *living* these values in contemporary times. Being literate is about *visioning* a future in which an Aboriginal *way of being* will continue to thrive. Meaningful Aboriginal literacy will develop and find expression in everything that is done. Consequently Aboriginal literacy programs must reflect a broad approach that recognizes the unique ways that Aboriginal people represent their experience and knowledge. [p. 26; italics in original]

Another example of how having some familiarity with other worldviews can affect our practice as adult educators is in understanding how many Asian students view aspects of the teaching-learning transaction. Their reticence to question or speak out in our classes is due to years of training that speaking out might cause someone (the teacher in particular) to lose face; the accepted strategy is to personally approach the teacher outside class. Further, "silence is used by east Asian collectivists as an indication of strength, power, and disagreement, whereas individualists see it as an indication of weakness, shyness, or trouble" (Liu, 2001, p. 190). Finally, Wang (2006) points out that for a Chinese student, sharing something personal in our adult education classes is seen as a sign of weakness, a loss of manners, or an attempt to seek help.

A final value in expanding our understanding of learning to include perspectives outside of our traditional Western views is that we will be personally enriched. Such exposure leads to reflecting on our own ideas in new ways, and hearing others' stories about their learning contributes to our own meaning-making. While we can

> acknowledge that no story perfectly evokes all that is true about our lives, . . . we must also acknowledge that the more stories we have available to us, the richer are our resources . . . the more voices and narratives to which we listen, the more abundantly we experience our lives. In fact, we often find that as different from ourselves as we may imagine the others who create those narratives to be, we can still find that the stories from their lives reflect something true about our own. In that case, for both their differences and their similarities, we can hardly afford to let some voices remain marginal and silenced and other voices dominate. [Brooks, 2000, p. 169]

For example, in one of our adult development classes an adult learner from India shared her story of living with her parents, as is the custom, until she was married at age thirty-two. She saw this as a great advantage in her learning to be a mature adult because she had her parents as constant role models. At the same time, she came to understand what aging meant for older adults and developed both compassion and admiration for the older generation.

THE WESTERN/NON-WESTERN DICHOTOMY, CULTURE, AND INDIGENOUS KNOWLEDGE

There are a number of concepts that are important to consider when stepping out of our Western-only perspective on learning. First to be considered is the dichotomy of Western versus non-Western. Culture and indigenous knowledge are two other concepts that inform this effort.

We have used "non-Western" in the title of this chapter to convey something different from the epistemology that many label "Western" that informs the rest of this book. This notion of dichotomies is itself a very Western concept, a fact not lost on us. Dichotomies such as *mind-body, nature-nurture, emotion-reason,* and *human-animal* are in fact an "obsession . . . that runs through Western intellectual history" (Nisbett, 2003, p. 154). And, of course, there are a number of anomalies in using these terms—for example, many indigenous peoples of North America do not adhere to a "Western" perspective. Also problematic is the suggestion that "Western" is the gold standard against which we measure non-Western, thus depriving non-Westerners of having legitimate knowledge apart from Western norms. So why do we use these categories? As Reagan (2005, p. 11) notes, "The biases inherent in the terms are in fact a significant and telling component of the phenomenon that we are concerned with studying. . . . Thus, what begins as a false dichotomy can emerge as an effective way of challenging and reforming racist and ethnocentric assumptions and biases."

A Western perspective is often traced to classical Greek culture where "personal freedom, individuality, and objective thought" (Nisbett, 2003, p. 30) were developed, brought to Europe, and extended to other parts of the world through European colonization. Still going on today is the intellectual "colonization" of the world, largely through Western science. "A key to comprehending the power of Western science involves its ability to depict its findings as universal knowledge. Modernist science produces universal histories, defines civilization, and determines reality: such capabilities legitimate particular ways of seeing and, concurrently, delegitimate others" (Semali & Kincheloe, 1999, p. 31).

The separation of knowledge from its context and its codification according to Western science has had an impact on educational thought and practice. We collapse education into "schooling," for example, so that in adult education learners have a difficult time thinking of their learning as anything but participation in formal classes. Informal learning, which adults engage in on a daily basis, hardly counts as "real" learning. "Western epistemological tyranny and the oppressive educational practices that follow it" (Semali & Kincheloe, 1999, p. 31) have resulted in our overlooking rich sources of knowledge. For example,

> Western epistemological exports to Africa . . . tend to limit reality
> to appearances with which they [Westerners] seek to justify, mostly
> without explanation, the so-called absolute and irrefutable truth.
> For Africans, the search for truth goes beyond appearances into
> some deep understanding of why the truth is truth. Sometimes the
> search for truth may be mystified as [when] recourse may be
> made to traditional religious performances. Among the Yoruba in

Nigeria, the *ifa* oracle of divination may be used to determine what the truth is. Magical understanding and interpretation of the truth is accepted in Africa and this is connected to the way in which people know. [Fasokun, Katahoire, & Oduaran, 2005, pp. 63–64]

The Western/non-Western dichotomy is one means of considering alternative perspectives to our understanding of learning and knowing. *Culture* is another, which is of course part of defining Western and non-Western perspectives. There are as many definitions of culture as there are individuals who write about it. Basically, culture consists of the shared behavior and symbolic meaning systems of a group of people. It is, as Hofstede (1984, p. 51) writes, "the collective programming of the mind which distinguishes the members of one category of people from another." Banks and Banks (1997, p. 8) have more recently defined it as follows:

> The essence of a culture is not its artifacts, tools, or other tangible cultural elements but how the members of the group interpret, use, and perceive them. It is the values, symbols, interpretations, and perspectives that distinguish one people from another in modernized societies; it is not material objects and other tangible aspects of human societies.

While we often link "Western" and "culture" together, "there is no single 'Western' culture in any really meaningful sense; rather, there are many different and distinct cultures that share certain elements of a common historical background that are manifested in different ways in the present" (Reagan, 2005, p. 37). What linking "Western" and "non-Western" to culture does is to provide a kind of shorthand for comparing two epistemological systems. For example, Jegede (1999) presents a table comparing African and Western systems of thought. In African culture "orality predominates," whereas in Western thought knowledge is "documented." Similarly, in Africa, "learning is communal," but in the West, "learning is an individual enterprise" (p. 125).

Abdullah (1996), a management consultant in Malaysia, compares what she calls "individualistic" or "more Western" with "collectivistic" or "more Eastern" cultural interpretations of values. With regard to group versus individual preference, for example,

"Westerners" value freedom and independence whereas "Easterners" value belonging, harmony, family, security, and guidance; success in the West is materialistic but in the East it is relationship- or friendship-based. The communication style in a more Western cultural orientation is direct, to the point, and emphasizes clarity; in a more Eastern culture communication is subtle, indirect, and often employs a third party. Understanding these and other differences in values, Abdullah points out, is crucial to managing a multinational and multicultural workplace.

What are presented as "Western" or "African" or "Eastern" values and systems of thought capture, imperfectly of course, some of the differences that in turn affect not only how we see the world but how learning experiences are interpreted. For example, in a study of the role of cultural values in shaping older adult learning in Malaysia, participants spoke of learning as a spiritual or philosophical quest, and as "a responsibility and a means of giving back to their communities" (Merriam & Muhamad, 2000, p. 60).

A third concept important for understanding learning and knowing from non-Western perspectives is that of *indigenous knowledge*. Like culture, indigenous knowledge has been defined in numerous ways. Most definitions consider it "local or community knowledge that is commonly generated and transmitted over a period of time in geographic and historic space" (Fasokun, Katahoire, & Oduaran, 2005, p. 61). It is knowledge generated to deal with local problems and issues "related to health, farming, warfare, education, culture and the environment" (p. 61). This is knowledge produced by people, who, according to the World Council of Indigenous Peoples, "occupied lands prior to populations who now share or claim such territories"; indigenous peoples may also "possess a distinct language and culture" (Semali & Kincheloe, 1999, p. 40). Dei, Hall, and Rosenberg (2000) point out that many indigenous cultures value the following: "seeing the individual as part of nature; respecting and reviving the wisdom of elders; giving consideration to the living, the dead, and future generations; sharing responsibility, wealth, and resources within the community; and embracing spiritual values, traditions and practices [with] reflection [on] connections to a higher order, to the culture, and to the earth" (p. 6).

Indigenous knowledge differs from official, academic knowledge in several ways. First, it is organic in the sense that it is generated during the daily lives of people in a local context rather than "by planned procedures and rules" (George, 1999, p. 80). This knowledge is typically passed on from one generation to the next in oral, rather than written form. Finally, "indigenous knowledge is not to be found in the school curriculum" (p. 80). So, too, the "pedagogy" of indigenous knowledge differs from traditional schooling or education. Knowledge is conveyed through "story-telling, poetry, metaphor, myth, ceremony, dreams and art; and honoring indigenous elders as 'cultural professor'" (Graveline, 2005, p. 308).

As many writers have pointed out, we have much to learn from indigenous knowledge systems throughout the world. What has until recently prevented us from accessing and learning from these systems is

> "Western" knowledge production—it is self-contained, self-sustaining, handy, convenient, and even tinged with a sense of righteousness. . . . Hermetically sealed, the closed system of "Western" knowledge production has been institutionalized, in a matter of several hundred years, to such a degree as to dismiss indigenous knowledges based on thousands of years of experience, analysis, and reflection as primitive (Allen, 1989; Deloria, 1997; Harjo & Bird, 1997). It is . . . intellectual apartheid. [Rains, 1999, p. 317]

By way of summarizing, it is our thinking that non-Western perspectives on learning and knowing include, for example, indigenous knowledge systems such as found in Africa, in Native American and First Nations peoples of North America, and in Maori people of New Zealand and Aboriginal people of Australia. Typically, however, major philosophical or religious systems of thought such as Buddhism, Islam, Hinduism, Confucianism, and so on are labeled "non-Western" rather than indigenous. Of course, how we group or label these systems is not what is important. What is important is that by becoming acquainted with other ways of learning and knowing we enrich our understanding of learning, and ultimately our practice with adults.

AN INTRODUCTION TO FIVE NON-WESTERN PERSPECTIVES ON LEARNING

Following is a sampling of five non-Western perspectives on learning. There are, of course, book-length descriptions of each of these, and there are many other non-Western and indigenous educational traditions that could be explored; however, it is not the intention of this chapter to be comprehensive with regard to these perspectives. Rather, we wish to introduce readers to the *possibilities* in learning about other ways of knowing. The perspectives included here were presented by their authors in a symposium held at the Forty-Sixth Annual Adult Education Research Conference at the University of Georgia, Athens, on June 4, 2005 (Merriam et al., 2005).

ADULT LEARNING FROM A CONFUCIAN WAY OF THINKING: YOUNGWHA KEE

The Confucian notions and perspectives on adult learning that I present here are based on four basic books about Confucianism: *Confucian Analects* (Sung, 1991a), *Mencius* (Sung, 1991d), *The Great Learning* (Sung, 1991c), and *The Doctrine of the Mean* (Sung, 1991b). Although *The Great Learning* focuses mainly on the Confucian way of learning, the other three books based on Confucian philosophy and ideas also contribute to our understanding of learning as proposed by Confucius (551–479 BC), who is also called Kung-tzu.

According to Chu Hsi, a twelfth-century scholar of Confucianism, the philosophy behind this conception of adult learning is to imitate the virtues of another person. According to Chu Hsi, a person who does not know how to act in a situation will follow the example of one who does know. Imitation of the conduct of the sages is true learning.

Confucius also expressed the concept of true learning with two characters *Hak* and *Seb*, which can be translated into the one word *learning* in English. Kung-tzu taught the principle of learning as *Hak-Yi-Shi-Seub*, which refers to the enjoyment of learning through daily experience. Seub, especially, has the literary meaning of a bird that is learning to fly by the continuous practice of flapping its wings in imitation of an example. Hak-Yi-Shi-Seub expresses a constant symbolic relationship with the world around us to feed off of—that is, learn from—the myriad situations we encounter as we go through our lives.

According to *The Great Learning*, the adult learning process is a highly complex process, involving commitment, continuous effort, and a holistic approach. This continuous learning process is constructed by learners through the inner self interacting with nature. It is a project that cannot be completed in a limited time frame. It emphasizes meditation to control oneself and internal integration between self and nature. And it is extended through continuous dialogues with others within the parameters of human relationships. It is a holistic approach to learning: to become fully human through self-rectification and spiritual study.

The purpose of adult learning is to enlighten the people, to love the people, and to rest in "the highest excellence." According to *The Great Learning*, eight steps should be followed to reach the highest excellence: investigation of things, extension of knowledge, sincerity of will, rectification of the mind, cultivation of one's personal life, regulation of the family, national order, and world peace. Adult learning is a guide to becoming fully human. Adult learning, according to Confucianism, cannot be used as a tool for achieving specific goals in a specific situation. For example, the contents of learning are not related to vocational or skill acquirement. Instead, adult learning is focused on spiritual development.

According to *The Great Learning* (Sung 1991c), adult learning highlights both learning on one's own and peer learning. *Confucian Analects* (Sung, 1991a, p. 139) mentions that "there must be a role model even when a few people take off on the road together." It emphasizes peer learning among adult learners. Moreover, *Confucian Analects* says that teachers must wait until adult learners understand by themselves; then, at this time, teachers must again help learners' understand through individual learning.

Finally, the relationship between teacher and students is not equal as it is in Western society. The teacher is respected by members of society, and learners are asked to obey their teachers. This comes from the Confucian idea expressed as gun (king), sa (teacher), bu (parent), ilche (the same body) in Chinese characters. This means: teacher, parent, and king are treated equally and have the same importance in one's lives. This idea is still prevalent in Confucian educational systems in Korea, Taiwan, and China.

THE HINDU PERSPECTIVE: SWATHI NATH THAKER

Imagine, for a moment, that you are interviewing people for a position and your next candidate is Indian. What characteristics come to mind? What types of knowledge do you think this particular individual possesses? Often when one thinks of an individual of Indian origin, one imagines a person with a strong aptitude for math, science, and technology. However, when one visits India, it is not technology that is readily apparent but rather a spiritual atmosphere that emanates from the people of this country. It is not simply religion but rather a holistic view of life. This view of life combines both cognition and spirituality to create individuals who view learning and the development of knowledge not merely as the acquisition of skills and facts but rather as a means to becoming unified beings. As Dr. Merriam has noted, Western notions of learning have dominated, and still dominate, the field of adult education, with issues such as somatic learning and spirituality emerging only recently. While much of the research and theory suggests that the mind and body are split, a number of cultures around the world do not believe in this dichotomy, and Hinduism is no exception.

Hinduism, which is said to be over four thousand years old, defines itself according to the Vedas, the most ancient body of religious literature. Although much of this content has long been unknown to most Hindus, it is still regarded as an absolute authority, revealing the fundamental truth. While the connection between mind and body is evident in these scriptures, the Vedas also chronicle the relationship between guru, or teacher, and student, which is believed to be sacred and revered. This connection between instructor and pupil is prevalent in early writings, such as the Mahabharat, an epic in itself, which contains a code of life, a philosophy of social and ethical relations that offers spiritual strength. The following story, contained within this literature, highlights the sacred relationship of guru and student:

> Ekalavya witnesses the archery skill of Drona and wishes him to be his guru. However, Drona refuses, for a number of reasons, chief among them because he already has a pupil, Arjuna, to whom he has promised the title of greatest archer in the world. Disappointed, Ekalavya takes it upon himself to secretly watch Drona

during his instruction. Through his absolute devotion to the art and ceaseless practice, Ekalavya's skills surpass those of Arjuna. Arjuna's dream is shattered and Drona inquires how the youth has learned such an art. Though it can be argued that it was Ekalavya's devotion and determination that developed his success, he honors Drona by kneeling before him. Drona becomes upset when he realizes that Ekalavya has been watching him, as he has a loyalty to Arjuna. Thus, Drona asks Ekalavya for his right thumb as payment for this "teaching," which he immediately offers out of gratitude, even though he knows he will no longer be able to practice archery.

This story illustrates both sides of the connection between student and master. Drona felt a strong bond to his disciple, Arjuna, and helping him fulfill his dream of becoming the world's greatest archer. Thus, he asks Ekalavya for his thumb, knowing full well that this will make it impossible for the youth to be an archer. In turn, Ekalavya feels a deep reverence for Drona because he views him as his master and guide. It is because of this respect that Ekalavya freely offers his thumb. While this tale does represent the notion of apprenticeship, because both Arjuna and Ekalavya were seeking to master a specific skill, it also highlights how, in Hindu philosophy, the guru-student relationship extends much further than that. Though Hinduism does allow for individuation, its focus is on spiritual growth, thus helping individuals to connect the mind and body.

The values and beliefs of Hinduism, such as karma (the law of cause and effect), are often learned not through readings but through oratory. While religious scriptures such as the Mahabharat, Ramayana, and the Bhagavad Gita are now in written form, much of their contents are taught through storytelling. Children grow up hearing tales, such as the one told earlier, from their parents and grandparents, that highlight the philosophical values of Hinduism. In this culture, items do not necessarily need to be written down in order to carry significance. Instead, the core underpinnings of Hinduism are passed from generation to generation through an oral tradition. This is especially true in relation to the Vedas, which are considered to be the heart of Hindu culture. Though many can no longer read these scriptures (the language of Sanskrit is a dying art), their message lives on in the stories that families share. It is the recounting of these generational tales, and not the written word, that keeps Hinduism alive. In addition, dance and music are used to share the lessons that are contained in the ancient texts. The use of these various art forms also helps keep Hindu traditions alive.

Throughout life, Hindus strive to become learned in multiple ways. It is not simply about developing cognitive skills, but rather to discover oneself, because this is the only means and path to liberation and wisdom. However, this self-discovery is not the end of the spiritual journey but rather a stepping-stone to gaining a more holistic understanding of the universe. Whereas Western belief teaches that an individual is empowered through himself or herself, Hinduism argues that true empowerment emerges through an understanding of the sources of knowledge, not just its components, thus leading to unity with the universe, which at times requires a renouncing of the self and worldly possessions. This is particularly poignant during the last stage of life, when individuals abandon their home and belongings and set forth on a pilgrimage or seek sanctuary in an ashram, which is a spiritual hostel. This type of journey still takes place today, because it is believed that this passage leads to true enlightenment through unification of the mind and body. Thus, life for a Hindu is not about the acquisition of knowledge but rather about developing wisdom through gaining an understanding of oneself in a holistic manner.

This notion of foregoing identity in order to reach a state of higher understanding is powerful, and often neglected in Western thought. There is a strong emphasis on individuation in the West that is not readily apparent in Hinduism. The Hindu learner continually strives to understand the larger picture and his or her connection to the universe as a whole. It can be argued that this mentality allows learners to open themselves to varying sources of knowledge. By allowing a variety of forms of knowledge, such as through meditation and stories, and not relying solely on the printed word, Hindu learners are able to obtain a level of spiritual being that is often difficult for Western students. As the Western educational system begins to value other ways of knowing, its learners will have an opportunity to focus less on the self and increasingly on forming a unity with the world at large.

MAORI CONCEPTS OF LEARNING AND KNOWLEDGE: BRIAN FINDSEN

He aha te mea nui o te ao? He tangata, he tangata, he tangata. (What is the most important thing in life? It's people, it's people, it's people.)

This proverb from Maori traditions stresses the centrality of people to any activity of living. Learning is no exception. Maori learning has always been lifelong and lifewide, long before these concepts became fashionable in adult education circles and beyond. *Ako,* the Maori word for learning, necessarily entails historical and cultural dimensions and is also the word for teaching. Before Freire (1970) explained the concepts of teacher-student and student-teacher, the term *ako* did not differentiate between those who dispense knowledge and those who acquire it. Knowledge is always a collective entity.

In this situation I need to state my positionality in relation to the construction of Maori knowledge. As a New Zealander and student of *Maoritanga* (things Maori), I offer an "insider" perspective; as a *Pakeha* (European), I offer an "outsider" viewpoint, unavoidably Eurocentric to a degree. I can never be bicultural in the same way as a Maori person who is immersed in the dominant culture and subject to its oppressive power relations; I choose as a member of the dominant colonizing group to better understand Maori concepts and perspectives.

The Treaty of Waitangi provides much of the policy context for Maori self-determination and what counts as knowledge in officially bicultural *Aotearoa* (the Maori word for New Zealand) today. In this contemporary society, the treaty, signed in 1840 by 512 chiefs of the Maori people and Governor Hobson, on behalf of the British Crown, functions as a blueprint for relations between *tangata whenua* (people of the land) and *tauiwi* (non-Maori), including relationships in the educational realm. Importantly, three principles derived from the treaty are prominent in current government social policy: protection (of *taonga,* or cherished possessions, such as language), partnership (moving forward on an equal power basis), and participation (the rights of Maori to active citizenry, including equality of educational opportunity and outcomes).

When discussing Maori concepts, traditional tribal structures need to be analyzed to provide the basis for the social construction of knowledge. Maori trace their *whakapapa* (genealogy) back to the Great Migration of the seven *waka* (canoes). Each waka claimed geographically different parts of Aotearoa for *iwi* (tribes). Within each iwi are *hapu* (subtribes) and within each hapu are *whanau* (extended families). Hence, the whanau serves as a fundamental unit for living and learning. Although iwi were originally concentrated in particular geographical areas, the reality now, after massive urbanization, is that Maori people are scattered through the country though usually still anchored to their tribal identity. Knowledge is a *taonga,* unevenly distributed, though highly valued; some of it is *tapu* (sacred) and controlled traditionally by *tohunga* (experts). While there is much in common among iwi, there are also significant differences, related to *marae* (community sites for hapu or iwi) protocol. Much knowledge is constructed and reinforced via *hui* (meetings) held on marae where local customs are emphasized and whanau socialization occurs. However, especially in urban settings, some of the traditional aspects of learning have been diminished and new social practices established.

One of the prominent features of New Zealand life is the increasing autonomy claimed by Maori in accord with *tino rangatiratanga* (self-determination). This bid by Maori for greater control over their lives is mirrored in other parts of the world where indigenous peoples are making serious efforts to reclaim political, economic, and educational sovereignty. As Maori have been disenfranchised from much of government-funded education (as evidenced by historical national statistics of underachievement), their solution has been to rebuild Maori collective consciousness by establishing their own sites of learning, where control is in their own hands. Knowledge is defined and constructed by Maori for Maori and learned in culturally appropriate ways. *Kohanga reo* (language nests) began in 1981; here, preschoolers are taught according to Maori customs in *te reo* (Maori language). Currently, over six hundred kohanga reo exist. Following this initiative are sixty *kura kaupapa Maori* (Maori elementary-secondary schools) and new *whare wananga* (houses of learning for adults). Hence, a lifelong education system, consisting of Maori education institutions, has been established by Maori, assisted to a modest extent by the public purse. The struggle has been hard but the rewards great.

In Maori education institutions, consistent with overarching principles derived from the treaty, there are six subprinciples adopted by prominent Maori educators (see Bishop & Glynn, 2003). They are as follows:

1. *Tino rangatiratanga* (relative autonomy). Organizers of the schools make all the required administrative, staffing, and pedagogical decisions.
2. *Taonga tuku iho* (cultural aspirations). To be Maori is to be normal. Maori language and knowledge are valued and legitimated.
3. *Ako* (reciprocal learning). Teaching and learning are connected to the real lives of Maori, cognizant of their life circumstances.
4. *Kia piki ake I nga raruraru o te kainga* (mediation of difficulties). Participation in kura reaches into the homes of Maori, and families are expected to participate in kura activities.
5. *Whanau* (extended families). Collectives of people work toward a common goal.
6. *Kaupapa* (collective vision or philosophy). There is a collective vision of what constitutes excellence in Maori education.

The fundamental essence of the kura kaupapa Maori is to assist Maori families to problem-solve in a culturally suitable fashion and to work alongside children in education and enhance their own lifelong learning aspirations.

ADULT LEARNING FROM AN ISLAMIC PERSPECTIVE: MAZANAH MUHAMAD AND MAZALAN KAMIS

The word *Islam* originates from three Arabic letters (Sim, Lam, Mim), making the root word which means to be in peaceful submission, to obey, to surrender, and peace. In the religious context it means "total submission to the will of Allah and obedience to His law." Muslims draw upon the Qur'an as a primary learning source and supplement it with the *hadith,* a collection of the recorded sayings of Prophet Muhammad.

Islam is a comprehensive way of life and it pays special attention to education and knowledge seeking. In some aspects, the Islamic perspective on learning differs from that of the West. Differences include the purpose of knowledge, communal obligation, responsibility to share knowledge, and the teacher-student relationship.

Learning is considered sacred and obligatory for an individual as well as for the community. It is a form of *jihad,* which means *struggle.* In the very first verse of the Qur'an, the Prophet was instructed to read: "Read! In the name of your Lord, Who has created (all that exists). Read! And your Lord is the most generous. Who has taught (the writing) by the pen. Has taught man that which he knew not" (Qur'an 96:1–5).

In Islam, the purpose of education is to bring humankind closer to God and His creation. Since God is "the source of knowledge, by knowing more they felt they were drawing near to God" (Husain & Ashraf, 1979, p. 11). The Qur'an also guides humans to investigate the phenomena of nature, so that they will recognize, worship, and serve Allah. The Islamic notion of education integrates the rational, spiritual, and social dimensions of a person (Cook, 1999). This notion is grounded in sincerity, where knowledge gained is meant to guide practice and espouse humility. The Prophet said: "Actions are but by intention and every man shall have only which he intended."

The emphasis on a communal learning obligation is unique because it stresses the believers' responsibility to society. Education and the acquisition of knowledge are good only if "they serve to engender virtue in the individual and elevate the whole community" (Cook, 1999, p. 349). Learners and society benefit from knowledge acquisition, "Are those who know equal to those who do not know?" (Qur'an, 39:9).

Islam recognizes that both learning and teaching are equally important. In his last sermon the Prophet said, "Let those who are present inform those who are not." In another hadith the Prophet calls for a person to "be a scholar/teacher, . . . or be a student who studies, or be a listener who listens to people who teach. Do not fall into the fourth category: hater of the above."

A teacher is a learned person who is a keeper of God's treasure—that is, knowledge. A teacher is like the sun, which being itself luminous, sheds light: "The passing away of a whole tribe is more tolerable than the death of one learned man" (Faris & Ashraf, 2003). The student-teacher relationship is, therefore, sacred. Thus, *adab* (discipline of body, mind, and spirit) must be observed when one interacts with one's teacher.

Finally, learning is lifelong. The Prophet said, "Seek knowledge from the cradle to the grave." The Prophet was forty years old and illiterate when the Qur'an was first revealed to him. A well-known Islamic scholar, Al-Imam Shaffie, described a person who ceases to learn as dead. Like a drop of water in the sea, one can never complete acquiring knowledge, a notion supported by the Qur'an (18:109). It is clear that age, gender, or ethnicity should not be a barrier or a prerequisite for learning. Seeking, reflecting, and sharing knowledge is noblest of all in Islam.

AFRICAN INDIGENOUS EDUCATION: GABO NTSEANE

Research on African traditional education (Morolong, 1996; Mautle, 2001; Magagula & Maziboku, 2004) reveals that education and learning are not recent interventions in traditional societies. They had specific principles, methods, and social institutions to foster learning. The literature also shows that a major principle of African indigenous knowledge systems is that to learn is to live usefully and happily with one's family, with one's community, one's society, and the spirits of one's ancestors—hence, the importance of the words *botho* in Setswana or *ubuntu* in Zulu, whose literal translation is "humanism of human beings collectively."

Informality, collective learning, oral modes of instruction, and acquisition of revealed knowledge through dreams and visions are also important. Unfortunately, current adult education practices have overlooked some of these important principles of African pedagogy. It is argued that a creative adult education practice that modernizes tradition but at the same time traditionalizes modernity is required.

In the African context, education is supposed to help groups of people reach the highest level of important societal values, such as *botho*, or humanism. By being botho the individual then becomes part of an empowered group of people who are honest, accommodating, sharing, committed to saving lives at all costs, and respecting of the young and the old. The opposite of botho is selfishness, greediness, and self-centeredness—characteristics not good for humanism because they do not promote cooperation between individuals, cultures, and nations.

However, the values of *ubuntu* have been marginalized in education because of the historical process of colonialism and a materialistic economy. The result is an education lacking in the ability to respond to the needs and interests of indigenous communities. Adult education has been accused of elevating technical rationality over other forms of knowledge, human thought, and discourse.

Locally based knowledge is generated through a systematic process of observing the local environment, experimenting with solutions, and readopting previously identified solutions to changing environmental factors. It is acquired and shared through empirically based observation, imitation, and continuous practice through a phased childhood and adolescence. It encourages *participatory education* through ceremonies and rituals, spiritual work, recreation work, and intellectual training such as storytelling and poetry. Knowledge is stored in cultural and religious beliefs, taboos, folklore, or myths and an individual's practical experience. The lack of hierarchy and theoretical concepts allow easy sharing of knowledge.

In oral societies such as in Africa, every normal person, besides being required to be a productive worker, also plays the double role of learner and teacher. A unique form of formal instruction is the acquisition of revealed knowledge through the processes of dreams and visions. For example, many herbalists in Botswana claim that the secrets of their medicine and how it should be administered were communicated to them mainly through dreams.

In the absence of literacy, Mautle (2001) observed that assessment in Botswana included performing group tasks and judging an individual's character in relation to the overall group's performance. Real graduation occurred only after a group had successfully initiated the cohort that followed it. Accreditation was not in the form of a certificate to an individual but rather the graduates were given a name for their cohort and assigned a community-based activity. The activity had to be relevant to the current needs of the society, such as building a corral for stray cattle.

Although I advocate for the recognition of African indigenous knowledge, I by no means advocate for a complete uprooting of the other cultural aspects of the current adult education curriculum. Only good aspects of African indigenous knowledge systems should be adapted.

COMMON THEMES ACROSS NON-WESTERN AND INDIGENOUS PERSPECTIVES

From this small sampling of non-Western and indigenous perspectives we can see a number of themes about learning that stand in contrast with Western views. The four themes of interdependent, communal, holistic, and informal learning highlight different *emphases* in learning, rather than suggesting an either/or stance.

First, there is an emphasis on *interdependence* instead of independence in learning. Western models of development and learning promote a movement toward being more independent; to be in control of one's life and learning, to be a productive member of society, is, in fact, what it means to be "mature" in our society (see Chapter Twelve). Andragogy, self-directed learning, and Mezirow's theory of transformational learning all focus on the individual becoming an independent learner who relies mostly on himself or herself in the process.

This notion is in stark contrast to non-Western learning traditions as is obvious in all five of the preceding vignettes. Identity, self-concept, and self-esteem are developed and enhanced only in relation to others. Recall Nah's (2000) research into self-directed learning in Korea mentioned earlier in this chapter wherein independence is considered immature and self-centered. Commenting on the African context, Fasokun, Katahoire, and Oduaran (2005, p. 10) note that while of course "no one is exclusively independent or interdependent" and some balance "is struck by each society, in most African cultures the individual gains significance from and through relationships with others."

Second, the notion of interdependence is linked to the *communal* nature of learning in non-Western systems, rather than the more isolated Western teaching-learning transaction. It is the responsibility of all in the community to teach and to learn. In commenting on seven traditions (African indigenous, Aztec, Native American, Confucian, Hindu and Buddhist, Rom, and Islamic) presented in his book, Reagan (2005) observes:

> The concept of some adults being *teachers* and others (presumably) being *non-teachers* is a somewhat alien one to many traditions. Furthermore, it is interesting to note that in none of the cases examined

here—even those with the most fully articulated formal educational systems—was there any explicit, formal training for those who would play teaching roles. The idea of teachers engaging in a profession, with specialized knowledge and expertise not held by others, appears to be a Western, and indeed relatively recent, innovation. [p. 249; italics in original]

Third, a *holistic* approach that includes the spirit, mind, body, and emotional components of learning, or some combination of these, is emphasized over the Western focus on the cognitive. In non-Western traditions, education and learning are in the service of developing more than just the mind. They are also to develop a good person, a moral person, a spiritual person, one who not only contributes to but also uplifts the community. Benally (1997) speaks of learning in the Navajo tradition: "Western tradition separates secular and sacred knowledge and thus fragments knowledge. Consequently, some learning is forgotten soon after academic program requirements are met because it was never grounded or connected to life processes" (p. 84). In contrast, "for the Navajo, knowledge, learning, and life itself are *sacred, inseparable, and interwoven parts of a whole.* The quality of each determines the quality of the other" (p. 84; italics in original). Because development of the whole person is imperative, instruction can take many forms to access these different dimensions, such as storytelling, poetry, ceremonies, dreams, meditation, and so on.

A fourth theme that cuts across non-Western perspectives is that learning is primarily *informal,* is embedded in everyday life, and is lifelong. While we in adult education might recognize the prevalence and power of learning that is integral to our daily lives, most Westerners think of learning as that which occurs in a formal teacher-led classroom dependent on books and curriculum materials. Formal assessment that often leads to some sort of certification or credit is part of this structure.

In contrast, learning in non-Western settings is structured by the community problem or issue needing attention, by accessing resources, including people and materials that can assist in the problem solving, and by "evaluating" the learning according to the effectiveness of its application to the situation. This is not to say that formal education has no place in non-Western systems; in today's world formal education has become a necessity. Rather, "the common tendency in our own society to conflate and confuse 'formal schooling' with 'education'—a tendency reflected in our concern with formal certification and degrees rather than with competence per se—has been far less common in non-Western traditions" (Reagan, 2005, p. 248). There appears to be more recognition of and value placed on learning that is what we would call informal in these non-Western traditions. In reference to Africa, Fasokun, Katahoire, and Oduaran (2005) sum up this emphasis on informal learning: "As in other parts of the world, informal learning by African adults involves learning through experience under enabling conditions that facilitate the development of knowledge, skills, attitudes, aptitudes, values and interests. This is done to enhance performance, bring about change or solve practical problems" (p. 36).

In summary, we have presented four themes or emphases in non-Western learning systems that contrast with our Western perspective. Non-Western systems appear to place a greater emphasis on interdependence as a value to be developed versus independence; to link communal or community concerns with learning; to see learning as a holistic activity with a spiritual aspect, in contrast to the cognitive emphasis of the West; and finally, to value and recognize informal learning as legitimate.

SUMMARY

This chapter on non-Western perspectives of learning and knowing has introduced the reader to other ways of thinking about learning than is found in the rest of this book. The value of engaging with other frameworks is that we are challenged to think about the purpose of education and learning as well as question the nature of knowledge production itself. Further, knowing something about other systems of learning can both lead to applications in our practice and contribute to our own personal meaning-making.

As part of this chapter we also briefly discussed some important concepts, including problematizing the Western/non-Western dichotomy itself, defining culture, and considering the nature of indigenous knowledge. These concepts and others frame our brief foray into traditions of learning and knowing unfamiliar to most of us. In light of this unfamiliarity, we offered short introductions to five non-Western perspectives: Confucianism, Hinduism, Maori, Islam, and African indigenous knowledge.

The final section of the chapter presented four themes that seem to span many systems of non-Western thought, themes that contrast with Western perspectives. First, non-Western systems emphasize interdependence versus independence. Second, and related to the first, is that learning in these frameworks is communal and in community, rather than an isolated activity. Third, a holistic perspective that includes spiritual, embodied, and emotional components of learning are given at least as much emphasis as purely cognitive approaches. Finally, informal learning is recognized and valued as much as, if not more than formal learning.

CHAPTER TEN

CRITICAL THEORY, POSTMODERN, AND FEMINIST PERSPECTIVES

Adult learning in North America has been most influenced by psychology, with its focus on individual learners, their growth and development, and their learning in and out of formal settings. In this chapter, where we approach adult learning from a critical, power relations framework, the camera moves from the individual learner to an analysis of the context where learning takes place. Considered are the larger systems in society, the culture and institutions that shape learning, and the structural and historical conditions framing, indeed defining, the learning event.

The learning process itself is less of a focus than the economic, historical, and sociocultural context in which that learning takes place. Questioning and critiquing taken-for-granted worldviews, structures, and institutions of society are the first steps in changing oppressive and nonemancipatory practices. Further, our assumptions about the nature of knowledge—including what counts as knowledge, where it is located (in the individual or in society), and how it is acquired—are also challenged. These questions about knowledge are particularly important for adult educators because presumably the construction and acquisition of knowledge are inherent in the teaching-learning transaction. Because this approach critiques and raises questions about the assumptions we make about the world around us, including those underlying the practice of adult education, this stance is often called *critical*, as in *critical adult education*.

explain what a critical theory is

A number of specific philosophical and theoretical orientations inform this approach to adult education and adult learning, including Marxism, critical theory, critical multiculturalism, critical race theory, postcolonialism, queer theory, postmodernism, and feminist theory. Although some adult educators are clearly identified with a specific orientation, a number of others draw from several theoretical perspectives. Hart's (1992) analysis of work and learning, for example, is anchored in Marxism, critical theory, and feminist theory. Tisdell (1998) draws from multiculturalism, feminist theory, and poststructuralism in proposing a model of feminist pedagogy for adult education classrooms. Hill (2004) combines critical theory and postmodernism in his analysis of activism around sexual orientation and gender identity. Grace (1996a, 1997) maintains that critical theory, feminism, and postmodernism inform one another to the extent that common themes or assumptions can be derived to guide adult learning practices. Further, many educators writing from several of these perspectives claim indebtedness to Paulo Freire's (1970) work. The noted Black feminist scholar bell hooks (1994, p. 46), for example, speaks of coming to Freire's work "just at that moment in my life when I was beginning to question deeply and profoundly the politics of domination, the impact of racism, sexism, class exploitation, and the kind of domestic colonization that takes place in the United States. . . . Paulo was one of the thinkers whose work gave me a language. He made me think deeply about the construction of an identity in resistance."

This chapter first provides a brief overview of some of the major themes, concepts, and terms that characterize perspectives derived from Marxist theory, critical theory, multiculturalism, critical race theory, postmodernism, and feminist theory. The chapter then focuses on three perspectives where contributions to adult learning have been most visible—critical theory, postmodernism, and feminist theory/pedagogy.

COMMON THEMES

An understanding of adult learning and adult education from the perspective of critique and empowerment mandates some familiarity with basic concepts and terminology. In this section, we discuss three themes that characterize this perspective: race, class, and gender, which figure prominently in a critical analysis of adult learning; power and oppression, both key concepts; and knowledge and truth, which are construed in different ways depending on the school of thought. These themes are, of course, highly interrelated; it is not possible to talk about racism, classism, sexism, and other "isms" without reference to power and oppression, nor can power be considered apart from issues surrounding knowledge construction. These themes are brought together later in the chapter in the discussions of critical theory, postmodernism, and feminist theory's contributions to adult learning.

RACE, CLASS, AND GENDER

Among the characteristics of people that provoke prejudice and oppression in American society, race, class, and gender are three of the most powerful and pervasive. The theoretical orientations discussed in this chapter place race, class, and gender and their interactions at center stage in analyzing the power dynamics and the distribution of resources in a particular context. The context can be defined as broadly as society, as an institution in society, or even as a specific adult education setting. The purpose in moving these issues to the foreground and analyzing systems of power and oppression, especially as they manifest themselves in adult education, is to bring about a more informed and democratic practice.

Race

While discussions of race focus primarily on African Americans, it should be noted that people other than White European Americans are also marginalized in our society. Native Americans, Hispanics, and Asian Americans all must grapple with discrimination and oppression based solely on their not being part of the White mainstream (Lee & Johnson-Bailey, 2004). Colin and Preciphs (1991, p. 62) define racism as "conscious or unconscious, and expressed in actions or attitudes initiated by individuals, groups, or institutions that treat human beings unjustly because of their skin pigmentation. . . . Racism is expressed in attitudes, behaviors, and institutions." The social impact of racism (and sexism) in America in economic terms is disturbing. The median income of

White workers in 2003 was $24,318 compared to $19,794 for Blacks and $17,974 for Hispanics (U.S. Bureau of the Census, 2004a). It is also common knowledge that women of color are overrepresented in low-skill, low-paid jobs, such as health aide and private household worker.

That these disparities based on race also exist in the practice of adult education is no surprise. Participation patterns alone have consistently borne out the fact that Blacks and other people of color are underrepresented in all types of adult education. Amstutz (1994) has suggested three reasons why racism (and sexism) persist in adult education despite well-intentioned efforts. First, she sees a discrepancy between the rhetoric of adult education that speaks of empowerment and equal access, and actual behaviors that more often than not are "unempowering" and "traditional." Second, most adult educators are themselves White and middle-class, have had little interaction with minorities of any kind, and have failed to examine their own beliefs, assumptions, prejudices, and biases. Third, she believes that most adult educators have an unwarranted faith in institutions, believing "that institutional practices are well meaning and that the policies under which their institutions operate are not biased" (p. 43).

The literature on multiculturalism has helped bring the issues of race and cultural diversity to the attention of educators at all levels. Even more recently, *critical multiculturalism* has emerged as "a term used to distinguish forms of multicultural education that specifically focus on challenging power relations based on *social structures* of race or culture, gender, class, etc. and on challenging the 'isms' that result from those power relations, as in ra*cism,* or sex*ism*" (Tisdell, 2005a, p. 163; italics in original).

Multiculturalism appears to be synonymous with what Guy (2005) calls "culturally relevant adult education." This educational approach attempts to "incorporate learners' cultural practices and values in the teaching-learning process" (Guy, 2005, p. 180). Culturally relevant adult education sees the micro social level of educational practice as it relates to "broader socio-cultural and societal issues of power and difference" (p. 183).

For some, multiculturalism and even critical multiculturalism do not go far enough in addressing the racism that permeates our society. Critical race theory (CRT) takes a more radical perspective in that it tries not only "to understand the relationships among race, racism, power, privilege, and oppression, but to challenge and transform these relationships" (Ianinska, Wright, & Rocco, 2003, p. 176). Drawing from a number of disciplines, CRT acknowledges that race, a socially constructed category, is "a fundamental organizing principle in U.S. society," that racism is systemic, and that "people of color have a unique voice in racial matters because of their social position and experiences with oppression" (Jeris & McDowell, 2003, pp. 188–189).

Ross-Gordon (1994) focuses on the intersections of race, class, and gender in reviewing the multicultural and critical pedagogy literature in order to extract elements of a multicultural pedagogy for adults. What this wide range of literature has in common, Ross-Gordon believes, is "an emphasis on deconstruction of hegemonic knowledge and structures, goals for emancipation of learners, and denial of claims to political neutrality for . . . any form of education" (p. 315). Finally, she develops a composite of ten principles for teaching and learning, including sharing power with learners, fostering collaboration, challenging all forms of oppression, and placing the culture of the student in a central rather than a marginal position. With regard to racism in particular, she finds the "Afrocentric/anti-racist discourse . . . unique in its concern with two concepts. One is the notion of centricity, that the student must find his or her culture to be central (not marginal) within the knowledge shared. Second is the emphasis on learning by teachers (or un-learning) through . . . programs that educate them to recognize and challenge racism, including their own" (p. 316).

In an approach similar to Ross-Gordon's, McDowell (2003) identified eleven themes from the literature on antiracist praxis that adult educators can use to inform their own antiracist orientation. Some of her suggestions are as follows: becoming knowledgeable about race and racism, attending to racial awareness, interrogating White power, integrating racially diverse voices into curricula, and acquiring skills to challenge racism.

As race and ethnicity shape learning transactions in educational settings, so too in the workplace. Ross-Gordon et al. (2005) reviewed the work-related learning literature from the three domains of continuing professional education, human resource development, and workforce development with regard to concerns about race in each domain. While their findings varied somewhat across domains, they were able to draw the following conclusions:

1. Institutionalized discrimination affects individual careers and program directions; (p. 379)
2. Personal determination and resourcefulness, peer and family support, mentors, and social networks are especially important to the career advancement of racialized minorities . . . ; (p. 380)
3. Whites are generally less aware of manifestations of racism and benefits of White privilege (HRD and CPE) and in some cases demonstrate resistance to examining these (CPE). . . . (p. 380)
4. A point of interconnection between HRD and CPE is seen in the degree to which literature focused on "cultural competence" was focused on the "helping" professions and organizations—those that require sensitivity to client perspectives in order to accomplish their "helping" goals/missions (p. 380).

Thus race not only permeates the workplace but all other aspects of our society as well, including adult education practice. Intertwined with race is socioeconomic class.

Class

When social class is the focus, the aim of the analysis and subsequent action is to bring about a change from a capitalist political economy to a classless socialist form of government. Drawing largely from Marxism, a class-based analysis emphasizes class struggle, alienation, and revolutionary activity. Workers find no connection or fulfillment through work; rather, the individual worker is but a cog in the production of goods and services, alienated from the self as well as others and society in general. It will be only through a revolutionary movement that this relationship between the person and his or her world can be changed. Freire (1970, p. 61) points out that those who are alienated are considered "marginal," "a pathology of the healthy society. . . . The truth is, however, that the oppressed are not 'marginals,' are not men [sic] living 'outside' society. They have always been 'inside'—inside the structure which made them 'beings for others.' The solution is not to 'integrate' them into the structure of oppression, but to transform that structure so that they can become 'beings for themselves.'" Thus a socialist Marxist framework for adult education would have, Youngman (1986, p. 197) suggests, the dual aims of challenging "the ideology and culture of capitalism" and developing "the general knowledge and technical expertise necessary to reorganise production and society in a fully democratic way."

Perhaps due in part to the collapse of Eastern European communist and socialist states, strict Marxist analysis is no longer in fashion. Nevertheless, some adult educators argue for its continued relevance (Collins & Collard, 1995; Schied, 1993, 1994; Youngman, 1996, 2000). Schied (1994) acknowledges that feminist and postmodern thought have questioned making the working class "the privileged agent of change" (p. 445); indeed, "the primacy of social class has been strongly challenged by notions of gender, race, and colonialism." In spite of this, "the economic dislocation and the exploitation of working people by international corporations is a reality. It is not merely constructed or read or produced by our theoretical perspective. This exploitation is real" (p. 446). Marxist analysis, if "conceived as a moral stance . . . provides adult educators a way to place their practice in some kind of social context" (p. 446). Collins and Collard (1995) concur with Schied. A class-based economic analysis is particularly relevant in today's world, they say, with the "re-emergence of what amounts to class warfare in connection with global economic restructuring" (p. 75). It is time "to make connections between the home, the workplace, and the community— between class and concerns around culture, gender and race" (p. 75). This is in fact what Hart (1992, 1995) does in her Marxist-feminist analysis of work, gender, and class. Youngman (1996, p. 7) agrees, calling for a robust political-economic analysis: "The central issue for a transformative political economy of adult education is how to adequately conceptualize the interconnections between the four main systems of domination in society, namely, those deriving from imperialism, class, gender, and race-ethnicity. It is clear that while none of these systems is reducible to another (for example, the basis of women's oppression is different from that of class oppression), they do affect each other (so that, for example, women's oppression has a class dimension)." Holst (2002), who also argues for a reassessment of the Marxist tradition, is concerned that new social movements around feminism, antiracism, and sexual and environmental issues might eclipse the working-class struggle against capitalism.

Gender

While multiculturalists, Marxists, and critical theorists have brought inequities based on economics and class to adult educators' attention, feminist scholars have placed gender, and gender as it intersects with race and class, at the forefront of a critical analysis. Although all versions of feminist theory are concerned with the status of women worldwide, theorists differ among themselves on two counts: how the problem is framed and what needs to be done to change the status of women. Tisdell's (1995, 2005b) categorization of feminist theories into individually focused theories, structural theories, and postmodern theories offers a useful framework for reviewing these theories.

As the category suggests, individually focused feminist theories are concerned with women as individuals, how they have come to internalize patriarchy as the norm, and what needs to be done to obtain equal access, rights, and opportunities. Psychoanalytic feminists, for example, maintain that the male domination of women (patriarchy) is deeply rooted in men's and women's subconscious and is perpetuated through gender socialization. Change cannot come about unless people "deal with the patriarchy in their unconscious" (Tisdell, 2005b, p. 254).

In contrast to an individual focus, structural feminist theories frame the problem in terms of societal structures and institutions that oppress women. Marxist feminists argue that the two systems of capitalism and patriarchy, in conjunction with each other, oppress women. "Socialist feminists," Tisdell (2005b, p. 255) explains, "would agree that two significant and interrelated systems of oppression to women are capitalism and patriarchy, but they also discuss the importance of examining other systems of oppression such as racial oppression and the intersections of gender, race, class, and sexual orientation in women's lives." Cultural feminists extend this analysis to the experience of women of color who also represent a particular cultural group, such as Latina, Black, and Asian or Asian Americans (Tisdell, 2005b).

Postmodern theorists take issue with the unit of analysis, or how the problem is framed by structuralists. One or even two systems of power and oppression do not adequately capture the reality of women's experience and oppression because "some groups are more privileged than others within the particular structural unit or units of analysis. Thus Marxism does not account for the fact that men are more privileged than women; Marxist feminism does not account for the fact that white women have more privilege than women of color" (Tisdell, 1995, p. 61). Postmodernists also take issue with the structuralists' overemphasis on locating power outside the individual. In a postmodern perspective, individuals have some power also—power to affect or resist the status quo. Postmodern feminist theories thus "tend to account for multiple systems of privilege and oppression and their intersections, along with people's capacity for agency or resistance" (p. 61). In this perspective, the "*connections between* individuals and social structures" (Tisdell, 2005b, p. 256; italics in original) and where one is positioned vis-à-vis multiple structures are the focus of analysis.

POWER AND OPPRESSION

In addition to the intersections of race, class, and gender, a second theme underlying these contemporary approaches is that social inequities, including those found in education, stem from power-based relationships: "Those wielding power can control others in varying ways, getting them to engage in activities not in the powerless's best interest" (Hansen, 1993, p. 2). And "because power is constructed in and through social interactions, it is always alterable and disruptable, hence the importance of understanding and using power in adult education" (Wilson & Nesbit, 2005, p. 454). One of the major tasks of a critical analysis is to uncover and expose these power relationships wherein the domination of one group's interests results in the oppression of other groups. Power and oppression are concepts that permeate the thinking and writing of radical adult educators. As Nesbit (1998, p. 174) explains, "Radical educators regard the world and its constituent societies as full of contradictions and marked by imbalances of power and privilege. Hence, they regard such problems as poverty or illiteracy neither as isolated incidents nor as manifestations of individual inadequacy, but as results of larger social issues. Furthermore, individuals, as social actors, both create and are created by their social worlds." Freire, for example, concluded that the Third World was "characterized by social, political, and economic oppression. . . . The various forms of oppression constitute the concrete problems or contradictions that are the task of [a] revolutionary pedagogy" (Elias & Merriam, 2005, p. 155).

The identification of systems of power and oppression as a lens through which to analyze society is a key component of critical theory. Critical theory originated in the 1940s with the German philosopher Jürgen Habermas and the Frankfurt School. With the advent of World War II, Habermas became disillusioned with Marxism, offering instead a view of society that is more optimistic, one that puts faith in the rationality of human beings to engage in critique and action to bring about a more just, free, and equitable society. The aim of critical theory, Welton (1995a, p. 37) writes, is "to help people to stop being passive victims who collude, at least partly, in their domination by external forces. Critical theory's liberating project is to name the enemies of human freedom, and to point to the possibility of freedom's enlargement." Inglis (1997, p. 4) goes a step further in suggesting that an analysis of power leads to empowerment or emancipation: "Empowerment involves people developing capacities to act successfully within the existing system and structures of power, while emancipation concerns critically analyzing, resisting and challenging structures of power."

Of concern to those writing from this perspective is the appropriation of the "lifeworld"—our everyday personal interactions in home, family, and community—by the "system." The system is conceived of as structures of power (institutions and organizations such as government) or the means to power (such as money in a capitalist economy, or knowledge in the information age). These systems have not only "colonized" the lifeworld but are oppressive: "Human beings as childrearers, partners, workers, clients, citizens, and consumers struggle against the process of being turned into objects of corporate and state management. Systemic imperatives, then, threaten to disempower men and women who have the capacity to be empowered, reflective actors" (Welton, 1993, p. 88). To fight the hegemony of the system (which includes corporate, government, legal, and media dimensions), citizens must engage in rational discourse about sources of power, knowledge, and oppression in the hope of redressing the current imbalance between the power of the lifeworld versus the system. Adult education can be a site for addressing power and oppression (Baptiste, 1998; Brookfield, 2005b; Rocco & West, 1998; Welton, 1995b).

KNOWLEDGE AND TRUTH

The various schools of thought that make up what in this chapter we call a power relations perspective all address, to some extent, the nature of truth and the construction of knowledge. Each of the three major orientations discussed in the next section—critical theory, postmodernism, and feminist pedagogy—has a somewhat different notion of knowledge and truth.

The primary spokesperson for critical theory, Jürgen Habermas, proposed that there are three types of knowledge: technical, practical, and emancipatory. Technical knowledge has to do with the world of facts, of material things that structure our world. This knowledge can be easily verified through checking with documents, authorities, and so on. A statement such as "an adult can obtain a high school diploma through making an acceptable score on the GED" is technical knowledge. To say, however, that "a GED diploma is just as good as a high school diploma" moves us into the practical realm of knowledge, where communication with others—dialogue—is necessary to establish validity. The validity or truth of the claim is arrived at through dialogical consensus; interpretation, judgment, and sincerity are important here. Finally, a question such as "Why doesn't the GED diploma have the same status in our society as a high school diploma?" is emancipatory in nature because it addresses the forces of society that empower or disempower some individuals over others; that is, one would ask *who* has determined that a GED diploma has less status? *Whose interests* does it serve to maintain this status differential? Not all knowledge, then, serves the same interests, nor does all knowledge construction hold the same potential for challenging the status quo or emancipating the individual. Clearly, emancipatory knowledge has the most power to address the oppressive forces in society.

From postmodernism comes the notion that there is no single truth or reality independent of the knower. Postmodernism criticizes the modern conception of knowledge as a set of underlying principles that can explain behavior or phenomena across individuals or settings. In the modern world, what constitutes and what is accepted as knowledge is determined by power: "Modernism privileges some ideas and people(s); it marginalizes others" (Cunningham & Fitzgerald, 1996, p. 49). Since "the goal of postmodernism is diversity/pluralism and its ethic is tolerance," knowledge "is either nonexistent or relative, and contradictory notions can all be considered equally true if locally held" (p. 49). Knowledge, then, is something that is part of the social and cultural context in which it occurs; how an individual or a community constructs knowledge and the type of knowledge constructed are socioculturally dependent. This view of knowledge goes hand in hand with how postmodernists view truth. There is no single, agreed-upon truth; there are many truths. This view leads to one of postmodernism's major strategies: deconstruction. As Hemphill (2001, p. 23) explains, if all truths are constructions, to deconstruct is "to uncover its [the term or concept's] evolution, unpacking the interests it serves and marginalizes." Further, postmodernism "encourages us to be critical of how knowledge is organized—whether in terms of broad disciplines or specific course curricula. All forms of organizing knowledge . . . are contingent, occurring due to existing organizations and constellations of power in a given moment—and not given in some cosmic hierarchy" (Hemphill, 2001, pp. 26–27).

Feminists who write from a poststructuralist or postmodern perspective hold the same view about knowledge and truth. That is, they assume there is no one Truth, and each woman's truth or knowledge is relative to the sociocultural context of which she is part. Feminist theory encompasses two other views of knowledge construction, however. The psychologically oriented feminist literature has been heavily influenced by Belenky, Clinchy, Goldberger, and Tarule's *Women's Ways of Knowing* (1986). From their interviews of 135 women, they identified five different ways women construct knowledge, ranging from silence to constructed knowing (see Chapter Thirteen). Their work suggests that knowledge is something that each individual constructs; the result of this process is a sense of individual empowerment, of gaining a voice along with the ability to effect change in their personal lives. In emancipatory feminist models, in contrast, knowledge is less personal. Drawing more from critical theory than psychology, these models "examine the political and social mechanisms that have controlled the knowledge production process and marginalized (or left out) the contributions of women and people of color" (Tisdell, 1995, p. 70).

In summary, assumptions underlying a power relations perspective on adult learning draw from a wide range of literature such as Marxist and feminist theory, critical race theory, multiculturalism, critical theory, and postmodernism. Any number of concepts and assumptions inform this perspective, but we chose three interlocking themes to set the stage for a discussion of contributions to adult learning from critical theory, postmodernism, and feminist theory/pedagogy. At the heart of all of these orientations is a critical assessment of the forces of economics, class, race, and gender that lead to systems of power and oppression. All also consider how knowledge is constructed and how the nature of its construction can liberate or dominate. We now turn to a more detailed discussion of critical theory, postmodernism, and feminist pedagogy, three of the contemporary perspectives that have had the greatest impact to date on adult learning.

CRITICAL THEORY AND ADULT LEARNING

In contrast to andragogy and even transformational learning, most practitioners in adult education are unaware of critical theory's potential for examining practice or illuminating the nature of adult learning. This is in part because the writing in this area is dense and obtuse, and operationalizing the concepts involved is difficult. Critical theory itself has been criticized for "asserting domination and reproducing a culture of silence in educational settings" due to its "technical jargon, obscure references, and ambiguous phrasing" (Pietrykowski, 1996, p. 84). In fact, we found only one article on critical theory in a practice-oriented publication. In "John's Story: An Exploration into Critical Theory in Education," deMarrais (1991) demonstrates how John's failure to learn to read can be understood as a systemic social problem rather than one individual's failure. The "system" in a critical theory analysis is an institution (such as government or education) that functions to reproduce the status quo, in particular the existing social class structure. Awareness of this oppression can lead to resistance and possibly change. Critical theory's strength, as noted earlier, lies in its critique of existing economic and social structures and resultant power dynamics. However, "it is a discourse that often leaves practitioners frustrated" (Finger, 2005a, p. 168) in suggesting workable strategies for effecting change.

A number of adult education intellectuals have brought critical theory, and in particular Habermas's version, to adult education. Welton (1993, 1995b) has articulated the ways in which critical theory can inform adult education theory and practice. He identifies several concepts from critical theory that have affected and can continue to affect adult education: three types of knowledge, ideal conditions for reflective discourse, institutions as learning communities, and the interplay of the system and the lifeworld.

The three types of knowledge discussed earlier in this chapter—technical, practical, and emancipatory—present a framework for understanding and critiquing adult education as a discipline and as a field of practice. Collins (1991, 1995a, 1995b), for example, finds the field of adult education to be overly concerned with technical knowledge (with the least attention to emancipatory) at the expense of social action designed to bring about a more just and equal society. According to Collins, the field is too preoccupied with "professionalizing," with "the cult of efficiency," and with "an eagerness to serve the conventional professions" (1995a, p. 79). This preoccupation with the technical has both distorted learning and diverted adult educators from providing a "context where shared commitments [practical knowledge] towards a socially more free, just, and rational society will coalesce" (1991, p. 119). By this, Collins means that adult educators are too concerned with how to plan programs or arrange a classroom at the expense of considering why some adults do not have access to education, for example.

In a similar approach, Wilson (1993) and Wilson and Hayes (2000b) use the tools of critical theory to trace the rise of technical rationality and professionalism represented in the field's handbooks. These handbooks, which are published approximately every ten years, are encyclopedic compilations of essays describing the field of adult education. For the field to become professionalized, a body of knowledge needed to be compiled with which to train adult educators. "This is what the discourse in the handbooks represents. Without this basis in a scientifically derived body of knowledge, there would be no professional activity to transact in a service economy" (Wilson, 1993, p. 14). It was not until the 2000 handbook (Wilson & Hayes, 2000a) that a more critical stance was taken in assessing the body of knowledge in the field. Both Collins and Wilson fear that the grip of professionalism and technical rationality prevents the field of adult education from attending to social action and emancipatory interests.

Closely related to forms of knowledge is Habermas's ideal conditions for reflective discourse. Habermas has identified four criteria or conditions that, if applied to interactions among adults, should result in mature, rational, candid, "authentic" discussions: comprehensibility, sincerity, truth, and legitimacy. Mezirow (1995, pp. 52–53), who has adopted these conditions as central to his transformative learning theory, explains how these conditions work in discussions:

> When we communicate or have doubts about the truth or authenticity of the assertion, the truthfulness of the speaker, or the appropriateness of what is asserted in light of relevant norms, we often seek the best judgment of the most informed, objective, and rational persons we can find. We engage them in a special form of dialogue which Habermas refers to as "discourse." Discourse involves an effort to set aside bias, prejudice, and personal concerns and to do our best to be open and objective in presenting and assessing reasons and reviewing the evidence and arguments for and against the problematic assertion to arrive at a consensus.

These criteria can form a basis for identifying the skills that learners need to possess in order to engage in more authentic discussions. Mezirow and others realize that these are ideal conditions; nevertheless, they give us a standard to work toward in adult learning transactions.

Critical theory has also contributed to adult education in considering how institutions themselves can become learning communities. According to Welton (1993, p. 89), "Habermas believes that while all institutions are educative, not all are true learning communities. An institution, whether family, corporation, or state agency, may be organized to block free and noncoerced learning processes. Habermas encourages us to ask whether our institutions, large and small, truly enable human beings to unfold their potentials (cognitive, oral, technical, aesthetic) in their daily routine interactions." Strategies to build learning organizations are efforts in this direction, as is the literature on classroom and planning practices that engage an emancipatory agenda (see Ellsworth, 1989; Fenwick, 2005a; Gouthro, 2003; Schied, Carter, Preston, & Howell, 1997; Tisdell & Perry, 1997; Wilson & Cervero, 2001). In view of this thinking, Welton (1995b, p. 151) even argues that the workplace has potential "as a site for emancipatory learning." Critical adult educators have a "mandate . . . to argue and struggle for workplaces that open up space for non-coerced, free communication pertaining to the organization, control and purposes of work" (p. 152).

Another contribution of critical theory to adult education, identified by Welton (1993), is the notion of the interplay between the lifeworld and the system. As already noted, the lifeworld is the informal, everyday interactions of daily life, and the system consists of those structures based on money and power (corporations, government, education, and so on) that have an impact on the lifeworld. These systems do more than intrude into the lifeworld; they oppress. Collins (1991, 1995a) is particularly articulate about how forces from the system, such as expertise, competency-based curricula, and much of workplace learning, have disempowered adults in their lifeworlds. In his opinion, spaces in our everyday world where discussions of social and political issues and what can be done about them could occur have been taken over by systems that promote technical learning. Self-directed learning, for example, has been touted for its value in creating "professionals." But

> the idea of "facilitating" self-directed learning, which Knowles recognized ordinary wide-awake adults already possess ("to be adult means to be self-directing"), makes no more sense than comfortable pedagogical chatter about empowering people. For a critical perspective on adult education the initial task is to identify social structures and practices which (mis)shape social learning processes and undermine capacities adults already possess to control their own education. [Collins, 1994, p. 100]

For Collins (1991, p. 119), critical practice means being engaged in "definable concrete projects for social change without which talk of justice, emancipation, and equality becomes hollow rhetoric."

Since the lifeworld and the system are interrelated, there is some merit in focusing on the interaction of the two, from a popular movement standpoint or a systems perspective. "The juxtaposition of lifeworld and system concepts is clearly significant in enabling us to 'think deeply and realistically about the systemic blockages to the achievement of a more fully democratized society'" (Collins, 1995b, p. 198). Hart's (1995) analysis of the workplace and the lifeworld of the family does just this, as does Hill's

(1995, 1998) study of Pennsylvania citizens' groups engaged in environmental conflicts. The citizens' groups and the government regulatory agency "were both instrumental in community learning" and community conflict (1995, p. 163).

The most recent work in critical theory by an adult educator is by Brookfield (2001, 2002, 2005a, 2005b). He proposes a critical theory framework for a theory of adult learning and education. At the center of this theory of adult learning is ideological critique: "A critical theory of adult learning should have at its core an understanding of how adults learn to recognize the predominance of ideology in their everyday thoughts and actions and in the institutions of civil society" (2001, pp. 20–21). More specifically, there are seven "learning tasks" embedded in critical learning theory:

1. Challenging ideology. This is "the basic tool for helping adults learn to penetrate the givens of everyday reality to reveal the inequity and oppression that lurk beneath" (Brookfield, 2005b, p. 42).
2. Contesting hegemony. Hegemony is the notion that "people learn to accept as natural and in their own best interest an unjust social order" (Brookfield, 2005b, p. 43).
3. Unmasking power. "Part of becoming adult is learning to recognize the play of power in our lives and ways it is used and abused" (Brookfield, 2005b, p. 47).
4. Overcoming alienation. "The removal of alienation allows for the possibility of freedom, for the unmanipulated exercise of one's creative powers. As such, claiming freedom and overcoming alienation are inextricably intertwined" (Brookfield, 2005b, p. 50).
5. Learning liberation. Adults need to learn to liberate themselves, individually and collectively, from the dominant ideology.
6. Reclaiming reason. "A major concern of critical theory is to reclaim reason as something to be applied in all spheres of life, particularly in deciding values by which we should live, not just in areas where technical decisions are called for" (Brookfield, 2005b, p. 56).
7. Practicing democracy. Adults must learn to live with the contradictions of democracy, "learning to accept that democracy is always a partially functioning ideal" (Brookfield, 2005b, p. 65).

We have illustrated how critical theory can inform both adult education theory and practice. However, as with any other theory, there are points of debate and critique. The notion that critical theory is a useful framework for better understanding adult learning has itself been critiqued. Ellsworth (1989), in her now classic article on problems with applying an emancipatory, dialogic approach to the classroom, found that "key assumptions, goals, and pedagogical practices fundamental to the literature on critical pedagogy—namely, 'empowerment,' 'student voice,' 'dialogue,' and even the term 'critical'—are repressive myths that perpetuate relations of domination" (p. 298). In experimenting with a college class on racism, Ellsworth discovered that she and the students were ill equipped to handle the unequal power relations in their own classroom. She writes:

> Our classroom was not in fact a safe space for students to speak out or talk back about their experiences of oppression both inside and outside of the classroom. . . . Things were not being said for a number of reasons. These included fear of being misunderstood and/or disclosing too much and becoming too vulnerable; . . . resentment that other oppressions (sexism, heterosexism, fat oppression, classism, anti-Semitism) were being marginalized in the name of addressing racism; . . . [and] confusion about levels of trust and commitment surrounding those who were allies to another group's struggles. [1989, pp. 315–316]

Collard (1995) concurs with Ellsworth, arguing that discourse (the conditions of ideal speech) "merely reintroduces an old elitism under the guise of a communicative ethic" (p. 68). Further, the ideal speech situation "tends to disregard difference and exclude those who have no voice—i.e., it is implicitly hierarchical" (p. 65). We also feel that while critical theory allows us to uncover the use and abuse of power, it is a particularly challenging perspective to put into practice. How do we as adult educators actually go about promoting rational discourse, or help adults "learn to liberate themselves" (Brookfield, 2005b, p. 65), for example?

Despite these criticisms, critical theory remains a particularly important underpinning to theory building in adult learning. For example, Mezirow's theory of perspective transformation, discussed in Chapter Six, draws heavily from Habermas. Critical theory has also informed analyses of professionalization, power and oppression, and the dynamics of the teaching and learning transaction.

POSTMODERNISM AND ADULT LEARNING

Uncertainty characterizes today's postmodern world. As Giroux (1992, p. 39) observes, "We have entered an age that is marked by a crisis of power, patriarchy, authority, identity, and ethics. This new age has been described, for better or worse, by many theorists in a variety of disciplines as the age of postmodernism." Unlike the modern world, which is characterized by "the scientific, industrial, and social programs, institutions, actions, and artifacts generated by the humanistic and Enlightenment search for the universal foundations of truth, morality, and aesthetics" (Bagnall, 1995, p. 81), in the postmodern era, things are much more diverse, fluid, illusionary, and contested, including the reality of the world itself. Identifying oppression, "defining the enemy" (Newman, 1994), and taking right forms of action are not so easy in a postmodern world. As Plumb (1995b, p. 188) observes, adult education from a "modern" world perspective "is poorly equipped to articulate how it can persist as a meaningful emancipatory practice without reinscribing itself as an institution that suppresses heterogeneity and difference." Newman (2006) however, is one writer who takes up this challenge, offering numerous strategies for social activists to channel their frustration, dismay, and anger into defiant action.

In a postmodern world, everything is "contested," up for grabs. What has been or is considered true, real, or right can be questioned; there are multiple interpretations depending on where one is standing and what factors are in juxtaposition with one another. There are no absolutes, no single theoretical framework for examining social and political issues. Hence, critical theory's goal of emancipation and overcoming oppression can itself be questioned because it represents a "logic" that "does not tolerate difference" (Pietrykowski, 1996, p. 90). At the same time, as Collins (1994, pp. 99–100) points out, postmodernism, in contrast to Habermasian critical theory, leaves us with no means of choosing "sensibly between one course of action and another. There is no truth to be found, only a plurality of signs, styles, interpretations, and meaningless process." Therefore, postmodernism can leave us with two almost diametrically opposed views. It can be seen as "offering a pessimistic, negative, gloomy assessment . . . of fragmentation, dis-integration, malaise, meaninglessness" (Rosenau, 1992, p. 15). Or it can be seen as hopeful—a world that is "nondogmatic, tentative, and nonideological" (p. 16), one in which adult education can play a major role.

Exactly how postmodernism can play a "major role" in adult education is only recently being articulated. Kilgore (2004), for example, begins by analyzing the nature of postmodern knowing, including the notion of multiple truths, that meaning lies not in text but in its interpretation, and that power, inextricably linked to knowledge, is "something that we exercise rather than possess" (p. 48). She goes on to point out that at the heart of a postmodern pedagogy is a "shaking up [of] the social positions of teacher and student and the power relationship between them. Such aspirations will require us to consider the death of the teacher, the subversion of the student, and the diffusion of power" (p. 48).

Others have focused on the postmodern notion of the self and its importance in adult learning. The self in postmodern thought is not the unified, integrated, authentic self of modern times. Rather, the self is multiple, ever changing, and some say, fragmented. As Gergen (1991, p. 7) argues, "Under postmodern conditions, persons exist in a state of continuous construction and reconstruction. . . . Each reality of the self gives way to reflexive questioning, irony, and ultimately the playful probing of yet another reality."

Such a notion of self has implications for adult learning and development. In an exploration of this question, Clark and Dirkx (2000, p. 112) find the notion of a unitary self "a little like trying to understand the universe by using a telescope with a fixed lens and position." Clark (1997, p. 111) argues that "learning from the assumption of a unified self privileges the rational, agenic self and thereby fails to recognize and to give voice to other dimensions of the self." A postmodern perspective of the self allows for "understanding, honoring, and fostering diversity" within the lives of our adult learners (Clark & Dirkx, 2000, p. 112). By extension, adult educators can be sensitive to "the noncognitive, emotive interests, inclination, and preferences of . . . participants (Bagnall, 1999, p. 135). That is, aesthetic, spiritual, affective, and experiential aspects of the self become as important as the rational. McLaren (1997, p. 25) writes that educators need to assist students in dealing with the following questions of identity:

How has the social order fashioned me in ways with which I no longer desire to identify? In what directions do I desire and why? To what extent are my dreams and my desires my own? What will likely be the consequences for me and others both like me and different from me? To what extent is society inventing me and by what moral, epistemological, political, or transcendental authority is this taking place? How am I to judge the world that made me and on what basis can I unmake myself in order to remake the world?

In the face of such a fragmented world, relationships, connectedness, and interdependence are the constants that hold us together. Finger (1995, p. 116) is explicit about moving to a collective action agenda to respond to

> the new challenges. . . . Experts must join groups of learners working collectively with real people on concrete problems. . . . Teaching and preaching ready-made solutions to individuals must be replaced with collaborative, vertical, horizontal, and cross-disciplinary learning. Such learning must be recognized as probably the only "resource" still available to us to get through and out of the ever accelerating vicious circle. This, of course, must be a collective and collaborative effort, because there is no individual way out.

Postmodernists celebrate diversity among people, ideas, and institutions. By accepting the diversity and plurality of the world, no one element is privileged or more powerful than another. Usher, Bryant, and Johnston (1997, p. 22) speak of the advantages of this perspective:

> Postmodernity has provided spaces for rising social groups such as the new middle classes, for new postmodern social movements and for hitherto oppressed and marginalised groups such as women, blacks, gays, and ethnic minorities to find a voice, to articulate their own "subjugated" knowledges and to empower themselves in a variety of different ways and according to their own specific agendas. In this situation, education stops being a univocal, predictable reality and consequently it makes no sense to speak of it simply as either functioning to reproduce the social order or as implicit social engineering, whether this be for domestication or liberation. . . . Linked with this is the impact of a reconfiguration of education away from its institutional and provider-led location.

Plumb (1995a, p. 246) observes that although so much fragmentation and diversity can be disempowering, it is also what is needed to challenge the equally disparate forces of oppression: "No longer is it sufficient to foster the emergence of a particular kind of identity sufficiently strong to overcome the inequitable norms of capitalism"; rather, "critical adult education must investigate new ways that identity can still productively be mobilized in the fragmenting environment of postmodernity."

Postmodernism has been criticized for its pessimism, its extreme relativism, its lack of a moral center. Furthermore, with few exceptions (see Clark & Dirkx, 2000; Kegan, 1994; Kilgore, 2004; Tisdell, 1995), it comes up lacking on specific techniques or strategies for dealing with the postmodern classroom or adult education program. What postmodernism does offer adult education is a respect for diversity, a moving of previously marginalized groups into a position of equal value to other groups, and a critique (or deconstruction, some would say) of the categories by which we have labeled aspects of our practice. What does it mean to be categorized as illiterate in our society, for example? The marginalized groups identified by Usher, Bryant, and Johnston (1997)—women, blacks, gays, and ethnic minorities—have not found an advocate until very recently in critical theory, which is focused primarily on rationality, economics, class, and power. From postmodernity's challenges to modern, rational thought and society comes a valuing of diversity and opportunities inherent in uncertainty and nondogmatic practices. Postmodern discourses "offer a path—albeit a frustrating and convoluted one—to understand present and future phenomena that are no longer well suited to modernist, rational explanations" (Hemphill, 2001, p. 27).

FEMINIST PEDAGOGY AND ADULT LEARNING

As the name implies, feminist pedagogy focuses on the concerns of women in the teaching-learning transaction. Feminist pedagogy is derived from feminist theory, or more accurately, feminist theories. There are, for example, liberal, radical, psychoanalytic, Black, Marxist, and postmodern versions of feminist theory. Based in feminist theory, feminist pedagogy is "a method of teaching and learning employing a political framework that involves consciousness-raising, activism, and a caring and safe environment" (Lee & Johnson-Bailey, 2004, p. 57).

However, just as there are many feminisms, there are also numerous strands of feminist pedagogy that have been categorized in various ways. Maher (1987), for example, has placed the various perspectives into one of two categories: liberatory models and gender models. Liberatory models draw from postmodernism and Marxist and critical theory. From this perspective, the structures of society, the systems that intrude on our lifeworlds, oppress through their power and control. The structured nature of power relations and interlocking systems of oppression based on gender, race, and class are seen as being reinforced through education; that is, institutions of learning and the classroom itself reproduce the power structures found in society at large. Liberatory pedagogy examines how these systems of oppression are reproduced and resisted in education. We ask, for example, why White males tend to dominate a classroom discussion (reproduction), or why Black working-class women shun formal education (resistance). Liberatory feminist educators attempt to recover women's voices, experiences, and viewpoints and use these to make systems of privilege, power, and oppression visible. Although influenced by Freire's emancipatory praxis and Marxist theory, liberatory feminists are critical of the lack of attention in these approaches to gender and to interlocking systems of oppression based on gender, race, and class (Gouthro, 2003).

In the gender model of feminist pedagogy, the focus is on how female identity has been socially constructed to be one of nurturer and how the individual woman can find her voice, becoming emancipated in the personal psychological sense. Drawing from psychoanalytic and humanistic psychology, educators from this stance look to how the educational environment and the learning transaction can be constructed so as to foster women's learning. In this model, a connected approach to learning is advocated, where life experiences are valued, where a woman can come to have a voice, and hence, an identity. "If a woman is to consider herself a real knower, she must find acceptance for her ideas in the public world" (Belenky, Clinchy, Goldberger, & Tarule, 1986, p. 220). The public world begins with a safe classroom where members can support and nurture each other. This connected environment will help women develop their own voices and see themselves as capable of being constructors of knowledge rather than just recipients. In their book *Knowledge, Difference, and Power: Essays Inspired by Women's Ways of Knowing* (1996), Goldberger, Tarule, Clinchy, and Belenky consider how to wed connected and separate knowing, what collaborative knowing might look like, and how color, class, and diversity affect women's learning.

Tisdell (1995, 1996, 1998, 2000) has moved feminist pedagogy forward by forging a synthesis of the liberatory and gender models that promotes both personal emancipation and public action. Tisdell first identifies four recurring themes in feminist pedagogy: how knowledge is constructed, the development of voice, the authority of the teacher and students, and dealing with differences. She finds the liberatory model particularly strong on recognizing differences based on race, class, and gender; nevertheless, such theories "focus too much on structures, and do not account for the individual's capacity for agency, the capacity to have some control outside of these social structures" (1996, p. 310). The gender or psychological model, in contrast, because it tends to emphasize similarities among women, does not much account for differences among women or differences in power relations based on race, class, sexual orientation, and so on. The way to take into account all four themes, Tisdell proposes, is through a poststructural feminist pedagogy, which weds the psychological orientation of the gender model with the structural factors of the liberatory perspective. Tisdell (1996, p. 311) explains:

> A synthesis of these models in the form of poststructural feminist pedagogies would take into account both the intellectual and emotional components of learning, the individual's capacity for agency, as well as the psychological and social and political factors that affect learning. It would emphasize the importance of relationship and connection to learning, but also account for the fact that power relations based on a multitude of factors including gender, race, and class are always present in the learning environment and affect both how knowledge is constructed on the individual level as well as the social and political factors that affect what counts as "official" knowledge and how it is disseminated.

Tisdell's poststructural feminist pedagogy model has several implications for the teaching and learning transaction. First, it speaks to differences among learners themselves: "Most women and some men may have different learning needs from men who represent the dominant culture" (1995, p. 73). Second, there is attention given to the role of power in the construction of knowledge itself—power's role in how knowledge is shaped and disseminated in the classroom, and in society at large. Third, a poststructural pedagogy, or what Tisdell (1995) also calls positional pedagogy, examines how "various positionalities—the gender, race, class, sexual orientation—of both the participants and the instructor matter and have an effect on the learning environment" (p. 75). Finally, this perspective problematizes the power and authority of the teacher and considers the ramifications of redistributing this power.

Tisdell's poststructuralist feminist pedagogy model highlights connections: connections between "the individual and the intersecting structural systems of privilege and oppression" and connections between "one's individual (constantly shifting) identity and social structures" (1998, p. 146). She suggests how these connections might lead to change in an adult learning setting:

> As learners examine how social systems of privilege and oppression have affected their own identity, including their beliefs and values, the "discourse" is disrupted, thus shifting their identity, as well as increasing their capacity for agency. For example, if one has embraced societal prescriptions of particular gender roles (or race roles, or sexual roles that are exclusively heterosexual), and one becomes conscious of and examines the social construction of such roles, one's identity is likely to shift, and one could develop new ways of acting in the world. One also begins to see that there are different "truths" and perhaps not one "Truth," and that social systems have allowed members of privileged groups to control what has counted as "knowledge" in determining the official curriculum through the politics of the knowledge production process. [Tisdell, 1998, p. 146]

Weiler (1996) identifies three issues from which a feminist pedagogy can be forged. The first is the role and authority of the teacher. The tension between feminist teachers' need "to claim authority in a society that denies it to them" (p. 139) and the sharing of authority in the community of the classroom needs to be addressed. Lee and Johnson-Bailey (2004) point out the complexity of sharing authority when the instructor is both female and a person of color: "Instead of sharing our limited power and authority, we believe it is first essential to claim our power and authority in the class. Claiming this authority purposely is never easy, particularly when our students already see us as academic impostors or feel threatened by our position" (p. 62). Second, space needs to be made for personal experience as a source of knowledge and truth—how much space and what kind of space in regard to other sources of knowledge need to be negotiated. Weiler cites the Black lesbian feminist Audre Lorde in articulating the challenge of incorporating feelings, "those hidden sources of power from where true knowledge and, therefore, lasting action comes," into the discourse around types of knowledge (cited by Weiler, 1996, p. 142). The third issue for Weiler is the question of difference. There is no unitary, universal women's experience on which to base a pedagogy of practice. Women who have been marginalized and oppressed by the dominant society, by the dominant female norms, have had very different experiences from those of the mainstream. "The turning to experience thus reveals not a universal and common women's essence, but, rather, deep divisions in what different women have experienced, and in the kinds of knowledge they discover when they examine their own experience. The recognition of the differences among women raises serious challenges to feminist pedagogy" (Weiler, 1996, p. 145). Brown, Cervero, and Johnson-Bailey's (2000) study of race, gender, and teaching in the adult education classroom underscores Weiler's point. They found that "the practices of African American women postsecondary mathematics teachers are significantly affected by their race and gender . . . dispel[ing] the myth of the universal teacher" (p. 286).

The work of Tisdell and Weiler is part of an expanding body of literature in adult education that addresses various aspects of adult teaching and learning contexts from a feminist pedagogy perspective. A number of writers have researched and presented guidelines for establishing collaborative and connected learning environments. Stalker's (1993b) feminist analysis of women teachers' mentoring women learners centers on women academics' location in a patriarchal system. Stalker (1993a) also examined sexual harassment in the adult learner–teacher relationship as a function of unequal power, authority, and control. Similarly, Jarvis and Zukas (1998) conducted a feminist analysis of teaching, research, and supervision in adult education, and Bierema and Cseh (2003) analyzed human resource development research from a feminist perspective. Finally, Gouthro and Grace (2000) use "positional" models of feminist pedagogy to analyze graduate women's experiences in adult and higher education. They conclude that these models can bring about a more relevant graduate experience for women that might include "changes in the goals and objectives graduate students set for themselves, changes in the time it takes to finish graduate school, altered student perceptions of the role and purpose of graduate education, and altered research interests and job and career ambitions" (p. 137).

With few exceptions, critical theory and postmodernism offer little guidance on how to manage the teaching and learning encounter to effect the theory's desired ends. There is much more in the feminist pedagogy literature, as the References indicate. Lee and Johnson-Bailey (2004) suggest the following strategies: using questioning and group debriefing, using technology to manage sensitive discussions, claiming authority as the instructor, facilitating the process of understanding new and contradictory knowledge, and selecting culturally diverse materials. Tisdell (1993, 1995, 1998) also includes the literature on multicultural education in her suggestions for creating inclusive learning environments:

- Integrate affective and experiential knowledge with theoretical concepts.
- Pay attention to the power relations inherent in knowledge production.
- Be aware that participants are positioned differently in relationship to each other and to the knowledge being acquired.
- Acknowledge the power disparity between the teacher/facilitator and the students.
- Identify all stakeholders and their positionality in the educational program.
- Consider the levels of inclusivity and the levels of contexts involved in the educational activity.

- Consider how curricular choices implicitly or explicitly contribute to challenging structured power relations.
- Adopt emancipatory teaching strategies.
- Be conscious of the ways in which unconscious behavior contributes to challenging or reproducing unequal power relations.
- Build a community based on both openness and intellectual rigor to create a democratic classroom. [Tisdell, 1995, p. 90]

In summary, of the three theoretical orientations of critical theory, postmodernism, and feminist theory/feminist pedagogy reviewed in the second half of this chapter, feminist pedagogy has most directly addressed the practice of adult education and in particular the teaching-learning transaction in the classroom. Critical theory and postmodernism focus more on critique and questioning of the status quo. A few writers have attempted what Grace (1996a) calls "an eclectic theoretical scaffolding . . . using insights from discourses including critical theory, feminism, and postmodernism" (p. 145). His model is based on several assumptions necessary for building an adult learning community. He suggests that actual classroom practices must acknowledge personal experience along with theoretical analyses through being sensitive to intersections of power "where race, ethnicity, class, gender, sexual orientation, ableness, and age impact learning, life, and work" (1996a, p. 147), through conflict and dialogue, and through practices that are inclusionary of the diversity of peoples and their knowledge.

SUMMARY

In this chapter we have presented an overview of several contemporary perspectives on adult learning, all of which deal with critique and power relations. The mound of writing and research, the plethora of viewpoints, and the complexity and density of language and concepts that make up this perspective have made this effort a daunting one. What we have done is to sketch the outlines, name some of the main concepts and players, and drawing from the work of colleagues in adult education, show how this perspective is shaping our understanding of adult learning and adult education practice.

To this end, and drawing from Marxist theory, critical theory, multiculturalism, critical race theory, postmodernism, and feminist theory, we briefly discussed three themes that characterize this perspective. The first theme—race, class, and gender—leads to the second theme—of how the intersections of race, class, and gender affect the distribution of resources and power so that some groups in our society are privileged and some are oppressed. The third theme—knowledge and truth—considers the nature and construction of knowledge as it relates to learning.

The second half of the chapter reviewed critical theory, postmodernism, and feminist pedagogy and their contributions to understanding adult learning. Drawing from Welton's (1993) framework, several aspects of critical theory were discussed: Habermas's three distinct types of knowledge and the conditions necessary for ideal discourse, how to make institutions sites for learning, and the relationship between systemic forces based on money and power and the everyday lifeworld of adults.

Postmodernism challenges the certainty and rationality that characterize modernity. Uncertainty, diversity, and multiplicity can be fragmenting and disempowering for some, energizing and powerful for others. Postmodernity's major contribution to adult education has been to bring to the foreground previously oppressed and marginalized groups.

Finally, feminist pedagogy—the application of feminist theory to education—was reviewed with attention to adult education. What Maher (1987) categorizes as liberatory (focusing on social structures) and gender (emphasizing the psychological) models of feminist pedagogy were presented, followed by Tisdell's (1995, 1996, 1998) synthesis of the two into a poststructural model of feminist pedagogy. The work of adult educators in applying feminist pedagogy to adult learning transactions and contexts was also reviewed.

LEARNING AND DEVELOPMENT

The adult learner is at the center of all learning activities. Understanding how we as adults develop and change as we age, and how developmental issues and the changes we encounter interface with learning in adulthood, are important considerations in facilitating meaningful learning. Equally informative is research that explores those cognitive factors that affect learning, such as intelligence, memory, brain functioning, and so on. Part Four of *Learning in Adulthood* is a set of chapters that offer foundational work on learning theory in general and developmental perspectives in particular. Drawing from psychology, sociology, neurobiology, and educational and developmental psychology, these chapters compile material from a wide range of research and theory and are designed as a *resource* for the reader who wants to explore particular aspects of learning in more depth. While much of this literature is not specific to adults, we have selected topics that are important to understanding adult learning, and wherever possible, made those links.

Part Four opens with Chapter Eleven, which reviews five traditional theories of learning. Beginning with the earliest developed orientation to learning, behaviorism, the chapter goes on to review humanism, cognitivism, social cognitive learning theory, and constructivism. Each of these orientations, which all offer very different explanations of learning, has something to contribute to our understanding of the learning process. We examine each theory in terms of its major proponents, its explanation of the learning process, the purpose of education, the role of the learner, and the influence it has had on adult education.

Research has shown that adults are often motivated to participate in learning activities by developmental issues and changes in their lives. Chapter Twelve explores the developmental characteristics of adults that are most clearly related to learning. In selecting the information from this large body of research that is most relevant to learning in adulthood, we chose to cover four areas: biological and psychological changes in adulthood, sociocultural factors, and what we term the integrative perspective on development. The biological perspective acknowledges the physical aging process brought on by the natural mechanisms of aging as well as environmental influences, health habits, and disease. For the most part, there are few effects on adult learning from these biological changes, except for those associated with deterioration of sight and hearing, a slowing of reaction time, and disease, especially diseases connected with the central nervous system.

Psychological models of development, where the focus is on internal, psychological change, can loosely be grouped into stage-of-life or chronological age categories. Erikson's famous stage theory and Levinson's model are discussed as exemplars of these foundational psychological models. As with other areas of adult learning, psychological perspectives on development have dominated our thinking as adult educators about the linkages between development and learning.

From the sociocultural perspective, change in adulthood is determined more by contextual influences, such as social, economic, and historical factors, than by internal mechanisms. Two strands of work from this perspective are highlighted: first, the importance of social roles and the timing of life events, and second, the socially constructed nature of the concepts of race, gender, ethnicity, and sexual orientation and how they shape development. The integrative perspective acknowledges the intersections among the biological, psychological, and sociocultural perspectives in framing developmental theory. To move to a richer understanding of learning in adulthood, we suggest that adult educators use multiple lenses or perspectives on development instead of relying on just a single paradigm of development.

Chapter Thirteen explores cognitive development in adulthood—that is, how adults' thinking patterns change over time. Beginning with a discussion of the pioneering work of Piaget (1972), we present alternative theories and models of adult cognitive development, including a contextual perspective, which has gained more prominence recently. Dialectical thinking, characterized by the tolerance for contradictions and ambiguity in ways of thinking about similar phenomena in adult life, and wisdom, one of the hallmarks of mature adult thought, are also discussed.

Chapter Fourteen focuses on the concept of intelligence. Beginning with the early work on intelligence tests used to measure whether young men were "mentally fit" to serve in the armed forces in World War I (Kaufman, 2000) and Thorndike's studies of intelligence and aging (Thorndike, Bregman, Tilton, & Woodyard, 1928), researchers and educators alike have sought to understand the nature of adult intelligence and how it might be affected by the aging process. This chapter traces the development of the concept of intelligence, highlighting first the more traditional theories and approaches to the study of intelligence. The fundamental question of whether intelligence declines with age has different answers, depending largely on how intelligence and the parameters of aging are defined, and the research designs and tests that are used in these studies. Challenges to the traditional approaches to intelligence have a promising potential for furthering the understanding of the nature of adult intelligence, providing that more empirical work is completed to validate both the basic components of these theories and the tests being developed to measure those components.

Chapter Fifteen focuses on memory and cognition and how brain structures and functioning affect learning. After reviewing how memory works, the chapter explores the different components of memory—sensory, working, and long-term memory—and how age may or may not affect an adult's ability to remember. Other important aspects of cognition are then discussed, including the concepts of declarative and procedural knowledge, expert versus novice learners, and the differences between cognitive style and learning style. Although the major work in cognition has been done primarily with children and computer modeling, many educators have generalized the findings to include learning in adulthood but without the necessary verification studies. The final area explored in Chapter Fifteen is one of the most fascinating frontiers in the study of learning: the neurobiological basis of learning. Although neurobiologists have provided captivating descriptions of how the human brain is organized and functions, only a few direct connections between what we have learned about the brain and specific learning interventions for adults are being explored. Rather, what we primarily have are tentative and often tantalizing hypotheses about the neurobiology of learning.

CHAPTER ELEVEN

TRADITIONAL LEARNING THEORIES

Learning, so central to human behavior yet so elusive to understanding, has fascinated thinkers as far back as Plato and Aristotle. Indeed, the views of these two philosophers underpin much modern research on learning conducted by psychologists and educators. The fact that so many people have thought about, investigated, and written about the process of learning over the years suggests the complexity of the topic. Learning defies easy definition and simple theorizing. This chapter reviews some of the main ways in which learning has been studied and delineates the contributions these orientations have made to our understanding of learning in adulthood.

Originally, learning was within the purview of philosophical investigations into the nature of knowledge, the human mind, and what it means to know. Plato believed that the physical objects in our everyday world have corresponding abstract forms that we can come to know through "introspection or self-analysis. . . . Only by turning away from the physical impure world to the world of ideas, pondered by the mind's eye, can we hope to gain true knowledge" (Hergenhahn & Olson, 2005, p. 31). Aristotle, in contrast, believed that all knowledge comes through the senses; these sense impressions can be pondered "to discover the lawfulness that runs through them" (p. 32). Plato's "rationalism" can be seen in Gestalt and cognitive psychology; Aristotle's "empiricism" is particularly evident in early behavioral psychology. Later philosophers presented variations on these two basic positions, ranging from Descartes' separation of mind and body to Kant's notion of innate mental faculties.

It was not until the nineteenth century that the study of the mind, of how people know, and by extension, of behavior became "scientifically" investigated. Hergenhahn and Olson (2005, p. 42) write that Hermann Ebbinghaus "emancipated psychology from philosophy by demonstrating that the 'higher mental processes' of learning and memory could be studied experimentally" and that many of his findings on learning and memory published in 1885 are still valid. Another pioneer, Wilhelm Wundt, set up the first psychological laboratory in Leipzig in 1879 and investigated how experience is assimilated into one's previous knowledge structures. Interestingly, Wundt felt that laboratory research was limited in its usefulness for studying "products of the mind" such as "religion, morals, myths, art, social customs, language, and law" and he spent years studying these products "through naturalistic observation" (Hergenhahn & Olson, 2005, p. 43). Thus, by the turn of the century, systematic investigations into human learning were well under way in Europe and North America.

In this chapter we first present a brief discussion of learning and learning theories in general, and then we focus on five different learning theories: behaviorist, humanist, cognitivist, social cognitive, and constructivist. These theories deal with learning in general; attempts to build theories of *adult* learning in particular were examined in the chapters in Part Two.

LEARNING AND LEARNING THEORIES

A common definition of learning, emanating from psychologists who investigated the phenomenon until the 1950s, is that learning is a change in behavior. This definition, however, fails to capture some of the complexities involved—such as whether one needs to perform in order for learning to occur or whether all human behavior is learned. As Hill (2002, p. 10) points out, "What is learned need not be 'correct' or adaptive (we learn bad habits as well as good), need not be conscious or deliberate (one of the advantages of coaching in a skill is that it makes us aware of mistakes we have unconsciously learned to make), and need not involve any overt act (attitudes and emotions can be learned as well as knowledge and skills)." The notion of change, however, still underlies most definitions of learning, although it has been modified to include the potential for change. And the idea that having an experience of some sort, rather than learning as a function of maturation, is important. Thus a reasonable definition of learning would be as follows: Learning is a process that brings together cognitive, emotional, and environmental influences and experiences for acquiring, enhancing, or making changes in one's knowledge, skills, values, and worldviews (Illeris, 2000; Ormrod, 1995).

Learning as a process (rather than an end product) focuses on what happens when the learning takes place. Explanations of what happens are called *learning theories,* and it is these theories that are the subject of this chapter. There are, however, many explanations of learning, some more comprehensive than others, that are called theories. How the knowledge base in this area is divided and labeled depends on the writer. Hilgard and Bower (1966), for example, review eleven learning theories and then note that they fall into two main families: stimulus-response theories and cognitive theories. Knowles (1984) uses Reese and Overton's (1970) organization, in which learning theories are grouped according to two different worldviews: mechanistic and organismic.

Gredler (1997) exemplifies the difficulties in deciding which "contemporary perspectives" are actual learning theories. She discusses seven "perspectives": Skinner's operant conditioning, Gagne's conditions of learning, cognitive learning principles, Piaget's cognitive-development theory, Vygotsky's sociohistorical theory, Bandura's social-cognitive theory, and Weiner's theory of motivation. However, three of these (Piaget, Vygotsky, and Weiner) "technically are not categorized as learning theories" but "have important implications for classroom practice" (p. 12).

Since there is little consensus on how many learning theories there are or how they should be grouped for discussion, we have organized this chapter according to orientations that present very different assumptions about learning and offer helpful insights into adult learning. With these criteria in mind, five basic orientations have been selected for discussion: behaviorist, humanist, cognitivist, social cognitive, and constructivist. As Hill (2002, p. 190) has observed, "For most of us, the various learning theories have two chief values. One is in providing us with a vocabulary and a conceptual framework for interpreting the examples of learning that we observe. These are valuable for anyone who is alert to the world. The other, closely related, is in suggesting where to look for solutions to practical problems. The theories do not give us solutions, but they do direct our attention to those variables that are crucial in finding solutions."

In each of the five orientations examined in this chapter, the following topics are covered: the major proponents, the view of the learning process itself, the locus of learning, the purpose of education, the role of the teacher, and the ways in which these theories are manifested in the practice of adult education. A summary of this information can be found in Table 11.1 at the end of the chapter.

BEHAVIORIST ORIENTATION

Behaviorism is a well-known orientation to learning that encompasses a number of individual theories. Developed by John B. Watson in the early decades of the twentieth century, behaviorism loosely includes the work of such people as Thorndike, Tolman, Guthrie, Hull, and Skinner (Ormrod, 1995). What characterizes these investigators is their underlying assumptions about the process of learning. In essence, three basic assumptions are held to be true. First, observable behavior rather than internal thought processes is the focus of study; in particular, learning is manifested by a change in behavior. Second, the environment shapes behavior; what one learns is determined by the elements in the environment, not by the individual learner. And third, the principles of contiguity (how close in time two events must be for a bond to be formed) and reinforcement (any means of increasing the likelihood that an event will be repeated) are central to explaining the learning process (Grippin & Peters, 1984).

Edward L. Thorndike, a contemporary of Watson, is "perhaps the greatest learning theorist of all time" (Hergenhahn & Olson, 2005, p. 54). A prolific researcher and writer, "he did pioneer work not only in learning theory but also in the areas of educational practices, verbal behavior, comparative psychology, intelligence testing, the nature-nurture problem, transfer of training, and the application of quantitative measures to sociopsychological problems (e.g., he developed scales with which to compare the quality of life in different cities)." In fact, the book *Adult Learning* published by Thorndike and his colleagues in 1928 (Thorndike, Bregman, Tilton, & Woodyard, 1928) was the first major report of research on learning with adults.

Thorndike's most significant contribution to understanding learning has come to be called *connectionism,* or the S-R theory of learning. Using animals in controlled experiments, Thorndike noted that through repeated trial-and-error learning, certain connections between sensory impressions, or stimuli (S), and subsequent behavior, or responses (R), are strengthened or weakened by the consequences of behavior. Thorndike formulated three laws of learning to explain his findings: the Law of Effect, which states that learners will acquire and remember responses that lead to satisfying aftereffects; the Law of Exercise, which asserts that the repetition of a meaningful connection results in substantial learning; and the Law of Readiness, which notes that if the organism is ready for the connection, learning is enhanced, and if it is not, learning is inhibited (Ormrod, 1995). Although Thorndike himself and later researchers modified these laws, they are nevertheless still applied widely in educational settings.

Thorndike's connectionism became refined and expanded on by his contemporaries and by those who followed (for a detailed discussion, see Hergenhahn & Olson, 2005; Ormrod, 1995). Working in Russia, Pavlov, for example, added concepts of reinforcement, conditioned stimulus, and extinction to the basic notion of the stimulus-response connection. Guthrie stated that one law of learning based on contiguity is all that is needed to make learning comprehensible: "Whatever you do in the presence of a stimulus, you do again when that stimulus is re-presented" (Grippin & Peters, 1984, p. 61). Important as the work of these and other researchers was, behaviorism was most developed as a theory of learning by B. F. Skinner.

Skinner's major contribution to understanding learning is known as *operant conditioning.* Simply stated, operant conditioning means "reinforce what you want the individual to do again; ignore what you want the individual to stop doing" (Grippin & Peters, 1984, p. 65). Reinforcement is essential to understanding operant conditioning. If behavior is reinforced or rewarded, the response is more likely to occur again under similar conditions. Behavior that is not reinforced is likely to become less frequent and may even disappear. Within this framework, even something as complex as personality can be explained by operant conditioning. Personality, according to Skinner (1974, p. 149), is a "repertoire of behavior imported by an organized set of contingencies"—in effect, a personal history of reinforcements. Skinner's research concentrated on positive and negative reinforcement schedules, the timing of reinforcements, and avoidance behavior. In essence, his work indicates that since all behavior is learned, it can be determined by arranging the contingencies of reinforcement in the learner's immediate environment. Behaviorists since Skinner have taken into account certain aspects of the human organism but still emphasize that it is environment that controls behavior, "not some mechanism within the individual" (Grippin & Peters, 1984, p. 71).

The behaviorist orientation has been foundational to much educational practice, including adult learning. Skinner in particular has addressed the application of his theory to educational issues. As he sees it, the ultimate goal of education is to bring about behavior that will ensure survival of the human species, societies, and individuals (Skinner, 1971). The teacher's role is to design an environment that elicits desired behavior toward meeting these goals and to extinguish undesirable behavior.

Several practices in education and adult education can be traced to behaviorism. Since behaviorism focuses on the measurable, overt activity of the learner, behavioral objectives that specify the behavior to be exhibited by learners after some intervention direct much instructional planning even today. Behavioral objectives specify the conditions (or stimuli), the behavior to be performed, and the criteria by which the behavior will be judged.

Closely linked to a behaviorist perspective is the demand at all levels of education for accountability. The current No Child Left Behind (NCLB) legislation is an example of efforts to make education accountable. Enacted in 2001, NCLB mandated that students, schools, districts, and states must be evaluated each year; those schools that fail to meet certain standards will be penalized. Another example of the accountability thrust in education is the current federal push for "scientifically based" or "evidence-based" practices; that is, funding sources want reliable evidence that an educational program or practice works. For example, the U.S. Department of Education's Institute of Education Sciences has called for "the integration of professional wisdom with the best empirical evidence in making decisions about how to deliver instruction" (Comings, 2003, p. 2). For many policymakers, "the best empirical evidence" consists of measurable, quantifiable changes in behavior that can be tied to the educational intervention. Evidence-based practice has found its way into adult basic education (ABE), adult English for speakers of other languages (ESOL), and adult secondary education (ASE). Literacy educators are being urged to use quantitative research methodologies such as experimental and quasi-experimental designs to assess the efficacy of their methods and practices.

In adult education in particular, behaviorism is the philosophy that most underlies adult career and technical education and human resource development. The emphasis in vocational education is on identifying the skills needed to perform in an occupation, teaching those skills, and requiring a certain standard of performance of those skills. The National Skills Standards Board (NSSB) determines the standards for skills needed in the workplace (see http://www.nssb.org/). Vocational educational programs teach to those standards and students are evaluated by those standards.

Human resource development (HRD) is most associated with training to enhance on-the-job performance in the workplace. Performance improvement, competency-based instruction, and accountability are all part of this behavioral orientation to HRD. Jacobs (1987), in particular, conceptualizes HRD as performance improvement: "Human performance technology is about engineering . . . technologies . . . based on what is known about the principles to change the outcomes of behavior" (p. 19). As Sleezer, Conti, and Nolan (2003) point out, "HRD professionals who rely on behaviorism and cognitivism emphasize rewards, the stimuli that learners receive from the environment, the systematic observation of behavior, and relating new information to previous learning" (p. 26). It should be noted that there are numerous educators and HRD and technical education professionals who do not ascribe to such a behaviorist orientation. Nevertheless, the behavioral orientation to learning has had a profound effect on our educational system. It has also been challenged by theorists from two radically different perspectives: humanism and cognitivism.

HUMANIST ORIENTATION

Humanist theories consider learning from the perspective of the human potential for growth. This shift to the study of the affective as well as cognitive dimensions of learning was informed in part by

Freud's psychoanalytic approach to human behavior. Although most would not label Freud a learning theorist, aspects of his psychology, such as the influence of the subconscious mind on behavior, as well as the concepts of anxiety, repression, defense mechanism, drives, and transference, have found their way into some learning theories. Sahakian (1984) even makes the case for psychoanalytic therapy as a type of learning theory.

Despite Freud's focus on personality, humanists reject the view of human nature implied by both behaviorists and Freudian psychologists. Identifying their orientation as a "third force," humanists refuse to accept the notion that behavior is predetermined by either the environment or one's subconscious. Rather, human beings can control their own destiny; people are inherently good and will strive for a better world; people are free to act, and behavior is the consequence of human choice; people possess unlimited potential for growth and development (Rogers, 1983; Maslow, 1970). From a learning theory perspective, humanism emphasizes that perceptions are centered in experience, and it also emphasizes the freedom and responsibility to become what one is capable of becoming. These tenets underlie much of adult learning theory that stresses the self-directedness of adults and the value of experience in the learning process. Two psychologists who have contributed the most to our understanding of learning from this perspective are Abraham Maslow and Carl Rogers.

Maslow (1970), considered the founder of humanistic psychology, proposed a theory of human motivation based on a hierarchy of needs. At the lowest level of his famous triangle hierarchy are physiological needs such as hunger and thirst, which must be attended to before one can deal with safety needs—those dealing with security and protection. The remaining levels are belonging and love, self-esteem, and finally, the need for self-actualization. This final need can be seen in a person's desire to become all that he or she is capable of becoming. The motivation to learn is intrinsic; it emanates from the learner. For Maslow self-actualization is the goal of learning, and educators should strive to bring this about. As Sahakian (1984) notes, learning from Maslow's point of view is itself "a form of self-actualization. Among the growth motivations was found the need for cognition, the desire to know and to understand. Learning is not only a form of psychotherapy . . . but learning contributes to psychological health" (p. 438).

Although self-actualization is the primary goal of learning, Maslow posits other goals (Sahakian, 1984, p. 439):

1. The discovery of a vocation or destiny
2. The knowledge or acquisition of a set of values
3. The realization of life as precious
4. The acquisition of peak experiences
5. A sense of accomplishment
6. The satisfaction of psychological needs
7. The refreshing of consciousness to an awareness of the beauty and wonder of life
8. The control of impulses
9. The grappling with the critical existential problems of life
10. Learning to choose discriminatively

Another major figure writing from a humanist orientation is Carl Rogers. His book *Freedom to Learn for the 80s* (1983) lays out his theory of learning, which he sees as a similar process in both therapy and education. In fact, his "client-centered therapy" is often equated with student-centered learning. In both education and therapy, Rogers is concerned with significant learning that leads to personal growth and development. Such learning, according to Rogers, has the following characteristics (p. 20):

1. Personal involvement: The affective and cognitive aspects of a person should be involved in the learning event.
2. Self-initiated: A sense of discovery must come from within.
3. Pervasive: The learning "makes a difference in the behavior, the attitudes, perhaps even the personality of the learner."
4. Evaluated by the learner: The learner can best determine whether the experience is meeting a need.
5. Essence is meaning: When experiential learning takes place, its meaning to the learner becomes incorporated into the total experience.

Quite clearly, Rogers's principles of significant learning and Maslow's views have been integrated into much of adult learning. Knowles's theory of andragogy, with its assumptions about the adult learner (see Chapter Four), and much of the research and writing on self-directed learning (see Chapter Five) are grounded in humanistic learning theories. As Caffarella (1993, p. 26) observes about self-directed learning, "The focus of learning is on the individual and self-development, with learners expected to assume primary responsibility for their own learning. The process of learning, which is centered on learner need, is seen as more important than the content; therefore, when educators are involved in the learning process, their most important role is to act as facilitators, or guides."

In addition to andragogy and self-directed learning, Mezirow's notion of perspective transformation (see Chapter Six) also has humanistic roots. In transformational learning theory the notion of individual development is both inherent in and an outcome of the process: "Meaning perspectives that permit us to deal with a broader range of experience, to be more discriminating, to be more open to other perspectives, and to better integrate our experiences are superior perspectives" (Mezirow, 1990b, p. 14).

In summary, adult education that is lodged in humanistic psychology is quite prevalent in the United States. Elias and Merriam (2005) attribute its popularity to its compatibility with a democratic political system and to adult education's voluntary nature: "Educational activities must meet the needs of adult learners in order to survive. Practical considerations thus necessitate an emphasis upon individual needs and interests" (p. 144).

COGNITIVE ORIENTATION

The earliest challenge to the behaviorists came in a publication in 1929 by Bode, a Gestalt psychologist. He criticized behaviorists for being too particularistic, too concerned with single events and actions, and too dependent on overt behavior to explain learning. *Gestalt* (a German word meaning *pattern* or *shape*) psychologists proposed looking at the whole rather than its parts, at patterns rather than isolated events. Through the research of Gestaltists Wertheimer, Kohler, Koffka, and later Lewin (Hergenhahn & Olson, 2005; Ormrod, 1995), Gestalt views of learning rivaled behaviorism by the mid-twentieth century. These views have been incorporated into what have come to be labeled *cognitive* or *information-processing* learning theories. Two key assumptions underlie this cognitive or information-processing approach: "(1) that the memory system is an active organized processor of information, and (2) that prior knowledge plays an important role in learning" (Gredler, 1997, p. 144).

Perception, insight, and meaning are key concepts in cognitivism for Gestalt learning theorists. According to cognitivists, "The human mind is not simply a passive exchange-terminal system where the stimuli arrive and the appropriate response leaves. Rather, the thinking person interprets sensations and gives meaning to the events that impinge upon his consciousness" (Grippin & Peters, 1984, p. 76). Learning involves the reorganization of experiences in order to make sense of stimuli from the environment. Sometimes this sense comes through flashes of insight. Hergenhahn and Olson (2005, p. 273) summarize the learning process according to Gestalt psychology: "Learning, to the Gestaltist, is a cognitive phenomenon. The organism 'comes to see' the solution after pondering a problem. The learner thinks about all the ingredients necessary to solve a problem and puts them together (cognitively) first one way and then another until the problem is solved. When the solution comes, it comes suddenly, that is, the organism gains an *insight* into the solution of a problem. The problem can exist in only two states: (1) unsolved and (2) solved; there is no state of partial solution in between." A major difference between Gestaltists and behaviorists, therefore, is the locus of control over the learning activity. For Gestaltists it lies with the individual learner; for behaviorists it lies with the environment. This shift to the individual—and in particular to the learner's mental processes—is characteristic of cognitivist-oriented learning theories.

A cognitive psychologist who clarified the focus on internal cognitive processes was Jean Piaget (1966). Influenced by both the behaviorist and Gestalt schools of thought, Piaget proposed that one's internal cognitive structure changes partly as a result of maturational changes in the nervous system and partly as a result of the organism's interacting with the environment and being exposed to an increasing number of experiences. His four-stage theory of cognitive development and its implications for adult learning are discussed more fully in Chapter Thirteen.

Currently, cognitive learning theory encompasses a number of perspectives, all of which take as their starting point the mental processes involved in learning (Wilson & Keil, 1999). Examples of specific areas of study include information-processing theories, memory and metacognition, theories of transfer, mathematical learning theory models, the study of expertise, computer simulations, cognition and culture, and artificial intelligence (see Chapter Fifteen). Converging with cognitive learning theory are theories of instruction that attempt to unite what is known about learning with the best way to facilitate its occurrence. Ausubel, Bruner, and Gagne provide good examples of how the understanding of mental processes can be linked to instruction.

Ausubel (1967) distinguishes between meaningful learning and rote learning. He suggests that learning is meaningful only when it can be related to concepts that already exist in a person's cognitive structure. Rote learning, in contrast, does not become linked to a person's cognitive structure and hence is easily forgotten. Ausubel's views have also been labeled *assimilation theory* since "most learning, especially in adulthood but in childhood as well, consists of assimilating new experience into one's existing cognitive structure" (Hill, 2002, p. 138). He suggests the use of "advance organizers" to prepare a person for new learning. Ausubel's work can be seen as an antecedent to current research on schema theory whereby schemata—structures that organize the learner's worldview—determine how people process new experiences (Anderson, 1996; Di Vesta, 1987; Ormrod, 1995).

Ausubel emphasizes the importance of the learner's cognitive structure in new learning. Bruner, whose views are often contrasted with Ausubel's, emphasizes learning through discovery. Discovery is "in its essence a matter of rearranging or transforming evidence in such a way that one is enabled to go beyond the evidence" and as a result, reconstruct additional new insights (Bruner, 1965, pp. 607–608). According to Knowles (1984), Bruner's instructional theory is based on a theory about the act of learning that involves "three almost simultaneous processes: (1) acquisition of new information . . . ; (2) transformation, or the process of manipulating knowledge to make it fit new tasks; and (3) evaluation, or checking whether the way we have manipulated information is adequate to the task" (p. 25).

Linking instruction to the acquisition and processing of knowledge has probably been most thoroughly developed by Gagne, Briggs, and Wager (1992). They contend that there are eight different types of knowledge—signal learning, stimulus-response, motor training, verbal association, discrimination learning, concept learning, rule learning, and problem solving—each with appropriate instructional procedures. Kidd (1973, p. 182) points out that the work of Gagne and others has been an important influence on the "learning how to learn" concept, which has been explored in some depth by Smith, who has been particularly interested in applying it to adult learning (Smith, 1982, 1987; Smith & Associates, 1990). According to Smith (1982, p. 19), "Learning how to learn involves possessing, or acquiring, the knowledge and skill to learn effectively in whatever learning situation one encounters." Three subconcepts are involved: the learner's needs; a person's learning style; and training, which is an organized activity, or instruction to increase competence in learning.

In addition to Smith's work on learning how to learn, the cognitive orientation can be seen in two other areas that have particular relevance for adult learning. First, interest in cognitive development in adulthood has been the subject of recent research (see Chapter Thirteen); second, the study of learning processes as a function of age (see Chapter Fifteen) draws from the cognitive focus on learning. (See also Tennant & Pogson, 1995.)

In summary, cognitively oriented explanations of learning encompass a wide range of topics with a common focus on internal mental processes that are under the learner's control. "Essential components of learning are the organization of the information to be learned, the learner's prior knowledge, and the processes involved in perceiving, comprehending, and storing information" (Gredler, 1997, p. 143). As Di Vesta (1987, p. 229) observes, "Rather than seeking the general all-encompassing laws for controlling and predicting behavior, as did the earlier grand theories of learning," cognitive learning theory "is directed toward miniature models of specific facets of cognition, such as models of discourse analysis, models of comprehension, ways of aiding understanding and meaningful learning, the nature of the schemata, the memory system, the development of cognitive skills, and the like."

SOCIAL COGNITIVE ORIENTATION

This learning theory, which combines elements from both behaviorist and cognitivist orientations, posits that people learn from observing others. By definition, such observations take place in a social setting—hence the label *observational* or *social* learning (Lefrancois, 1999). Specifically, "social cognitive learning theory highlights the idea that much human learning occurs in a social environment. By observing others, people acquire knowledge, rules, skills, strategies, beliefs, and attitudes. Individuals also learn about the usefulness and appropriateness of behaviors by observing models and the consequences of modeled behaviors, and they act in accordance with their beliefs concerning the expected outcomes of actions" (Schunk, 1996, p. 102). Just how the learning occurs has been the subject of several investigations.

Miller and Dollard in the 1940s were the first to explore how people learn through observation. Drawing from stimulus-response and reinforcement theory, they argued that people do not learn from observation alone; rather, they must imitate and reinforce what they have observed. "If imitative responses were not made and reinforced, no learning would take place. For them, imitative learning was the result of observation, overt responding, and reinforcement" (Hergenhahn & Olson, 2005, p. 339). These ideas are totally congruent with the behaviorist orientation to learning. Not until the 1960s, however, with the work of Bandura, did social learning theory break from a purely behaviorist orientation.

Bandura focused more on the cognitive processes involved in the observation than on the subsequent behavior. Central to his theory is the separation of observation from the act of imitation. One can learn from observation, he maintains, without having to imitate what was observed (Lefrancois, 1999). In fact, the learning can be vicarious: "Virtually all learning phenomena resulting from direct experiences can occur on a vicarious basis through observation of other people's behavior and its consequences for the observer" (Bandura, 1976, p. 392). In addition to being cognitive and vicarious, Bandura's observational learning is characterized by the concept of self-regulation. He contends that "persons can regulate their own behavior to some extent by visualizing self-generated consequences" (p. 392).

Observational learning is influenced by the four processes of attention, retention or memory, behavioral rehearsal, and motivation (Hergenhahn & Olson, 2005). Before something can be learned, the model must be attended to; some models are more likely than others to be attended to, such as those thought to be competent, powerful, attractive, and so on. Information from an observation then needs to be retained or stored for future use. Retention can be through symbols or words: "Imaginally stored symbols are pictures or mental images of past experiences, whereas verbal symbols capture the complexities of behavior in words. Bandura notes that conceptual representations often comprise both images and verbal symbols" (Gibson, 2004, p. 197). Finally, the modeled behavior is stored until a person is motivated to act on it.

More recently, Bandura has focused on self-efficacy, that is, our own estimate of how competent we feel we are likely to be in a particular environment. This self-assessment influences how effective we are in interactions with others and with our environment (Lefrancois, 1999). Bandura's approach first became known as social learning theory, but as his research and writing began to emphasize cognitive components, it is now known as social *cognitive* theory (Hergenhahn & Olson, 2005; Hill, 2002). As Bandura himself explained in the preface to his book, *Social Foundations of Thought and Action: A Social Cognitive Theory* (1986, p. xii), "The theoretical approach of this book is designated as *social cognitive theory*. The social portion of the terminology acknowledges the social origins of much human thought and action; the cognitive portion recognizes the influential causal contribution of thought processes to human motivation, affect, and action."

Bandura's theory has particular relevance to adult learning in that it accounts for both the learner and the environment in which he or she operates. Behavior is a function of the interaction of the person with the environment. This is a reciprocal concept in that people influence their environment, which in turn influences the way they behave. This three-way interactive model of the learning, the individual, and the environment is pictured by Bandura (1986) as a triangle in which learning is set solidly in a social context.

The social situation is also central to Rotter's (1954) theory, which includes strands from behaviorism, cognitivism, and personality theory. Rotter's theory is framed by seven propositions and attendant corollaries that delineate relationships among the concepts of behavior, personality, experience, and environment. Rotter's theory assumes that "much of human behavior takes place in a meaningful environment and is acquired through social interactions with other people" (Phares, 1980, p. 406). Key to understanding "which behavior (once acquired) in the individual's repertoire will occur in a given situation" (p. 407) are the concepts of expectancy and reinforcement. Expectancy is the likelihood that a particular reinforcement will occur as the result of specific behavior: "The way in which the person construes or psychologically defines the situation will affect the values of both reinforcement and expectancy, thereby influencing the potential for any given behavior to occur" (p. 408). "Rotter's theory says that when subjective beliefs contradict prior experiences . . . people are more likely to act on the basis of belief than experience" (Schunk, 1996, p. 107).

Several useful concepts emerge from social cognitive learning theory. For example, the motivation to engage in adult learning activities might be partly explained by Rotter's (1954) notion of locus of control. Some people attribute their successes and failures to factors over which they feel they have no control—they exhibit an external locus of control—whereas others attribute successes and failures to personal, internal factors. An example of how this might relate to motivation and participation in adult education would be the case of someone who is out of work. This person's unemployment might be blamed on factors over which he feels he has no control such as "the economy," outsourcing of jobs to cheaper labor markets, lack of public transportation, or age, gender, or skin color. Another person, whose locus of control is more internal, might decide that her being unemployed is more likely due to her inability to get along with coworkers, her lack of computer skills, and so forth. This person is much more likely to engage in learning activities to make herself more employable.

Another connection to adult learning is the importance of context and the learner's interaction with the environment to explain behavior. That is, explanations of learning may need to focus on more than overt behavior, mental processes, or personality. Bandura, in fact, has advanced a model of *triadic reciprocality* "in which behavior, cognitive and other personal factors, and environmental events all operate as interacting determinants of each other" (1986, p. 18). Studying the interaction of all these factors may result in a more comprehensive explanation of how adults learn. Moreover, Bandura's work on observational learning and modeling provides insights into social role acquisition and the nature of mentoring, a topic explored in depth by several adult educators (see Cohen, 1995; Daloz, 1999; Galbraith & Cohen, 1995; Mullen, 2005). Finally, Gibson (2004) makes a strong case for the influence of social cognitive theory in HRD theory building, research, and practice. In the area of practice, for example, she points out the prevalence of behavior-modeling techniques in both formal classroom situations and informal workplace interactions. Self-efficacy and its relationship to training and development of employees and employee socialization and on-the-job training are other areas of practice where social cognitive learning theory is evident.

CONSTRUCTIVIST ORIENTATION

Like some of the other theories already reviewed, constructivism encompasses a number of related perspectives. Basically, a constructivist stance maintains that learning is a process of constructing meaning; it is how people make sense of their experience. Beyond that basic assumption, constructivists differ as to the nature of reality, the role of experience, what knowledge is of interest, and whether the process of meaning-making is primarily individual or social (Steffe & Gale, 1995).

In an essay underscoring the variety of perspectives that are labeled constructivist, Phillips (1995) identifies six major strands: von Glaserfeld's work in math and science education, Kant's notions of knowledge and experience, feminist theorists' views on knowledge construction, Kuhn's work on scientific paradigms and revolutions, Piaget's theory of cognitive development, and Dewey's assumptions about knowledge and experience. Where these strands seem to converge is in the debate over the individual versus the social.

Driver and her colleagues (Driver, Asoko, Leach, Mortimer, & Scott, 1994) frame the issue as one of personal versus social constructivism. Drawing heavily on Piaget, they state that learning as an individual or personal activity involves a "progressive adaptation of [an] individual's cognitive schemes to the physical environment" (p. 6). Meaning is made by the individual and is dependent on the individual's previous and current knowledge structure. Learning is thus an internal cognitive activity. Teaching from the personal constructivism perspective involves providing "experiences that induce cognitive conflict and hence encourage learners to develop new knowledge schemes that are better adapted to experience. Practical activities supported by group discussions form the core of such pedagogical practices" (Driver et al., 1994, p. 6).

The social constructivist view, in contrast, posits that knowledge is "constructed when individuals engage socially in talk and activity about shared problems or tasks. Making meaning is thus a dialogic process involving persons-in-conversation, and learning is seen as the process by which individuals are introduced to a culture by more skilled members" (Driver et al., 1994, p. 7). This approach involves learning the culturally shared ways of understanding and talking about the world and reality. Vygotsky (1978) is credited with developing the foundation of this view because he proposed that learning is socially mediated through a culture's symbols and language, which are constructed in interaction with others in the culture. Vygotsky's work is also considered foundational to what's known as *activity theory* (AT). Activity theory "conceptualises learning as involving a subject (the learner), and object (the task or activity) and mediating artifacts (for example, a computer, laws)" (Issroff & Scanlon, 2002, p. 77). Activity theory, or what is better known as situated cognition in the United States (Wilson, 2005), combines the individual and the social (including culture and history) in understanding an activity such as learning.

Phillips (1995) posits that the various forms of constructivism can be graphed on a number of continua or axes and in so doing some would be close together on one dimension and far apart on another. For example, the personal, more psychological, orientation of, say, Piaget would contrast with the social perspective of feminist epistemologists. Other constructivists would be more in the middle of this continuum in that they "believe that their theories throw light on both the question of how individuals build up bodies of knowledge and how human communities have constructed the public bodies of knowledge known as the various disciplines" (p. 7). Cobb (1994, p. 13), for example, suggests viewing mathematical learning as "both a process of active individual construction and a process of enculturation into the mathematical practices of wider society." However, regardless of one's position on the continuum, there are important pedagogical implications to be derived, "each of which has a degree of credibility that is independent of the fate of the respective epistemologies" (p. 10). All forms of constructivism understand learning to be an active rather than passive endeavor. Consequently, learning occurs through dialogue, collaborative learning, and cooperative learning. "One learns through engaging, incorporating, and critically exploring the views of others, and new possibilities of interpretations are opened through the interaction" (Gergen, 1995, p. 34).

This view, of course, is quite congruent with what we know about adult learning.

Writing from a predominantly social constructivist perspective, Candy (1991, p. 275) discusses how this view translates to adult education: "Becoming knowledgeable involves acquiring the symbolic meaning structures appropriate to one's society, and, since knowledge is socially constructed, individual members of society may be able to add to or change the general pool of knowledge. Teaching and learning, *especially for adults*, is a process of negotiation, involving the construction and exchange of personally relevant and viable meanings" (italics in original).

Much of our adult learning theory is constructivist in nature. For example, "the constructivist view of learning is particularly compatible with the notion of self-direction, since it emphasizes the combined characteristics of active inquiry, independence, and individuality in a learning task" (Candy, 1991, p. 278). Transformational learning theory (see Chapter Six), especially as presented by Mezirow, focuses on both the individual and social construction of meaning. Perspective transformation is a highly cognitive process in which one's meaning schemes and meaning perspectives undergo radical change (Mezirow & Associates, 2000). This change is mediated through personal reflection and dialogue with others. The central role of experience in adult learning is another point of connection. Andragogy and other models of adult learning see life experience as both a resource and a stimulus for learning; constructivism too begins with the learner's interaction with experience.

Finally, much of what the field of adult learning draws from situated cognition is constructivist in nature (see Chapter Seven). Concepts such as cognitive apprenticeship, situated learning, reflective practice, and communities of practice are found in both adult learning and constructivist literature. Two adult education practice arenas in particular where constructivist and situated cognition concepts are having an impact are in continuing professional education (Ferry & Ross-Gordon, 1998) and human resource development (Stamps, 1997). As Wegner (cited by Stamps, 1997, pp. 38–39) explains, "What is shared by a community of practice—what makes it a community—is its practice. The concept of practice connotes doing, but not just doing in and of itself. It is doing in a historical and social context that gives structure and meaning to what we do. . . . Learning is the engine of practice, and practice is the history of that learning. Indeed, practice is ultimately produced by its members through the negotiation of meaning."

SUMMARY

Learning, a process central to human behavior, has been of interest to philosophers, psychologists, educators, and politicians for centuries. Since the late nineteenth century, the systematic investigation of this phenomenon has resulted in many explanations of how people learn. This chapter has reviewed some of these theories. Because there are dozens of learning theories and volumes written describing them, we have explored different orientations to learning, any of which might include numerous learning theories. The behaviorist, humanist, cognitivist, social cognitive, and constructivist orientations were chosen for their diversity and for their insights into learning in adulthood. Table 11.1 summarizes these five orientations. Since each is based on different assumptions about the nature of learning, the strategies one might use to enhance learning will depend on one's orientation. Instructors and program developers can use this review of major learning theories to identify their own theory of learning and discover the strategies for facilitating learning that are most congruent with their theory.

In brief, behaviorists define learning as a change in behavior. The focus of their research is overt behavior, which is a measurable response to stimuli in the environment. The role of the teacher is to arrange the contingencies of reinforcement in the learning environment so that the desired behavior will occur. Findings from behavioral learning theories can be seen in training and vocational adult education.

In contrast to behaviorism is the humanistic orientation to learning. Here the emphasis is on human nature, human potential, human emotions, and affect. Theorists in this tradition believe that learning involves more than cognitive processes and overt behavior. It is a function of motivation and involves choice and responsibility. Much of adult learning theory, especially the concepts of andragogy and many of the models of self-directed learning, are grounded in humanistic assumptions.

TABLE 11.1. FIVE ORIENTATIONS TO LEARNING.

Aspect	Behaviorist	Humanist	Cognitivist	Social Cognitive	Constructivist
Learning theorists	Guthrie, Hull, Pavlov, Skinner, Thorndike, Tolman, Watson	Maslow, Rogers	Ausubel, Bruner, Gagne, Koffka, Kohler, Lewin, Piaget	Bandura, Rotter	Candy, Dewey, Lave, Piaget, Rogoff, von Glaserfeld, Vygotsky
View of the learning process	Change in behavior	A personal act to fulfill development	Information processing (including insight, memory, perception, metacognition)	Interaction with and observation of others in a social context	Construction of meaning from experience
Locus of learning	Stimuli in external environment	Affective and developmental needs	Internal cognitive structure	Interaction of person, behavior, environment	Individual and social construction of knowledge
Purpose of learning	To produce behavioral change in desired direction	To become selfactualized, mature, autonomous	To develop capacity and skills to learn better	To learn new roles and behaviors	To construct knowledge

continued

TABLE 11.1. *Continued*

Aspect	Behaviorist	Humanist	Cognitivist	Social Cognitive	Constructivist
Instructor's role	Arrange environment to elicit desired response	Facilitate development of whole person	Structure content of learning activity	Model and guide new roles and behaviors	Facilitate and negotiate meaning-making with learner
Manifestation in adult learning	• Behavioral objectives • Accountability • Performance improvement • Skill development • HRD and training	• Andragogy • Self-directed learning • Cognitive development • Transformational learning	• Learning how to learn • Social role acquisition • Intelligence, learning, and memory as related to age	• Socialization • Self-directed learning • Locus of control • Mentoring	• Experiential learning • Transformational learning • Reflective practice • Communities of practice • Situated learning

Also in contrast to behaviorists, researchers working from a cognitivist perspective focus not on external behavior but on internal mental processes. Cognitivists are interested in how the mind makes sense out of stimuli in the environment—how information is processed, stored, and retrieved. This orientation is especially evident in the study of adult learning from a developmental perspective. The major concerns are how aging affects an adult's ability to process and retrieve information and how it affects an adult's internal mental structures.

The fourth orientation discussed here is social cognitive learning. This perspective differs from the other three in its focus on the social setting in which learning occurs. From this perspective, learning occurs through the observation of people in one's immediate environment. Furthermore, learning is a function of the interaction of the person, the environment, and the behavior. Variations in behavior under the same circumstances can be explained by idiosyncratic personality traits and their unique interaction with environmental stimuli. Social learning theories contribute to adult learning by highlighting the importance of social context and explicating the processes of modeling and mentoring.

Finally, constructivism, representing an array of perspectives, posits that learners construct their own knowledge from their experiences. The cognitive process of meaning-making is emphasized as both an individual mental activity and a socially interactive interchange. Aspects of constructivism can be found in self-directed learning, transformational learning, experiential learning, situated cognition, and reflective practice.

CHAPTER TWELVE

ADULT DEVELOPMENT

At age eighty, John reflects on the many changes he has experienced. Although his eyes are now clouded by cataracts, he remembers when family and friends nicknamed him "Eagle-Eye Johnny" because of his excellent eyesight. He also recalls his friends' surprise when he married at age forty and went on to have two children. He explains, "I guess I was a late bloomer. Having kids in my forties kept me young, though." John recollects that his priorities have changed over time. In high school and college, he wanted to "be [his] own man" and after college he focused on his career. John recalls, "In my mid-thirties, I realized that I wanted to give back to the community. I also wanted to be married and have a family." John continues to give back to people in his small town by visiting people in the nursing home and sponsoring a support group for men who have had heart surgery. John admits that lately he has spent more time "remembering the good times." He continues, "I've had a good life. In some ways, I'm still the same person I was at twenty. For example, I've always valued being organized and efficient. In other ways, I've changed a lot."

The concept of development is most often equated with change. Development has been defined as "systematic change within an individual or a group of individuals that results from a dynamic interaction of heredity and environmental influences" (Lerner, 1998, as cited in Bee & Bjorkland, 2004, p. 14). However, it is important to remember that there is a sense of both stability and change in development (Bee & Bjorkland, 2004). For example, John's sense of organization has been a constant in his life. However, his values have changed somewhat. In the next section we will briefly introduce the approaches to development that wrestle with the importance of nature and nurture in the developmental process, including biological, psychological, sociocultural, and integrated perspectives.

FOUR APPROACHES TO ADULT DEVELOPMENT

The biological perspective acknowledges the role of nature in our development. It recognizes that "we are physical beings" and that change in our physical being can be "driven by natural aging, the environment, our own health habits or by an accident or disease process" (Clark & Caffarella, 1999, p. 5). The psychological perspective "focuses on how we develop as individuals and examines primarily internal development processes" (p. 5). Psychological models of development have been used to explore faith development (Fowler, 1981), moral development (Kohlberg, 1976), identity development (Erikson, 1968; Loevinger, 1976), and intellectual development (Perry, 1999). The sociocultural approach posits that adult development cannot be understood apart from the historical context in which it occurs (Miller, 2002). The influence of society is taken into account in this perspective. The integrative approach to development combines several influences on adult development. For example, Bronfenbrenner's (2001) ecological model delineates changes that occur in people as the result of their interaction with peers or the interaction between a person's workplace and community.

We discuss the four approaches to adult development in this chapter. First, we explore biological aging and its impact on learning. Next, we examine psychological models of development, including Erikson's (1963, 1978) psychosocial model and Levinson's (Levinson, Darrow, Klein, Levinson, & McKee, 1978; Levinson & Levinson, 1996) model of personal development, among others. Third, we discuss how sociocultural factors affect development, including the influence of the timing of life events and the influence of race, class, and gender on development. The last section of the chapter presents integrative models of development, which demonstrate a more holistic approach.

Biological Development

Biological aging is a fact of life, although rarely a welcome one in American culture. Anti-aging products abound because people are fascinated with maintaining a youthful appearance. The top ten facial moisturizers (some of which advertise antiwrinkle properties) sold at supermarkets, drugstores, and discount stores produced $262.8 million in sales in 2004, and professional skin care products sold at spas and salons netted an additional $285 million ("Beauty at Every Age Is the Maxim," 2005). Antiwrinkle creams, hair color, sexual enhancement medications, and laser treatments temporarily keep the signs of aging at bay. Yet, people cannot escape the inevitability of biological aging.

Biological development refers to the physical and biological changes that occur over the life span. In this section, we discuss biological aging. We briefly explore theories of primary aging. In addition, we discuss age-related changes in vision, hearing, and the central nervous system.

Although life expectancy has increased from 49.2 years in 1900 to 76.5 years in the United States in 2000 (Guyer, Freedman, Strobino, & Sondik, 2000), our capacity to live longer does not mean we have been able to halt the primary process of aging— those time-related physical changes governed by some kind of maturational process, as in vision and hearing, for example—that happen to all of us (Bee & Bjorkland, 2004). Theories as to *why* primary aging occurs are plentiful, but all theories need further research. One theory asserts that cellular damage occurs during "the normal metabolism of oxygen" and this cellular damage builds up with age (Bee & Bjorkland, 2004, p. 61). Some scholars blame physical aging on the cell's lessening ability to repair daily breaks in DNA strands (Bee & Bjorkland, 2004; Carey, 2003). A third theory asserts that primary aging is related to "how many calories we metabolize per day" (Bee & Bjorkland, 2004, p. 63). Bee and Bjorkland note, "This theory is based on the premise that the hypothalamus serves as a glandular clock of some kind that measures age in the number of calories metabolized by the body" (p. 63).

Although life expectancy has increased, the human life span, usually given as 110 to 120 years, has not changed. Rather, our increased longevity stems from overcoming some of the problems related to secondary aging—aging that occurs due to "the . . . changes that are the result of disease, health habits or environmental influences" (Bee & Bjorkland, 2004, p. 60). These changes do not happen to everyone and can often be prevented. Improved nutrition, hygiene, discoveries in the medical and mental health fields, and lifestyle changes have accounted for most of this increased longevity.

It is important to note, however, that racial and ethnic health disparities have an impact on longevity. Black men are more likely to suffer from prostate, lung, colorectal, and stomach cancer than White men, and Black men and women are more likely than their White counterparts to suffer from hypertension ("Health Disparities Experienced by Black or African Americans," 2004). Numerous factors, including access to preventive services and racial discrimination, contribute to these disparities. In a study of three hundred thousand Medicare patients, research completed with Black patients found that they received different treatment than Whites (Schneider, Zaslavsky, & Epstein, 2002). Blacks were less likely than Whites to receive beta-blockers after a heart attack or aftercare following a hospitalization for mental illness. The researchers controlled for income, education, and quality of the clinic the patients visited.

While racial and ethnic disparities in health care persist, biological aging affects us all. However, decline in the actual functioning of the major biological systems is slow. The fourth and fifth decades tend to be the physiological turning point for most adults, although the effects of these changes may not be felt until the sixth or seventh decade of life (Bee & Bjorkland, 2004). The most obvious changes are changes in appearance. Suddenly, we notice our skin is not as firm and elastic as it once was. Our hair may become increasingly gray and turn white or we may experience hair loss. Yet these changes, although noticeable, really have little effect on our physical functioning. Less obvious are the more pervasive internal changes. For example, most adults begin to experience changes in vision, cardiovascular systems, bones and connective material, respiratory system, and reproductive function (for women) sometime in their forties or early fifties.

Although it appears that we will all experience many major changes in our physical beings at some point in our lives, the effect of these changes on our capacity to learn is largely unknown. In fact, many of these changes may prove to be very minor, except in cases of underlying disease processes. We will briefly discuss physical changes that have been shown to affect learning in adulthood: age-related changes in two of the senses and changes in the central nervous system. In addition, vision and hearing disorders common to older adulthood are discussed.

SENSES

Deterioration in the ability to see and to hear can create problems with the learning process. Specific changes in vision are well documented (Pesce, Guidetti, Baldari, Tessitore, & Capranica, 2005; Stuen & Faye, 2003). One of the most notable changes is in the ability to perceive small detail on the printed page and computer screen. A loss of close vision begins for many people between the ages of forty and fifty and results primarily from the lens becoming larger and denser and losing elasticity (Meisami, Brown, & Emerle, 2003; Stuen & Faye, 2003). This problem can be corrected by eyeglasses or various types of surgery. A second major sight-related change concerns light. As people age, the pupil of the eye becomes smaller and allows less light to enter the eye (Stuen & Faye, 2003). Hence people need more illumination to see both near and far (Bee & Bjorkland, 2004; Marsh, 1996). These latter changes make people less responsive to sudden changes in illumination, such as oncoming headlights. In addition, "peripheral vision, depth perception, color vision, and adaption to the dark also become poorer and sensitivity to glare increases" with age (Lefrancois, 1996, p. 505).

In addition to age-related vision changes, there are age-related vision disorders. Cataracts are the most common of these age-related eye conditions; in this condition, there is a clouding of the lens that reduces passage of light (Meisami, Brown, & Emerle, 2003; Stuen & Faye, 2003). Cataract surgery is a common remedy for this condition. A second common eye malady is age-related macular degeneration, which "is the leading cause of vision loss among people over age 60" (Stuen & Faye, 2003, p. 9). Seeing detail and reading become difficult. Caucasians and people with light eye color are more at risk for this disease than African Americans or people with dark eye color. A third age-related eye disease is glaucoma, usually caused by very high eye pressure, which results in damage to the optic nerve and causes damage to peripheral vision and sometimes blindness. Treatment includes surgery and eyedrops. Those of African ancestry, individuals with diabetes, and people with a history of glaucoma in the family are at increased risk for the disease (Stuen & Faye, 2003).

While changes in vision happen primarily at set periods in life, hearing loss is a progressive but gradual process throughout adulthood generally starting in the thirties (Bee & Bjorkland, 2004). Most adults do not notice any discernible change until their fifties and sixties, when sounds, especially in the high-frequency range, become more difficult to hear (Kline & Scialfa, 1996). Males suffer this type of hearing impairment more often than females (Bee & Bjorkland, 2004). By age sixty-five, over 25 percent of adults have a hearing difficulty, and for males over age seventy-five approximately 50 percent experience hearing loss (Bee & Bjorkland, 2004). The basic cause appears to be from "gradual changes in the inner ear" that result in structures in the inner ear becoming less responsive to sound (Rados, 2005, p. 22).

Some hearing deficits can be compensated for with the use of hearing aids. However, most older adults who could benefit from hearing aids do not use them because they do not feel the need, do not want to be associated with a device that makes them "look old," or simply cannot afford them. Other devices to assist hearing include hardwire systems, infrared systems, or FM devices (Montano, 2003). In addition, cochlear implants, which directly stimulate the auditory nerve through wires inserted in the cochlea, appear to improve the life of those with significant hearing difficulties (Meisami, Brown & Emerle, 2003).

Tinnitus, a ringing noise in the head or ears with no external stimuli present, is another common hearing disturbance in older adults (Whitbourne, 2005). Thirty-five to fifty million Americans experience this hearing impairment and two to three million are debilitated by this symptom (Ahmad & Seidman, 2004). Men are more commonly affected than women. The use of antibiotics, aspirin, and anti-inflammatory medications may contribute to tinnitus (Whitbourne, 2005). Other causes for the disturbance include injuries or infections of the ear, neck injuries, head trauma, stress, seizure disorders, possible nutritional deficiencies, and metabolic disturbances (Ahmad & Seidman, 2004).

Except for major degenerative and other disease processes, corrective measures, such as the wearing of eyeglasses and teaching people to find alternative ways of communicating, can help ensure the best use of the vision and hearing that remain. Further, advances in technology such as closed captioning of lectures and discussions (Schmidt & Haydu, 1992) and computer programs that assist low-vision individuals to read texts, help older adults navigate new learning in both formal and informal settings. Both teachers and learners must see to it that the educational environment is conducive to all adult learners, ensuring, for example, that rooms are adequately illuminated and acoustics are good.

THE CENTRAL NERVOUS SYSTEM

Consisting of the brain and the spinal cord, the central nervous system forms the primary biological basis for learning. We continue to learn how changes in this system may affect cognitive functioning (Bee & Bjorkland, 2004). Research on the aging brain has shifted from seeing "aging as an inevitable process of brain damage and decline" to aging as "a complex phenomenon characterized by reorganization, optimization and enduring functional plasticity that can enable the maintenance of a productive—and happy—life" (Reuter-Lorenz & Lustig, 2005, p. 249). For example, instead of seeing the decrease in brain cells as a sign of inevitable cognitive decline, we now know that although we lose brain cells or neurons through the aging process, the remaining neurons increase their connections with each other. This plasticity of the brain allows the aging brain to maintain much of its function (Bee & Bjorkland, 2004; Timiras, 2003). Further, brain scans have shown that deficits in one area of the brain may be compensated for in other areas (Cabeza, Anderson, Locantore, & McIntosh, 2002; Reuter-Lorenz & Lustig, 2005). In addition, older adults may also maintain higher levels of brain activity to compensate for deficits. However, higher levels of brain activity may not, for some, necessarily represent compensation but inefficient processing (Reuter-Lorenz & Lustig, 2005).

A consistent finding related to changes in the central nervous system concerns declining reaction time as people age (Bee & Bjorkland, 2004; Schaie & Willis, 2002). Reaction time is usually measured as the time it takes a person to complete a psychomotor task such as putting together a puzzle or responding to a specific stimulus by hitting a lighted button. Although "it is not true that all elderly people are markedly slower than young people . . . , on the average people over the age of 65" react less rapidly (Lefrancois, 1996, p. 506). Numerous explanations have been posited for this change, such as possible sensory deprivation (Baltes & Lindenberger, 1997) or changes in actual brain activity (Baltes & Lindenberger, 1997; Schaie & Willis, 2002). Factors such as the nature of the task and a person's familiarity with it also affect reaction time. In addition, physical activity seems to improve reaction times in older adults (Schaie & Willis, 2002).

In sum, while our life expectancy in the United States has increased from 49.2 years in 1900 to 76.5 years in 2000—although racial disparities in health care affect longevity for African Americans—the human life span remains at approximately 110 to 120 years. Regardless of race, changes in vision, hearing, and reaction time are an inevitable part of the aging process. However, new technologies such as cochlear implants and laser surgery for cataracts help older adults remain active and they can continue learning well into old age. In addition, technology has demonstrated the brain's elasticity. Older adults who show deficits in one area of the brain may compensate for it in other areas.

PSYCHOLOGICAL DEVELOPMENT

Most of the work in adult development has been driven by the psychological tradition and focuses on the individual's *internal* process of development. A myriad of models concerning faith development (Fowler, 1981), identity development (Erikson, 1963), and self-development (Gould, 1978; Josselson, 1996; Kegan, 1994) have been based on this perspective. In this view, little attention is paid to the society's influence on the person's development. The psychological perspective also underlies models used to explain race identity development (Helms, 1990), gay identity development (Cass, 1979), and more recently, biracial identity development (Henriksen & Trusty, 2004). In short, the psychological model of development, which explores the internal experiences of the individual, continues to be a favorite of developmental psychologists even among those studying socially constructed identities of race and gender.

In this next section, we will touch on two foundational psychological models of development: namely, Erikson's model of psychosocial development and Levinson's model of personal

Models of psychological development fall into two main categories. In stage theories, there is a stepwise upward movement, but it is not necessarily tied to chronological age (for example, Erikson, 1963, 1978; Fowler, 1981). These scholars assert that these stages are hierarchical in nature and therefore build on one another. There is disagreement about what causes the movement between stages and whether this movement is upward only to higher stages or whether it is back and forth across stages. Age-graded models, in contrast, tie specific ages to particular tasks (for example, Levinson et al., 1978; Levinson & Levinson, 1996).

Erikson's Psychosocial Development Model

Erikson's (1963) psychosocial development model is representative of the stage-related view of development. Considered "the most influential view of adult development proposed thus far" (Bee & Bjorklund, 2004, p. 33), Erikson's theory consists of eight stages of development, each representing a series of crises or issues to be dealt with over the life span. At each stage, there is a choice between opposites—one negative and the other positive—and it is imperative that persons achieve a favorable ratio of positive over negative prior to moving to the next stage. In young adulthood, the successful resolution between intimacy versus isolation results in love. In middle adulthood, resolving the tensions between generativity and self-absorption allows people to care for others; in older adulthood, resolutions between integrity versus despair provide the capacity for wisdom. Although Erikson tied his fifth stage—identity versus identity confusion—primarily to the period of adolescence, researchers in adult development have also included the examination of this stage as part of their research on adults (for example, Josselson, 1987). Erikson maintains that as adults we may revisit earlier stages to resolve or re-resolve conflicts from earlier periods in different ways. For example, because of the loss of a spouse, we may need to work again through issues of both intimacy and identity. In addition, Erikson, Erikson, and Kivnick (1986) go on to suggest that vital involvement in old age and interdependence among people allow adults to complete the life cycle successfully and leave a positive legacy for the next generation.

Erikson's theory continues to stimulate discussion and research. One recent work, for example, seeks to realign his eight stages into a decade-by-decade formulation (Capps, 2004), in essence making Erikson's model an age-based one, rather than stage-of-life; generativity would then be most prominent in one's sixties, and ego integrity the task for the seventies. In terms of research, Westermeyer (2004) has recently reported on a thirty-two-year longitudinal study applying Erikson's theory to healthy men. In 1959, ninety-four male students completed a seven-hundred-item questionnaire assessing dimensions of Erikson's theory. After thirty-two years, eighty-six of the original ninety-four were assessed again. Fifty-six percent of the participants had achieved generativity, the appropriate task for adults in their late fifties. Likewise, Norman, McCluskey-Fawcett, and Ashcraft (2002) assessed developmental differences between women in their sixties and women in their eighties. The young-old group more so than the old-old women "identified with the positive aspects of Erikson's developmental stages such as fidelity, wisdom, and satisfaction with their lives, work, and accomplishment" (pp. 37–38). The authors speculated that the older women were dealing with widowhood, physical limitations and decreased resources, which may have caused them to revisit earlier issues of trust and identity.

LEVINSON'S AGE-GRADED MODEL

Levinson and his colleagues (Levinson & Levinson, 1996; Levinson et al., 1978) provide an often-quoted description of an age-graded model. Levinson and Levinson (1996), for example, from their studies of both men and women, suggest that people evolve through an orderly sequence of stable and transitional periods that correlate with chronological age. One's life structure, that is, "the underlying pattern or design of a person's life at any given time" (p. 22), tends to be established and maintained during stable periods and then questioned and changed during transitional periods. For example, the authors indicate that the early life transition occurs between the ages of seventeen and twenty-two. This is followed by the entry into the life structure at age twenty-two to twenty-eight, followed by the age thirty transition, which occurs from the ages of twenty-eight to thirty-three, and the culmination of the life structure occurring between ages thirty-three and forty. The model ends with the era of late adulthood, starting at age sixty.

Among the components of this changing life are marriage and family, occupation, friendships, religion, ethnicity, and community. The "*central components* are those that have the greatest significance for the self and the life. They receive the greatest share of one's time and energy, and they strongly influence the character of the other components" (Levinson & Levinson, 1996, p. 23).

Although Levinson and his colleagues hold that both men and women follow these alternating sequences of structure building and transitional periods, these periods "operate somewhat differently in females and males" (Levinson & Levinson, 1996, p. 36), largely because of *gender splitting*, which "refers not simply to gender differences but of a splitting asunder—the creation of a rigid division between male and female, masculine and feminine, in human life" (p. 38). They elucidate four forms of gender splitting: (1) public sphere (male)/domestic sphere (female), (2) within marriage breadwinner (male)/homemaker (female), (3) "men's work"/"women's work," and (4) splitting of the psyche as male and female.

This framework of relating development to specific age periods has led a number of educators to propose a link between age-appropriate tasks and behavior and the fostering of learning activities for adults. Havighurst (1972) was one of the earliest writers to link these ideas into what he termed *the teachable moment*. The idea of the teachable moment is grounded in the concept of developmental tasks—tasks that arise at a certain period in a person's life, such as selecting a mate, starting a family, and getting started in an occupation. Although the time frame and some of the tasks Havighurst suggested are somewhat dated, the idea of specific life tasks giving rise to a teachable moment is not. Knowles (1980, p. 51) has also viewed developmental tasks as producing "a 'readiness to learn' which at its peak presents a 'teachable moment'" and outlines his own list of "life tasks" for young, old, and middle-aged adults.

OTHER MODELS

The psychological paradigm has been embraced by some who have constructed models of racial identity development and sexual identity development. While some of these models implicitly recognize the influence of society on racial and sexual orientation identity development, they still primarily focus on the experience of the individual, with little mention of society's influence on these types of development. For example, Helms (1990, 1995) proposes a process model of White racial identity that consists of two phases: abandoning racism and creating a nonracist identity. The process of abandoning racism is as follows (Helms, 1990): Initially, Whites are oblivious to racism, until they encounter an incident or series of incidents that alert them to racism. During the *disintegration* stage, they recognize that racial discrimination exists and may experience confusion or guilt because of their White privilege. During *reintegration* they often believe there is an element of truth to negative stereotypes about people of color. They avoid associating with or may even act violently toward people of color. As Whites focus on developing a nonracist identity, they traverse through a *pseudo-independent* stage where they begin to recognize that Whites are not superior to people of color, but they may still perpetuate the idea of White superiority through their actions or behaviors, while in the *immersion/emersion* stage individuals encourage others to abandon racism and come to terms with their Whiteness. In the last phase, *autonomy*, they abandon racism and commit to its eradication on a personal and societal level. Maintaining this perspective is a continual process (Richardson & Silvestri, 1999).

Biracial identity development has received more attention from researchers in the past fifteen years (Bowles, 1993; Collins, 2000a, 2000b; Herring, 1995; Pinderhughs, 1995). Research has explored conflicts about dual racial identity, self-esteem and identity, and identity development, among others (Rockquemore & Brunsma, 2002). Like Helms's model, the focus of a recent biracial identity development model constructed by Henriksen and Trusty (2004) is on the experience of the individual, with less explicit attention given to the impact of society on this development. Their model of recursive Black-White biracial identity development, developed from interviews with biracial women, describes six periods that individuals undergo during their biracial identity development. These periods are *neutrality, acceptance, awareness, experimentation, transition,* and *recognition*. During the neutrality period, individuals are unaware of racial differences (Henriksen & Trusty, 2004). Acceptance occurs when people realize that they are racially different from others and that they "[do] not have a racial reference group" (p. 72). This difference and the lack of a racial reference group promote feelings of isolation during the awareness period. People "try to fit into one part of their racial identity" (p. 72) by associating mostly with Blacks or Whites in an effort to find where they fit in (Henriksen & Trusty, 2004). During transition, women realize they cannot identify as Black or White. Last, the recognition period is one of acceptance of their biracial identity.

Early models of sexual identity development also relied on the psychological paradigm. Cass's (1979) foundational model of gay or lesbian identity development is one of the most well-known. Cass proposes a six-stage model. The first stage, identity confusion, is marked by feelings of confusion as an individual begins to realize that he or she may be gay or lesbian. This is followed by the identity comparison stage, when the person begins to realize that he or she is gay or lesbian but denies the identity on some level. During the second stage, the individual may believe that his or her attraction to the same sex is temporary. In the third stage, identity tolerance, the person becomes more open to the idea of a gay or lesbian identity but does not yet fully embrace the identity. Identity acceptance occurs during Stage 4. Individuals have increased contact with other gays or lesbians and evaluate them more positively. This is followed by the identity pride stage, where the person discloses the identity to others and may be more immersed in the gay or lesbian subculture. Last, the gay or lesbian identity is synthesized into one's self.

Even recent models of women's midlife development have used a psychological perspective (Barrett, 2005; Josselson, 2003; Tangri, Thomas, Mednick, & Lee, 2003). Implicit in these developmental stages is the influence of society on midlife women, but the focus is still on the internal experiences of the women. Howell and Beth (2002) interviewed eleven women (seven Caucasian and four African-American) between the ages of forty and sixty in an urban environment to understand their midlife experiences. A three-stage (nonlinear) process emerged: *Rejecting Midlife Stereotypes, Exploring Midlife Realities,* and *Adjusting Attitudes, Behaviors, and Circumstances.* Rejecting Midlife Stereotypes included an awareness of midlife changes and a denial of the label "middle-aged" (which they associated with negative stereotypes) as applying to themselves (Howell & Beth, 2002). In Stage 2, the denial of being middle-aged gave way to the second stage, Exploring Midlife Realities, where women mourned midlife losses, including losses in relationships due to divorce, death, or estrangement, their changing bodies, and concern about finances. Participants also clarified their values as a result of their losses and looked for role models that they felt were successfully negotiating midlife changes. During the third stage, Adjusting Attitudes, Behaviors, and Circumstances, women acted on their newfound values.

A second study expanded the findings of the Howell and Beth 2002 investigation. The study concentrated on midlife development in lesbians. It revealed that while lesbians experienced some of the same stages as heterosexual women, there were differences. For example, because of the "coming out" process that the women journeyed through earlier in their lives they had "a stronger sense of who they were and were less concerned with what others thought of them" (Howell & Beth, 2004, p. 133). They were much less concerned about ageism than their heterosexual counterparts. The earlier coming out process for participants equated with the Rejecting Midlife Stereotypes stage for heterosexual women. For example, both groups of women struggled with self-esteem. In addition, both groups coped with social rejection. Lesbians felt rejected by some members of society because of their sexual orientation. Middle-aged heterosexual women felt rejected by others because they were growing older. They experienced ageism (Howell & Beth, 2004). Lesbians experienced losses in the Exploring Midlife Realities stage but "they experienced grief with the pragmatism of individuals who had already been through many difficult experiences" because many had experienced losses during the coming out process (p. 143). Stage 3, Adjusting Attitudes, Behaviors, and Circumstances, was similar for lesbians and heterosexuals.

How do psychological models of adult development relate to learning? Educators who accept that their job is to help learners achieve the highest level of development possible could encourage students to examine their assumptions, and facilitate critical reflection on these assumptions (Daloz, 1986, 1999; Levine, 1989; Mezirow, 2000). Through mentoring and learning activities designed with development in mind, facilitators can enable the "transformational journeys" of their students (Daloz, 1986, p. 16).

In sum, psychological models of development explore the internal experiences of the individual. Models of psychological development primarily fall into two categories. For stage theorists, there is a stepwise upward movement, but it is not necessarily tied to chronological age (for example, Erikson, 1963, 1978; Fowler, 1981), nor is it always linear (Howell & Beth, 2002). Age-graded models tie specific ages to particular tasks (for example, Levinson et al., 1978; Levinson & Levinson, 1996). Despite the knowledge that society affects adults' development, the psychological model continues to be popular.

SOCIOCULTURAL FACTORS

The sociocultural perspective on adult development acknowledges how the social world in which we live influences our development (Dannefer, 1996; Gardiner & Kosmitzki, 2005; Shaffer, 2005). This perspective recognizes that factors such as age, race, gender, ethnicity, socioeconomic status, and sexual orientation affect how society defines us. We offer two salient strands of work from the literature on the sociocultural perspective on adulthood that provide us with different ways of looking at adult development. We examine how adult social roles and the timing of life events affect development. We then review how socially constructed notions of race, ethnicity, gender, and sexual orientation affect development.

SOCIAL ROLES AND THE TIMING OF LIFE EVENTS

The earlier work on the sociocultural dimensions of adulthood focused on the taking of social roles and the notion of the timing of life events. Social roles are defined as both positions and associated expectations determined primarily by normative beliefs held by society (Bee & Bjorkland, 2004). Examples of these various roles include parent, spouse, worker, child, and friend. Changes in one's social position result from modifications of these roles (such as redefining the role of parent when both parents assume employment) and the taking on of new roles (such as wife to widow or paid worker to retired person). These changes may be initiated by the individual or by others; a parent might ask an older child to take on the role of worker to help pay for her college expenses, for example, or changes in legislative policy might give a specific group in society, such as minorities or women, more or perhaps less control over their own lives.

Research on role transitions has migrated from a "life problem" approach to a "life trajectory" approach (Ferraro, 2001, p. 316). Early research on role transitions in the United States in the 1950s through the mid-1970s focused on loss of roles, such as the loss of the worker role after retirement. It was thought that such losses led to disengagement from society. Studies in the 1970s and 1980s moved from a concentration on role loss and gain to one of role *transitions* as life circumstances change (Bee & Bjorkland, 2004; Ferraro, 2001). More rigorous research designs and longitudinal studies on role transitions brought to light the complexities of role transition outcomes. Role transition outcomes could be positive or negative instead of solely negative. In the 1990s, research began to focus on the place of role transitions and role salience in the life course. Scholars investigated "how role transitions are both influenced by earlier life experiences and shape subsequent paths of personal adjustment" (Ferraro, 2001, p. 315). In research on role salience (Krause, 1999; Reitzes, 2003), people have multiple roles or identities, such as mother, sister, parent, or worker, which are arranged hierarchically according to their salience. The role's importance or salience is determined by how much the person values that role and how detrimental the loss of the role would be to a person's self-concept. This spotlight on social roles has fostered a number of research traditions in such areas as career development and marriage and family roles (see Bee & Bjorkland, 2004; Berger, 1998; Ferraro, 2001; Kalmijin, 2004).

The scholarship on the timing of life events, which is exemplified by the work of Neugarten and others (Neugarten, 1976, 1979; Neugarten & Datan, 1973), suggests that "every society is age-graded, and every society has a system of social expectations regarding age-appropriate behavior. The individual passes through a socially regulated cycle from birth to death as inexorably as he [sic] passes through the biological cycle: a succession of socially delineated age-statuses, each with its recognized rights, duties and obligations" (Neugarten, 1976, p. 16). Although the timing of events has changed somewhat and the deadlines for completing such events have become more variable since Neugarten completed her original work, being "off-time" or "on-time" regarding certain major life events still holds merit (Bee & Bjorkland, 2004; Pinhey & Pinhey, 2002). It is not the events themselves that necessarily precipitate crisis or change. Life events that occur "off-time," such as going through menopause at an early age, becoming a widower at age thirty, or having children later in life, can be stressful (Bee & Bjorkland, 2004; Pinhey & Pinhey, 2002). From this vantage point, the study of adult development then becomes a study of life events construed from socially constructed beliefs, whereas in the psychological tradition, the focus is on the life events themselves as markers and processes.

The idea that learning in adulthood is related to appropriate role taking, as defined by society's expectations, has a long history in adult education, from the early citizenship education programs for immigrants to today's workplace learning programs. Several writers have suggested that programs be developed related to the social roles of adults. Some thirty years ago, Kidd (1973) and Knox (1977), for example, explored how changes in social roles can be related to learning activities. In particular, Kidd (1973) outlined a taxonomy suggested by Malcolm Knowles at a UNESCO seminar in Hamburg in 1972 that takes into account not only roles but also the competencies related to those roles. The implied assumption underlying this taxonomy is that learning programs could be built to address these competencies for adults going through role changes or wishing to become more competent in their current roles (for example, family member, worker, and citizen). Even learning on our own may be driven by what society expects of us, such as learning parenting skills or taking care of aging parents. For the most part, adult educators have developed programs around role taking to the age-normative times of life events and have not taken into account those people who are "off-time." More recently there has been some change in this thinking. For example, hospice programs, which both offer support and teach caretakers how to care for dying people, do not discriminate whom they will serve based on either the age of the patient or the age of the caretaker.

SOCIALLY CONSTRUCTED NOTIONS OF RACE, ETHNICITY, GENDER, AND SEXUAL ORIENTATION

Researchers have been especially interested over the past two decades in the socially constructed notions of race, ethnicity, gender, and sexual orientation as they relate to adult development (Alderson, 2003; Cross & Vandiver, 2001; Ponterotto, Casas, Suzuki, & Alexander, 2001; Worthington, Savoy, Dillion, & Vernaglia, 2002). Discussing these different constructs in relation to development is challenging because they often overlap and have been given different meanings by researchers. For example, some people use the terms *race* and *ethnicity* interchangeably, whereas others clearly distinguish between these two concepts. What makes it even more difficult to establish the connection between these ideas and development is the intersection of various positionalities, that is, where one stands or where one's "position" is in relation to others. As Kincheloe and Steinberg (1993, p. 302) write: "We are never independent of the social and historical forces that surround us—we are caught at a particular point in the web of reality. The post-formal project is to understand what that point in the web is, how it constructs our vantage point, and the ways it insidiously restricts our vision." A person's race, class, gender, and sexual orientation, among other positionalities, intersect to influence the development of that person. For example, a middle-class White lesbian may face different developmental challenges than a wealthy, heterosexual Black man because of their different positionalities. There has been increasing interest in examining these intersections and their impact on adult development (Bowman et al., 2001; Etter-Lewis & Foster, 1996).

Most approaches to Black identity development appear to be sociocultural. Black identity development models take three approaches: mainstream, underground, and multidimensional. The mainstream approach focuses on how racial identity can be viewed in relation to other identities. This view of Black identity development emphasizes coping with the stigma associated with a marginalized identity but does not examine "the qualitative meanings associated with particular ethnic and racial identity" (Sellers, Smith, Shelton, Rowley, & Chavous, 1998, p. 21). The underground approach recognizes the importance of history and culture in the "experiential meaning associated with being Black" (p. 21). The multidimensional approach combines the mainstream and underground perspectives.

Cross's (1971) theory exemplifies an underground approach to Black identity development and offers several propositions. First, Black racial identity contains two dimensions: "a personal identity component (PI) and a reference group component (RGO)" (Cross & Vandiver, 2001, p. 380). Second, the "core of the theory is on the various ways Black people make sense of themselves as social beings" (p. 380). Third, the theory addresses how Black identity is "*enacted* in everyday interactions with Black and White people" and while there are four stages that contain a total of eight "identity exemplars" (p. 375), Cross recognizes the myriad ways people experience their Nigrescence.

Cross's model has grown from five identity stages (Cross, 1971) to multiple identity clusters at each of four stages (Cross & Vandiver, 2001). The four main stages are *pre-encounter, encounter, immersion-emersion,* and *internalization.* An individual in the pre-encounter stage generally does not interact with Black culture or problems. In the encounter stage, the individual may have an experience or series of experiences that "*shatter* the relevance of the person's current identity and worldview, and at the same time provide some hint of the new direction the person must now take" (Cross, 1995, p. 105; italics added). Generally, this new worldview is followed by Stage 3, immersion-emersion, where the individual immerses himself or herself in Black culture. The last stage, internalization, is marked by an "inner peace," and the person's idea of Blackness "tends to be more open, expansive, and sophisticated" (Cross, 1995, p. 114). Furthermore, an internalization-biculturalist engages in Black issues and is committed to Black concerns but he or she also enjoys aspects of the dominant culture (Cross & Vandiver, 2001). An internalization-nationalist stresses the Afrocentric perspective. The internalization-multiculturalist feels a part of the Black community but appreciates many cultures and "prefers solutions . . . that address multiple oppressions" (p. 376).

As noted, mainstream and underground perspectives are combined in the multidimensional approach to racial identity development (Sellers et al., 1998). Racial identity is composed of four elements: racial salience, racial centrality, racial regard, and racial ideology. *Racial salience* "refers to the extent to which one's race is a relevant part of one's self-concept at a particular moment or in a particular situation" (p. 24). *Centrality* concerns how central race is to the person's self-definition. *Racial regard* refers to how positively or negatively a person feels about his or her race. This includes how the individual believes others view African Americans as well as how he or she feels about being African American. *Ideology* "is composed of the individual's beliefs, opinions, and attitudes with respect to the way she or he feels that the members of the race should act" (p. 27). Various ideologies include that of the nationalist, oppressed minority, assimilationist, and humanist. People with a nationalist ideology "stress the uniqueness of being Black," while oppressed minority ideologists compare the oppression faced by Blacks with other groups and support building coalitions with other groups in an effort to fight oppression (p. 27). The assimilationist emphasizes similarities between cultures and works within the existing power structure to change the system, while the humanist "emphasize[s] the similarities among all humans" and is concerned with oppression of all people and global issues such as hunger and environmental issues (p. 28).

The sociocultural approach to development is not limited to scholars who investigate racial identity development. Researchers have also used this approach to explore gay sexual identity development. For example, Cox and Gallois's (1996) social identity perspective on gay and lesbian identity development explicitly acknowledges the importance of society in the construction of a gay or lesbian sexual identity. Their model, grounded in social identity theory, "examines the identity processes which occur within the individual . . . [and] explores the effect that the larger social and societal forces have on these processes" (p. 10). Identity development involves two processes: self-categorization and social comparison. Cox and Gallois (1996) assert that people can possess a personal identity (self-categorization) that is not part of their social identity. In short, people can self-categorize as gay or lesbian but not have a gay or lesbian social identity. They note that when people adopt a gay or lesbian social identity they may use several strategies in order to address the stigma, which include putting down heterosexuals. For example, they may call heterosexuals "breeders" (p. 21) in order to feel better about being gay or lesbian.

A second model of gay identity development takes an ecological approach (Alderson, 2003). This model examines the myriad influences that help or hinder the person in the process of claiming a gay identity. In the Before Coming Out stage, influences that can serve as catalysts to continue the process or can hinder the process include parents, culture, church, peers, and society. These influences continue in the During Coming Out phase, when a person experiences conflicting emotions, learns new behaviors, and works at reducing his or her own internalized homophobia. In the Beyond Coming Out phase, the person commits to the gay identity, has integrated the gay identity with other parts of the self, and has reintegrated into the heterosexual world (Alderson, 2003).

Numerous scholars, primarily over the past decade, have acknowledged the importance of the socially constructed notions of race, ethnicity, gender, and sexual orientation to understanding learning in adulthood and the teaching-learning transaction (Hayes & Colin, 1994; Flannery & Hayes, 2001; Lee & Johnson-Bailey, 2004; Johnson-Bailey & Cervero, 1998; Maher & Tetreault, 1994; Mojab, 2005; Tisdell, 1995). Lee and Johnson-Bailey (2004) examine their experiences as teachers of color in the White academy. While explaining their feminist classroom practice, they unearth issues of racism, sexism, and power in the classroom and its effect on the teaching-learning transaction. They write, "In those early days, we were often the only women of color in a sea of white women and men who felt free to vocalize their surprise that we were their instructors and to ask openly whether or not we belonged in that environment" (p. 56). In another study, Johnson-Bailey and Cervero (1998) compared graduate student perceptions of a White male full professor and a Black female assistant professor. Race had an impact on the messages students received from each professor. The White professor, who discussed race as a central topic in his class, was not seen as having an agenda associated with race. His competence and fairness to students was not questioned. In contrast, the Black professor, who did not discuss race as a central topic in class, was seen as having a racial agenda and her fairness and competence were questioned (Johnson-Bailey & Cervero, 1998). Tisdell (1995), among others, has pointed out the important role that power plays when introducing socially constructed notions of race, ethnicity, gender, and sexual orientation into formal and even nonformal programs of adult learning. Tisdell observes that "what counts as knowledge in a particular learning context—and decisions about what gets included in the curriculum for a given learning activity—are decisions made with attention to the politics of this particular educational context and to what is seen as 'real' knowledge relevant to this educational context" (p. 11). Teaching strategies that allow participants to connect the material to their own life experiences, allow for reflective time, confront differences, and bring together theory and practice seem to provide useful starting points for doing this (Caffarella, 1992; Wlodkowski & Ginsberg, 1995).

To summarize, the sociocultural approach to adult development acknowledges how the social world influences our development. This perspective recognizes that the intersection of various positionalities affects how society defines us. In addition, the social roles we take on and the timing of life events such as marriage and having children affect our development. Cross and Vandiver's (2001) model of Black identity development and Cox and Gallois's (1996) model of gay and lesbian identity development were two models that were highlighted that come from the sociocultural paradigm.

INTEGRATIVE PERSPECTIVES

There have been attempts to respond to the call for a more integrated theory of adult development by combining two or more of the perspectives reviewed in this chapter. Four models of adult development—those proposed by Baltes (1982, 1987), Magnusson (1995), Perun and Bielby (1980), and Bronfenbrenner (2001) are illustrative of this wave of theory building.

Baltes (1982, p. 18) introduced one of the earlier comprehensive models that emphasized a "multicausal and interactive view" of adult development. Drawing on the work of Havighurst, Neugarten, and others, he hypothesized that biological and environmental forces constitute the basic determinants of development. These are then influenced by three major sets of factors: normative age-graded influences (forces normally correlated with age), normative history-graded influences (events that are widely experienced by one age group of people), and nonnormative influences (factors significant to one particular person). The interaction of these influences results in developmental changes over the life span. Baltes hypothesized that the relative significance of the three developmental influences may vary at different points in the life span—"for example, age-graded influences may be especially important . . . in old age, whereas history-graded non-normative influences may predominate in early and middle adulthood" (Baltes, 1982, p. 22).

Within this life-span perspective, writes Bee (1996, p. 74), Baltes and his colleagues assume "there is *lawfulness* to the changes we see in adult life. . . . Our task . . . is to uncover and understand the nature of that lawfulness. They do not assume that the specific pathways followed by adults will necessarily all be the same; they do not assume that all pathways lead toward either decline or toward higher efficacy. They do assume that the underlying lawfulness will create many surface patterns." Baltes has also stressed the need for new "development-specific" research methodologies to address the more interactive and complex models of adult development.

One response to Baltes's concern about methodology is an integrative model proposed by Magnusson (1995). Grounded in four basic assumptions, Magnusson argues that his model "can serve as a general theoretical framework for planning, implementation, and interpretation of empirical research on specific aspects of individual development" (p. 19). His four assumptions are as follows (pp. 25–29):

1. The individual functions and develops as a total integrated organism. Development does not take place in single aspects, taken out of context. . . .
2. The individual functions and develops in a continuously ongoing, reciprocal process of interaction with his or her environment. . . .
3. At each specific moment, individual functioning is determined in a process of continuous, reciprocal interaction between mental factors, biological factors, and behavior—on the individual side—and situational factors. . . .
4. The individual develops in a process of continuous reciprocal interaction among psychological, biological, and environmental factors. . . .

What is key to this model is that "individuals do not develop in terms of single variables but as total integrated systems. In this perspective, all changes during the life span of a person are characterized by lawful continuity" (p. 39). Magnusson emphasizes that his model "does not imply that the whole system of an individual must be studied at the same time. The essential function of the model is that it enables us to formulate problems at different levels of the functioning of the total organism, to implement empirical studies, and to interpret the results in a common, theoretical framework" (p. 50).

The third model we discuss is not widely known, but we have found it useful in framing development from the integrative perspective. Perun and Bielby (1980) view adulthood as "consisting of a large number of temporal progressions—sequences of experiences or internal changes, each of which follow some timetable" (Bee, 1996, p. 75). Pictured as a set of disks, similar to machine gears rotating on a central rod, each disk represents a part of the developmental picture: physical changes, changes in nuclear family roles (like marrying and having children), changes in other family roles (such as death of a parent), changes in work roles, and changes in emotional and personal tasks of adulthood (Perun & Bielby, 1980). Each of these gears or disks moves at different rates for different people, "thus creating a unique pattern for each adult" (Bee, 1996, p. 76). For example, one person may delay having children until her early forties so she can establish herself in a career, while another may start a family in her teens and then start a career once her children are grown. The first person would have speeded up her career or work progression while slowing down her family life cycle, while the second person would have done just the opposite. In addition, the entire developmental process is embedded in historical time, which also affects the developmental progression in each of the major areas.

In this model, developmental changes come from two sources. The first is the basic changes that happen during each of the temporal progressions, some of them inevitable and others chosen. Second, *asynchrony*, which "occurs when one or more dimensions is off-time in relation to others" (Perun & Bielby, 1980, p. 105), triggers other changes. For example, when a person's spouse or partner dies in early adulthood, the nuclear family roles and possibly the work roles often change dramatically, especially if there are minor children involved. Bee (1996, p. 77) has outlined a number of "intriguing and potentially useful implications or expansions of this model." Among these are that the rate of movement along any of the temporal dimensions may be influenced by gender, race, class, ethnicity, and sexual orientation.

Last, Bronfenbrenner's (2001) bioecological systems theory delineates five layers of the environment or systems that influence development. Although his emphasis was on child development, his theory has implications for adults. The *microsystem* includes the "activities, roles, and interpersonal relations" in the person's immediate environment, which include the home, school, peers, and workplace (Bronfenbrenner, 2001). The *mesosystem* is defined as the relationships between these microsystems. An example of a mesosystem is the relationship between a person's workplace and the community. The *exosystem* is a larger social system in which the person may not function directly but which has an effect on his or her microsystem. For a child, this may be the relationship between the home and the parent's workplace. For an adult, this may be the relationship between the child's school and a community group (Bronfenbrenner, 2001). The fourth system is the *macrosystem,* which contains the cultural values, mores, and laws that affect the previously mentioned systems. For example, if the cultural belief is that women should marry and raise children, opportunities for aspiring career women may be limited and affect their development and standing in society. Last, the *chronosystem* refers to the influence of time as it relates to the person's environment and subsequent development. Examples include the timing of historical events such as the Depression or personal events such as the timing of a parent's death.

Although application of these integrated models to learning in adulthood has been limited, the message conveyed by the theorists is clear: to understand development in adulthood fully, one must move beyond explanations fostered only by one or two perspectives. Educators of adults must be mindful of the impact of single-perspective theories "on shaping and maintaining conventionally held views about what it means to be a mature and healthy adult" (Tennant, 1988, p. 65). The psychological perspective, which has been used as the major lens through which educators of adults have viewed development, can be widened to include the other lenses of biological, sociocultural, and integrated perspectives. Tennant and Pogson (1995) observe that "the raw material[s] in the process of development are the organism, with its constitutionally endowed equipment, and the social environment, with its historical and cultural formations. Development thus proceeds through a constant interaction between the person and the environment.

[Further], because development is contested, and because different versions of development serve the interests of different groups, it is as much a political as it is a psychological construct" (pp. 198–199). Therefore, it is important to foster a multiperspective focus in our study and practice of how adult development theory is linked to learning in adulthood.

Summary

Adult developmental theory and research offer a rich array of material from which numerous implications can be drawn about learning in adulthood. This chapter has reviewed the developmental characteristics of adults from four perspectives: biological aging, psychological change, the influence of sociocultural factors on development, and the integrative paradigm. With regard to biological aging, all adults experience some changes as they age. Many of these changes vary from person to person and may have little effect on learning thanks to advances in technology. Psychological changes in adulthood have been charted by a number of researchers. The sequential models of development of Erikson and Levinson are representative of those that attempt to delineate the common themes of adult life according to what phase or stage of life one is in.

From the sociocultural perspective, change in adulthood is determined more by sociocultural factors, such as social roles, race, and gender, than by individual maturation. Two strands of work from the sociocultural perspective were described, and implications for this work for adult learning were addressed. Discussed first was the importance of social roles, such as parent, worker, or friend. Social roles are determined primarily by societal expectations and change over time. Adult educators have often designed programs tied to social roles, such as parenting classes or workshops on retirement. Society still determines at what age we ought to be engaged in which life events, although some would argue that the age norms for events are much more flexible than they were in the past.

Addressed next was the socially constructed nature of the concepts of race, gender, ethnicity, and sexual orientation and how defining these concepts as social constructions versus individual traits has affected the way we think about adult development.

Research in this area has exploded in the past fifteen years. Representative theories on racial and sexual identity development were discussed.

The chapter concluded with a description of integrated perspectives on development with salient examples of theorists who have included the biological, psychological, and sociological perspectives in their models of adult development (for example, Baltes and Magnusson). To understand fully how adult development is linked to adult learning, we suggested that educators of adults move to multiple explanations of what adulthood is all about, rather than rely on just one or two paradigms. We especially need to acknowledge perspectives beyond the psychological lens that has driven our research and practice on learning in adulthood for the past three decades. The more we know about adult learners, the changes they go through, and how these changes motivate and interact with learning, the better we can structure learning experiences that both respond to and stimulate development.

CHAPTER THIRTEEN

COGNITIVE DEVELOPMENT IN ADULTHOOD

Andrew lives his life certain that for every situation there is a "right way" and a "wrong way" to view it. He sees the world in absolutes. According to Andrew, the taking of a human life for any reason is wrong. Hence, he is against such things as capital punishment, abortion, and assisted suicide. In contrast, for his sister Marie, everything is relative. Abortion, the death penalty, and assisted suicide may be appropriate in particular situations, according to Marie. Andrew and Marie represent different ways of thinking about the same issue. Scholars continue to be fascinated with the myriad of ways people think and whether adults' thinking patterns change with age. If so, what might these changes in thinking patterns look like over the adult life span?

The study of pathways of adult cognitive development—that is, how thinking patterns change over time—is often linked to a combination of factors, primarily the interaction of maturational and environmental variables. As in other research traditions on learning, the major studies on cognitive development have been primarily carried out with children and adolescents. When this research is extended to adulthood, the underlying assumption has often been that adults move toward a final stage of cognitive development, however that is defined, or if that stage has been attained, work at maintaining that stage. Still other theorists have posited models of cognitive development that may be unique to adulthood.

Explored first in this chapter is the foundational work of Piaget (1972) and how scholars have used and extended this work. We then discuss alternative conceptualizations of cognitive development that are linear or categorical in nature (for example, Belenky, Clinchy, Goldberger, & Tarule, 1986; Perry, 1999). This discussion is followed by an exploration of dialectical thinking and models that are representative of this form of thinking. Then, the contextual perspective on cognitive development and key theorists who represent this perspective are presented. Last, wisdom—the hallmark of adult thinking—is discussed. Representative conceptions of wisdom, including those of Holliday and Chandler, Sternberg, and Bassett, are reviewed.

FOUNDATIONAL WORK ON COGNITIVE DEVELOPMENT

When we speak of cognitive development, Jean Piaget immediately comes to mind. Although Piaget's work is entirely focused on childhood cognitive development, his theory has provided the foundation for work with adults. Piaget proposed four invariant stages of cognitive development that are age related. These stages represent "qualitatively different ways of making sense, understanding, and constructing a knowledge of the world" (Tennant, 1988, p. 68). In Piaget's view, children's thought processes move from innate reflex actions (sensory-motor stage, birth to two years), to being able to represent concrete objects in symbols and words (preoperational stage, two to seven years), to an understanding of concepts and relationships of ideas (concrete operational stage, seven to eleven years), to an ability to reason hypothetically, logically, and systematically (formal operational stage, twelve-plus years). Piaget contended that normal children have the capacity to reach this final stage of formal operations between the ages of twelve and fifteen, which he later revised upward to ages fifteen to twenty (Piaget, 1972). It is this final stage, characterized by the ability to think abstractly, that characterized the apex of mature adult thought for Piaget.

Piaget's model has its limitations in that it accepts "a mechanistic worldview that is caught up in a cause-effect, hypothetico-deductive system of reasoning. Unconcerned with questions of power relations and the way they structure our consciousness, formal operational thinkers accept an objectified, unpoliticized way of knowing that breaks a social or educational system down into its basic parts in order to understand how it works. . . . [F]ormal thought operates on the assumption that resolution must be found for all contradictions" (Kincheloe & Steinberg, 1993, p. 297).

Those who came after Piaget (neo-Piagetians) have challenged some aspects of Piaget's principles. First, they recognize that these qualitative changes (for example, moving from concrete operational thought to formal operational thought) may not occur for all aspects of thinking, but rather tend to be "local and domain specific in nature" (Knight & Sutton, 2004, p. 49). This explains why people can use concrete operations in one context and formal operations in another.

Second, several neo-Piagetian scholars have found evidence of postformal thought (see Arlin, 1975; Sinnott, 1998). Knight and Sutton (2004) note, "Whereas Piagetian formal operational thinking implies the ability to think systematically within a set of logical parameters, a more advanced level involves an individual's ability not only to think logically but also to reflect on this logical thinking" (p. 51). People who possess postformal thought believe the following: First, they know that all knowledge is incomplete and subjective. However, they recognize that they must act despite the limits of their knowledge. They understand that there is not one "Truth" but many "truths" and they commit to one set of beliefs knowing that there are many. Further, they understand that contradiction and subjectivity are inherent in all logical and objective observations (Sinnott, 1998). They go beyond problem-*solving* behaviors, as is common in formal operations where they seek a solution to a problem, to *problem-finding* behaviors, characterized by "creative thought vis-à-vis 'discovered' problems" (Arlin, 1975, p. 603). In short, formal operational thought "presume[s] logical consistency within a single logical system" (Sinnott, 1998, p. 25). In contrast, postformal operations "presume somewhat necessarily subjective selection among logically contradictory formal operational systems, each of which is internally consistent and absolute" (p. 25).

In addition to recognizing the existence of postformal operational thought, neo-Piagetians focus on the importance of context in learning and development. In his later work, Piaget acknowledged that learning and development were more dependent on context than previously thought (Knight & Sutton, 2004). However, neo-Piagetians concentrate on the *specific* context in which the learning occurs and assert that "new learning is most robust in the context in which it was constructed" (p. 51). The further away a person gets from the context in which the learning was constructed, the more difficult it is to access the learning that occurred.

So, how has Piaget's theory enhanced our understanding of cognitive development in adulthood? Tennant (1988, p. 77) noted Piaget's most salient contributions:

- The emphasis on qualitative rather than quantitative developmental changes in cognition (and his related "structuralist" approach to cognitive development)
- The importance attached to the active role of the person in constructing his or her knowledge (with the implication that learning through activity is more meaningful [than passive learning])
- A conception of mature adult thought (that is, formal operations)

With the discovery of postformal operational thought, neo-Piagetians have further expanded our understanding of cognitive development. They have helped us recognize that cognitive development occurs into adulthood (Knight & Sutton, 2004). Further, the importance of contextual support such as "familiar materials, opportunities for practice, analysis [and] interaction with others" (p. 52) for adult learners cannot be underestimated. The more types of support adult learners have, the more likely they are to perform at high levels and to retain the learned information. Conversely, if they are not given the support or challenged to think at higher levels, the understanding and retention of material will be lower (Knight & Sutton, 2004).

Neo-Piagetian theories offer several implications for adult educators. First, students come to our classes at different cognitive levels and thus interpret our course material and activities in different ways. They operate at different levels *during* a class period. In addition, assert Knight and Sutton (2004), older students have a higher level of functioning than younger students and can access their optimal levels more easily than younger students. They add, "Consequently, in the college classroom, the cognitive gap is even wider than a simple comparison of optimal levels would suggest. Therefore, we add even more complex challenges to the educator of adults" (p. 57).

In sum, Jean Piaget's four stages of cognitive development provided the foundation for other models of cognitive development. Neo-Piagetians augmented Piaget's original theory in the following ways: First, they recognized that people could use formal operational thought in one context and concrete operational thought in another. Hence, cognitive change was not systemwide but localized. Second, they introduced the idea of postformal thought; that is, there is development past formal operations. These discoveries have implications for adult educators. Adult educators now know that cognitive development occurs in adulthood and that learning affects this development. In addition, the importance of context in adult learning is acknowledged.

Linear and Categorical Models of Adult Cognitive Development

There are other models of cognitive development that differ from Piaget's and yet are also linear or categorical in nature. These writers come from a variety of disciplines and interests (for example, college student development, women's development, psychology), but all have the same interest in exploring how adult thinking changes over time. A discussion of a number of these linear or categorical models of cognitive development follows.

Perry's Developmental Scheme

Perry's (1970, 1999) map of cognitive development is perhaps the best known and has been used the most often in the study of young adults, most of whom have been college students. Based on a study of the thinking patterns of Ivy League, White male college students, Perry proposed a model of cognitive development consisting of nine positions, each position representing a qualitatively different way of interpreting learning experiences. Perry purposely chose the word *position* over *stage* because "the notion of 'position' is happily appropriate to the image of 'point of outlook' or 'position from which a person views his [sic] world'" (Perry, 1999, p. 54). As in

Piaget's work, each position is conceptualized as hierarchical and sequential and moves from relatively simple thinking patterns to highly complex ways of perceiving and evaluating knowledge. People move from viewing knowledge in "dualistic" terms, as either right or wrong, to an acceptance of knowledge and values as "relativistic"—that is, the context of the knowledge is as important as the knowledge itself. Perry places as much emphasis on the transitions between each position as on the positions themselves and observes: "Perhaps development is all transitions and 'stages' [are] only resting points along the way" (1981, p. 78). Some examples of Perry's proposed positions and the transitions between them are outlined as follows (see Perry, 1970, 1981, 1999 for a complete description):

Position 1: Authorities know, and if we work hard, read every word, and learn the Right answers, all will be well.

Transition between Positions 1 and 2: But what about those Others I hear about? And different opinions? And uncertainties? Some of our own Authorities disagree with each other or don't seem to know, and some give us problems instead of answers.

Position 2: True Authorities must be Right, the Others are frauds. We remain Right. Others must be different and wrong. . . .

Transition between Positions 5 and 6: But if everything is relative, am I relative too? How can I know I'm making the Right Choice?

Position 6: I see I'm going to have to make my own decisions in an uncertain world with no one to tell me I'm Right. . . .

Transition between Positions 8 and 9: Things are getting contradictory. I can't make logical sense out of life's dilemmas.

Position 9: This is how life will be. I must be wholehearted while tentative, fight for my values yet respect others, believe my deepest values are right yet be ready to learn. I see that I shall be retracing this whole journey over and over—but, I hope, more wisely. [Perry, 1981, p. 79]

Within this schema one can see shades of the conceptually complex notions of dialectical thinking, which is discussed later in this chapter, as well as the major theme of becoming more relativistic in one's thought patterns as one matures.

Each position is descriptive of individual cognitive growth, and in addition, Perry's positions have also been used to describe how people view instructors' roles and their own roles as learners. Learners at the lowest positions, for example, tend to view instructors as authority figures; their job as learners is to filter out the right answers from the material presented. Those at the higher end of the continuum view knowledge in a contextual sense and search for relationships between ideas; they see instructors more as guides.

The increasing diversity of the college student population has prompted scholars to investigate the generalizability of Perry's scheme with various student populations. Zhang (1999, 2004) investigated the applicability of Perry's scheme to both American and Chinese college students. He conducted five studies between 1994 and 2000 using the Zhang Cognitive Development Inventory (ZCDI), which is based on Perry's schemes. In the five studies that he conducted, he found that Chinese college students' cognitive development was *opposite* that of Perry's scheme. That is, students traversed from a more relativistic viewpoint toward a more dualistic viewpoint. In the two studies in which Americans were included, the dualistic-relativistic-commitment progression did not hold for American students in the second study, but it did in the first. Zhang (2004) hypothesized that changing American values may explain why Perry's order of cognitive development was not evident. He indicated that mainland China's approach to higher education, which limits students' opportunities for making choices, may explain why students in the study moved toward more dualistic thinking. He cautioned, however, that these conclusions were not final and recommended that qualitative research procedures and longitudinal studies would give a richer picture of Chinese students' cognitive development. Likewise Johnson (2000) noted that Perry's scale, normed on White, traditional-age college students, did not account for cultural differences between Whites and African Americans.

Most of the work using Perry's schema with older adults has produced contradictory results. Lavallee, Gourde, and Rodier (1990) and Wilson (1996) found that the majority of their respondents were at Positions 3 or 4 (multiplicity) on Perry's scheme, while Cameron's (1983) subjects were primarily at Position 2 (dualist). In a cross-sectional study, Hood and Deopere (2002) found that "as age increased, relativism scores tended to decrease" even when researchers controlled for intelligence and education (p. 233). This finding reinforces the stereotype that older people are more set in their ways and "less capable or willing to handle complexity in their thought processes" (p. 233). In addition, the findings of Wilson (1996) and Lavallee, Gourde, and Rodier (1990) differed on the importance of the level of education in terms of reaching higher levels of cognitive development. Wilson (1996) and Hood and Deopere (2002) found that those with a higher education scored higher on Perry's scale while Lavallee, Gourde, and Rodier (1990) concluded that level of education had little effect on the cognitive development of their subjects.

In sum, Perry's cognitive development model, based on the thinking patterns of White, Ivy League traditional-age college students, suggests that individuals move from dualistic (right-wrong) thinking toward dialectical thinking, where students are able to hold contradictory notions in their mind. Recent studies have indicated that the model may not account for cultural differences (Johnson, 2000; Zhang, 2004). Further, some studies show that older adults may show more dualistic thinking than younger adults (Hood & Deopere, 2002; Wilson, 1996).

THE REFLECTIVE JUDGMENT MODEL

King and Kitchener, like Perry, have also constructed a stage model. Influenced by the developmental traditions of Perry (1970), Piaget (1972), and Kohlberg (1981), they examine the development of "epistemic assumptions" or "reflective thinking from late adolescence through adulthood" (King & Kitchener, 2004, pp. 5–6). The authors focus on how people make judgments about complex or "ill-structured" problems that "cannot be defined with a high degree of completeness, and . . . cannot be solved with a high degree of certainty" (p. 5). Examples include such controversial issues as "the accuracy of news reporting, the creation of human beings, and the safety of nuclear power" (pp. 10–11).

According to this complex stage model, people move through seven stages, with the final two stages encompassing the more mature thinking patterns of what King and Kitchener call *reflective thinking* (King & Kitchener, 1994, 2004). In Stages 1, 2, and 3 (labeled *prereflective thinking*), people assume that knowledge comes from authority figures or is gained through personal experience. Individuals in these stages do not see problems as ill-structured, but rather view all problems as having complete and right answers. In Stages 4 and 5 *(quasi-reflective reasoning),* people define knowledge in terms of uncertainty and are more subjective in their thinking. Although they understand that ill-defined problems exist, they have trouble dealing with the ambiguity of those problems and tend to respond in very individualistic ways. In the final two stages of thinking (Stages 7 and 8), knowledge is no longer a given. Rather, knowledge, especially knowledge used to solve life's ill-structured problems, may have to be constructed by the person, and this knowledge must be understood in the context in which it was generated. Decisions and judgments people make, although they must be grounded in relevant data, should remain open to evaluation and reevaluation (King & Kitchener, 1994, 2004). It is important to note that individuals do not fit neatly into one particular stage. People can use Stage 4 reasoning and can also evidence Stage 3 epistemic assumptions. King and Kitchener note that the development of reflective thinking is more like "waves across a mixture of stages, where the peak of the wave is the most commonly used set of assumptions" (King, Kitchener, & Wood, 1994, p. 140).

The sample for their original ten-year longitudinal study consisted of male and female students. The sample included twenty high school juniors, forty twenty-one-year-old college juniors, and twenty doctoral students whose average age was twenty-eight (King & Kitchener, 2002). Subsequent studies have included nonstudent adults. As the result of thousands of interviews, King and Kitchener (2004) have come to the following conclusions: "(a) There are striking differences in people's underlying assumptions about knowledge or epistemic assumptions; (b) these differences in assumptions are related to the way people make and justify their own judgments about ill-structured problems; and (c) there is a developmental sequence in the patterns of responses and judgments about such problems" (p. 5).

A great deal of research has been completed using the reflective judgment model (see King & Kitchener, 1994, 2002). Research has centered on validating whether the stages in the model form a developmental sequence. In addition, scholars have examined the impact of education, gender, and ethnicity on reflective judgment and the relationship of reflective judgment to other intellectual and personality constructs (King & Kitchener, 2002). As previously noted, there appears to be a developmental sequence to the model. Further, there is a trend for older, more educated participants to score higher on the reflective judgment model than younger, less-educated individuals. Results on differences in reflective judgment by gender are mixed. King and Kitchener caution readers that "samples differ on many variables beyond gender (such as ability and educational level), and [we] suggest that these should be examined when interpreting gender differences" (p. 49).

There has been scant research on reflective judgment and ethnicity. Two studies that examined ethnicity (Latino-Latina and African American) revealed similar reflective judgment scores to Whites (King & Kitchener, 2002). King and Kitchener report, "Prior studies have show that RJ [reflective judgment] is related to but not the same as academic aptitude, verbal ability, formal operations, or traditional measures of critical thinking" (2002, p. 50). There also appears to be some overlap with Belenky et al.'s (1986) *Women's Ways of Knowing,* but "only to the extent that the Belenky et al. interview asks epistemic questions and scores for that category" (p. 51). Regarding the relationship between reflective judgment and personality constructs, there seems to be moderate correlations between RJ and tolerance for diversity. Kozak (1996, as cited in King & Kitchener, 2002) found that people with higher reflective judgment scores "can access their feelings in the process of decision making, but aren't ruled by their feelings" (p. 53). The authors conclude that although personality variables may be related to reflective judgment, reflective judgment is a separate construct.

Recent research utilizing the reflective judgment model includes an investigation of the relationship between personality traits and reflective judgment among female undergraduates and graduates in teacher education programs (Friedman, 2004), the epistemological development of Finnish adults (Pirttilä-Backman & Kajanne, 2001), and the reflective judgment scores of seminarians over time (Dale, 2005). In the study concerning the epistemological development of Finnish adults, fifty-nine adults were interviewed in the mid-1980s and again in the early 1990s using King and Kitchener's Reflective Judgment Interview. Participants ranged in age from twenty-four to fifty in the follow-up interviews.

Their post–high school education included graduation from a vocational institute or university in the technical, medical-nursing, or social science fields. Formal education contributed to "epistemic development . . . through middle adulthood" (Pirttilä-Backman & Kajanne, 2001, p. 90). In addition, being exposed to a variety of information and diverse associations with others appeared to promote epistemic development in adulthood.

There seem to be similarities between the Perry scheme and the model developed by King and Kitchener. For example, both start with the assumption that people progress from a dualistic to a relativistic form of thinking. However, King and Kitchener incorporate the idea of knowledge construction in their model while Perry focuses on expanding his ideas of using relativistic thinking in a responsible way. Although a great deal of research has been completed using the reflective judgment model, few studies have been completed with adults outside the higher education setting. Attention to adult populations outside of the higher education setting would increase the generalizability of the reflective judgment model and would expand the understanding of people's personal epistemology.

Women's Ways of Knowing

In reaction to the early work of Perry (1970), Kohlberg (1973), and others in which primarily male samples were used, researchers became more interested in hearing the voices of women on developmental issues. The most prominent and often-quoted study on cognitive development using a sample of women is the work of Belenky, Clinchy, Goldberger, and Tarule: *Women's Ways of Knowing* (1986). These researchers interviewed women from diverse social and ethnic backgrounds from two major settings: different types of academic institutions and parenting classes. From their in-depth interviews of 135 women of different ages, classes, and ethnic backgrounds, "based on the theoretical and empirical work of Perry, Kohlberg, and Gilligan" (p. 14), Belenky et al. grouped women's perspectives on knowing into five major categories:

1. *Silence*—a position in which women experience themselves as mindless and voiceless and subject to the whims of external authority. (They are passive, feel incompetent, and are defined by others.)

2. *Received knowledge*—a perspective from which women conceive of themselves as capable of receiving, even reproducing, knowledge from the all-knowing external authorities but not capable of creating knowledge on their own. (They listen to the voices of others; their world is literal and concrete, good or bad.)

3. *Subjective knowledge*—a perspective from which truth and knowledge are conceived of as personal, private, and subjectively known or intuited. (The locus of truth shifts to the self; intuition is valued over logic and abstraction; here women begin to gain a voice. Half the women in the study were in this category.)

4. *Procedural knowledge*—a position in which women are invested in learning and applying objective procedures for obtaining and communicating knowledge. (This position takes two forms: separate knowing—the self is separate from the object of discourse, making it possible to doubt and reason—and connected knowing—there is intimacy and equality between the self and the object of discourse, based on empathetic understanding.)

5. *Constructed knowledge*—a position in which women view all knowledge as contextual, experience themselves as creators of knowledge, and value both subjective and objective strategies for knowing. (This stage is characterized by the development of an authentic voice.)

These categories, which are not necessarily fixed or universal, move from the simple to the complex—from having no voice, to being able to value and create different ways of knowing that are contextual in nature. Although these authors do not assert that the categories constitute specific stages of cognitive development, they appear to present them as such, and some people continue to interpret them in this way (Goldberger, 1996b).

Reflecting on fifteen years of research, Clinchy (2002) lent some additional insight to a couple of positions. She realized the Silence position was much more common than previously realized, regardless of class. She also noted that the categorization of women into five broad categories did not allow for subtle distinctions between women in that category. For example, she indicated that most Received Knowers in their sample were young college students or older, poor women. Clinchy stated, "Received Knowing may take a different form among, say, a sample of prosperous middle-aged people. . . . Received Knowing cannot be quite the same for a first-year student in an elite college . . . and a fifty-year-old with minimal formal education" (pp. 68–69).

Scholars see similarities and differences between the *Women's Ways of Knowing* (WWK) positions and other epistemological models. Clinchy (2002) states that there are parallels between Perry's (1970) dualistic position and *Women's Ways of Knowing* position of received knowledge. In both cases, the knowers see "the world in terms of black and white, right and wrong" (Clinchy, 2002, p. 66). Likewise, subjective knowledge has similarities to Perry's (1970) multiplicity position, and WWK's constructed knowing is similar to Perry's Position 5—relativism (Clinchy, 2002). However, Baron (2003), who used "factor, correlational, and comparative analysis" to assess the relationships between Perry's scale and WWK, found that "the two theories are largely independent of each other" (p. x). Baron believes that Perry does not address "the concept of knowing in relationship and caring" while WWK explicitly acknowledges these factors (p. 55). Further, Perry presents his theory in a sequential fashion, whereas the WWK authors do not see cognitive development as a linear progression.

WWK's final category of constructed knowing seems comparable with the findings of King and Kitchener (1994, 2004) and Baxter Magolda (1992; Baxter Magolda's work is reviewed in the following section). For example, King and Kitchener (2004) speak to the importance of contextual knowing and constructing one's own knowledge as characteristic of their final two stages, and Baxter Magolda (1992) stresses the integration of relational (subjective) and impersonal (objective) knowing as key to what she terms contextual knowing. These apparent similarities add confirmation to the work of Belenky and her colleagues and are in line with their original interpretations of their research.

As with other epistemological models, scholars have several criticisms of the WWK theory. First, they argue that it is essentialist rather than constructivist. Clinchy refutes this criticism, saying, "We did not argue that the positions we described applied only to women, although we speculated that for various reasons, the positions might take somewhat different form in men" (2002, p. 79). Second, critics note that the theory does not take into consideration "the role of social positionality and oppression in the construction of knowledge" (Goldberger, 1996b, p. 8). Goldberger agrees that this is a weakness of the theory, but says they have "listened to and learned from women of color and other culture theorists . . . , [and] have become much more alert to the situational and cultural determinants of knowing and to the relationship of power and knowledge" (p. 8). Cultural differences were also not explored in the WWK theory. However, the influence of culture on knowing has become of interest to the authors as the result of subsequent conversations. Last, the theory is thought to "endorse . . . the superiority of antirationalist, subjectivist epistemologies" (p. 9). Goldberger (1996b) replies that the authors value both connected and separate knowing and do not champion one above the other.

The WWK theory has generated much discussion around issues of gender and epistemological development. Clinchy (2002, p. 85) recommends that future research examine "development within rather than across domains" in the form of longitudinal case studies in order to get a better understanding of what factors promote epistemological development.

EPISTEMOLOGICAL REFLECTION MODEL

Marcia Baxter Magolda (1992) originally developed the epistemological reflection model to demonstrate the epistemological reasoning of college students. Later, she extended her work to young adults beyond their college experience. Like others who have studied cognitive development, Baxter Magolda's work is grounded in the assumption that ways of knowing are socially constructed and context bound.

Baxter Magolda (1992, p. 29) followed a group of seventy predominantly White male and female college students over five years, interviewing them yearly, and discovered "four qualitatively different ways of knowing, each characterized by a core set of epistemic assumptions": *absolute knowing, transitional knowing, independent knowing,* and *contextual knowing*. Students told stories of moving from being certain about what they knew, to uncertainty, and finally to being able to integrate information from diverse points of view in order to apply that knowledge in a particular context. Baxter Magolda noted that only a small percentage of students used contextual knowing while in college. Like Perry's (1999) and

King and Kitchener's (2004) work, Baxter Magolda provides excellent descriptions of what this work means for practice in higher education.

Unlike the work on the Perry (1981) and King and Kitchener (1994) schemes, Baxter Magolda found patterns of thinking within each of the ways of knowing that were gender related. Baxter Magolda (2004) explains, "I use the term gender related to convey that women or men in the project used one pattern more but the patterns were not exclusive to one gender" (p. 34). For example, in the absolute knowing category, two patterns emerged: listening-recording and mastery. Women focused on listening and recording information to learn from authorities while men were more likely to use the mastery pattern, which meant they participated in class and actively showed their mastery of material (Baxter Magolda, 2004).

Baxter Magolda (2004) extended her original study and followed students for another two years after they graduated from college. She found that when her participants exhibited contextual knowing, their ways of knowing were no longer gender related. Rather, as they took on different adult roles, their patterns of thinking within this contextual framework became more integrated. More specifically, the patterns of relational and impersonal modes of knowing, which characterize contextual knowing, were used in an integrative fashion: "Contextual knowing required connecting to others and to the subject to be known, yet at the same time required standing back to analyze the situation" (pp. 37–38). (Her descriptions of contextual knowing echo somewhat the descriptions of "constructed knowledge" described by Belenky, Clinchy, Goldberger, & Tarule, 1986.) However, Baxter Magolda was puzzled at recent college graduates' need to continue to "look to external sources for guidance" despite their advanced epistemological positions (Baxter Magolda, 2004, p. 38). She stated, "On leaving college, longitudinal participants did what they had been taught to do best—follow authorities' leads to manage uncertainty" (p. 38). She continued to interview participants "for 12 years after their college graduation" (p. 39) and found that participants put external authority in perspective as they began to author their own lives. Baxter Magolda (2004) explained, "Becoming the author of one's life meant taking responsibility for one's beliefs, identity, and relationships. The internal voice became the coordinator of meaning-making in all three dimensions of development" (p. 40). As a result, people opened themselves to change and ambiguity and authored their own epistemologies.

From these longitudinal interviews with undergraduates, Baxter Magolda and King (2004) developed a learning partnerships model where they "identified conditions that promote self-authorship" (p. 41). The authors listed three assumptions and three key principles of educational practice. The assumptions were as follows: First, environments that promoted self-authorship conveyed "knowledge as complex and socially constructed" (p. 41). Individuals had to grapple with multiple interpretations and ambiguity. Second, these environments recognized that "self is central to knowledge construction" (p. 42). Third, "authority and expertise were shared in the mutual construction of knowledge" (p. 42). These assumptions were demonstrated by educators and employers in connection with the three principals of educational practice. The first principle was "validating learners' capacity to know" (p. 42). Employers and teachers solicited students' opinions and demonstrated that knowledge is constructed. Second, employers situated learners' experiences. Employees' knowledge was used as a "basis for continued learning and decision making" (p. 43). The last principle, "mutually constructing meaning" (p. 43), was shown when experts and learners constructed knowledge together to arrive at more complex understandings of the material.

THE TRANSCENDENCE VIEW

A very different view of cognitive development has emerged from scholars writing from the perspective of transpersonal psychology. Washburn (2000), among others (see Wilber, 1990), has extended models of cognitive development beyond the rational level by identifying deeper structures in the mind that undergird higher or transpersonal levels of consciousness. An important component of these theories is Consciousness of human beings, with a capital C, which denotes "the unlimited reservoir from which we draw personal, ego-centered awareness. Our individual Consciousness is an infinitesimal spark within the eternal flame of Universal Consciousness" (Nuernberger, 1994, p. 96). When we allow ourselves to move beyond our own individual limits of time and space—our individual Consciousness—a whole new world of expanded Consciousness with limitless boundaries, almost mystical in nature, is open to us.

Washburn (2000) cites several characteristics of transpersonal cognition. First, our consciousness goes beyond ourselves or our egos. We are more open to images. Second, transpersonal cognition is not only a cognitive occurrence but includes "feeling, instinct . . . a sense of being in the midst of or infused by an awesome energy" (p. 204). This energy amplifies our awareness. Third, transpersonal cognition is initially unstable and becomes more stable as it develops. In short, transpersonal cognition is a deep awakening. Washburn writes, "As Socrates put it, wisdom cannot be taught; we must awaken to it, and this awakening is not an isolated cognitive event but is, rather, a transformation of our whole being" (p. 207).

Wilber's (1986) model of transpersonal cognitive development has nine stages. The last two levels illustrate well the transpersonal nature of the theory. The subtle level, Level 7, is based on "a truly trans-rational structure . . . not emotionalism or merely felt meaning . . . or hunch" (Wilber, 1982, p. 30). Rather, phrases such as *illumination of the spirit, intuition as an elemental sense,* and *mystical awareness* characterize the thinking of this developmental level. The eighth level, the causal state, indisputably moves individuals beyond themselves. As described by Wilber (1983, p. 97), "This is total and utter transcendence and release into Formless Consciousness, Boundless Radiance. There is here no self, no God, no final-God, no subjects, no thingness, apart or other than consciousness as such."

In reviewing these and other theoretical models of adult cognitive development, what becomes apparent is there are two themes that many of these theories address: first, higher stages of cognitive development in some models suggest the presence of dialectical thinking in adulthood—that is, the acceptance of inherent contradictions and alternative truths—and second, context, including the acceptance of cultural differences, is critical in determining what thinking patterns in adulthood really mean. The discussions of dialectical thinking have a long history in adult cognitive development, beginning with the work of Riegel (1973) and others. In contrast, viewing the contextual dimensions of development is more recent. Both of these themes, and representative work illustrating the themes, are discussed in the next two sections.

DIALECTICAL THINKING

Our modern world is rife with contradictions and paradoxes. We have the capability to clone cells, with the possibility for great advances in medicine and many other areas, yet at the same time we fear what might be constructed with this technology. We eradicate one dreaded disease and other vicious diseases take its place. We can replace most body parts at will, but ethically cannot decide who should get the limited supply of these parts. And the list keeps expanding to the point where Kegan (1994), among others, views us literally "in over our heads" in responding to a world of continuous change and disparities.

Conflict and contradictions in adult life are not new phenomena; rather, they may just be more apparent now because we can often see and hear them up close through television and other technological formats. In addition, what used to be intensely personal, such as the beginning and the end of life, has also become public knowledge. Should a woman be allowed to decide to abort an unwanted child? Who has the right to end someone's life? These are just a few of the questions debated in the public forum. In responding to life's inherent contradictions and complexities, a number of authors have posited that dialectical ways of thinking must become part of the way adults think. In essence, thinking in a dialectic sense allows for the acceptance of alternative truths or ways of thinking about similar phenomena that abound in everyday adult life. One might abhor killing, for example, and yet silently applaud the gentle person who switches off the life-support system of her spouse who is suffering beyond relief from a terminal illness.

One of the earliest and most thoughtful theorists to describe dialectical thinking was Riegel (1973, 1975, 1976). According to Riegel (1973, p. 350), "[D]ialectic conceptualization characterizes the origin of thought in the individual and in society [and] represents a necessary synthesis in the development of thought toward maturity." In describing the dialectic thought process, Riegel (1973, 1975) proposed a corresponding mode of dialectic operations to stand beside Piaget's formal system. The key to this alternative system is the inclusion of the dialectic, or the acceptance of inherent contradictions and ambiguities in thought processes, at all developmental levels and not just as part of the more mature thought of adulthood. "The skills and competence in one area of concern, for instance in sciences, might be of the type of formal dialectic operations, while in everyday business transactions, might be of the type of concrete dialectic operations," and so on (Riegel, 1973, p. 365). Riegel's basic assumptions are that people do not have to pass through any of the Piagetian levels to reach the higher levels of thinking within the dialectic framework and that people can operate simultaneously on all levels. In proposing this system, Riegel (1973, p. 366) argued that people are not only ready to live with life's inherent contradictions and ambiguities but will accept "these contradictions as a basic property of thought and creativity."

Unlike Riegel, however, some writers view dialectical thought as evolving from the formal stages Piaget proposed. Benack and Basseches (1989, p. 98), for example, in exploring dialectical thinking as a postformal stage of thought, have developed a "dialectical schemata framework" consisting of twenty-four schemata representing different "moves in thought that dialectical thinkers tend to make." These schemata were abstracted from "writings reflecting dialectic world-outlooks" (Basseches, 1984, p. 72) and interviews with college students and professors about the nature of education. Basseches claims that "some of the dialectical schemata describe ways of introducing dialectical perspectives on existence and knowledge into processes of inquiry. Others describe ways of maintaining dialectical movement within one's own thought" (p. 73). Based on his research, Basseches has suggested that there are actually four phases to the development of mature dialectical thinking. (See Basseches, 1984, and Benack & Basseches, 1989, for a full description of these phases.)

Kegan (1994), framing his work from both a psychological and contextual approach, proposes a level-of-consciousness model that incorporates dialectical thinking as part of the highest level of consciousness. His assumption in proposing this model is that the "hidden curriculum" of modern life necessitates different ways of thinking and "a new conception of *consciousness thresholds* individuals may have to reach in order to satisfy contemporary expectations of love and work" (p. 11). Through examples of real-world demands on our private lives (parenting and partnering) and our public lives (work, dealing with differences, healing, and learning), Kegan (1994) explains how our thinking must continue to evolve through several levels of consciousness in order to navigate our complex lives. First, adults need to discern how to use their mental capacities in social situations. This form of thinking moves adults from the concrete world (having a point of view), to abstractions (being able to build inferences and hypotheses), to abstract systems (conceiving relations between abstractions), and finally to dialectical thinking (testing of paradoxical and contradictory formulations). Dialectical thinking thus becomes the hallmark of mature adult thinking.

Kegan argues that this pressing demand for dialectical thinking comes from our need as adults to respond to what he terms "culture's curriculum"—that is, the mental demands the postmodern world places on us. Kegan, like Riegel and Kramer, also views contradictions and paradoxes as inevitable and at the heart of the dialectical process. He then adds a new framework to this process: trans-systems thinking. What is key in this trans-systems way of thinking is that the parties or systems in conflict move beyond trying to "win" for their position, even the most desired of outcomes—the "win-win" position. Rather, what is needed is the recognition that "the other side will not go away, [and] probably *should* not. The conflict is potentially a reminder of our tendency to pretend to completeness when we are in fact incomplete" (Kegan, 1994, p. 319). Therefore, we must acknowledge and value the thought processes that brought about these conflictual relationships, knowing they are often based in fundamental ideological differences. We need to work within these relationships, miserable as that might be, to advance our ways of thinking and working.

In working together, the parties or systems in these conflictual relationships must then focus on transforming who they are versus trying to solve the conflict. As Kegan (1994, p. 345) goes on to observe:

> This view does not mean that the challengers are co-opted into the status quo. It means that the old status quo is replaced by a new status quo. It does not mean that blacks can come into the office only if they act white. It does not mean that women's experience is included in the curriculum simply by changing pronouns and making a "Michael" example into a "Mary" example. It means that formerly marginalized people will come into the office, and they will

have their own distinctive way of seeing things, setting the agenda, getting the goals accomplished; and it means that these ways will be recognized, acknowledged, and respected, provided that some common ground can be found where all contending "cultures" in their wholeness and distinctness can stand. This common ground becomes, in effect, a new status quo and a new ideology, but a much more wholesome one.

From his longitudinal work, Kegan (1994) has found that most people do not even enter the fourth level of consciousness until their forties. Kegan sees our expanded life span as a wonderful opportunity to develop our consciousness to this fifth level. From Kegan's perspective, "Highly evolved people do not mate and create highly evolved children. The evolution of human consciousness requires long preparation. We may gradually become ever more ready to engage the curriculum of the fifth order because we have found ways to increase the number of years we live" (p. 352).

Some studies on dialectical thought include the view that culture shapes the process. Peng and Nisbett (1999) describe differences between Western and Eastern thought. First, they delineate three principles to Chinese dialectical epistemology. First is the principle of change, which says that reality is a dynamic, flexible process. Existence does not consist of two categories: life and death. Instead, life is a "constant passing of one stage to another" (p. 743). Second is the principle of contradiction, which says that reality is full of contradictions. "Two sides of any contradiction exist in an active harmony, opposed but connected and mutually controlling" (p. 743). Third is the "principle of relationship or holism" (p. 743). Everything is connected and an entity is more than the sum of its parts. Next, Peng and Nisbett maintain that Western thought rests on laws of formal Aristotelian logic. The law of identity dictates that everything is what it is. A equals A. The law of noncontradiction says that "no statement can be both true and false" (p. 744).

Peng and Nisbett (1999) selected Chinese and American dialectical and nondialectical proverbs for American and Chinese undergraduates to read. A dialectical proverb, for example would be "Beware of your friends, not your enemies," which contradicts the very definition of friendship (p. 744). A nondialectical proverb might be "One against all is certain to fall" (p. 744). Americans preferred nondialectical American proverbs, while the Chinese preferred dialectical Chinese proverbs. In a separate study, Chinese and American undergraduates were asked to read vignettes and suggest resolutions to the conflicts. Americans suggested nondialectical solutions more often than their Chinese counterparts, while Chinese proposed dialectical solutions more often than their American colleagues. Peng and Nisbitt determined that Westerners take a more analytic approach to problems, while Easterners have a more holistic approach.

Caroline Ho (2004) takes issue with these findings in her dissertation. She examined the dialectical reasoning of 196 Chinese Canadians and European Canadians. She found no difference between groups in dialectic reasoning ability, suggesting that "dialectical thinking skills may be more universal; however, the "tendency to display those skills may be more culture specific" (p. ii).

Nisbett's 2003 book, *The Geography of Thought: How Asians and Westerners Think Differently . . . and Why,* explores these cultural differences in detail. He contends that that we do think quite differently, in part because of the Greek heritage of the West versus the Confucian-Chinese philosophy of the East:

> The ancient Greeks were fond of categories and used them as the basis for discovery and application of rules. They also believed in stability and understood both the physical and social worlds in terms of fixed attributes or dispositions. These are not unrelated facts, nor is it a coincidence that the ancient Chinese were uninterested in categories, believed in change, and understood the behavior of both physical and social objects as being due to the interaction of the object with the surrounding field of forces. . . . [For example], there is the whiteness of the horse or the whiteness of the snow in ancient Chinese philosophy, but not whiteness as an abstract, detachable concept that can be applied to almost anything. [pp. 152–153]

Clearly, there are intriguing questions yet to be explored about the role of culture in cognitive development—and "if the nature of thought is not everywhere the same" (Nisbett, 2003, p. 211), then what are the implications for educators?

THE CONTEXTUAL PERSPECTIVE

When we read through the many theories of cognitive development, some of us might resonate better than other people with these theories. We may wrestle with ideas presented in various theories and reflect later on how powerful being exposed to different ways of thinking has been. Acknowledging the contextual factors of cognitive development—that is, taking into account how social, cultural, economic, and political forces shape the development of adult thinking—completes the picture. Our theories and models need to be altered and perhaps totally revamped when these contextual aspects are seriously considered by scholars studying adult cognitive development. The work of Labouvie-Vief (1992) and the work of Goldberger (1996a) are used to illustrate how scholars consider context as central to cognitive development.

Labouvie-Vief (1980, 1984) was one of the earlier scholars to acknowledge the importance of contextual factors in cognitive development. Labouvie-Vief challenged the more accepted notion at that time that the perfection of formal logic was the ultimate goal of adult thinking. Rather, Labouvie-Vief contends that a different form of thinking must be integrated into one's model of adult cognitive development: "While the theme of youth is flexibility, the hallmark of adulthood is commitment and responsibility. Careers must be started, intimacy bonds formed, children raised. In short, in a world of a multitude of logical possibilities, one course of action must be adopted. This conscious commitment to one pathway and the deliberate disregard of other logical choices may mark the onset of adult maturity" (1980, p. 153). Therefore, what may have been conceived of as a regression in later life to Piaget's notion of concrete thought patterns is, rather, a positive adaptation to the realities of adult life. One key factor in being able to adapt to these new ways of thinking is the ability to accept and even thrive on contradiction. This in turns leads to acceptance of the notion of inherent relativity of knowledge and the ability to be self-regulating in choosing one's worldview.

Labouvie-Vief (1990, p. 256), expanding on her earlier work, postulates that "it may be variables related [more] to one's social context than to one's age that account for particular developmental gradients" in cognition. Therefore, if one wishes to discover changes and patterns in cognitive development, it might be more fruitful to examine groups of people who share pertinent life events and experiences versus people of a certain chronological age group. For example, age has been most often cited as the marker by which cognitive declines are measured. Labouvie-Vief (1990) instead asks the question of whether a major life event, such as retirement, "could be the cause of the ubiquitous decline in cognitive functioning" (p. 263). In posing this framework, Labouvie-Vief is echoing the sentiments of those studying personal and intellectual development from a sociocultural or contextual perspective.

In more recent work, Labouvie-Vief has examined the relationship between cognitive complexity and cognitive-affective integration (Labouvie-Vief & Diehl, 2000). A person's cognitive complexity was shown by tests that measured crystallized intelligence (cultural knowledge), fluid intelligence (on-the-spot reasoning not dependent on experience but tied to how fast we can respond to stimuli), and reflective cognition (the complexity of thought demonstrated in thinking about oneself). Cognitive-affective integration was demonstrated by the level of a person's coping strategies and defense mechanisms as shown by answers to the California Psychological Inventory–based coping and defense scales. The study showed an interconnection between cognitive complexity and cognitive-affective integration. Those who were more "culturally advantaged and of higher cognitive complexity are more likely to show integrated coping" (p. 501). However, for those who "feel a sense of vulnerability vis-à-vis their family of origin, the two domains may be somewhat disconnected" (p. 501). In short, the study demonstrated the importance of environment on cognitive-affective integration.

Goldberger (1996a), from interviews with approximately sixty bicultural individuals, primarily women, living in the United States, has added different dimensions of meanings to all of the original categories of knowing that she and Belenky, Clinchy, Goldberger, and Tarule (1986) had described. Goldberger found that the position of "not knowing," that of silence, for example, is a much more complicated phenomenon than was described in *Women's Ways of Knowing*. Rather, how silence is defined can be culturally determined and is actually a positive way of knowing for some. In American Indian cultures, "silence is taught [as something to be respected] within their tribal groups. . . . Allaq [a member of the Inuit nation] remembers the 'nice silence' of many children in a room, listening as the elders told stories. Hard Rider [a member of the Canadian West Coast Dtidahy band], struggling to learn from his grandfather how to be a tribal leader, had already recognized the advantages of silent and respectful listening" (Goldberger, 1996a, p. 343). Goldberger also highlights the importance of silence for others, such as African-American women, as a tactical strategy for "negotiating life in white communities or workplaces" (p. 345). This distinction of types of silence has led Goldberger to differentiate between those who are truly silenced "by oppressive and demeaning life conditions who feel powerless, mindless, and truly without words . . . from individuals who resort to strategic or culturally and ritually endorsed silence, but who may have other well-developed ways of acquiring, even constructing knowledge" (p. 346). In reframing the original categories from a contextual perspective, Goldberger views them more as strategies for knowing than as "person types" to which individuals are assigned based on their response patterns. In conceptualizing these categories as knowing strategies, one can then explore how contextual factors limit or expand our ways of knowing and allow us to speak of different uses or even meanings of each of the ways of knowing.

In this review of the work of Labouvie-Vief, Goldberger, and others on the contextual perspective of cognitive development, two important points become apparent.

First, the majority of the mainstream theory in adult cognitive development is "based largely on the findings from a mainly White, well-educated U.S. population" (Hofer & Pintrich, 1997, p. 89). There is a paucity of studies that incorporate people of color or different social classes or that examine cross-cultural differences. It appears from studies where the contextual aspect is acknowledged that people from varying backgrounds may define and value knowledge quite differently. Goldberger (1996a), for example, shares three stories from bicultural women living in the United States: Kat, a South American–born woman of mestizo background who is a counselor; Allaq, a Native Alaskan of the Inuit people and a health worker; and Toshi, an African-American professor recently granted tenure:

Kat: My grandmother [who is a shaman] would teach me the difference between thinking that you know something and knowing it. She would take me out into the woods and have me sense becoming things. Not just looking and describing what I saw. I had to be the tree, I had to be the rock, I was the bird. Some of that [kind of knowing] is helped with the sacred medicine plants. They allow one to open up many different channels and get all the information possible. Whereas [simply] thinking about something feels like it is a very narrow band, a very narrow channel.

Allaq: As a child, I learned a lot just listening to the elders. They talked about the way of living of the Yupik people. . . . Knowledge is part of the soul. You have to learn it spiritually in every aspect of life—spiritually, mentally, emotionally, physically, socially, as a whole person. Yugarag is passed through generations. . . . In my world everything is interrelated. Everything interrelates.

Toshi: Black people have a different way of relating to the world. Even intellectually active black people. And that way is more experientially related than cognitively related. We think less about something but react more. I like being able to go from my experience, rather than having to think about it. As a Black person, I don't have to hold it in. I can express it. [pp. 336–337]

What is evident in these stories, and those from other writers (for example, Goldberger, Tarule, Clinchy, & Belenky, 1996; Reybold, 1997), is that culture and personal experience shape what and how people develop their distinctive ways of knowing.

The second point regarding the contextual perspective, as observed by Goodnow (1990, p. 82), is that social context is not, as it is often presented, "a relatively benign, neutral, or free market" commodity. Rather, the social world in which we live "takes an active and managing interest in the ideas people acquire" (p. 93). This active and managing interest manifests itself in two ways related to adult cognitive development. The first is that the dominant culture may subvert ways of knowing it does not value. Because these ways of knowing may not be valued by the dominant culture, they may be hidden or lost, and worse, viewed as illegitimate or not needed in our modern world. And second, scholars themselves may choose to study only the development of the ways of knowing that they are familiar with and value. This bias will continue to block the construction of alternative models and theories that acknowledge contextual factors as a critical aspect of adult cognitive development.

WISDOM: THE HALLMARK OF ADULT THINKING

Wisdom is often seen as the pinnacle or hallmark of adult thinking. It is something we all speak about and sometimes yearn for as we face the many challenges of adult life. Should we tell our teenage grandchildren they are making horrendous decisions? Should we make a major career change, especially if it means losing our financial security? What do we say to a very dear friend who is dying of cancer? Questions like these haunt many of us, and we wish we had the wisdom of the elders to make the "right" decisions. Yet this notion of wisdom continues to be a fluid and elusive idea that is most often characterized by the acceptance of ambiguity as one of its many virtues.

Wisdom is not a new concept; it has been discussed through the ages by great philosophers and theologians of all backgrounds and persuasions. Psychologists and educators have defined and studied wisdom from a variety of perspectives. Robinson (1990) noted that the definition of wisdom has changed over time, differing in ancient Greek, traditional Christian, and contemporary conceptions. Baltes and Smith (1990) define wisdom as expertise in everyday life, while Kramer and Baccelar (1994) link wisdom to being able to think in a dialectic way, while Becvar (2005) states that "being wise has to do with higher awareness," one which allows us to acknowledge the "many possible paradigms, worldviews, reality tunnels and epistemologies, each of which is a plausible explanation of the way the world really is" (p. 29). Therefore, the problems we face as adults are value- and context-specific, and wisdom then becomes a process versus a state of being. And Sternberg (1996b, p. 276) has noted the importance of the social-interaction nature of wisdom, which stresses "that wisdom by definition will hardly ever be found in an individual, but rather in cultural or social interactive products." These and other definitions point to the complexity of the concept. Most researchers do agree, however, that wisdom is the province of adulthood, although *older* is not always equated with *wiser.*

Researchers and writers on wisdom have attempted to delineate its major components and its relationship to the aging process. Holliday and Chandler (1986), for example, have sought to provide empirical parameters for the term *wisdom* in three interlocking studies. They first collected general descriptions of wise people from which they formulated the basic description of wisdom in a second study. In the third phase of their research, they "examined the influence of the wise prototype on people's information processing strategies" (p. 44). The 458 subjects in their study represented all age cohorts of adults: young, middle-aged, and older. They concluded that wisdom is a multidimensional construct consisting of more than objective and context-free aspects of thought. In their view, "Wise people must be able to solve problems—but not in an abstract sense. The type of problems that wise people presumably deal with appear to have strong practical and emancipatory components. That is, wisdom problems are problems endemic to life and to the human condition. . . . Consequently, the problems typically involve or center on values" (p. 90).

In a somewhat different way, Sternberg (1986b, pp. 177–178) sought to discover people's conceptions or implicit theories of wisdom by exploring "the nature and the interrelationships of intelligence, wisdom, and creativity." Through a series of studies with both laypersons (community volunteers and students) and specialists (college professors from a variety of disciplines), Sternberg found that people not only have implicit theories about intelligence, wisdom, and creativity but use them to evaluate others. Moreover, he found differences in the way laypersons and specialists perceived each of the three constructs, including the notion of wisdom.

Laypersons perceived the wise individual to have much the same analytic reasoning ability one finds in the intelligent person. "But the wise person has a certain sagacity that is not necessarily found in the intelligent person. He or she listens to others, knows how to weigh advice, and can deal with a variety of different kinds of people. . . . The wise individual is especially well able to make clear, sensible, and fair judgments and is perceived to profit from the experiences of others and . . . learn from others' mistakes, as well as from his or her own" (p. 186). The specialists, in contrast, tend to emphasize certain aspects of wisdom as more critical than others. The art professors, for example, "emphasize insight, knowing how to balance logic and instinct . . . and sensitivity," while the business professors emphasize such things as "maturity of judgment, understanding of the limitations of one's own actions . . . and appreciation of the ideologies of others" (pp. 186–187). Sternberg concludes that the three major constructs of intelligence, wisdom, and creativity are indeed distinct and yet interrelated, and moreover, that we must pay as much attention to wisdom and creativity as we do to intelligence.

Sternberg and associates, using the findings from this 1986b study, have expanded on this earlier work through an expansive research program over the last twenty years to further delineate the nature of wisdom (Sternberg, 2000a; Sternberg & Jordan, 2005, Sternberg & Lubart, 2001; Sternberg et al., 2000). Sternberg has often linked this research, which is both theoretical and empirical, to his study of intelligence, and more specifically to his triarchic, successful, and practical theories of intelligence (see Chapter Fourteen). Sternberg's current theory of wisdom "views successful intelligence and creativity as the basis for wisdom" (2003b, p. 152). Termed the balance theory of wisdom, Sternberg contends that wisdom is mediated by the values that underlie achieving the common good. Thus wisdom is "about balancing various self-interests (intrapersonal) with the interests of others (interpersonal) and of other aspects of the context in which one lives (extrapersonal). Wisdom also involves creativity, in that the wise solution to a problem may be far from the obvious" (p. 152).

In a recent handbook on wisdom, edited by Sternberg and Jordan (2005), Sternberg (2005a) takes a different view of wisdom through his discussion of the absence of wisdom, or what he has characterized as *foolishness*. His message is very clear—"the costs of foolishness can be very high" (p. 349), especially from the actions of people who possess incredible power and wealth. Their foolishness has led us into wars, polarizations among those who could make a positive difference, and inconceivable hardships for people worldwide. It is Sternberg's contention, as echoed in his earlier work, that being bright does not necessary equate with being wise. Rather, based on his balance theory of wisdom, he not only views wisdom as a continuous balancing act among individuals, groups, and societal interests "but also of three possible courses of action in response to this balancing: adaptation of oneself and others to existing environments; shaping of environments to render them more compatible with oneself or others; and selection of new environments" (pp. 346–347). What is critical is taking action, as echoed earlier by Sternberg (2003b) and will be seen later in this chapter in the work of Bassett (2005) and Thorpe (2005)—in "wisdom, one seeks a common good, realizing this common good may be better for some than for others"(Sternberg, 2005a, p. 345).

Bassett (2005) also has developed a model of wisdom. This model, the Emergent Wisdom model, is based on in-depth interviews with twenty-four adults whom she describes as "thoughtful, insightful people of public distinction from many walks of life" (p. 6). Using a grounded theory approach, the model that emerged from these interviews comprises four major components: discerning, respecting, engaging, and transforming. *Discerning* includes the cognitive functions of wisdom, meaning that wise people have "the ability to distinguish often quite subtle variations in different qualities and characteristics of others" (p. 7). Or as one of her respondents observed: "Wise people are able to look at the 'underlying forces and not be distracted by surface symptoms'" (p. 7). *Respecting* is an affective function that allows adults to express "a kind of caring for the other, even another we might not agree with, feel empathy for, or 'love.' Respect manifests gratitude and an expanded sphere of consideration" (p. 9) for both other people and the many interconnected parts of the environments where we live. *Engaging* means that we push ourselves to action, do things we never thought we could do and in some cases are afraid of doing. Engagement displays itself "in the wider world as committed action for the common good, what is good for many of us, not just me and the people like me" (p. 9). *Transforming* is a reflective process that allows us to think more deeply about "the fundamental patterns and relationships, expanded spheres of consideration, and actions" (p. 10) that are often associated with the common good. This domain allows us to live with ourselves, even with the "many possible, plausible, and competing worldviews and epistemologies" we are confronted with as we move through life. In essence, "the self becomes understood not as a *unit* seeking stability, but rather as a *process* where the sub-parts constantly shift, adjust, and change" (p. 11; italics in original). In addition, included in the model for each dimension are "proficiencies (skilled behaviors), a main manifestation and several learning prompts or developmental stimuli whose practice can lead to wisdom" (p. 7).

Bassett (2005) views this model or "map of wisdom" not as a single path to follow but as a "spiral, circling ever wider and deeper" (p. 10). Therefore, we can keep moving forward, survive, and perhaps even thrive again, through even the most perplexing and painful situations, like the loss of a child, or being left with nothing from nature's wrath of earthquakes, tsunamis, and hurricanes. Do these types of challenges we all face as adults leave us wiser? Not necessarily so. However, by embracing the Emergent Wisdom model, we may find a deeper acceptance of paradox and recognition of the interdependence of all living systems—"in short, the whole mystery of the world and of wisdom" (p. 11).

Thorpe (2005), in her essay on wisdom, asks different kinds of questions: "Does wisdom ever appear in the same place as violence and madness? What if madness came to town—and we had to deal with it?" (p. 34). Could we—or would we, especially those of us who are warm, well-fed, and relaxed—"have good sense, unusual discernment and judgment, in the face of firsthand violence or would we too be swept away in the hysteria?" (p. 34). Often we look for answers to these questions from great men and women throughout the ages, but she asks if the response to these questions really comes more from ordinary people, without aspiration, who find themselves in extraordinary situations. To answer these questions she followed the stories of three ordinary men who lived during the 1800s who found themselves embroiled in extraordinary times. What she discovered in their stories were numerous themes about wisdom that were a part of each of their stories. A sampling of these themes contains ideas that are both similar and different to what we have discussed previously in our discussion of wisdom.

- *Wisdom is not the same thing as peace, serenity, or personal insight.* When madness is flying all about, no one is peaceful, serene, nor afforded the luxury of inner contemplation. . . .
- *Wisdom is neither moderation nor relativism.* It is not about giving equal weight to all perspectives, nor about compromise.

[Rather,] it is seeing beyond the immediate positions and knowing what is beyond them that is more fundamental—and more permanent. . . .

- *Wisdom cannot be identified through benchmarks of time and place.* The standards of time and place do not predict or denote wisdom. However, the little streams of wisdom that people leave in other times and places grow into rivers that change the benchmark over time towards systems that work better. [Thorpe, 2005, pp. 41–42; italics in original]

Thorpe concludes "that wisdom appears when we most need it" (p. 43). If wisdom could not appear in times of war, madness, and polarization, those "tiny rivulets of sanity" that save us and society from exploding into oblivion would not be forthcoming.

Despite the different perspectives from which wisdom has been studied and the lack of consensus on its precise dimensions, several points of agreement have emerged. Wisdom is grounded in life's rich experiences and therefore can be developed throughout our adult lives. Although book learning may be a part of developing wisdom, it is not a requirement. Rather, being able to respond well to the pragmatics of life seems to form the core of being wise. Moreover, wisdom seems to consist of the ability to move away from absolute truths, to be reflective, and to make sound judgments for the common good related to our daily existence, whatever our circumstances.

Recently, Sternberg (2005b) published a comprehensive review of the literature on the relationship between wisdom and age. He presents a number of conclusions with respect to this question. First, there is no single position on the relationship between age and wisdom—studies have reported it decreasing with age, increasing with age, and remaining stable with age. He also concludes that "there are almost certainly widespread individual differences in the trajectory of wisdom"; wisdom appears to lie "in situational rather than personal variables" and research results depend on how wisdom is defined and measured (p. 20). Finally, he concludes that while research suggests that people have the ability to become more wise, "whether wisdom actually will develop depends not so much on age as upon cognitive variables, personality variables, and life experiences" (p. 21).

In reflecting on this study of wisdom and how it might enrich learning in adulthood, we are struck by observations made by Dychtwald and Flower (1989) about "the third age"—that part of life beyond age sixty, a time of life that more and more people are experiencing as healthy and vital individuals. Dychtwald and Flower contend that this third age allows for the "further development of the interior life of the intellect, memory, and imagination, of emotional maturity, and of one's personal sense of spiritual identity" (p. 53). It is a time for people to give back to society through their wisdom, power, and spirituality "the lessons, resources, and experiences accumulated over a lifetime" (p. 53). They then quote Monsignor Fahey, the director of Fordham University's Third Age Center: "People in the third age should be the glue of society, not its ashes" (p. 53). Their conclusion is clear and dramatic: "Think about it. We know even with the best care overall fitness will decline gradually over the years. While the strength of the senses is weakening, what if the powers of the mind, heart, and the spirit are rising? If life offers the ongoing opportunity for increased awareness and personal growth, think how far we could evolve, given the advantage of extra decades of life!" (p. 52). Their observations of using our later years to further develop our cognitive thinking abilities are similar to Kegan's (1994), discussed earlier. In incorporating the concept of wisdom in our thinking about cognitive development, mature adult cognition is more than just abstract logic, complex reasoning, and dialectical thinking; it also encompasses the ability to think, feel, and act "wisely" in life.

Summary

Cognitive development refers to the change in thinking patterns that occurs as one grows older. Much of the earlier work on cognitive development in adulthood has been grounded primarily in the work of Piaget. One line of research has focused on how Piaget's stages play out in adulthood. A more fruitful research tradition, grounded in Piaget's work, has been the conceptualization of adult stages of cognition beyond that of formal operations, such as the work of Arlin (1975). Other researchers have posited entirely new schemes of adult cognitive development. These alternative theories range from the traditional stage theories of development, such as the work of Perry (1970, 1999) and King and Kitchener (1994, 2004), to those theories that bring in new voices (Belenky, Clinchy, Goldberger, & Tarule, 1986; Goldberger, Tarule, Clinchy, & Belenky, 1996) and different ways of framing development, represented by Baxter Magolda (1992, 2004) and Labouvie-Vief (1980, 1990; Labouvie-Vief & Diehl, 2000).

In the review of the many theories of adult cognitive development, two major themes became apparent: dialectical thinking is important and contextual factors are critical in determining how we develop our thinking patterns as adults. Dialectical thinking, as represented by the work of Riegel (1973) and Kegan (1994), allows for the acceptance of alternative truths or ways of thinking about the many contradictions and paradoxes that we face in everyday life. To be able to engage in dialectical thinking is viewed by some as the only way to navigate our postmodern world successfully. Bringing in the contextual perspective on adult cognitive development acknowledges that the world around the thinker makes a difference in how adults develop their thinking patterns. Social, cultural, economic, and political forces help shape both how we think and what kind of knowledge we value.

The chapter concluded with a discussion of wisdom, often regarded as the hallmark of mature adult thinking. Although it has been discussed over the ages by the great philosophers and theologians, this area of study has received little attention in the literature on cognitive development and learning in general. Representative conceptions of wisdom, including those of Holliday and Chandler (1986), Sternberg (1996b, 2003b, 2005a), and Bassett (2005), were reviewed. Despite the different perspectives from which wisdom is viewed, scholars seem to agree that wisdom involves special types of experience-based knowledge and is characterized by the ability to move away from absolute truth, to be reflective, to take action for the common good, and to make sound judgments related to everyday life.

Chapter Fourteen

Intelligence and Aging

One of the authors of this book vividly remembers her mother coming home after a trip into town, "just fit to be tied." She was thoroughly disgusted with how she had been treated by a bank employee. The employee had insinuated that as a "little old lady" there was no way she could understand her different account options. As this mother reflected on her experience, still in an angry mood, she said, "I may be old and little, but I have not lost my mind and neither am I stupid." This powerful myth—that adults lose their intellectual ability as they age—still prevails, even in the literature on intelligence and aging. However, over the past twenty-five years other scholars have put to rest that myth, backed up with a strong knowledge base that substantiates that for most adults intellectual functioning is alive and well throughout most of their lifetimes.

Intelligence is defined in a number of ways. From the perspective of the casual observer, intelligence is often equated with "being smart"—that is, being able to act intelligently when dealing with everyday life. But there is another definition of intelligence that many adults have carried with them since their elementary school days: intelligence is a specific measurement of their ability to learn. While not actually knowing their IQ scores, many adults have vague recollections of being labeled an "average," "above-average," or "below-average" student. Worse still are the memories of using IQ tests to be placed in a "slow" reading or math group, while watching a best friend be put in the "high" group. Although the concept of intelligence affects the lives of many adults, both through earlier and current experiences, what intrigues us is that educators of adults have given little attention to the study of intelligence in adulthood.

In this chapter, we first discuss the more traditional approaches to and theories of intelligence, focusing on those traditions that continue to have a very strong influence on intelligence in adulthood. We then argue that these traditional approaches continue to be foundational in how scholars both study and interpret the effect of aging on intelligence. Next, we explore the more recent challenges raised by scholars to these traditional approaches. In this section we examine key theoretical and empirical work that has promise for expanding how adult intelligence is conceptualized and in the future could have a significant effect on our basic understanding of aging and intelligence. The chapter concludes with a discussion of three ideas about intellectual functioning in adulthood that are particularly intriguing and useful for educators of adults.

TRADITIONAL APPROACHES TO INTELLIGENCE

There are two reasons why it is important to understand what are often termed "the traditional approaches" to intelligence. The first is that the different lenses these researchers use "come not only from ideological biases affecting what is said, but also from what defines the concept of intelligence" (Sternberg, Lautrey, & Lubart, 2003, p. 3). And second, many of the ideas from these traditions still dominate the thinking and practice related to how intelligence is viewed, and hence, often unbeknownst to us, frame our practice as educators of adults.

Three areas within the more traditional approaches have been foundational in our thinking about adult intelligence: the biological approach, the individual differences approach, and the cognitive processes approach. Described more in depth in the next two subsections are the first two approaches. The third tradition, the cognitive processes approach, exemplified by the work of Piaget and Vygotsky, arises "from the construction of cognitive structures that materialize as a function of the interaction of the organism with the environment" (Sternberg, Lautrey, & Lubart, 2003, p. 3). While Piaget's (1952) work called our attention primarily to our biological maturation, Vygotsky (1978) was most interested in how the social environment around us influenced our intellectual development.

Although both of these authors and their colleagues are often quoted in the literature on adulthood, very little empirical work with adults has been completed from this tradition (see Chapter Thirteen).

THE BIOLOGICAL APPROACH

Although the biological approach to intelligence is not often discussed by educators of adults, "nearly everyone believes that intelligence resides in the brain, and is virtually synonymous with brain power" (Richardson, 1999, p. 180). If we can only discover where in the human brain "intelligence resides" and how it fits into the way the brain operates, we will have the key to exactly what intelligence is. Tracing this rationale further, with this knowledge at some point the brain could be manipulated so that all humans could both become smarter and stay that way throughout their lives. Unfortunately, the knowledge we have gained about "the smart brain" has little practical application and is tentative at best. Rather, what scholars over the past two or three decades "have produced is an outpouring of interesting new facts and ideas. But it has to be admitted that psychologists and neuroscientists have not yet managed to weave these into a clear, or clearly agreed theory about how the brain produces, or is otherwise involved in human intelligence" (Richardson, 1999, p. 181). This search for the biological correlates of human intelligence is still strong, but it also needs to be more theoretically driven (Haier, 2003; Vernon, Wickett, Bazana, & Stelmack, 2000).

Another avenue in the biology of intelligence couples it with the genetics of intelligence. This interest has been stimulated by those who assert that intelligence is an inheritable quality, and that people are born highly intelligent, "just so-so," or way below the mean for functioning normally in society. There is no agreement in the current literature on the influence that genetic factors have on intelligence. Rather, there is a very wide spread of variations, with estimates ranging from 20 to 80 percent (Bronfenbrenner, 2005). Even among researchers who argue that "genes play a sizeable part in influencing differences in mental ability between people" (Deary, 2001, p. 88), there is scant knowledge about what these genes are. However, with the ever-widening interdisciplinary approach to the study of human genetics, there are those who predict that we will discover, at some point in the future, the genetic composition of intelligence (Grigorenko, 2000). If indeed these specific genetic markers are able to pinpoint intelligence, there will be a need to carefully consider both the practical and ethical issues that would be involved with such a discovery.

THE INDIVIDUAL DIFFERENCES APPROACH

The individual differences approach has and continues to have an enormous impact on the study of adult intelligence. In many ways this tradition has served the field well. First, scholars from this approach have provided a systematic means for studying individual differences. Second, "the theories embedded within this tradition have proved to have many and diverse applications. [In addition] they have provided a model for how theory and measurement can evolve in synchrony" (Sternberg, Lautrey, & Lubart, 2003, p. 2).

Grounded in the psychometric tradition, viewing the concept of intelligence from this approach assumes that intelligence is a measurable construct. Although testing for individual differences in intelligence is most often done with children and adolescents, this form of testing still has a significant influence on how adults continue to be sorted, left out, or included in educational, work, and even living situations. Using the psychometric approach there are two primary ways that individual differences in intelligence are conceptualized: general intelligence (or the "g" factor) and multiple factors (Embretson & Schmidt McCollam, 2000).

Jensen (2002) observes that in "the state of the art in the field of psychology, a clear conclusion is warranted: That is, a century of research on intelligence suggests there are abilities and processes in intellectual functioning that are truly general, very strong in their affect and always present" (p. 5). Numerous scholars agree with Jensen's view that the g factor is alive, well, and thriving, and tests that measure this factor are used in numerous settings with adults (Deary, 2001; Sternberg & Grigorenko, 2002). The central tenant of theory building and research related to the g factor is that a person's performance on one or more scales can be explained as a single underlying ability (Sternberg & Grigorenko, 2002). Therefore, scores from diverse tests or subscales can be combined to form a general intelligence quotient, commonly known as the g factor.

Spearman (1904, 1927) and Binet (1916) are representative of the early researchers who sought to understand the nature of intelligence as a single well-defined construct. The first massive use of intelligence testing with adults using the g factor as the norm was with men entering the army in World War I. As large numbers of recruits needed to be tested quickly, two IQ tests were developed (Kaufman, 2000). The practical consequences of the development of these tests were many. For example, "IQ tests [using the g factor] were found to be useful for adults, not just children; were perceived to be valuable for high functioning people, not just the lower extreme," and the data analysis from huge samples (almost two million) led to intense controversies, from "cries of racism and inferiority, to debates about the value of IQ tests and their social implications" (Kaufman, 2000, p. 446). Examples of often-quoted current scholars who study the g factor are Carroll (1993), Jenson (2002), Humphreys and Stark (2002), and Petrill (2002, 2003).

The more prevalent use of IQ tests with adults to measure individual differences is with those that include multiple factors of intelligence, such as spatial ability, perceptual speed, numerical ability, verbal relations, words, memory, and induction. Of the earlier theorists who advocated this point of view, Horn and Cattell (1966, 1967) have had the widest influence on conceptualizing intelligence as multiple factors. In addition, their work has been foundational to the study of intelligence in adulthood. The Horn-Cattell theory viewed intelligence as consisting of two broad areas: *fluid intelligence* (Gf) and *crystallized intelligence* (Gc). The fluid arena captured those tasks that "demanded new problem solving with minimal dependency on school learning or acculturation" (Kaufman, 2000, p. 460), and was therefore viewed as more innate and dependent on a neurophysiological base. In contrast, the crystallized domain was viewed as education dependant and more associated with accumulated information.

Horn (1985, 1989) expanded this Gf-Gc theory by shifting his focus to a group of eight to ten abilities, with the measure of each being "purer" and with no overlap between the factors. "From current Horn theory, tasks are only categorized as Gf if they emphasize reasoning ability and as Gc if they stress comprehension and knowledge base" (Kaufman, 2000, p. 460). In addition, Horn (1985, p. 289) changed one of the basic assumptions of this theory, which is that "there are good reasons to believe that Gf is learned as much as Gc, and that Gc is inherited as much as Gf." Instead, he believes that both types of intelligence can be nurtured, at least until very old age. This assertion has led researchers to study whether fluid intelligence, which was thought to be primarily innate, can be either restored (if loss has been shown) or strengthened as people age (Lohman & Scheurman, 1992; Schaie & Willis, 1986; Willis & Schaie, 1994). Schaie (1996b) has provided a clear and cogent summary of this work.

Psychometric tests using the multiple factors methods are most often used with adults in assessing people in the workplace for job placement, in clinical settings for appropriate treatment plans, and in the military, where a certain score is required for entry. In addition, these types of intelligence tests have been used in research to determine how intellectual abilities change as people age. The three tests that measure multiple factors of intelligence most often used in both research and practice with adults are the Kaufman Adolescent and Adult Intelligence Test (KAIT; Kaufman & Kaufman, 1993), the Wechsler Adult Intelligence Scale, which is now in its third edition (the WAIS-III), and the Primary Mental Abilities (PMA) test, the most recent version being the Schaie-Thurston Adult Mental Abilities Test (STAMAT; Schaie, 1979, 1985). Each of these tests appears to primarily assess mental abilities, such as verbal and reasoning ability, related more to formal schooling than everyday intelligence (Deary, 2001; Sternberg et al., 2000). In a challenge to this idea, Schaie and others (Schaie, 1996b; Willis & Schaie, 1986) found that, at least in later adulthood, certain primary mental abilities do predict competent behavior in specific situations—for example, "competence in active situations was predicted by spatial ability and inductive reasoning, and competence in passive situations was predicted by verbal abilities" (Schaie & Willis, 1986, p. 290). Therefore, to these researchers, the findings suggest "a strong relationship between the 'building blocks' of intelligence and abilities on real life tasks" (p. 290).

Two of these intelligence tests, the Kaufman Adolescent and Adult Intelligence Test (Kaufman & Kaufman, 1993) and the Wechsler Adult Intelligence Scale-Third Edition (Wechsler, 1997), are examples of measures that have been primarily constructed using the work of Horn and Cattell. Within the KAIT framework (Kaufman & Kaufman, 1993), fluid intelligence "measures a person's adaptability and flexibility when faced with new problems." Crystallized intelligence evaluates "the acquisition of facts and problem-solving ability using stimuli that are dependent on formal schooling, cultural experiences, and verbal conceptual development" (Kaufman & Kaufman, 1993, p. 7).

The WAIS-III is designed for adults ages sixteen to eighty-nine. The WAIS-III, like its predecessors (the WAIS-R and the WAIS), consists of six regular verbal subtests and five mandatory performance tasks. Several of the WAIS-III subtests are often grouped together for measuring Horn's expanded concepts of fluid and crystallized intelligence. Like the KAIT, the WAIS-III also may present problems in the testing of the elderly, and more specifically those seventy-five and above. However, "The WAIS-III is likely to follow in the footsteps of the WAIS-R, which has proven itself as a leader in the field of adult assessment" (Kaufman, 2000, p. 459).

The third test of adult intelligence, the Primary Mental Abilities test, is often associated with the work of Schaie and colleagues on intelligence and aging (Schaie, 1979, 1985, 1996a). The underlying assumption of the PMA test, originally developed by Thurstone and Thurstone (1941), is that intelligence is actually several distinct abilities. Purported to measure five relatively independent factors, the PMA test battery consists of five subtests: (1) verbal meaning, which is the ability to understand ideas expressed in words; (2) space, describing the ability to think about an object in two or three dimensions; (3) reasoning, involving the ability to solve logical problems; (4) number, the ability to handle arithmetic problems; and (5) word fluency, concerning the speed and ease with which words are used.

As we demonstrate in the next section, the individual differences approaches to intellectual development continues to dominate how scholars have argued whether adults lose or perhaps even gain in intellectual abilities as we age. Central to this discussion of linking age and intelligence is whether adults, and especially older adults, will be as intellectually capable in their sixties and seventies as they were in their twenties and thirties.

AGE AND INTELLECTUAL ABILITIES

"The study of the depth and breadth of interest in intellectual changes during adulthood has increased dramatically in recent decades" (Dixon, 2003, p. 152). The fundamental question that researchers have struggled with over the years is: Does intelligence decline with age? In their pioneering work in this arena, Thorndike, Bregman, Tilton, and Woodyard (1928) were among the first scholars who challenged the fundamental notion that learning ability peaks very early in life. Using primarily laboratory or schoolroom tasks, Thorndike measured the speed of the performance of people from ages fourteen to fifty on a variety of tasks, from memorizing poetry to acquiring an artificial language (Kidd, 1973). Thorndike et al. (1928, pp. 178–179) concluded from their many studies that "in general, teachers of adults of age twenty-five to forty-five should expect them to learn at nearly the same rate and in nearly the same manner as they would have learned the same thing at twenty." In reflecting on Thorndike's work, Kidd (1973) noted two major contributions. The first was to raise the age of onset of the downhill slide of a person's ability to learn from twenty years of age to forty-five; second, and even more important, Thorndike "helped to stimulate colleagues to reject traditional views and formulas" (p. 79) about learning in adulthood.

Naturally, this question related to whether intelligence declines with age is of no small interest to current scholars and also to many adults who wonder if in fact they will become less "with it" as they age. Responses to this question are mixed and often have been controversial. They range from the contention that intelligence definitely enters a process of irreversible decline as we age (though that age does differ from scholar to scholar) to those who argue that intelligence is relatively stable through the adult years, with substantial changes occurring very late in life. Underlying these highly diverse responses are issues of *universality, directionality,* and *reversibility* in intellectual functions over the life span. Do changes in intelligence "occur generally or differently in normal aging adults?" (Dixon, 2003, p. 153). Are these changes progressive or regressive in nature? And what is the potential for adults to alter or compensate for any of these changes? One way to respond to these underlying questions is through understanding how scholars who study intelligence and aging define the concept of intelligence, delineate the parameters of aging, and select the designs and measures they use in this research.

Concept of Intelligence

In looking at the concept of intelligence we can see how the different ways this construct is defined provide different responses to the questions of directionality and reversibility of intelligence. As noted earlier, although there is no universal agreement as to what constitutes intelligence, the study of intelligence and aging is deeply rooted in the individual differences approach. Because this approach assumes that intelligence is a measurable construct, when we speak of intelligence and aging our observations come primarily from a comparison of test scores. These tests are designed to investigate a specific theory or theories and factors thought to be the major components that constitute intelligence. For example, the PMA test defines intelligence as five relatively distinct measures of psychological competence, versus a single general intelligence factor.

From Schaie's perspective, when intelligence is defined as a unitary property, the research tends to confirm that intelligence does indeed decline with age, although again the point of departure for that decline often varies (Schaie & Willis, 1986). Yet when intelligence is viewed as consisting of multiple factors, the response tends to be that some of our abilities decline, while others remain stable or even increase (Baltes, 1993; Berg, 2000; Dixon, 2003; Schaie, 1996b).

Other authors, including Baltes and Schaie, have added important properties to their definitions of intelligence. Two of those properties—plasticity and compensation processes—are key in addressing the issue of whether adults can in some way change the course of their intellectual development. Again, these added properties need to be placed in the context of the data sources used, which are primarily empirical studies based on traditional intelligence tests.

Plasticity refers to the ability for people to change and yet also maintain a certain durability as they age. Research on "the plasticity of intelligence has focused on the modifiability of intelligence through intervention" (Berg, 2000, p. 122). Dixon (2003) asserts in his review of literature related to intervention research that "it is possible to train normal older adults to perform better on challenging cognitive tasks" (p. 156). He contends that researchers have demonstrated that older adults can improve their performance on intelligence tests through self-directed practice and formal training on higher-level tasks. In addition, those adults who have received this formal training can also perform more effectively on some cognitive tasks in everyday life. Based on these studies, Dixon goes on to observe: "Theoretically this implies that some degree of normally observed decline in intellectual aging may be the result of disuse and that potential for improvement may be present in older adults" (p. 157).

Compensation is among the most promising expansions to the nature of intelligence. Embedded in the individual differences and in the information processing approaches to intelligence, *compensation* refers to ways that adults adapt to losses in cognitive processes that may affect their intelligence as they age, and can take many forms. For example, adults can invest more time and effort in a task, learn new ways to perform the same task, and adjust their goals and criteria for success to accommodate any losses or deficits. For example, one of the authors has a ninety-one-year-old friend who has chosen to live in her own apartment rather than in another, alternative living arrangement available to her in the complex where she lives. Due to severe arthritis this woman can no longer use her hands to complete many household tasks, so, instead, she has learned to do these tasks, like making a bed, with her feet. She has also chosen to play bridge every day versus only twice a week so she does not lose her competitive edge, and she makes sure she takes a cocktail before dinner in a common lounge with other residents to maintain her contact with those who live in the same area. "Compensation may occur automatically at the level of the brain or may be trained deliberately in impaired individuals" (Dixon, 2003, p. 157).

PARAMETERS OF AGING

The question of directionality—that is, whether we gain or lose our intellectual abilities as we age—is also addressed when we discuss how scholars define the parameters of aging. Whether or not one believes intelligence declines with age depends on the ages of the adults included in the study. Are we talking about adults in early, middle, or later adulthood? In reviewing data on early and middle adulthood, our response would be that intelligence does not decline with age. In fact, some intellectual functions, no matter what testing procedures are employed, seem to increase over the course of the years. Our response to whether intelligence declines in later adulthood is not as clear-cut (Baltes, 1993; Schaie, 1996a, 2005). Most agree that some decline in functioning occurs between age sixty and the early seventies, but the precise nature of that decline, and more important, its practical effect on learning ability are still in question.

In line with this observation, although there have been numerous studies of older adults (Schaie & Hofer, 2001), only a few have addressed the intellectual abilities of healthy adults after age 70. In one longitudinal comparison of subjects ranging in age from 73 to 99, researchers found that although many of the subjects showed some decline in abilities, more than half displayed no such changes, even at the older ages (Field, Schaie, & Leino, 1988). In a more recent study of eighteen people between the ages of 100 and 106, these "centenarians reported rich late-life learning experiences, the majority of [which] occurred through social interactions" (Fenimore, 1997, p. 57).

Research Designs and Measures

The questions that surround the issues of directionality and universality are important issues raised by those who discuss how research designs and measures affect our thinking about intelligence and aging. The research designs employed in investigations of changes in intelligence over the life span also are a major point of discussion in the literature. Results from the two most often used designs, cross-sectional and longitudinal, usually provide very different findings. Data from cross-sectional studies, which compare onetime test scores of different age groups (for example, twenty-year-olds and sixty-year-olds) predominately show that as we age our intelligence declines (Schaie, 1994, 1996a; Schaie & Hofer, 2001). Findings from longitudinal studies, however, usually support a very different conclusion. Based primarily on readministration of intelligence tests over time and to the same group of people, various longitudinal investigations demonstrate that intellectual abilities of groups of older people are remarkably stable over time (Rabbitt, Donlan, Brent, McInnes, & Abson, 1993; Schaie, 1996b, 2005).

Cross-sectional designs only allow inferences about differences of intellectual abilities for specified age groups, such as adults in their twenties and those in their sixties. In addition, even in the claims that are made based on these data there are numerous limitations inherent to this design. For example, cohort differences, such as level of formal education and health status, may cloud results. In addition, "as the 20th century progressed, the whole population's scores on some well-known mental tests were improving when compared with same-age people generations earlier" (Deary, 2001, p. 104), which further confounds these cross-sectional comparisons between the young and the old.

In contrast, longitudinal studies permit scholars to draw a broader picture of intellectual development through the adult life span. By providing information on both cohort-age-specific and individual differences in adults as they age, they allow researchers to explore more complex issues and questions. For example, researchers are able to address whether there are individual differences or similarities in intellectual abilities as adults age. They also are able to investigate how other factors, such as health, social interactions, and psychological attributes, may contribute to the continued stability or decline in intellectual functioning. As with cross-sectional designs, longitudinal studies also have built-in limitations, such as selective attrition and dropout, and retaking the same or similar performance tests over time. In addition, "effects thought to be age-dependent must be carefully disaggregated from those due to historical limited events and environmental impacts" (Schaie & Hofer, 2001, p. 56).

In response to the limitations and problems associated with both cross-sectional and longitudinal designs, researchers have adopted alternative designs to control for some of the biases inherent when only a cross-sectional or longitudinal design is used. Schaie and his associates, as part of the Seattle Longitudinal Study, provide the best example of the work using one of these alternative designs (Schaie, 1994, 1996b, 2005; Schaie, Willis, & O'Hanlon, 1994). The primary variables for this study were the five factors that represent the primary mental abilities of adults. The data for the study were collected from more than five thousand subjects over a thirty-five-year period in six testing cycles. With six cross-sectional studies, in addition to longitudinal data, the researchers were able to do a number of different forms of analysis. In essence, the cross-sectional data showed a typical pattern of intellectual decline, while the longitudinal data suggested little if any decline of any practical consequence until after the mid- to late sixties. Even "this decrement is modest until the 80s are reached, and for most individuals it is not a linear phenomenon but occurs in stair-step fashion" (Schaie, 1994, p. 308). Schaie and others attributed the differences in findings between the two research designs to cohort variation—differences between the generations versus differences in the ages of subjects. These cohort variations are, in turn, attributed to higher educational levels of succeeding generations and overall better nutrition and health care.

In addition to providing answers to the question of directionality, the findings from the Seattle Longitudinal Study and studies of like nature (Schaie & Hofer, 2001) also offer helpful insights into whether these changes in intelligence as we age are universal or occur differently in normal aging, and are progressive or regressive in nature. Schaie and his associates, for example, "emphasized that considerable individual differences exist in both degrees of intellectual decline and the age of onset" (Dixon, 2003, p. 153). Seven variables were identified that reduce the risk of cognitive decline in old age: absence of cardiovascular and other chronic diseases, living in favorable environmental circumstances, substantial involvement in activities, maintenance of high levels of perceptual processing speed into old age, being married to a spouse of high cognitive status, and rating one's self as satisfied with one's life. We would conjecture that health, economic means, and feeling good about life are central to continued intellectual vitality and that the other variables might just be a plus, or perhaps go with having economic means.

In exploring the other side of the question—which factors predict earlier-than-average decline—four were identified: significant decrease in being flexible in one's approach to life, low educational attainment, being male, and a low satisfaction with life success (Schaie, 1994). Except for gender, of course, some of these variables may be amenable to change using the typical interventions recommended to offset and even possibly restore decreases in intellectual capabilities (Dixon, 2003). They may also suggest different kinds of interventions, like personal counseling and enrolling in formal educational programs.

Most research on the effects of intelligence and aging has been conducted using either the Weschler scales (WAIS-III or the earlier WAIS-R) or a form of the PMA test. One big question, still strongly debated today, is whether either of these two measures, and others of this nature, capture more than the academic or "mental abilities" versus intelligence in everyday life. Sternberg and associates (Sternberg, 2000b; Sternberg et al., 2000) would respond with a resounding *no*, although Sternberg does see the value of tests of this nature used in concert with measures of practical intelligence. Scholars like Gardner (1999b, 2003) and Tennant and Pogson (1995) would argue that these tests do not capture the more complex nature of intelligence.

A second question raised on both of these tests, and others like them, has been their inclusion of timed items. All of the PMA subtests, and about half of the subtests in the WAIS-III are timed. Are timed tests, particularly ones involving perceptual motor functions, valid measures of adult intelligence, especially for older adults? Some scholars strongly argue that speeded tests should be eliminated in assessing adult intelligence, whereas others make compelling augments that timed items should be included, because mental speed is a critical component of intellectual functioning (Deary, 2001).

In summary, our answer to the fundamental question "Does intelligence decline with age?" leads us back to our discussions of the concept of intelligence, age parameters, and research designs and measures. With these factors in mind, our response to this question is that intelligence may decline, remain relatively stable until late adulthood, or even be enhanced as we age. One school of thought contends that intellectual functioning is a process of irreversible decline in the adult years, although the hypothesized onset and the extent of that decline are still unknown. The majority of those who argue this position are relying on data from cross-sectional studies or are firmly entrenched in the belief that intelligence is an inheritable trait.

Others say that intelligence is relatively stable through the adult years, with substantial intellectual changes occurring only very late in life, and then primarily "in abilities that were less central to the individual's life experience and thus perhaps less practiced"

(Schaie, 1996b, p. 2). In essence, we have enough brain capacity to do almost anything we choose, until serious illness or when we are in highly challenging, complex, or stressful situations. Still others argue that intelligence declines in some respects, remains stable in others, and may even increase in some functions, depending on a person's educational level, life experiences, overall health, and outlook on life (Dixon, 2003; Kaufman, Kaufman, Chen, & Kaufman, 1996; Raykov, 1995). Those who assert the latter two points of view primarily point to longitudinal or mixed-design studies on aging and intelligence and define intelligence as multifaceted.

As will be discussed in the next section, it is hoped that more recent and future research on different approaches to adult intelligence will provide further insight into whether the individual differences approach can continue to be used as the best predictor of how intelligence changes with age. Or, might these alternative ways of thinking about adult intelligence possibly provide a clearer and perhaps even a more complex picture of the effects of aging on intellectual functioning?

CHALLENGES TO THE MORE TRADITIONAL CONCEPTS OF INTELLIGENCE

Major challenges about the nature of intelligence have been made by a number of scholars in the past twenty years. These critiques have come from numerous sources, but they center on three main issues. The first is the major focus on the individual, and more specifically, differences between individuals as measured by psychometric tests. Second, there is, in the words of Sternberg, Lautrey, and Lubart (2003), "a fighting for the 'truth' . . . with the underlying notion . . . that only one model or theory could be correct" (p. 11). Third, the majority of these traditional ways of thinking about intelligence in adulthood do not take into account "real-world" or "everyday" intelligence. Theorists who advocate that the basic nature of intelligence has to be reframed most often view intelligence as a combination of biological, psychological, social, cultural, life experiences, and environmental factors. Rather than focusing on just one or two of these frames, scholars from this tradition argue that intelligence consists of multiple domains and most often is conceived as an interaction among three or more of them.

Tennant and Pogson (1995) have provided a thoughtful treatise on why these challenges to intelligence have been overlooked for so long, especially by scholars representing Western culture. They assert that "historically, Western culture has taken a lower view of manual work than of cognitive activity" (p. 37), which has led to "the exaltation of the theoretical or contemplative over the practical" (p. 39). More specifically, they cite the attributes of verbal, abstract, and complex thinking as far more valued than either those of concrete and sensual thought or the active use of knowledge.

In discussing these alternative ways of defining the nature of intelligence, we focus on Gardner's theory of multiple intelligences (the MI theory); practical intelligence, illustrated by the work of Sternberg and his colleagues; and emotional intelligence. We also explore the way culture affects how intelligence is viewed. We chose these specific theories and studies to illustrate these alternative stances because educators of adults have gravitated to these viewpoints of intelligence, considering them more applicable to adult learners.

GARDNER'S THEORY OF MULTIPLE INTELLIGENCES

Gardner is representative of theorists who broke away from the psychometric tradition of intelligence during the early 1980s. From Gardner's perspective, the concept of intelligence has been too narrowly limited to the realm of logical and linguistic abilities, primarily by the way intelligence has been measured. He argues that "there is persuasive evidence for the existence of several relatively autonomous human intellectual competencies that can be fashioned and combined in a multiplicity of adaptive ways by individuals and cultures" (Gardner, 1993, pp. 8–9). From a number of unrelated sources, such as studies of prodigies, brain-damaged patients, and normal children and adults, Gardner originally identified seven different forms of intelligence, with an eighth added in the mid-1990s. The original seven forms of intelligence include "not only the standard academic ones of linguistic, logical-mathematical, and spacial (the visual skills exhibited by a painters or architect) but also musical, "bodily-kinesthetic," and two "personal" intelligences involving a fine-tuned understanding of oneself and others" (Levine, 1987, p. 54). Gardner's eighth form of intelligence, naturalist intelligence, takes us to a different realm. The intelligence of naturalists is in recognizing and categorizing natural objects and patterns in their environment. This type of intelligence is exemplified in the work of formal scientists, such as biologists and environmentalists, but also people who are highly skilled in applying "folk taxonomies," such as natural healers, and other abilities, like farming and hunting (see Gardner, 1983, 1993, 1999b, for a complete description of his eight intelligences). Gardner has also discussed another possible form of intelligence—"existential intelligence." Adults who exhibit existential intelligence capture and ponder "the fundamental questions of existence": spiritual leaders and philosophical thinkers are among such people (Gardner, 1999a, p. 22). Gardner has not yet added this form of intelligence to his current eight due to its perplexing nature and its distance from the other intelligences. "At the most, I am willing, Fellini-style, to joke about '8 and 1/2 intelligences'" (Gardner, 1999b, p. 66).

In introducing the theory of multiple intelligences, Gardner (1993) emphasized that the idea has a rich history, recognized even in early Greek times. He makes only two strong claims about the theory. The first is that all humans possess all of these intelligences: indeed, they can collectively be considered a definition of Homo sapiens, cognitively speaking. The second claim is that just as we all look different and have unique personalities and differences, we also have different patterns of intelligence (Gardner, 1999a). Therefore, in Gardner's framework, our tendency to label people as being generally bright, average, or dull just does not fit. Rather, a person may exhibit high intelligence in one or more areas, such as music and math, and yet demonstrate only average intelligence in other respects. In other words, you can be very talented in specific areas and have some or little capacity in others. In addition, Gardner views MI theory as presenting a critique of the predominant model of "psychometrics-as-usual" in measuring intelligence. Therefore, although scholars have made some attempts to develop and use tests that measure multiple intelligences (for example, Rosnow, Skleder, Jaeger, & Rind, 1994; Shearer & Jones, 1994), Gardner (1995) himself argues that any assessments of multiple intelligences must be "'intelligent fair'; that is, in ways that examine the intelligence directly rather than through the lens of linguistic or logical intelligence (as ordinary pencil and paper tests do)" (p. 202).

When Gardner proposed his MI theory, he was interested in both promoting theory building on the nature of intelligence with his fellow psychologists and having scholars examine the educational implications of his theory. His work has stirred a great deal of theoretical debate among scholars, but what Gardner was unprepared for was the almost overwhelming positive response among educators of preschool and elementary-school-age children, which then spread even to the secondary and college levels (Gardner, 1993, 1995, 1999b; Rosnow, Skleder, Jaeger, & Rind, 1994; Shearer & Jones, 1994). For example, MI theory was almost immediately put into practice and whole curricula for school-age children have been developed using the theory. The conclusion that Gardner (1999a) himself has reached "is that the MI theory is best thought of as a tool rather than an educational goal" (p. 21).

The use of MI theory has been much more limited in applications to situations of adult life. Gardner (1999b) noted that, more recently, "a growing number of businesses have been attracted to the themes of MI: as input to the human resources department, as a means for creating or marketing products, or as training for a more effective learning environment" (p. 202). But Gardner also cautions that, although there are some applications to individuals and perhaps even to organizations, in the work world "what is important is whether people can do their jobs, not what particular intelligences they happen to be applying" (p. 198).

One example of a highly systematic use of the MI theory has been with programs of adult literacy. The Adult Multiple Intelligences (AMI) study was a project under the auspices of the National Center for the Study of Adult Learning and Literacy (NCSALL) at Harvard University (Viens & Kallenbach, 2004). In Phase 1 of the study, ten teachers of ESOL, ABE, GED, or diploma preparation programs from five New England states "took on the challenge to help their students identify and use diverse pathways to learning English, basic skills, and content utilizing the MI theory" (p. ix). One result of their work was a draft sourcebook for adult literacy teachers who wanted to learn about and use MI theory in their classrooms. In Phase 2, twelve additional adult literacy teachers from four diverse locations around the United States piloted a first draft of this sourcebook. One of the most important outcomes of that pilot study is *Multiple Intelligences and Adult Literacy: A Sourcebook for Practitioners* (Viens & Kallenbach, 2004). This sourcebook provides a very clear description of MI theory and its promises and challenges; useful resources on how to develop various learning strategies that can tap into students' strengths; and "stories" from students and teachers, some of whom found using the MI theory very helpful as part of the learning process and others who found it rather cumbersome to their central tasks.

We do see significant value in integrating Gardner's MI theory into our research and practice of learning in adulthood. But we are also well aware that there is a major need for more systematic validation studies of the basic dimensions of the MI theory, and more specifically, whether this theory is applicable to adults, and if so, for whom, where, and how. We recommend paying heed to Gardner's (1995) position that there is no "single educational approach based on the MI theory, [and] that educators are in the best position to determine the uses to which MI theory can and should be used" (p. 206).

PRACTICAL INTELLIGENCE

Sternberg and his associates have been the most active and prolific scholars responding to the challenge to reframe the concept of intelligence. Like Gardner, they too have broken from the tradition of framing intelligence as primarily a measure of what they have come to call "academic intelligence" to one that includes problem solving for everyday life. More specifically, they argue that "the problems faced in everyday life often have little relationship to the knowledge and skills acquired through formal education or the abilities used in classroom activities" (Sternberg et al., 2000, p. 32). Consider, for example, an adult who returns to school to earn his RN license. He does extremely well in his classes and clinical experiences. Yet he finds through his first job as a nurse in an acute care hospital that his overall performance is less than adequate. He has great difficulty keeping up with all the demands of the doctors and the needs of his patients, and even worse, he panics in emergency situations.

The theoretical framework used most often by Sternberg and his associates, and also by other scholars who study practical intelligence, is the triarchic theory of intelligence. According to Sternberg (1985, 1986a, 1988), the triarchic theory is composed of three subtheories: a componential subtheory, describing the internal analytical mental mechanisms and processes involved in intelligence; an experiential subtheory, focusing on how a person's experience combined with insight and creativity affects how she thinks; and a contextual subtheory, emphasizing the role of the external environment in determining what constitutes intelligent behavior in a situation. The first part of the subtheory, the mental mechanisms of intelligence, is posited as universal: "Although individuals may differ in what mental mechanisms they apply to a given task or situation, the potential set of mental mechanisms underlying intelligence is claimed to be the same across all individuals, social classes, and cultural groups" (Sternberg, 1986a, pp. 23–24). The other two parts of Sternberg's theory, which emphasize the experience of the learner and the real-world context, are seen as having both universal and relativistic components. The universal aspect has to do with areas being studied within each of these sub-parts of the theory (such as the processes of automation, environmental adaptation, and shaping). These processes are seen as important no matter what the cultural milieu or the person's experience with the tasks or situations chosen to measure these aspects. The relativistic nature of these parts of the theory comes from the recognition that what constitutes intelligent behavior is not the same for all groups of people. As Sternberg puts it, "Parts of the theory are culturally universal, and parts are culturally relative" (1986a, p. 24).

Sternberg and colleagues are still in the process of validating an empirical test of the triarchic theory of intelligence. A revised version of Sternberg's Triarchic Abilities Test (STAT) has been developed, focusing on additions to the measurements used for creative and practical intelligence. In addition to the presentation of problems through verbal, quantitative, and figural representations, they have added other types of items. For example, they are now asking participants "to write and tell stories or captions for cartoons, and [to solve] everyday problems presented in films, and by an office-based situational judgment inventory" (Sternberg, 2003a, p. 61). Studies of this revised edition are still in progress, and it is our understanding that the STAT is still not being used beyond the experimental phase of test validation (Brody, 2003; Sternberg, 2003a; Sternberg, Castejón, Prieto, Hautamäki, & Grigorenko, 2001). In addition, we could locate only one study in which adults were the audience for this continuing evaluation of the STAT (Sternberg, 2003a).

Sternberg (1997, 2003b) has expanded on the triarchic theory further through his research on "successful intelligence." His view of successful intelligence is grounded in the same basic components as those in his triarchic theory, although these underlying components are labeled a bit differently, and also, the basic meaning of those components has changed somewhat. "To be successfully intelligent is to think well in three ways: analytically, creatively, and practically" (Sternberg, 1997, pp. 126–128). Sternberg highlights that it is not enough just to have these three abilities; rather, people are successfully intelligent when they are able to choose how and when to use these abilities effectively. For example, students in graduate programs often develop research studies that meet the test of being highly analytical in nature. Nonetheless, the problems they choose to study may not be important to their fields (lack creative intelligence) or have little practical significance (something valued in educational research).

Sternberg and associates (Sternberg, 1996b, 1997; Sternberg et al., 2000; Sternberg & Horvarth, 1999; Wagner, 2000) have further delineated one of the three components that compose the theories of triarchic and successful intelligence by exploring in more depth the concept of contextual or practical intelligence. These scholars argue that tacit knowledge is a central component of practical intelligence. Tacit knowledge is defined as "knowledge that reflects the practical ability to learn from experience and to apply that knowledge in the pursuit of personally valued goals" (Sternberg et al., 2000, p. 104). In their opinion, it is this tacit knowledge that allows adults to successfully adapt to, select, or shape real-world environments.

Sternberg et al. (2000) present a clear and cogent discussion of how tacit knowledge has been measured with adults, ranging from critical incidents and simulations to the initial development and testing of tacit knowledge inventories. The research on building tacit knowledge inventories was conducted with a variety of adult populations (for example, academic psychologists, business managers, people who enroll in general leadership training programs, and military leaders). Among their findings are "that individuals who exhibit the ability to acquire and use tacit knowledge are more effective in their respective performance domains" (Sternberg et al., 2000, p. 223). In addition, "although the acquisition of tacit knowledge appears to be influenced, to some extent, by 'g' and by the amount of experience, tacit knowledge inventories are not simply new measures of these constructs" (p. 223). Overall, Sternberg et al. conclude that "tacit knowledge appears to reflect a single underlying ability, which [they] label practical intelligence" (p. 223). Sternberg et al. do caution that although there is excitement about the promise of this new generation of measures of practical intelligence, they "are the first to admit that existing evidence for the new measures does not yet match that available for traditional cognitive-academic tests. Consequently, the use of both kinds of measures explain more variance in performance than reliance on either kind alone" (p. 224).

The work of Sternberg and his colleagues has provided the most useful insights over time into different ways of framing intelligence in adulthood. First, although the work discussed is more widely used with children, the theory building, research, and applications have also been used with a variety of adult groups in systematic ways. Therefore, there is a twenty-year research history that provides a different level of credibility to this work than to that of Gardner, or, as we next explore, to the concept of emotional intelligence. For educators of adults it provides rich evidence that adult intelligence is much more than academic abilities and measures on the more traditional IQ tests, but also encompasses what many of us have believed it to include all along: everyday or practical intelligence. Second, Sternberg and his colleagues have provided us with initial inventories of both successful and practical intelligence. Although, as was discussed previously, additional validation studies need to be completed on these inventories, we hope that at some point they will be as accepted as the current traditional battery of tests of intelligence in adults. And finally, Sternberg and his colleagues have added their voices to those who have said that intelligence can be taught (see Grotzer & Perkins, 2000, for an overview) and offer resources that can be used with adults in the instructional process (for example, Sternberg, 1986a, 1988, 1997).

EMOTIONAL INTELLIGENCE

The term emotional intelligence became almost a household word with the publication of Goleman's popular book *Emotional Intelligence* (1995). Goleman's suggestion that "emotional intelligence can be as powerful and at times more powerful than IQ" (p. 24) created excitement especially among practitioners. Grounding his work in the new discoveries of the emotional architecture of the brain, Goleman asserts that we have two very different ways of knowing—the rational and the emotional—which are, for the most part, intertwined and "exquisitely coordinated; feelings are essential to thought, thought to feelings" (p. 9). Yet, in Goleman's beliefs, it is the emotional mind—in his terms, emotional intelligence— that is the major determiner of success in life. His model of emotional intelligence has five primary domains, which he attributes to the earlier model of Salovey and Mayer (1990): knowing one's emotions, managing one's emotions, motivating oneself, recognizing emotions in others, and handling relationships. Goleman believes that self-awareness of one's feelings is the key to emotional intelligence, but one must also be attuned to the emotions of others.

Both Salovey and Mayer's (1990) and Goleman's (1995) descriptions of how adults might display their emotional intelligence are similar to Gardner's concept of personal intelligence. For example, all the authors speak to the need for people to make personal connections and be empathetic as well as to have access to their own internal feelings. In addition, their ideas about emotional intelligence are echoed in Sternberg's list of the characteristics and attributes of people who display successful intelligence.

Although Goleman's work has been quoted and used most often as a base for practice with both children and adults, there is little if any empirical evidence to support the majority of his basic assertions about emotional intelligence. Rather, as observed by Mayer, Salovey, and Caruso (2000) and Brody (2004), Goleman's very strong claims on emotional intelligence are based primarily in proprietary research and not published in peer-review journals. In addition, Goleman ascribes his five-domain model of emotional intelligence as one that was conceptualized by Salovey, citing an earlier work of Salovey and Mayer (1990), as his source. However, in our review of the original source for that model it was our observation that Goleman's model is not a good representation of the work of either the original model Salovey and Mayer proposed (1990) or of their more recent work (Mayer & Salovey, 1997; Mayer, Salovey, & Caruso, 2000). In essence, the Mayer and Salovey model has four branches: "(a) perceiving emotions, (b) using emotions to facilitate thought, (c) understanding emotions, and (d) managing emotions"

(Mayer & Salovey, 1997, as cited by Salovey & Pizarro, 2003, p. 263). Although some of the language is similar to that of Goleman's description of emotional intelligence, the actual meanings are quite different. First, Mayer and Salovey's work is situated in a rich body of both theory and research. Second, the Mayer and Salovey model has become foundational for some highly sophisticated work on emotional intelligence that both these authors and other scholars continue to revise and use in their research (Mayer, Salovey, & Caruso, 2000; Palmer, Gignac, Manocha, & Stough, 2005; Salovey & Pizarro, 2003).

In addition to the work completed on building theories and models of emotional intelligence, there is also work done in developing measures of this construct (Bar-On, 1997; Simmons & Simmons, 1997; Mayer, Salovey, & Caruso, 2002, 2003). The Mayer-Salovey-Caruso Emotional Intelligence Test (MSCEIT) has received the greatest scrutiny. For example, Palmer, Gignac, Manocha, and Stough (2005) have recently completed a psychometric evaluation of the MSCEIT Test Version 2. Two major conclusions resulted from their study: (1) "the reliability of the MSCEIT at the total scale, area, and branch levels was found to be good" (p. 1); and (2) there is a need for the "addition of valid items to the current subscales, as well as the creation of more subscales in general" (p. 21).

Still others have explored the practical application of emotional intelligence in the workplace (Weisinger, 1998; Opengart, 2005; McEnrue & Groves, 2006). Opengart (2005) conducted a literature search on two very different but related concepts: emotional intelligence and emotional work. She concluded that employees need to have both the capacity to act in emotional situations (that is, emotional intelligence) and in-depth knowledge of how their specific place of employment allows for the expression of emotion and in what ways. McEnrue and Groves (2006) have provided an excellent review and critique on current tests on emotional intelligence used in the workplace. They are advocating using the MSCEIT "on the basis of its psychometric properties and HRD application potential" (p. 38) as the test of choice at this time, although they acknowledge the test is still undergoing further refinement.

Even though the writings and research on emotional intelligence in adulthood have made us think about the importance of emotion to learning, we need to be mindful that this concept of intelligence has little empirical evidence to support it as a separate construct of intelligence. Therefore, we should not consider emotional intelligence as a given fact, nor design programs that teach others how to develop and use a certain "type" of emotional intelligence. Rather, we should continue to critically explore the many ways that emotional intelligence has been presented and reflect on how these might enhance our practice as educators of adults.

We move next in this section to a discussion of the contextual perspective of intelligence. There is some overlap among researchers who include contextual components in their theories and models. Representative theories and models of intelligence where this overlap can easily be seen are successful intelligence (Sternberg, 1997), practical intelligence (Sternberg et al., 2000; Wagner, 2000), and emotional intelligence (Mayer & Salovey, 1997; Salovey & Pizarro, 2003)

THE CONTEXTUAL PERSPECTIVE OF INTELLIGENCE

Acknowledging the contextual dimension of intelligence in adulthood moves our thinking beyond the realm of individual learners. Inside the broad framework of this perspective, two main threads emerge. The first thread is that intellectual abilities lie at the intersection of the mind and the many changes we experience over time in our everyday lives. For example, many of us have wondered why some people can be successful in more than one employment setting, even when those settings are radically different, while others fail miserably when they change their places of employment, even when they are doing similar work. One explanation that is often given is that people who succeed across settings have the capacity to scan and adapt to new environments. Unless an individual is able to understand and actively participate in new situations, a contextual theorist would observe, being cognitively competent internally may make little, if any, difference in that person's success in most realms. In essence, the contextual perspective captures the adaptive functions of intelligence—being able to act intellectually in a number of different contexts, based on the accumulation of both generalized and specialized knowledge and abilities (Berg, 2000). Berg (2000) advocates that this process of adaptation should be dynamic, in which individuals' intellectual "abilities and processes as well as the context are simultaneously shaped" (p. 127). Berg also observes that research on the intersection of the mind and our everyday experiences within the contextual framework "is in its relative infancy compared with the work on individual abilities and processes that reside within the individual" (p. 128).

The second thread in the contextual framework is based on the assumption that intelligence often has different meanings to different social, ethnic, and cultural groups (Davidson & Downing, 2000; Luttrell, 1989; Serpell, 2000; Sternberg, 2004). As Davidson and Downing (2002) state: "What is considered to be intelligent behavior in one culture is sometimes thought to be rather idiotic in other cultures" (p. 40).

In line with this thinking, Kohl de Oliveira (1995, p. 245) notes: "Individuals, growing up in their cultural settings, develop their own conceptions about intellectual competence, acquisition and use of cognitive abilities, and organization of these abilities within different situations." For example, respondents in Luttrell's study (1989, p. 37) of working-class Black women and White women judged people as intelligent by their ability "to cope with everyday problems in an everyday world." In other words, they saw using common sense as an important intellectual skill. But even in their definitions of common sense, each group described the formulation and value of this commonsense know-how very differently. White women valued the commonsense knowledge of working-class men, such as manual and craft knowledge, more highly than their own intuitive knowledge springing from their domestic responsibilities. In contrast, Black women viewed as important the knowledge and abilities they gained through caretaking and domestic work. In addition, working-class Black women considered their racial identity and relationships with "extended kin" and the Black community as critical to both what they knew and how they used this knowledge.

Serpell (2000) has raised a very different kind of cultural issue: the culture of academic scholars who possess incredible power over those who try to break out of the mainstream way of conceptualizing and studying intelligence. More specifically, he addresses how a "culturally particular" conception of intelligence, in this case one that is dominant in contemporary Western, industrialized societies, continues to be the prevailing view of how intelligence is defined and researched. Troubling are Serpell's (2000) observations, similar to ones made earlier in this chapter, that this cultural paradigm, for example, "informs the development of most of the standardized tests in the United States, which in turn have emerged from a tradition that has dominated the design of intelligence tests elsewhere around the world" (pp. 567–568). In his discussion of an editorial with fifty-two signatures published in the journal *Intelligence* (Gottfredson, 1997), Serpell critiques three significant cultural themes raised in the editorial that, from the perspective of the editorial's signatories, drive the majority of the research in intelligence: "decontextualization, quantification, and biologization" (Gottfredson, 1997, as cited by Serpell, 2000, p. 568). We agree with Serpell's intriguing critique of these themes, and also offer our own observations. We find the first theme especially problematic because there are researchers, especially in the last two decades, who have argued that historical, sociocultural, and biographical contexts are central to the study of intelligence in adulthood (Schaie, 1994; Sternberg, 2003b; Sternberg et al., 2000). We also question the second theme of whether all forms of intelligence can or even should be quantifiable. In addition, although the biological perspective, the third theme, may hold great promise for a better understanding of intelligence, we cannot state for sure that this knowledge will be useful in our practice as educators of adults.

Other scholars have crossed the boundaries of Western culture, through cross-cultural studies, to gain a clearer understanding of how culture affects the way intelligence is defined. Sternberg et al. (2000), for example, describe a number of studies Sternberg and others conducted in Asia and Africa. The groups studied were quite varied in their backgrounds, countries of origin, and the type of environments in which they lived, ranging from adults residing in cities in Taiwan to villagers in rural areas of Africa. Although the populations differed in so many aspects, there was one main similarity among these groups—a stronger emphasis in both African and Asian cultures on social aspects of intelligence "to a much greater extent than in the conventional Western view" (p. 17). Even though this greater emphasis existed, "these cultures still recognize the importance of the cognitive aspects" (p. 17) of intelligence.

Issues of race, ethnicity, and social class, in addition to culture, are also studied. Kohl de Oliveira (1995, p. 262), for example, in

her longitudinal study of how adults in a *favela* (squatter settlement) in the city of São Paulo, Brazil, understand intelligence is
one example of a study that takes into account social class as well
as culture. She found that her respondents "characterized intelligent people as those who are able, basically, to 'make things,' to
create concrete products with their own hands: build houses, do
woodwork, do mechanical work, paint, make objects in straw,
ceramics, and so on." These people, who were living in a squatter
settlement, defined intelligence as the ability to cope with their
everyday lives, which in essence meant possessing the skills to make
things with their own hands and having the ability to learn easily
and quickly things that could assist them in their daily survival.

Sternberg (2004), as editor of a recent handbook, *The International Handbook of Intelligence,* has provided us with a wide variety of
examples of cross-cultural studies on intelligence from many
regions of the world. He includes studies that focus on theory,
research, and testing in the Nordic countries, Israel, Turkey, and
Japan. In addition, other authors explore whether it is possible to
study intelligence without using the concept of intelligence, if diligence can make people smart, and the validity and usefulness of
local versus universal models and theories of intelligence.

INTELLIGENCE, AGING, AND ADULT LEARNING

Among the many new ideas about intellectual functioning in adulthood, four surface as the most intriguing and useful to educators.
The first is that the individual differences approach to intelligence
continues to be the dominant paradigm in the study of adult intelligence. In essence, most of our knowledge about intelligence in
adulthood, including the effects of the aging process on intelligence, is still grounded in the more traditional measures of IQ.
Our hypothesis, as stated earlier, is that many educators of adults
may not be aware of the enormous influence that intelligence, as
defined from the individual differences approach, has had on
adult lives. For example, some adults were tracked into ability
groups early in their schooling days through these types of IQ tests,
which may have lifetime effects on how they and others perceive
their ability to learn. In addition, other educators and adults alike

have believed for a long time that, as adults age, they really cannot think as well as they once did. For these people this premise may be a "fact of life" that becomes a self-fulfilling prophecy, no matter what evidence is presented to the contrary.

The second development is the expansion of alternative conceptions of adult intelligence. Adults are especially attracted to the work of Gardner on multiple intelligences and Sternberg's notion of practical intelligence, because these ideas resonate with their adult lives. These alternative perspectives on adult intelligence have great potential for assisting adult educators and learners to think differently about what it means to be intelligent. For example, "unschooled adults" often view themselves as not very bright. Yet, in telling stories of some of their favorite activities they often describe hobbies or other tasks that are quite complex and require higher-order thinking. Assisting these individuals in understanding what practical intelligence is all about might change their own self-image as learners.

Third, Sternberg (1996c, 1997) has also challenged us to think in very different ways about how individuals and the circumstances in which they find themselves interact to shape intellectual functioning in adulthood. He offers a novel illustration to help us gain a clearer picture of what he means by "the mind in context": the "luck" and "whoops" factors (Sternberg, 1994b). Each of us is born with different gifts and into different circumstances. Some of us are lucky enough to find ourselves in places where our gifts have been prized and nurtured (the luck factor), while others, no matter what their individual efforts, are never recognized or are blocked by circumstances beyond their control (the whoops factor). As the world around us becomes more complex, so does the entanglement of the whoops with the luck factors. What may be termed a luck factor one day may often without warning become a whoops factor the next. The truly intelligent adult must be able to grapple with these often paradoxical situations, which can become highly frustrating and even daunting to those caught up in tragic events. We think of the many families who were left homeless and jobless as a result of Hurricane Katrina. Many of them have had to progress up a very steep learning curve to get back on their feet, often in circumstances that were at best tolerable, but often horrible. Those who have made their way back to a life of some normalcy are excellent examples of adults who display high levels of intellect—and also, perhaps, have a little luck along the way.

Fourth, researchers such as Schaie (1994, 1996a, 1996b) and Sternberg (1986a, 1986b; Sternberg et al., 2000) are creating a clearer understanding of how adults can both retain and even enhance their intellectual abilities as they age. These researchers view adult intelligence as consisting of a number of factors or components. Sternberg, for example, identifies people who really "shine"—that is, are highly intelligent—as those who can weave their academic know-how, however it was learned, their creativity, and their "street smarts" into meeting life "head-on," no matter the circumstances. Based on this definition, very different strategies for keeping one's intelligence intact are needed than when intelligence is viewed primarily as academic or mental ability. Therefore, based on the varying definitions of intelligence, adult educators need to think carefully about which intellectual abilities might be the most useful for adults, both young and old, to have addressed by educational interventions.

To ensure that they continue to maintain their intellectual functioning, learners themselves can take part in both informal and formal educational programs aimed at keeping their intellectual capacities intact. Adult educators can offer formal learning experiences, grounded in a solid knowledge base about intelligence and aging, while also providing advice to learners on useful resources they might consult. In addition, Peterson and Masunaga (1998) and Ramey and Ramey (2000) advocate that we need to expand our role in educational policies related to learning in adulthood, and more specifically, in policies that speak directly to the intellectual functioning of adults. A basic assumption that influences Ramey and Ramey's commitment in this arena is that all citizens in a democratic society are responsible for acting intelligently in their roles as voters, members of governing boards, and spokespeople for specific causes related to intellectual functioning in adulthood. Examples of specific issues are to ensure that IQ tests used as part of a major policy initiative for adults are appropriate and valid and that public funding is adequate to meet the needs of older adults for specific interventions to maintain their intellectual capacities.

SUMMARY

In this chapter we discussed the more traditional approaches to intelligence, including the biological, the individual differences, and the cognitive processes approaches, which have been foundational to our thinking about adult intelligence. The most often used paradigm among these traditional approaches is the individual differences approach, which assumes that intelligence is a measurable quantity. First conceptualized from this approach as a single factor of general ability, the construct has broadened to include the notion that there are multiple factors of intellectual ability, such as those proposed by Horn and Cattell (1967), and Thurstone and Thurstone (1941). Commonly used tests of adult intelligence that fit into this psychometric tradition include the Wechsler Adult Intelligence Scale and the Primary Mental Abilities test. The three issues that have surfaced with the use of these types of tests are what they measure, the inclusion of timed items, and the social and policy implications of IQ scores.

The question of whether adults retain their intellectual abilities as they age has not yet been definitively answered. Set primarily within the individual differences perspectives, three key factors on which the age and intelligence controversies center are defining the concept of intelligence, delineating the parameters of aging, and choosing which research designs and tests to use to measure intelligence. Some researchers contend that intellectual functioning is a process of irreversible decline. However, most scholars agree that intelligence either remains relatively stable through the adult years, with substantial intellectual changes occurring only very late in life, or that intelligence declines in some respects, remains stable in others, and may even increase in some functions, depending on a person's educational level, life experiences, and overall health. In addition, a number of variables reducing the risk of intellectual decline in old age have been isolated, such as living in favorable circumstances and maintaining substantial involvement in activities.

Challenges to the individual differences approach have come primarily from scholars who question whether what is measured as intelligence through this tradition presents a comprehensive picture of intellectual abilities, has any relationship to real-world or practical intelligence, and the effects that context has on intelligence. Three of the most prominent theorists who represent this alternative view of intelligence are Gardner (1999b), Sternberg (1985, 1997, 2003b), and Mayer and Salovey (1997). The contextual perspective on intelligence, which often includes the notion of practical and emotional intelligence, recognizes the importance of the intersection of the mind and the outside world as critical in gaining a clearer understanding of intelligence. Acknowledging this perspective means that intelligence has been defined differently by people of varying cultural backgrounds, social classes, and ethnicity.

The chapter concluded with an exploration of four ideas about intellectual functioning in adulthood that are particularly important for educators of adults: the continued predominance of the individual differences approach to the study of intelligence in adulthood; the expansion of alternative conceptions of adult intelligence; how individuals and the circumstances they find themselves in interact to shape intellectual functioning in adults; and a clearer understanding of how adults can retain and enhance their intellectual abilities, including the roles learners and adult educators can play using instructional and policy interventions.

CHAPTER FIFTEEN

MEMORY, COGNITION, AND THE BRAIN

One of the predominant views about adult learning is that learning is an internal process; it involves something happening inside our heads. Cognitive scientists, primarily from the discipline of psychology, have had the longest history of research in this arena. What cognitive scientists do is "attempt to discover the mental functions and processes that underlie observed behavior" (Bruer, 1997, p. 10). These mental functions and processes include, but are not limited to, the study of how people receive, store, retrieve, transform, and transmit information. Neurobiologists, in contrast, "study the anatomy, physiology, and pathology of the nervous system" (Taylor, 1996, p. 301), including the brain and related systems. They are primarily interested in the structures of the brain and how the brain actually works, including its electrical and chemical systems. With more recent technological advances, like magnetic resonance imaging (MRI) and positron emission tomography (PET), neurobiologists are generating actual pictures of how the brain operates.

Care must be taken in using work from both the cognitive and neurobiological sciences to talk about learning in adulthood, because the majority of studies in these two areas have been done with children (in the cognitive sciences) or with animals and people with severe brain damage (in the neurosciences). Still, there are some intriguing ideas that have informed the study of adult learning from both perspectives. With the advent of more sophisticated technology and a trend in the sciences toward interdisciplinary research, the knowledge base in these two areas has already expanded immensely. Although at this stage most of what we know about memory and how our brains function is laboratory-based, this ever expanding knowledge base has enormous potential for the study of adult learners and the way we practice our craft.

The work with adult populations related to cognition has been primarily in the area of memory and aging. This chapter first highlights that work, presenting an overview of the information processing framework. Next, we explore the concept of knowledge structures or schemas, the effect of prior knowledge and experience on learning, and cognitive and learning styles. These three topics, which are grounded in the cognitive sciences, are important for educators of adults to understand. Key ideas relating to neurobiology and learning are then reviewed. A description of how the brain has been viewed differently through the ages is followed by a discussion of the structures and the functions of the brain. As part of this discussion we describe how cognitive psychologists, neurobiologists, and scientists from other disciplines have joined forces in the study of the brain, with the result being a new field of study: cognitive neuroscience. We explore next connecting what we know about the brain to our practice as adult educators. The chapter concludes by raising some intriguing questions of what we are discovering about the brain from the perspective of the cognitive neurosciences and how this knowledge might change the way we think about adult learning and our practice as adult educators.

HUMAN MEMORY

Fear of memory loss is a common concern of people as they age. Parents often observe how much more easily their children can remember such simple things as telephone numbers and computer access codes, while many older adults seem to remember childhood events vividly but sometimes have difficulty remembering the names of people they just met. These observations and images foster the idea that memory loss is a normal result of aging and thus is something we all must accept. Are these perceptions of memory loss accurate, and if so, what effects do they have on learning in adulthood? Often, memory functions are equated with learning or are seen as one of the primary mental processes associated with learning (Hoyer & Roodin, 2003). If adults do suffer major changes, especially decline, in their memory functions, it follows that the learning process may also be impaired. To understand how memory can be affected by the aging process, we first need to examine how the process of memory from the cognitive framework is conceptualized.

Since the 1960s, human memory has been studied primarily from the information processing approach. The mind was until recently visualized as a computer, with information being entered, stored, and then retrieved as needed. Conceptualizing where people store or file what they learn, termed the *structural aspect of memory*, was the first major focus of study from this perspective. Three categories have been traditionally used to describe the different structures of memory: sensory memory, short-term memory, and long-term memory. More recently there has been a movement away from dividing up the structure of memory in such a definitive manner. This change in thinking has stemmed primarily from the study of *working memory*, and our knowledge of how the brain functions, which is discussed later in this chapter. Working memory has been conceptualized in three different ways: as part of long-term memory, as part of or the same as short-term memory, or as the mediator between sensory memory and either long- or short-term memory (Anderson, 2005; Ormrod, 1999). For the purposes of our discussion, we discuss human memory within the framework of sensory, working, and long-term memory. What is important to keep in mind when discussing memory as a process is that the different forms of memory do not exist in specific "places" in the brain, but rather are metaphors for each of the main processing components.

Sensory memory, also called the sensory register, "holds incoming information long enough for it to undergo preliminary cognitive functioning" (Ormrod, 1999, p. 179). Primarily through the senses of vision, hearing, and touch, images, sounds, and vibrations are entered into our memory systems. Sensory memory has a very brief storage time of only milliseconds before it either enters our working memory system or is lost. *Working memory,* or what some label short-term memory, entails "the active and simultaneous processing and storing of information" (Hoyer & Roodin, 2003, p. 277). Hoyer and Roodin compare working memory to a desktop:

During the course of a day, new pieces of information (memos, reports, work requests, and maybe empty pizza boxes) constantly accumulate on an individual's desk. The individual has to determine (1) which information is the most important, (2) which pieces of information require further processing, (3) which processing strategy to use, and (4) which pieces of information are cluttering up the desktop and should either be discarded or stored. Working memory tasks require individuals to simultaneously select, coordinate, and process incoming information. [pp. 277–278]

The storage capacity of working memory is estimated to be from five to thirty seconds. *Long-term memory,* however, has an enormous capacity for storage and is that part of the memory structure that retains information for long periods of time. "It includes memory for specific events and general knowledge that has been gleaned from those events over the years" (Ormrod, 1999, p. 192). Long-term memory has been conceptualized as the most complicated component of the memory system, and therefore has received the most attention in the research literature.

In recent years our understanding of long-term memory has moved from viewing it as one monolithic system "to one that is less hierarchical, involving several different kinds of memory, each playing a significant role" (Taylor, 1997b, p. 263). Most of the research on long-term memory has involved *explicit* (or declarative) memory, which is "the term used to describe knowledge that we can consciously recall" (Anderson, 2005, p. 234). "This form of memory is more sensitive and prone to interference, but it is also invaluable, providing the ability for personal autobiography and cultural evolution" (Taylor, 1997b, p. 263). *Implicit* (or nondeclarative) memory, in contrast, "concerns memories that we are not conscious we have" (Anderson, 2005, p. 234). Although these memories are developed unconsciously and thus form a hidden world we know little about, "people are influenced by [these types of memories] without any awareness they are remembering" (Schacter, 1996, p. 161). Classic examples of implicit memories are riding a bike, using a computer keyboard, and the "acquisition of rules often found in grammar [involving categorical knowledge]. Grammar is a particularly good example of implicit memory, where people have acquired abstract rules, but are unable to articulate what guides their speech and writing" (Taylor, 1997b, p. 264).

How we process information is integrally related to the cognitive processes involved in memory. Usually the memory process is divided into three phases (Anderson, 2005; Ormrod, 1999; Schacter, 1996). The *encoding* or *acquisition phase* is the initial process in which the information is entered into the system. Filing this material for future use is termed the *storage* or *retention phase*. The final phase, *retrieval,* describes how we get material out of storage when needed. Two of the most common methods of retrieval are *recall,* or bringing forth "to-be-remembered" information, and *recognition,* which involves choosing from a group of possible answers. As we well remember from our school testing days of essay versus multiple-choice exams, recalling the "correct" answer is considered to be more difficult than recognizing the correct answer among other possibilities presented (Hoyer & Roodin, 2003). Research has demonstrated that as we get older, we have more problems encoding and retrieving memories; the actual retention or storage of our memories remains fairly constant, however.

Memory from the information processing perspective works as follows: Information from our environment is registered within sensory memory through our visual, auditory, and tactile senses. Material is then selectively transferred or encoded into working memory. The control system of selective attention determines what is important enough to be moved into working memory. There is considerable flexibility with what can be done with the information in working memory. It "can be used as a cue to retrieve other information from long-term memory, it can be elaborated, it can be used to form images, it is used in thinking, it can be structured to be placed in long-term or secondary memory, or if nothing is done with it, it can be discarded" (Di Vesta, 1987, p. 211).

Because the functions of working memory are complex and its time and capacity are limited, two major control processes are used to sort and file the data: *chunking* and *automatization.* Chunking essentially is organizing the information in groups or patterns (a phone number in three chunks: 970-351-2119, for example), while automatization allows for a chunk of information to become so familiar that a person can handle it without recall thinking (Ormrod, 1999). The material structured in working memory for long-term memory is then encoded into that memory bank for permanent storage. Because individuals organize information received in different ways, attending to different cues, and associating similar pieces of information together, what is stored is not likely to be exactly what was received. "As a result, several people witnessing the same event often store very different things in their long-term memories" (Ormrod, 1999, p. 208). This type of processing is sometimes referred to as deep processing versus the shallow processing done at the working memory level. The information is then retrieved as needed from this long-term storage.

MEMORY AND AGING

A great deal of research from the information processing framework has been conducted on the topic of memory and aging. The general consensus from that work is that certain memory functions do decline with age. Nevertheless, a number of authors have cautioned that because of methodological considerations and the variables being studied, this work must be interpreted with care. The great majority of it has focused on comparing young adults (usually college students) with older adults by using cross-sectional designs. These two factors combined make it difficult to generalize across age groups because of subject and cohort bias. Subject bias comes from using people in a study who do not necessarily represent the general population (such as college students versus the broad population of young adults). Cohort bias or effect "is any difference between groups of adults of varying ages that is due not to any maturation or developmental process, but simply to the fact that the different age groups have grown up under different historical and cultural circumstances" (Bee & Bjorklund, 2004, p. 10). In addition, although the focus of the research is memory and aging, some of the authors of these memory and aging studies do not define *older adult*, not even in terms of age ranges (Naveh-Benjamin, Hussain, Guez, & Bar-On, 2003; Rodgers & Fisk, 2001). Rodgers and Fisk, for example, provide a very through review and critique of the literature on understanding how age may affect the role of attention in older adults. However, except for one of many studies included in their review, they neither describe nor critique the study participants. What is especially interesting, but also ironic, is that in that particular study the age range of the older adult group was from fifty to eighty. Moreover, most of this research has been conducted primarily in laboratory settings using memory tasks and activities, such as repeating back nonsense words and lists of random numbers. The primary criticism leveled against this type of research on memory is that these tasks and skills are generally artificial and taken out of the context of everyday life. A response to this criticism in recent years has been to design "ecologically valid" research that takes into account the everyday learning demands of adults (Anderson, 2005; Hoyer & Roodin, 2003; Langer, 1997; Rodgers & Fisk, 2001). With these limitations in mind, we offer a summary of this research on memory in adulthood.

Sensory and Working Memory

In general, few clearly defined changes have been found in sensory memory as people age. Because there are fairly major changes with age in both vision and hearing, one would expect to see these changes reflected in sensory memory. If you do not hear someone's name in an introduction, for example, there is no way it can be registered for recall later. However, it is often difficult with testing procedures to distinguish between age-related physiological decline in the senses *themselves,* especially hearing, and actual decrements in the process of sensory memory.

Working memory, in contrast, is more problematic as we age, especially "if people are asked to do anything with the information they are holding in short-term memory—to rearrange it, or recall it in some order other than the one in which it was given, or repeat back only the words of a particular type" (Bee & Bjorklund, 2004, p. 143). Bee and Bjorklund suggest three reasons for a decline in working memory. One possibility is that older adults "don't have the mental energy or attentional resources that younger people do and their short-term memory system becomes overloaded as tasks become more complex" (p. 143). A second possibility is that older adults do not employ the same strategies for dealing with working memory tasks as do younger people. The third commonly cited reason for this decline in working memory is that older adults appear to process materials more slowly, especially ones that are more complex in nature. One of the explanations for this slowing of the processing of information seems to be the "older adults' capacity to simultaneously perform a cognitive task while trying to remember some of the information for a later memory task"

(Smith, 1996, p. 241). In other words, it appears to be more difficult for older adults to both respond immediately to whatever stimulus triggered working memory and store pertinent information in long-term memory. Finally, older adults are less likely to even attempt to deal with "irrelevant and confusing information" (Bee & Bjorklund, 2004, p. 143).

LONG-TERM MEMORY

As with working memory, age deficits are also more commonly found in long-term memory. Three major differences have surfaced in long-term memory for older versus younger learners: changes in the encoding or acquisition of material, the retrieval of information, and the speed of processing. Few changes have been noted in the storage or retention capacity of long-term memory over the life span.

The question that often surfaces in reviewing the process related to long-term memory is whether it is more difficult for adults as they age to get information into the system (to encode it) or to get it out (to retrieve it). The response to this question appears to be both. It is not yet clear which part of the process creates more difficulty (Bee & Bjorklund, 2004; Ormrod, 1999). Encoding problems are most often associated with the organization of information. Specifically, older adults appear to be less efficient at organizing new material. Possible explanations of why organization is a problem relates to the amount and type of prior knowledge they already possess. While it is clear that the more we can relate new information to already stored information, the better we will remember it, it may also be that "storage of new information sometimes affects previously learned information. . . . Learners sometimes distort new material to fit their existing beliefs. Yet in other situations, a new piece of information may help learners recognize that something they stored earlier is inaccurate or that two previously learned pieces of information are related in a way they have not previously recognized" (Ormrod, 1999, p. 228). Further, information that is so at odds with a person's belief system may be ignored. In other words, this type of information may never enter long-term memory because it is incompatible with what the person already knows.

On the retrieval side, changes are most often noted in the recall versus recognition of information. In tests of recall, for example, major differences have been demonstrated for older and younger people, whereas in recognition activities, the differences are small or nonexistent, although the retrieval time may be slower. However, if older adults "are given some type of *environmental support* such as strategy instructions at encoding or cues at retrieval (or both), their recall performances increase and approach the levels of the younger adults' recall ability" (Bee & Bjorklund, 2004, p. 143; italics in original). Another aspect of retrieval that is often taken as a given is that older persons can retrieve "ancient memories" better than younger people, along with the accompanying myth that older people can clearly remember events in their distant past but have trouble recalling recent events. Rather, it appears that this reversal of memory strengths—remote memories are stronger than recent memories—may be a natural phenomenon that occurs at all ages, not just with older people. Further, we all "possess varying amounts of knowledge in selected domains of work, sports, hobbies, music, and other areas. Access to such knowledge is unaffected by aging. Individuals maintain their ability to use well-learned knowledge, strategies, and skills throughout middle age and into old age (Rybash, Hoyer, & Roodin, 1986). Tests of factual knowledge (e.g., vocabulary or news events) typically show no decline from young adulthood to old age (Hoyer & Touron, 2002)" (Hoyer & Roodin, 2003, p. 295).

In summary, in relation to long-term memory it appears that older adults may not acquire or retrieve information as well as do younger adults, nor organize information as effectively. This line of research may have limited generalizability because of the research designs, the subjects, the memory activities tested, and the separation of the research from the real world of the adult learner.

MEMORY IN CONTEXT

In response to some of the criticisms of memory research just cited, a different approach has been taken by placing memory tasks in the context of everyday adult lives, called *functional memory* by some researchers. This strand of research, which fosters what has been termed *ecological validity,* has received little attention, primarily because it is affected by so many different variables and is still considered controversial by some researchers. The term ecological validity assumes that the tasks being studied are meaningful to the person and accurately reflect real-life adult experiences. These studies use a variety of memory tests, from "memory for text" formats, which include reviews of sentences, paragraphs, and stories versus single words and symbols, to memory skills for everyday activities, such as keeping appointments and remembering what items to buy at the grocery store (Anderson, 2005; Knopf, 1995; Ormrod, 1999). These studies also address some of the other concerns voiced by scholars of the contextual approach, such as the person's needs and motivation, the specificity of the task, and situational variables. Other factors that might affect differences in memory are the person's "attitudes, interests, health status, intellectual abilities, and style of learning" (Hoyer & Roodin, 2003, p. 302). However, in sum, the extent to which noncognitive factors such as health and level of education affect age and memory is not as clear; the effect of cognitive factors such as speed of processing have more research support (Hoyer & Roodin, 2003).

FOSTERING MEMORY CAPACITY AND SKILLS

The assumption underlying the research on memory is that memory capacity and skills form one of the keys to how adults learn. Formal memory training, the most structured approach to building memory skills, has been shown to be useful in helping older adults cope with memory deficits (Bee & Bjorklund, 2004; Hoyer & Roodin, 2003). This training has most often focused on the teaching of encoding strategies, such as practicing rehearsal information or using mnemonics (devices for helping people improve their memory; Carney & Levine, 1998).

Adult educators have suggested ways to integrate training in memory skills into formal learning programs for adults: providing both verbal and written cues, such as advance organizers and overheads, when introducing new material to learners; using mnemonics and rehearsal strategies; and giving opportunities to apply the new material as soon after the presentation as possible. Adults learning on their own may also find it helpful to use memory aids in their learning activities. These can come in many forms, from

structured checklists for learning a new skill to personal note taking on items of interest. Bee and Bjorklund (2004) report on a
study by Burack and Lachkman (1996) that there were no significant differences between young and older adults for those who
made lists in word recognition and recall tests. Interestingly, participants who were told they could use their lists, but were "actually not allowed to use them" benefited as much as subjects who
made lists and used them—"suggesting that the activity of list making improves memory even when the list is not available at recall"
(Bee & Bjorklund, 2004, p. 145).

Cognitive psychologists, in addition to their work on memory
and aging, have provided us with a number of other important concepts related to learning in adulthood. Three of those concepts—
knowledge structures, the role of prior knowledge and experience,
and learning and cognitive styles—are discussed next in the
chapter.

KNOWLEDGE STRUCTURES

Within the cognitive framework, the emphasis is on what learners
know versus how they behave. This knowing involves both the
acquisition of knowledge, discussed in the section on human memory, and the actual structure of that knowledge (Anderson, 2005;
Bruer, 1993). In this perspective, considerable importance is
placed on prior knowledge as well as on new knowledge being
accumulated. Since it is assumed that most adults have a greater
store of prior knowledge than children, understanding the role
that this knowledge plays in learning is critical. In thinking through
the possible connections of prior knowledge to learning in adulthood, the concept of schemas provides a useful framework.

Schemas "represent categorical knowledge . . . [that is,] what specific things tend to have in common" (Anderson, 2005, p. 158). "People often form schemas about events as well as objects; such event
schemas are often called scripts. . . . For example, what things usually
happen when people go to a doctor's office?" (Ormrod, 1999, p.
255). These schemas, which may be embedded within other schemas
or may stand alone, are filled with descriptive materials and are seen
as the building blocks of the cognitive process. Schemas are not just
passive storehouses of experience, however; they are also active
processes whose primary function is to facilitate the use of knowledge.

We all carry around with us our own individualized set of schemata that reflect both our experiences and our worldview. Therefore, as adult learners, each of us comes to a learning situation with a somewhat different configuration of knowledge and how it can be used. For example, some participants in a workshop on diversity in the workplace may bring to that experience firm beliefs that achieving diversity is a worthwhile goal based on their positive experiences with women and people of color. Others may not believe in the principle of diversity at all, and view it as an easy way for "some people" to get hired. And still others may be downright angry, believing they have either been discriminated against or passed over for a promotion because they were of the "wrong color" or gender. Therefore, each learner in the workshop not only comes with different schema sets but also departs having learned very different things—even though all were exposed to basically the same material.

In categorizing schema types, two kinds of knowledge are most often distinguished: declarative knowledge and procedural knowledge. Anderson (1993) describes declarative knowledge as "factual knowledge that people can report or describe"; procedural knowledge, by contrast, "is knowledge people can only manifest in performance" (p. 18). We may be able to describe two or three different models for instruction (declarative knowledge), for example, but when we try to put these models into action (procedural knowledge), we may fail miserably. Because the question is open whether learning facts or knowing how to perform comes first, the scenario just described could also be reversed: a person may be an excellent instructor and yet have no specific knowledge of instructional models.

Educators, however, are well aware that most learning in adulthood goes far beyond the simple memorization of facts. The expectation is that adults will be able to put those facts to good use in their everyday living, whether as workers, parents, spouses, friends, and so on. Therefore, the processes of tuning and restructuring of information, as well as both declarative and procedural knowledge, become vital in adult learning. The general processes of problem solving and critical thinking are good examples of the importance of these constructs. Specifically, in most problem-solving situations, we are trying to fit new ideas (declarative knowledge) and ways of acting (procedural knowledge) into earlier patterns of thinking and doing (our current schemas). If we are unable to change our earlier thought patterns (that is, fine-tune or restructure them), our chances of being able to frame and act on problems from a different perspective are remote, if not impossible.

Cognitive scientists also cite the importance of *metacognition,* defined as "people's knowledge of their own learning and cognitive processes and their consequent regulation of those processes to enhance learning and memory" (Ormrod, 1999, p. 319). A related term, *metamemory,* refers to the self-ratings of memory performance, or the self-appraisal or self-monitoring of memory. "Some studies have found that older persons' metamemory is mostly accurate, whereas other studies have found that older adults exaggerate their memory failures (Hertzog & Hultsch, 2000)" (Hoyer & Roodin, 2003, p. 274). Researchers have speculated, though, that the discrepancies between people's opinion of their memory performance and their actual ability may be largely due to older adults assuming memory loss or failure as they age.

PRIOR KNOWLEDGE AND EXPERIENCE

Many writers, as discussed in Chapter Seven, have spoken about the importance of acknowledging adults' prior knowledge and experience as integral to the learning process. In exploring the role of prior knowledge and experience in learning, two ideas are important: the *amount* of prior knowledge and experience and the *nature* of that knowledge and experience.

In terms of the amount of prior knowledge and experience one possesses, the difference between those who know a great deal about what they are experiencing (termed experts) and those who know very little (novices) is key. A person can be an expert in a variety of areas, from growing tomatoes to skiing. According to Sternberg and Horvath (1995, p. 10), "Perhaps the most fundamental difference between experts and novices is that experts bring more knowledge to solving problems . . . and do so more effectively than novices." In addition, experts are able to solve problems faster and in a more economical way, have stronger self-monitoring skills, and are able to view and solve problems at a deeper level than novices (Ferry & Ross-Gordon, 1998; Sternberg &

Horvath, 1995; Tennant & Pogson, 1995). Similar to Ferry and Ross-Gordon, Sternberg and Horvath, and Tennant and Pogson, Anderson (2005) has observed that experts "learn to perceive problems in ways that enable more effective problem-solving procedures to apply" (p. 295). Further, experts learn strategies to organize problem solving that are "optimally suited to problems in a particular domain" (p. 295). And "as people become more expert in a domain, they develop a better ability to store problem information in long-term memory and to retrieve it" (p. 302). Finally, "no one develops expertise without a great deal of hard work . . . [and] the difference between relative novices and relative experts increases as we look at more difficult problems" (p. 280).

As Anderson (2005) and others have pointed out, being an expert is related to certain domains or subject matter areas. Educators have often observed that being an expert in one area does not necessarily translate into being an expert in another, no matter what the learner's motivation or background. Many graduate students, for example, although very perceptive and advanced in their own fields of study, may have a great deal of trouble completing statistical and advanced research design courses that are quantitatively based. This issue is especially true of students who are not mathematically inclined. Moreover, some people become experts in carpentry or tracing genealogy, while others view these tasks as beyond their capabilities.

Therefore, in helping adults connect their current experience to their prior knowledge and experience, we need to be knowledgeable about the amount of prior knowledge they possess in a particular area and design our learning activities accordingly. For example, in teaching a group of expert instructors of adults, it probably does little good to outline just one instructional model, even when this model is the newest and supposedly the most complete model. They will probably think of every exception under the sun as to why this model will not work with all of their learners. It would make more sense to ask these instructors to look at alternative models, including this new model, and then have them problem-solve which of these models or parts of these models have worked best for them in what type of situations. By following this plan, the participants' level of expertise would be acknowledged, they would be asked to think more deeply about the many situations they have faced in teaching, and they would need to use their problem-solving abilities related to their prior knowledge and experience as instructors.

It would be helpful, in addition, to know how the transition between being a novice and being an expert takes place in order to facilitate learning from prior knowledge and experience. To this end, Anderson (2005), Lajoie (2003), Pillay and McCrindle (2005), and Sternberg and Horvath (1995), among others, have provided comprehensive descriptions of the development of expertise that are useful in designing learning activities to assist adults in moving along the continuum from novice to expert. Although there are differences among these authors' portrayals of expertise, there are also a number of commonalities in their descriptions of what constitute its main dimensions. Using primarily the framework of expert knowledge in the professions (for example, teaching, veterinarians) these scholars agree that experts:

- Require extensive knowledge in one or more specific domains (content areas).
- Recognize the importance of the sociocultural context of their work, including, as applicable, their own professions.
- Are challenged by complex and novel situations and problems.
- Process complex information quickly.
- Arrive faster at more creative and accurate solutions.

Additional research is needed to distill further the main dimensions of expertise, which would be helpful to educators in planning programs that would assist novices not to become just "more experienced novices" but indeed experts in areas that are significant to who they are and also significant to the common good.

In an example of what such a program might encompass, Lajoie (2003) has identified two different approaches to fostering expertise development. The first, dynamic assessment, is "defined as a moment-by-moment assessment of learners during problem solving so that feedback can be provided in the context of the activity" (p. 22). This approach, framed in the concept of situated cognition, was explored in more depth earlier in Chapter Seven. Second, Lajoie advocates "making the expertise trajectory visible to learners through models of expertise, feedback, or examples that promote the active transfer of knowledge and self-monitoring. This requires openness on the part of experts to share what they know, rather than having novices "learn the ropes" by trial and error, although that might be part of the learning process. For example, in some professions many of the experts do not have the time to share their expertise with novice learners on any meaningful level, nor are the organizations they work for willing to change the workday to allow for that time. Unfortunately, there are also experts in every field who are unwilling to pass along their "trade secrets" because doing so might erode their power and dominant positions in their organizations.

Cognitive Style and Learning Style

Another important aspect of cognition related to learning in adulthood is the notion of *cognitive style*. Cognitive styles are characterized as consistencies in information processing that develop in concert with underlying personality traits. They are reflected in "how individuals typically receive and process information" (Joughin, 1992, p. 4) and encompass the ways people see and make sense of their world and attend to different parts of their environment. Some people tend to look at problems from a global perspective, while others are more interested in taking in the detail (Flannery, 1993). The latter types, which Flannery labels *analytical information processors,* want information in a step-by-step manner and tend to perceive information in an abstract and objective manner. In contrast, "the global learners process information in a simultaneous manner. The ideas or experiences are seen all at once, not in any observable order" (Flannery, 1993, p. 16). In addition, global learners perceive information in a concrete and subjective manner.

A number of cognitive-style dimensions, including the concepts of global and analytical processing styles, have been identified through research (Cassidy, 2004; Joughin, 1992; Messick, 1996). The outstanding feature of these varying dimensions is their tendency to be bipolar. In contrasting people's cognitive styles, we tend to label people as being at either end of the continuum, and for the most part, cognitive styles are considered relatively stable.

Although a great deal of research has been conducted on cognitive styles, much of it has been done with children, and "no style has led to clear implications with respect to adult learning" (Joughin, 1992, p. 4). Therefore, it is still unclear how this work may relate to helping adults learn more effectively. Hiemstra and Sisco (1990) have conjectured that knowledge about cognitive styles might assist instructors in predicting how learners are "likely to form typical learning tasks such as remembering, selecting, comparing, focusing, reflecting, and analyzing" information (p. 241). In addition, Flannery (1993) has asserted that "teaching, texts and structures can be adapted to teach to different" cognitive styles (p. 19).

A related yet somewhat different phenomenon is the concept of *learning style.* The literature describing cognitive and learning style is rather confusing; some authors use the two terms interchangeably, others view cognitive style as the more encompassing term, and still others see learning style as the more inclusive term. Clearly there is no common definition of learning style, nor is there a unified theory on which this work is based (Cassidy, 2004; Desmedt & Valcke, 2004; Hall & Moseley, 2005). Learning style "attempts to explain learning variation between individuals in the way they approach learning tasks" (Toye, 1989, pp. 226–227). More specifically, Cranton (2005, p. 362) defines learning styles as "preferences for certain conditions or ways of learning, where learning means the development of meaning, values, skills, and strategies." Although this definition and other parallel definitions of learning style are quite similar to cognitive style, it appears that the real difference between these two concepts lies in the emphasis placed by learning style researchers on the practical learning situation versus the more general notion of how people perceive, organize, and process information. Therefore, those who study learning style usually place the emphasis on both the learner and the learning environment. Desmedt and Valcke (2004, p. 459), after reviewing the voluminous literature on cognitive style and learning style, summarize the differences as follows:

> Most cognitive style models are developed in laboratory or clinical settings to explain individual differences in cognitive processing, and they are applied in various fields. The recurrent features of the concept seem to be stability, pervasiveness, bipolarity and a strong interdependence with personality.
>
> The learning style models are developed and used in various educational contexts to explain and accommodate individual differences in learning. Learning styles are generally defined as relatively stable and consistent. It is however acknowledged that the characteristics of the learning environment and learning experiences influence their development.

Cranton (2005, p. 362) has identified "at least six approaches to learning style in the adult education literature: (a) experience, b) social interaction, c) personality, d) multiple intelligences and emotional intelligence, e) perceptions, and f) conditions or needs." The experience, personality, and the perception preferences approaches have received the most attention in the literature in adult education, as well as the various learning style instruments that are associated with each of these approaches. The experience approach addresses the issue that "learners have different styles or preferences when it comes to making meaning out of and learning from experiences" (pp. 362–363). Kolb's Learning Style Inventory, which is the most often used instrument to assess learning styles in adult education, classifies learning styles into four different categories: accommodators, divergers, convergers, and assimilators (see Kolb, 1984, and Kolb & Kolb, 2005, for a more complete description of each style). The personality approach is a more encompassing way of assessing learning style in that its gives a broader and more in-depth picture of individual learners. The Myers-Briggs Type Indicator (Myers, 1985, as cited by Cranton, 2005) is the most often used measure to assess learning styles based on psychological type preferences. Learners' visual, auditory, and kinesthetic learning preferences are the central focus of the perceptions approach to determining learning styles. Often practitioners think that this approach constitutes what they mean by learning styles.

It is also important to acknowledge that learning styles may be in part culturally based. Anderson (1988, p. 4), for example, asserts that "it would seem feasible that different ethnic groups, with different cultural histories, different adaptive approaches to reality, and different socialization practices, would differ concerning their respective learning styles." He goes on to observe that "there is no such thing as one style being 'better than another,' although in our country [the United States] the Euro-American style is projected by most institutions as the one which is most valued" (p. 6). Anderson characterizes the Euro-American style as primarily field-independent, analytic, and nonaffective, which to him reflects primarily male and acculturated minority views. In contrast, he views a non-Western style (meaning such groups as American Indians, African Americans, and many Euro-American females) as field-dependent, relational and holistic, and affective. Bell's (1994) research with African Americans confirms some of Anderson's thinking on learning styles. Bell's findings support "a holistic African American learning style . . . which consistently reflects a relational style. . . . The relational style has been defined as a preference for a whole-to-parts (rather than parts-to-whole) analysis of information, a perceptual vigilance for person social cues over object cues, and a preference for contextually 'rich' over contextually 'sterile' (abstract) learning/problem-solving structures" (p. 57). As learning style inventories are primarily Euro-American in their orientation, researchers "need to question the usefulness of conducting cross-cultural compassions using assessment strategies based on Western conceptualizations of learning style" (Cranton, 2005, p. 365).

Despite the lack of uniform agreement about which elements constitute a learning style, it seems apparent that learning-style inventories, unlike most cognitive-style instruments, have proved useful in helping learners and instructors alike become aware of their personal learning styles and their strengths and weaknesses as learners and teachers. What must be remembered in using these instruments, however, is that each inventory measures different things, depending on how the instrument's author has defined learning style. In using the variety of learning-style inventories available, it is important that learners understand how the author(s) of the instrument has conceptualized learning style. It is also important to remember that "learning style instruments are best used as tools to create awareness that learners differ and as starting points for individual learners' continued investigation of themselves as learners" (Hiemstra & Sisco, 1990, p. 240). For those who use learning style instruments regularly as part of their education and training must impress upon their learners that their learning styles are not the only, nor necessarily "the best way" for them learn. In addition, they also need to dispel the myth that these styles are "fixed and" change very little. This careful use of learning-style inventories, especially in making programming decisions about learners, is especially crucial. James and Blank (1993, p. 55) have observed that "although various authors claim strong reliability and validity for their instruments, a solid research base for many of these claims does not exist." Their analysis is confirmed by Cassidy's (2004) recent review of more than twenty learning style measures. For each instrument Cassidy presents the model or theory upon which it is based, a description of the measurement itself, and comments about the instrument and research conducted on the instrument. He concludes that "what is necessary is further empirical work to provide evidence to assess the validity of many of the proposed models" (p. 440). Coffield, Moseley, Hall, and Ecclestone (2004, as cited by Della Porta, 2006), using similar procedures as Cassidy (2004), found that just three instruments, the Allison and Hayes Cognitive Style Index, Apter's Motivational Style Profile, and Vermunt's Inventory of Learning Styles came close to demonstrating "both internal consistency and test-retest reliability *and* construct and predictive validity" (Coffield et al., 2004, p. 56, as cited by Porta, 2006). Della Porta went on to observe that "most surprising is the fact that some of the most widely used instruments, including the Myers-Briggs' Type Indicator and Kolb's Learning Style Inventory did not meet the minimum criteria for a psychometric instrument" (p. 10).

Sternberg (1994a, 1996a) has proposed a new term, *thinking styles,* which seems very similar, if not identical, to learning styles. Sternberg (1994a) defines a thinking style as "a preferred way of using one's abilities. It is not in itself an ability but rather a preference. Hence, various styles are not good or bad" (p. 36). Although Sternberg has described his theory of thinking styles primarily in the context of children, and more specifically childhood education, many components of his theory would also be useful in understanding the thinking patterns of adults. His work on thinking styles is grounded in ten general characteristics of styles, such as "styles can vary across tasks and situations, people differ in strengths of stylistic preferences, styles are socialized, and styles can vary across the life span—they are not fixed" (Sternberg, 1996a, pp. 349–350). He uses the concept of mental self-government, patterned after the kind of governments and government branches that exist worldwide, to describe his theory of thinking styles: "According to this theory, people can be understood in terms of the functions, forms, levels, scope, and leanings of government" (p. 351). Sternberg (1994a, p. 39) emphasizes the importance of taking into account people's thinking styles in designing learning programs and cautions that most instructors are best at teaching people "who match their own styles of thinking and learning . . . and tend to overestimate the extent to which their students share their own styles."

In summary, scholars studying learning from a cognitive perspective have added a great deal to our knowledge about learning in adulthood. Some of the major contributions described thus far in this chapter are our understanding of memory and how aging may affect memory processes, how our knowledge is organized into schemas, what effect prior knowledge and experience have on learning, and the concepts of cognitive and learning style. We reviewed in Chapter Seven another view of learning, situated cognition, to which cognitive scientists have also contributed. We now turn to a discussion of one of the newest research arenas related to adult learning: the neurobiology of learning.

NEUROBIOLOGY AND THE BRAIN

It is hard not to miss the latest goings-on in brain research. Stories about what researchers are finding about how our brain functions abound in popular outlets, such as *Time, Newsweek,* and our daily papers and newscasts. For example, *Time* magazine in 2004 and 2005 carried three very different stories about how brain imaging could assist "corporate America" and politicians to better get their messages across (McCarthy, 2005), what a brain "in love" looks like (Fisher, 2004), and how the brains of men and women differ in size and the processing of emotion (Ripley, 2005). Although these stories are certainly interesting, the data for these stories come from experiments in laboratories. Thus, much of our knowledge about the brain is currently only in the form of working hypotheses. On a more serious note, what we might learn from scientists who study the physical functions of the brain and its related systems has the possibility of moving our understanding of learning significantly forward. For example, recent research has shown "how a particular protein in the brain is responsible for converting short-term memories into long-term memories (Frankland et al., 2001)" (Hoyer & Roodin, 2003, p. 300). Viewing the devastation of the memory and learning capacity of a person with advanced Alzheimer's disease or a massive stroke brings home to each of us the innate and yet almost mystical ways in which the brain functions.

DIFFERING VIEWS OF THE BRAIN

Restak (2000) observes that when we "speak of the mind—making up our mind, improving our mind, changing our mind—we are actually referring to activities carried out by our brain" (p. 6). However, this assumption that the brain and the mind are one and the same has not always been the way that philosophers, religious scholars, and scientists conceptualized the mind-body relationship. "The ancient Egyptians thought so little of the brain matter that they made a practice of scooping it out . . . of the dead leader before packing the skull with cloth before burial. This practice was grounded in the belief that "consciousness resided in the heart" (Shreeve, 2005, p. 4). Aristotle, and a legacy of medieval thinkers, shared a very similar belief in that they "attributed all life forces to the heart and considered the brain to be nothing more than a cooling system for the blood" (Restak, 2000, p. 6).

In contrast, the Greek physician Hippocrates, considered the Father of Medicine, argued that the brain was the centrality of all thought. In his words, "Not only the pleasure, our joy, and our laughter but also our sorrow, plain, grief, and tears arise from the brain and the brain alone. With it we think and understand, see and hear, and we discriminate between . . . what is pleasant and unpleasant, and between good and evil" (Hippocrates, as cited by Restak, 2000, p. 8). The meaning of the phrase "the brain is center of our thinking" took on many forms, involved many winding roads, detours, and blind alleys, and has become a continuous journey, joined by scholars from many disciplines. For example, scientists and philosophers debated whether the actual brain tissues, which can be seen, or the fluid-filled cavities, which lie deep within, are more relevant to the operation of the brain; others believed that a person's character could be determined from bumps and other irregularities of the skull (phrenology). In addition, research focused on what parts of the brain are "in charge" of specific behavioral and cognitive functions, which originated in latter part of the eighteenth century, remains a hot topic of debate among scholars (Albert & Killiany, 2001; Albright & Neville, 1999; Restak, 2000).

The Structures and Functions of the Brain

The way the brain is structured and functions has captured, as noted earlier, the notice of the general public, in addition to study among the scientific community. "For good reason, the brain is sometimes hailed as the most complex object in the universe. It comprises a trillion cells, 100 billion of them neurons linked in networks that give rise to intelligence, creativity, emotion, consciousness and memory" (Fischback, 1992, p. 51). Since the 1950s, the study of the structures and functions of the brain, including how underlying electrical and chemical processes carry messages throughout the brain, has been dominated by neurobiologists, cognitive psychologists, and physicians. Although most of this work until recently has used animals as subjects, there have also been studies of people with a wide range of brain disorders. The studies on humans have relied primarily on what could be observed during brain surgery, the behavior and abilities of people with severe brain damage, or postmortem examinations. With the advent of noninvasive imaging techniques, researchers are also beginning to include healthy humans as subjects (Albert & Killiany, 2001).

These newer noninvasive techniques allow scientists "to see into the brain," with little risk to humans, whether they are well or in need of medical care. "These imaging techniques can loosely be divided into two basic types: structural scans and functional scans. The structural scans, using computerized tomography (CT) and magnetic resonance imaging (MRI), "produce highly detailed images of the brain" (Albert & Killiany, 2001, p. 163). With the more advanced forms of these technologies the images produced "look very similar in detail to that . . . seen on postmortem examination of brain tissue. . . . Functional scans, on the other hand, provide an indication of the activity of the brain, but do not tend to produce anatomical detail" (p. 163). Protein emission tomography (PET) and functional MRI (fMRI) are the scanning procedures used most often to gather functional data about the brain. Although these newer scanning methods have shown that "while it's true that certain areas [of the brain] are specialized for specific purposes, this organ can only be understood as one highly complex and integrated functional unit" (Restak, 2000, p. 25). For example, rather than each hemisphere of the brain operating separately, when the processing of information "within each hemisphere commences, the hemispheres rapidly send signals back and forth" (Robertson, 2005, p. 21). The result is a lot of "cross-talk" among the neurons rather than a direct response from one side or the other. "The large association cortex [the corpus callosum] is responsible for this information flow from one part of the brain to another" (Restak, 2000, p. 25).

These newer forms of technology have also allowed us to gain a clearer picture of the architecture of the brain. One of the most striking structures of the brain "are the large, seemingly symmetric cerebral hemispheres" (p. 48) that sit on a central core or base. The two hemispheres are connected by the corpus callosum, a large band of nerve fibers that, as just described, allows the two hemispheres to collaborate on many tasks.

Other structures of the brain that have generated more interest in recent years are those connected to emotion. "Emotion was largely neglected by neuroscience during most of the twentieth century, but it is now the focus of intense scrutiny, and not a moment too soon considering its importance in human lives. The neurobiological underpinning of the emotions have begun to be elucidated and it has become clear that the brain handles different emotions with the help of different components" (Damasio, 2000, p. 14). These components [structures] include the amygdale, the ventral and medial prefrontal cortex, and the hypothalamus. This "discovery offers important clues in the investigation of diseases such as depression and mania" (p. 16). In addition, Damasio argues that gaining further knowledge about what the interactions are among these parts of the brain underscore "the degree to which emotion and feeling are inextricably interwoven with the mechanisms that ensure the maintenance of life" (p. 16).

Pert (1997), although in agreement with Damasio's basic assumptions, has challenged researchers on the idea that the brain is the only part of us that can gather, process, and share information related to emotions. Based on her findings that chemical substances and their receptors are found in the body's nerves of all kinds, she argues that emotions could be stored and mediated by other parts of the body. This fairly recent discovery is important for appreciating how memories are stored not only in the brain but in a psychosomatic network that "can extend out to the very surface of our skin" (Pert, 1997, p. 143). This recognition that emotion and memory are clearly linked—whether these functions are based primarily in the brain or throughout our bodies—could have enormous implications for how we understand learning in adulthood.

Three other structures—the hypothalamus, the pituitary gland, and the pineal gland—control bodily functions, such as temperature regulation, hormone production, and sleep and wakefulness. In addition, two other crucial structures form the central core or base of the brain. These are the medulla, which contributes to the control of central life functions (including respiration, circulation, and digestion), and the cerebellum, which coordinates movement and plays a vital role in the processing of information (Restak, 2000). We hypothesize that all of these deeper structures of the brain, depending on their operational effectiveness, could affect how adults learn.

There has also been a change in the last twenty-five years, albeit a slow one, of adding cognitive scientists to the mix of researchers who study brain functions, including the addition of the new field cognitive neuroscience. "The term alone suggests a field that is pregnant and full of promise. It is a large field of study, uniting concepts and techniques from many disciplines, and its boundaries are rangy and often loosely defined. At the heart of cognitive neuroscience, however, lies the fundamental question of knowledge and its representation by the brain—characterized not inappropriately by William James (1842–1910) as 'the most mysterious thing in the world' (James, Vol. 1, 216)" (Albright & Neville, 1999, p. li.). Thus, rather than relying on either neurobiology or cognitive sciences, the promise of connecting what we know about how the brain functions and learning comes primarily from the merger of the two sciences. Bruer (1997) has used the metaphor of the bridge to illustrate this point. On the one hand, we have a "well-established bridge" of knowledge about learning from the cognitive sciences. On the other hand, we have a newer bridge between cognitive psychology and neuroscience. "This newer bridge is allowing us to see how mental function maps onto brain structures." When neuroscientists are able to "provide useful insights for educators about instruction and educational practice, those insights will be the extensive traffic over the second bridge" (p. 4).

Even though the cognitive neurosciences have amassed an amazing amount of information about the structures and functions of the brain, this information has generated more questions than answers. As Albright and Neville (1999) observe, "[T]he applications of new experimental techniques [in this case, more sophisticated, noninvasive imaging techniques] have often raised more questions than they have answered. But such are the expansion pains of a thriving science" (p. lvii). In addition, because the primary research in this field is laboratory-based and involves experimental designs, direct applications of this knowledge to educational practice may still be in the far future. Rather, the breakthroughs that have been made as a result of research in the cognitive neurosciences appear to relate more indirectly to learning in adulthood. For example, Shreeve (2005) tells the fascinating story of how, before removing a cancerous tumor from a young woman, the physicians and a neuropsychologist needed to find the exact "address" for Corina's language abilities. In doing so they had a good chance of being able to retain her language functions, which are a vital dimension of the learning process. However, this search is not an easy one because "every person's brain is as unique as their face" (p. 9). In this case the surgery was a marvelous success, and as the main surgeon observed: "Corina's brain is the most beautiful object that exists, for it allows her to perceive beauty, have a self, and know about existence in the first place" (p. 8).

CONNECTIONS TO LEARNING IN ADULTHOOD

Connecting what we know about the brain and related systems to learning in adulthood is at best a set of working hypotheses. Although some educators have tried to make very direct correlations by devising what they term *brain-based learning programs* (for example, Caine & Caine, 1994; Jensen, 2000), we still have a long way to go before we can make any really useful linkages that are theoretically and empirically sound. This gap between the theoretical and empirical knowledge of how the brain and related systems work and practical applications of that knowledge has created a number of questionable educational practices.

Two main practices have surfaced related to how educators have applied this knowledge to their practice. The first is the applications some educators have made based on supposed factual knowledge about the brain. As Bruer (1997, p. 4) argues, "Currently we do not know enough about brain development and neural function to link that understanding directly, in any meaningful, defensible way, to instruction and educational practice." He goes on to observe that even neuroscientists, "while interested in how their research might find application outside the laboratory and clinic, are more guarded in their claims. Often they are puzzled by the neuroscientific results educators choose to cite, by the interpretations educators give those results, and by the conclusions educators draw from them" (p. 4). For example, one of these applications of brain research to learning in adulthood has been educators designing programs that purport to increase the functions of the left or right brain. By the end of these programs, sponsors claim that participants will have fully developed their untapped potential of the right or left brain. Although, indeed, there is localization of functions that different parts of the brain support, more current research definitely debunks the myth that our brains are divided neatly into two halves, with the left brain being the seat of logic while the right brain houses our creative and artistic abilities. In fact, there are no definitive maps, as discussed earlier, that provide guides to which of the many structures of the brain controls what. Rather, what has been hypothesized is that it is the interactions among various structures that may be the key to understanding how our brain functions.

The second practice is the linking of specific instructional techniques to the knowledge we have of the brain. Vella (2002), for example, bases her argument for "teaching as dialogue" in the notion of quantum learning. She defines quantum learning as learning "which uses all of the neural networks in the brain, putting them together in personal ways to make significant meaning" (p. 73). Although we are intrigued with her discussion of the principles and practices that are necessary for the dialogue approach to learning to work well, we can see no real connections between how she defines quantum learning as a neurological function and the actual outcomes of what she terms quantum learning. As educators of adults we would be on more solid ground if we provided excellent descriptions of different kinds of learning processes, as Vella did, rather than attributing those processes to unproven neurological assumptions about learning.

New Directions and Discoveries

Until the theoretical and empirical knowledge from the cognitive neurosciences on the brain have moved out of the laboratory and into the context of everyday life, educators of adults would be better off not using our limited knowledge of the brain as a source of information for understanding adult learning. Because these types of arguments are not yet available, we suggest that information of this nature be framed as hypotheses or new discoveries that may someday lead to a greater understanding of learning in adulthood. However, research into the link between cognitive neuroscience and learning in adulthood offers some promising discoveries and new directions that may well have direct links to adult learning. A sampling of some of these intriguing ideas and questions are summarized as follows:

- Could our increasingly fast-paced lives have the potential to limit our capacity in our information processing systems to the point that they will create bottlenecks in our ability to process information? More specifically, Marois (2005) focuses on three areas in which our capacities as learners could be negatively affected: conscious visual perception, short-term memory, and action and decision making.
- Are there actual differences in male and female brains that affect both what and how we learn (Baron-Cohen, 2005)? If so, how might taking these differences into consideration change our current practices as educators?
- Will brain injury no longer be considered hopeless based "on the plasticity model of brain function and repair" (Restak, 2000)? Is so, what are the roles of adult educators in assisting these adults to become the normal learners they once were?
- Do the techniques that Buddhists have employed for over twenty-five hundred years "to guide their mental state away from destructive emotions and towards a more compassionate, happier frame of being" change how the mind works (Shreeve, 2005)? If so, how can using these techniques change our way of thinking and being as educators of adults?

- Are there interdependent relationships that exist between emotion and reason, exhibited in how the brain functions, that are crucial components of how adult learn? If so, what are the impacts of these relationships on learning, and how can adult educators best facilitate these impacts?

In closing, one of the authors remembers well a lecture given by Professor Houle in the early 1980s at a meeting of the Commission of Professors of Adult Education. Houle was a very strong believer that all adults could learn. In this lecture he related a personal story that had changed these beliefs. Two of his colleagues at the University of Chicago had recently been diagnosed with Alzheimer's disease. What he recognized, with great sadness, is that there are times in the lives of adults when they cannot learn and that the foundations of our knowledge of adult learning need to add another dimension. Houle urged adult educators to join hands with the biological sciences to expand our understanding of learning in adulthood. Houle's argument, given over twenty-five years ago, has indeed proven prophetic, and it promises in the future to enhance our understanding of learning in adulthood and our practice as educators.

SUMMARY

The internal workings of the learning process have fascinated scientists for decades. Researchers from the cognitive sciences have the longest history of research in this important arena, and more recently scholars from the neurobiological sciences are offering new hypotheses about how the brain and related systems are involved in learning. Perhaps the most exciting new arena of study, with the greatest potential for expanding our knowledge base of the internal processes of learning, are the combined efforts of cognitive scientists and neuroscientists working together to address how and where learning happens in the brain.

Cognitive scientists, primarily from the discipline of psychology, describe how people receive, store, retrieve, transform, and transmit information. Most of this work has focused on memory and aging, with the resulting conclusion that there are some apparent losses as people age in both working and long-term memory. How this loss affects the everyday learning activities of adults is still an unanswered question, although we know that most older adults take a longer time to process complex information. Other important aspects of cognition reviewed in this chapter are the concepts of schemas, the effect of prior knowledge and experience on learning, and cognitive and learning-style theories. The concept of schemas has provided a useful framework for thinking about both the forms of knowledge (declarative and procedural) adults have accumulated over time and how that knowledge is transformed and used. In exploring the effects of prior knowledge and experience on learning, the concepts of novice and expert learners were stressed. The differences between cognitive and learning styles were discussed as well, with the resulting observation that learning styles seem to be a more useful concept. The learning-style inventories, although many have questionable reliability and validity from a research standpoint, appear to have proved effective in helping both learners and instructors gain some basic understanding of their strengths and weaknesses as learners and instructors.

Cognitive neuroscience, a new field that bridges the gap between the cognitive sciences and neurobiology, as well as added other disciplines to the mix, has provided some fascinating descriptions of how the brain is organized and functions. Especially with the newer imaging techniques, such CT, PET, and fMRI scans, we can catch glimpses of how our brains are structured and operate during differing types of learning episodes. Direct connections between what we see and have learned about the brain and learning interventions are yet to come. What we have now are tentative hypotheses about the neurobiology of learning.

With this caveat in mind, we described how the brain has been viewed differently throughout the ages, and discussed how the brain is structured and organized and information is exchanged inside the structures of the brain. We then commented on how educators have tried to apply this knowledge, with limited, if any, success because of the lack of definitive knowledge about the relationships between brain functioning and learning. We concluded by outlining some intriguing questions being raised about the brain from the perspective of the cognitive neurosciences and how this knowledge could inform the way we think about adult learning and our practice as adult educators.

CHAPTER SIXTEEN

REFLECTIONS ON LEARNING IN ADULTHOOD

This book is testimony to the fact that we know quite a lot about learning in adulthood. Each chapter speaks to some aspect of learning, whether it be the context, the learner, the process, or some combination of these factors. In the process of reviewing and reflecting on all of this material, we arrived at our own understanding of learning in adulthood. This last chapter is our opportunity to articulate what we ourselves have learned about this phenomenon.

Many who have written on the topic of adult learning have tried to delineate principles summarizing what has been learned from research or observed in practice and axioms that can be applied to practice. Knowles's (1980) assumptions underlying andragogy, discussed in Chapter Four, are a good example of a set of principles about adult learners that has implications for practice. Others have advanced similar lists, often with a distinctive orientation. Smith (1982) distinguishes the learning process from the learners. He presents six observations about learning, such as "learning is a personal and natural process" and "learning has its intuitive side" (p. 35), and notes four critical characteristics of adult learners: a different orientation to education and learning, an accumulation of experience, special developmental trends, and anxiety and ambivalence. In a popular version of this approach, Zemke and Zemke (1995) in an update of their 1981 article, listed "thirty things we know for sure about adult learning" dividing these "thirty things" into the three categories of adult motivation, curriculum design, and classroom practice. MacKeracher (1996), who makes sense of adult learning through looking at the complex interaction of cognitive, affective, physical, social, and spiritual aspects of learning, offers practical advice to both learners and facilitators for enhancing the learning activity. Learners, for example, should "trust the process," be willing to take risks, and be "open to new ideas and experiences" (p. 243). Instructors should be reflective, passionate, responsive, and "keep in mind that you are a model for learners whether you want to be or not" (p. 253).

A few more recent publications reflect the orientation of the authors. For example, Taylor, Marienau, and Fiddler's (2000) book focuses on developmental goals for adult learners, including toward knowing as a dialogical process, toward a dialogical relationship to oneself, toward being a continuous learner, toward self-agency and self-authorship, and toward connection with others. Writing from a critical theory perspective, Brookfield (2005b) has identified the following "series of learning tasks" that are central to becoming critical learners:

> Learning to recognize and challenge ideology that attempts to portray the exploitation of the many by the few as a natural state of affairs, learning to uncover and counter hegemony, learning to unmask power, learning to overcome alienation and thereby accept freedom, learning to pursue liberation, learning to reclaim reason, and learning to practice democracy. [p. 39]

We considered doing a meta-analysis of the principles, concepts, and characteristics found in these sources as well as those delineated elsewhere in this book and in some of our own work. That undertaking, however, would probably have resulted in another set of principles that would not truly capture what we have come to understand about learning in adulthood. Furthermore, there is some question in our minds as to the usefulness of any one set of principles for guiding either research or practice. If, as we have tried to bring out in previous chapters, learning in adulthood is embedded in its context, a single set of principles is not likely to hold true for the wide-ranging diversity of learners and learning situations.

What we have done, therefore, is to step back and think about how learning in adulthood can be distinguished from learning in childhood. This was, after all, the question that stimulated much of the research, writing, and debate in the field's early efforts to distinguish itself from other subfields of education. Our answer, in essence a summary of the book, is that learning in adulthood can be distinguished from childhood in terms of the learner, the context, and to some extent, the learning process. Furthermore, it is not just that differences can be seen in these areas. Equally important, the configuration of learner, context, and process together makes learning in adulthood distinctly different from learning in childhood. In this chapter we first explore these differences and then discuss how well our understanding of the phenomenon is addressed by theory and practice. Finally, we speculate on the next steps in furthering our understanding of adult learning.

THE LEARNER

The focus on the individual learner, grounded primarily in the psychological paradigm, drove research and practice in adult learning until the 1990s. Representative lines of inquiry from this perspective include the ways we have traditionally framed the life experiences of individual learners, the linking of the psychological frame of development to learning, much of our research on motivation and participation, the information processing framework of cognition and memory, and the neurobiology of learning.

The comparatively richer life experiences of individual adults have been cited by nearly all writers as a key factor in differentiating adult learning from child learning. As Kidd (1973) noted over thirty years ago, "Adults have more experiences, adults have different kinds of experiences, and adult experiences are organized differently." It is these experiences that set adults "off from the world of children" (p. 46). If accumulated life experiences differentiate children from adults, they also differentiate one adult from another. A group of sixty-year-olds will have less in common than a group of twenty-year-olds.

Experience is an assumption "that can arguably lay claim to be viewed as a 'given' in the literature of adult learning" (Brookfield, 1986, p. 98). Knowles (1980, p. 44) conceives of it in terms of a "growing reservoir of experience" that functions as "a rich resource for learning." It also establishes a person's self-identity: "Adults derive their self-identity from their experience. They define who they are in terms of the accumulation of their unique sets of experiences."

And "because adults define themselves largely by their experience, they have a deep investment in its value" (p. 50).

Experience, however, can be quite varied as Fenwick (2003, p. 13) points out, including the following:

> *Direct embodied experience,* an immediate encounter in the here-and-now, planned or unplanned, involving us physically, emotionally, sensually, mentally, and perhaps spiritually; . . . *vicarious experience* [in which we] . . . imagine ourselves immersed in the encounter. We sometimes are exposed to *simulated experience,* a direct experience planned to be like something real. . . . We can experience through *reliving* a past encounter. . . . There is also *collaborative experience,* joining others in a shared community of experience whose meaning is constructive together amid conversation and joint action. . . . [Finally], *introspective experience,* such as mediation or dreaming, or reading, are powerful forms of experience occurring in a special psychic space. . . . All of these dimensions suggest different ways to understand whatever is construed to be learning in each context.

Whatever the type of experience, it functions in several ways that are particular to adult learning. First, as Knowles observed, adult learners themselves become important resources for learning. Adults can call on their experiences in the formulation of learning activities, as well as serve as resources for others in a learning event. Second, the need to make sense out of one's life experiences is often an incentive for engaging in a learning activity in the first place. Third, the actual engagement of past experiences with learning is somewhat different for adults than for children. An adult's major use of experience in learning is on reintegrating or transforming meanings and values, while children tend to use their experiences in accumulating new knowledge and skills. As Mezirow (2000, p. 5) points out, "[L]earning is understood as the process of using a prior interpretation to construe new or revised interpretation of the meaning of one's experience as a guide to future action." Finally, it should be noted that an adult's past experiences can become obstacles to new learning. Some may have to unlearn negative attitudes toward learning, old ways of doing things, prejudicial views, and so on.

The arena of development from a psychological perspective is another way in which adults are differentiated from children. While it is true that both adults and children are involved in developmental processes, the nature of the processes is qualitatively different. This difference can be clearly illustrated with Havighurst's (1972) developmental tasks for different life stages. From infancy through adolescence, the tasks reflect physical maturation (learning to walk, getting ready to read) or preparatory activities needed for future adult roles. Beginning with the tasks of young adulthood, there is a shift to functioning well as an adult—bringing up young children, managing a home, achieving adult civic and social responsibilities, and so on. Erikson's (1963) life stages also reflect a shift from childhood dependence to adult-oriented dilemmas. In the first five stages of infancy through adolescence, the child deals with establishing trust, autonomy, initiative, industry, and identity. Adults struggle with intimacy, generativity, and integrity, characteristics manifested in adult roles of spouse, parent, worker, and citizen. In at least one developmental theory, the notions of adult experience and development converge. Part of Kohlberg's (1973) theory of moral development stipulates that one cannot attain the higher stages of development until one has experienced irrevocable moral decision making. Fowler (1981), whose stages of faith build on Kohlberg's idea, also maintains that later stages cannot be attained until adult life. Even some models of cognitive change and development assume an accumulation of experience with age. Mezirow (1991, p. 193), for example, asserts that "transformations likely to produce developmentally advanced meaning perspectives usually appear to occur after the age of thirty," while Kegan (1994) asserts that most people do not even enter the highest levels of consciousness until their forties.

In addition to a sequential stage-phase view of development, life events and transitions differentiate adult learning from child learning. Many of the life events and transitions that adults face are peculiar to adulthood and require adjustments—adjustments often made through systematic learning activity. It is these transitions and life events that are likely to result in significant, meaningful learning (Merriam & Clark, 2006). They are also what motivate many adults to seek out learning. Aslanian and Brickell (1980), for example, found that 83 percent of adult learners in their study were involved in learning to cope with a transition. The transitions were primarily career related (56 percent), followed by family life transitions (35 percent). "To know an adult's life schedule," they concluded, "is to know an adult's learning schedule" (pp. 60–61).

There is little doubt that there is a strong link between the motivation to participate in a learning activity and an adult's life experiences and developmental issues. From studies of participation and motivation that document that adult roles, especially that of worker, are prime motivators for learning, to Mezirow's (1991) process of perspective transformation that is precipitated by a "disorienting dilemma"—that is, one's familiar patterns of coping with life events prove ineffective—learning in adulthood is a function of social roles and developmental issues.

Research on human memory and how the brain functions also has the learner center stage in understanding learning. From these perspectives learning has been conceived as something that primarily goes on inside the heads of individual learners. Through studying memory we continue to try to decipher how adults receive, store, transform, and retrieve information and how these processes are affected as we age. We have even tried to see if we could improve these processes through formal learning activities, and more recently, by using various forms of pharmaceutical interventions. One of the most intriguing knowledge bases on which to draw about learning in adulthood in the last few years is neurobiological. By discovering more about how the brain actually functions, we have a better chance of unlocking lifelong learning disabilities and such disastrous diseases as Alzheimer's and Parkinson's, which can render adults incapable of learning even at a rudimentary level. There is a great deal of potential to enhance what we know about individual learners, especially when we merge the ideas from the cognitive and neurobiological sciences.

In addition to what is happening in the mind of an adult learner, there is a burgeoning literature looking at learning as an embodied, emotional, perhaps spiritual occurrence (see Chapter Eight). While this research and writing still focuses on the individual learner, it is at the same time expanding our understanding of learning beyond an information processing, cognitive activity.

Just being an adult is thus a crucial factor in distinguishing between learning in adulthood and learning in childhood. The accumulation of experience, the nature of that experience, the developmental issues adults address, how the notions of development and experience relate to learning, and how aging affects our memory and the more general neurological basis for learning—all of these differentiate adult learners from children.

THE CONTEXT

Historically, adult educators in social action and community-based learning programs have taken the context into account in their work. From Jane Adams's Hull House immigrant programs to Highlander's Research and Education Center's involvement in labor movements, civil rights, and environmental action, the adult learner was seen as affected by, and having an effect on, his or her social context. However, it has not been until the last fifteen years or so that context has received more systematic attention in the literature on adult learning. There are at least two ways to think about context in this more recent work. The first is the notion that learning is a product of the individual *interacting* with the context. Recent theories of situated cognition, reflective practice, and cognitive development are representative of this interactive view. A second way to view the importance of context in learning is to consider how the structures and institutions of society affect learning. These *structural* dimensions include factors such as race, class, gender, cultural diversity, and power and oppression.

The interactive dimension of the context acknowledges that an adult's life situation is quite different from that of a child. A child's life situation is usually characterized by dependency on others for his or her well-being. The majority of adults, in contrast, are adults because they have assumed responsibility for managing their own lives. As Paterson (1979, p. 10) reminds us, "To say that someone is an adult is to say that he [sic] is entitled, for example, to a wide-ranging freedom of life-style and to a full participation in the making of social decisions; and it is also to say that he is obliged, among other things, to be mindful of his own deepest interests and to carry a full share of the burdens involved in conducting society and transmitting its benefits. His adulthood consists in his full employment of such rights and his full subjection to such responsibilities." The taking on of social roles characteristic of adulthood—roles such as worker, spouse or partner, voting citizen, and parent—differentiates adults from children better than chronological age does.

This difference in the social position of adults and children is reflected in contextual differences in their lives and their learning. A child's life is bounded by home and school, whereas an adult's life situation is defined primarily by work, family, and community. Through home and school, children learn to be adults; going to school is a full-time job. Theoretically at least, both home and school are sites where young people learn how to function as adults. The curriculum in both settings is determined primarily by others, who decide what is important to know in order to become responsible members of society. Education, even undergraduate education for traditional-age students, is basically preparatory—young people are "prepared" for the world of work.

Adults, in contrast, typically add the role of learner to other full-time roles and responsibilities. The learning that adults do arises from the context of their lives, which is intimately tied to the sociocultural setting in which they live. As Jarvis (1992, p. 11) has observed: "Learning . . . is about the continuing process of making sense of everyday experience." Jarvis also draws a connection between motivation and context: "The reason for participation does not always lie within the learner but in the dynamic tension that exists between the learner and [the] socio-cultural world" (1983, p. 67). The potential for learning occurs "at the intersection of us and our world" (Jarvis, 2006, p. 10). For example, an assembly-line worker whose job has been outsourced will need to retrain for other employment; a nurse will need to keep up with changes in the health care system and technology. Zoning and tax laws, waste disposal management, and so on that affect citizens' lives in communities also lead to new learning. Thus learning in adulthood is characterized by an interaction between the adult and his or her lifeworld and the duties and responsibilities inherent in the adult roles of worker, spouse, partner, parent, and citizen.

The differences in context between the lives of children and adults and how these differences influence learning are highlighted in an article by Resnick (1987) contrasting learning in school and outside school. She writes that "school is a special place and time for people—discontinuous in some important ways with daily life and work" (p. 13). There are several ways that school learning differs from other (mostly adult) learning. First, in school, individual cognition has, until recently, been primarily rewarded, whereas outside school shared cognition is the norm. In school "a student succeeds or fails at a task independently of what other students do. . . . In contrast, much activity outside school is socially shared. Work, personal life, and recreation take place within social systems, and each person's ability to function successfully depends on what others do and how several individuals' mental and physical performances mesh" (p. 13). Second, "school is an institution that values thought that proceeds independently, without aid of physical and cognitive tools," at least in testing situations (p. 13). In the real world, people use all sorts of tools on a regular basis, such as books, notes, calculators, and computers, to solve problems and function more effectively. Resnick points out that it is the use of tools that allows "people of limited education to participate in cognitively complex activity systems" and cites Brazilian black market bookies' use of prepared probability tables for functioning in a demanding mathematical system (p. 14). In our own society, personnel in fast food restaurants ring up orders on a computer where the food items are keyed by picture and word.

Resnick also points out that too often school learning is decontextualized, resulting in little transfer between school and real-world reasoning. Finally, generalized learning occurs in school, but situation-specific competencies are needed out of school: "Schools aim to teach general, widely usable skills and theoretical principles. . . . Yet to be truly skillful outside school, people must develop situation-specific forms of competence" (p. 15). What people in all settings (including, Resnick points out, adult technical training, management, and continuing professional education) need to learn is "to be good adaptive learners, so that they can perform effectively when situations are unpredictable and task demands change" (p. 18). Resnick's analysis underscores the contextual differences between learning in childhood and in adulthood and acknowledges the importance of the more recent work on situated cognition and reflective practice (see Chapter Seven).

In delineating differences between children and adults regarding the context, we note that these differences have ramifications with regard to social and ethical issues. Since children's education is preparatory, for example, they are expected to learn certain social and moral values as well as specific bodies of knowledge. Adult education struggles with issues of provision and access to learning opportunities, perhaps because adult education is primarily a voluntary activity, whereas schooling for children is compulsory. Similarly, the ethical issues involved in adult learning differ somewhat in that an adult's learning is often intimately tied to his or her life situation and status as an adult. Questions thus arise regarding agency and responsibility in the learning activity, as well as the outcomes of that interaction. Daloz's (1988) now famous article titled "The Story of Gladys Who Refused to Grow: A Morality Tale for Mentors" explores this very issue of how much adult educators should "push" the development of their adult students.

The context, then, in which adult learning takes place generally differs from the context of most childhood learning. Moreover, every adult learning situation differs from every other situation, whether the learning is done in a formal or nonformal setting or on one's own. Certainly informal learning contexts, including social action and community-based learning, are where much of adult learning takes place. While these contexts vary from individual to individual, they all hold the potential for learning and in fact organize our learning. We need only see them as sites for learning. In a delightful and insightful book on the integration of learning and living, Bateson (1994, p. 9) writes, "When the necessary tasks of learning cannot be completed in a portion of the life cycle set aside for them, they have to join life's other tasks and be done concurrently. We can carry on the process of learning in everything we do, like a mother balancing her child on her hip as she goes about her work with the other hand or uses it to open the doors of the unknown. Living and learning, we become ambidextrous." At another point, she comments on the unfortunate tendency of our society to compartmentalize: "If only for tax purposes, we are forced to label activities as work, or play, or learning, or therapy, or exercise, or stress reduction, missing the seriousness of play, the delight of good work, the healing that happens in the classroom. For adults, learning is rarely the only activity going on. . . . By emphasizing a single thread of activity, we devalue the learning running throughout" (p. 108).

The importance of context is not just that it is interactive with one's learning. There are structural dimensions to our social context, often unseen and unacknowledged, that subtly affect learning. This aspect of context recognizes that our society has become highly multicultural and diverse, and that political and economic conditions often shape the learning experience. It is no longer a question of *whether* in adult learning situations we need to address issues of race, class, gender, culture, ethnicity, and sexual orientation but rather a question of *how* we should deal with these issues, the power dynamics involved, and so on. We are beginning to recognize that it is important to know the backgrounds and experiences of our learners not only as individual learners but also as members of social and culturally constructed groups such as women and men; poor, middle-class, and rich; black, white, and brown. These socially constructed notions of who our learners are and who we are as educators and the subsequent power dynamics should be given the same attention in teaching and learning, planning, and administrative functions as the "technology" (that is, program design, instructional strategies) of our practice. (See Alfred, 2002, Hansman & Sissel, 2001, and St. Clair & Sandlin, 2004, for discussions of sociocultural and political contexts and their impact on adult learning.)

Further, exposure to other groups of people and cultures has been greatly expanded through travel, participation in the global marketplace, and technological wonders such as the World Wide Web. These changes afford all adults opportunities to learn from others and to expand their worldviews. Bateson (1994, p. 17) explains how this kind of exposure can lead to learning: "Each person is calibrated by experience, almost like a measuring instrument for difference, so discomfort [in encountering difference] is informative and offers a starting point for new understanding." She goes on to say that "it is contrast that makes learning possible" (p. 27). The inclusion in this edition of *Learning in Adulthood* of a chapter on non-Western perspectives on learning and knowing acknowledges the still-nascent but growing influence of other epistemological systems on our understanding of adult learning.

THE LEARNING PROCESS

Of the three areas of learner, context, and process, in the learning process there are fewer dramatic differences between adults and children. Houle (1972), one of the field's most respected adult educators, maintained that the process of learning is fundamentally the same for adults and children. Research, however, has uncovered some differences—differences that when linked with context and learner help distinguish adult learning from child learning.

Two process factors in particular—speed and meaningfulness—have been shown to affect adult learning. Speed refers to the time a person has to examine a problem or respond to a situation. An adult's ability to respond slows with age, and time limits and pressures have a negative effect on learning performance. With regard to meaningfulness, perhaps because an adult's learning is so closely tied to his or her life situation, adults are not inclined to engage in learning unless it is meaningful. Adults are thus likely to do poorly on recall of nonsense syllables, for example, compared with younger learners, who are more conditioned by school experiences to learn material that may not be immediately relevant. Linked to the meaningfulness of material is the variable of motivation. MacKeracher (1996, p. 80) defines motives as "the needs that learners feel when starting a learning activity. They may relate to unmet needs or unwanted conditions in life and to the pursuit of positive growth toward desired goals. As learners proceed toward meeting unmet needs, resolving unwanted conditions, or reaching desired goals, motives for learning tend to change in relation to any feelings and experiences of success/failure and satisfaction/dissatisfaction." In summarizing the literature on motivation, MacKeracher observes that "the tendencies which are labeled 'motives' arise from within the learner. Despite encouragement from some writers to 'motivate learners,' facilitators cannot do this directly" (p. 79).

In addition, there are other age-related factors that may affect learning in adulthood. Adults are more likely than children to have health problems. Fatigue, medication, interference from previous learning, environmental conditions, and so on certainly affect new learning. Acquisition of information may become more difficult, because the rate at which working memory processes information seems to be slower with age. The point to be made here is that the nature of the learning process in adulthood is likely to be different from a child's because of the greater incidence of these occurrences and the greater impact of these factors on older learners.

By linking an adult's greater experiential base to learning, a case can be made that cognitive functioning in adulthood may also be qualitatively different from childhood. Recognizing that the prior accumulation of knowledge is crucial to the integration of new learning, and that adults have accumulated more knowledge than children, by extension, learning potential, at least in some areas, would naturally increase with age. Research on fluid and crystallized intelligence bears this generalization out. Other scholars, especially those writing from a transformational learning perspective, do not focus so much on the accumulation of knowledge as on the *transformation* of experience as a characteristic of adult learning.

Finally, it should be noted that those who posit stages of cognitive development in adulthood that are different from those unfolding in childhood contribute to our understanding of how the learning process may be different for adults. Kegan (1994), for example, proposes a level of consciousness model in which dialectical thinking becomes the hallmark, or highest level, of mature adult thinking. Framed from the assumption that our postmodern world necessitates this form of thinking in order to respond effectively to the demands of adult life, Kegan asserts that adults rarely expand their thinking to this level until in their forties or fifties. As Kegan observes, "I suggest that we are gradually seeing more adults working on a qualitatively different order of consciousness than did adults one hundred years ago because we live twenty or more years longer than we used to" (p. 352).

THE CONFIGURATION OF LEARNER, CONTEXT, AND PROCESS

We believe that learning in adulthood can be distinguished from childhood learning by the way in which learner, context, and some aspects of the learning process blend in adulthood. The configuration looks different than it does in childhood. In our discussion of each component, we noted how adults are different from children, how the context of adult learning is different from the context of child learning, and how certain features of the learning process are unique to adults. Although we have attempted to discuss these components separately, our discussion reflects their natural interaction. An adult's life experiences, for example, are a function of the sociocultural environment and the learner's personality. We can think about this interaction with regard to an adult's work experiences. As everyone is aware, the context of work has changed dramatically with the emergence of a global marketplace, advances in technology, and the shift from an industrial to a service and knowledge-based economy. Some adults are training for jobs that did not exist five years ago, many are changing jobs often, and a growing number are experimenting with alternative job structures, such as consulting, telecommuting, and job sharing. Previous experiences as well as one's personality will determine how these changes are accommodated, which in turn affects both one's self-concept as a worker and notions of career development.

How an adult processes information from the sociocultural context, and even what an adult *attends* to in the environment, is wrapped up with the developmental concerns of the moment. A parent of teenagers, for example, is much more likely to notice and perhaps attend a workshop on teenagers and drugs than someone not involved with that age group. And the state of the economy is likely to be of great interest to someone nearing retirement, who might then design a learning project on the topic. In both examples, the sociocultural context, the accumulated life experiences, developmental concerns, and presumably the nature of ensuing learning experiences converge to make learning in adulthood qualitatively different from learning in childhood.

In summarizing the material on learning in adulthood, we also asked ourselves to what extent theory and practice might reflect this integrated perspective of adult learning. The work on self-directed learning or participation, for example, by definition focuses on a particular aspect of the phenomenon. The self-directed learning frameworks emphasize the process, and to a lesser extent, the context and the learner. Similarly, the research on participation does not deal with the learning process per se; rather, the context and the learner are the most important variables.

Some theories or models of adult learning focus on adult characteristics (for example, Knowles, 1980), some emphasize an adult's life situation (for example, McClusky, 1970), and others center on changes in consciousness (for example, Freire, 1970; Mezirow, 2000). These three emphases can be loosely equated with the adult, the context, and the learning process. Knowles's (1980) still-popular notion of andragogy is almost entirely focused on how the adult learner is different from a preadult learner. McClusky (1970) attends to the adult's life situation and social context from which the need or motivation to learn arises.

For both Freire (1970) and Mezirow (2000) learning in adulthood is a transformative rather than an additive process. It requires the ability to reflect critically on one's thoughts and assumptions—a particularly adult skill. Both theories also account for adult characteristics, and in particular, life experiences and developmental concerns unique to adulthood. And in both theories the sociocultural context is a critical component. It is in the sociocultural context that adults have experiences that must be processed. The two differ, however, in the notion of being emancipated through this learning process. Mezirow, while not discounting social change as an outcome of perspective transformation, emphasizes personal psychological change. And while Mezirow's theory of perspective transformation perhaps comes closest to taking into account our notions of context, learner, and process, there are still some questions as to just how comprehensive his theory is. Is the process he outlines unique to adulthood? What about adults who do not reflect critically? Can transformations occur through other mechanisms? His theory seems most appropriate for informal, self-directed learning situations, although several have sought application in more institutionally based settings (Cranton, 1996, 1997; Mezirow & Associates, 1990, 2000; Taylor, Marienau, & Fiddler, 2000).

For Freire, in contrast, being emancipated from false consciousness requires political action aimed at changing society. Critical theory and feminist pedagogy share with Freire their emphases on emancipation and empowerment. Further, both of these orientations begin with the sociopolitical context of people's lives. Critical theory attends to socioeconomic class as the major variable creating inequities and oppression, while feminists look to gender as well as the intersection of race, class, and gender. Both perspectives call for adults to reflect critically on power and oppression and engage with other like-minded adults in a radical restructuring of society.

How well does practice account for the uniqueness of adult learning? This question is difficult to answer without looking at a specific learning situation. Furthermore, it is basically a question of the relationship between theory and practice. To what extent is the knowledge that we have accumulated about adult learning— knowledge reviewed in this book—reflective of what actually happens in practice? Moreover, to what extent is the knowledge that we do have derived from practice, and to what extent does it inform our practice? Cervero (1991) has delineated four positions relative to the interaction between knowledge and practice, each of which can be applied to adult learning. His framework allows us to see how the knowledge presented in this book and practice are related.

The first position posits that the practice of adult learning has been carried out without reference to what is known about how adults learn. This position in fact characterizes much of adult learning, since only a small percentage of teachers, administrators, program developers, and others have had any formal training in adult education. From this position, those working with adult learners rely on common sense and trial-and-error learning, a less formal but certainly no less valuable source of guidance for practice.

The second position is that a systematically collected knowledge base illuminates practice. It is thought that if this knowledge is disseminated through professional preparation, in-service staff development, and so on, practice will be strengthened. Lists of principles and guidelines, for example, such as those reviewed at the beginning of the chapter, are often disseminated through workshops and in-house publications, ostensibly to improve one's practice in adult learning. There are also numerous publications that attempt to show how knowledge about context, learner, and process could be put into practice. *Andragogy in Action* (Knowles & Associates, 1984), for example, presents thirty-six case studies of how characteristics of adult learners can be incorporated into the planning of learning activities in settings ranging from business and government to universities and volunteer organizations. In another publication, *Improving Higher Education Environments for Adults* (1989), Schlossberg, Lynch, and Chickering show how adult life experiences and adult developmental theory can form the basis for programs and support services for learners in higher education. Finally, Cranton's *Transformative Learning in Action: Insights from Practice* (1997) and Mezirow and Associates' *Fostering Critical Reflection in Adulthood* (1990) and *Learning as Transformation* (2000) review exemplary programs and suggest methods "for precipitating and fostering transformative learning in the context of the classroom, in special workshops, in informal group settings, in collective social action, in counseling sessions, and in the workplace" (Mezirow & Associates, 1990, p. xv).

The third position on the relationship between knowledge and practice is that educators operate intuitively with an understanding of adult learning whether or not that knowledge is articulated. This theory-in-practice position holds that "practitioners actually do operate on the basis of theories and knowledge" and that "theory can be derived from practice by systematically articulating the subjective meaning structures that influence the ways that real individuals act in concrete situations" (Cervero, 1991, pp. 26–27). This notion has been investigated with regard to professional practice (Schön, 1987, 1991, 1996) and is now being promoted in adult education, especially in the work of Cervero and Wilson (1994, 2005).

With regard to the learning situation and other aspects of adult education, the central task of this approach is to "describe educational practice and help practitioners become more reflective about their own individual actions" (Cervero, 1991, p. 29). The orientation of our book—in particular, our attending to context and exploring social issues—reflects the critical stance toward practice inherent in this position.

The fourth position on theory and practice is that they are indivisible. Here the focus is on "what counts as knowledge and how, where, and by whom this knowledge is produced" (Cervero, 1991, p. 31). Understanding the production of knowledge is emancipating. This perspective is best illustrated by critical theory, postmodernism, and feminist theoretical assumptions about knowledge and learning. More than the first three positions, this perspective—that theory and practice are indivisible—takes into account the political, economic, and sociocultural context in which learning occurs. Examples of adult education practice from this perspective are community-based literacy programs, feminist pedagogy, critical pedagogy, popular education programs and movements, and participatory research activities (Merriam, 1991). Participatory research "has faith in people's ability to produce their own knowledge through collective investigation of problems and issues, collective analysis of the problems, and collective action to change the conditions that gave rise to the problems in the first place" (Gaventa, 1988, p. 19). This method of producing knowledge, indeed this perspective on the relationship between theory and practice, makes space for alternative knowledge systems that have been excluded from the "official" body of knowledge. While we recognize that, for the most part, the material presented in this book is representative of "official" knowledge, we hope that some of the less mainstream information that we have included will stimulate further research to make such unconventional knowledge more visible.

SOME CONCLUDING THOUGHTS

In this final chapter, we have articulated our understanding of learning in adulthood and assessed how well learner, context, and process as a unique configuration in adulthood are reflected in theory and in practice. We conclude with some observations and suggestions. First, we think the field has developed a significant knowledge base about learning in adulthood, much of it fairly recent. We are optimistic that learning in adulthood will continue to interest researchers and educators and that we will know quite a bit more within the next several years. Second, the nature of contributions in this area is changing. Adult educators are moving from description to theory building and looking at adult learning more holistically, as attested to by our two new chapters: "Embodied, Spiritual, and Narrative Learning" and "Learning and Knowing: Non-Western Perspectives." The field is also considering the sociocultural context in which learning takes place, how race, class, gender, able-bodiedness, sexual orientation, and so on affect learning, thus shifting from a primarily psychological orientation to a broader contextual view. We are indeed more cognizant of the social issues and dilemmas involved in the provision and practice of adult learning. And we are examining notions about how knowledge about adult learning itself is produced and legitimized.

We are hopeful that learners themselves will be a great source of our understanding of learning in adulthood. In fact, we suggest that future research in adult learning be collaboratively designed with adults who are learning on their own or in informal ways, as well as with participants in formal and nonformal learning activities. Focusing on adults would counter some of the research on the learning process itself, which more often than not employs nonadults or select populations such as college students. We also suggest that research that takes into account the sociocultural and political context of adult learning might well advance our understanding of the problems of access and opportunity that continue to trouble the field. While this book has drawn from a voluminous literature base, we still feel there is much to be learned about learning in adulthood. We hope that readers will be inspired to think about their practice with adult learners and contribute in some way to our further understanding of this very complex phenomenon.

REFERENCES

Abdullah, A. (1996). *Going glocal: Cultural dimensions in Malaysian management*. Kuala Lumpur: Malaysian Institute of Management.

Ahmad, N., & Seidman, M. (2004). Tinnitus in the older adult: Epidemiology, pathophysiology and treatment options. *Drugs & Aging, 21*(5), 297–305.

Ahteenmaki-Pelkonen, L. (1994). From self-directedness to interdependence? An analysis of Mezirow's conceptualization of self-directed learning. In S. Tosse, B. Wahlgren, J. Manninen, & M. Klasson (Eds.), *Social change and adult education research: Adult education research in Nordic countries 1992/93* (pp. 173–183). Linkoping, Sweden: Linkoping Adult Education Research Group, Linkoping University. (ERIC Document Reproduction Service No. ED 374 213)

Albert, M. S., & Killiany, R. J. (2001). Age-related cognitive change and brain-behavior relationships. In J. E. Birren & K. S. Schaie (Eds.), *Handbook of psychology and aging* (5th ed., pp.161–185). San Diego, CA: Academic Press.

Albright, T. D., & Neville, H. J. (1999). Neurosciences. In R. A. Wilson & F. C. Keil (Eds.), *The MIT encyclopedia of the cognitive sciences* (pp. li–lxxii). Boston: Massachusetts Institute of Technology Press.

Alderson, K. G. (2003). The ecological model of gay male identity. *The Canadian Journal of Human Sexuality, 12*(2), 75–85.

Alfred, M. V. (2000). Philosophical foundations of andragogy and self-directed learning: A critical analysis from an Africentric feminist perspective. . . . In M. Glowacki-Dudka (Ed.), *Proceedings of the 19th Annual Midwest Research to Practice Conference in Adult, Continuing, and Community Education* (pp. 21–26). Madison: University of Wisconsin.

Alfred, M. V. (Ed.). (2002). *Learning and sociocultural contexts: Implications for adults, community, and workplace education*. New Directions for Adult and Continuing Education, No. 96. San Francisco: Jossey-Bass.

Alfred, M. V. (2004). Immigration as a context for learning: What do we know about immigrant students in adult education? In E. E. Clover (Ed.), *Proceedings of the Joint International Conference of the 45th Annual Adult Education Research Conference and the Canadian Association for the*

Study of Adult Education (pp. 13–18). Victoria, Canada: University of Victoria.

Allen, I. E., & Seaman, J. (2004). *Entering the mainstream: The quality and extent of online education in the United States, 2003 and 2004.* Needham, MA: Sloan Center for Online Education.

Amann, T. (2003). Creating space for somatic ways of knowing within transformative learning theory. In C. A. Wiessner, S. R. Meyer, N. L. Pfhal, & P. G. Neaman (Eds.), *Proceedings of the Fifth International Conference on Transformative Learning* (pp. 26–32). New York: Teacher's College, Columbia University.

Amstutz, D. D. (1994). Staff development: Addressing issues of race and gender. In E. Hayes & S.A.J. Colin III (Eds.), *Confronting racism and sexism* (pp. 39–51). New Directions for Adult and Continuing Education, No. 61. San Francisco: Jossey-Bass.

Anderson, J. R. (1988). Cognitive styles and multicultural populations. *Journal of Teacher Education, 39*(1), 2–9.

Anderson, J. R. (1993). *Rules of the mind.* Hillsdale, NJ: Erlbaum.

Anderson, J. R., Reder, L. M., & Simon, H. A. (1996). Situated learning and education. *Educational Researcher, 25*(4), 5–11.

Anderson, J. R. (2005). *Cognitive psychology and its implications* (6th ed.). New York: Freeman.

Anderson, N. H. (1996). *A functional theory of cognition.* Hillsdale, NJ: Erlbaum.

Andruske, C. L. (2000). Self-directed learning as a political act: Learning projects of women on welfare. In T. Sork, V. Chapman, & R. St. Clair (Eds.), *Proceedings of the 41st Annual Adult Education Research Conference* (pp. 11–15). Vancouver: University of British Columbia.

Antone, E. M., & Gamlin, P. (2004). Foundations for Aboriginal adult literacy. In D. E. Clover (Ed.), *Proceedings of the Joint International Conference of the 45th Adult Education Research Conference and the Canadian Association for the Study of Adult Education* (pp. 25–30). Victoria, Canada: University of Victoria.

Argyris, C., & Schön, D. A. (1978). *Organizational learning: A theory of action perspective.* San Francisco: Jossey-Bass.

Argyris, C., & Schön, D. A. (1996). *Organizational learning II—Theory, method, practice.* Reading, MA: Addison-Wesley.

Arlin, P. K. (1975). Cognitive development in adulthood: A fifth stage? *Developmental Psychology, 11,* 602–606.

Arlin, P. K. (1984). Adolescent and adult thought: A structural interpretation. In M. L. Commons, F. A. Richards, & C. Armon (Eds.), *Beyond formal operations: Late adolescent and adult cognitive development* (pp. 258–271). New York: Praeger.

Aslanian, C. B. (2001). *Adult students today.* New York: College Board.

Aslanian, C. B., & Brickell, H. M. (1980). *Americans in transition: Life changes as reasons for adult learning.* New York: College Entrance Examination Board.

Association for Clinical Pastoral Education. (n.d.). *Assessment tool description and definition.* http://www.ncracpe.org. Accessed September 22, 2003.

Ausubel, D. P. (1967). A cognitive structure theory of school learning. In L. Siegel (Ed.), *Instruction: Some contemporary viewpoints* (pp. 207–260). San Francisco: Chandler.

Bagnall, R. G. (1995). Discriminative justice and responsibility in post-modernist adult education. *Adult Education Quarterly, 45*(2), 79–94.

Bagnall, R. G. (1999). *Discovering radical contingency: Building a postmodern agenda in adult education.* New York: Peter Lang.

Baltes, P. B. (1982). Life-span development psychology: Some conveying observations on history and theory. In K. W. Schaie & J. Geiwitz (Eds.), *Readings in adult development and aging* (pp. 12–25). Boston: Little, Brown.

Baltes, P. B. (1987). Theoretical propositions of life-span developmental psychology: On the dynamics between growth and decline. *Developmental Psychology, 23,* 611–626.

Baltes, P. B. (1993). The aging mind: Potential and limits. *Gerontologist, 33*(5), 580–594.

Baltes, P. B., & Lindenberger, U. (1997). Emergence of a powerful connection between sensory and cognitive functions across the adult life span: A new window to the study of cognitive aging? *Psychology and Aging, 12*(1), 12–21.

Baltes, P. B., & Smith, J. (1990). Toward a psychology of wisdom and its ontogenesis. In R. J. Sternberg (Ed.), *Wisdom: Its nature, origins, and development* (pp. 87–120). Cambridge, MA: Harvard University Press.

Bandura, A. (1976). Modeling theory. In W. S. Sahakian (Ed.), *Learning: Systems, models, and theories* (2nd ed., pp. 391–409). Skokie, IL: Rand McNally.

Bandura, A. (1986). *Social foundations of thought and action: A social cognitive theory.* Englewood Cliffs, NJ: Prentice Hall.

Banks, J. A., & Banks, C.A.M. (1997). *Multicultural education: Issues and perspectives* (3rd ed.). Needham Heights, MA: Allyn & Bacon.

Baptiste, I. (1998). Towards a pedagogy of disempowering our enemies. In J. Kimmel (Ed.), *Proceedings of the 39th Annual Adult Education Research Conference* (pp. 13–18). San Antonio: University of the Incarnate Word and Texas A&M University.

Baron, C. E. (2003). The study of the intersection of Perry's scheme of intellectual development and women's ways of knowing epistemological perspectives. *Dissertation Abstracts International, 64*(02), 415A. (UMI No. 3080570)

Bar-On, R. (1997). *The Emotional Quotient Inventory (EQ-i). Technical manual.* Toronto: Multi-Health System.

Baron-Cohen, S., (2005). The essential difference: The male and female brain. *Phi Kappa Phi Forum, 85*(1), 23–27.

Barrett, A. E. (2005). Gendered experiences in midlife: Implications for age identity. *Journal of Aging Studies, 19*(2), 163–183.

Basseches, M. (1984). *Dialectical thinking and adult development.* Norwood, NJ: Ablex.

Bassett, C. (2005). Emergent wisdom: Living in widening circles. *ReVision: A Journal of Consciousness and Transformation,* 27(4), 6–11.

Bateson, M. C. (1994). *Peripheral visions: Learning along the way.* New York: HarperCollins.

Baum, J. (1980). Testing the Theory of Margin using a population of widows. In *Proceedings of the 21st Annual Adult Education Research Conference* (pp. 17–21). Vancouver: University of British Columbia.

Baumgartner, L. M. (2001). An update on transformative learning. In S. Merriam (Ed.), *The new update on adult learning theory* (pp. 15–24). New Directions for Adult and Continuing Education, No. 89. San Francisco: Jossey-Bass.

Baumgartner, L. M. (2002). Living and learning with HIV/AIDS: Transformative tales continued. *Adult Education Quarterly, 53*(1), 44–59.

Baumgartner, L. M., & Merriam, S. B. (1999). *Adult development and learning: Multicultural stories.* Malabar, FL: Krieger.

Baxter Magolda, M. (1992). *Knowing and reasoning in college: Gender-related patterns in students' intellectual development.* San Francisco: Jossey-Bass.

Baxter Magolda, M. (2004). Evolution of a constructivist conceptualization of epistemological reflection. *Educational Psychologist, 39*(1), 31–42.

Baxter Magolda, M. B., & King, P. M. (Eds.). (2004). *Learning partnerships: Theory and models of practice to educate for self-authorship.* Sterling, VA: Stylus.

Beard, C., & Wilson, J. P. (2002). *The power of experiential learning: A handbook for trainers and educators.* London: Kogan Page.

Beauty at Every Age Is the Maxim. (2005, March 7). *Business and Industry MMR, 22*(5), 14. http://www.highbeam.com/library/doc3.asp?DOCID=1G1:130722681&num=1&ctrlInfo=Round19%3AProd%3ASR%3AResult&ao=1&FreePremium=BOTH. Accessed July 29, 2005.

Beckett, D., & Morris, G. (2001). Ontological performance: Bodies, identities and learning. *Studies in the Education of Adults, 33*(1), 35–48.

Becvar, R. J. (2005). On wisdom and becoming wise. *ReVision: A Journal of Consciousness and Transformation,* 27(4), 28–32.

Beder, H. (1987). Dominant paradigms, adult education, and social justice. *Adult Education Quarterly, 37*(2), 105–113.

Beder, H., & Darkenwald, G. (1982). Differences between teaching adults and pre-adults: Some propositions and findings. *Adult Education, 32*(3), 142–155.

Bee, H. L. (1996). *The journey of adulthood* (3rd ed.). Englewood Cliffs, NJ: Prentice Hall.

Bee, H. L., & Bjorkland, B. R. (2004). *The journey of adulthood.* (5th ed.). Englewood Cliffs, NJ: Prentice Hall.

Belanger, P. (1996). Trends in adult education policy. *Adult Education and Development, 47,* 19–29.

Belenky, M. F., Clinchy, B. M., Goldberger, N. R., & Tarule, J. M. (1986). *Women's ways of knowing: The development of self, voice, and mind.* New York: Basic Books.

Bell, Y. R. (1994). A culturally sensitive analysis of Black learning style. *Journal of Black Psychology, 20*(1), 47–61.

Belzer, A. (2004). "It's not like normal school": The role of prior learning contexts in adult learning. *Adult Education Quarterly, 55*(1), 41–59.

Benack, S., & Basseches, M. A. (1989). Dialectical thinking and relativistic epistemology: Their relation in adult development. In M. L. Commons, J. D. Sinnott, F. A. Richards, & C. Armon (Eds.), *Adult Development: Vol. 1: Comparisons and applications of developmental models* (pp. 95–109). New York: Praeger.

Benally, H. J. (1997). The pollen path: The Navajo way of knowing. In R. P. Foehr & S. A. Schiller (Eds.), *The spiritual side of writing* (pp. 84–94). Portsmouth, NH: Boynton/Cook.

Benn, R. (1997). Participation in adult education: Breaking boundaries or developing inequalities? In P. Armstrong, N. Miller, & M. Zukas (Eds.), *Crossing Borders, Breaking Boundaries: Proceedings of the 27th Annual SCUTREA Conference* (pp. 31–34). London: Birbeck College, University of London.

Benson, H., Corliss, J., & Cowley, G. (2004, September 27). Brain check. *Newsweek,* pp. 45–47.

Berg, C. A. (2000). Intellectual development in adulthood. In R. J. Sternberg (Ed.), *Handbook of intelligence* (pp. 117–137). New York: Cambridge University Press.

Berger, K. S. (1998). *The developing person through the life span* (4th ed.). New York: Worth.

Berger, N. (1990). *A qualitative study of the process of self-directed learning.* Unpublished doctoral dissertation, Virginia Commonwealth University, Richmond.

Beswick, D. M., Chuprina, L., Canipe, J. B., & Cox, B. (2002). *Investigating self-directed learning in culture, learning styles, and creativity.* Columbus, OH: ERIC Clearinghouse on Adult and Vocational Education. (ERIC Document Reproduction Service No. ED 473 804)

Bierema, L. L. (2005). Critical human resource development education: A review of the literature and recommendations for teaching. In D. Vlosak, G. Kielbaso, & J. Radford (Eds.), *Proceedings of the 6th International Conference on Transformative Learning* (pp. 35–46). East Lansing: Michigan State University.

Bierema, L. L., & Cseh, M. (2003). Evaluating HRD research using a feminist research framework. *Human Resource Development Quarterly, 14*(1), 5–26.

Bills, D. B. (2004). *The sociology of education and work.* Malden, MA: Blackwell.

Binet, A. (1916). *The development of intelligence in children* [the Binet-Simon Scale]. Baltimore: Williams & Williams.

Bishop, R., & Glynn, T. (2003). *Culture counts: Changing power relations in education.* London: Zed Books.

Blacksher, B. (2001). Education to self-knowledge: Students' self-awareness through reflection in response to literature by African American women. *Dissertation Abstracts International, 62*(07), 2356A. (UMI No. 3021249)

Bolhuis, S. (2003). Towards process-oriented teaching for self-directed lifelong learning: A multidimensional perspective. *Learning and Instruction, 13*(3), 327–347.

Bolman, L., & Deal, T. E. (1995). *Leading with soul: An uncommon journey of spirit.* San Francisco: Jossey-Bass.

Boshier, R. (1991). Psychometric properties of the alternative form of the education participation scale. *Adult Education Quarterly, 41*(3), 150–167.

Boshier, R. (2005). Lifelong learning. In L. M. English (Ed.), *International encyclopedia of adult education* (pp. 373–378). New York: Palgrave Macmillan.

Boshier, R., & Collins, J. B. (1985). The Houle typology after twenty-two years: A large-scale empirical test. *Adult Education Quarterly, 35*(3), 113–130.

Boucouvalas, M. (1988). An analysis and critique of the concept of self in self-directed learning: Toward a more robust construct for research and practice. In M. Zukas (Ed.), *Papers from the transatlantic dialogue: SCUTREA 1988* (pp. 56–61). Leeds, England: School of Continuing Education, University of Leeds.

Boucouvalas, M. (1993). Consciousness and learning: New and renewed approaches. In S. Merriam (Ed.), *An update on adult learning theory* (pp. 57–70). New Directions for Adult and Continuing Education, No. 57. San Francisco: Jossey-Bass.

Boud, D., Keogh, R., & Walker, D. (1985). *Reflection: Turning experience into learning.* New York: Kogan Page.

Boud, D., Keogh, R., & Walker, D. (1996). Promoting reflection in learning: A model. In R. Edwards, A. Hanson, & P. Raggatt (Eds.), *Boundaries of adult learning* (pp. 32–56). New York: Routledge.

Boud, D., & Walker, D. (1991). *Experience and learning: Reflection at work.* Geelong, Victoria: Deakin University Press.

Boudard, E., & Rubenson, K. (2003). Revisiting major determinants of participation in adult education with a direct measure of literacy skills. *International Journal of Educational Research, 39*(3), 265–281.

Bowles, D. D. (1993). Bi-racial identity: Children born to African American and White couples. *Clinical Social Work Journal, 21*(4), 417–428.

Bowman, S. L., Rasheed, S., Ferris, J., Thompson, D. A., McRae, M., & Weitzman, L. (2001). Interface of feminism and multiculturalism: Where are the women of color? In J. G. Ponterotto, J. M. Casas, L. A. Suzuki, & C. M. Alexander (Eds.), *Handbook of multicultural counseling* (2nd ed., pp. 779–798). Thousand Oaks, CA: Sage.

Boyd, R. D. (1989). Facilitating personal transformations in small groups: Part I. *Small Group Behavior, 20*(4), 459–474.

Boyd, R. D. (1991). *Personal transformations in small groups: A Jungian perspective.* New York: Routledge.

Boyd, R. D., & Myers, J. G. (1988). Transformative education. *International Journal of Lifelong Education, 7*(4), 261–284.

Brady, E. M., & Sky, H. Z. (2003). Journal writing among older learners. *Educational Gerontology, 29,* 151–163.

Brandt, B. L., Farmer, J. A. Jr., & Buckmaster, A. (1993). Cognitive apprenticeship approach to helping adults learning. In D. Flannery (Ed.), *Applying cognitive learning theory to adult learning* (pp. 69–78). San Francisco: Jossey-Bass.

Brennan, B. (1997). Reconceptualizing non-formal education. *International Journal of Lifelong Education, 16*(3), 185–200.

Briskin, A. (1996). *The stirring of soul in the workplace.* San Francisco: Jossey-Bass.

Brockett, R. G. (1985). Methodological and substantive issues in the measurement of self-directed learning readiness. *Adult Education quarterly, 36*(1), 15–24.

Brockett, R. G. (1994). Resistance to self-direction in adult learning: Myths and misunderstandings. In R. Hiemstra & R. G. Brockett (Eds.), *Overcoming resistance to self-directed adult learning* (pp. 5–12). New Directions for Adult and Continuing Education, No. 64. San Francisco: Jossey-Bass.

Brockett, R. G. (2000). Is it time to move on? Reflections on a research agenda for self- directed learning in the 21st century. In T. Sork, V. Chapman, & R. St. Clair (Eds.), *Proceedings of the 41st Annual Adult Education Research Conference* (pp. 543–544). Vancouver: University of British Columbia.

Brockett, R. G., & Hiemstra, R. (1991). *Self-direction in adult learning: Perspectives on theory, research, and practice.* New York: Routledge.

Brockman, J. (2001). A somatic epistemology for education. *Educational Forum, 65*(4), 328–334.

Brody, N. (2003). Construct validation of the Sternberg Triarchic Abilities Test. *Intelligence, 31*(4), 319–329.

Brody, N. (2004). Review of the book *Emotional intelligence: Science and myth. Intelligence, 32*(1), 109–111.

Bronfenbrenner, U. (2001). Human development, bioecological theory of. In N. J. Smelser & P. B. Battles (Eds.), *International encyclopedia of the social and behavioral sciences* (pp. 6963–6970). Washington, DC: American Psychological Association.

Bronfenbrenner, U. (2005). Is 80% of intelligence genetically determined? In U. Bronfenbrenner (Ed.), *Making human beings human: Bioecological perspective on human development* (pp. 234–245). Thousand Oaks, CA: Sage.

Brookfield, S. (1984). Self-directed adult learning: A critical paradigm. *Adult Education Quarterly, 35*(2), 59–71.

Brookfield, S. (1985). Self-directed learning: A critical review of research. In S. Brookfield (Ed.), *Self-directed learning: From theory to practice* (pp. 5–16). New Directions for Continuing Education, No. 25. San Francisco: Jossey-Bass.

Brookfield, S. (1986). *Understanding and facilitating adult learning.* San Francisco: Jossey-Bass.

Brookfield, S. (1987). *Developing critical thinkers.* San Francisco: Jossey-Bass.

Brookfield, S. (1993). Self-directed learning, political clarity, and the critical practice of adult education. *Adult Education Quarterly, 43*(4), 227–242.

Brookfield, S. (1994). Tales from the dark side: A phenomenography of adult critical reflection. In M. Hyams, J. Armstrong, & E. Anderson (Compilers), *Proceedings of the 35th Annual Adult Education Research Conference* (pp. 55–60). Knoxville: University of Tennessee.

Brookfield, S. (1996). Breaking the code: Engaging practitioners in critical analysis of adult educational literature. In R. Edwards, A. Hanson, & P. Raggatt (Eds.), *Boundaries of Adult Learning* (pp. 57–81). New York: Routledge.

Brookfield, S. (2000). Transformative learning as ideology critique. In J. Mezirow & Associates (Eds.), *Learning as transformation: Critical perspectives on a theory in progress* (pp. 125–148). San Francisco: Jossey-Bass.

Brookfield, S. (2001). Repositioning ideology critique in a critical theory of adult learning. *Adult Education Quarterly, 52*(1), 7–22.

Brookfield, S. (2002). Overcoming alienation as a practice of adult education: The contribution of Erich Fromm to a critical theory of adult learning and education. *Adult Education Quarterly, 52*(2), 96–111.

Brookfield, S. (2005a). Overcoming impostership, cultural suicide and lost innocence: Implications for teaching critical thinking in the community college. In C. M. McMahon (ed.), *Special issue: Critical thinking: Unfinished business* (pp. 49–57). New Directions for Community Colleges, No. 130. San Francisco: Jossey-Bass.

Brookfield, S. (2005b). *The power of critical theory: Liberating adult learning and teaching.* San Francisco: Jossey-Bass.

Brooks, A. K. (2000). Cultures of transformation. In A. L. Wilson & E. R. Hayes (Eds.), *Handbook of adult and continuing education* (pp. 161–170). San Francisco: Jossey-Bass.

Brooks, A. K., & Clark, C. (2001). Narrative dimensions of transformative learning. In R. O. Smith, J. M. Dirkx, P. L. Eddy, P. L. Farrell, & M. Polzin (Eds.), *Proceedings of the 42nd Annual Adult Education Research Conference* (pp. 65–70). East Lansing: Michigan State University.

Brown, A. H., Cervero, R. M., & Johnson-Bailey, J. (2000). Making the invisible visible: Race, gender and teaching in adult education. *Adult Education Quarterly, 50*(4), 273–288.

Brown, A. J. (2000). Social influences on individual commitment to self-directed learning at work. In G. A. Straka (Ed.), *Conceptions of self-directed learning* (pp. 23–36). New York: Waxmann.

Brown, J. S., Collins, A., & Duguid, P. (1989). Situated cognition and the culture of learning. *Educational Researcher, 18*(1), 32–42.

Bruce, L., Aring, M., & Brand, B. (1998). Informal learning: The new frontier of employee & organizational development. *Economic Development Review, 15*(4), 12–18.

Bruer, J. T. (1993). *Schools for thought: A science of learning in the classroom.* Cambridge, MA: MIT Press.

Bruer, J. T. (1997). Education and the brain: A bridge too far. *Educational Researcher, 26*(8), 4–16.

Bruner, J. (1965). The art of discovery. In R. C. Anderson & D. P. Ausubel (Eds.), *Readings in the psychology of cognition* (pp. 606–620). New York: Holt, Rinehart.

Bruner, J. (1986). *Actual minds, possible worlds.* Cambridge, MA: Harvard University Press.

Brysk, A. (2003). Globalization and human rights: It's a small world after all. *Phi Kappa Phi Forum, 83*(4), 21–24.

Burack, O. R., & Lachkman, M. E. (1996). The effects of list-making on recall in young and elderly adults. *Journal of Gerontology: Psychological Sciences, 51*(4), 226–233.

Cabeza, R., Anderson, N. D., Locantore, J. K., & McIntosh, B. R. (2002). Aging gracefully: Compensatory brain activity in high-performing older adults. *NeuroImage, 17*, 1394–1402.

Caffarella, R. S. (1992). *Psychosocial development of women: Linkages to teaching and leadership in adult education.* Information Series No. 350. Columbus, OH: ERIC Clearinghouse of Adult, Career, and Vocational Education.

Caffarella, R. S. (1993). Self-directed learning. In S. B. Merriam (Ed.), *An update on adult learning theory* (pp. 25–36). New Directions for Adult and Continuing Education, No. 57. San Francisco: Jossey-Bass.

Caffarella, R. S. (2000). Goals of self-directed learning. In G. A. Straka (Ed.), *Conceptions of self-directed learning: Theoretical and conceptual considerations* (pp. 37–48). Berlin, Germany: Waxmann.

Caffarella, R. S., & O'Donnell, J. M. (1987). Self-directed adult learning: A critical paradigm revisited. *Adult Education Quarterly, 37,* 199–211.

Caffarella, R. S., & O'Donnell, J. M. (1989). *Self-directed learning.* Nottingham, England: Department of Adult Education, University of Nottingham.

Caine, R. N., & Caine, G. (1994). *Making connections: Teaching and the human brain.* Reading, MA: Addison-Wesley.

Cajete, G. (1994). *Look to the mountain: An ecology of indigenous education.* Skyland, NC: Kivaki Press.

Cameron, S. W. (1983). The Perry Scheme: A new perspective on adult learners. In R. Cervero, M. Collins, M. Even, & N. Robbins (Eds.), *Proceedings of the 24th Annual Adult Education Research Conference* (pp. 38–43). Montreal: Université de Montreal, Faculté de l'Education Permanente.

Candy, P. C. (1987). Evolution, revolution or devolution: Increasing learner control in the instructional setting. In D. Boud & V. Griffin (Eds.), *Appreciating adults learning: From the learner's perspective* (pp. 159–178). London: Kogan Page.

Candy, P. C. (1991). *Self-direction for lifelong learning.* San Francisco: Jossey-Bass.

Canipe, J. B., & Fogerson, D. L. (2004, February). *The literature on self-directed learning: Dissertations.* Paper presented at the meeting of the 18th International Self-Directed Learning Symposium, Cocoa Beach, FL.

Canipe, J. B., Fogerson, D. L., & Duffley-Renow, P. (2005, February). *A content analysis of articles on self-directed learning in ERIC: 1993–2003.* Paper presented at the meeting of the 19th International Self-Directed Learning Symposium, Cocoa Beach, FL.

Capps, D. (2004). The decades of life: Relocating Erikson's stages. *Pastoral Psychology, 53*(1), 3–32.

Carey, J. R. (2003). Theories of life span and aging. In P. Timiras (Ed.), *Physiological basis of aging and geriatrics* (pp. 85–95). New York: CRC Press.

Carney, R. N., & Levine, J. R. (1998). Mnemonic strategies for adult learners. In M. C. Smith & T. Poucot (Eds.), *Adult learning and development: Perspectives from educational psychology* (pp. 159–175). Mahwah, NJ: Erlbaum.

Carroll, J. B. (1993). *Human cognitive abilities: A survey of factor analytic studies*. Cambridge, UK: Cambridge University Press.

Carter, T. J. (2000). The voice of relationship: Transformative learning through developmental relationships in the lives of mid-career women. *Dissertation Abstracts International, 61*(12), 4976A. (UMI No. 9999877)

Cass, V. C. (1979). Homosexual identity formation: A theoretical model. *Journal of Homosexuality, 4*(3), 219–235.

Cassidy, S. (2004). Learning styles: An overview of theories, models, and measures. *Educational Psychology, 24*(4), 419–444.

Cattell, R. B. (1963). Theory of fluid and crystallized intelligence: A critical experiment. *Journal of Educational Psychology, 54,* 1–22.

Cattell, R. B. (1987). *Intelligence: Its structure, growth and action*. Amsterdam: Elsevier.

Caudron, S. (1999). Free agent learner. *Training & Development, 53*(8), 26–30.

Cavaliere, L. A. (1992). The Wright brothers' odyssey: Their flight of learning. In L. A. Cavaliere & A. Sgroi (Eds.), *Learning for personal development* (pp. 51–60). New Directions for Adult and Continuing Education, No. 53. San Francisco: Jossey-Bass.

Cervero, R. M. (1988). *Effective continuing education for professionals*. San Francisco: Jossey-Bass.

Cervero, R. M. (1991). Relationships between theory and practice. In J. Peters & P. Jarvis (Eds.), *Adult Education: Evolution and Achievements in a Developing Field of Study* (pp. 19–41). San Francisco: Jossey-Bass.

Cervero, R. M., & Wilson, A. L. (1994). *Planning responsibly for adult education: A guide to negotiating power and interests*. San Francisco: Jossey-Bass.

Cervero, R. M., & Wilson, A. L. (2005). *Working the planning table: Negotiating democratically for adult, continuing and workplace education*. San Francisco: Jossey-Bass.

Chapman, V. (2002). "Knowing one's self": Selfwriting, power and ethical practice. In J. M. Pettitt (Ed.), *Proceedings of the 43rd Annual Adult Education Research Conference* (pp. 73–78). Raleigh: North Carolina State University.

Chene, A. (1983). The concept of autonomy: A philosophical discussion. *Adult Education Quarterly, 34,* 38–47.

Cheville, J. (2005). Confronting the problem of embodiment. *International Journal of Qualitative Studies in Education, 18*(1), 85–107.

Cho, D. (2002). The connection between self-directed learning and the learning organization. *Human Resource Development Quarterly, 13*(4), 467–470.

Choi, J., & Hannafin, M. (1995). Situated cognition and learning environments: Roles, structures, and implications for design. *Educational Technology Research and Design, 43*(2), 53–69.

Chua, A. (2003). Globalization and ethnic hatred. *Phi Kappa Phi Forum,* *83*(4), 13–16.

Clancey, W. J. (1997). *Situated cognition: On human knowledge and computer representations.* New York: Cambridge University Press.

Clardy, A. (2000). Learning on their own: Vocationally oriented self-directed learning projects. *Human Resource Development Quarterly, 11*(2), 105–126.

Clark, M. C. (1997). Learning as a non-unitary self: Implications of postmodernism for adult learning theory. In P. Armstrong, N. Miller, & M. Zukas (Eds.), *Crossing Borders, Breaking Boundaries: Proceedings of the 27th Annual SCUTREA Conference* (pp. 108–111). London: Birbeck College, University of London.

Clark, M. C., & Caffarella, R. S. (1999). Theorizing adult development. In M. C. Clark & R. S. Caffarella (Eds.), *An update on adult development theory: New ways of thinking about the life course* (pp. 3–8). New Directions for Adult and Continuing Education, No. 84. San Francisco: Jossey-Bass.

Clark, M. C., & Dirkx, J. M. (2000). Moving beyond a unitary self: A reflective dialogue. In A. L. Wilson & E. R. Hayes (Eds.), *Handbook of adult and continuing education* (pp. 101–116). San Francisco: Jossey-Bass.

Clark, M. C., & Wilson, A. L. (1991). Context and rationality in Mezirow's theory of transformational learning. *Adult Education Quarterly, 41*(2), 75–91.

Clinchy, B. M. (2002). Revisiting women's ways of knowing. In B. K. Hofer & P. R. Pintrich (Eds.), *Personal epistemology: The psychology of beliefs about knowledge and knowing* (pp. 63–88). Hillsdale, NJ: Erlbaum.

Cobb, P. (1994). Where is the mind? Constructivist and sociocultural perspectives on mathematical development. *Educational Researcher, 23*(7), 13–20.

Coffield, F., Moseley, D., Hall, E., & Ecclestone, K. (2004). *Should we be using learning styles? What research has to say about practice?* London: Learning & Skills Center.

Cognition and Technology Group at Vanderbilt. (1990). Anchored instruction and its relation to situated cognition. *Educational Researcher, 19*(6), 2–10.

Cognition and Technology Group at Vanderbilt. (2000). Adventures in anchored instruction: Lessons from beyond the ivory tower. In R. Glaser (Ed.), *Advances in instructional psychology: Educational design and cognitive science* (Vol. 5, pp. 35–100). Hillsdale, NJ: Erlbaum.

Cohen, N. H. (1995). *Mentoring adult learners: A guide for educators and trainers.* Melbourne, FL: Krieger.

Cole, T. B., & Glass, R. M. (2004). Learning associated with participation in journal-based continuing medical education. *Journal of Continuing Education in the Health Professions, 24*(4), 205–212.

Colin, S.A.J. III, & Preciphs, T. K. (1991). Perceptual patterns and the learning environment: Confronting white racism. In R. Hiemstra (Ed.), *Creating environments for effective adult learning* (pp. 61–70). New Directions for Adult and Continuing Education, No. 50. San Francisco: Jossey-Bass.

Collard, S. (1995). Remapping adult education: Beyond social movement and professionalization. In P. Collette, B. Einsiedel, & S. Hobden (Eds.), *Proceedings of the 36th Annual Adult Education Research Conference* (pp. 63–68). Edmonton, Alberta: University of Alberta.

Collins, J. F. (2000a). Biracial-bisexual individuals: Identity coming of age. *International Journal of Sexuality and Gender Studies, 5*(3), 221–253.

Collins, J. F. (2000b). Biracial Japanese American identity: An evolving process. *Cultural Diversity and Ethnic Minority Psychology, 6*(2), 115–133.

Collins, M. (1988). Self-directed learning or an emancipatory practice of adult education: Re-thinking the role of the adult educator. In C. Warren (Ed.), *Proceedings of the 29th Annual Adult Education Research Conference* (pp. 61–66). Calgary, Canada: University of Calgary.

Collins, M. (1991). *Adult education as vocation.* New York: Routledge.

Collins, M. (1994). From self-directed learning to post-modernist thought in adult education: Relocating our object of theory and practice. In M. Hyams, J. Armstrong, & E. Anderson (Eds.), *Proceedings of the 35th Annual Adult Education Research Conference* (pp. 97–102). Knoxville: University of Tennessee.

Collins, M. (1995a). Critical commentaries on the role of the adult educator: From self- directed learning to postmodernist sensibilities. In M. R. Welton (Ed.), *In defense of the lifeworld* (pp. 71–98). Albany: State University of New York Press.

Collins, M. (1995b). In the wake of postmodernist sensibilities and opting for a critical return. In M. R. Welton (Ed.), *In defense of the lifeworld* (pp. 195–201). Albany: State University of New York Press.

Collins, M. (1996). On contemporary practice and research: Self-directed learning to critical theory. In R. Edwards, A. Hanson, & P. Raggatt (Eds.), *Boundaries of adult learning: Adult learners, education and training* (pp. 109–127). New York: Routledge.

Collins, M. A., Brick, J. M., & Kim, K. (1997). The measurement of participation in adult education. In R. Nolan & H. Chelesvig (Eds.), *Proceedings of the 38th Annual Adult Education Research Conference* (pp. 61–66). Stillwater: Oklahoma State University.

Collins, M., & Collard, S. (1995). Examining the case for class analysis in adult education research. In P. Collette, B. Einsiedel & S. Hobden (Eds.), *Proceedings of the 36th Annual Adult Education Research Conference* (pp. 69–76). Edmonton, Alberta: University of Alberta.

Comings, J. P. (2003). *Establishing an evidence-based adult education system.* NSCALL Occasional Paper. Cambridge, MA: National Center for the Study of Adult Learning and Literacy.

Commission for a Nation of Lifelong Learners. (1997). *A nation learning: Vision for the 21st century.* Albany, NY: Commission for a Nation of Lifelong Learners (www.regents.edu).

Commission of the European Communities. (2000). *A memorandum on lifelong learning.* Brussels: European Commission.

Conrad, D. (2005). Online learning. In L. M. English (Ed.), *International encyclopedia of adult education* (pp. 442–446). New York: Palgrave Macmillan.

Cook, B. J. (1999). Islam versus Western conceptions of education: Reflections on Egypt. *International Review of Education, 45*(3/4), 339–357.

Coombs, P. H. (1985). *The world crisis in education: A view from the eighties.* New York: Oxford University Press.

Coombs, P. H. (1989). Formal and nonformal education: Future strategies. In C. J. Titmus (Ed.), *Lifelong education for adults: An international handbook* (pp. 57–60). New York: Pergamon Press.

Coombs, P. H., with Prosser, R. C., & Ahmed, M. (1973). *New paths to learning for children and youth.* New York: International Council for Educational Development.

Cope, P., Cuthbertson, P., & Stoddart, B. (2000). Situated learning in the practice of placement. *Journal of Advanced Nursing, 31*(4), 850–856.

Courtenay, B. C., Arnold, G. W., & Kim, K. (1994). An examination of the empirical basis for involving adult learners in planning their learning experiences. *International Journal of Lifelong Education, 13*(4), 291–300.

Courtenay, B. C., Merriam, S. B., Reeves, P. M., & Baumgartner, L. M. (2000). Perspective transformation over time: A two-year follow-up study of HIV-positive adults. *Adult Education Quarterly, 52*(2), 102–119.

Courtenay, B. C., & Milton, J. (2004). Spirituality in adult education: From the voices of educators and learners. In D. E. Clover (Ed.), *Proceedings of the Joint International Conference of the 45th Annual Adult Education Research Conference and the Canadian Association for the Study of Adult Education* (pp. 101–106). Victoria, Canada: University of Victoria.

Courtney, S. (1992). *Why adults learn: Toward a theory of participation in adult education.* New York: Routledge.

Cowen, T. (2003). Does globalization kill ethos and diversity? *Phi Kappa Phi Forum, 83*(4), 17–20.

Cox, S., & Gallois, C. (1996). Gay and lesbian identity development: A social identity perspective. *Journal of Homosexuality, 30*(4), 1–30.

Cranton, P. (1996). *Professional development as transformative learning.* San Francisco: Jossey-Bass.

Cranton, P. (Ed.). (1997). *Transformative learning in action: Insights from practice.* New Directions for Adult and Continuing Education, No. 74. San Francisco: Jossey-Bass.

Cranton, P. (2002). Teaching for transformation. In J. M. Ross-Gordon (Ed.), *Contemporary viewpoints on teaching adults effectively* (pp. 63–71). New Directions for Adult and Continuing Education, No. 93. San Francisco: Jossey- Bass.

Cranton, P. (2005). Learning styles. In L. M. English (Ed.), *International encyclopedia of adult education* (pp. 111–117). New York: Palgrave McMillan.

Cranton, P., & Dirkx, J. M. (2005). Integrating theoretical perspectives through online dialogue. In D. Vlosak, G. Kielbaso, & J. Radford (Eds.), *Proceedings of the 6th International Conference on Transformative Learning* (pp. 91–97). East Lansing: Michigan State University.

Cranton, P., & Lin, L. (2005). Transformative learning about teaching: The role of technology. In D. Vlosak, G. Kielbaso, & J. Radford (Eds.), *Proceedings of the 6th International Conference on Transformative Learning* (pp. 99–104). East Lansing: Michigan State University.

Creighton, S., & Hudson, L. (2002). *Participation trends and patterns in adult education: 1991 to 1999.* Washington, DC: National Center for Educational Statistics, Office of Educational Research and Improvement, U.S. Department of Education.

Criticos, C. (1993). Experiential learning and social transformation for a post-apartheid learning future. In D. Boud, R. Cohen, & D. Walker (Eds.), *Using experience for learning* (pp. 157–168). Buckingham, England, and Bristol, PA: Society for Research into Higher Education and Open University Press.

Cropley, A. J. (1989). Factors in participation. In C. J. Titus (Ed.), *Lifelong education for adults: An international handbook* (pp. 145–147). New York: Pergamon Press.

Cross, W. (1971, July). The Negro-to-Black conversion experience. *Black World, 20,* 13–27.

Cross, W. E. Jr. (1995). The psychology of Nigrescence: Revising the Cross model. In J. G. Ponterotto, J. M. Casa, L. A. Suzuki, & C. M. Alexander (Eds.), *Handbook of multicultural counseling* (pp. 93–122). Thousand Oaks, CA: Sage.

Cross, W. E. Jr., & Vandiver, B. J. (2001). Nigrescence theory and measurement: Introducing the Cross racial identity scale (CRIS). In J. G. Ponterotto, J. M. Casa, L. A. Suzuki, & C. M. Alexander (Eds.), *Handbook of multicultural counseling* (2nd ed., pp. 371–393). Thousand Oaks, CA: Sage.

Crowdes, M. S. (2000). Embodying sociological imagination: Pedagogical support for linking bodies to minds. *Teaching Sociology, 28*(1), 24–40.

REFERENCES

Crowther, J. (2000). Participation in adult and community education: a discourse of diminishing returns. *International Journal of Lifelong Education, 19*(6), 479–492.

Cunningham, J., & Fitzgerald, J. (1996). Epistemology and reading. *Reading Research Quarterly, 31*(1), 36–60.

Cunningham, P. M. (1988). The adult educator and social responsibility. In R. G. Brockett (Ed.), *Ethical issues in adult education.* New York: Teachers College Press.

Cunningham, P. M. (2000). A sociology of adult education. In A. L. Wilson & E. R. Hayes (Eds.), *Handbook of adult and continuing education* (pp. 573–591). San Francisco: Jossey-Bass.

Dale, J. A., Glowacki-Dudka, M., & Hyslop-Margison, E. J. (2005). Lifelong learning as human ontology: A Freirean response to human capital education. In R. J. Hill & R. Kiely (Eds.), *Proceedings of the 46th Annual Adult Education Research Conference* (pp. 109–114). Athens: University of Georgia.

Dale, J. T. (2005). Reflective judgment: Seminarians: Epistemology in a world of relativism. *Journal of Psychology and Theology, 33*(1), 56–64.

Daloz, L. A. (1986). *Effective teaching and mentoring: Realizing the transformational power of adult learning experiences.* San Francisco: Jossey-Bass.

Daloz, L. A. (1988). The story of Gladys who refused to grow: A morality tale for mentors. *Lifelong Learning: An Omnibus of Practice and Research, 11*(4), 4–7.

Daloz, L. A. (1999). *Mentor: Guiding the journey of adult learners* (2nd ed.). San Francisco: Jossey-Bass.

Daloz, L. A. (2000). Transformative learning for the common good. In J. Mezirow & Associates (Eds.), *Learning as transformation: Critical perspectives on a theory in progress* (pp. 103–124). San Francisco: Jossey-Bass.

Damasio, A. R. (2000). The fabric of the mind: A neurobiological perspective. NOW/Huygens Lecturer. Rotterdam, Netherlands: The Netherlands Organization for Scientific Research.

Danis, C. (1992). A unifying framework for data-based research into adult self-directed learning. In H. B. Long & others, *Self-directed learning: Application and research* (pp. 47–72). Norman: Oklahoma Research Center for Continuing Professional and Higher Education, University of Oklahoma.

Danis, C., & Tremblay, N. A. (1987). Propositions regarding autodidactic learning and their implications for teaching. *Lifelong Learning: An Omnibus of Practice and Research, 10*(7), 4–7.

Danis, C., & Tremblay, N. A. (1988). Autodidactic learning experiences: Questioning established adult learning principles. In H. B. Long & others, *Self-directed learning: Application and theory* (pp. 171–197). Athens: Adult Education Department, University of Georgia.

Dannefer, D. (1996). Commentary. *Human Development, 39,* 150–152.

Darkenwald, G. G., & Valentine, T. (1985). Factor structure of deterrents to public participation in adult education. *Adult Education Quarterly, 35*(4), 177–193.

Davenport, J., & Davenport, J. (1985). A chronology and analysis of the andragogy debate. *Adult Education Quarterly, 35*(3), 152–159.

Davidson, J. E., & Downing, C. L. (2000). Contemporary models of intelligence. In R. J. Sternberg (Ed.), *Handbook of intelligence* (pp. 34–49). New York: Cambridge University Press.

Davis, D. C. (2003). Dialogue of the soul: Transformative dimensions of the experience of spirit. In C. A. Weissner, S. R., Meyer, N. L. Pfhal, & P. G. Neaman (Eds.), *Proceedings of the 5th International Conference on Transformative Learning* (pp. 130–135). New York: Teachers College, Columbia University.

Davis, D. C. (2004). Thrown from the train: Experiences that contribute to the spiritual growth of males in mid-life. In D. E. Clover (Ed.), *Proceedings of the Joint International Conference of the 45th Annual Adult Education Research Conference and the Canadian Association for the Study of Adult Education* (pp. 119–124). Victoria, Canada: University of Victoria.

Davis-Harrison, D. (1996). Nonparticipation in adult education programs: Views of blue-collar male workers with low literacy skills. In H. Reno & M. Witte (Eds.), *Proceedings of the 37th Annual Adult Education Research Conference* (pp. 85–90). Tampa: University of South Florida.

Deary, I. J. (2001). *Intelligence: A very short introduction.* Oxford, United Kingdom: Oxford University Press.

Dei, G. J., Hall, B. L., & Rosenberg, D. G. (2000). Introduction. In G. J. Dei, B. L. Hall, & D. G. Rosenberg (Eds.), *Indigenous knowledges in global contexts* (pp. 3–17). Toronto: University of Toronto Press.

Della Porta, T. (2006). A perspective on the use of learning style instruments in adult education. Unpublished manuscript, Cornell University, Ithaca, New York.

deMarrais, K. (1991). John's story: An exploration into critical theory in education. *Adult Learning, 2*(8), 9–10.

Demko, D. J. (1982). Human resources correlates of older adult participation in self- selected community college settings. *Dissertation Abstracts International, 43*(06A), 1792. (UMI No. 8224936)

Desimone, R., Werner, J., & Harris, D. (2002). *Human resource development* (3rd ed.). Mason, OH: South-Western.

Desmedt, E., & Valcke, M. (2004). Mapping the learning styles "jungle": An overview of the literature based on citation analysis. *Educational Psychology, 24*(4), 446–464.

Dewey, J. (1938). *Experience and education.* New York: Collier Books.

Dirkx, J. (1998). Transformative learning theory in the practice of adult education: An overview. *PAACE Journal of Lifelong Learning, 7,* 1–14.

Dirkx, J. (2001a). Images, transformative learning and the work of the soul. *Adult Learning, 12*(3), 15–16.

Dirkx, J. (2001b). The power of feelings: Emotion, imagination and the construction of meaning in adult learning. In S. B. Merriam (Ed.), *The new update on adult learning theory* (pp. 63–72). New Directions for Adult and Continuing Education, No. 89. San Francisco: Jossey-Bass.

Dirkx, J. M., Pratt, D., & Taylor, E. (2002). Archetypes of teaching: Tethers in the wind or flashlights in the dark? In J. M. Pettitt (Ed.), *Proceedings of the 43rd Annual Adult Education Research Conference* (pp. 91–96). North Carolina State University, Raleigh.

Dirkx, J. M., & Smith, R. (2005). Transformative learning in adult online collaborative groups: The dialectic of will and willness. In D. Vlosak, G. Kielbaso, & J. Radford (Eds.), *Proceedings of the Sixth International Conference on Transformative Learning* (pp. 113–119). East Lansing: Michigan State University.

Di Vesta, F. J. (1987). The cognitive movement in education. In J. Glover & R. Ronning (Eds.), *Historical foundations of education* (pp. 203–233). New York: Plenum.

Dixon, N. M. (1997). The hallways of learning. *Organizational Dynamics, 25*(4), 23–34.

Dixon, R. A. (2003). Themes in the aging of intelligence: Robust decline with intriguing possibilities. In R. J. Sternberg, J. Lautrey, & T. I. Lubart (Eds.), *Models of intelligence: International perspectives* (pp. 151–167). Washington, DC: American Psychological Association.

Dominice, P. (2000). *Learning from our lives: Using educational biographies with adults.* San Francisco: Jossey-Bass.

Driver, R., Asoko, H., Leach, J., Mortimer, E., & Scott, P. (1994). Constructing scientific knowledge in the classroom. *Educational Researcher, 23*(7), 5–12.

Dunlap, J., & Grabinger, S. (2003). Preparing students for lifelong learning: A review of instructional features and teaching methodologies. *Performance Improvement Quarterly, 16*(2), 6–25.

Durr, R., Guglielmino, L. M., & Guglielmino, P. J. (1996). Self-directed learning readiness and occupational categories. In G. N. McLean (Ed.), *Human Resource Development Quarterly, 7*(4), 349–358.

Dychtwald, K., & Flower, J. (1989). The third age. *New Age Journal, 6*(1), 50–59.

Edwards, R., & Usher, R. (2000). Lifelong learning: The postmodern condition of education? In T. J. Sork, V. Chapman, & R. St. Clair (Eds.), *Proceedings of the 41st Annual Adult Education Research Conference* (pp. 96–100). Vancouver: University of British Columbia.

Elias, D. (1997). It's time to change our minds: An introduction to transformative learning. *ReVision, 20*(1), 2–6.

Elias, J. L. (1979). Critique: Andragogy revisited. *Adult Education, 29,* 252–255.

Elias, J. L, & Merriam, S. B. (2005). *Philosophical foundations of adult education* (3rd ed.). Malabar, FL: Krieger.

Ellinger, A. D. (2004). The concept of self-directed learning and its implications for human resource development. In B. Yang (Ed.), *Advances in Developing Human Resources, 6*(2), 129–145.

Ellinger, A. D., Ellinger, A. E., Yang, B., & Howton, S. W. (2002). The relationship between the learning organization concept and firms' financial performance: An empirical assessment. *Human Resource Development Quarterly, 13*(1), 5–21.

Ellsworth, E. (1989). Why doesn't this feel empowering? Working through the repressive myths of critical pedagogy. *Harvard Educational Review, 59*(3), 297–324.

Embretson, S. E., & Schmidt McCollam, K. (2000). Psychometric approaches to understanding and measuring intelligence. In R. J. Sternberg (Ed.), *Handbook of intelligence* (pp. 423–444). New York: Cambridge University Press.

English, L. M. (2000). Spiritual dimensions of informal learning. In L. M. English & M. A. Gillen (Eds.), *Addressing the spiritual dimensions of adult learning: What educators can do* (pp. 29–38). New Directions for Adult and Continuing Education, No. 85. San Francisco: Jossey-Bass.

English, L. M. (2005a). Historical and contemporary explorations of the social change and spiritual directions of adult education. *Teachers College Record, 107*(6), 1169–1192.

English, L. M. (Ed.). (2005b). *International encyclopedia of adult education.* New York: Palgrave Macmillan.

English, L. M., Fenwick, T. J., & Parsons, J. (2003). *Spirituality of adult education and training.* Malabar, FL: Krieger.

Erickson, D. M. (2002). A developmental constructivist examination of meaning making capacity among peer instructors in learning in retirement programs. *Dissertation Abstracts International, 63*(05), 1668A. (UMI No. 3052875)

Erikson, E. H. (1963). *Childhood and society* (2nd ed., rev.). New York: Norton.

Erikson, E. H. (1968). *Identity, youth and crisis.* New York: Norton.

Erikson, E. H. (1978). *Adulthood.* New York: Norton.

Erikson, E. H., Erikson, J. M., & Kivnick, H. O. (1986). *Vital involvement in old age.* New York: Norton.

Etter-Lewis, G., & Foster, M. (Eds.). (1996). *Unrelated kin: Race and gender in women's personal narratives.* New York: Routledge.

Eurich, N. (1990). *The learning industry.* Princeton, NJ: Carnegie Foundation for the Advancement of Teaching.

Faris, N. A., & Ashraf, S. A. (2003). *The book of knowledge: Being a translation with notes of Kitab al-'Ilm of Al-Ghazzalis's Ihya' "Ulum al-Din.* http://www.al-Ghazali.org. Accessed September 8, 2004.

Fasokun, T., Katahoire, A., & Oduaran, A. (2005). *The psychology of adult learning in Africa*. Hamburg, Germany: UNESCO Institute for Education and Pearson Education South Africa.

Faure, E., Herrera, F., Kaddoura, A., Lopes, H., Petrovsky, A. J., Rahnema, M., & Ward, F. C. (1972). *Learning to be: The world of education today and tomorrow*. Paris: UNESCO.

Feinstein, B. C. (2004). Learning and transformation in the context of Hawaiian ecological knowledge. *Adult Education Quarterly, 54*(2), 105–120.

Fenimore, M. A. (1997). 'My brain is still working!': Conversations with centenarians about learning in adulthood. *Canadian Journal for the Study of Adult Education, 11*(1), 57–70.

Fenwick, T. J. (2001). *Experiential learning: A theoretical critique from five perspectives*. Information Series No. 385. Columbus, OH: ERIC Clearinghouse on Adult, Career and Vocational Education, Center on Education and Training for Employment.

Fenwick, T. (2003). *Learning through experience: Troubling orthodoxies and intersecting questions*. Malabar, FL: Krieger.

Fenwick, T. (2005a). Conceptions of critical HRD: Dilemmas for theory and practice. *Human Resource Development International, 8*(2), 225–238.

Fenwick, T. (2005b). Organizational learning. In L. M. English (Ed.), *International encyclopedia of adult education* (pp. 446–450). New York: Palgrave Macmillan.

Fenwick, T., & English, L. (2004). Dimension of spirituality: A framework for adult educators. *Journal of Adult Theological Education, 1*(1), 49–64.

Fenwick, T., English, L., & Parsons, J. (2001). Dimensions of spirituality: A framework for adult educators. In T. Nesbit (Ed.), *Proceedings of the 20th Annual Conference of the Canadian Association for the Study of Adult Education* (CASAE). Quebec: Laval University. http://www.oise.utoronto.ca/CASAE/cnf2001/fenwicketal.htm. Accessed January 5, 2003.

Ferraro, K. F. (2001). Aging and role transitions. In R. H. Birnstock & L. K. George (Eds.), *Handbook of aging and the social sciences* (pp. 313–330). San Francisco: Academic Press.

Ferry, N., & Ross-Gordon, J. (1998). An inquiry into Schön's epistemology of practice: Exploring links between experience and reflective practice. *Adult Education Quarterly, 48*(2), 98–112.

Field, D., Schaie, K. W., & Leino, V. E. (1988). Continuity in intellectual functioning: The role of self-reported health. *Psychology and Aging, 3*(4), 385–392.

Finger, M. (1995). Adult education and society today. *International Journal of Lifelong Education, 14*(2), 110–119.

Finger, M. (2005a). Critical theory. In L. M. English (Ed.), *International Encyclopedia of Adult Education* (pp. 165–168). London: Palgrave Macmillan.

Finger, M. (2005b). Globalization. In L. M. English (Ed.), *International Encyclopedia of Adult Education* (pp. 269–273). London: Palgrave Macmillan.

Fischback, G. D. (1992). Mind and brain. *Scientific American, 267*(3), 48–57.

Fisher, H. (2004, January 19). Your brain in love. *Time.*

Flannery, D. D. (1993). Global and analytical ways of processing information. In D. D. Flannery (Ed.), *Applying cognitive learning theory to adult learning* (pp. 15–24). New Directions for Adult and Continuing Education, No. 59. San Francisco: Jossey-Bass.

Flannery, D., & Hayes, B. (2001). Challenging adult learning: A feminist perspective. In V. Sheared & P. Sissel (Eds.), *Making space: Merging theory and practice in adult education.* (pp. 29–41). New York: Bergin & Garvey.

Foehr, R. P. (1997). Writing the spirit: Interviews with John Bradshaw, Larry Dossey, M.D., and Thomas Moore. In R. P. Foehr & S. A. Schiller (Eds.), *The spiritual side of writing* (pp. 44–68). Portsmouth, NH: Boynton/Cook.

Fogerson, D. L. (2005). *Readiness factors contributing to participant satisfaction in online higher education courses.* Unpublished doctoral dissertation, University of Tennessee, Knoxville.

Fowler, J. W. (1981). *Stages of faith: The psychology of human development and the quest for meaning.* New York: HarperCollins.

Freed, S. A. (2003). Metaphors and reflective dialogue online. *New Horizons in Adult Education, 17*(3), 4–19.

Freire, P. (1970). *Pedagogy of the oppressed.* New York: Seabury Press.

Freire, P. (1985). *The politics of education: Culture, power, and liberation.* New York: Bergin & Garvey.

Freire, P. (2000). *Pedagogy of the oppressed* (20th anniversary ed.). New York: Continuum.

Friedman, A. A. (2004). The relationship between personality traits and reflective judgment among female students. *Journal of Adult Development, 11*(4), 297–304.

Fujita-Starck, P. J. (1996). Motivations and characteristics of adult students: Factor stability and construct validity of educational participation scale. *Adult Education Quarterly, 47*(1), 29–40.

Gagne, R. M., Briggs, L. J., & Wager, W. W. (1992). *Principles of instructional design* (4th ed.). Orlando: Harcourt Brace.

Galbraith, M. W., & Cohen, N. H. (Eds.). (1995). *Mentoring: New strategies and challenges.* New Directions for Adult and Continuing Education, No. 66. San Francisco: Jossey-Bass.

Gardiner, H. W., & Kosmitzki, C. (2005). *Lives across cultures: Cross-cultural human development.* Needham Heights, MA: Allyn & Bacon.

Gardner, H. (1993). *Multiple intelligences: The theory in practice.* New York: Basic Books.

Gardner, H. (1995). Reflections on multiple intelligences: Myths and messages. *Phi Delta Kappan, 77*(3), 200–209.

Gardner, H. (1999a). A multiplicity of intelligences. *Intelligence, 9*(4), 19–23.

Gardner, H. (1999b). *Intelligence reframed: Multiple intelligences for the 21st century.* New York: Basic Books.

Gardner, H. (2003). Three distinct meanings of intelligence. In R. J. Sternberg, J. Lautrey, & T. I. Lubart (Eds.), *Models of intelligence: International perspectives* (pp. 43–54). Washington, DC: American Psychological Association.

Gardner, P. (1996). Transitions: Understanding economic and workplace changes at the end of the century. *Journal of Cooperative Education, 31*(2), 41–57.

Garrison, D. R. (1986). An analysis and reformulation of McClusky's concept of margin for predicting adult dropout. In K. Landers (Ed.), *Proceedings of the 27th Adult Education Research Conference* (pp. 112–117). Syracuse, NY: Syracuse University.

Garrison, D. R. (1992). Critical thinking and self-directed learning in adult education: An analysis of responsibility and control issues. *Adult Education Quarterly, 42*(3), 136–148.

Garrison, D. R. (1997). Self-directed learning: Toward a comprehensive model. *Adult Education Quarterly, 48*(1), 18–33.

Gaventa, J. (1988). Participatory research in North America. *Convergence, 21*(2–3), 19–28.

Geissler, K. A. (1996). Adult education in modern times—development and quality. *Adult Education and Development, 47,* 31–54.

George, J. M. (1999). Indigenous knowledge as a component of the school curriculum. In L. M. Semali & J. L. Kincheloe (Eds.), *What is indigenous knowledge? Voices from the academy* (pp. 79–94). New York: Falmer Press.

Gergen, K. J. (1991). *The saturated self.* New York: Basic Books.

Gergen, K. J. (1995). Social construction and the educational process. In L. P. Steffe & J. Gale (Eds.), *Constructivism in education* (pp. 17–39). Hillsdale, NJ: Erlbaum.

Gibson, S. K. (2004). Social learning (cognitive) theory and implications for human resource development. In B. Yang (Ed.), *Advances in Developing Human Resources, 6*(2), 193–210.

Giroux, H. (1992). *Border crossings: Cultural workers and the politics of education.* New York: Routledge.

Glastra, F. J., Hake, B. J., & Schedler, P. E. (2004). Lifelong learning as transitional learning. *Adult Education Quarterly, 54*(4), 291–307.

Goldberger, N. R. (1996a). Cultural imperatives and diversity in ways of knowing. In N. R. Goldberger, J. M. Tarule, B. M. Clinchy, & M. F. Belenky (Eds.), *Knowledge, difference and power: Essays inspired by women's ways of knowing* (pp. 335–364). New York: Basic Books.

Goldberger, N. R. (1996b). Looking backward, looking forward. In N. R. Goldberger, J. M. Tarule, B. M. Clinchy, & M. F. Belenky (Eds.), *Knowledge, difference and power: Essays inspired by women's ways of knowing* (pp. 1–21). New York: Basic Books.

Goldberger, N. R., Tarule, J. M., Clinchy, B. M., & Belenky, M. F. (Eds.). (1996). *Knowledge, difference, and power: Essays inspired by Women's Ways of Knowing.* New York: Basic Books.

Goldenberg, J. L., Pyszczynski, T., Greenberg, J., & Solomon, S. (2000). Fleeing the body: A terror management perspective on the problem of human corporeality. *Personality and Social Psychology Review, 4*(3), 200–218.

Goleman, D. (1995). *Emotional intelligence: Why it can matter more than IQ.* New York: Bantam Books.

Goodnow, J. J. (1990). Using sociology to extend psychological accounts of cognitive development. *Human Development, 33,* 81–107.

Gorard, S., & Selwyn, N. (2005). Towards a learning society? The impact of technology on patterns of participation in lifelong learning. *British Journal of Sociology of Education, 26*(1), 71–89.

Gorham, J. (1985). Differences between teaching adults and pre-adults: A closer look. *Adult Education quarterly, 35*(4), 194–209.

Gottfredson, L. S. (1997). Mainstream science on intelligence: An editorial with 52 signatories, history, and bibliography. *Intelligence, 24*(1), 13–23.

Götz, I. L. (2001). Spirituality and the body. *Religious Education, 96*(1), 2–19.

Gould, R. (1978). *Transformations: Growth and change in adult life.* New York: Simon & Schuster.

Gouthro, P. A. (2003). Feminist perspectives on Habermasian theory: Implications for the development of critical feminist theoretical discourses in adult education. In D. Flowers, M. Lee, A. Jalipa, E. Lopez, A. Schelstrate, & V. Sheared (Eds.), *Proceedings of the 44th Annual Adult Education Research Conference* (pp. 145–150). San Francisco: San Francisco State University.

Gouthro, P. A., & Grace, A. P. (2000). Feminist pedagogies and graduate adult and higher education for women students: Matters of connection and possibility. In T. J. Sork, V. Chapman, & R. St. Clair (Eds.),

Proceedings f the 41st Annual Adult Education Research Conference (pp. 134–138). Vancouver: University of British Columbia.

Grace, A. P. (1996a). Adult educators as border crossers: Using transformative pedagogy to inform classroom practice. In H. Reno & M. Witte (Eds.), *Proceedings of the 37th Annual Adult Education Research Conference* (pp. 145–150). Tampa: University of South Florida.

Grace, A. P. (1996b). Taking a critical pose: Andragogy—missing links, missing values. *International Journal of Lifelong Education, 15*(5), 382–392.

Grace, A. P. (1997). Taking it to practice: Building a critical postmodern theory of adult learning community. In R. Nolan & H. Chelesvig (Eds.), *Proceedings of the 38th Annual Adult Education Research Conference* (pp. 126–131). Stillwater: Oklahoma State University.

Graveline, F. J. (2005). Indigenous learning. In L. M. English (Ed.), *International encyclopedia of adult education* (pp. 304–309). New York: Palgrave Macmillan.

Graves, R. L. (1997). Grace, in pedagogy. In R. P. Foehr & S. A. Schiller (Eds.), *The spiritual side of writing* (pp. 15–24). Portsmouth, NH: Boynton/Cook.

Gredler, M. E. (1997). *Learning and instruction: Theory into practice* (3rd ed.). Englewood Cliffs, NJ: Prentice Hall.

Greeno, J. (1997). On claims that answer the wrong question. *Educational Researcher, 27*(1), 5–17.

Griffith, W. S., & Fujita-Starck, P. J. (1989). Public policy and financing of adult and continuing education. In S. B. Merriam & P. M. Cunningham (Eds.), *Handbook of adult and continuing education* (pp. 168–180). San Francisco: Jossey-Bass.

Grigorenko, E. L. (2000). Heritability and intelligence. In R. J. Sternberg (Ed.), *Handbook of intelligence* (pp. 53–91). New York: Cambridge University Press.

Grippin, P., & Peters, S. (1984). *Learning theory and learning outcomes.* Lanham, MD: University Press of America.

Grotzer, T. A., & Perkins, D. N. (2000). Teaching intelligence: A performance conception. In R. J. Sternberg (Ed.), *Handbook of intelligence* (pp. 492–515). New York: Cambridge University Press.

Grow, G. (1991). Teaching learners to be self-directed: A stage approach. *Adult Education Quarterly, 41*(3), 125–149.

Grow, G. (1994). In defense of the staged self-directed learning model. *Adult Education Quarterly, 44*(2), 109–114.

Guglielmino, L. M. (1977). *Development of the self-directed learning readiness scale.* Unpublished doctoral dissertation, University of Georgia.

Guglielmino, L. M. (1997). *Contributions of the self-directed learning readiness scale (SDLRS) and the learning preference assessment (LPA) to the definition and measurement of self-direction in learning.* Paper presented at the First World Conference on Self-Directed Learning, Montreal, Canada.

Guglielmino, P. J., & Guglielmino, L. M. (2005). *The relationship of self-directed learning readiness, culture, productivity and income in seven countries.* Paper presented at the meeting of the Self-Directed Learning Conference, Jupiter, FL.

Guglielmino, P. J., & Roberts, D. G. (1992). A comparison of self-directed learning readiness in U.S. and Hong Kong samples and the implications for job performance. *Human Resource Development Quarterly, 3*(3), 261–271.

Guy, T. C. (2005). Culturally relevant adult education. In L. M. English (Ed.), *International encyclopedia of adult education* (pp. 180–184). London: Palgrave Macmillan.

Guyer, B., Freedman, M. A., Strobino, D. M., & Sondik, E. J. (2000). Annual summary of vital statistics: Trends in the health of Americans during the 20th century. *Pediatrics, 106*(6), 1307–1317.

Hadfield, J. (2003). Recruiting and retaining adult students. In D. Kilgore & P. J. Rice (Eds.), *Meeting the special needs of adult students* (pp. 17–25). New Directions for Student Services, No. 102. San Francisco: Jossey-Bass.

Haier, R. J. (2003). Brain imaging studies of intelligence: Individual differences and neurobiology. In R. J. Sternberg, J. Lautrey, & T. I. Lubart (Eds.), *Models of intelligence: International perspectives* (pp. 185–193). Washington, DC: American Psychological Association.

Hall, A. G., & Donaldson, J. F. (1997). An exploratory study of the social and personal dynamics that deter underserved women from participating in adult education activities. In R. Nolan & H. Chelesvig (Eds.), *Proceedings of the 38th Annual Adult Education Research Conference* (pp. 96–101). Stillwater: Oklahoma State University.

Hall, E., & Moseley, D. (2005). Is there a role for learning styles in personalized education and training? *International Journal of Lifelong Education, 24*(3), 243–255.

Hamil-Luker, J., & Uhlenberg, P. (2002). Later life education in the 1990s: Increasing involvement and continuing disparity. *Journals of Gerontology Series B: Psychological Sciences & Social Sciences, 57B*(6), S324-S331.

Hammond, M., & Collins, R. (1991). *Self-directed learning: Critical practice.* London: Nichols/GP Publishing.

Hanpachern, C., Morgan, G. A., & Griego, O. V. (1998). An extension of the theory of margin: A framework for assessing readiness for change. *Human Resource Development Quarterly, 9*(4), 339–350.

Hansen, A. H. (1988). Model of deficit/growth motives and learning needs of older participants. *Dissertation Abstracts International, 149*(12A), 3588. (UMI No. 8904357)

Hansen, T. L. (1993). What is critical theory? An essay for the uninitiated organizational communication scholar. Paper presented at the Speech Communication Association of America Convention, Miami. (ERIC Document Reproduction Service No. ED 368 008)

Hansman, C. A. (2001). Context-based adult learning. In S. Merriam (Ed.), *The new update on adult learning* (pp. 43–51). New Directions for Adult and Continuing Education, No. 89. San Francisco: Jossey-Bass.

Hansman, C. A., & Sissel, P. A. (Eds.). (2001). *Understanding and negotiating the political landscape of adult education.* New Directions for Adult and Continuing Education, No. 91. San Francisco: Jossey-Bass.

Hanson, A. (1996). The search for a separate theory of adult learning: Does anyone really need andragogy? In R. Edwards, A. Hanson, & P. Raggatt (Eds.), *Boundaries of adult learning* (pp. 99–108). New York: Routledge.

Hart, M. (1990). Liberation through consciousness-raising. In J. Mezirow & Associates, *Fostering critical reflection in adulthood: A guide to transformative and emancipatory learning* (pp. 47–73). San Francisco: Jossey-Bass.

Hart, M. (1992). *Working and educating for life: Feminist and international perspectives on adult education.* New York: Routledge.

Hart, M. (1995). Motherwork: A radical proposal to rethink work and education. In M. R. Welton (Ed.), *In defense of the lifeworld* (pp. 99–126). Albany: State University of New York Press.

Hart, M., & Holton, D. (1993). Beyond God the father and the mother: Adult education and spirituality. In P. Jarvis & N. Walters (Eds.), *Adult education and theological interpretations* (pp. 237–258). Malabar, FL: Krieger.

Hartree, A. (1984). Malcolm Knowles' theory of andragogy: A Critique. *International Journal of Lifelong Education, 3*(3), 203–210.

Harvie, P.H.B. (2004). Transformative learning in undergraduate education. *Dissertation Abstracts International, 65*(10), 3717A. (UMI No. NQ94535).

Havighurst, R. J. (1972). *Developmental tasks and education* (3rd ed.). New York: McKay. (Original work published 1952)

Hayes, E. R. (2005). An extra life: Living and learning in virtual worlds. In R. J. Hill & R. Kiely (Eds.), *Proceedings of the 46th Annual Adult Education Research Conference* (pp. 193–198). Athens: University of Georgia.

Hayes, E., & Colin, S.A.J. III (Eds). (1994). *Confronting racism and sexism.* New Directions for Adult and Continuing Education, No. 61. San Francisco: Jossey-Bass.

Health Disparities Experienced by Black or African Americans. (2004, August 27). *MMWR Weekly 53*(33), 755. http://www.cdc.gov/mmwr/preview/mmwrhtml/mm5333a1.htm. Accessed August 1, 2005.

Heany, T. (2005). *Issues in Freirean pedagogy.* http://www3.nl.edu/academics/cas/ace/resources/Documents/FreireIssues.cfm#conscientization. Accessed June 8, 2005.

Hecker, D. (2001). Occupational employment projections to 2010. *Monthly Labor Review, 124*(11), 57–84.

Hecker, D. (2004). Occupational employment projections to 2012. *Monthly Labor Review, 127*(2), 80–105.

Heclo, H. (1994). Move to cut high-tech is growing. *Atlanta Journal/Atlanta Constitution,* September 11, pp. B1–B2.

Helms, J. E. (1990). *Black and white racial identity: Theory research and practice.* Westport, CT: Greenwood.

Helms, J. E. (1995). An update on Helms' White and people of color racial identity development models. In J. G. Ponterotto, J. M. Casa, L. A. Suzuki, & C. M. Alexander (Eds.), *Handbook of multicultural counseling* (pp. 188–198). Thousand Oaks, CA: Sage.

Hemphill, D. F. (1996). Flexibility, innovation, and collaboration: A regional view of community-based organizations in adult education. *Adult Learning, 7*(6), 21–22.

Hemphill, D. F. (2001). Incorporating postmodernist perspectives into adult education. In V. Sheared & P. A. Sissel (Eds.), *Making space: Merging theory and practice in adult education* (pp. 16–27). New York: Bergin & Garvey.

Henderson, J. (2002). Transformative learning in the executive suite: CEOs and the role of context in Mezirow's theory. *Dissertation Abstracts International, 62*(12), 4026A. (UMI No. 3037824)

Henriksen, R. C. Jr., & Trusty, J. (2004). Understanding and assisting Black/White biracial women in their identity development. In A. R. Gillem & C. A. Thompson (Eds.), *Biracial women in therapy: Between the rock of gender and the hard place of race* (pp. 65–84). Binghamton, NY: Hawthorn Press.

Hergenhahn, B. R., & Olson, M. H. (2005). *An introduction to theories of learning* (7th ed.). Englewood Cliffs, NJ: Prentice Hall.

Herring, R. D. (1995). Developing biracial ethnic identity: A review of the increasing dilemma. *Journal of Multicultural Counseling and Development, 23*(1), 29–38.

Hersey, P., & Blanchard, K. (1988). *Management of organizational behavior: Utilizing human resources* (5th ed.). Englewood Cliffs, NJ: Prentice Hall.

Hicks, A., & Rowel, R. (2004). Indigenous learning: Weaving the fabric of our histories for success. In D. E. Clover (Ed.), *Proceedings of the Joint International Conference of the 45th Annual Adult Education Research Conference and the Canadian Association for the Study of Adult Education* (pp. 221–226). Victoria, Canada: University of Victoria.

Hiemstra, R. (1992). Individualizing the instructional process: What we have learned from two decades of research on self-direction in learning. In H. B. Long & others, *Self-directed learning: Application and research* (pp. 323–344). Norman: Oklahoma Research Center for Continuing Professional and Higher Education, University of Oklahoma.

Hiemstra, R. (1993). Three underdeveloped models for adult learning. In S. B. Merriam (Ed.), *An update on adult learning theory* (pp. 37–46). New Directions for Adult and Continuing Education, No. 57. San Francisco: Jossey-Bass.

Hiemstra, R., & Brockett, R. G. (1994). *Overcoming resistance to self-direction in adult learning.* New Directions for Adult and Continuing Education, No. 64. San Francisco: Jossey-Bass.

Hiemstra, R., & Sisco, B. (1990). *Individualizing instruction: Making learning personal, empowering, and successful.* San Francisco: Jossey-Bass.

Hilgard, E. R., & Bower, G. H. (1966). *Theories of learning.* Englewood Cliff, NJ: Appleton-Century-Crofts.

Hill, L. H. (2001). The brain and consciousness: Sources of information for understanding adult learning. In S. Merriam (Ed.). *The new update on adult learning theory* (pp. 73–82). New Directions for Adult and Continuing Education, No. 89. San Francisco: Jossey-Bass.

Hill, R. J. (1995). Fugitive and codified knowledge: The struggle to control the meaning of environmental hazards. In P. Collette, B. Einsiedel & S. Hobden (Eds.), *Proceedings of the 36th Annual Adult Education Research Conference* (pp. 163–170). Edmonton, Alberta: University of Alberta.

Hill, R. J. (1998). From motherhood to sister-solidarity: Homemaking as a counterdiscourse to corporate environment polluting. In J. Kimmell (Ed.), *Proceedings of the 39th Annual Adult Education Research Conference* (pp. 179–184). San Antonio: University of the Incarnate Word and Texas A&M University.

Hill, R. J. (2004). Activism as practice: Some queer considerations. In R. St. Clair & J. A. Sandlin (Eds.), *Promoting critical practice in adult education* (pp. 85–94). New Directions for Adult and Continuing Education, No. 102. San Francisco: Jossey-Bass.

Hill, W. F. (2002). *Learning: A survey of psychological interpretations* (7th ed.). Needham Heights, MA: Allyn & Bacon.

Ho, C. (2004). Cultural and individual differences in rational thinking. *Dissertation Abstracts International, 65*(05), 2608A. (UMI No. NQ91748)

Hockly, N. (2000). Modelling and "cognitive apprenticeship" in teacher education. *ELT Journal, 54*(2), 118–125.

Hofer, B. K., & Pintrich, P. R. (1997). The development of epistemological theories: Beliefs about knowledge and knowing and their relation to learning. *Review of Educational Research, 67*(1), 88–140.

Hofstede, G. (1984). National cultures and corporate cultures. In L. A. Samovar & R. E. Porter (Eds.), *Communication between cultures* (pp. 52–88). Belmont, CA: Wadsworth.

Holford, J., & Jarvis, P. (2000). The learning society. In A. L. Wilson & E. R. Hayes (Eds.), *Handbook of adult and continuing education* (pp. 643–659). San Francisco: Jossey-Bass.

Hollenbeck, C. R. (2005). Online anti-brand communities as a new form of social action in adult education. In R. J. Hill & R. Kiely (Eds.), *Proceedings of the 46th Annual Adult Education Research Conference* (pp. 205–210). Athens: University of Georgia.

Holliday, S. G., & Chandler, M. J. (1986). *Wisdom: Explorations in adult competence: Contributions to human development* (Vol. 17). Basel: Karger.

Holst, J. D. (2002). *Social movements, civil society, and radical adult education.* New York: Bergin & Garvey.

Holton, E. F., & Swanson, R. A. (1999). Reframing the andragogical model of learning. In K. P. Kuchinke (Ed.). *Academy of Human Resource Development (AHRD) Conference Proceedings,* Vol. 1 (pp. 20–28). Arlington, VA.

Holton, E. F. III, Swanson, R. A., & Naquin, S. S. (2001). Andragogy in practice: Clarifying the andragogical model of adult learning. *Performance Improvement Quarterly, 14*(1), 118–143.

Hood, A. B., & Deopere, D. L. (2002). The relationship of cognitive development to age, when education and intelligence are controlled for. *Journal of Adult Development, 9*(3), 229–234.

hooks, b. (1994). *Teaching to transgress: Education as the practice of freedom.* London: Routledge.

Hopkins, R. L. (1994). *Narrative schooling: Experiential learning and the transformation of American education.* New York: Teachers College Press.

Horn, J. L. (1985). Remodeling old models of intelligence. In B. B. Wolman (Ed.), *Handbook of intelligence: Theories, measurements, and applications.* New York: Wiley.

Horn, J. L. (1989). Cognitive diversity: A framework of learning. In P. L. Ackerman, R. J. Sternberg, & R. Glaser (Eds.), *Learning and individual differences* (pp. 61–116). New York: Freeman.

Horn, J. L., & Cattell, R. B. (1966). Refinement and test of the theory of fluid and crystallized intelligence. *Journal of Educational Psychology, 57*, 233–270.

Horn, J. L., & Cattell, R. B. (1967). Age differences in fluid and crystallized intelligence. *Acta Psychologica, 26*, 107–129.

Houle, C. O. (1972). *The design of education.* San Francisco: Jossey-Bass.

Houle, C. O. (1988). *The inquiring mind* (2nd ed.). Madison: University of Wisconsin Press & Norman: Oklahoma Research Center for Continuing Professional and Higher Education. (Original work published 1961)

Howell, L. C., & Beth, A. (2002). Midlife myths and realities: Women reflect on their experiences. *Journal of Women and Aging, 14*(3/4), 189–204.

Howell, L. C., & Beth, A. (2004). Pioneers in our own lives: Grounded theory of lesbians' midlife development. *Journal of Women and Aging, 16*(3/4), 133–147.

Hoyer, W. J., & Roodin, P. A. (2003). *Adult development and aging* (5th ed.). New York: McGraw-Hill.

Humphreys, L. G., & Stark, S. (2002). General Intelligence: Measurement, correlates, and interpretations of the cultural-genetic construct. In R. J. Sternberg & E. L. Grigorenko (Eds.), *The general factor of intelligence: How general is it?* (pp. 87–115). Hillsdale, NJ: Erlbaum.

Husain, S. S., & Ashraf, S. M. (1979). *Crisis in Muslim education.* London: Hodder and Stoughton.

Hwang, I. (2004). The relationships between discipleship training and transformative learning in Korean Presbyterian congregations. *Dissertation Abstracts International, 65*(05), 1625A. (UMI No. 31324775). http://proquest.umi.com/pqdweb?index=0&did=766026451&SrchMode=1&sid=1&Fmt=2&VInst=PROD&VType=PQD&RQT=309&VName=PQD&TS=1143990562&clientId=30345. Accessed July 29, 2005.

Ianinska, S., Wright, U., & Rocco, T. S. (2003). Critical race theory and adult education: Critique of the literature in *Adult Education Quarterly.* In D. Flowers, M. Lee, A. Jalipa, E. Lopez, A. Schelstrate, & V. Sheared (Eds), *Proceedings of the 44th Annual Adult Education Research Conference* (pp. 175–180). San Francisco: San Francisco State University.

Illeris, K. (2002). *Three dimensions of learning.* Roskilde, Denmark: Roskilde University Press/Leicester, UK: NIACE.

Illeris, K. (2004a). *Adult education and adult learning.* Malabar, FL: Krieger.

Illeris, K. (2004b). Transformative learning in the perspective of a comprehensive learning theory. *Journal of Transformative Education, 2*(2), 79–89.

Inglis, T. (1997). Empowerment and emancipation. *Adult Education Quarterly, 48*(1), 3–17.

Internet World Stats. (2005). *Internet usage statistics—The big picture.* http:www.internetworldstats.com/stats. Accessed August 7, 2005.

Issroff, K., & Scanlon, E. (2002). Using technology in higher education: An Activity Theory perspective. *Journal of Computer Assisted Learning, 18,* 77–83.

Jacobs, R. (1987). *Human performance technology: A systems-based field for the training and development profession.* Information Series No. 326. Columbus, OH: ERIC Clearinghouse on Adult, Career, and Vocational Education.

James, J. M. (1986). *Instructor-generated load: An inquiry based on McClusky's concepts of margin.* Unpublished doctoral dissertation, University of Wyoming, Laramie.

James, W. B., & Blank, W. E. (1993). Review and critique of available learning style instruments for adults. In D. D. Flannery (Ed.), *Applying cognitive learning theory to adult learning* (pp. 47–58). New Directions for Adult and Continuing Education, No. 59. San Francisco: Jossey-Bass.

Jarvis, C., & Zukas, M. (1998). Feminist teaching, feminist research, feminist supervision: Feminist praxis in adult education. In J. Kimmel (Ed.), *Proceedings of the 39th Annual Adult Education Research Conference* (pp. 197–202). San Antonio: University of the Incarnate Word and Texas A&M University.

Jarvis, P. (1983). *Adult and Continuing Education: Theory and Practice.* London: Croom Helm.

Jarvis, P. (1985). *The sociology of adult and continuing education.* London: Croom Helm.

Jarvis, P. (1986). *Sociological perspectives on lifelong education and lifelong learning.* Athens: Adult Education Department, University of Georgia.

Jarvis, P. (1987). *Adult learning in the social context.* London: Croom Helm.

Jarvis, P. (1992). *Paradoxes of learning: On becoming an individual in society.* San Francisco: Jossey-Bass.

Jarvis, P. (2001). *Learning in later life: An introduction for educators and careers.* London: Kogan Page.

Jarvis, P. (2004). *Adult education and lifelong learning: Theory and practice* (3rd ed.). London and New York: Routledge/Falmer Press.

Jarvis, P. (2006). *Towards a comprehensive theory of human learning.* London and New York: Routledge/Falmer Press.

Jegede, O. J. (1999). Science education in nonwestern cultures: Towards a theory of collateral learning. In L. M. Semali & J. L. Kincheloe (Eds.), *What is indigenous knowledge? Voices from the academy* (pp. 119–142). Bristol, PA: Falmer Press.

Jensen, A. R. (2002). *Psychometric g: Definition and substantiation.* In R. J. Sternberg & E. L. Grigorenko (Eds.), *The general factor of intelligence: How general is it?* (pp. 39–53). Hillsdale, NJ: Erlbaum.

Jensen, E. (2000). *Brain-based learning.* San Diego: CA: The Brain Store.

Jeris, L., & McDowell, T. (2003). Journal literature through the lens of critical race theory: A model for examining racism and social justice in the professions. In D. Flowers, M. Lee, A. Jalipa, E. Lopez, A. Schelstrate, & V. Sheared (Eds.), *Proceedings of the 44th Annual Adult Education Research Conference* (pp. 187–191). San Francisco: San Francisco State University.

Johnson, J. B. (2000). A comparison of cognitive development between Whites and African Americans based on William Perry's scheme of intellectual and ethical development. *Dissertation Abstracts International, 61*(02), 522A. (UMI No. 9961423)

Johnson, J. K. (2001). The sexual offender in treatment: An analysis of the cognitive- affective meaning-making process. *Dissertation Abstracts International, 62*(4), 1299A. (UMI No. 3011734)

Johnson-Bailey, J., & Alfred, M. (2006). Transformational teaching and the practice of Black women adult educators. In E. W. Taylor (Ed.), *Fostering transformative learning in the classroom: Challenges and innovations.* New Directions in Adult and Continuing Education. San Francisco: Jossey-Bass.

Johnson-Bailey, J., & Cervero, R. M. (1998). Power dynamics in teaching and learning practices: An examination of adult education classrooms. *International Journal of Lifelong Education, 17*(6), 389–399.

Johnstone, J.W.C., & Rivera, R. J. (1965). *Volunteers for learning: A study of the educational pursuits of adults.* Hawthorne, NY: Aldine de Gruyter.

Jonassen, D. H., & Hernandez-Serrano, J. (2002). Case-based reasoning and instructional design: Using stories to support problem solving. *Educational Technology Research and Development, 50*(2), 65–77.

Josselson, R. (1987). *Finding herself: The story of women's identity from college to midlife.* New York: Oxford University Press.

Josselson, R. (1996). *Revising herself: The story of women's identity from college to midlife.* New York: Oxford University Press.

Josselson, R. (2003). Revisioning: Processes of development in midlife women. In J. Demick & C. Andreoletti (Eds.), *Handbook of adult development* (pp. 431–441). New York: Kluwer Academic/Plenum.

Joughin, G. (1992). Cognitive style and adult learning principles. *International Journal of Lifelong Education, 11*(1), 3–14.

Jung, J., & Cervero, R. M. (2002). The social, economic and political contexts of adults' participation in undergraduate programs: A state-level analysis. *International Journal of Lifelong Education, 21*(4), 305–320.

Kalmijin, M. (2004). Marriage rituals as reinforcers of role transitions: An analysis of weddings in the Netherlands. *Journal of Marriage and Family, 66*(3), 582–594.

Kappel, P. L., & Daley, B. J. (2004). Transformative learning and the urban context. In L. G. Martin & E. E. Rogers (Eds.), *Adult education in the urban context: Problems, practices, and programming for inner city communities* (pp. 69–81). New Directions for Adult and Continuing Education, No. 101. San Francisco: Jossey-Bass.

Karpiak, I. (2000). Writing our life: Adult learning and teaching through autobiography. *Canadian Journal of University Continuing Education, 26*(1), 31–50.

Kasworm, C. E. (1992). The adult's learning projects: A fresh approach to theory and practice in adult learning (2nd ed.). In G. J. Confessore & S. J. Confessore (Eds.), *Guideposts to self-directed learning: Expert commentary on essential concepts* (pp. 55–73). King of Prussia, PA: Organizational Design and Development.

Kasworm, C. E., Sandmann, L., & Sissel, P. (2000). Adult learners in higher education. In A. L . Wilson & E. R. Hayes (Eds.), *Handbook of adult and continuing education* (pp. 449–463). San Francisco: Jossey-Bass.

Kaufman, A. S. (2000). Tests of intelligence. In R. J. Sternberg (Ed.), *Handbook of intelligence* (pp. 445–476). New York: Cambridge University Press.

Kaufman, A. S., & Kaufman, N. L. (1993). *Manual for Kaufman Adolescent & Adult Intelligence Test* (KAIT). Circle Pines, MN: American Guidance Service.

Kaufman, A. S., Kaufman, J. C., Chen, T., & Kaufman, N. L. (1996). Differences on six horn abilities for 14 age groups between 15–16 and 75–94 years. *Psychological Assessment, 8*(2), 161–171.

Keen, S., & Valley-Fox, A. (1989). *Your mythic journey: Finding meaning in your life through writing and storytelling.* New York: Tarcher/Putnam.

Kegan, R. (1982). *The evolving self: Problem and processes in human development.* Cambridge, MA: Harvard University Press.

Kegan, R. (1994). *In over our heads: The mental demands of modern life.* Cambridge, MA: Harvard University Press.

Kegan, R. (2000). What "form" transforms? A constructive-developmental perspective on transformational learning. In J. Mezirow & Associates (Eds.), *Learning as transformation: Critical perspectives on a theory in progress* (pp. 35–70). San Francisco: Jossey-Bass.

Kelland, J. H. (2005). Distance learning: Access and inclusion issues. In R. J. Hill & R. Kiely (Eds.), *Proceedings of the 46th Annual Adult Education Research Conference* (pp. 253–258). Athens: University of Georgia.

Kerka, S. (1999). *Self-directed learning.* Myths and Realities No. 3. Columbus, OH: ERIC Clearinghouse on Adult, Career, and Vocational Education. (ERIC Document Reproduction Service No. ED 435 834)

Kerka, S. (2000). *Journal writing as an adult learning tool.* ERIC Digest No. 174. Columbus, OH: ERIC Clearinghouse on Adult, Career, and Vocational Education. (ERIC Document Reproduction Service No. ED 399 413)

Kerka, S. (2002). *Somatic/embodied learning and adult education.* Trends and Issues Alert No. 32. ERIC Clearinghouse on Adult, Career, and Vocational Education, Columbus, OH (ERIC Document Reproduction Service No. ED 462 550).

Kessels, J.W.M., & Poell, R. F. (2004). Andragogy and social capital theory: The implications for human resource development. *Advances in Developing Human Resources, 6*(2), 146–157.

Kidd, J. R. (1973). *How adults learn* (rev. ed.). New York: Association Press.

Kiely, R. C. (2003). A chameleon with a complex: Searching for social justice in transformational learning. In D. Floers, M. Lee, A. Jalipa, E. Lopez, A. Schelstrate, & V. Sheared (Eds.), *Proceedings of the 44th Annual Adult Education Research Conference* (pp. 217–222). San Francisco: San Francisco State University.

Kilgore, D. (2004). Toward a postmodern pedagogy. In R. St. Clair & J. A. Sandlin (Eds.), *Promoting critical practice in adult education* (pp. 45–54). New Directions for Adult and Continuing Education, No. 102. San Francisco: Jossey-Bass.

Kim, K., Collins Hagedorn, M., Williamson, J., & Chapman, C. (2004). *Participation in adult education and lifelong learning: 2000–01* (NCES 20004–050). U.S. Department of Education, National Center for Education Statistics. Washington, DC: U.S. Government Printing Office.

Kim, K., & Creighton, S. (2000). Participation in adult education in the United States: 1998–1999. *Education Statistics Quarterly, 2*(1), 123–128.

Kincheloe, J. L., & Steinberg, S. R. (1993). A tentative description of postformal thinking: The critical confrontation with cognitive theory. *Harvard Educational Review, 63*(3), 296–320.

King, P. M., & Kitchener, K. S. (1994). *Developing reflective judgment.* San Francisco: Jossey-Bass.

King, P. M., & Kitchener, K. S. (2002). The reflective judgment model: Twenty years of research on epistemic cognition. In B. K. Hofer & P. R. Pintrich (Eds.), *Personal epistemology: The psychology of beliefs about knowledge and knowing* (pp. 37–61). Hillsdale, NJ: Erlbaum.

King, P. M., & Kitchener, K. S. (2004). Reflective judgment: Theory and research on the development of epistemic assumptions through adulthood. *Educational Psychologist, 39*(1), 5–18.

King, P. M., Kitchener, K. S., & Wood, P. K. (1994). Research on the reflective judgment model. *Developing reflective judgment: Understanding and promoting intellectual growth and critical thinking in adolescents and adults.* San Francisco: Jossey-Bass.

Kirshner, D., & Whitson, J. A. (Eds.). (1997). *Situated cognition: Social, semiotic and psychological perspectives.* Hillsdale, NJ: Erlbaum

Kline, D. W., & Scialfa, C. T. (1996). Visual and auditory aging. In J. E. Birren & K. W. Schaie (Eds.), *Handbook of the psychology of aging* (4th ed., pp. 181–203). Orlando, FL: Academic Press.

Knight, C. C., & Sutton, R. E. (2004). Neo-Piagetian theory and research. Enhancing pedagogical practice for educators of adults. *London Review of Education, 2*(1), 47–60.

Knopf, M. (1995). Memory for action events: Structure and development in adulthood. In F. E. Weinert & W. Schneider (Eds.), *Memory performance and competencies: Issues in growth and development* (pp. 127–138). Hillsdale, NJ: Erlbaum.

Knowles, M. S. (1968). Andragogy, not pedagogy. *Adult Leadership, 16*(10), 350–352, 386.

Knowles, M. S. (1970). *The modern practice of adult education: Andragogy versus pedagogy.* New York: Cambridge Books.

Knowles, M. S. (1973). *The adult learner: A neglected species.* Houston: Gulf.

Knowles, M. S. (1975). *Self-directed learning.* New York: Association Press.

Knowles, M. S. (1980). *The modern practice of adult education: From pedagogy to andragogy* (2nd ed.). New York: Cambridge Books.

Knowles, M. S. (1984). *The adult learner: A neglected species* (3rd ed.). Houston: Gulf.

Knowles, M. S. (1989). *The making of an adult educator: An autobiographical journey.* San Francisco: Jossey-Bass.

Knowles, M. S., & Associates. (1984). *Andragogy in action: Applying modern principles of adult learning.* San Francisco: Jossey-Bass.

Knox, A. B. (1977). *Adult development and learning.* San Francisco: Jossey-Bass.

Kohl de Oliveira, M. (1995). The meaning of intellectual competence: Views from a favela. In J. Valsiner (Ed.), *Child development within culturally structured environments: Comparative-cultural and constructivist perspectives.* Norwood, NJ: Ablex.

Kohlberg, L. (1973). Continuities in childhood and adult moral development. In P. Baltes & K. Schaie (Eds.), *Life-Span Developmental Psychology: Personality and Socialization* (pp. 180–204). Orlando: Academic Press.

Kohlberg, L. (1976). Moral stages and moralization: The cognitive-developmental approach. In T. Lickona (Ed.), *Moral development and behavior: Theory, research, and social issues* (pp. 31–53). Austin, TX: Holt, Rinehart & Winston.

Kohlberg, L. (1981). *The philosophy of moral development: Moral stages and the idea of justice.* San Francisco: HarperSanFrancisco.

Kolb, A. Y., & Kolb, D. A. (2005). Learning styles and learning spaces: Enhancing experiential learning in higher education. *Academy of Management Learning and Education, 4*(2), 193–212.

Kolb, D. A. (1984). *Experiential learning: Experience as the source of learning and Development.* Englewood Cliffs, NJ: Prentice Hall.

Kovan, J. T., & Dirkx, J. M. (2003). "Being called awake": The role of transformative learning in the lives of environmental activists. *Adult Education Quarterly, 53*(2), 99–118.

Kramer, D. A., & Baccelar, W. T. (1994). The educated adult in today's world: Wisdom and the mature learner. In J. D. Sinnott (Ed.), *Interdisciplinary handbook of adult lifespan learning.* Westport, CT: Greenwood Press.

Krause, N. (1999). Stress and the devaluation of highly salient roles in later life. *Journal of Gerontology: Social Sciences, 54B,* S99–S108.

Labouvie-Vief, G. (1980). Beyond formal operations: Uses and limits of pure logic in life-span development. *Human Development, 23,* 141–161.

Labouvie-Vief, G. (1984). Logic and self-regulation from youth to maturity: A model. In M. L. Commons, F. A. Richards, & C. Armon (Eds.), *Beyond formal operations: Late adolescent and adult cognitive development* (pp. 158–179). New York: Praeger.

Labouvie-Vief, G. (1990). Models of cognitive functioning in the older adult: Research needs in educational gerontology. In R. H. Sherron & D. B. Lumsden (Eds.), *Introduction to educational gerontology* (3rd ed., pp. 243–268). New York: Hemisphere.

Labouvie-Vief, G. (1992). A new-Piagetian perspective on adult cognitive development. In R. J. Sternberg & C. A. Berg (Eds.), *Intellectual Development* (pp. 197–228). New York: Cambridge University Press.

Labouvie-Vief, G., & Diehl, M. (2000). Cognitive complexity and cognitive-affective integration: Related or separate domains of adult development. *Psychology and Aging, 15*(3), 490–504.

Laiken, M. E. (2001). Models of organizational learning: Paradoxes and best practices in the post industrial workplace. NALL Working Paper #24–2001. http://www.nall.ca/res/25MarilynLaiken.pdf. Accessed July 29, 2005.

Lajoie, S. P. (2003). Transitions and trajectories for studies of expertise. *Educational Researcher, 32*(8), 21–25.

Lamb, S. (2003). Best practices on fostering transformative learning in the workplace. In C. A. Weissner, S. R., Meyer, N. L. Pfhal, & P. G. Neaman (Eds.), *Proceedings of the 5th International Conference on Transformative Learning* (pp. 263–268). New York: Teachers College, Columbia University.

Langer, E. J. (1997). *The power of mindful learning.* Reading, MA: Addison-Wesley.

Lavallee, M., Gourde, A., & Rodier, C. (1990). The impact of lived experience on cognitiveoethical development of today's women. *International Journal of Behavioral Development, 13*(4), 407–430.

Lave, J. (1988). *Cognition in practice: Mind, mathematics and culture in everyday life.* Cambridge: Cambridge University Press.

Le Cornu, A. (2005). Building on Jarvis: Towards a holistic model of the process of experiential learning. *Studies in the Education of Adults, 37*(2), 166–181.

Lee, M. (2003). Andragogy and foreign-born learners. In L. M. Baumgartner, M. Lee, S. Birden, & D. Flowers (Eds.), *Adult learning theory: A primer* (pp. 11–16). Information Series No. 392. Columbus, OH: Center on Education and Training for Employment. (ERIC Document Reproduction Service No. ED 482 337)

Lee, M. Y., & Greene, G. J. (2003). A teaching framework for transformative multicultural social work education. *Journal of Ethnic and Cultural Diversity in Social Work, 12*(3), 1–28.

Lee, M., & Johnson-Bailey, J. (2004). Challenges to the classroom authority of women of color. In R. St. Clair & J. A. Sandlin (Eds.), *Promoting critical practice in adult education* (pp. 55–64). New Directions for Adult and Continuing Education, No. 102. San Francisco: Jossey-Bass.

Lefrancois, G. R. (1996). *The lifespan* (5th ed.). Belmont, CA: Wadsworth.

Lefrancois, G. R. (1999). *The lifespan* (6th ed.). Belmont, CA: Wadsworth.

Lemkow, A. F. (2005). Reflections on our common lifelong learning journey. In J. P. Miller, S. Karsten, D. Denton, D. Orr, & I. C. Kates (Eds.), *Holistic learning and spirituality in education* (pp. 17–26). Albany: State University of New York Press.

Lennox, S. L. (2005). Contemplating the self: Holistic approaches to transformative learning in higher education. In D. Vlosak, G. Kielbaso, & J. Radford (Eds.), *Proceedings of the Sixth International Conference on Transformative Learning* (pp. 281–287). East Lansing: Michigan State University.

Levine, S. L. (1989). *Promoting adult growth in schools: The promise of professional development.* Needham Heights, MA: Allyn & Bacon.

Levinson, D. J., Darrow, C. N., Klein, E. B., Levinson, M. H., & McKee, B. (1978). *The seasons of a man's life.* New York: Knopf.

Levinson, D. J., & Levinson, J. D. (1996). *The seasons of a woman's life.* New York: Ballantine.

Lewis, M. T., Adams, J., & Southern, N. (2005). Transformative learning communities at a distance. In D. Vlosak, G. Kielbaso, & J. Radford (Eds.), *Proceedings of the 6th International Conference on Transformative Learning* (pp. 301–307). East Lansing: Michigan State University.

Lindeman, E. C. (1961). *The meaning of adult education in the United States.* New York: Harvest House.

Lindeman, E. C. (1989). *The meaning of adult education in the United States.* Norman: Oklahoma Research Center for Continuing Professional and Higher Education, University of Oklahoma. (Original work published 1926)

Liu, J. (2001). *Asian students' classroom communication patterns in U.S. universities: An emic perspective.* Norwood, NJ: Ablex.

Livingstone, D. W. (2001). *Adult's informal learning: Definitions, findings, gaps and future research.* NALL Working Paper #21–2001. http://www.nall.ca/res/21adultsifnormallearning.htm. Accessed August 6, 2005.

Loevinger, J. (1976). *Ego development.* San Francisco: Jossey-Bass.

Lohman, D. F., & Scheurman, G. (1992). Fluid abilities and epistemic thinking: Some prescriptions for adult education. In A. Tuijnman & M. van der Kamp (Eds.), *Learning across the lifespan: Theories, research, policies.* New York: Pergamon Press.

Londoner, C. A. (1993). The theory of margin as an HRD problem-solving tool for coping with life stresses. In L. Mathis & K. Mizer (Eds.), *Proceedings of Quest for Quality: National research conference on human resource development* (pp. 117–126). College Station: Texas A&M University.

Ludwig, G. D. (2005). Transforming our spiritual self through critical thinking. In D. Vlosak, G. Kielbaso, & J. Radford (Eds.), *Proceedings of the Sixth International Conference* (pp. 315–320). East Lansing: Michigan State University.

Luttrell, W. (1989). Working-class women's ways of knowing: Effects of gender, race and class. *Sociology of Education, 62*(1), 33–46.

Lyman, P., & Varian, H. R. (n.d.). *How much information? 2003.* Berkeley: University of California, School of Information Management and Systems. http://www.sims.berkeley.edu/how-much-info-2003. Accessed September 11, 2005.

Machles, D. (2004). A qualitative study of situated learning in occupational safety. *Dissertation Abstracts International, 65*(11), 4072A. (UMI No. 3154328)

MacKeracher, D. (1996). *Making sense of adult learning.* Toronto, Canada: Culture Concepts.

Maehl, W. H. (2000). *Lifelong learning at its best: Innovative practices in adult credit programs.* San Francisco: Jossey-Bass.

Magagula, C. M., & Maziboku, E. Z. (2004). Indigenization of African formal education system. *The African Symposium: An On-line Educational Research Journal, 4*(2), 1–9.

Magnusson, D. (1995). Individual development: A holistic, integrated model. In P. Moen, G. H. Elder, & K. Lusher (Eds.), *Examining lives in context: Perspectives on the ecology of human development* (pp. 19–60). Washington, DC: American Psychological Association.

Maher, F. A. (1987). Toward a richer theory of feminist pedagogy: A comparison of "liberation" and "gender" models for teaching and learning. *Journal of Education, 169*(3), 91–100.

Maher, F. A., & Tetreault, M. K. (1994). *The feminist classroom.* New York: Basic Books.

Malinen, A. (2000). *Towards the essence of experiential learning: A reading of the theories of Knowles, Kolb, Mezirow, Revans, and Schön.* Jyväskylä, Finland: SoPhi, University of Jyväskylä Press.

Maples, M. F., & Webster, J. M. (1980). Thorndike's connectionism. In G. B. Gazda & R. J. Corsini (Eds.), *Theories of learning* (pp. 1–28). Itasca, IL: Peacock.

Marois, R. (2005). Capacity limits of information processing in the brain. *Phi Kappa Phi Forum, 85*(1), 30–33.

Marsh, G. R. (1996). Perceptual changes with aging. In E. W. Bussee & D. G. Blazer (Eds.), *Textbook of geriatric psychiatry.* Washington, DC: American Psychiatric Press.

Marsick, V. J., & Watkins, K. E. (1990). *Informal and incidental learning.* London: Routledge.

Marsick, V. J., & Watkins, K. E. (2005). Learning organization. In L. M. English (Ed.), *International encyclopedia of adult education* (pp. 355–360). New York: Palgrave Macmillan.

Maslow, A. H. (1970). *Motivation and personality* (2nd ed.). New York: HarperCollins.

Mason, R. (2003). Global education: Out of the ivory tower. In M. G. Moore & W. G. Anderson (Eds.), *Handbook of distance education* (pp. 743–752). Hillsdale, NJ: Erlbaum.

Matthews, J. C. (1998). Somatic knowing and education. *Educational Forum, 62*(3), 236–242.

Mautle, G. (2001). Formal education among peoples of Botswana before 1840. *Mosenodi, 9*(2), 25–33.

Mayer, J. D., & Salovey, P. (1997). What is emotional intelligence? In P. Salovey & D. Sluyter (Eds.), *Emotional development and emotional intelligence: Implications for educators* (pp. 3–31). New York: Basic Books.

Mayer, J. D., Salovey, P., & Caruso, D. (2000). Models of emotional intelligence. In R. J. Sternberg (Ed.), *Handbook of intelligence* (pp. 396–420). New York: Cambridge University Press.

Mayer, J. D., Salovey, P., & Caruso, D. (2002). *Mayer-Salovey-Caruso Emotional Intelligence Test (MSCEIT): User's manual.* Toronto, Ontario, Canada: Multi-Health Systems.

Mayer, J. D., Salovey, P., & Caruso, D. (2003). Measuring emotional intelligence with the MSCEIT V2.0. *Emotion, 3,* 97–105.

Mayer, R. E., Mautone, P., & Prothero, W. (2002). Pictorial aids for learning by doing in a multimedia geology simulation game. *Journal of Educational Psychology, 94*(1), 171–185.

McCarthy, T. (2005, November 9). Getting inside your head. *Time.*

McClenaghan, P. (2000). Social capital: Exploring the theoretical foundations of community development education. *British Educational Research Journal, 26*(5), 565–582.

McClusky, H. Y. (1963). The course of the adult life span. In W. C. Hallenbeck (Ed.), *Psychology of Adults* (pp. 10–19). Washington, DC: Adult Education Association.

McClusky, H. Y. (1970). An approach to a differential psychology of the adult potential. In S. M. Grabowski (Ed.), *Adult learning and instruction* (pp. 80–95). Syracuse, NY: ERIC Clearinghouse on Adult Education. (ERIC Document Reproduction Service No. ED 045 867)

McClusky, H. Y. (1971). *Education: Background.* Report prepared for the 1971 White House Conference on Aging. Washington, DC: White House Conference on Aging.

McDonald, B. (2002). We make spirit by waling: An application of Kovel's spirituality to the life and work of committed environmentalists. In J. M. Pettitt (Ed.), *Proceedings of the 43rd Annual Adult Education Research Conference.* Raleigh: North Carolina State University.

McDonald, B., Cervero, R. M., & Courtenay, B. C. (1999). An ecological perspective of power in transformational learning: A case study of ethical vegans. *Adult Education Quarterly, 50*(1), 5–23.

McDowell, T. (2003). Answering the call for anti-racist praxis in adult education. *Proceedings of the 44th Annual Adult Education Research Conference* (pp. 279–283). San Francisco: San Francisco State University.

McEnrue, M. P., & Groves, K. (2006). Choosing among tests of emotional intelligence: What is the evidence? *Human Resource Development Quarterly, 17*(1), 9–42.

McLaren, P. (1997). Revolutionary praxis: Toward a pedagogy of resistance and transformation. *Educational Researcher, 26*(6), 23–26.

McLaren, P. (2000). Paulo Freire's pedagogy of possibility. In S. F. Steiner, H. M. Krank, P. McLaren, & R. E. Bahruth (Eds.), *Freirean pedagogy, praxis, and possibilities: Projects for the new millennium. Vol. 19: Critical Education Practice* (pp. 1–22). New York: Falmer Press.

Meisami, E., Brown, C. M., & Emerle, H. F. (2003). Sensory systems: Normal aging, disorders, and treatments of vision and hearing in humans. In P. Timiras (Ed.), *Physiological basis of aging and geriatrics* (pp. 141–165). New York: CRC Press.

Merriam, S. B. (1991). How research produces knowledge. In J. M. Peters & P. Jarvis (Eds.), *Adult education: Evolution and achievements in a developing field of study* (pp. 42–65). San Francisco: Jossey-Bass.

Merriam, S. B. (2004). The role of cognitive development in Mezirow's transformational learning theory. *Adult Education Quarterly, 55*(1), 60–68.

Merriam, S. B., & Brockett, R. G. (1997). *The profession and practice of adult education.* San Francisco: Jossey-Bass.

Merriam, S. B., & Clark, M. C. (2006). Learning and development: The connection in adulthood. In C. Hoare (Ed.), *Handbook of adult development and learning* (pp. 27–51). London: Oxford University Press.

Merriam, S. B., Doraisamy, L., Findsen, B., Kamis, M., Kee, Y., Muhamad, M., Ntseane, G., & Thaker, W. N. (2005). Challenging the hegemony of Western views of learning. In R. J. Hill & R. Kiely (Eds.), *Proceedings of the 46th Annual Adult Education Research Conference* (pp. 295–305). Athens: University of Georgia.

Merriam, S. B., Mott, V. W., & Lee, M. (1996). Learning that comes from the negative interpretation of life experience. *Studies in Continuing Education, 18*(1), 1–23.

Merriam, S. B., & Muhamad, M. (2000). How cultural values shape learning in older adulthood: The case of Malaysia. *Adult Education Quarterly, 51*(1), 45–63.

Messick, S. (1996). Human abilities and modes of attention: The issue of stylistic consistencies in cognition. In I. Dennis & P. Tapsfield (Eds.), *Human abilities: Their nature and measurement* (pp. 77–96). Hillsdale, NJ: Erlbaum.

Mezirow, J. (1981). A critical theory of adult learning and education. *Adult Education, 32*(1), 3–27.

Mezirow, J. (1985). A critical theory of self-directed learning. In S. Brookfield (Ed.), *Self-directed learning: From theory to practice* (pp. 17–30). New Directions for Continuing Education, No. 25. San Francisco: Jossey-Bass.

Mezirow, J. (1990a). Conclusion: Toward transformative learning and emancipatory education. In J. Mezirow & Associates (Eds.), *Fostering critical reflection in adulthood: A guide to transformative and emancipatory learning* (pp. 354–376). San Francisco: Jossey-Bass.

Mezirow, J. (1990b). How critical reflection triggers transformative learning. In J. Mezirow & Associates (Eds.), *Fostering critical reflection in adulthood: A guide to transformative and emancipatory learning* (pp. 1–20). San Francisco: Jossey-Bass.

Mezirow, J. (1991). *Transformative dimensions of adult learning.* San Francisco: Jossey-Bass.

Mezirow, J. (1992). Transformation theory: Critique and confusion. *Adult Education Quarterly, 42*(2), 250–252.

Mezirow, J. (1993). How adults learn: The meaning of adult education. *Proceedings of the 34th Annual Adult Education Research Conference* (pp. 185–190). University Park: Penn State University.

Mezirow, J. (1995). Transformation theory of adult learning. In M. R. Welton (Ed.), *In defense of the lifeworld* (pp. 39–70). New York: State University of New York Press.

Mezirow, J. (1996). Contemporary paradigms of learning. *Adult Education Quarterly, 46*(3), 158–172.

Mezirow, J. (1997a). Transformative learning: Theory to practice. In P. Cranton (Ed.), *Transformative learning in action: Insights from practice* (pp. 5–12). New Directions for Adult and Continuing Education, No. 74. San Francisco: Jossey-Bass.

Mezirow, J. (1997b). Transformative theory out of context. *Adult Education Quarterly, 48*(1), 60–62.

Mezirow, J. (1998). On critical reflection. *Adult Education Quarterly, 48*(3), 185–198.

Mezirow, J. (2000). Learning to think like an adult: Core concepts of transformation theory. In J. Mezirow & Associates, *Learning as transformation: Critical perspectives on a theory in progress* (pp. 3–33). San Francisco: Jossey-Bass.

Mezirow, J., & Associates. (1990). *Fostering critical reflection in adulthood: A guide to transformative and emancipatory learning.* San Francisco: Jossey-Bass.

Mezirow, J., & Associates. (2000). *Learning as transformation: Critical perspectives on a theory in progress.* San Francisco: Jossey-Bass.

Michelson, E. (1996). Beyond Galileo's telescope: Situated knowledge and the assessment of experiential learning. *Adult Education Quarterly, 46*(4), 185–196.

Michelson, E. (1998). Re-membering: The return of the body to experiential learning. *Studies in Continuing Education, 20*(2), 217–233.

Miettinen, R. (2000). The concept of experiential learning and John Dewey's theory of reflective thought and action. *International Journal of Lifelong Education, 19*(1), 54–72.

Mikolaj, E. D. (1983). The intrapersonal role conflicts of adult women undergraduate students. *Dissertation Abstracts International, 144*(11A), 3247. (UMI No. 8403550)

Miller, P. H. (2002). *Theories of developmental psychology* (4th ed.). New York: Freeman.

Mitroff, I. I., & Denton, E. (1999). *A spiritual audit of corporate America.* San Francisco: Jossey-Bass.

Mojab, S. (2005). Class and race. In T. Nesbit (Ed.), *Class concerns: Adult education and social class* (pp. 73–82). New Directions for Adult and Continuing Education, No. 106. San Francisco: Jossey-Bass.

Montano, J. J. (2003, Spring). Emerging technologies for hearing loss: An ecological approach. *Generations, 27*(1), 71–77.

Moore, M. G. (2001). *Distance education in the United States: The state of the art.* Series of lectures on the education use of ICT and virtual education by UOC. http:www.uoc.edu/web/eng/art/uoc/moore/moore.html. Accessed July 1, 2004.

Moore, M. G., & Kearsley, G. (1996). *Distance education: A systems view.* Belmont, CA: Wadsworth.

Moore, T. (2005). Educating for the soul. In J. P. Miller, S. Karsten, D. Denton, D. Orr, & I. C. Kates (Eds.), *Holistic learning and spirituality in education* (pp. 9–16). Albany: State University of New York Press.

Morolong, B. L. (1996, April 10–13). *Indigenous knowledge and development: Any space for this in the provision of adult education and social transformation?* Paper presented at the International Conference on Adult Education and Social Transformation, Maseru, Lesotho.

Mullen, C. (2005). *The mentorship primer.* New York: Peter Lang.

Mulvihill, M. K. (2003). The Catholic Church in crisis: Will transformative learning lead to social change through the uncovering of emotion? In C. A. Wiessner, S. R. Meyer, N. L. Pfhal, & P. G. Neaman (Eds.), *Proceedings of the Fifth International Conference on Transformative Learning* (pp. 320–325). New York: Teacher's College, Columbia University.

Myers, I. (1985). *Gifts differing* (7th ed.). Palo Alto, CA: Consulting Psychologists.

Nah, Y. (2000). Can a self-directed learner be independent, autonomous and interdependent? Implications for practice. *Adult Learning, 18,* 18–19, 25.

Naisbitt, J., & Aburdene, P. (1990). *Megatrends 2000: Ten new directions for the 1990s.* New York: Morrow.

Naveh-Benjamin, M., Hussain, Z., Guez, J., & Bar-On, M. (2003). Adult age differences in episodic memory: Further support for an associative-deficit hypothesis. *Journal of Experimental Psychology: Learning Memory and Cognition, 29*(5), 826–837.

Nesbit, T. (1998). The social reform perspective: Seeing a better society. In D. Pratt & others, *Five perspectives on teaching in adult and higher education* (pp. 173–199). Malabar, FL: Krieger.

Neugarten, B. (1976). Adaptation and the life cycle. *Counseling Psychologist, 6,* 16–20.

Neugarten, B. (1979). Time, age, and the life cycle. *American Journal of Psychiatry, 136,* 887–893.

Neugarten, B., & Datan, N. (1973). Sociological perspectives on the life cycle. In P. Baltes & K. W. Schaie (Eds.), *Life span developmental psychology: Personality and socialization* (pp. 53–69). Orlando: Academic Press.

Neuhauser, P. C. (1993). *Corporate legends and lore: The power of storytelling as a management tool.* New York: McGraw-Hill.

Newman, M. (1994). *Defining the enemy: Adult education in social action.* Sydney: Stewart Victor.

Newman, M. (2006). *Teaching defiance: Stories and strategies for activist educators.* San Francisco: Jossey-Bass.

Nisbett, R. E. (2003). *The geography of thought: How Asians and Westerners think differently . . . and why.* New York: Free Press.

Nordhaug, O. (1990). Structured determinants of publicly subsidized adult education. *Adult Education Quarterly, 40*(4), 197–206.

Norman, S. M., McCluskey-Fawcett, K., & Ashcraft, L. (2002). Older women's development: A comparison of women in their 60s and 80s on a measure of Erikson's developmental tasks. *International Journal of Aging and Human Development, 54*(1), 31–41.

Nuernberger, P. (1994). The structure of mind and its resources. In M. E. Miller & S. R. Cook-Greuter (Eds.), *Transcendence and mature thought in adulthood: The further reaches of adult development* (pp. 89–115). Lanham, MD: Rowman & Littlefield.

Oddi, L. F. (1986). Development and validation of an instrument to identify self-directed continuing learners. *Adult Education Quarterly, 36*(2), 97–107.

Oddi, L. F., Ellis, A. J., & Roberson, J.E.A. (1990). Construct validity of the Oddi continuing learning inventory. *Adult Education Quarterly, 40*(3), 139–145.

Opengart, R. (2005). Emotional intelligence and emotion work: Examining constructs from an interdisciplinary framework. *Human Resource Development Review, 4*(1), 49–62.

Organization for Economic Cooperation and Development (OECD). (1996). *Learning for all.* Paris: OECD.

Ormrod, J. E. (1995). *Human learning* (2nd ed.). Englewood Cliffs, NJ: Merrill.

Ormrod, J. E. (1999). *Human learning* (3rd ed.). Englewood Cliffs, NJ: Merrill.

Osterman, K. F., & Kottkamp, R. B. (2004). *Reflective practice for educators: Professional development to improve student learning* (2nd ed.). Thousand Oaks, CA: Corwin Press.

O'Sullivan, E. (1999). *Transformative learning: Educational vision for the 21st century.* London: Zed Books.

O'Sullivan, E. (2002). The project and vision of transformative education: Integral transformative learning. In E. O'Sullivan, A. Morrell, & M. A. O'Conner (Eds.), *Expanding the boundaries of transformative learning: Essays on theory and praxis* (pp. 1–12). New York: Palgrave.

O'Sullivan, E. (2005). Emancipatory hope: Transformative learning and the "strange attractors." In J. P. Miller, S. Karsten, D. Denton, D. Orr, & I. C. Kates (Eds.), *Holistic learning and spirituality in education* (pp. 69–78). Albany: State University of New York Press.

Over 60 and overlooked. (2002, August 10). *The Economist*, pp. 51–52.

Owen, T. R. (2002). *Self-directed learning in adulthood: A literature review.* Columbus, OH: ERIC Clearinghouse on Adult, Career, and Vocational Education. (ERIC Document Reproduction Service No. ED 461 050)

Pachnowski, L. M., & Jurczyk, J. P. (2000). *Correlating self-directed learning with distance learning success.* Paper presented at the annual meeting of the Eastern Educational Research Association, Clearwater, FL. (ERIC Document Reproduction Service No. ED 441 000)

Padberg, L. F. (1994). The organizing circumstance revisited: Environmentally structured learning projects among adults with low formal education. In H. B. Long & others, *New ideas about self-directed learning*. Norman: Oklahoma Research Center for Continuing Professional and Higher Education, University of Oklahoma.

Page, G. A. (2005). Adult education and technology in a rural county: The irony of persistent poverty and "progress" in the information age. In R. J. Hill & R. Kiely (Eds.), *Proceedings of the 46th Annual Adult Education Research Conference* (pp. 331–336). Athens: University of Georgia.

Palmer, B. R., Gignac, G., Manocha, R., & Stough, C. (2005). A psychometric evaluation of the Mayer-Salovey-Caruso emotional intelligence test version 2.0. *Intelligence, 33*(3), 285–305.

Paterson, K. W. (1979). *Values, education, and the adult.* New York: Routledge.

Pearson, E., & Podeschi, R. (1997). Humanism and individualism: Maslow and his critics. In R. Nolan & H. Chelesvig (Eds.), *Proceedings of the 38th Annual Adult Education Research Conference* (pp. 203–207). Stillwater: Oklahoma State University.

Peng, K., & Nisbett, R. E. (1999). Culture, dialectics, and reasoning about contradiction. *American Psychologist, 54*(9), 741–754.

Penland, P. R. (1979). Self-initiated learning. *Adult Education, 29,* 170–179.

Perry, W. G. (1970). *Forms of intellectual and ethical development in the college years.* Austin, TX: Holt, Rinehart & Winston.

Perry, W. G. (1981). Cognitive and ethical growth: The making of meaning. In A. W. Chickering (Ed.), *The modern American college* (pp. 76–116). San Francisco: Jossey-Bass.

Perry, W. G. (1999). *Forms of intellectual and ethical development in the college years: A scheme.* San Francisco: Jossey-Bass.

Pert, C. B. (1997). *Molecules of emotion: Why you feel the way you feel.* New York: Scribner.

Perun, P. J., & Bielby, D. D. (1980). Structure and dynamics of the individual life course. In K. W. Back (Ed.), *Life course: Integrative theories and exemplary populations* (pp. 97–119). Boulder, CO: Westview Press.

Pesce, C., Guidetti, L., Baldari, C., Tessitore, A., & Capranica, L. (2005). Effects of aging on visual attention focusing. *Gerontology, 51*(4), 266–276.

Peterson, D. A., & Masunaga, H. (1998). Policy for older adult education. In J. C. Fisher & M. A. Wolf (Eds.), *Using learning to meet the challenges of older adulthood.* New Directions for Adult and Continuing Education, No. 77. San Francisco: Jossey-Bass.

Petrella, R. (1997). The snares of the market economy for future training policy: Beyond the heralding there is a need for denunciation. *Adult Education and Development, 48,* 19–26.

Petrill, S. A. (2002). The case for general intelligence: A behavioral genetic perspective. In R. J. Sternberg & E. L. Grigorenko (Eds.), *The general factor of intelligence: How general is it?* (pp. 281–298). Hillsdale, NJ: Erlbaum.

Petrill, S. A. (2003). The development of intelligence: Behavioral genetic approaches. In R. J. Sternberg, J. Lautrey, & T. I. Lubart (Eds.), *Models of intelligence: International perspectives* (pp. 81–89). Washington, DC: American Psychological Association.

Phares, E. J. (1980). Rotter's social learning theory. In G. M. Gazda & R. J. Corsini (Eds.), *Theories of learning* (404–446). Itasca, IL: Peacock.

Phillips, D. C. (1995). The good, the bad, and the ugly: The many faces of constructivism. *Educational Researcher, 24*(7), 5–12.

Piaget, J. (1952). *The origins of intelligence in children.* New York: International Universities Press.

Piaget, J. (1966). *The origins of intelligence in children.* New York: International Universities Press.

Piaget, J. (1972). Intellectual evolution from adolescent to adulthood. *Human Development, 16,* 346–370.

Pietrykowski, B. (1996). Knowledge and power in adult education: Beyond Freire and Habermas. *Adult Education Quarterly, 46*(2), 82–97.

Pillay, H., & McCrindle, A. R. (2005). Distributed and relative nature of professional expertise. *Studies in Continuing Education, 27*(1), 67–88.

Pinderhughs, E. (1995). Biracial identity—asset or handicap? In H. W. Harris, H. C. Blue, & E.E.H. Griffith (Eds.), *Racial and ethnic identity: Psychological development and creative expression* (pp. 73–93). New York: Routledge.

Pinhey, T. K., & Pinhey, D. L. (2002). Life event timing and the emotional consequences of surgical menopause for Asian-Pacific women in Guam. *Women and Health, 36*(4), 43–54.

Pirttilä-Backman, A. M., & Kajanne, A. (2001). The development of implicit epistemologies during early and middle adulthood. *Journal of Adult Development, 8*(2), 81–97.

Piskurich, G. M. (1993). *Self-directed learning: A practical guide to design development, and implementation.* San Francisco: Jossey-Bass.

Plumb, D. (1995a). Critical adult education and identity in postmodernity. *Proceedings of the 36th Annual Adult Education Research Conference* (pp. 241–248). Edmonton, Alberta: University of Alberta.

Plumb, D. (1995b). Declining opportunities: Adult education, culture, and postmodernity. In M. R. Welton (Ed.), *In defense of the lifeworld* (pp. 157–194). Albany: State University of New York Press.

Ponterotto, J. G., Casas, J. M., Suzuki, L. A., & Alexander, C. M. (2001). *Handbook of multicultural counseling* (2nd ed). Thousand Oaks, CA: Sage.

Potter, E. (2003). Telecommuting: The future of work, corporate culture, and American society. *Journal of Labor Research, 24*(1), 73–84.

Poulton, M. K., Derrick, M. G., & Carr, P. B. (2005). The relationship between resourcefulness and persistence in adult autonomous learning. *Adult Education Quarterly, 55*(2), 116–128.

Pratt, D. D. (1988). Andragogy as a relational construct. *Adult Education Quarterly, 38*(3), 160–181.

Pratt, D. D. (1993). Andragogy after twenty-five years. In S. B. Merriam (Ed.), *An update on adult learning theory* (pp. 15–24). New Directions for Adult and Continuing Education, No. 57. San Francisco: Jossey-Bass.

Progoff, I. (1975). *At a journal workshop: The basic text and guide for using the intensive journal.* New York: Dialogue House Library.

Quigley, B. A. (1990). Hidden logic: Reproduction and resistance in adult literacy and adult basic education. *Adult Education Quarterly, 40*(2), 103–115.

Rabbitt, P., Donlan, C., Brent, N., McInnes, L., & Abson, V. (1993). The University of Manchester Age and Cognitive Performance Research Centre and the North East Age Research longitudinal programmes, 1982 to 1997. *Zeitschrift fur Gerontologie, 26,* 176–183.

Rachal, J. (1989). The social setting of adult and continuing education. In S. B. Merriam & P. M. Cunningham (Eds.), *Handbook of adult and continuing education* (pp. 3–14). San Francisco: Jossey-Bass.

Rachal, J. (2002). Andragogy's detectives: A critique of the present and a proposal for the future. *Adult Education Quarterly, 52*(3), 210–227.

Rados, C. (2005, May-June). Sound advice about age-related hearing loss. *FDA Consumer, 3,* 20–27.

Rager, K. B. (2003). The self-directed learning of women with breast cancer. *Adult Education Quarterly, 53*(4), 277–293.

Rains, F. V. (1999). Indigenous knowledge, historical amnesia and intellectual authority: Deconstructing hegemony and the social and political implications of the curricular "other." In L. M. Semali & J. L. Kincheloe (Eds.), *What is indigenous knowledge? Voices from the academy* (pp. 317–331). New York: Falmer Press.

Ramey, C. T., & Ramey, S. (2000). Intelligence and public policy. In R. J. Sternberg (Ed.), *Handbook of intelligence* (pp. 534–548). New York: Cambridge University Press.

Randall, W. L. (1996). Restorying a life: Adult education and transformative learning. In J. E. Birren, G. M. Kenyon, J. Ruth, J. Schroots, & T. Svensson (Eds.), *Aging and biography: Explorations in adult development* (pp. 224–247). New York: Springer.

Ratinoff, L. (1995). Global insecurity and education: The culture of globalization. *Prospects, 25*(2), 147–174.

Raykov, T. (1995). Multivariate structural modeling of plasticity in fluid intelligence of aged adults. Multivariate Behavioral Research, *30*(2), 255–287.

Reagan, T. (2005). *Non-Western educational traditions: Indigenous approaches to educational thought and practice* (3rd ed.). Hillsdale, NJ: Erlbaum.

Reese, H. W., & Overton, W. F. (1970). Models of development and theories of development. In L. R. Goulet & P. B. Balltes (Eds.), *Life-span developmental psychology: Interventions* (pp. 115–145). Orlando: Academic Press.

Reitzes, D. C. (2003). Social and emotional engagement in adulthood. In M. H. Borstein & L. Davidson (Eds.), *Well-being: Positive development across the life course* (pp. 425–447). Hillsdale, NJ: Erlbaum.

Resnick, L. (1987). Learning in school and out. *Educational Researcher, 16*(9), 13–20.

Restak, R. (2000). *Mysteries of the mind.* Washington, DC: National Geographic Society.

Reuter-Lorenz, P., & Lustig, C. (2005). Brain aging: Reorganizing discoveries about the aging mind. *Current Opinion in Neurobiology, 15*(2), 245–251.

Reybold, L. E. (1997). A sociocultural perspective on knowing: A grounded theory of epistemological development of Malaysian women. In R. Nolan & H. Chelesvig (Eds.), *Proceedings of the 38th Annual Adult Education Research Conference* (pp. 208–213). Stillwater: Oklahoma State University.

Richardson, K. (1999). *The making of intelligence.* London: Weidenfeld & Nicolson.

Richardson, T. Q., & Silvestri, T. J. (1999). White identity formation: A developmental process. In R. H. Sheets & E. R. Hollins (Eds.), *Racial and ethnic identity in school practices: Aspects of human development* (pp. 49–65). Hillsdale, NJ: Erlbaum.

Riegel, K. F. (1973). Dialectic operations: The final period of cognitive development. *Human Development, 16,* 346–370.

Riegel, K. F. (1975). Adult life crises: A dialectical interpretation of development. In N. Datan & L. H. Ginsberg (Eds.), *Life-span developmental psychology: Normative life crises* (pp. 99–128). Orlando: Academic Press.

Riegel, K. F. (1976). The dialectics of human development. *American Psychologist, 31,* 689–700.

Ripley, A. (2005, February 27). Who says a woman can't be Einstein? *Time.*

Roberson, D. N. (2003). *How older adults utilize self-directed learning in late life adjustments.* Unpublished doctoral dissertation, University of Georgia, Athens.

Roberson, D. N., & Merriam, S. B. (2005). The self-directed learning process of older, rural adults. *Adult Education Quarterly, 55*(4), 269–287.

Robertson, L. C. (2005). The bilateral brain: Are two better than one? *Phi Kappa Phi Forum, 85*(1), 19–22.

Robinson, D. N. (1990). Wisdom through the ages. In R. J. Sternberg (Ed.), *Wisdom: Its nature, origins, and development.* New York: Cambridge University Press.

Rocco, T. S., & West, W. (1998). Deconstructing privilege: An examination of privilege in adult education. *Adult Education Quarterly, 48*(3), 171–184.

Rockquemore, K. A., & Brunsma, D. L. (2002). *Beyond Black: Biracial identity in America.* Thousand Oaks, CA: Sage.

Rodgers W. A., & Fisk, A. D. (2001). Understanding the role of attention in cognition and aging research. In J. E. Birren & K. S. Schaie (Eds.), *Handbook of psychology and aging* (5th ed., pp. 267–287). San Diego, CA: Academic Press.

Rogers, C. R. (1961). *On becoming a person: A therapist's view of psychotherapy.* Boston: Houghton Mifflin.

Rogers, C. R. (1983). *Freedom to learn for the 80s.* Columbus, OH: Merrill.

Root, T. L. (2000). Getting there: A study of adult undergraduate persistence to graduation in an adult-centered degree program. *Dissertation Abstracts International, 61*(01), 108. (UMI No. 9958846)

Rosenau, P. M. (1992). *Post-modernism and the social sciences.* Princeton, NJ: Princeton University Press.

Rosenblum, S., & Darkenwald, G. (1983). Effects of adult learner participation in course planning on achievement. *Adult Education Quarterly, 33*(3), 147–160.

Rosnow, R. L., Skleder, A. A., Jaeger, M. E., & Rind, B. (1994). Intelligence and the epistemics of interpersonal acumen: Testing some implications of Gardner's theory. *Intelligence, 19*(1), 93–116.

Ross, J. (2000). Art education in the information age: A new place for somatic wisdom. *Arts Education Policy Review, 101*(6), 27–32.

Ross-Gordon, J. (1994). Toward a critical multicultural pedagogy for adult education. In M. Hyams, J. Armstrong, & E. Anderson (Eds.), *Proceedings of the 35th Annual Adult Education Research Conference* (pp. 312–317). Knoxville: University of Tennessee.

Ross-Gordon, J., Brooks, A. K., Clunis, T., Munox, L., Parsells, R., & Parker, U. (2005). An analysis of work-related learning literature focusing on race and ethnicity. In R. J. Hill & R. Kiely (Eds.), *The 46th Annual Adult Education Research Conference* (pp. 375–380). Athens: University of Georgia.

Rossiter, M. (2002). Narrative and stories in adult teaching and learning. *Clearinghouse Digest.* (ERIC Documentation Reproduction Service No. ED 473 147)

Rossiter, M. (2005). Narrative. In L. M. English (Ed.), *International encyclopedia of adult education* (pp. 418–422). New York: Palgrave Macmillan.

Rossiter, M., & Clark, M. C. (in press). *Narrative and the practice of adult education.* Malabar: FL: Krieger.

Rotter, J. B. (1954). *Social learning and clinical psychology.* Englewood Cliffs, NJ: Prentice Hall.

Rowland, R., & Volet, S. (1996). Self-direction in community learning: A case study. *Australian Journal of Adult and Community Education, 36*(2), 89–102.

Rubenson, K. (1989). Sociology of adult education. In S. B. Merriam & P. M. Cunningham (Eds.), *Handbook of adult and continuing education* (pp. 51–69). San Francisco: Jossey-Bass.

Rubenson, K. (1998). Adults' readiness to learn: Questioning lifelong learning for all. *Proceedings of the Adult Education Research Conference, No. 39.* (pp. 257–262). San Antonio: University of the Incarnate Word and Texas A&M University.

Sahakian, W. S. (1984). *Introduction to the psychology of learning* (2nd ed.). Itasca, IL: Peacock.

Salovey, P., & Mayer, J. D. (1990). Emotional intelligence. *Imagination, Cognition and Personality, 9*(3), 185–211.

Salovey, P., & Pizarro, D. A. (2003). The value of emotional intelligence. In R. J. Sternberg, J. Lautrey, & T. I. Lubart (Eds.), *Models of intelligence: International perspectives* (pp. 263–278). Washington, DC: American Psychological Association.

Sandlin, J. (2000). The politics of consumer education materials used in adult literacy classrooms. *Adult Education Quarterly, 50*(4), 289–307.

Sandlin, J. (2005). Andragogy and its discontents: An analysis of andragogy from three critical perspectives. *PAACE Journal of Lifelong Learning, 14,* 25–42.

Sawyer, L. L. (2003). Transformative learning at the intersection of body, mind and spirit. In C. A. Weissner, S. R., Meyer, N. L. Pfhal, & P. G. Neaman (Eds.), *Proceedings of the 5th International Conference on Transformative Learning* (pp. 369–374). New York: Teachers College, Columbia University.

Sawyer, L. L. (2004). Seeding and sustaining transformative learning, development and spiritual growth in higher education: A case study. *Dissertation Abstracts International, 65*(12), 4431A. (UMI No. 3155999)

Schacter, D. L. (1996). *Searching for memory: The brain, the mind, and the past.* New York: Basic Books.

Schaie, K. W. (1979). The primary mental abilities in adulthood: An exploration in the development of psychometric intelligence. In P. B. Baltes & O. G. Brim (Eds.), *Life-span development and behavior* (Vol. 2). Orlando: Academic Press.

Schaie, K. W. (1985). *Manual for the Schaie-Thurston adult mental abilities test* (STAMAT). Palo Alto: Consulting Psychologists Press.

Schaie, K. W. (1994). The course of adult intellectual development. *American Psychologist, 49*(4), 304–313.

Schaie, K. W. (1996a). Intellectual development in adulthood. In J. E. Birren & K. W. Schaie (Eds.), *Handbook of the psychology of aging* (4th ed., pp. 266–286). Orlando: Academic Press.

Schaie, K. W. (1996b). *Intellectual developmental in adulthood: The Seattle longitudinal study.* Cambridge, UK: Cambridge University Press.

Schaie, K. W. (2005). *Developmental influences on adult intelligence: The Seattle longitudinal study.* New York: Oxford University Press.

Schaie, K. W., & Hofer, C. (2001). Longitudinal studies in aging research. In J. E. Birren & K. W. Schaie (Eds.), *Handbook of the psychology of aging* (5th ed., pp. 53–77). Orlando: Academic Press.

Schaie, K. W., & Willis, S. L. (1986). *Adult development and aging* (2nd ed.) Boston: Little, Brown.

Schaie, K. W., & Willis, S. L. (2002). *Adult development and aging* (5th ed.). Englewood Cliffs, NJ: Prentice Hall.

Schaie, K. W., Willis, S. L., & O'Hanlon, A. M. (1994). Perceived intellectual performance change over seven years. *Journal of Gerontology: Psychological Sciences, 49*(3), 103–118.

Schawo, A. (1997). The relationship between the margin in life and perception of the ideal adult classroom of adult female college students. *Dissertation Abstracts International, 57*(09), 3848. (UMI No. 9705283)

Schied, F. (1993). *Learning in social context: Workers and adult education in nineteenth century Chicago*. DeKalb, IL: LEPS Press.

Schied, F. (1994). Neo-Marxist perspectives and adult education. *Proceedings of the 35th Annual Adult Education Research Conference* (pp. 445–446). Knoxville: University of Tennessee.

Schied, F. M., Carter, V. K., Preston, J. A., & Howell, S. L. (1997). The HRD factory: An historical inquiry into the production of control in the workplace. In P. Armstrong, N. Miller, & M. Zukas (Eds.), *Crossing Borders, Breaking Boundaries: Proceedings of the 27th Annual SCUTREA Conference* (pp. 404–408). London: Birbeck College, University of London.

Schied, F. M., Mulenga, D., & Baptiste, I. (2005). Lifelong learning in a global context: Towards a reconceptualization of adult education. In R. J. Hill & R. Kiely (Eds.), *Proceedings of the 46th Annual Adult Education Research Conference* (pp. 395–399). Athens: University of Georgia.

Schlossberg, N. K. (1984). *Counseling adults in transition*. New York: Springer.

Schlossberg, N. K. (1987). Taking the mystery out of change. *Psychology Today, 21*(5), 74–75.

Schlossberg, N. K., Lynch, A. Q., & Chickering, A. W. (1989). *Improving higher education environments for adults*. San Francisco: Jossey-Bass.

Schmidt, M. J., & Haydu, M. L. (1992). The older hearing-impaired adult in the classroom: Real-time closed captioning as a technological alternative to oral lecture. *Educational Gerontology, 18*(3), 273–276.

Schneider, E. C., Zaslavsky, A. M., & Epstein, A. M. (2002). Racial disparities in the quality of care for enrollees in Medicare managed care. *JAMA: Journal of the American Medical Association, 287*(10), 1281–1294.

Schön, D. A. (1983). *The reflective practitioner: How professionals think in action*. New York: Basic Books.

Schön, D. A. (1987). *Educating the reflective practitioner.* New York: Basic Books.

Schön, D. A. (Ed.). (1991). *The reflective turn: Case studies in and on educational practice*. New York: Teachers College Press.

Schön, D. A. (1996). From technical rationality to reflection-in-action. In R. Edwards, A. Hanson, & P. Raggatt (Eds.), *Boundaries of adult learning* (pp. 8–31). London: Routledge.

Schrader-Naef, R. (2000). Foundations of self-directed lifelong learning. In G. A. Straka, *Conceptions of self-directed learning* (pp. 143–169). New York: Waxmann.

Schugurensky, D. (2000). The forms of informal learning: Towards a conceptualization of the field. NALL Working Paper #19–2000. http://www.nall.ca/res/19formsofinformal.htm. Accessed August 5, 2005.

Schunk, D. H. (1996). *Learning theories: An educational perspective.* Englewood Cliffs, NJ: Prentice Hall.

Scott, S. M. (1997). The grieving soul in the transformation process. In P. Cranton (Ed.), *Transformative learning in action* (pp. 41–50). New Directions for Adult and Continuing Education, No. 74. San Francisco: Jossey-Bass.

Selingo, J. (2005, June 17). U. of Phoenix owes rapid growth to use of technology, its president says. *Chronicle of Higher Education,* p. A23.

Sellers, R. M., Smith, M. A., Shelton, J. N., Rowley, S.A.J., & Chavous, T. M. (1998). Multidimensional model of racial identity: A reconceptualization of African American racial identity. *Personality and Social Psychology Review, 2*(1), 18–39.

Semali, L. M., & Kincheloe, J. L. (1999). Introduction: What is indigenous knowledge and why should we study it? In L. M. Semali & J. L. Kincheloe (Eds.), *What is indigenous knowledge? Voices from the academy* (pp. 3–57). New York: Falmer Press.

Senge, P. M. (1990). *The fifth discipline: The art and practice of the learning organization.* New York: Doubleday.

Serpell, R. (2000). Intelligence and culture. In R. J. Sternberg (Ed.), *Handbook of intelligence* (pp. 549–577). New York: Cambridge University Press.

Shaffer, D. L. (2005). *Social and personality development* (5th ed). Belmont, CA: Wadsworth/Thomson Learning.

Shank, P., & Sitze, A. (2004). *Making sense of online learning.* San Francisco: Jossey-Bass/Pfeiffer.

Sheared, V. (1994). Giving voice: An inclusive model of instruction—A womanist perspective. In E. Hayes & S.A.J. Colin III (Eds.), *Confronting racism and sexism in adult education* (pp. 27–37). New Directions for Continuing Education, No. 61. San Francisco: Jossey-Bass.

Shearer, C. B., & Jones, J. A. (1994). *The validation of the hillside assessment of perceived intelligences (HAPI): A measure of Howard Gardner's theory of multiple intelligences.* Washington, DC: National Institute on Disability and Rehabilitation Research. (ERIC Document Reproduction Service No. ED 372 077)

Shreeve, J. (2005). Beyond the brain. *Journal of the National Geographic Society, 207*(3), 2–31.

Siegesmund, R. (2004). Somatic knowledge and qualitative reasoning: From theory to practice. *Journal of Aesthetic Education, 37*(1), 54–64.

Simmons, S., & Simmons, J. C. (1997). *Measuring emotional intelligence.* Arlington, TX: Summit.

Sinnott, J. D. (1998). *The development of logic in adulthood: Postformal thought and its applications.* New York: Plenum Press.

Sipe, R. B. (1995). Teacher as learners: An exploration into the learning worlds of experimentally open teachers. *Dissertation Abstracts International, 55*(12), 3716. (UMI No. 9513934)

Sissel, P. A. (1997). Participation and learning in Head Start: A sociopolitical analysis. *Adult Education Quarterly, 47*(3/4), 123–137.

Skinner, B. F. (1971). *Beyond freedom and dignity.* New York: Knopf.

Skinner, B. F. (1974). *About behaviorism.* New York: Knopf.

Sleezer, C. M., Conti, G. J., & Nolan, R. E. (2003). Comparing CPE and HRD programs: Definitions, theoretical foundations, outcomes, and measures of quality. *Advances in Developing Human Resources, 6*(1), 20–34.

Sloan, D. (2005). Education and the modern assault on being human: Nurturing body, soul, and spirit. In J. P. Miller, S. Karsten, D. Denton, D. Orr, & I. C. Kates (Eds.), *Holistic learning and spirituality in education* (pp. 27–46). Albany: State University of New York Press.

Smith, A. D. (1996). Memory. In J. E. Birren & K. W. Schaie (Eds.), *Handbook of the psychology of aging* (pp. 236–250). Orlando: Academic Press.

Smith, P. J. (2002). "Modern" learning methods: Rhetoric and reality— further to Sadler-Smith et al. *Personnel Review, 31*(1), 103–113.

Smith, R. M. (1982). *Learning how to learn: Applied learning theory for adults.* Chicago: Follett.

Smith, R. M. (1987). *Theory building for learning how to learn.* Chicago: Educational Studies Press.

Smith, R. M., & Associates. (1990). *Learning to learn across the life span.* San Francisco: Jossey-Bass.

Snyder, K. M. (2000). Asynchronous learning networks and cognitive apprenticeship: A potential model for teaching complex problem-solving skills in corporate environments. *Dissertation Abstracts International, 60*(12), 4392. (UMI No. 9955733)

Somerville, M. (2004). Somatic knowledge and qualitative reasoning: From theory to practice. *Journal of Aesthetic Education, 38*(4), 80–96.

Spear, G. E. (1988). Beyond the organizing circumstance: A search for methodology for the study of self-directed learning. In H. B. Long & others, *Self-directed learning: Application and theory.* Athens: Department of Adult Education, University of Georgia.

Spear, G. E., & Mocker, D. W. (1984). The organizing circumstance: Environmental determinants in self-directed learning. *Adult Education Quarterly, 35*(1), 1–10.

Spearman, C. E. (1904). "General intelligence," objectively determined and measured. *American Journal of Psychology, 15,* 201–293.

Spearman, C. E. (1927). *The abilities of man.* New York: Macmillan.

Stacy, N., & To, D. (1994). Adult education and training markets. In T. Husen & T. N. Postlethwaite (Eds.), *The international encyclopedia of education* (Vol. 1, 2nd ed., pp. 103–111). New York: Pergamon Press.

Stalker, J. (1993a). Sexual harassment: The dark side of the adult learner/teacher relationship. In D. Flannery (Ed.), *Proceedings of the 34th Annual Adult Education Research Conference* (pp. 263–268). University Park: Penn State University.

Stalker, J. (1993b). Women teachers mentoring women learners: On the inside working it out. In D. Flannery (Ed.), *Proceedings of the 34th Annual Adult Education Research Conference* (pp. 269–274). University Park: Penn State University.

Stamps, D. (1997). Learning is social. Training is irrelevant? *Training, 3*(2), 35–42.

St. Clair, R. (2002). *Andragogy revisited: Theory for the 21st century?* Myths and Realities No. 19. Columbus, OH: ERIC Clearinghouse on Adult, Career, and Vocational Education. (ERIC Document Reproduction Service No. ED 468 612)

St. Clair, R., & Sandlin, J. A. (Eds.). (2004). *Promoting critical practices in adult education.* New Directions in Adult and Continuing Education, No. 102. San Francisco: Jossey-Bass.

Steffe, L. P., & Gale, J. (Eds.). (1995). *Constructivism in education.* Hillsdale, NJ: Erlbaum.

Sternberg, R. J. (1985). *Beyond IQ: A triarchic theory of human intelligence.* New York: Cambridge University Press.

Sternberg, R. J. (1986a). *Intelligence applied: Understanding and increasing your intellectual skills.* San Diego: Harcourt Brace.

Sternberg, R. J. (1986b). Intelligence, wisdom, and creativity: Three is better than one. *Educational Psychologist, 21*(3), 175–190.

Sternberg, R. J. (1988). *The triarchic mind: A new theory of human intelligence.* New York: Viking/Penguin.

Sternberg, R. J. (1994a). Allowing for thinking styles. *Educational Leadership, 52*(3), 36–40.

Sternberg, R. J. (1994b). PRSVL: An integrative framework for understanding mind in context. In R. J. Sternberg & R. K. Wagner (Eds.), *Mind in context: Interactionist perspectives on human intelligence.* New York: Cambridge University Press.

Sternberg, R. J. (1996a). Styles of thinking. In P. B. Baltes & U. M. Staudinger (Eds.), *Interactive minds: Life-span perspectives on the social foundation of cognition* (pp. 347–365). Cambridge, MA: Cambridge University Press.

Sternberg, R. J. (1996b). *Successful intelligence: How practical and creative intelligence determine success in life.* New York: Simon & Schuster.

Sternberg, R. J. (1996c). Myths, countermyths, and truths about intelligence. *Educational Researcher, 25*(2), 11–16.

Sternberg, R. J. (1997). *Successful intelligence.* New York: Plume.

Sternberg, R. J. (2000a). Intelligence and wisdom. In R. J. Sternberg, J. Jautrey, & T. I. Lubart (Eds.), *Models of intelligence: International perspectives* (pp. 631–645). Washington, DC: American Psychological Association.

Sternberg, R. J. (2000b). The concept of intelligence. In R. J. Sternberg (Ed.), *Handbook of intelligence* (pp. 3–15). New York: Cambridge University Press.

Sternberg, R. J. (2003a). Construct validity of the theory of successful intelligence. In R. J. Sternberg, J. Lautrey, & T. I. Lubart (Eds.), *Models of intelligence: International perspectives* (pp. 55–77). Washington, DC: American Psychological Association.

Sternberg, R. J. (2003b). *Wisdom, intelligence, and creativity synthesized.* Cambridge, UK: Cambridge University Press.

Sternberg, R. J. (Ed.). (2004). *The international handbook of intelligence.* New York: Cambridge University Press.

Sternberg, R. J. (2005a). Foolishness. In R. J. Sternberg & J. Jordan (Eds.), *A handbook of wisdom: Psychological perspectives* (pp. 331–352). Cambridge, UK: Cambridge University Press.

Sternberg, R. J. (2005b). Older but not wiser? The relationship between age and wisdom. *Ageing International, 30*(1), 5–26.

Sternberg, R. J., Castejón, J. L., Prieto, M. D., Hautamäki, J., & Grigorenko, E. L. (2001). Confirmatory factor analysis of the Sternberg triarchic abilities test in three international samples. *European Journal of Psychological Assessment, 17*(1), 1–16.

Sternberg, R. J., Forsythe, G. B., Hedlund, J., Horvath, J. A., Wagner, R. K., Williams, W. M., et al. (2000). *Practical intelligence in everyday life.* New York: Cambridge University Press.

Sternberg, R. J., & Grigorenko, E. L. (Eds.). (2002). *The general factor of intelligence: How general is it?* Hillsdale, NJ: Erlbaum.

Sternberg, R. J., & Horvath J. A. (1995). A prototype view of expert teaching. *Educational Researcher, 24*(6), 9–17.

Sternberg, R. J., & Horvath, J. A. (1999). *Tacit knowledge in professional practice.* Hillsdale, NJ: Erlbaum.

Sternberg, R. J., & Jordan, J. A. (Eds.). (2005). *A handbook of wisdom: Psychological perspectives.* Cambridge, UK: Cambridge University Press.

Sternberg, R. J., Lautrey, J., & Lubart, T. I. (2003). Where are we in the field of intelligence, how did we get here, and where are we going? In R. J. Sternberg, J. Lautrey, & T. I. Lubart (Eds.), *Models of intelligence: International perspectives* (pp. 3–25). Washington, DC: American Psychological Association.

Sternberg, R. J., & Lubart, T. I. (2001). Wisdom and creativity. In J. E. Birren & K. W. Schaie (Eds.), *Handbook of the psychology of aging* (pp. 500–522). Orlando: Academic Press.

Stevenson, J. J. (1980). Load, power and margin in older adults. *Geriatric Nursing, 1*(2), 50–55.

Stinson, S. W. (1995). Body of knowledge. *Educational Theory, 45*(1), 43–54.

Stockdale, S. L. (2003). *Development of an instrument to measure self-directedness.* Unpublished doctoral dissertation, University of Tennessee, Knoxville.

Stubblefield, H. W., & Keane, P. (1994). *Adult education in the American experience.* San Francisco: Jossey-Bass.

Stuen, C., & Faye, E. E. (2003). Vision loss: Normal and not normal changes among older adults. *Generations, 27*(1), 8–14.

Sung, B. (1991a). *Confucian analects.* Seoul, Korea: Association of Traditional Culture Study.

Sung, B. (1991b). *The doctrine of the mean.* Seoul, Korea: Association of Traditional Culture Study.

Sung, B. (1991c). *The great learning.* Seoul, Korea: Association of Traditional Culture Study.

Sung, B. (1991d). *Mencius.* Seoul, Korea: Association of Traditional Culture Study.

Tangri, S. S., Thomas, V. G., Mednick, M. T., & Lee, K. S. (2003). Predictors of satisfaction among college-educated African American women at midlife. *Journal of Adult Development, 10*(2), 113–125.

Taylor, E. W. (1994). Intercultural competency: A transformative learning process. *Adult Education Quarterly, 44*(3), 154–174.

Taylor, E. W. (1996). Rationality and emotions in transformative learning theory: A neurobiological perspective. In H. Reno and M. Witte (Eds.), *Proceedings of the 37th Annual Adult Education Research Conference* (pp. 301–306). Tampa: University of Southern Florida.

Taylor, E. W. (1997a). Building upon the theoretical debate: A critical review of the empirical studies of Mezirow's transformative learning theory. *Adult Education Quarterly, 48*(1), 34–59.

Taylor, E. W. (1997b). Implicit memory and transformative learning theory: Unconscious cognition. In R. E. Nolan and H. Chelesvig (Eds.), *Proceedings of the 38th Annual Adult Education Research Conference* (pp. 263–268). Stillwater: University of Oklahoma.

Taylor, E. W. (2000a). Analyzing research on transformative learning theory. In J. Mezirow & Associates (Eds.), *Learning as transformation: Critical perspectives on a theory in progress* (pp. 285–328). San Francisco: Jossey-Bass.

Taylor, E. W. (2000b). Fostering Mezirow's transformative theory in the adult education classroom: A critical review. *Canadian Journal for the Study of Adult Education, 14*(2), 1–28.

Taylor, E. W. (2001). Transformative learning theory: A neurobiological perspective of the role of emotions and unconscious ways of knowing. *International Journal of Lifelong Education, 20*(3), 218–236.

Taylor, E. W. (2003). Looking back five years: A critical review of transformative learning theory. In C. A. Weissner, S. R., Meyer, N. L. Pfhal, & P. G. Neaman (Eds.), *Proceedings of the Fifth International Conference on Transformative Learning* (pp. 396–402). New York: Teachers College, Columbia University.

Taylor, E. W. (2005a). Making meaning of the varied and contested perspectives of transformative learning theory. In D. Vlosak, G. Kielbaso, & J. Radford (Eds.), *Proceedings of the 6th International Conference on Transformative Learning* (pp. 459–464). East Lansing: Michigan State University.

Taylor, E. W. (2005b). Teaching beliefs of nonformal consumer educators: A perspective of teaching in home improvement retail stores in the United States. *International Journal of Consumer Studies, 29*(5), 448–457.

Taylor, E. W., & Caldarelli, M. (2004). Teaching beliefs of non-formal environmental educators: A perspective from state and local parks in the United States. *Environmental Education Research, 10*(4), 451–469.

Taylor, K. (2000). Teaching with developmental intention. In J. Mezirow & Associates (Eds.), *Learning as transformation: Critical perspectives on a theory in progress* (pp. 151–180). San Francisco: Jossey-Bass.

Taylor, K., Marienau, C., & Fiddler, M. (2000). *Developing adult learners.* San Francisco: Jossey-Bass.

Tennant, M. C. (1988). *Psychology and adult learning.* New York: Routledge.

Tennant, M. C. (1991). The psychology of adult teaching and learning. In J. M. Peters, P. Jarvis, & Associates (Eds.), *Adult Education: Evolution and achievements in a developing field of study* (pp. 191–216). San Francisco: Jossey-Bass.

Tennant, M. C. (1993). Perspective transformation and adult development. *Adult Education Quarterly, 44*(1), 34–42.

Tennant, M. C. (2000). Adult learning for self-development and change. In A. L. Wilson & E. R. Hayes (Eds.), *Handbook of adult and continuing education* (pp. 87–100). San Francisco: Jossey-Bass.

Tennant, M. C., & Pogson, P. (1995). *Learning and change in the adult years: A developmental perspective.* San Francisco: Jossey-Bass.

Theil, J. P. (1984). Successful self-directed learning styles. *Proceedings of the 25th Annual Adult Education Research Conference* (pp. 327–242). Raleigh: North Carolina State University.

Thomas, W. H. (2004). *What are old people for? How elders will save the world.* Acton, MA: VanderWyk & Burnham.

Thorndike, E. L., Bregman, E. O., Tilton, J. W., & Woodyard, E. (1928). *Adult learning.* New York: Macmillan.

Thorpe, M. O. (2005). Wisdom in war: Ordinary people in extraordinary times. *ReVision: A Journal of Consciousness and Transformation, 27*(4), 34–43.

Thurstone, L. L., & Thurstone, T. G. (1941). *Factorial studies of intelligence.* Psychometric Monographs, No. 2. Chicago: University of Chicago Press.

Timiras, P. S. (2003). The nervous system: Structural and biological changes. In P. S. Timiras (Ed.), *Physiological basis of aging and geriatrics* (pp. 99–118). New York: CRC Press.

Tisdell, E. J. (1993). Feminism and adult learning: Power, pedagogy, and praxis. In S. A. Merriam (Ed.), *An update on adult learning theory* (pp. 91–104). New Directions for Adult and Continuing Education, No. 57. San Francisco: Jossey-Bass.

Tisdell, E. J. (1995). *Creating inclusive adult learning environments: Insights from multicultural education and feminist pedagogy.* Information Series No. 361. Columbus, Ohio: ERIC Clearinghouse on Adult, Career, and Vocational Education.

Tisdell, E. J. (1996). Feminist pedagogy and adult learning: Underlying theory and emancipatory practice. *Proceedings of the 37th Annual Adult Education Research Conference* (pp. 307–312). Tampa: University of South Florida.

Tisdell, E. J. (1998). Poststructural feminist pedagogies: The possibilities and limitations of a feminist emancipatory adult learning theory and practice. *Adult Education Quarterly, 48*(3), 139–156.

Tisdell, E. J. (2000). Feminist pedagogies. In E. R. Hayes & D. D. Flannery with A. K. Brooks, E. J. Tisdell, & J. M. Hugo (Eds.), *Women as learners: The significance of gender in adult learning* (pp. 155–183). San Francisco: Jossey-Bass.

Tisdell, E. J. (2003). *Exploring spirituality and culture in adult and higher education.* San Francisco: Jossey-Bass.

Tisdell, E. J. (2005a). Critical multiculturalism. In L. M. English (Ed.), *International encyclopedia of adult education* (pp. 162–165). London: Palgrave Macmillan.

Tisdell, E. J. (2005b). Feminism. In L. M. English (Ed.), *International encyclopedia of adult education* (pp. 254–257). London: Palgrave Macmillan

Tisdell, E. J. (2005c). In the new millennium: The role of spirituality and the cultural imagination in dealing with diversity and equity in the higher education classroom. *Teacher's College Record.* http://www.tcrecord.org. ID No. 12223. Accessed April 10, 2006.

Tisdell, E. J., & Perry, C. (1997). A collaborative inter-racial "border" pedagogy in adult multicultural education classes. In P. Armstrong, N. Miller, & M. Zukas (Eds.), *Crossing Borders, Breaking Boundaries: Proceedings of the 27th Annual SCUTREA Conference* (pp. 441–444). London: Birbeck College, University of London.

Tomlin, M. E. (1997). Changing what and how we teach for a changing world. *Adult Learning, 8*(5/6), 19–21.

Tough, A. (1967). *Learning without a teacher.* Educational Research Series, No. 3. Toronto: Ontario Institute for Studies in Education.

Tough, A. (1971). *The adult's learning projects: A fresh approach to theory and practice in adult learning.* Toronto: Ontario Institute for Studies in Education.

Tough, A. (1978). Major learning efforts: Recent research and future directions. *Adult Education, 28*(4), 250–263.

Tough, A. (1979). *The adult's learning projects: A fresh approach to theory and practice in adult learning* (2nd ed.). Toronto: Ontario Institute for Studies in Education.

Toye, M. (1989). Learning styles. In C. J. Titmus (Ed.), *Lifelong education for adults: An international handbook.* Oxford: Pergamon Press.

Ulrich, D. (1998). A new mandate for human resources. *Harvard Business Review, 76*(1), 124–134.

U.S. Bureau of the Census. (2000). *Educational attainment by sex.* http://factfinder.census.gov/servlet/SAFFPeople?_sse=on. Accessed September 15, 2005.

U.S. Bureau of the Census. (2004a). *Income in 2003 by educational attainment.* http://www.census.gov/population/socdem/education/cps2004/tab08–1.pdf. Accessed October 2, 2005.

U.S. Bureau of the Census. (2004b). *U.S. Interim projections by age, sex, race, and Hispanic origin.* http://www.census.gov/ipc/www/usinterimproj. Accessed August 27, 2005.

U.S. Bureau of the Census. (2005). *National population estimates by characteristics.* http://www.census.gov/popest/national/asrh/NC-EST2004-sa.html. Accessed August 27, 2005.

U.S. Bureau of Labor Statistics. (2005). *The employment situation: August 2005.* http://www.bls.gov/cps/cps_over.htm#overview. Accessed September 7, 2005.

U.S. Department of Education. (1986). *Bulletin.* Office of Educational Research and Improvement, Center for Statistics. Washington, DC: Department of Education.

U.S. Department of Labor. (n.d.). *Women in the labor force in 2004.* http://www.dol.gov/wb/factsheets/Qf-laborforce-04.htm. Accessed September 11, 2005.

Usher, R., Bryant, I., & Johnston, R. (1997). *Adult education and the postmodern challenge: Learning beyond the limits.* New York: Routledge.

Usher, R., & Edwards, R. (1994). *Postmodernism and education.* New York: Routledge.

Valente, J. (2005). *The role of self-directed learning in older adult's healthcare.* Unpublished doctoral dissertation, University of Georgia, Athens.

Valentine, T. (1997). United States of America: The current predominance of learning for the job. In P. Belanger & S. Valdivielso (Eds.), *The emergence of learning societies: Who participates in adult learning?* (pp. 95–108). New York: Elsevier.

Valentine, T., & Darkenwald, G. G. (1990). Deterrents to participation in adult education: Profiles of potential learners. *Adult Education Quarterly, 41*(1), 29–42.

Velazquez, L. C. (1996). Voices from the fields: Community-based migrant education. In P. Sissel (Ed.), *A community-based approach to literacy programs: Taking learners' lives into account* (pp. 27–36). New Directions for Adult and Continuing Education, No. 70. San Francisco: Jossey-Bass.

Vella, J. (1994). *Learning to listen, learning to teach: The power of dialogue in educating adults.* San Francisco: Jossey-Bass.

Vella, J. (2000). A spirited epistemology: Honoring the adult learner as subject. In L. English & M. Gillen (Eds.), *Addressing the spiritual dimensions of adult learning: What educators can do* (pp. 7–16). New Directions for Adult and Continuing Education, No. 85. San Francisco: Jossey-Bass.

Vella, J. (2002). *Quantum learning: Teaching as dialogue.* New Directions for Adult and Continuing Education, No. 3, 73–83.

Vernon, P. A., Wickett, J. C., Bazana, P. G., & Stelmack, R. M. (2000). The neuropsychology and psychophysiology of human intelligence. In R. J. Sternberg (Ed.), *Handbook of intelligence* (pp. 245–264). New York: Cambridge University Press.

Viens, J., & Kallenbach, S. (2004). *Multiple intelligences and adult literacy: A sourcebook for practitioners.* New York: Teachers College, Columbia University.

Vygotsky, L. S. (1978). *Mind in society: The development of higher psychological processes.* Cambridge, MA: Harvard University Press.

Wagner, R. K. (2000). Practical intelligence. In R. J. Sternberg (Ed.), *Handbook of intelligence* (pp. 380–395). New York: Cambridge University Press.

Walker, B. H. (1996). *Margin-in-life scale: A predictor of persistence for nontraditional students in higher education.* Unpublished doctoral dissertation, University of Georgia, Athens.

Walker, D. P. (2003). Enhancing problem-solving disposition, motivation and skills through cognitive apprenticeship. *Dissertation Abstracts International 65*(1), 127. (UMI No. 3119217)

Walters, S. (2005). Learning region. In L. M. English (Ed.), *International encyclopedia of adult education* (pp. 360–362). New York: Palgrave Macmillan.

Wang, H. (2006). Teaching Asian students online: What matters and why? *PAACE Journal of Lifelong Learning, 15,* 69–84.

Washburn, M. (2000). Transpersonal cognition in developmental perspective. In T. Hart, P. L. Nelson, & K. Puhakka (Eds.), *Transpersonal knowing: Exploring the horizon of consciousness* (pp. 185–212). Albany: State University of New York Press.

Watkins, K. E., & Marsick, V. J. (1993). *Sculpting the learning organization: Lessons in the art and science of systemic change.* San Francisco: Jossey-Bass.

Wechsler, D. (1997). *Manual for the Wechsler Adult Intelligence Scale-III.* New York: Psychological Corporation.

Weiler, K. (1996). Freire and a feminist pedagogy of difference. In R. Edwards, A. Hanson, & P. Raggatt (Eds.), *Boundaries of adult learning* (pp. 128–151). New York: Routledge.

Weiman, E. R. (1987). McClusky's power-load-margin theory and adult students. *Dissertation Abstracts International, 50*(11), 3450. (UMI No. 8922403)

Weisinger, H. (1998). *Emotional intelligence at work.* San Francisco: Jossey-Bass.

Wellington, B., & Austin, P. (1996). Orientations to reflective practice. *Educational Researcher, 38*(3), 307–316.

Welsh, M. A., & Dehler, G. E. (2004). P(l)aying attention: Communities of practice and organized reflection. In M. Reynolds & R. Vince (Eds.), *Organizing reflection* (pp. 15–29). Burlington, VT: Ashgate.

Welton, M. R. (1993). The contribution of critical theory to our understanding of adult learning. In S. B. Merriam (Ed.), *An update on adult learning theory* (pp. 81–90). New Directions for Adult and Continuing Education, No. 57. San Francisco: Jossey-Bass.

Welton, M. R. (1995a). The critical turn in adult education theory. In M. R. Welton (Ed.), *In defense of the lifeworld* (pp. 11–38). Albany: State University of New York Press.

Welton, M. R. (1995b). In defense of the lifeworld: A Habermasian approach to adult learning. In M. R. Welton (Ed.), *In defense of the lifeworld* (pp. 127–156). Albany: State University of New York Press.

Westermeyer, J. F. (2004). Predictors and characteristics of Erikson's life cycle model among men: A 32-year longitudinal study. *International Journal of Aging & Human Development, 58*(1), 29–48.

Whitbourne, S. K. (2005). *Adult development and aging: Biopsychosocial perspectives* (2nd ed). New York: Wiley.

Whitson, D. L., & Amstutz, D. D. (1997). *Accessing information in a technological age.* Malabar, FL: Krieger.

Wiener, W. J., & Rosenwald, G. C. (1993). A moment's monument: The psychology of keeping a diary. In R. Josselson & A. Lieblich (Eds.). *The narrative study of lives* (Vol. 1, pp. 30–58). Thousand Oaks, CA: Sage.

Wiessner, C. A., & Mezirow, J. (2000). Theory building and the search for common ground. In J. Mezirow & Associates, *Learning as transformation: Critical perspectives on a theory in progress* (pp. 329–358). San Francisco: Jossey-Bass.

Wilber, K. (1982). *A sociable God.* New York: McGraw-Hill.

Wilber, K. (1983). *Eye to eye.* New York: Doubleday.

Wilber, K. (1986). The spectrum of development. In K. Wilber, K. Engler, & D. P. Brown (Eds.), *Transformations of consciousness: Conventional and contemplative perspectives on development.* (pp. 65–105). Boston: New Science Library.

Wilber, K. (1990). Two patterns of transcendence: A reply to Washburn. *Journal of Humanistic Psychology, 30*(3), 113–136.

Williams, B. (2001). The theoretical links between problem-based learning and self- directed learning for continuing professional nursing education. *Teaching in Higher Education, 6*(1), 85–98.

Williamson, A. (1997). You're never too old to learn! Third-age perspectives on lifelong learning. *International Journal of Lifelong Education, 16*(3), 173–184.

Willis, S. L., & Schaie, K. W. (1986). Practical intelligence in later adulthood. In R. Sternberg & R. Wagner (Eds.), *Practical intelligence: Nature and origin of competency in the everyday world* (pp. 266–270). Cambridge, UK: Cambridge University Press.

Willis, S. L., & Schaie, K. W. (1994). Cognitive training in the normal elderly. In F. Forette, Y. Christensen, & F. Boller (Eds.), *Plasticité cerebrale et stimulation cognitive* [Cerebral plasticity and cognitive stimulation]. Paris: Fondation Nationale de Gerontologie.

Wilson, A. L. (1993). The common concern: Controlling the professionalization of adult education. *Adult Education Quarterly, 44*(1), 1–16.

Wilson, A. L. (2005). Activity theory. In L. M. English (Ed.), *International encyclopedia of adult education* (pp. 25–30). London: Palgrave Macmillan.

Wilson, A. L., & Cervero, R. M. (2001). Adult education and the struggle for knowledge and power: Practical action in a critical tradition. In R. O. Smith, J. M. Dirkx, P. L. Eddy, P. L. Farrell, & M. Polzin (Eds.), *Proceedings of the 42nd Annual Adult Education Research Conference* (pp. 423–428). East Lansing: Michigan State University.

Wilson, A. L., & Hayes, E. R. (Eds). (2000a). *Handbook of adult and continuing education.* San Francisco: Jossey-Bass.

Wilson, A. L., & Hayes, E. R. (2000b). A selective history of the adult education handbooks. In A. L. Wilson & E. R. Hayes (Eds.), *Handbook of adult and continuing education* (pp. 3–14). San Francisco: Jossey-Bass.

Wilson, A. L., & Nesbit, T. (2005). The problem of power. In R. J. Hill & R. Kiely (Eds.), *The 46th Annual Adult Education Research Conference* (pp. 449–454). Athens: University of Georgia.

Wilson, B. A. (1996). *A descriptive and interpretive study: The intellectual development of adults.* Paper presented at the annual meeting of the American Educational Research Association, New York. (ED 393 976).

Wilson, R. A., & Keil, F. C. (Eds.) (1999). *The MIT encyclopedia of the cognitive sciences.* Boston: Massachusetts Institute of Technology Press.

Wink, P., & Dillon, M. (2002). Spiritual development across the adult life course: Findings from a longitudinal study. *Journal of Adult Development, 9*(1), 79–94.

Wlodkowski, R. J., & Ginsberg, M. G. (1995). *Diversity and motivation: Culturally responsive teaching.* San Francisco: Jossey-Bass.

Wolfin, R. (1999). Understanding overloaded adults' readiness level for learning: McClusky's theory of margin refuted. In A. Austin, G. Hynes, & R. Miller (Eds.), *Proceedings of the 18th Annual Midwest Research-to-Practice Conference in Adult, Continuing, and Community Education* (pp. 280–285). St. Louis: University of Missouri.

World Bank. (2003). *Lifelong learning in the global economy: Challenges for developing countries.* Washington, DC: World Bank.

Worthington, R. L., Savoy, H. B., Dillion, F. R., & Vernagalia, E. R. (2002). Heterosexual identity development: A multidimensional model of individual and social identity. *Counseling Psychologist, 30*(4), 496–531.

York-Barr, J., Sommers, W. A., Ghere, G. S., & Montie, J. (2001). *Reflective practice to improve schools: An action guide for educators.* Thousand Oaks, CA: Corwin Press.

Yorks, L., & Marsick, V. J. (2000). Organizational learning and transformation. In J. Mezirow & Associates, *Learning as transformation: Critical perspectives on a theory in progress* (pp. 253–284). San Francisco: Jossey-Bass.

Yorks, L., & Sharoff, L. (2001). An extended epistemology for fostering transformative learning in holistic nursing education and practice. *Holistic Nursing Practice, 16*(1), 21–29.

Yoshida, A. (2005). Interface of holistic changes in Japanese schools and Waldorf education. In J. P. Miller, S. Karsten, D. Denton, D. Orr, & I. C. Kates (Eds.), *Holistic learning and spirituality in education* (pp. 129–134). Albany: State University of New York Press.

Young, M. F. (1993). Instructional design for situated learning. *Educational Technology Research and Development, 41*(1), 43–58.

Youngman, F. (1986). *Adult education and socialist pedagogy.* London: Croom Helm.

Youngman, F. (1996). A transformative political economy of adult education: An introduction. In P. Wangoola & F. Youngman (Eds.), *Towards a transformative political economy of adult education* (pp. 3–30). DeKalb, IL: LEPS Press.

Youngman, F. (2000). *The political economy of adult education and development.* London: NIACE & Zed Books.

Zemke, R., & Zemke, S. (1981). "30 things we know for sure about adult learning." *Training, 18,* 45–49.

Zemke, R., & Zemke, S. (1995). Adult learning: What do we know for sure? *Training, 32*(6), 31–34, 36, 38, 40.

Zhang, L. F. (1999). A comparison of U.S. and Chinese university students' cognitive development: The cross-cultural applicability of Perry's theory. *Journal of Psychology, 133*(4), 425–439.

Zhang, L. F. (2004). The Perry scheme: Across cultures, across approaches to the study of human psychology. *Journal of Adult Development, 11*(2), 123–138.

Zohar, D., & Marshall, I. (2000). *SQ: The ultimate intelligence.* London: Bloomsburg.

Name Index

A

Abdullah, A., 223–224
Abson, V., 370
Aburdene, P., 11, 21
Adamms, Jane, 427
Adams, J., 156
Adult Education Research Conference, 226
Ahmad, N., 303
Ahmed, M., 29
Ahteenmaki-Pelkonen, L., 124
Albert, M. S., 412, 413
Albright, T. D., 412, 415, 416
Alderson, K. G., 315, 317–318
Alexander, C. M., 315
Alfred, M., 132, 142, 143
Alfred, M. V., 10, 89, 431
Allen, 225
Allen, I. E., 40
Amann, T., 151, 156, 194, 215, 216
American Cancer Society, 36
American Medical Association, 199
Amstutz, D. D., 20–21, 244
Anderson, J. R., 179, 393, 394, 395, 397, 400, 401, 402, 404, 405, 408, 409
Anderson, N. D., 304
Anderson, N. H., 286
Andruske, C. L., 109
Antone, E. M., 220
Argyris, C., 42
Aring, M., 73
Aristotle, 275, 412
Arlin, P. K., 327, 357
Arnold, G. W., 90

Ashcraft, L., 307
Ashraf, S. A., 234
Ashraf, S. M., 234
Aslanian, C. B., 62–63, 92
Asoko, H., 291–292
Association for Clinical Pastoral Education, 96
Austin, P., 173–174
Ausubel, D. P., 286, 295–296

B

Bacclear, W. T., 351
Bagnall, R. G., 259, 260
Baldari, C., 302
Baltes, P. B., 305, 319–320, 324, 351, 367, 369
Bandura, A., 277, 288, 289, 295–296
Banks, C.A.M., 223
Banks, J. A., 223
Baptiste, I., 15, 23, 24, 250
Bar-On, R., 382, 396
Baron-Cohen, S., 418
Barrett, A. E., 310
Basseches, M. A., 343
Bassett, C., 326, 354–355, 358
Bateson, M. C., 430, 431
Baum, J., 95
Baumgartner, L. M., 133, 154, 157, 210
Baxter Magolda, M., 337, 338, 339–340, 358
Bazana, P. G., 361
Beard, C., 165–166
Beckett, D., 190, 196–197
Becvar, R. J., 351

504

Subject Index